ATLAS OF ELECTROCHEMICAL EQUILIBRIA IN AQUEOUS SOLUTIONS

ATLAS OF ELECTROCHEMICAL EQUILIBRIA

IN AQUEOUS SOLUTIONS

BY

MARCEL POURBAIX

Translated from the French by

JAMES A. FRANKLIN

(except Sections I, III 5 and III 6, which were originally written in English)

NATIONAL ASSOCIATION of CORROSION ENGINEERS

Houston, Texas, USA

CEBELCOR

Brussels

National Association of Corrosion Engineers
2400 West Loop South, Houston, Texas 77027

Centre Belge d'Etude de la Corrosion CEBELCOR, 50 Av. F. D. Roosevelt, Bruxelles 5

First English Edition 1966
Pergamon Press Ltd.

Second English Edition 1974
National Association of Corrosion Engineers

Library of Congress Catalog Card No. 65-11670

PRINTED IN THE USA BY

NATIONAL ASSOCIATION OF CORROSION ENGINEERS
2400 West Loop South
Houston, Texas 77027

In memory of

F. E. C. SCHEFFER

and in tribute to

U. R. EVANS

as a testimony of gratitude.

ACKNOWLEDGEMENTS

It is for me a pleasant duty to express on behalf of Cebelcor and myself our sincere gratitude to the contributors, the Union Minière du Haut-Katanga, "U.M.H.K.", the Institut pour l'Encouragement de la Recherche Scientifique dans l'Industrie et dans l'Agriculture, "I.R.S.I.A.", and the Air Force Material Laboratory Research and Technology Division, U.S. Air Force System Command, whose collaboration and help have assisted in the preparation of this Atlas, as well as to the members of the Administrative Council of Cebelcor.

Special acknowledgement is made to Mr. Félix Leblanc, President of the Administrative Council of Cebelcor and President of Université Libre de Bruxelles, to Mr. Jacques Errera and to Mr. Louis Baes, Honorary Professors at this University. Mr. Baes, who was formerly Vice-President of Cebelcor, followed with great interest the progress of this book, which he helped to inspire, up until his death on 29 October 1961 (prior to its publication in French). He will be remembered with gratitude.

My thanks are also due to Miss Nina de Zoubov and Mr. Jean Van Muylder who, besides the important part they played in the preparation of this work, have shared the difficult task of collating and correcting the text and figures.

M. Pourbaix

CONTENTS

LIST OF CONTRIBUTORS

*BESSON, J., University of Grenoble, France.

*BRENET, J. P., University of Strasbourg, France.

*BURGERS, W. G., Technical University, Delft, Netherlands.

*CHARLOT, G., University of Paris, France.

*DELAHAY, P., University of Louisiana, Bâton Rouge, La., U.S.A.

DELTOMBE, E., Belgian Centre of Corrosion Study (at present with the Société des Laboratoires Labaz, Brussels, Belgium).

DE ZOUBOV, N., Belgian Centre of Corrosion Study, Brussels, Belgium (at present Harvard University, Cambridge, Mass., U.S.A.).

*GARRELS, R. M., Northwestern University, Evanston, Ill., U.S.A.

*HOAR, T. P., University of Cambridge, Great Britain.

*JOLAS, F., "Les Piles Wonder" Company, Saint-Ouen, France.

*KUNZ, W., University of Saarbrücken, W. Germany.

*MARAGHINI, M., University of Rome, Italy.

*MOUSSARD, M., "Les Piles Wonder" Company, Saint-Ouen, France.

*PIONTELLI, R., Milan Polytechnic, Italy.

PITMAN, A. L., Naval Research Laboratory, Washington D.C., U.S.A.

POURBAIX, M., Belgian Centre of Corrosion Study, Brussels, Belgium.

SCHMETS, J., Belgian Centre of Corrosion Study, Brussels, Belgium (at present with the Centre d'Étude de l'Énergie Nucléaire, Mol, Belgium).

*SCHWABE, K., University of Dresden, Germany.

*VALENSI, G., University of Poitiers, France.

*VANLEUGENHAGHE, C., Belgian Centre of Corrosion Study, Brussels, Belgium (at present with S.E.R.A.I., Brussels).

*VAN MUYLDER, J., Belgian Centre of Corrosion Study, Brussels, Belgium.

*VAN RYSSELBERGHE, P., Stanford University, Stanford, Calif., U.S.A.

* Members of the International Committee of Thermodynamics and Electrical Kinetics, "C.I.T.C.E.", and/or of the Commission of Electrochemistry of the International Union of Pure and Applied Chemistry, "I.U.P.A.C."

LIST OF MEMBERS OF CEBELCOR

(January 1974)

EFFECTIVE MEMBERS

BELGIUM

1. Administration.

Institut Royal du Patrimoine Artistique.
Ministère des Communications.
Ministère des Travaux Publics.
Régie des Télégraphes et des Téléphones (R.T.T.).
Société Nationale des Chemins de Fer Belges (SNCB).

2. Fédérations et Groupements.

Association des Industriels de Belgique (AIB).
Association des Métalliseurs de Belgique.
Association Vinçotte.
Centre Scientifique et Technique de la Construction (CSTC).
Fédération des Entreprises de l'Industrie des Fabrications Métalliques (FABRIMETAL).
Laboratoire Belge de l'Industrie Électrique (LABORELEC).
Laboratoire IVP.

3. Teaching, Research, and Information Institutions.

Centre Belge d'Information du Cuivre.
Centre Belgo-Luxembourgeois d'Information de l'Acier.
Centre d'Enseignement et de Recherches des Industries Alimentaires et Chimiques (CERIA).
Centre d'Etude de l'Energie Nucléaire (CEN).
Centre National d'Information de l'Aluminium.
Centre de Recherches Métallurgiques (CRM).
Institut Belge de l'Emballage (IBE).
Institut Belge de Normalisation (IBN).
Rijksuniversiteit Gent. Laboratorium voor Anorganische Technische Chemie.
Rijksuniversiteit Gent. Laboratorium voor non-ferro metallurgie.
Université Libre de Bruxelles.—Service Corrosion.
Université Libre de Bruxelles.—Services Techniques et des Constructions.
Université de Liège.—Institut du Génie Civil.

4. Construction and Building.

Association Momentanée Entreprises François & Fils et Bâtiments & Ponts.
Bureau de Contrôle pour la Sécurité de la Construction en Belgique (SECO).
Limpens et Cie.
Société d'Etudes et de Réalisations Thermodynamiques (SERT).

5. Chemical and Food Industries.

Brasserie Wielemans Ceuppens.
Citrique Belge.
Degussa-Antwerpen.
Kronos.
Metraco.
Polysar Belgium.
Pourdreries Réunies de Belgique (PRB).
Procter et Gamble.—European Technical Center.
Raffinerie Tirlemontoise.
Savonnerie Klaar.
Solvay & Co.

6. Petroleum Industry.

Albatros.
Petrofina.
Texaco Belgium.

7. Mining and Metallurgy.

Allegheny Longdoz.
Cockerill-Ougrée-Providence'—Groupe A Sidérurgie, Liège.
Ets De Kriek.
Iternational Nickel Benelux.
Métallurgie Hoboken-Overpelt.
Métallurgique Hainaut-Sambre.
Sidmar.
Société Générales des Minerais.
Vieille-Montagne-Angleur.
Visseries et Tréfileries Réunies de Haren (VTR).

8. Metallic Fabricators

Ateliers de Construction d'Appareils de Chauffage et de Ventilation (ACV).
Tréfileries Léon Bekaert.
Belgonucléaire.
F.M.C. Food Machinery Europe.
Idéal-Standard.
Lion Rapide.
Sidal.
Société Anonyme Belge de Constructions Aéronautiques (SABCA).
Soprindus.
Veha.

9. Energy.

Intercommunale Belge d'Électricité.—Département Intervapeur.
Westinghouse Research Laboratory Europe.

10. Electronics.

Manufacture Belge de Lampes et de Matériel Électronique (MBLE).
Ets Mornard.

11. Protection Against Corrosion.

Distrigaz.
Epuro.
Guldager Electrolyse.
Hommema Delectron.
Tecnimétal.
Ets Trachet.
Travail Mécanique de la Tôle (TMT).
Trimetal Paint Co' Belgium.

12. Textile Industry.

Kortrijkse Katoenspinnerij.

13. Miscellaneous.

L. Hage-Aerts, architecte et géologue.

ASSOCIATE MEMBERS

ALGERIA.

Sonatrach.

ARGENTINA.

Centro Argentino de Estudios de la Corrosion (CEARCOR).
Gas del Estado.

AUSTRALIA.

Australasian Corrosion Association.
John Lysaght (Australia) Limited.
Commonwealth Scientific and Industrial Research Organization (C.S.I.R.O.).

BRAZIL.

COPPE. Universidade Federal do Rio de Janeiro.
Sacor Siderotecnica.

CANADA.

Du Pont of Canada.
Corrosion Service Company Limited.
Ecole Polytechnique de Montreéal.
National Science Library.

CHILI.

Instituto de Investigaciones y Ensayes de Materiales de Universidad de Chile (I.D.I.E.M.).

DENMARK.

Korrosionscentralen—Tilknyttet Akademiet for Tekniske Videnskaber.

EGYPT.

National Information & Documentation Centre (NIDOC).

FINLAND.

Central Chemical Association.

FRANCE.

Atelier de Construction de Tarbes.
Cegedur G. P.
Centre Expérimental du Bâtiment et des Travaux Publics (CEBTP).
Centre Scientifique et Technique du Bâtiment (CSTB).
Centre Technique des Industries Mécaniques.—Centre de Documentation Mécanique.
Centre Technique du Zinc.
Compagnie pour la Protection Intégrale des Matériaux (COPIM).
Dia-Prosim.
École Nationale Supérieure d'Électrochimie et d'Électrométallurgie.
Électricité de France.—Département d'Étude des Matériaux.
Électricité de France.—Service Central Production Thermique.
Éstablissements des Constructions et Armes Navales.
Framatome.
Gaz de France.—Service d'Essais et de Protection des Ouvrages.
Gaz Intégral.
Institut de Recherches de la Sidérurgie Française (IRSID).
Laboratoire d'Etudes et de Recherches des Emballages Métalliques.
Laboratories de Marcoussis.
Laboratoire National d'Essais.
Péchiney—Centre de Recherches de Voreppe.
Société Chimique des Charbonnages (SCC).

Société d'Etude contre la Corrosion (SECCO).
Société Nationale des Pétroles d'Aquitaine (SNPA).
Service Technique des Constructions et Armes Navales (STCAN).
Tréfimétaux.
Tuyaux Bonna.
Ugine Kuhlmann, Laboratoire d'Ugine.
Ugine Kuhlmann, Centre de Recherches de Lyon.
Ugine Kuhlmann, Centre Technique Aciers.

Université de Clermont.–Centre Universitaire des Sciences et Techniques (CUST).
Université de Poitiers.–Laboratoire de Thermodynamique Chimique et d'Electrochimie.
Université de Toulouse.–Institut du Génie Chimique.
Usinor.
Vallourec–Centre d'Étude (CEV).

ERMANY.
Ludwig Taprogge.
Ruhrgas Aktiengesellschaft.
Technische Universitat Hannover–Bibliothek und Technische Informationsbibliothek.
Zentralstelle für Atomkernenergie–Dokumentation ZAED.

RAN.
Iranian Documentation Centre.
National Iranian Oil Company (N.I.O.C.).

TALY.
Centro Sperimentale Metallurgico (C.S.M.).
Consiglio Nazionale delle Ricerche–Centro di Studio per la Chimica e la Chimico-fisica applicata alle Caratteristiche di Impiego dei Materiali.
Consiglio Nazionale delle Ricerche–Laboratorio per la Corrosione Marina dei Metalli.
Italsider.
Oronzio de Nora.–Impianti Elettrochimici.
Pirelli, S.p.A.

JAPAN.
Kyoto University–Department of Metallurgy.

LUXEMBURG.
ARBED.
Syndicat des Eaux du Sud.

NETHERLANDS.
Dow Chemical Nederland.
N.V. tot Keuring van Elektrotechnische Materialen KEMA.
Koninklijk Instituut voor de Marine.
Thomassen & Drijver–Verblifa.

NORWAY.
Norwegian Defence Research Establishment.
Norwegian Institute for Air Research.
Norges Tekniske Hogskole–Institutt for Mekanisk Teknologi.
Norges Tekniske Hogskole–Institutt for Teknisk Elektrokjemi.
Ship Research Institute of Norway.

PORTUGAL.
Companhia Uniao Fabril (CUF).
Instituto Nacional de Investigaçao Industrial (I.N.I.I.).
Société Sacor.

RUMANIA.
Institutul Politehnic Timisoara.

SWEDEN.
Swedish Corrosion Institute.
Vattenbyggnadsbyran VBB.

SWITZERLAND.
Association Susse des Électriciens (Commission de Corrosion).

TURKEY.
Université d'Istanbul–Institut de Chimie Industrielle.

UNITED KINGDOM.
BISRA–The Corporate Laboratories of the British Steel Corporation.
Central Electricity Research Laboratories.
National Lending Library for Science and Technology.
National Reference Library of Science and Invention (Holborn Division).
Royal Aircraft Establishment.

U.S.A.
Aluminium Company of America (ALCOA).
Anaconda American Brass Co.
Babcock & Wilcox Co.
Bethlehem Steel Corp.
Center for Research Libraries.
Corrosion Center Ohio State University (OSU).
General Electric Co.–Nucleonics Laboratory.
General Motors Corp.–Research Laboratories.
International Lead Zinc Research Organization (ILZRO).
Michigan Technological University.
National Bureau of Standards (NBS).
Naval Air Development Center.
Naval Research Laboratory (NRL).
Reynolds Metals Co.
Surface Research Inc.
Union Carbide Corp.
University of California, Los Angeles (UCLA).
University of Florida.
University of Wisconsin, Milwaukee.

YUGOSLAVIA.
COPOH–Centar za Odrzavanje Opreme Hrvatske.

FOREWORD

THE introduction into electrochemistry of potential–pH diagrams in the form originated by Pourbaix marks a new era in the study of electrochemical reactions occurring in an aqueous medium near an electrode. By means of them it is possible to predict, on a thermodynamic basis, for a given element, the equilibrium states of all the possible reactions between this element, its ions and its solid and gaseous compounds in the presence of water. Of course, application of the data contained in these diagrams is limited by the reactions which have been considered in establishing them as well as by the values assumed for the standard chemical potentials of the substances taking part in these reactions; in certain cases, for solid compounds, these chemical potentials may vary with the perfection of the crystalline state. Moreover, the diagrams are based on the activities of ions, and not on their real concentrations. However, even with these restrictions, it is evident that in a good many cases the diagrams provide data which lead to important conclusions concerning the possible reactions; these conclusions are particularly important in the study of corrosion in aqueous media.

It is only through the indomitable energy and perseverance of Pourbaix and his collaborators that this Treatise, the *Atlas of Electrochemical Equilibria*, comprising data for 90 elements, could have been produced.

Those who are acquainted with the history of these diagrams know that it goes back to Pourbaix's "doctorate thesis", presented at the Technical University of Delft in 1945 with the encouragement of my late colleague, F. E. C. Scheffer. However, this thesis was only a modest beginning compared with the "complete" *Atlas*. I sincerely hope that this *Atlas* will find a welcome appropriate to the enormous amount of work that has been necessary to produce it.

W. G. BURGERS

PREFACE

R. PIONTELLI

THE publication of the *Atlas of Electrochemical Equilibria* is a most rewarding culmination of all the efforts of Dr. M. Pourbaix since the appearance in 1945 of his doctorate thesis, which was presented in Delft with the encouragement of the late Professor F. E. C. Scheffer and of Professor W. G. Burgers, and which was translated into English in 1949 by J. N. Agar at the invitation of Dr. U. R. Evans.

Dr. Pourbaix, President-in-Charge of CITCE, has for many years been the driving-force of this organization, within which the activity of the "Potential–pH Diagrams" commission has been most intense and productive, counting also on the enlightened collaboration of its members, in particular Prof. Charlot, Prof. Delahay, Dr. Garrels, Dr. Hoar, Prof. Valensi and Prof. Van Rysselberghe.

Through the efforts of Dr. Pourbaix and his collaborators at CEBELCOR, and with the generous support of the Union Minière du Haut Katanga, the Institut pour l'Encouragement de la Recherche Scientifique dans l'Industrie et dans l'Agriculture (IRSIA), and CEBELCOR's Commission des Études Fondamentales et Applications CEFA, the gathering of data has made continual progress in volume and precision, thus enabling this *Atlas* to be produced.

Collected here in a condensed, logical and standardized form are the data which characterize the equilibrium conditions at 25°C of a very considerable number of processes. These processes involve water, hydrogen peroxide and 90 elements of the periodic system and are in direct relationship with the electrochemistry of aqueous solutions, both theoretical and applied: the extraction of metals, their finishing, corrosion and protection, analytical chemistry and other fields such as geology, whose connection with electrochemistry is not often very apparent.

Potential–pH equilibrium diagrams were originated for the theoretical prediction of oxidation-reduction catalysts (according to a method devised by Michaelis) and of the conditions under which oxidation and reduction reactions are possible or impossible in the presence of aqueous solutions (in a manner related to the experimental work of Travers and Thiesse). The method and technique used in establishing them are the same as those used previously by their originator in work on the prediction of catalysts in gas reactions; thus these potential–pH equilibrium diagrams result from the extrapolation to electrochemical systems involving an aqueous solution of work carried out on chemical systems involving a gaseous phase. Each of these two groups of work is based on the formulation of the equilibria of *all* the reactions possible in a given system as a function of *two* independent variables (the other possible variables being considered to be parameters). These two independent variables are chosen in such a way that the equilibrium formulae are linear (or practically linear): they are the logarithm of the oxygen partial pressure $\log p_{O_2}$ and the reciprocal of the absolute temperature $1/T$ in the case of chemical systems involving a gaseous phase, and the equilibrium electrode potential and the pH of the solution in the case of electrochemical systems involving an aqueous solution. By this method the equilibrium conditions of all the reactions possible in a given system are represented on a plane diagram by families of straight lines. An investigator who constructs such diagrams must have a certain appreciation both of science and art: the science is necessary in plotting the lines (i.e. above all in knowing the relevant thermodynamic data) and the art in using the lines to create pictures which are as simple and useful as possible, and which can, as U. R. Evans wrote in his Preface to the English translation of the Delft thesis, "diagrams embodying a vast amount of pertinent information in a small space".

The diagrams, which were originated for catalysis studies, have rapidly evolved towards problems of the electrochemistry of metals, and corrosion in particular. The productiveness of the method caused them to be applied to all the elements—metals and non-metals, and its applications have developed greatly, spreading to other branches of electrochemistry and related fields.

For each of the elements in turn, it is a question of characterizing the equilibrium conditions (both where there is a possibility of exchanging electrical work with the exterior and where there is not) for systems whose constituent species are: the element in question and its ions in aqueous solution, water and its constituents (H^+ and OH^- ions, gaseous hydrogen and oxygen) and the products of the reactions of the element with these species (oxides and hydroxides, hydrides, etc.).

Corresponding to each reaction which is chemically possible there is a "free enthalpy of reaction" (referred by differentiation to unit variation in the degree of advancement of the reaction), whose value and sign determine the tendency of the system to react and the direction of the reaction. Under fixed physical conditions this free enthalpy of reaction can be expressed as the sum of a standard free enthalpy (which is constant for fixed physical conditions characteristic of a standard reference state) and a linear combination of logarithms of the activities of the substances taking part in the reaction. When the reaction is accompanied by the circulation of an electric current in a galvanic cell, the free enthalpy of reaction per unit electric charge gives us the value of the equilibrium potential difference at the terminals of the cell (or electromotive force) which corresponds to a state of equilibrium of the reaction considered.

An external source of electric current, such as that causing the circulation of "stray" currents in the ground, or the current supply of an electrolysis bath, can impose on a system the circulation of a current in a given direction and hence the production of a reaction in a given direction, subject to the condition (which is necessary but not sufficient) that the source is capable of maintaining a potential difference at the terminals which exceeds the equilibrium value, which is then called the "decomposition voltage". An "electrochemical" presentation of the free enthalpies of reaction is thus quite natural for reactions produced by an external current source. It is concerned with the very nature of the phenomena both in this case in which electrochemical reactions are caused by the external supply of electric current and also in the case of electrochemical reactions which produce electric current; spontaneous corrosion processes of the metallic elements are of the latter type.

Since 1792 (i.e. shortly after the discovery of galvanism) when Fabbroni clearly stated the hypothesis of the galavanic nature of corrosion processes together with his chemical theory of galvanic phenomena, throughout the studies of Davy, Thénard and De La Rive and up to the most recent ones, the electrochemical conception of corrosion has never ceased to be strengthened and confirmed. Systems in which spontaneous corrosion processes take place can thus be compared to galvanic systems which do not exchange electrical work with the outside world, for which the conditions necessary for the occurrence of modifications, or sufficient for their absence, can again be represented in an essentially electrochemical form.

Let us consider a galvanic couple in which one of the two electrodes is the standard hydrogen electrode, and for which one can represent the chemical modification as being the resultant of two complementary partial oxidation-reduction reactions, taking place respectively at each of the two electrodes with the participation of electrons in the phases having metallic conduction, the stoichiometric coefficients of the electrons having equal values and opposite signs for the two partial reactions.

The most common conventions concerning reference states for the thermodynamic properties of gaseous hydrogen and the hydrogen ion in aqueous solution automatically cancel out the contribution of the standard hydrogen electrode in the expression for the free enthalpy of reaction. One can thus consider the value of this free enthalpy as being inherent to the reaction taking place at the other electrode. The potential differences at the terminals of the galvanic couple are adopted, by definition, as values of the potentials (or "relative potentials") of this electrode with respect to the standard hydrogen electrode.(1) A series of such potentials will give us the scale of the "affinities" of the partial electrode

(1) With regard to the sign of these relative electrode potentials, the convention adopted by Dr. Pourbaix is in accordance with the IUPAC recommendations (Stockholm, 1953), and is the so-called "European Convention".

Using the notation of the writer of this Preface, the above choice is equivalent to using the values E^{MH} to express the relative

(*Footnote continued opposite*)

reactions, referred to the reaction proceeding at the standard hydrogen electrode as a conventional reference level.

For the cell obtained by coupling *any* two electrodes, the equation of the overall reaction, the value of the free enthalpy of reaction and hence the value of the equilibrium potential difference can be deduced by simple algebraic addition of those corresponding to the cells formed by coupling each of these two electrodes in turn with the reference electrode; the exactitude of the result depends on the possible "liquid junction" contributions. In this way the study of redox reactions can be reduced to a study of partial electrode reactions (or "electrochemical" reactions involving free electrons or electrons in phases having metallic conduction); the other reactions will be studied in the way which is classical for purely chemical reactions not involving free electrons.

The equilibrium conditions can thus be represented in the general case of electrochemical reactions by a relation between the equilibrium potential, the standard free enthalpy of reaction (in the form of a standard equilibrium potential), and a linear combination of logarithms of activities. In the particular case of non-electrochemical reactions the equilibrium conditions assume a simpler form as no equilibrium potential is involved; these conditions are then expressed by a relation between the standard free enthalpy of reaction (in the form of an equilibrium constant) and a linear combination of logarithms of activities.

With a view to the graphical representation of the equilibrium conditions on a plane diagram, the choice of the relative electrode potential as one of the coordinates imposes itself in the more general case of reactions involving electrons.

In view of the exceptional place occupied by H^+ ions among the species whose activities appear in the equilibrium relations to be considered here, it was natural to choose a function of the activity of H^+ ions as the second coordinate; the pH was chosen in order to linearize the equilibrium relations, despite the difficulties inherent to the individual thermodynamic properties of ionic species.[1]

The linear combination of the logarithms of the activities of the species different from H^+, whose thermodynamic level in the electrolytic medium is also variable, will be given the nature of a "parameter", which is variable from one curve to another in each family of equilibrium curves.

For electrochemical reactions which do not involve hydrogen ions the loci of points representing equilibrium conditions will be straight lines parallel to the pH axis; for "purely chemical" reactions involving hydrogen ions they will be straight lines parallel to the potential axis. When there is only one species of variable thermodynamic level, the parameter, which is then proportional to the logarithm of the activity of this species, characterizes the conditions of "practical existence" of this species in the medium, i.e. the domain of conditions under which the equilibrium can be realized in the presence of appreciable concentrations of the species. Let us consider a system consisting of a metal in contact with solution of its simple ions, these being the only ones which can exist; if the concentration of these ions which is compatible with the equilibrium conditions is lower than a fairly low conventional limit, one can then speak of a state of thermodynamic *immunity* of this metal. When the number of species of variable thermodynamic level is two, the parameter, which includes in general the ratio of their activities, gives these domains of relative predominance, which can become practically total for one to the exclusion of the other.

The diagrams thus give us a panoramic view of the "chemical configurations" of our systems, predicted on a thermodynamic basis. An examination of the properties of the potential–pH diagrams

---

potential of an electrode M with respect to the hydrogen electrode (the sign convention is indicated here by the order of the letters M and H). The "American" convention would correspond on the other hand, to using the value E^{HM}. There are arguments for considering the first choice as being the more "natural" one. It is, however, a question of adopting a simple convention, without touching on the scientific prestige of nations or schools, which at different periods and with numerous alternatives have preferred one or the other of the two conventions.

(1) For the purposes envisaged by Pourbaix's diagrams one can assume that the pH gives us, in an indirect and approximate way the potential of an electrode, which, like the standard reference electrode is a hydrogen electrode and is saturated with gaseous hydrogen at 1 atm, but is immersed in the solution studied. One can also postulate that in this way one defines a quantity which has an operational significance and which is also capable of characterizing the thermodynamic level of the H^+ ions (and hence that of the OH^- ions due to the dissociation equilibrium of water), with regard to their participation in any equilibrium.

suggests certain aspects which it is useful to know in order to apply them appropriately. It is evident that the electrochemical behaviour of a metallic phase, immersed in an electrolytic medium, depends on the composition of the layer of solution which is in immediate contact with this phase. This composition may differ considerably from the mean or initial composition of the medium on account of the absolute and relative rates of the possible processes of electrolysis and matter transport (by migration, diffusion and convection). This same observation is valid for the phases formed by the compounds of the metal, and must be considered carefully in using the diagrams.

When the metal forms soluble complexes of great stability with other substances (such as cyanides or ammonia), the equilibrium diagrams for the binary system metal–water must be modified: one must then take into account the equilibrium conditions of these complexes, for example by plotting equilibrium diagrams for a ternary system. This may modify appreciably the domains of relative predominance of the dissolved species and the domains of thermodynamic stability. In these cases one must therefore be very careful, particularly because only when a dissolved species is greatly predominant, in the case of dilute solutions at least, can one assume, as has been done in this *Atlas*, that the activities are virtually the same as the molarities.

Use of the diagrams therefore renders necessary corrections of activities with respect to molarities (or molalities); these corrections, which may be important for all the diagrams when one considers concentrated solutions, may also be important when one envisages the use of binary diagrams for studying ternary systems which involve stable complexes.

Amongst the reactions considered in establishing the diagrams a special place is held by those which involve a metal or its ions and oxygen or the ions derived from it, and which produce oxides or hydroxides. The equilibrium conditions concerning these phases have a fundamental interest, not only when they are the main subject of study but also when one considers the behaviour of the metal in electrochemical processes, such as those of corrosion. From this point of view the diagrams, in spite of their essentially thermodynamic nature, can give us information about one of the most important kinetic factors in the electrochemical behaviour of metals. Indeed, in the case of electrochemical reactions, amongst the factors which can be named "resistances to reaction" and which, in spite of the affinity available, determine the kinetics of the reaction, a most important place is occupied by those which depend on the formation of surface layers on the metallic phases. A fairly detailed study of these phenomena has suggested, quite recently, that one should distinguish between *passivation phenomena*, corresponding to an increase of resistance to ionic exchange reactions between a metal and a solution due to their separation by a surface layer, and *states of passivity* in which this resistance is sufficient to reduce the rates of these reactions below limits at which they are appreciable in spite of there being an affinity for the conversion of the metal into its corrosion products.

The solid compounds (oxides, hydroxides, basic salts) formed by the various metals with water represent the most common and important source of passivation of metals in an aqueous medium by a surface layer. Thus a knowledge of the conditions of thermodynamic stability of these oxides, hydroxides and basic salts can enable one to characterize the domains of passivation predicted by thermodynamics. The passivation may result in a state of passivity, which may be local or complete, depending on the structural properties of the phases involved. Indeed, in any branch of electrochemistry, theoretical and applied investigations can be carried out thoroughly only if one takes into account three types of factors: thermodynamic, kinetic and structural ones. It must be realized that thermodynamic studies are insufficient, even in conjunction with kinetic studies; structural studies are indispensable. This is the case first of all because they give us information on the deviation of the real phases from the ideal ones considered by theoretical thermodynamics and kinetics; moreover, they alone enable us to analyse, to control if possible, and sometimes to predict the properties of our galvanic deposits or passivating layers, the selectivity of the attack processes, and all those properties which determine to a large extent the success of the electrochemical processes of production, finishing and protection of metals, or the consequences of corrosion phenomena. While the scale of relative potentials gives us the degree of "thermodynamic nobility" of the various electrode processes, a knowledge of their "practical nobility" requires that one should also take into account kinetic laws and the influence of structural factors on these laws.

For those metals whose ionic exchanges at 25°C in aqueous media are rapid (metals which we have defined as being of "normal" electrochemical behaviour), the behaviour is in accordance with thermodynamic predictions, both when they are attacked anodically and when they are deposited cathodically, e.g. in a refining or electrodeposition bath, or in a displacement reaction, or in a corrosion process. For those metals whose ionic exchanges are slow, on the other hand, or even very slow (metals with "electrochemical inertia"), the divergence between the thermodynamic nobility and the practical nobility is sometimes very great, even when there is no passivation. For these metals a knowledge of these kinetic aspects of their behaviour is an indispensable complement to the information given by the equilibrium diagrams. One of the most important kinetic features in many branches of electrochemistry is the influence of the anions, as essential constituents of the metal solution double layers; as real catalysts of ionic exchanges (according to various mechanisms, such as competitive adsorption at the surface, excluding constituents which have an inhibiting action); or as destroyers of the surface layers, or as agents which can exploit their weak points, or as structural factors in cathodic deposition, or as selectivity factors in anodic attack. In all branches of the electrochemistry of metals the specific participation of anions, even independently of any complexing action and of their influence on the ionic activity values, can play an important part, which must often be considered to complete the information that one can obtain from the diagrams.

At present the potential–pH diagrams concern only pure metals and non-metals (there is also an attempt to apply them to sodium amalgams); these diagrams cannot therefore give us information about the behaviour of alloys, which often differs from that of the pure metals, with regard to all three factors mentioned above. It is fairly obvious that the corrosion behaviour of a bronze, or of a brass, is a fairly complex resultant of the properties of the constituent metals, and this is even more true of a stainless steel. On the other hand, a knowledge of the thermodynamic properties of the products of attack of the metals constituting an alloy can sometimes enable us to predict its passivation conditions too. The study of equilibrium conditions and kinetic conditions is fairly simple for galvanic systems consisting of two electrodes, each of which can be considered to be the site of a single well-determined reaction. In practice, systems in which corrosion phenomena occur are very often multiple electrode systems in which several reactions can occur simultaneously. Here, therefore, is a new source of complication, involving once again kinetic aspects of the phenomena in particular.

The considerations which I have just discussed help us to recognize the limits to the application of potential–pH equilibrium diagrams to concrete problems, either of theoretical or applied electrochemistry, or of some other nature, within the limits of accuracy of the available thermodynamic data. For anyone who might have claimed to find the answer in these diagrams to any theoretical or practical problem without exception, the above analysis may have brought some disillusionments.

The author of this *Atlas* himself has stated most explicitly the opinion that only a clear understanding of the limits of the diagrams, and hence a rational and appropriate use of them, can enable us to appreciate their great utility which justifies the generous, passionate and profitable efforts of Dr. Pourbaix and all those who have worked with him to realize this *Atlas*, whose success can easily be foreseen.

GLOSSARY

CORROSION: The reaction of a metal with its non-metallic environment that results in the continuing destruction of the metal.

IMMUNITY: The state of a metal in which corrosion is thermodynamically impossible in a particular environment.

PASSIVITY: The state of a metal in which corrosion in a particular environment is prevented by modifications of its surface, for instance, by the formation of a thin protective layer of oxide.

PASSIVATION: The process leading to more or less perfect passivity of a material.

Passivation can be obtained by electrochemical means (for instance the anodic polarization of iron in a solution of sodium bicarbonate) or by chemical means (for instance immersion of iron in fuming nitric acid).

CATHODIC PROTECTION: The establishment of a state of immunity by cathodic polarization, i.e. by making the electric potential of the electrode (or electrode tension) more negative. After the completion of the present *Atlas* (1960), it has been observed(1) that pitting of stainless steels (and of other passivable metals and alloys) due to chlorides may often be avoided by a cathodic treatment under conditions which do not lead to immunity, but lead to perfect passivity.

Taking this fact into account, cathodic protection may be defined more generally as *the establishment of a state of immunity or of perfect passivation by cathodic polarization.*

A state of cathodic protection can be obtained by the use of an e.m.f. applied through an external source or by means of a galvanic anode (such as zinc or magnesium for the protection of iron or steel).

INHIBITOR: A substance capable, in the form of small additions to a reactive medium, of stopping or of slowing down a chemical or an electrochemical reaction at a metal surface. When this reaction would result in corrosion the inhibitor is called a *corrosion inhibitor*.

ELECTRODE POTENTIAL (or tension): The difference $E = \varphi_1 - \varphi_2$ between the electric potential φ_1 of a terminal lead of a metallic electrode dipping in a electrolyte solution and the electric potential φ_2 of the terminal lead of a reversible reference electrode in contact with this solution, this difference of potential being corrected on account of the potential difference at the liquid junction which may exist between these two electrodes. The two leads are made of the same metal, copper for instance. In general the electrode tensions or potentials E will be expressed in volts with respect to the standard hydrogen electrode, i.e. an electrode of platinized platinum on which an equilibrium is established between gaseous hydrogen under a pressure of 1 atm. and an aqueous solution of pH = 0.

(1) See CEBELCOR's Rapports Techniques R.T. 102, 103, 104, 120 (1962); cf. *Corrosion Science* **3**, 239–59 (1963).

NOTATION AND ABBREVIATIONS

A	ampere
abs.	absolute
ac.	acid
act.	activity
anh.	anhydrous
anhydr.	anhydride
aq.	aqueous, dissolved
atm.	atmosphere
b.c.cub.	body-centred cubic
°C	degree centigrade
cal.	calorie
cm	centimetre
cm^2	square centimetre
def.	deformed
diox.	dioxide
E	electrode potential (or electrode tension)
E_0	equilibrium value of E (equilibrium potential)
$\dot{E}_0$	standard value of E_0 (standard equilibrium potential)
E_0^0	standard value of E_0 at 25°C (standard equilibrium potential at 25°C)
e^-	negatively charged electron
e.m.f.	electromotive force
f.c.cub.	face-centred cubic
g	gaseous
g	gram
g-at/l	gram-atom per litre
g-ion/l	gram-ion per litre
g/l	gram per litre
g-mol/l	gram-molecule per litre
h	hour
h	enthalpy of formation
$h^{\cdot}$	standard enthalpy of formation
h^0	standard enthalpy of formation at 25°C
hex.	hexagonal
hydr.	hydrated
hydrox.	hydroxide
I	electrolytic current
i	reaction current
i_0	reaction current at the equilibrium (exchange current)
°K	degree Kelvin
kcal.	kilocalorie
kg	kilogram
l	litre
ln	Napierian logarithm
log	logarithm to base 10
M	molar, i.e. 1 gram-molecule per litre
M	symbol for a chemical substance
(M)	fugacity of a gaseous substance, or activity of a dissolved substance M
m	metre
mA	milliampere
mg	milligram
mn (or min)	minute
monocl.	monoclinic
mV	millivolt
μ	chemical potential
$\mu^{\cdot}$	standard chemical potential
μ^0	standard chemical potential at 25°C
μA	microampere
μm	micrometre (or micron)
N	normal, i.e. 1 gram-equivalent per litre
ν	stoichiometric coefficient
n	stoichiometric coefficient of the electron e^-
ox.	oxide
orthorh.	orthorhombic (or rhombic)
pentox.	pentoxide
p.p.m.	parts per million
quad.	quadratic (or tetragonal)
rhomb.	rhombohedral (or ternary)
sesquiox.	sesquioxide
s	second
s	solid
s	entropy of formation
$s^{\cdot}$	standard entropy of formation
s^0	standard entropy of formation at 25°C
soln.	solution
solub.	solubility
tetrox.	tetroxide
tricl.	triclinic
V	volt
Z	oxidation number

In all tables, formulae and diagrams which appear in Chapter IV of the present *Atlas*, the physical state of the substances considered will be indicated as follows:

M solid substances, *M* gaseous substances,
M liquid substances, M dissolved substances (in aqueous solutions).

CHAPTER I

INTRODUCTION

INTRODUCTION

REMARKS ON ELECTROCHEMICAL THERMODYNAMICS AND KINETICS

PIERRE VAN RYSSELBERGHE
Stanford University, California, U.S.A.

THE excellent Preface by Professor R. Piontelli provides a perfect basis for this Introduction which can thus be reduced to a few remarks concerning certain fundamental points, all the details of the calculation and of the construction of the tension–pH diagrams being presented by M. Pourbaix in the following chapters.

We shall begin by examining the meaning of the very name given to the diagrams in the present book. Let us recall that, for many years, their name has been both in French and in English, "potential–pH diagrams". Commission No. 2 of the International Committee for Electrochemical Thermodynamics and Kinetics (CITCE), "Electrochemical Nomenclature and Definitions", has presented in yearly reports since 1951 a critical study of electrochemical concepts and has made a number of recommendations concerning the exact significance of various terms currently used and, in some cases, it has found useful to insist on the adoption of certain new terms or of new and more precise definitions of old terms. In particular, Commission No. 2 of CITCE has presented in recent reports a systematic treatment of the various tensions—electrochemical, electric, chemical—which should be considered in the fundamental theory of electrochemical equilibria and of irreversible electrochemical phenomena. Up to now this vocabulary of tensions has received general approval among French-speaking electrochemists and, with the very precise translation *tension* = *Spannung*, that of their German-speaking colleagues. The situation seems to be the same in most of the other languages, but as far as English is concerned, certain resistances have been encountered, and some of these have been rather strong. On the other hand, encouragement has been forthcoming from some quarters in the United States, and statements of adoption of the new terms have been made, in Australia for instance.

Before entering into a brief discussion of the question it is advisable to note that the word "potential" has been used in thermodynamics, physics, etc., in so many different senses that the appellation "potential–pH diagram" appears to be really too vague, particularly in view of the fact that the potentials here involved are actually combinations of differences of inner electric potentials of the various phases or linear combinations of chemical potentials reduced to the unit of charge. The objection can, of course, immediately be made that the word "tension" has also been used in many different senses, but, when one has to distinguish between inner, outer and surface potentials; chemical potentials, electrochemical potentials; oxidation, reduction and redox potentials; thermodynamic potentials, etc., the three very precisely defined types of tensions, which are always differences or linear combinations (reduced to the unit of charge) of the corresponding potentials, certainly introduce a considerable amount of clarity.

In the general name "tension–pH diagrams" the word tension is used without adjective. We shall immediately see that it can be understood as referring to equilibrium electric tensions, but also, and, we submit, chiefly to reduction chemical tensions, which are also called in the CITCE reports reduction affinities per unit of charge and correspond to one of the possible types of the quantities which are rather currently called "electromotive forces".

As far as pH is concerned, the diagrams presented in this *Atlas* use it in the well-known operational sense. Commission No. 2 of CITCE has been examining for some time the possibility of establishing a rational definition of pH, but we shall not enter here into these theoretical considerations.

In order to define the various tensions as briefly and clearly as possible, let us first examine the typical example of the Daniell cell, which we shall represent by the following diagram:

$$\underset{1}{Cu} \;/\; \underset{2}{Cu^{++}} \;//\; \underset{3}{Zn^{++}} \;/\; \underset{4}{Zn} \;/\; \underset{1'}{Cu}$$

followed by an external circuit 1′ − 1.

The inner electric potentials of the various phases are represented by $\varphi^1, \varphi^2, \ldots$ The electric tension U of the cell, considered from left to right in the direction of the numbering of the phases, is

$$U = \varphi^1 - \varphi^{1'}, \tag{1}$$

whether a current passes through the cell (U is then an irreversible electric tension) or not (U is then the reversible electric tension, if one leaves out of consideration the electric tension $\varphi^2 - \varphi^3$ of the liquid junction between solutions 2 and 3, either by neglecting it or by estimating it numerically and subtracting it from the total electric tension). The terminals 1 and 1′ being chemically identical, we may write

$$U = \frac{\mu^1_{e-} - F\varphi^1}{-F} - \frac{\mu^{1'}_{e-} - F\varphi^{1'}}{-F}, \tag{2}$$

where $\mu^1_{e-} = \mu^{1'}_{e-}$ represent the chemical potential of the electron in copper and F represents the Faraday. Measuring instruments, potentiometers and voltmeters, always give us differences of electric potentials between chemically identical phases which should then always be associated to the phases of the electrochemist's galvanic and electrolytic cells. In general the copper wires used as connections will belong to the electrochemical systems under study.

Introducing the electrochemical potentials

$$\tilde{\mu}^1_{e-} = \mu^1_{e-} - F\varphi^1, \qquad \tilde{\mu}^{1'}_{e-} = \mu^1_{e-} - F\varphi^{1'}, \tag{3}$$

we have

$$U + \frac{\tilde{\mu}^{1'}_{e-} - \tilde{\mu}^1_{e-}}{-F} = 0, \tag{4}$$

where, in the denominator of the second term on the left-hand side, the charge −F is that transported by 1 mole of electrons passing from 1′ to 1 through an external conductor. The difference of electrochemical potentials in the numerator is equal to the electrochemical affinity of the process

$$e^-(1') \rightarrow e^-(1), \qquad \tilde{A} = \tilde{\mu}^{1'}_{e-} - \tilde{\mu}^1_{e-}. \tag{5}$$

If we reverse the mode of writing of the process, its electrochemical affinity changes sign:

$$e^-(1) \rightarrow e^-(1'), \qquad \tilde{A} = \tilde{\mu}^1_{e-} - \tilde{\mu}^{1'}_{e-}. \tag{6}$$

The charge transported from 1′ to 1 by the external circuit when the process occurs once is now +F. We thus see that the quotient of the electrochemical affinity by the charge transported in the direction of the numbering of the phases is invarient in magnitude and in sign. It is called *electrochemical tension* of this process and we write, designating by E this electrochemical tension,

(7) $$U + \frac{\tilde{A}}{zF} = U + \tilde{E} = 0,$$

where z is the number of charges transported, expressed in Faradays. We have $z = -1$ for case (5) and $z = +1$ for case (6).

At the Zn/Cu contact between phases 4 and 1′ there is always electrochemical equilibrium for the transfer of electrons, intermetallic contacts being considered as unpolarizable. We then have, for the process

(8) $$e^-(4) \rightarrow e^-(1'),$$

the electrochemical equilibrium condition

(9) $$\tilde{A} = \tilde{\mu}^4_{e^-} - \tilde{\mu}^{1'}_{e^-} = 0$$

and (4) can then be written

(10) $$U + \frac{\tilde{\mu}^4_{e^-} - \tilde{\mu}^1_{e^-}}{-F} = 0$$

whether there is, for the whole cell, equilibrium (zero current) or non-equilibrium (current passing either in the spontaneous direction, here from Zn, phase 4, to Cu, phase 1, in the cell, or in the non-spontaneous direction thanks to a suitable electric tension applied from the external current).

In the absence of current there is electrochemical equilibrium at the contact Cu (phase 1)/Cu^{++} (phase 2) and at the contact Zn^{++} (phase 3)/Zn (phase 4). We then have, for the processes

(11) $$Cu(1) \rightarrow Cu^{++}(2) + 2e^-(1),$$

(12) $$Zn^{++}(3) + 2e^-(4) \rightarrow Zn(4),$$

the respective electrochemical equilibrium conditions

(13) $$2\tilde{\mu}^1_{e^-} = \mu^1_{Cu} - \tilde{\mu}^2_{Cu^{++}},$$

(14) $$2\tilde{\mu}^4_{e^-} = \mu^4_{Zn} - \tilde{\mu}^3_{Zn^{++}}.$$

From (10) we then obtain, but only for equilibrium (at all interfaces, 2/3 excepted) which we indicate by the subscript $I = 0$ (zero current):

(15) $$U_{I=0} = -\frac{\tilde{\mu}^2_{Cu^{++}} + \mu^4_{Zn} - \mu^1_{Cu} - \tilde{\mu}^3_{Zn^{++}}}{-2F}.$$

Let us decompose the electrochemical potentials into their chemical and electric terms:

(16) $$U_{I=0} = -\frac{\mu^2_{Cu^{++}} + \mu^4_{Zn} - \mu^1_{Cu} - \mu^3_{Zn^{++}}}{-2F} + (\varphi^2 - \varphi^3)_{I=0},$$

the difference $(\varphi^2 - \varphi^3)_{I=0}$ being the electric tension of the liquid junction at zero current.

Let us introduce the *chemical tension* (or electromotive force) E of the cell reaction, equal to the chemical affinity of the reaction

(17) $$Cu^{++}(2) + Zn(4) \rightarrow Cu(1) + Zn^{++}(3)$$

divided by its reaction charge $-2F$, or to the chemical affinity of the reaction

(18) $$Cu(1) + Zn^{++}(3) \rightarrow Cu^{++}(2) + Zn(4)$$

divided by its reaction charge + 2F. We then have

(19) $$U_{I=0} = -\frac{A}{zF} + (\varphi^2 - \varphi^3)_{I=0} \quad \text{or} \quad U_{I=0} + E = (\varphi^2 - \varphi^3)_{I=0}.$$

The difference between $U_{I=0}$ and U at I different from zero given by (10) can be written

(20) $$U_{I=0} - U_I = \frac{\mu^2_{Cu^{++}} + 2\mu^1_{e^-} - \mu^1_{Cu}}{2F} + \frac{\mu^4_{Zn} - \mu^3_{Zn^{++}} - 2\mu^4_{e^-}}{2F} + (\varphi^2 - \varphi^3)_{I=0} - (\varphi^1 - \varphi^4)_I.$$

The first fraction on the right-hand side is equal to $(\varphi^1 - \varphi^2)_{I=0}$, the second fraction is equal to $(\varphi^3 - \varphi^4)_{I=0}$ and we have

(21) $$U_{I=0} - U_I = (\varphi^1 - \varphi^2)_{I=0} - (\varphi^1 - \varphi^2)_I + (\varphi^3 - \varphi^4)_{I=0} - (\varphi^3 - \varphi^4)_I - (\varphi^2_I - \varphi^3_I),$$

in which the difference $\varphi^2_I - \varphi^3_I$ is equal to plus or minus the internal ohmic drop in the cell. The differences of differences appearing in (21) are the anodic and cathodic *overtensions* at the electrodes of the cell. When the current passes through the cell in the direction corresponding to that in which the cell reaction takes place spontaneously, hence from left to right according to (17), there is a displacement of positive charges from right to left in the cell diagram, copper being deposited on electrode 1 and zinc dissolving in solution 3. The cathodic overtension η_c being always negative and the anodic overtension η_a always positive, we have at the cathode 1/2:

(22) $$(\varphi^1 - \varphi^2)_{I=0} - (\varphi^1 - \varphi^2)_I = -\eta_c > 0$$

and at the anode 4/3:

(23) $$(\varphi^3 - \varphi^4)_{I=0} - (\varphi^3 - \varphi^4)_I = +\eta_a > 0,$$

with

(24) $$\varphi^3_I - \varphi^2_I = RI$$

and (21) can thus be written

(25) $$U_{I=0} - U_I = |\eta_c| + \eta_a + RI > 0.$$

If the current passes through the cell from left to right, the cell reaction takes place from left to right according to (18), copper dissolving in solution 2 and zinc depositing on electrode 4. We have at the anode 1/2:

(26) $$(\varphi^1 - \varphi^2)_{I=0} - (\varphi^1 - \varphi^2)_I = -\eta_a < 0$$

and at the cathode 3/4:

(27) $$(\varphi^3 - \varphi^4)_{I=0} - (\varphi^3 - \varphi^4)_I = +\eta_c < 0,$$

with

(28) $$\varphi^2_I - \varphi^3_I = RI$$

and (21) is now written

(29) $$U_I - U_{I=0} = \eta_a + |\eta_c| + RI > 0.$$

Let us now consider the *tensiometric cell*

$$\underset{A}{Cu} \;/\; \underset{1}{Zn} \;/\; \underset{2}{Zn^{++}} \;//\; \underset{3}{H^+(a_{H^+} = 1)} \;/\; \underset{4}{H_2}(p_{H_2} = 1 \text{ atm.}), \quad Pt \;/\; \underset{B}{Cu}$$

in which the electrode on the right is a standard hydrogen electrode. The cell reaction is

(30) $$Zn(1) + 2H^+(3) \rightarrow Zn^{++}(2) + H_2(4)$$

with the reaction charge +2F or

(31) $$Zn^{++}(2) + H_2(4) \rightarrow Zn(1) + 2H^+(3)$$

with the reaction charge $-2F$. As in (19) we have, neglecting the electric tension of the liquid junction,

(32) $$U_{I=0} = \varphi^A - \varphi^B = -\frac{A_{oxid.}}{+2F} = -\frac{A_{red.}}{-2F} = \frac{A_{red.}}{2F},$$

where $A_{oxid.}$ represents the chemical affinity of reaction (30), which is the oxidation of Zn by H^+ at $a_{H^+} = 1$, and $A_{red.}$ represents the chemical affinity of reaction (31), which is the reduction of Zn^{++} by H_2 at $p_{H_2} = 1$ atm. We also have

(33) $$U_{I=0} = \frac{\mu^2_{Zn^{++}} - \mu^1_{Zn} - (2\mu^3_{H^+} - \mu^4_{H_2})}{2F} = E_{red.}$$

Since Pourbaix represents by the symbol E_0 this electric tension at zero current or "equilibrium tension", our symbol $U_{I=0}$ corresponds to this symbol E_0 which is to be found in all the formulae and diagrams of the present *Atlas.*

The reversible electric tension of the tensiometric cell here considered is thus equal to the *reduction chemical tension,* which is identical with the reduction affinity per unit charge, as indicated in (32).

The chemical potentials $\mu^3_{H^+}$ and $\mu^4_{H_2}$ are the standard chemical potentials of H^+ and H_2, $\mu^{\bullet}_{H^+}$ and $\mu^{\bullet}_{H_2}$. The universal usage is to take the standard hydrogen electrode as reference electrode at all temperatures. Moreover one takes conventionally

(34) $$2\mu^{\bullet}_{H^+} - \mu^{\bullet}_{H_2} = 0$$

at all temperatures, with, specially, at 25°C:

(35) $$\mu^0_{H^+} = 0 \quad \text{and} \quad \mu^0_{H_2} = 0.$$

Formula (33) is then written

(36) $$U_{I=0} = E_{red.} = \frac{\mu^2_{Zn^{++}} - \mu^1_{Zn}}{2F}.$$

At the standard state of 25°C the Zn/Zn^{++} electrode has a reversible electric tension of $-0{\cdot}76$ V. We thus have

$$U^0_{I=0} = -0.76\ \text{V}, \qquad E^0_{red.} = -0.76\ \text{V},$$

with

(37) $$E^0_{oxid.} = -E^0_{red.} = +0.76\ \text{V}.$$

If we take, still at 25°C, $\mu^0_{Zn} = 0$, we obtain $\mu^0_{Zn^{++}} = -0{\cdot}76 \times 2 \times 96\,500 = -146\,700$ J or $-0{\cdot}76 \times 2 \times 23 = -35$ kcal., a quantity which thus represents the standard free enthalpy of formation of the Zn^{++} ion, equal to minus the standard chemical affinity of the reaction.

(38) $$Zn + 2H^+(a_{H^+} = 1) \rightarrow Zn^{++}(a_{Zn^{++}} = 1) + H_2(p_{H_2} = 1\ \text{atm.}).$$

Let us now consider the general case of the electrode reaction

(39) $$aA + mH^+ + ne^- \rightarrow bB + cH_2O,$$

in which A may represent a simple metallic ion and B the corresponding metal ($a = b = 1$, $m = c = 0$), but in which A and B may also both be dissolved species, for instance Fe^{+++}, Fe^{++} and FeO_2H^-, or both oxides or hydroxides, etc. When the reagents and products do not include a metal, the electrons are furnished or liberated by an inert noble metal such as platinum. The reversible electric tension of a cell in which the electrode on the left is that at which reaction (39) can occur, the electrode on the right being always the standard hydrogen electrode is given by

(40) $$U_{I=0} = E_{red.} = \frac{a\mu_A + m\mu_{H^+} - b\mu_B - c\mu_{H_2O}}{nF},$$

an expression in which convention (34) has been taken into account.

The chemical potentials being of the form

(41) $$\mu_i = \mu_i^0(T, p) + RT \ln a_i$$

we have

(42) $$U_{I=0} = E_{red.} = E_0^{\cdot} + \frac{RT}{nF} \ln \frac{(a_A)^a \cdot (a_{H^+})^m}{(a_B)^b \cdot (a_{H_2O})^c},$$

with

(43) $$E_0^{\cdot} = \frac{a\mu_A^0 + m\mu_{H^+}^0 - b\mu_B^0 - c\mu_{H_2O}^0}{nF}.$$

The tension–pH diagrams presented in this *Atlas* apply to the temperature of 25°C. We then make $\mu_{H^+}^0 = 0$ in (43). The activity of water a_{H_2O}, exactly equal to the ratio of the vapor pressure of the solution to that of the pure solvent, is taken as practically equal to one. We then have, at 25°C and in terms of pH,

(44) $$U_{I=0} = E_{red.} = E_0^0 + \frac{0.059}{n} \log \frac{(a_A)^a}{(a_B)^b} - 0.059 \frac{m}{n} \text{ pH}.$$

The systematic use of equations of this type in the construction of the tension–pH diagrams is discussed in detail in the chapters contributed by Pourbaix. The outline of theory presented in this Introduction has as main goal to bring out the fact that the tensions represented in the diagrams can be regarded as being either reversible or equilibrium electric tensions or reduction chemical tensions. In the majority of cases the experimentally accessible tensions are those derived from thermodynamic data, free enthalpies or affinities, obtainable themselves from thermochemical data (heats of formation and entropies), the electrically measurable tensions, at electrodes which must necessarily function reversibly, being definitely in a minority. In any case, the two types of tensions are immediately convertible into each other.

It can also be deduced from the above discussion, particularly from our brief mention of the overtensions, that, out of equilibrium, the reduction chemical tensions remain unchanged as long as the composition of the system, temperature and pressure remain unchanged, while the electric tensions vary on account of the overtensions and of the ohmic drops. It follows that the tension–pH diagrams continue to play a fundamental part out of equilibrium. They represent then, for an element and the ions, oxides and hydroxides resulting from its interaction with water, the various reduction chemical tensions to which one may compare, when they are experimentally obtained by means of polarization curves and plotted on the diagrams, the irreversible electric tensions corresponding to different values of the current or of the reaction velocity.

It is the role of electrochemical kinetics to unravel the mechanisms of irreversible oxidation and reduction processes and to furnish theoretical foundations for the interpretation of the empirical relations between overtensions and currents. In spite of the considerable progress in this field during the last few years and of the abundant experimental and theoretical literature appearing at a constantly accelerated rate, it must be recognized that electrochemical kinetics is still far from having reached a satisfactory degree of logic and coherence.

When the concentration and resistance polarizations have been separated from the total polarization and the activation polarization remains alone to be considered, it is generally found that a law of the

Tafel type applies at sufficiently large overtensions and currents. For a cathodic process, for instance, we have

$$|\eta_c| = a + b \ln I \tag{45}$$

or

$$|\eta_c| = \frac{RT}{\alpha z F} \ln \frac{I}{I_0}, \tag{46}$$

the transfer coefficient α and the exchange current I_0 being empirically obtained from the slope and the extrapolation of the "Tafel straight line". In the range of overtensions and currents for which the velocity of the reverse process, here an oxidation, is not negligible, one writes

$$I = I_0\left[\exp\left(\frac{\alpha z F |\eta_c|}{RT}\right) - \exp\left(-\frac{\beta z F |\eta_c|}{RT}\right)\right], \tag{47}$$

the transfer coefficient β of the reverse process being generally taken equal to $1 - \alpha$. Finally, in the range of very small overtensions, it is possible to retain only the first two terms of the developments in series of the two exponentials and we have

$$I = I_0 \frac{(\alpha + \beta) z F}{RT} |\eta_c|, \tag{48}$$

a formula which expresses the proportionality in the vicinity of equilibrium between current or reaction velocity and electrochemical affinity. It is thus a typical formula of the thermodynamics of irreversible processes.

A complete theoretical deduction of these formulae explaining the exact significance of the transfer coefficient and determining the influence of the composition of the system on the exchange current remains to be established. At the eleventh yearly meeting of CITCE held in Vienna around 1st October 1959, we have suggested, on the basis of earlier communications and of a preliminary study presented in our *Electrochemical Affinity* (Hermann, Paris, 1955), that the use in electrochemistry, for each elementary step of a reaction mechanism, of the Marcelin–De Donder formula (see our article "Reaction rates and affinities", *J. Chem. Phys.* **29**, 640 (1958)), could lead to considerable clarification. This is of the form

$$v = \vec{v}_e\left(\exp\frac{\vec{A} - \vec{A}_e}{RT} - \exp\frac{\overleftarrow{A} - \overleftarrow{A}_e}{RT}\right), \tag{49}$$

in which v is the reaction velocity, $\vec{V}_e = \overleftarrow{V}_e$ is the exchange velocity at equilibrium, $\vec{A}$ and $\overleftarrow{A}$ are the opposed partial affinities equal to the sums of chemical potentials of reagents and products (we have $\vec{A} - \overleftarrow{A} = A$). $\vec{A}_e = \overleftarrow{A}_e$ is the common value of these affinities at equilibrium. In the case of electrochemical reactions these various affinities become sums of electrochemical potentials. We had already insisted in 1949 (*J. Chem. Phys.* **17**, 1226 (1949)) on the advisability of using systematically the electrochemical potentials in the typical case of hydrogen overtensions. Current theoretical studies in the field of electrochemical kinetics combine in general the principles of purely chemical kinetics with empirical considerations intended to describe the role of the electric field in the transition layer from metal to solution. It is, however, clear that the total influence, chemical and electric, of a charge constituent on the velocity of a reaction in which it participates results from the value of its electrochemical potential at the spot where the reaction act takes place. This influence cannot then result from separate and functionally different contributions of the local chemical and electric potentials.

Among the numerous current and future applications of the tension–pH diagrams assembled in this *Atlas* it appears certain that they will serve as foundations for numerous investigations in the field of electrochemical kinetics to the great benefit of this discipline.

CHAPTER II

METHOD OF ESTABLISHING POTENTIAL–pH EQUILIBRIUM DIAGRAMS

METHOD OF ESTABLISHING POTENTIAL–pH EQUILIBRIUM DIAGRAMS(¹)

M. POURBAIX

SUMMARY

1. INTRODUCTION

WHEN iron corrodes in the presence of air in tap water from a town water supply (Fig. 1), a large number of reactions take place simultaneously: the iron corrodes with evolution of hydrogen and the water becomes alkaline according to the reaction $Fe + 2H_2O \rightarrow Fe^{++} + H_2 \nearrow + 2OH^-$; in strongly aerated regions the ferrous ions thus formed are oxidized to ferric ions by dissolved oxygen according to the reaction $4Fe^{++} + O_2 + 2H_2O \rightarrow 4Fe^{+++} + 4OH^-$, and these ferric ions react with the hydroxyl ions according to the reaction $4Fe^{+++} + 12OH^- \rightarrow 4Fe(OH)_3 \downarrow$ to form a brown deposit of ferric hydroxide; in less aerated regions the action of oxygen leads to the separation, not of ferric hydroxide, but of magnetite Fe_3O_4. In general these oxides are deposited in the form of rust at a certain distance from the place where the iron dissolves, in which case the corrosion of the metal proceeds

(¹) Detailed accounts of this have been given in the following publications:

[1] M. POURBAIX, *Thermodynamique des solutions aqueuses diluées. Représentation graphique du rôle du pH et du potentiel* (*Thesis*, Delft, 1945; Béranger, Paris and Liège). 3rd Edition, Cebelcor 1963. *Thermodynamics of Dilute Aqueous Solutions, with Applications to Electrochemistry and Corrosion* (foreword by U. R. EVANS), Arnold, London, 1950.

[2] M. POURBAIX, *Leçons sur la Corrosion électrochimique* (2e fascicule) (Rapport technique RT.30 of CEBELCOR, 1956).

[3] M. POURBAIX, *Leçons sur la Corrosion électrochimique* (3e fascicule) (Rapport technique RT.49 of CEBELCOR, 1957).

The author expresses his gratitude to P. Van Rysselberghe and R. Defay for numerous discussions relating to the present text.

in a permanent manner; sometimes these oxides are deposited in an adherent form at the actual place where the iron dissolves, in which case they can cover the metal with a more or less protective coating. Other changes can occur simultaneously with these reactions: the local alkalinization of the water due to the evolution of hydrogen or the reduction of oxygen causes the conversion of bicarbonate ions, according to the reaction $HCO_3^- + OH^- \rightarrow CO_3^{--} + H_2O$, into carbonate ions, which react with the dissolved calcium ions to form calcium carbonate according to the reaction $CO_3^{--} + Ca^{++} \rightarrow CaCO_3 \downarrow$. If this calcium carbonate is deposited on the metal, which frequently happens with tap water, it can form on the surface, in combination with ferric oxide or hydroxide, an adherent coating which effectively protects the metal against further corrosion.

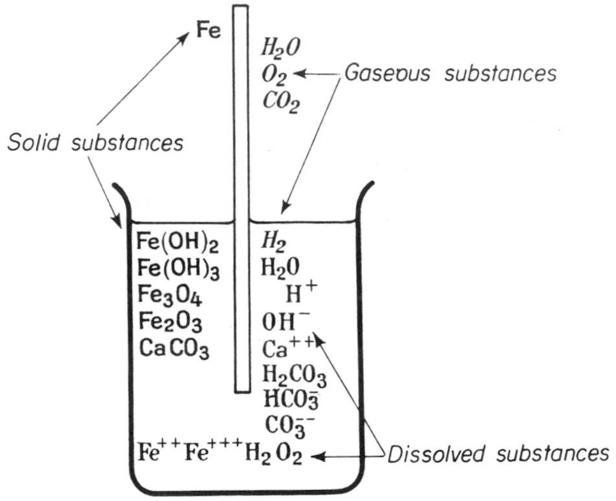

FIG. 1. Iron in the presence of tap water from a town water supply.

Finally, in the course of this corrosion of iron, other reactions can lead to the formation of small quantities of hydrogen peroxide.

Under these conditions, therefore, the corrosion of iron gives rise to the formation of a large number of substances in the dissolved, solid and gaseous states; these substances react chemically and electrochemically among themselves, and we are faced with an inextricable problem if we try to study these reactions separately. For the study of these complex phenomena it is best to employ graphical methods which enable us to study simultaneously the equilibria of *all* the entangled reactions,([2]) both chemical and electrochemical, that may occur.

It is for the study of such problems that the electrochemical equilibrium diagrams discussed here are intended.

2. CONVENTIONS FOR WRITING THE REACTIONS. CHEMICAL REACTIONS AND ELECTROCHEMICAL REACTIONS

2.1. GENERAL

Throughout this *Atlas* we shall concern ourselves in particular with the study of equilibrium states of reactions, which are the same in whichever direction one considers the reactions. We shall therefore

([2]) The idea of "entangled equilibria" was introduced by P. Montagne in his treatise *Calcul numérique des équilibres chimiques en phase gazeuse homogène; applications à l'étude théorique des combustions*, Gauthier-Villars, Paris, 1934.

write these reactions in a manner that does not necessarily imply that the reaction takes place in a definite direction (for instance from left to right, a convention which the majority of authors use at present) rather than in the other direction (from right to left).

For example, the equation $2H_2O = 2H_2 + O_2$ will not necessarily be taken to represent the dissociation of water $2H_2O \rightarrow 2H_2 + O_2$; it will represent equally well the synthesis of water $2H_2O \leftarrow 2H_2 + O_2$. The equation $H_2 = 2H^+ + 2e^-$ will not necessarily be taken to represent the oxidation $H_2 \rightarrow 2H^+ + 2e^-$; it will also represent the reduction $H_2 \leftarrow 2H^+ + 2e^-$.

2.2. CHEMICAL REACTIONS

A *chemical reaction* is a reaction in which only neutral molecules and positively or negatively charged ions take part, with the exclusion of electrons (see later on the definition of an electrochemical reaction).

The following reactions are examples:

Dissociation of water vapour	$2H_2O_{(g)}$	$\rightarrow$	$2H_{2(g)} + O_{2(g)}$
Electrolytic dissociation of liquid water	$H_2O_{(l)}$	$\rightarrow$	$H^+_{(aq.)} + OH^-_{(aq.)}$
Precipitation of ferrous hydroxide	$Fe^{++}_{(aq.)} + 2OH^-_{(aq.)}$	$\rightarrow$	$Fe(OH)_{2(s)}$
Dissolution of gaseous CO_2	$CO_{2(g)} + H_2O_{(l)}$	$\rightarrow$	$H_2CO_{3(aq.)}$
Corrosion of iron with evolution of hydrogen	$Fe_{(s)} + 2H^+_{(aq.)}$	$\rightarrow$	$Fe^{++}_{(aq.)} + H_{2(g)}$
Oxidation of ferrous ions by permanganate	$MnO^-_{4(aq.)} + 8H^+_{(aq.)} + 5Fe^{++}_{(aq.)}$	$\rightarrow$	$Mn^{++}_{(aq.)} + 4H_2O_{(l)} + 5Fe^{+++}_{(aq.)}$.

These reactions can be written in the general form

(1) $$\nu'_1 M'_1 + \nu'_2 M'_2 + \ldots = \nu''_1 M''_1 + \nu''_2 M''_2 + \ldots,$$

in which the "stoichiometric coefficients" $\nu'_1, \nu'_2, \ldots$ and $\nu''_1, \nu''_2 \ldots$ are positive numbers.

By bringing all the terms to one side of the equation, we can write the reaction equation (1) in a shortened form

(2) $$\boxed{\Sigma \nu M = 0,}$$

in which the stoichiometric coefficients ν have the same numerical values as in (1) but bear either a + or a − sign; *as a sign convention* we say that the coefficients ν are positive for the reacting substances M on the right-hand side of the reaction equation (1), and negative for the reacting substances on the left-hand side.

For example, the following reaction written in form (1)

$$MnO_4^- + 8H^+ + 5Fe^{++} \rightarrow Mn^{++} + 4H_2O + 5Fe^{+++}$$

will be written in form (2)

$$Mn^{++} + 4H_2O + 5Fe^{+++} - MnO_4^- - 8H^+ - 5Fe^{++} = 0.$$

By writing the reaction in form (1) or form (2) we do not assume that we know the direction in which the reaction is really proceeding. Depending on the circumstances, reaction (1) can take place from left to right, using up certain quantities of substances M′ to produce substances M″, or conversely from right to left, producing substances M′ at the expense of substances M″. When the reaction takes place from left to right we say in general that it takes place in the positive direction; when it takes place from right to left, we say in general that it retrogresses, or takes place in the negative direction.

In short, by choosing the direction in which to write a reaction, we do not assert that it will proceed in this direction; we merely choose the direction which will be taken as positive; when a reaction takes place from left to right, we say moreover, that it takes place in the direction in which it is written.

The rule for the signs of the stoichiometric coefficients in the reaction equation (2) can be stated very simply as follows: when reaction (1) takes place in the direction in which it is written, the constituents which appear have positive stoichiometric coefficients in (2) and those which disappear have negative stoichiometric coefficients.

2.3. ELECTROCHEMICAL REACTIONS

We shall define *an electrochemical reaction* (or electrode reaction) as being a reaction involving, besides molecules and ions, negative electrons e^- arising from a metal or other substance by metallic conduction. Such reactions will be *oxidations* if they proceed in the direction corresponding to the liberation of electrons; they will be *reductions* if they proceed in the direction corresponding to the absorption of electrons.

Some examples of electrochemical reactions are:

Reduction of hydrogen ions to gaseous hydrogen	$2H^+_{(aq.)} + 2e^- \rightarrow H_{2(g)}$
Reduction of gaseous oxygen to hydroxyl ions	$O_{2(g)} + 2H_2O_{(l)} + 4e^- \rightarrow 4OH^-_{(aq.)}$
Reduction of permanganate to manganous ions	$MnO^-_{4(aq.)} + 8H^+_{(aq.)} + 5e^- \rightarrow Mn^{++}_{(aq.)} + 4H_2O_{(l)}$
Oxidation of iron to ferrous ions	$Fe_{(s)} \rightarrow Fe^{++}_{(aq.)} + 2e^-$
Oxidation of ferrous ions to ferric ions	$Fe^{++}_{(aq.)} \rightarrow Fe^{+++}_{(aq.)} + e^-.$

These reactions can be written in the general form

(3) $$\nu'_1 M'_1 + \nu'_2 M'_2 + \ldots + n e^- = \nu''_1 M''_1 + \nu''_2 M''_2 + \ldots$$

or

(4) $$\boxed{\Sigma \nu M + n e^- = 0.}$$

2.4. METHOD OF WRITING THE REACTIONS

It is well known that, *for every chemical reaction* involving, among other substances, gases and/or dissolved substances, there exists an *equilibrium constant* whose value for a given temperature and total pressure is a certain function of the *partial pressures* (or the *fugacities*) of the gaseous reacting substances and of the *concentrations* (or the *activities*) of the dissolved reacting substances. Some examples of such equilibrium constants are:

dissociation in the gaseous phase (Guldberg and Waage's constant, mass action constant):

$$2H_2O_{(g)} = 2H_{2(g)} + O_{2(g)}, \qquad K = \frac{(p_{H_2})^2 \cdot p_{O_2}}{(p_{H_2O})^2};$$

dissociation in solution (Ostwald's constant, dissociation constant, ionic product of water):

$$H_2O_{(l)} = H^+_{(aq.)} + OH^-_{(aq.)}, \qquad K = C_{H^+} \cdot C_{OH^-};$$

dissolution of sparingly soluble solid substances (solubility product):

$$Fe(OH)_{2(s)} = Fe^{++}_{(aq.)} + 2OH^-_{(aq.)}, \qquad K = C_{Fe^{++}} \cdot C^2_{OH^-};$$

$$As_2O_{3(s)} + H_2O_{(l)} = 2HAsO_{2(aq.)}, \qquad K = C_{HAsO_2};$$

dissolution of gaseous substances:

$$CO_{2(g)} + H_2O_{(l)} = H_2CO_{3(aq.)}, \qquad K = \frac{C_{H_2CO_3}}{p_{CO_2}}.$$

It is possible to show(3) that, *for every electrochemical reaction* involving gases and/or dissolved substances, there also exists an *equilibrium constant* whose value, for a given temperature and total pressure, is a function, not only of the partial pressures (or fugacities) of the gaseous reacting substances and of the concentrations (or activities) of the dissolved reacting substances, but also of a *difference of electric potential* (or *electrode tension*).

Consequently, if, in order to establish equilibrium diagrams as a function of pH and electrode potential, we concern ourselves with investigating the influence of the *pH* and the *electrode potential* on the equilibrium characteristics of the different reactions that we are interested in, it is as well to write these reactions in a certain specified manner which makes clearly apparent in the reaction equation any H^+ ions and electric charges e^- that may take part in the reaction.

For this purpose we shall in general use the *following convention for writing the reactions*: for example in writing the reaction for the conversion of permanganate ions MnO_4^- into manganous ions Mn^{++} (reduction of permanganate in acid solution) we proceed as follows: we write the symbols for these two substances on either side of the = sign.

	MnO_4^-	$= Mn^{++}$
We balance the O's with H_2O:	MnO_4^-	$= Mn^{++} + 4H_2O$
We balance the H's with H^+:	$MnO_4^- + 8H^+$	$= Mn^{++} + 4H_2O$
We balance the electric charges with e^-:	$MnO_4^- + 8H^+ + 5e^-$	$= Mn^{++} + 4H_2O$.

Below are some other examples (reduction of permanganate in non-acid solution, and reduction of dichromate):

MnO_4^-	$= MnO_2$	$Cr_2O_7^{--}$	$= 2Cr^{+++}$
MnO_4^-	$= MnO_2 + 2H_2O$	$Cr_2O_7^{--}$	$= 2Cr^{+++} + 7H_2O$
$MnO_4^- + 4H^+$	$= MnO_2 + 2H_2O$	$Cr_2O_7^{--} + 14H^+$	$= 2Cr^{+++} + 7H_2O$
$MnO_4^- + 4H^+ + 3e^-$	$= MnO_2 + 2H_2O$	$Cr_2O_7^{--} + 14H^+ + 6e^-$	$= 2Cr^{+++} + 7H_2O$;

Also for the precipitation of ferrous hydroxide, for example, we shall not write:

$$Fe^{++} + 2OH^- = Fe(OH)_2,$$

but we shall write instead

$$Fe^{++} + 2H_2O = Fe(OH)_2 + 2H^+.$$

In general, the reaction for the conversion of an oxidized substance A into a reduced substance B, for instance, will be written:

$$aA + cH_2O + ne^- = bB + mH^+.$$

By applying the general equilibrium formulae that we are about to deduce to reactions written in this way, we shall obtain equilibrium relations which will automatically be expressed as a function of the pH and the electrode potential;

the pH measures the effect of the H^+ ions;

the electrode potential measures the effect of the charges e^-.

3. GENERAL FORMULA FOR CHEMICAL EQUILIBRIA

Let us consider a *chemical reaction*

$$\Sigma \nu M = 0, \quad (2)$$

which involves gaseous substances and/or substances dissolved in aqueous solution.

---

(3) See *loc. cit.* [1].

The affinity A of this reaction can be expressed by the equation

(5) $$A = -\Sigma \nu\mu,$$

in which μ represents the "chemical potentials" of the various reacting substances M.

If we use the common symbol (M) to represent the fugacity or "corrected" partial pressure of the gaseous substances (expressed in atmospheres), and the activity or "corrected" concentration of the dissolved substances (expressed as a molality, i.e. in gram-molecules or gram-ions per kilogram of solvent), the values of the chemical potentials μ of each of the reacting substances M can be expressed by the following equation:[4]

(6) $$\mu = \mu^\circ + RT \ln (M),$$

in which

μ° is the "standard chemical potential" of the substance considered;
R is the ideal gas constant (1·985 cal.-deg. mole);
T is the absolute temperature;
ln represents a Napierian logarithm.

In the case of a gaseous constituent, the standard chemical potential μ° depends solely on the temperature; it is the chemical potential of the substance when it is by itself at the temperature considered and under such a pressure that its fugacity is 1 atm. (760 mm Hg).

In the case of a condensed constituent, μ° is the chemical potential of the pure substance in this condensed state; it depends on the temperature T and the pressure p.

In the case of a solution, the standard chemical potential of the solvent is the chemical potential of the pure solvent at the temperature and pressure considered; the standard chemical potential of a dissolved substance is the chemical potential of this substance at the pressure and temperature considered, in a reference state chosen according to certain conventions in which the substance is attributed an activity of unity.

Now the chemical potential μ of a constituent can be expressed by the equation

(7) $$\mu = h - Ts,$$

in which h is the specific molar enthalpy of this constituent and s is its specific molar entropy, under the conditions of medium, pressure, temperature and concentration experienced by the constituent.

For the chemical reaction $\Sigma \nu M = 0$ we can write, on the basis of equations (5) and (7):

(8) $$-A = \Sigma \nu\mu = \Sigma \nu h - T \Sigma \nu s$$

or, representing the summation $\Sigma \nu x$ by the notation ΔX:

(9) $$-A = \Delta G = \Delta H - T \Delta S,$$

in which G represents the free enthalpy $G = H - TS$; we point out, however, that although the X corresponding to $x = \mu$ is being represented more and more widely by the symbol G, it is still often represented by the symbol F used by G. N. Lewis and his collaborators.

Equation (9) can be written in particular for reagents and reaction products considered separately in the pure state and under the same conditions of temperature and pressure. For example, if we consider the reaction

$$H_{2(g)} + \frac{1}{2} O_{2(g)} \rightarrow H_2O_{(l)}$$

representing the formation of liquid H_2O starting from the substances H_2 and O_2 in the gaseous state, we have

$$\Delta G = \mu_{H_2O_{(l)}} - \mu_{H_{2(g)}} - \frac{1}{2} \mu_{O_{2(g)}}$$

(4) See *loc. cit.* [2], p. 9.

A very widely adopted convention consists of assigning the value zero to the chemical potentials of elements in their normal molecular state at 25°C and 1 atm. pressure. If H_2 and O_2 are both considered at 1 atm. pressure we have therefore,

$$\Delta G = \mu_{H_2O_{(l)}},$$

which shows that the free enthalpy of formation of liquid H_2O starting from its elements at 25°C and 1 atm. is the same as the chemical potential of liquid H_2O, a substance which is then in its standard state.

In view of this, and taking into account equation (5), the condition for thermodynamic equilibrium of a chemical reaction, i.e. the condition which expresses that the affinity of such a reaction is zero, can be written

(10) $$\Sigma \nu \mu = 0$$

or, substituting into this equation the values of the chemical potentials μ shown in equation (6),

(11) $$\Sigma \nu \mu^{\circ} + RT\, \Sigma \nu \ln(M) = 0$$

or further, by replacing the ideal gas constant R by its numerical value, and changing from Napierian logarithms to decimal logarithms:

(12) $$\Sigma \nu \mu^{\circ} + 4.575\, T\, \Sigma \nu \log(M) = 0$$

that is

(13) $$\boxed{\Sigma \nu \log(M) = -\frac{\Sigma \nu \mu^{\circ}}{4.575\, T}}$$

which can be written

(14) $$\Sigma \nu \log(M) = \log K,$$

(15) $$\log K = -\frac{\Sigma \nu \mu^{\circ}}{4.575\, T} \quad (^5)$$

Now the formulation

(2) $$\Sigma \nu M = 0$$

of a reaction equation is equivalent to the usual formulation

(1) $$\nu'_1 M'_1 + \nu'_2 M'_2 + \ldots = \nu''_1 M''_1 + \nu''_2 M''_2 + \ldots.$$

The stoichiometric coefficients ν of the formulation (2) are usually considered as being positive for the substances M″ on the right-hand side of the usual formulation; they are considered as being negative for the substances M′ on the left-hand side. Equation (13) can therefore be expressed in the form

(16) $$\log \frac{(M''_1)^{\nu''_1} . (M''_2)^{\nu''_2} \ldots}{(M'_1)^{\nu'_1} . (M'_2)^{\nu'_2} \ldots} = -\frac{\Sigma \nu \mu^{\circ}}{4.575\, T}$$

or

(17) $$\frac{(M''_1)^{\nu''_1} . (M''_2)^{\nu''_2} \ldots}{(M'_1)^{\nu'_1} . (M'_2)^{\nu'_2} \ldots} = 10^{-\frac{\Sigma \nu \mu^{\circ}}{4.575\, T}}$$

---

(5) It would be as well to point out that the formulation (15) of the value of the equilibrium constant K is equivalent to the usual equation

$$\ln K = -\frac{\Sigma \nu \mu^{\circ}}{RT}$$

and to the equation

$$K = e^{\frac{A^{\circ}}{RT}},$$

in which A° is the standard affinity of the reaction, i.e. the affinity of the reaction in the particular case when all the reacting substances are in the standard state.

or

(18) $$\frac{(M''_1)^{\nu''_1}.(M''_2)^{\nu''_2}\ldots}{(M'_1)^{\nu'_1}.(M'_2)^{\nu'_2}\ldots} = K,$$

(19) $$\log K = -\frac{\Sigma \nu\mu^{\cdot}}{4.575\,T}.$$

Consequently for every chemical reaction $\Sigma\nu M = 0$, the equilibrium condition at a temperature T can be expressed by the equation

(14) $$\Sigma \nu \log(M) = \log K,$$

i.e. the algebraic sum $\Sigma \nu \log(M)$ of the logarithms of the fugacities, and activities (M) of the gaseous and dissolved reacting substances is a constant which is the logarithm of an "equilibrium constant" K. The value of this equilibrium constant is connected with the values of the standard chemical potentials $\mu^{\cdot}$ of the reacting substances and with the absolute temperature by the equation

(15) $$\log K = -\frac{\Sigma \nu\mu^{\cdot}}{4.575\,T}.$$

When the temperature is $t = 25{\cdot}0°C$, i.e. $T = 298{\cdot}1°K$, as is considered throughout this *Atlas*, equilibrium conditions (13), (14) and (15) become respectively

(20) $$\Sigma \nu \log(M) = -\frac{\Sigma \nu\mu^{0}}{1363},$$

(14) $$\Sigma \nu \log(M) = \log K,$$

(21) $$\log K = -\frac{\Sigma \nu\mu^{0}}{1363},$$

in which $\mu°$ represents the standard chemical potentials at 25°C of the reacting substances M.

Relation (20) [and relations (14) and (21) which are derived from it] is the *general formula for chemical equilibria* (or physicochemical ones) at 25°C.

This relation expresses that, when the equilibrium state of a chemical or physicochemical change is obtained at a given temperature and pressure, the algebraic sum $\Sigma \nu \log(M)$ of the logarithms of the fugacities and activities (M) of the gaseous and dissolved reacting substances is equal to a constant log K, whose value depends only on the temperature and pressure, and can be calculated from relation (21) if the values of the standard chemical potentials $\mu°$ of all the reacting substances are known for the standard reference state, which is:

for condensed substances (solid or liquid), the pure state;

for gaseous substances, the state having a fugacity (or "corrected" partial pressure) of 1 atm.;

for dissolved substances, the state having an activity (or "corrected" molality) of 1 g-mol (or 1 g-ion) per kilogram of solvent.

Given below are some examples of the calculation of the equilibrium constant, for the four types of chemical reactions considered in paragraph 2.4, and also for the vaporization of water, based on the following standard chemical potentials $\mu°$ at 25°C; [6]

H_2O (gaseous)	− 54 635 cal	$Fe(OH)_2$ (solid)	− 115 570 cal
H_2 (gaseous)	0 „	Fe^{++} (dissolved)	− 20 300 „
O_2 (gaseous)	0 „	As_2O_3 (solid)	− 137 680 „
H_2O (liquid)	− 56 690 „	$HAsO_2$ (dissolved)	− 96 250 „
H^+ (dissolved)	0 „	CO_2 (gaseous)	− 94 260 „
OH^- (dissolved)	− 37 595 „	H_2CO_3 (dissolved)	− 149 000 „

[6] *Enthalpies libres de formation standard* (Rapport technique RT. 87 of CEBELCOR, 1960).

Homogeneous reaction in the gaseous phase:

$2H_2O_{(g)} = 2H_{2(g)} + O_{2(g)}$:

$$\log \frac{(p_{H_2})^2 \cdot p_{O_2}}{(p_{H_2O})^2} = -\frac{2\mu^0_{H_2} + \mu^0_{O_2} - 2\mu^0_{H_2O}}{1\,363} = -\frac{0 + 0 + 109\,270}{1\,363}$$

$$= -80.16$$ [Guldberg and Waage's law of dissociation in the gaseous phase (mass-action law)].

Homogeneous reaction in aqueous solution:

$H_2O_{(l)} = H^+_{(aq.)} + OH^-_{(aq.)}$:

$$\log C_{H^+} \cdot C_{OH^-} = -\frac{\mu^0_{H^+} + \mu^0_{OH^-} - \mu^0_{H_2O}}{1\,363} = -\frac{0 - 37\,595 + 56\,690}{1\,363}$$

$$= -14.00$$ (Oswald's law of electrolytic dissociation).

Heterogeneous reactions—solid/solution type:

$Fe(OH)_{2(s)} = Fe^{++}_{(aq.)} + 2\,OH^-_{(aq.)}$:

$$\log C_{Fe^{++}} \cdot (C_{OH^-})^2 = -\frac{\mu^0_{Fe^{++}} + 2\mu^0_{OH^-} - \mu^0_{Fe(OH)_2}}{1\,363} = -\frac{-20\,300 + 75\,190 + 115\,570}{1\,363}$$

$$= -14.73$$ (solubility product law);

$As_2O_{3(s)} + H_2O_{(l)} = 2HAsO_{2(aq.)}$:

$$\log C_{HAsO_2} = -\frac{1}{2}\,\frac{2\mu^0_{HAsO_2} - \mu^0_{As_2O_3} - \mu^0_{H_2O}}{1\,363}$$

$$= -\frac{-192\,500 + 137\,680 + 56\,690}{2\,726} = -0.68$$ (solubility).

Heterogeneous reaction—gas/solution type:

$CO_{2(g)} + H_2O_{(l)} = H_2CO_{3(aq.)}$:

$$\log \frac{C_{H_2CO_3}}{p_{CO_2}} = -\frac{\mu^0_{H_2CO_3} - \mu^0_{CO_2} - \mu^0_{H_2O}}{1\,363}$$

$$= -\frac{-149\,000 + 94\,260 + 56\,690}{1\,363} = -1.43$$ (Henry's gas solubility law).

Conversion from condensed phase (solid or liquid) to gaseous phase:

$H_2O_{(l)} = H_2O_{(g)}$:

$$\log p_{H_2O} = -\frac{\mu^0_{H_2O_{(g)}} - \mu^0_{H_2O_{(l)}}}{1\,363} = -\frac{-54\,635 + 56\,690}{1\,363} = -1.505.$$

that is

$$p_{H_2O} = 10^{-1.505}\ \text{atm.} = 0.0313\ \text{atm.} = 23.7\ \text{mm Hg}.$$ (vapour pressure law).

It is important that we should be well aware of the fact that *the different equilibrium laws which these equations express are only particular cases of a single law of physico-chemical equilibrium*

(14) $$\boxed{\Sigma\,\nu\,\log(M) = \log K,}$$

or

(21) $$\boxed{\log K = -\frac{\Sigma\,\nu\mu^0}{1\,363},}$$

in which the constant K is known by different names, according to the nature of the change that is being studied: Guldberg and Waage's constant (mass–action constant), Ostwald's constant (dissociation constant, ionic product of water), solubility product, solubility, Henry constant, vapour pressure. *The value of each of these equilibrium constants* K *is connected with the values of the standard free enthalpies formation (or standard chemical potentials)* μ° *of the substances taking part in the change, by the same relation, which is at* 25°C:

$$\log K = -\frac{\Sigma \nu \mu^0}{1363}. \tag{21}$$

4. GENERAL FORMULA FOR ELECTROCHEMICAL EQUILIBRIA (7)

4.1. GALVANIC CELLS

We have defined an electrochemical reaction (or electrode reaction) as being a reaction involving both chemical substances M (neutral molecules and/or positively or negatively charged ions) and free electric charges (for instance negative electrons e^- arising from a metal or other substance with metallic conduction):

$$\Sigma \nu M + n e^- = 0 \quad (7) \qquad \text{for example} \quad Zn_{(s)} = Zn^{++}_{(aq.)} + 2e^-.$$

Such reactions can be brought about by the coupling of two electrodes at which take place respectively absorption and liberation of electrons, for instance according to the reactions

$$\Sigma \nu_1 M_1 + n_1 e^- = 0,$$
$$\Sigma \nu_2 M_2 - n_1 e^- = 0,$$

leading to the overall chemical reaction

$$\Sigma \nu_1 M_1 + \Sigma \nu_2 M_2 = 0. \tag{22}$$

These galvanic cells may operate either without the external addition of electrical energy (in which case the overall chemical reaction takes place in the direction suggested by its affinity), or with the external addition of electrical energy (in which case the overall chemical reaction takes place in the opposite direction to that suggested by its affinity alone). In the first case, which is obtained in the discharge of batteries and accumulators and in the spontaneous corrosion of metals, there is oxidation at the negative electrode of the cell and reduction at the positive electrode(8); in the second case, which is obtained in electrolysis and in the charging of accumulators, there is reduction at the negative electrode and oxidation at the positive electrode; in the two cases we call the electrode where there is oxidation the *anode*, and the electrode where there is reduction the *cathode*.

For example (Figs. 2 and 3), the synthesis of water in a hydrogen/oxygen gas cell and the discharge of a zinc/copper Daniell cell take place according to the following reactions:

− ve Electrode (oxidation)	$2H_2 \rightarrow 4H^+ + 4e^-$	$Zn \rightarrow Zn^{++} + 2e^-$
+ ve Electrode (reduction)	$O_2 + 4H^+ + 4e^- \rightarrow 2H_2O$	$Cu^{++} + 2e^- \rightarrow Cu$
Overall reaction	$2H_2 + O_2 \rightarrow 2H_2O$	$Zn + Cu^{++} \rightarrow Zn^{++} + Cu$.

(7) See *loc. cit.* [3], pp. 5–14.

(8) Here we call the electrode attached to the negative terminal of the cell the negative electrode, and the electrode attached to the positive terminal of the cell the positive electrode.

Conversely, the electrolysis of water and the charging of a Daniell cell take place as follows:

− ve Electrode (reduction)	$4H^{+} + 4e^{-} \rightarrow 2H_2$	$Zn^{++} + 2e^{-} \rightarrow Zn$
+ ve Electrode (oxidation)	$2H_2O \rightarrow O_2 + 4H^{+} + 4e^{-}$	$Cu \rightarrow Cu^{++} + 2e^{-}$
Overall reaction	$2H_2O \rightarrow 2H_2 + O_2$	$Zn^{++} + Cu \rightarrow Zn + Cu^{++}$.

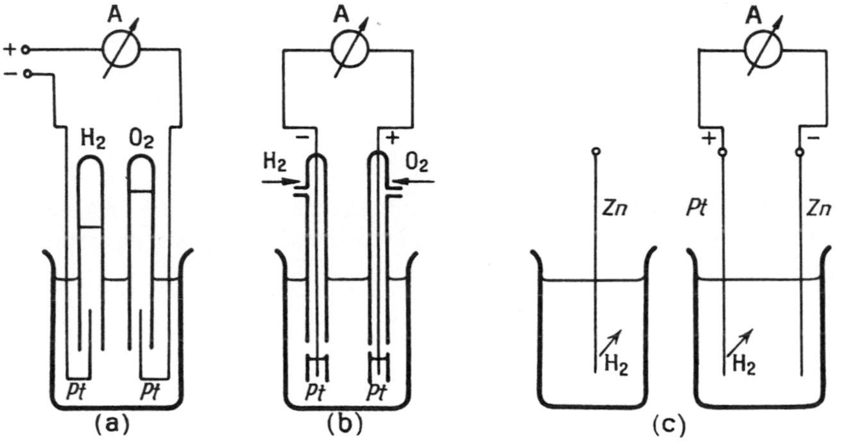

FIG. 2. Electrochemical realization of chemical reactions.

(*a*) Decomposition of water (electrolysis): $2H_2O \rightarrow 2H_2 + O_2$.
(*b*) Synthesis of water (gas cell): $2H_2 + O_2 \rightarrow 2H_2O$.
(*c*) Corrosion of zinc with the evolution of hydrogen: $Zn + 2H^{+} \rightarrow Zn^{++} + H_2$.

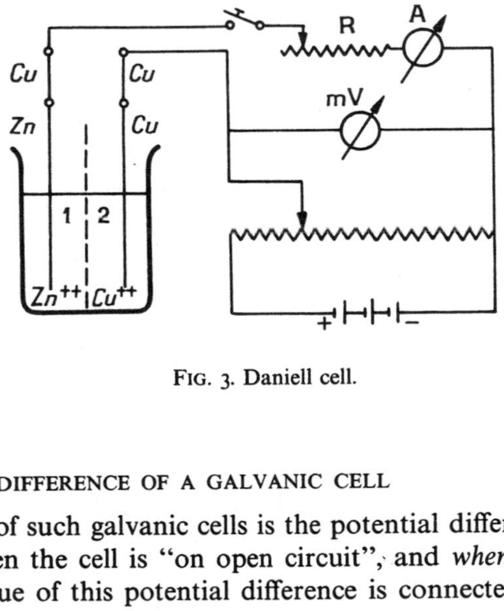

FIG. 3. Daniell cell.

4.2. EQUILIBRIUM POTENTIAL DIFFERENCE OF A GALVANIC CELL

The electromotive force of such galvanic cells is the potential difference $\varphi_1 - \varphi_2$ ([9]) (or tension at the terminals of the cell) when the cell is "on open circuit", and *when the whole system is in electrochemical equilibrium.* The value of this potential difference is connected with the value of the affinity $A_{1.2}$ of the overall chemical reaction (22) by the relation

(23)
$$\varphi_1 - \varphi_2 = -\frac{A_{1.2}}{n_1 F}$$

([9]) φ_1 and φ_2 represent respectively the internal electric potentials of chemically identical terminals (both made of copper for instance) attached to the two electrodes of the cell. The electromotive force (or chemical tension) of the cell is $A_{1.2}/nF$.

or, since

(24) $$A_{1.2} = -(\Sigma\nu_1\mu_1 + \Sigma\nu_2\mu_2),$$

(25) $$\varphi_1 - \varphi_2 = \frac{\Sigma\nu_1\mu_1 + \Sigma\nu_2\mu_2}{n_1 F}.$$

This difference of electric potentials, or electric "tension", is the *equilibrium potential difference* of the galvanic cell.

If we express the electric potentials in volts and the chemical potentials μ in calories per mole, equation (25) becomes

(26) $$\varphi_1 - \varphi_2 = \frac{\Sigma\nu_1\mu_1 + \Sigma\nu_2\mu_2}{23\,060\,n_1}.$$

Let us consider, for example, a Daniell cell in which the Zn^{++} and Cu^{++} ions are in the standard state (activities: 1 g-ion/l at 25°C), and for which the chemical potentials have the following values (according to Latimer):

$$\mu^0_{Zn} = 0 \text{ cal.,} \qquad \mu^0_{Cu} = 0 \text{ cal.,}$$
$$\mu^0_{Zn^{++}} = -35\,184 \text{ »} \qquad \mu^0_{Cu^{++}} = +15\,530 \text{ »}$$

Equation (22) gives

$$\varphi_{Zn} - \varphi_{Cu} = \frac{-35\,184 - 0 + 0 - 15\,530}{46\,120} = -\frac{50\,714}{46\,120} = -1.099 \text{ V}.$$

The potential at the terminals of this Daniell cell in the equilibrium state is 1·099 V; the zinc is the negative electrode, i.e. the copper wire which is attached to it is negative with respect to the other terminal of the cell.

4.3. ELECTRODE POTENTIAL. EQUILIBRIUM POTENTIAL OF AN ELECTROCHEMICAL REACTION

With a view to studying any electrochemical reaction $\Sigma\nu_1 M_1 + n_1 e^- = 0$, let us consider a galvanic cell of a special type (Fig. 4) made up of an electrode 1 on which is taking place the reaction that we

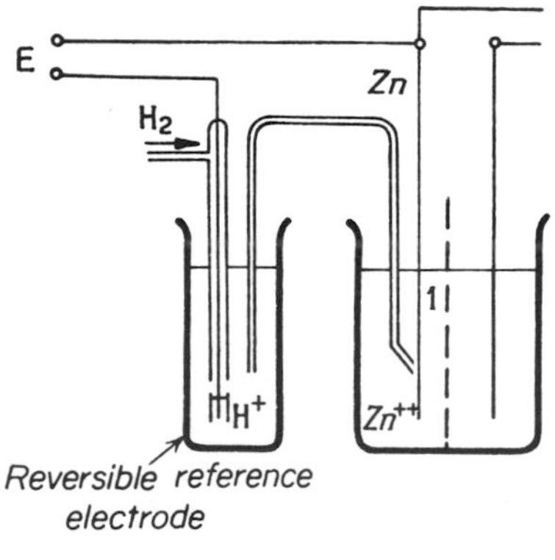

FIG. 4. Measurement of electrode potential. (Haber and Luggin's method.)

wish to study, and a *reversible reference electrode* (hydrogen electrode, calomel electrode, silver chloride electrode) *on which the state of thermodynamic equilibrium of the electrochemical reference reaction is obtained.* It must be understood that this reference electrode is connected to the reaction solution by means of a siphon to avoid the existence of a diffusion potential between the two solutions (for instance a siphon of agar-agar jelly saturated with KCl) and which, when an electric current flows in the reaction solution, *emerges in this solution in the immediate neighbourhood of the metallic surface on which the reaction to be studied is taking place* (Haber and Luggin's siphon or Piontelli's siphon). The equation

(27) $$\varphi_1 - \varphi_{ref} = \frac{\Sigma \nu_1 \mu_1 + \Sigma \nu_{ref} \mu_{ref}}{23\,060\, n_1}$$

which is deduced from equation (24) gives the value of the equilibrium potential difference of the cell formed by coupling the electrode studied and the reference electrode, i.e. the value of the potential difference when the whole of the system is in electrochemical equilibrium. Now the reference electrode is, by definition, in a state of equilibrium. *Equation* (27) *therefore expresses the equilibrium condition of the electrochemical reaction studied.*

Consequently a general electrochemical reaction *r*, i.e. $\Sigma \nu_r M_r + n_r e^- = 0$, will be in a state of equilibrium if the difference between the potential φ of the electrode on which this reaction is taking place and the potential φ_{ref} of a given [10] reversible reference electrode has a fixed value, given in

(28) $$\varphi_r - \varphi_{ref} = \frac{\Sigma \nu_r \mu_r - \Sigma \nu_{ref} \mu_{ref}}{23\,060\, n_r}.$$

We shall call the difference of potential thus measured between an electrode and a reversible reference electrode the "potential" of this electrode, or *electrode potential* E, and we shall call this electrode potential the *equilibrium potential of a reaction* in the particular case when it corresponds to the state of equilibrium of an electrochemical reaction taking place on this electrode. If we use the symbol E_{0r} to denote the equilibrium potential of a reaction *r* written in the form $\Sigma \nu_r M_r + n_r e^- = 0$, equation (28) can be written

(29) $$E_{0r} = \frac{\Sigma \nu_r \mu_r - \Sigma \nu_{ref} \mu_{ref}}{23\,060\, n_r}.$$

If we use as a reference electrode the standard hydrogen electrode for which the chemical potentials of the constituents H^+ (at pH = 0) and H_2 (at 1 atm. pressure) are taken to be zero, the equilibrium condition (27) takes the simpler form

(30) $$\boxed{E_{0r} = \frac{\Sigma \nu_r \mu_r}{23\,060\, n_r}.}$$

Consequently, *for any given electrochemical reaction taking place under fixed physico-chemical conditions* (to which correspond fixed values of the chemical potentials μ_r) *there exists a fixed value of the electrode potential at which the equilibrium state of the reaction is obtained.*

If we consider a metal–solution system at the interface of which an electrochemical reaction can occur (for example zinc in a zinc sulphate solution, in which the reaction $Zn = Zn^{++} + 2e^-$ can take place; or platinum in a solution of ferrous and ferric ions, in which the reaction $Fe^{++} = Fe^{+++} + e^-$ can take place; or any metal in a solution saturated with gaseous hydrogen, in which the reaction $H_2 = 2H^+ + 2e^-$ can take place), there exists a value of the electrode potential of the metal for which the equilibrium state of the reaction is obtained. When the potential of the metal has this value, the reaction canhot take place either in the oxidation direction or in the reduction direction: for example there can be neither corrosion nor electrodeposition of zinc, neither oxidation of ferrous ions nor reduction of ferric ions, neither evolution nor oxidation of hydrogen. For any other value of the electrode

[10] It is understood that this difference of potential is measured by Haber and Luggin's method mentioned above (Fig. 4). The electric potentials in question here are those of chemically identical terminals (e.g. copper) attached to the electrodes of the cell.

potential, the state of thermodynamic equilibrium will not be obtained, and it is possible, from the energetic point of view, for the reaction to take place, either in the oxidation direction (if the electrode potential is above the equilibrium potential of the reaction), or in the reduction direction (if the electrode potential is below this equilibrium potential).

As P. Van Rysselberghe has shown in his excellent *Introduction* to this *Atlas*, the *equilibrium potential* E_0 of an electrochemical reaction is equal to the *reduction affinity* per unit charge, i.e. the affinity of the chemical reaction obtained by combining, in the reduction direction, the electrochemical reaction studied with the electrochemical reference reaction.

For example, in the case of the reaction $Fe_{(s)} = Fe^{++}_{(aq.)} + 2e^-$ for which the standard equilibrium potential at 25°C, measured with respect to the standard hydrogen electrode, is $E^0_0 = -0{\cdot}440$ V, the reduction affinity, relating to the reaction $Fe^{++}_{(aq.)} + H_{2(g)} \rightarrow Fe_{(s)} + 2H^+_{(aq.)}$ taking place under standard conditions, is $-0{\cdot}440$ V; the oxidation affinity, relating to the reaction $Fe_{(s)} + 2H^+_{(aq.)} \rightarrow Fe^{++}_{(aq.)} + H_{2(g)}$ is $+0{\cdot}440$ V.

4.4. FORMULATION OF ELECTROCHEMICAL EQUILIBRIA

The equation

(31) $$\boxed{E_0 = \frac{\Sigma \nu \mu}{23\,060\, n}} \quad (^{11})$$

(which gives in magnitude and sign the value of the equilibrium potential of a given electrochemical reaction $\Sigma \nu M + ne^- = 0$) expresses in short the condition of thermodynamic equilibrium of this reaction. Indeed, the affinity A of an electrochemical reaction can be expressed by the equation

(32) $$A = -\Sigma \nu \mu + 23\,060\, n\, E$$

and the equation

(33) $$\Sigma \nu \mu - 23\,060\, n\, E_0 = 0$$

which is equivalent to equation (29) expresses that the affinity of the electrochemical reaction is zero at the equilibrium.

Equation (33) enables us to compare the equilibrium condition for chemical reactions and the equilibrium condition for electrochemical reactions:

	Reactions	
	Chemical	Electrochemical
Reaction equation	$\Sigma \nu M = 0$	$\Sigma \nu M + ne^- = 0$
Equilibrium condition	$\Sigma \nu \mu = 0$	$\Sigma \nu \mu - 23\,060\, nE = 0$

We see that in the same way that the equation of an electrochemical reaction differs from that of a chemical one only by the presence of a term which indicates the presence of free electrons e^-, the equilibrium condition of an electrochemical reaction differs from that of a chemical one only by the presence of a term which expresses the energetic influence of these electrons, in the form of an electrode potential E.

By manipulating equation (33) as we manipulated equation (8) relating to chemical equilibria, in paragraph 3, we obtain successively, by substituting fugacities and activities (M) and standard chemical potentials μ°:

(34) $$\Sigma \nu \mu^\circ + 4.575\, T\, \Sigma \nu \log (M) - 23\,060\, n\, E = 0.$$

(11) Equation (31) is equation (30) in which the indices *r* have been omitted to simplify the discussion. However, all the symbols arising in this equation concern a definite electrochemical reaction.

which becomes at 25°C

(35) $$\Sigma \nu \mu^0 + 1\,363\,\Sigma \nu \log(M) - 23\,060\, n\, E = 0$$

or

(36) $$E_0 = E_0^0 + \frac{0{,}0591}{n} \Sigma \nu \log(M),$$

(37) $$E_0^0 = \frac{\Sigma \nu \mu^0}{23\,060\, n},$$

in which

E_0 is the *equilibrium potential* of the electrochemical reaction;
E_0^0 is the *standard equilibrium potential* of the reaction at 25°C, i.e. its equilibrium potential for the particular case in which all the reacting substances are in the standard state at 25°C: fugacity, 1 atm. for gaseous substances; activity, 1 g-mol/l (or 1 g-ion/kg of water) for dissolved substances.

The value of the standard equilibrium potential E_0^0 can easily be calculated from equation (37) if we know the standard chemical potentials μ° of all the substances taking part in the reaction.

Given below are some examples of standard equilibrium potentials and the corresponding equilibrium formulae, based on the following values of standard chemical potentials μ° ([6]):

Fe^{++} (dissolved)	– 20 300 cal	H_2O (liquid)	– 56 690 cal
Fe^{+++} (dissolved)	– 2 530 „	O_2 (gaseous)	0 „
Fe (solid)	0 „	H^+ (dissolved)	0 „

Homogeneous reaction in aqueous solution:

$Fe^{++}_{(aq.)} = Fe^{+++}_{(aq.)} + e^-$:

$$E_0^0 = \frac{\mu^0_{Fe^{+++}} - \mu^0_{Fe^{++}}}{23\,060} = \frac{-2\,530 + 20\,300}{23\,060} = +0.771 \text{ V.}$$

$$E_0 = +0.771 + 0.0591 \log \frac{(Fe^{+++})}{(Fe^{++})} \quad \text{(volt)} \qquad \text{(redox tension)}$$

Solid/solution reaction:

$Fe_{(s)} = Fe^{++}_{(aq.)} + 2e^-$:

$$E_0^0 = \frac{\mu^0_{Fe^{++}} - \mu^0_{Fe}}{23\,060 \times 2} = \frac{-20\,300 - 0}{46\,120} = -0.440 \text{ V,}$$

$$E_0 = -0.440 + 0.0295 \log(Fe^{++}) \quad \text{(volt)} \qquad \text{(metal solution tension)}$$

Gas/solution reaction:

$2H_2O_{(l)} = O_{2(g)} + 4H^+_{(aq.)} + 4e^-$:

$$E_0^0 = \frac{\mu^0_{O_2} + 4\mu^0_{H^+} - 2\mu^0_{H_2O}}{23\,060 \times 4} = \frac{0 + 0 + 113\,380}{92\,240} = +1.228 \text{ V.}$$

$$E_0 = +1.228 - 0.0591\, pH + 0.0148 \log p_{O_2} \quad \text{(volt)} \qquad \text{(gas electrode tension)}$$

It follows from the above that the *redox tensions* (or "redox potentials"), the *metal solution tensions* (or "metal solution potentials") and the *gas electrode tensions* (or "gas electrode potentials") are only three particular cases of the *equilibrium tension of an electrochemical reaction.*

5. CONSTRUCTION OF POTENTIAL–pH EQUILIBRIUM DIAGRAMS(12)

In view of the above we shall now show how to proceed with the construction of potential–pH equilibrium diagrams. We shall consider, by way of an example, the particular case of the system iron–water at 25°C, which is treated in detail in Section 12.1 of Chapter IV.

5.1. STANDARD CHEMICAL POTENTIALS

We draw up a list of all the substances that we propose to consider and find out from chemical literature the values of the standard chemical potentials μ° of all these substances. Except where indicated, these values have been taken from Latimer.(*) We make a table of these values (in small calories) grouping separately the condensed substances (solid substances and liquid substances other than water), the solvent (water) and the dissolved substances, and the gaseous substances. In each of these groups we classify the derivatives of the element considered in order of increasing oxidation number Z. In the case of hydroxides or other hydrated oxides, the chemical potentials are preferably calculated for the anhydrous oxide which would have the same stability(13); when the same oxide exists in different forms (allotropic modifications, or differently hydrated oxides) we classify these forms in order of decreasing stability, i.e. in order of increasing value of chemical potential calculated for the same chemical formula (which is the anhydrous form here), and we label these forms by the indices *a*, *b*, *c*, . . .

Concerning the values accepted for the standard chemical potentials, we indicate their degree of accuracy by writing in italics the figures which cannot reasonably be considered exact, the last of the figures not in italics nevertheless being subject to caution.

For example, here are the values of the standard chemical potentials μ° which we have taken in the case of iron:

Oxidation Number (Z).	Solid Substances		Solvent and dissolved Substances	
-	-	-	H_2O	— 56 690 cal.
-	-	-	H^+	0 »
0	Fe	0 cal.	-	-
+2	FeO hydr. ($Fe(OH)_2$)	— 58 880 »	Fe^{++}	— 20 300 »
»	-	-	$HFeO_2^-$	— 90 627 »
+2.67	Fe_3O_4	—242 400 »	-	-
+3	*a*. Fe_2O_3	—177 100 »	Fe^{+++}	— 2 530 »
»	*b*. Fe_2O_3 hydr. ($Fe(OH)_3$)	—161 930 »	$FeOH^{++}$	— 55 910 »
»	-	-	$Fe(OH)_2^+$	—106 200 »
+6	-	-	FeO_4^{--} ?	—111 685 »

5.2. REACTIONS

We write the equations of the various reactions in which these substances can take part two by two in the manner shown in paragraph 2 above, i.e. possibly introducing, apart from these two substances A and B, water H_2O, the H^+ ion, and the free electric charge e^-.

(12) A similar account giving in detail the method of construction of the potential–pH equilibrium diagram relating to the system copper–water, has been published elsewhere (*Leçons sur la corrosion électrochimique* (3e fascicule), pp. 28–34, Rapport technique RT.49 of CEBELCOR, 1957).

(13) The chemical potential of this anhydrous oxide is calculated by adding to the chemical potential of the hydrated oxide as many times 56 690 cal., (i.e. $-\mu^0_{H_2O\,(liquid)}$) as there are water molecules in the chemical formula of the hydrated oxide. For example $\mu^0_{Fe(OH)_2} = -115\,570$ cal. corresponds to $\mu^0_{FeO} = -115\,570 + 56\,690 = -58\,880$ cal.

(*) W. M. Latimer, *The Oxidation States of the Elements and their Potentials in Aqueous Solutions*, 2nd. ed., Prentice-Hall, New York, 1952; *Recent References to Thermodynamic Data*, University of California, 1954.

These reaction equations will therefore have the following general form:

$$a\,A + c\,H_2O + n\,e^- = b\,B + m\,H^+ \quad ([14]).$$

We group these reactions as follows according to the physical state of the substances A and B, indicating, for each reaction, the oxidation numbers Z of the element in each of these two forms:

a. homogeneous reactions (two dissolved forms);
b. heterogeneous reactions involving two condensed substances (generally two solid forms);
c. heterogeneous reactions involving one condensed substance (generally solid) and one dissolved substance.

When the system considered includes substances in the gaseous state, we also consider all or some of the groups of reactions below (group *d* will not be considered when there is only one substance in the gaseous state):

d. heterogeneous reactions involving two gaseous substances;
e. heterogeneous reactions involving one gaseous substance and one dissolved substance;
f. heterogeneous reactions involving one gaseous substance and one condensed substance (generally solid).

In each of these groups, we consider separately the chemical reactions, in which the forms A and B have the same oxidation number Z and in which electrons e^- do not appear (the coefficient n of the electron is then equal to zero), and the electrochemical reactions in which the forms A and B have different oxidation numbers, and in which electrons appear (the coefficient n is then not equal to zero).

In each of these groups the chemical reactions are classified in order of increasing oxidation number; the electrochemical reactions are classified in increasing oxidation number of the least oxidized form, and following this successively in increasing oxidation number of each of the more oxidized forms in turn.

Each reaction is given an identification number, with the intention that we reject those reactions which, at a later stage of the work, appear to present no practical interest.

Thus we have below the reactions that we considered in the case of iron([15]):

(*a*) *Homogeneous reactions* (two dissolved forms):

Z.	n°	
+2	1.	$Fe^{++} + 2H_2O = HFeO_2^- + 3H^+$
+3	2.	$Fe^{+++} + H_2O = FeOH^{++} + H^+$
»	3.	$FeOH^{++} + H_2O = Fe(OH)_2^+ + H^+$
+2 → +3	4.	$Fe^{++} = Fe^{+++} + e^-$
»	5.	$Fe^{++} + H_2O = FeOH^{++} + H^+ + e^-$
»	6.	$Fe^{++} + 2H_2O = Fe(OH)_2^+ + 2H^+ + e^-$
»	7.	$HFeO_2^- + H^+ = Fe(OH)_2^+ + e^-$
+2 → +6	8.	$HFeO_2^- + 2H_2O = FeO_4^{--} + 5H^+ + 4e^-$
+3 → +6	9.	$Fe^{+++} + 4H_2O = FeO_4^{--} + 8H^+ + 3e^-$
»	10.	$FeOH^{++} + 3H_2O = FeO_4^{--} + 7H^+ + 3e^-$
»	11.	$Fe(OH)_2^+ + 2H_2O = FeO_4^{--} + 6H^+ + 3e^-$

([14]) By the convention discussed in paragraph 2, this equation can represent equally well the oxidation

$$a\,A + c\,H_2O + n\,e^- \leftarrow b\,B + m\,H^+$$

and the reduction

$$a\,A + c\,H_2O + n\,e^- \rightarrow b\,B + m\,H^+$$

([15]) In the equations below, the chemical symbols in heavy type represent solid substances; the symbols in normal type represent water and substances dissolved in aqueous solution.

(*b*) *Heterogeneous reactions involving two solid substances:*

$0 \rightarrow +2$	12.	$Fe + H_2O =$	FeO	$+ 2H^+$	$+ 2e^-$
$0 \rightarrow +2.67$	13.	$3Fe + 4H_2O =$	Fe_3O_4	$+ 8H^+$	$+ 8e^-$
$0 \rightarrow +3$	14.	$2Fe + 3H_2O =$	Fe_2O_3	$+ 6H^+$	$+ 6e^-$
$+2 \rightarrow +2.67$	15.	$3FeO + H_2O =$	Fe_3O_4	$+ 2H^+$	$+ 2e^-$
$+2 \rightarrow +3$	16.	$2FeO + H_2O =$	Fe_2O_3	$+ 2H^+$	$+ 2e^-$
$+2.67 \rightarrow +3$	17.	$2Fe_3O_4 + H_2O =$	$3Fe_2O_3$	$+ 2H^+$	$+ 2e^-$

(*c*) *Heterogeneous reactions involving one solid substance and one dissolved substance:*

$+2$	18.	$Fe^{++} + H_2O =$	FeO	$+ 2H^+$	
»	19.	$FeO + H_2O =$	$HFeO_2^-$	$+ H^+$	
$+3$	20.	$2Fe^{+++} + 3H_2O =$	Fe_2O_3	$+ 6H^+$	
»	21.	$2FeOH^{++} + H_2O =$	Fe_2O_3	$+ 4H^+$	
»	22.	$2Fe(OH)_2^+ =$	Fe_2O_3	$+ H_2O + 2H^+$	
$0 \rightarrow +2$	23.	$Fe =$	Fe^{++}		$+ 2e^-$
»	24.	$Fe + 2H_2O =$	$HFeO_2^-$	$+ 3H^+$	$+ 2e^-$
$0 \rightarrow +3$	25.	$Fe =$	Fe^{+++}		$+ 3e^-$
$+2 \rightarrow +2.67$	26.	$3Fe^{++} + 4H_2O =$	Fe_3O_4	$+ 8H^+$	$+ 2e^-$
»	27.	$3HFeO_2^- + H^+ =$	Fe_3O_4	$+ 2H_2O$	$+ 2e^-$
$+2 \rightarrow +3$	28.	$2Fe^{++} + 3H_2O =$	Fe_2O_3	$+ 6H^+$	$+ 2e^-$
»	29.	$2HFeO_2^- =$	Fe_2O_3	$+ H_2O$	$+ 2e^-$

5.3. EQUILIBRIUM CONDITIONS FOR THE REACTIONS

For each of these reactions we evaluate the equilibrium condition, by applying the following equations, established in paragraph 3 and 4.4:

for *chemical reactions:*

$$\Sigma\nu \log(\mathrm{M}) = \log \mathrm{K}, \quad \text{where} \quad \log \mathrm{K} = -\frac{\Sigma\nu\mu^0}{1363},$$

for *electrochemical reactions:*

$$\mathrm{E}_0 = \mathrm{E}_0^0 + \frac{0.0591}{n}\Sigma\nu \log(\mathrm{M}), \quad \text{where} \quad \mathrm{E}_0^0 = \frac{\Sigma\nu\mu^0}{23\,060\,n}$$

and we write these equations in such a way as to make explicit the influence of pH, which occurs implicitly in the term $\Sigma\nu \log(\mathrm{M})$.

In the case of *chemical reactions* written in the form

$$a\mathrm{A} + c\mathrm{H_2O} = b\mathrm{B} + m\mathrm{H^+}, \tag{38}$$

in which B is the alkaline form and A is the acid form of the element in question, the condition for equilibrium will be of the form

$$\log\frac{(\mathrm{B})^b}{(\mathrm{A})^a} = \log \mathrm{K} + m\,\mathrm{pH} \tag{39}$$

and, in the most common case when $a = b = 1$, and the reaction is $\mathrm{A}+c\mathrm{H_2O} = \mathrm{B}+m\mathrm{H^+}$

$$\log\frac{(\mathrm{B})}{(\mathrm{A})} = \log \mathrm{K} + m\,\mathrm{pH}. \tag{40}$$

This equation shows that the ratio of the fugacity (or activity) of the alkaline form to the fugacity (or activity) of the acid form increases linearly with the pH.

In the case of *electrochemical reactions* written in the form

(41) $$a\,A + c\,H_2O + n\,e^- = b\,B + m\,H^+,$$

in which A is the oxidized form and B the reduced form of the element in question, the condition for equilibrium will be of the form

(42) $$E_0 = E_0^0 - \frac{0.0591\,m}{n}\,pH + \frac{0.0591}{n}\log\frac{(A)^a}{(B)^b}$$

and in the most common case when $a = b = 1$, and the reaction is $A + cH_2O + ne^- = B + mH^+$

(43) $$E_0 = E_0^0 - \frac{0.0591\,m}{n}\,pH + \frac{0.0591}{n}\log\frac{(A)}{(B)}.$$

It is as well to note that the fugacity (or activity) of the oxidized form A occurs *in the numerator* of the term log (A)/(B): the equilibrium tension E_0, increases when the percentage of the oxidized form increases.

The equilibrium formulae for the twenty-nine reactions quoted in paragraph 5.2 can be found in paragraph 2 of section 12.1 of Chapter IV (p. 308).

In the particular case of solid substances existing in different varieties having different free formation enthalpies (labelled in 5.1 by the indices *a, b, c*, ...) we label the corresponding equilibrium constants and standard tensions with these same indices [see, for example, equations (17) and (20) concerning anhydrous Fe_2O_3 and hydrated Fe_2O_3 (or $Fe(OH)_3$)].

Finally, if we put (A) = (B) in equilibrium relations of the type (40) or (42), we obtain the following equations which express the conditions of pH and electrode potential for which the activities (or the fugacities) of these two forms are equal([16]), being valid for the case when the forms A and B of the element in question are either both in the dissolved state or both in the gaseous state:

(44) $$pH = \frac{1}{m}\log K,$$

(45) $$E_0 = E_0^0 - \frac{0.0591\,m}{n}\,pH.$$

Such equations, concerning the reactions between the dissolved forms of iron according to reactions (1)–(11) are given under numbers 1′–11′ of paragraph 2 of section 12.1 of Chapter IV (p. 309).

5.4. CONSTRUCTION OF THE EQUILIBRIUM DIAGRAMS

Considering the electrode potential and the pH as independent variables and the logarithmic function of the concentrations and/or pressures of the substances A and B as a parameter, we can now proceed to establish potential-pH equilibrium diagrams on millimetre paper on which we have previously drawn the lines *a* and *b*:

$$E_{0a} = 0.000 - 0.0591\ pH\ \text{(volt)} \qquad \text{(line } a)$$
$$E_{0b} = 1.228 - 0.0591\ pH\ \text{(volt)} \qquad \text{(line } b)$$

which express respectively the reduction equilibrium of water according to the reaction $H_2 = 2H^+ + 2e^-$ (*a*) and its oxidation equilibrium according to the reaction $2H_2O = O_2 + 4H^+ + 4e^-$ (*b*) at a hydrogen or oxygen pressure of 1 atm.

([16]) These simple relationships can only be applied when the formulae of the two substances A and B refer to the same number of atoms of the substance under consideration, e.g. Fe^{++}/Fe^{+++}. For example this is not the case for the systems Cr_2O_7/Cr^{+++} or N_2/NO; relationships have to be modified by allowing for the total concentration C (or activity) of the element in the two forms in solution $Cr_2O_7^{--} + Cr^{+++}$) or the total pressure P (or fugacity) of the two gaseous forms (N_2 + NO).

The drawing of lines expressing the conditions under which the concentrations (or activities) of the two dissolved substances are equal [equations (1')–(11') relating to iron] enables us to represent in Fig. 1 (section 12.1 of Chapter IV) the *domains of relative predominance of the dissolved forms in question:* Fe^{++}, $HFeO_2^-$, $FeOH^{++}$, $Fe(OH)_2^+$ and FeO_4^{--}.

The drawing of lines which express the equilibrium conditions for two solid substances [equations (12)–(17)] enables us to represent the *domains of relative stability of the solid substances in question.* Such a representation can be made, not only for stable equilibria ($Fe/Fe_3O_4/Fe_2O_3$), but also for unstable equilibria [$Fe/Fe(OH)_2/Fe(OH)_3$].

By superimposing these two diagrams, we can easily pick out the conditions of potential and pH under which a given solid substance and a given dissolved substance can be simultaneously stable. By giving a definite value (for instance zero) to the logarithmic term which, in the equilibrium equation for this solid substance and this dissolved substance [relations (18)–(29)], expresses the value of the concentration (or activity) of the dissolved substance (for instance $10^0 = 1$ g-ion/l), we define a line which represents the conditions under which the *solubility* of the solid substance considered, in the dissolved form considered, has this value. In this way it is easy to draw, step by step, a line which represents the locus of the points of the diagram for which the *solubility of the different solid substances in all the different dissolved forms* has the same value. It is often useful to establish such "equisolubility" lines for different solubility values (for example, 10^0, 10^{-2}, 10^{-4} and 10^{-6} g-atm. of the element considered per kilogram of water([17])). We thus obtain, after omitting those lines or parts of lines which have no practical interest, figures such as Figs. 4 and 5 which are two electrochemical equilibrium diagrams for the systems $Fe–H_2O$; Fig. 4 represents only stable equilibria; Fig. 5 represents, with regard to $Fe(OH)_2$ and $Fe(OH)_3$, unstable equilibria.

It is as well to note that each of the lines indicating the solubility of the different condensed substances in all the different dissolved forms changes direction abruptly at the places where the composition of the system changes abruptly (for example in Fig. 4, when we pass from the domain of relative stability of Fe to the domain of relative stability of Fe_3O_4); these lines change direction progressively when the composition of the system changes progressively, that is in the neighbourhood of the lines which separate the domains of relative predominance of the dissolved substances (for example Fe^{++} and Fe^{+++}). The drawing of these curved portions of the equisolubility lines can be done by a graphical method that we have described elsewhere([18]). These equal solubility lines therefore have sharp points at the limits of the domains of stability of the condensed substances, they have gradual curves near the limits of the domains of predominance of the dissolved substances.

Such diagrams are valid only for solutions in the presence of which the metal or metalloid considered can exist only in the forms that have been considered in establishing the diagram. When the solutions contain substances capable of forming soluble complexes with the metal or metalloid (for instance cyanides forming ferro- and ferricyanides) or insoluble salts (for instance phosphates forming ferrous and ferric phosphates), it is necessary to modify the diagram by adding to it a representation of the stability conditions of these dissolved or solid substances. It is then necessary to establish diagrams for systems which are not binary such as $Fe—H_2O$, but ternary such as $Fe—CN^-—H_2O$ or $Fe—PO_4^{---}—H_2O$.

([17]) We shall often use, from the point of view of simplification, the fact that solubilities expressed per litre of aqueous solution are almost the same as solubilities expressed per kilogram of water.

([18]) *Leçons sur la corrosion électrochimique*, 2e fascicule (Rapport technique RT. 30 of CEBELCOR, 1956, pp. 22 and 23).

CHAPTER III

USE OF POTENTIAL–pH EQUILIBRIUM DIAGRAMS

SECTION 1

GENERALITIES

M. Pourbaix

In the important preface that R. Piontelli has kindly written for this *Atlas*, he has brought out the practical significance of potential–pH equilibrium diagrams and has pointed out the limitations which we must be aware of when using them. In the accounts which follow, the reader will find some examples of the application of these diagrams to the study of concrete problems of inorganic chemistry, analytical chemistry, corrosion, electrodeposition and geology. Elsewhere can be found some examples of their application to catalysis([1]) and the study of batteries and accumulators([2]).

We shall therefore be very brief here, and content ourselves with reviewing a few particularly important fundamental ideas.

We know well the tremendous scope given to chemistry by *chemical thermodynamics*, which is the science of the application of energetics to chemistry and is based on the concept of chemical equilibrium. Chemical thermodynamics, whose fundamental basis was established around 1876 by J. Willard Gibbs, and whose applications have greatly developed since the beginning of this century, has enabled us to understand a large number of formerly mysterious chemical phenomena; it has allowed us to predict certain facts prior to experiment; and it has greatly helped in the perfection of numerous processes of chemistry and metallurgy.

Electrochemical thermodynamics can, within limits, provide for electrochemistry a help analogous to that provided for chemistry by chemical thermodynamics. The potential–pH equilibrium diagrams have the essential purpose of supplying a thermodynamic framework for electrochemical reactions involving an aqueous solution.

In electrochemistry as in chemistry, the fact that a reaction is thermodynamically possible does not entail that this reaction actually takes place. Such a conformity between theoretical possibility and reality exists only for reactions which are practically reversible; the world of electrochemical reactions is full of irreversible changes which, like many chemical reactions can take place only on the condition that there is an appreciable affinity, and their speed is influenced by the presence of catalysts; the chemical synthesis of water, although thermodynamically possible between 25° and 100°C, generally takes place only extremely slowly under these conditions, and can be accelerated by the presence of catalysts such as platinum; similarly, the electrochemical synthesis of water, which occurs in a hydrogen/oxygen gas cell, takes place only in a very irreversible manner at these temperatures and is affected by the catalytic action of the metals constituting the electrodes.

Electrochemical reactions (or electrode reactions) differ from chemical reactions in that they involve, apart from chemical reagents, an electric reagent (the negative electron) which acts at the

---

([1]) M. Pourbaix, *Sur l'interpretation thermodynamique des courbes de polarisation* (Rapport technique RT.1 of CEBELCOR, 1952). The utility of thermodynamic Interpretation of Polarization Curves—J. Electrochem. Soc. *101*, 217–221c (1954).

([2]) See the work of Commission No. 6 of CITCE, *Batteries and Accumulators*, presided over by J. P. Brenet.

interface between a metal (or another phase with metallic conduction) and a solution of electrolytes. This fact has a fundamental consequence from the expeŕimental point of view: the affinity of the reaction can be measured in magnitude and sign by an *electrode potential*, or rather by the difference $E-E_0$ between the electrode potential E of the metallic surface and the equilibrium potential E_0 of the reaction; if these two potentials are *equal*, the affinity is zero and the state of *thermodynamic equilibrium* of the reaction is obtained; if the electrode potential is *above the equilibrium potential*, the affinity is positive and the reaction can take place only in the *oxidation* direction; if the electrode potential is *below the equilibrium potential*, the affinity is negative and the reaction can take place only in the *reduction* direction. If we denote the speed of the electrochemical reaction by the magnitude *i* of the electric current which corresponds to it by Faraday's Law, considering this reaction current to be positive in the case of oxidation and negative in the case of reduction, the relations above between the sign of the difference in potentials $E-E_0$ (which we can define to be the *overpotential* of the reaction on the electrode studied) and the direction of the reaction can be expressed by the inequality

$$(E - E_0)\, i \geqq 0$$

according to which the reaction current *i* is always either zero, or of the same sign as the overpotential $E-E_0$.(3)

Consequently, if we wish to know in which direction a certain electrochemical reaction of known equilibrium potential will proceed on a metallic surface in contact with an aqueous solution, it is sufficient to measure the electrode potential of this surface and compare the value of this electrode potential with the value of the equilibrium potential of this reaction. This is true, not only in the particular case in which a single reaction is possible, but also in the general case in which several reactions can occur. If we know the potential–pH equilibrium diagrams for such a set of reactions, we can pick out the point on these diagrams which represents the conditions of potential and pH of the interface studied; all those reactions whose equilibrium potentials are below the potential of this point can take place only in the oxidation direction; all those reactions whose equilibrium potentials are above the potential of this point can take place only in the reduction direction.

If, for example, we consider a surface of iron and ferric oxide Fe_2O_3 immersed in an aerated aqueous solution of pH = 4 containing 10^{-4} g-at Fe/l (6·0 mg/l), and if this iron surface has an electrode potential of −0·20 V, the electrochemical equilibrium diagram for iron (Fig. 4 of section 12.1, Chapter IV) leads to the following conclusions: the iron tends to corrode according to the reaction $Fe \rightarrow Fe^{++} + 2e^-$ (23) without evolution of hydrogen, but with reduction of oxygen according to the reaction $O_2 + 4H^+ + 4e^- \rightarrow 2H_2O$ (*b*) and with reduction of ferric oxide according to the reaction $Fe_2O_3 + 6H^+ + 2e^- \rightarrow 2Fe^{++} + 3H_2O$ (28).(4)

If, for this same pH and potential the solution contains hydrogen peroxide, the latter will tend to be reduced to water according to the reaction $H_2O_2 + 2H^+ + 2e^- \rightarrow 2H_2O$ (2) (see Section 1.2, Chapter IV); if the solution contains cupric ions, a cement of copper can be formed by the reduction $Cu^{++} + 2e^- \rightarrow Cu$ (15) (see section 14.1, Chapter IV); if it contains a chromate, a deposit of Cr_2O_3 capable of passivating the metal can be formed by the reduction $2CrO_4^{--} + 10H^+ + 6e^- \rightarrow Cr_2O_3 + 5H_2O$ (54) (see section 10.1, Chapter IV).

It must be understood that the electrode potentials and pH considered here are the characteristics of a metal/solution interface, and not of some other part of the metal or solution. In the very frequent

(3) A detailed account of this is outside the scope of the present Treatise; see principally M. POURBAIX, Thesis, Delft, 1945 (*loc. cit.*), and *Vue d'ensemble sur le comportement électrochimique des métaux* (2e partie) (Recueils de Mémoires RM. 5 of CEBELCOR, 1953).

The relation $(E - E_0)i \geqslant 0$ results from the adaptation to electrochemical reactions of De Donder's relation $Av \geqslant 0$ which connects the direction of a chemical reaction (fixed by the sign of its speed *v*) with the sign of its affinity A.

(4) The numbers in brackets are those under which these reactions have been classified in Chapter IV in section 12.1 for iron, section 1.2 for hydrogen peroxide, section 14.1 for copper, and section 10.1 for chromium.

case in which the metal or solution is the site of electric currents or chemical changes, it is necessary to make sure that the chemical composition assumed for the solution (and consequently its pH) is that of the fraction of the solution in direct contact with the metal, since this composition can differ greatly from the mean composition of the solution; careful note must also be taken that the electrode potential of the metal is measured in such a way as to avoid any effects of ohmic fall or diffusion potential; for this purpose, it is best to use Haber and Luggin's capillary siphon method or Piontelli's method.

Finally, we cannot insist too much on the fact that the equilibrium diagrams discussed here can only, by themselves, solve a very limited number of problems, as Piontelli has made very clear in the final part of his preface. They are only tools at the disposal of the electrochemist and they must always be used in conjunction with other means of investigation. Among these means, a particularly important place is held by studies of electrochemical kinetics, which are based on the experimental determination of potential–current curves (for example by intensiostatic or potentiostatic methods) and which enable us to establish the laws connecting the speed i of an electrochemical reaction and its affinity $E - E_0$.(5) A bright future can be predicted for groups of investigators who are competent at the same time in thermodynamics, kinetics, and physics and physical chemistry of metals.

(5) See *loc. cit.* (1).

SECTION 2

GENERAL CHEMISTRY

G. Valensi

SUMMARY

1. *Introduction.*
2. *Redox couples.*
3. *Coexistence potentials.*
4. *Mixed couples.*
5. *Graphical representation.*
6. *Disproportionation.*
7. *Amphoterization.*
8. *Rates of reactions which are thermodynamically possible.*
9. *Conclusion.*

1. INTRODUCTION

The electrochemical diagram of an element summarizes in an extremely condensed form the most salient features of its solution chemistry. To cover such a vast domain necessarily requires a certain complexity of the diagrams, the basic features of which may thus escape a first examination.

It is perhaps not superfluous, therefore, before considering some concrete examples, to remind the reader of certain concepts introduced in the preceding articles, but at the same time relating them more directly to chemical considerations.

2. REDOX COUPLES

Solution reactions, in particular those of inorganic chemistry, very often involve a transfer of electrons e^- from a reducing agent R_1 to an oxidizing agent O_2. The possibility of the reverse process under different conditions implies that R_1 is converted into a conjugate oxidizing agent O_1 while O_2 is converted into a conjugate reducing agent R_2. Thus the action of chlorine on ferrous salts can be represented by the scheme:

$$\overset{R_1}{Fe^{2+}} + \frac{1}{2}\overset{O_2}{Cl_2} \rightleftharpoons \overset{O_1}{Fe^{3+}} + \overset{R_2}{Cl^-}$$

$$\underbrace{Fe^{2+} \xrightarrow{e^-} Cl_2} \qquad \underbrace{Fe^{3+} \xleftarrow{e^-} Cl^-}$$

In general, if the stoichiometric coefficients are chosen so that the reaction involves only one electron (for the sake of convenience), the free enthalpy of a so-called *redox* reaction:

$$(1) \qquad a_1 R_1 + b_2 O_2 \rightleftharpoons b_1 O_1 + a_2 R_2$$

is given by the expression

$$(2) \qquad \Delta G = \Delta G^0 + RT \operatorname{Log} \frac{(O_1)^{b_1}(R_2)^{a_2}}{(R_1)^{a_1}(O_2)^{b_2}} = \Delta G^0 + 2.3\, RT \log \frac{(O_1)^{b_1}(R_2)^{a_2}}{(R_1)^{a_1}(O_2)^{b_2}}.$$

R denotes the gas constant; T, the absolute temperature; Log, a natural logarithmic; log, a decimal logarithm; the symbols in brackets denote the fugacities or activities of the corresponding constituents, i.e. to a first approximation, the pressure for all gaseous substances, the molality (number of moles per kilogram of solvent) for all dissolved substances; the mole fraction for each liquid or solid solvent; in particular, the activity is unity for a pure condensed substance, and almost unity for the water in an aqueous solution when sufficiently dilute. The first term ΔG^0 represents the standard free enthalpy of reaction, i.e. the free enthalpy of reaction, ΔG, when all the fugacities and activities involved are unity.

By choosing a reference couple under specific conditions at the temperature considered, generally the couple $\underset{(1\ \text{atm.})}{H_2} \Big| \underset{(\text{act. } 1)}{H^+}$, it is possible to decompose (1) into two half-reactions:

$$a_1 R_1 + \underset{(\text{act. } 1)}{H^+} \rightleftharpoons b_1 O_1 + \underset{(1\ \text{atm.})}{\tfrac{1}{2} H_2},$$

and

$$\underset{(1\ \text{atm.})}{\tfrac{1}{2} H_2} + b_2 O_2 \rightleftharpoons \underset{(\text{act. } 1)}{H^+} + a_2 R_2,$$

whose free enthalpies are respectively

$$\Delta G_1 = \Delta G_1^0 + RT \operatorname{Log} \frac{(O_1)^{b_1}}{(R_1)^{a_1}},$$

and

$$-\Delta G_2 = -\Delta G_2^0 - RT \operatorname{Log} \frac{(O_2)^{b_2}}{(R_2)^{a_2}}.$$

At the temperature considered (usually 25°C) and at a given pressure (usually 1 atm.), reaction (1) is thermodynamically possible only if

$$\Delta G = \Delta G_1 - \Delta G_2 < 0 \quad \text{i.e.} \quad \Delta G_1 < \Delta G_2.$$

Now, the half-reaction corresponding to a redox couple i can theoretically be brought about reversibly by means of the electrochemical cell

$$\text{Pt} \left| \begin{matrix} O_i, R_i \\ \text{aq.} \end{matrix} \right| \cdot \left| \begin{matrix} \underset{(\text{act. } 1)}{H^+} \\ \text{aq.} \end{matrix} \right| \text{Pt}, \underset{(1\ \text{atm.})}{H_2},$$

of which the *reversible potential difference* (electric potential of the first pole less that of the second when there is a perfect potentiometric compensation) is

$$(3) \qquad E_i = \frac{\Delta G_i}{F} = \frac{\Delta G_i^0}{F} + \frac{2.3\, RT}{F} \log \frac{(O_i)^{b_i}}{(R_i)^{a_i}} = E_i^0 + \frac{2.3\, RT}{F} \log \frac{(O_i)^{b_i}}{(R_i)^{a_i}}.$$

$E_i^0 = \Delta G_i^0/F$ may be termed the *standard potential* associated with the couple i; F represents one Faraday in the system of units employed. The M.K.S. system implies that E_i and E_i^0 should be expressed in volts; R in joules $mol^{-1}\ deg^{-1}$; F in coulombs. $equivalent^{-1}$. At 25°C, 2·3RT/F is therefore equal to 0·0591 V, as seen in Chapter II.

Tables such as those of W. M. Latimer[1] list numerical values of E_i^0 for x couples, enabling us to predict the thermodynamic possibility of $2x(x - 1)$ redox reactions under the most varied conditions: the reducing agent R_1 of a couple 1 reacts with the oxidizing agent O_2 of a couple 2 when $E_1 < E_2$.

It should be noted that in tables of this kind the half-reactions are written:

$$a_i R_i \rightleftharpoons b_i O_i + ne^-, \tag{4}$$

(as is done systematically in this *Atlas*), instead of

$$a_i R_i + \underset{(\text{act. } 1)}{H^+} \rightleftharpoons b_i O_i + \frac{1}{2} \underset{(1 \text{ atm.})}{H_2}. \tag{5}$$

With regard to calculating the free enthalpy, and on account of the standard potential given in (3), the result is the same, it being understood that the state of the electrons considered is their aqueous dissolution equilibrium (producing an unknown electron concentration) in the reference couple. Let us suppose first of all that $n = 1$: the free enthalpy of the reaction

$$e^-_{aq.} + \underset{(\text{act. } 1)}{H^+} \rightleftharpoons \frac{1}{2} \underset{(1 \text{ atm.})}{H_2} \tag{6}$$

is zero. Now reaction (5), whose free enthalpy is given by formula (3), is the sum of reactions (4) and (6). Since their free enthalpies are also additive, it follows that (4) and (5) have the same free enthalpy. When $n \neq 1$, one can divide both sides of equation (4) by n to replace (3) by the more general equation

$$E_i = E_i^0 + \frac{2.3\,RT}{F} \log \frac{(O_i)^{\frac{b_i}{n}}}{(R_i)^{\frac{a_i}{n}}} = E_i^0 + \frac{2.3\,RT}{nF} \log \frac{(O_i)^{b_i}}{(R_i)^{a_i}}. \tag{3'}$$

3. COEXISTENCE POTENTIALS

In the initial absence of O_1 and R_2, $\Delta G = -\infty$ from (2). This means that a redox reaction can always begin, but the question is to know how far it can continue. One may consider it to be practically significant when more than 50 per cent of the reducing agent R, put into the system can disappear. Thus it is useful to consider for each couple i a coexistence potential i for equal parts of R_i and O_i. We will provisionally denote this potential by $E_i^{(0.5)}$. Let α_i, β_i be the atomicities of the element involved in its respective forms R_i, O_i (e.g. $\alpha_i = 1$ for Cl^-; $\beta_i = 2$ for Cl_2) and let C_i be the overall concentration of the system (which may consist of one or several phases) in gram-atoms of this element per kilogram of water present: C_i remains constant throughout any reaction which produces only a small amount of additional water, e.g. when the reagent employed is solid or gaseous or when it is in a very concentrated solution. Let us denote by x_i the fraction of the active element of couple i present in the oxidized state O_i. There are three principal cases to be considered.

3.1. O_i and R_i are two constituents dissolved in the aqueous phase. One then has

$$\beta_i(O_i) = x_i C_i; \qquad \alpha_i(R_i) = (1 - x_i) C_i.$$

Substituting in (3′) we obtain

$$E_i = E_i^0 + \frac{0.0591}{n} \log \frac{\alpha_i^{a_i}}{\beta_i^{b_i}} + \frac{0.0591\,(b_i - a_i)}{n} \log C_i + \frac{0.0591}{n} b_i \log x_i - \frac{0.0591}{n} a_i \log(1 - x_i),$$

[1] *Oxidation Potentials*, 2nd ed., Prentice-Hall, New York, 1952.

E_i, which varies in the same sense as x_i is thus a real measure of the fraction oxidized. In order to obtain the coexistence potential $E_i^{(0\cdot5)}$, one merely puts $x_i = 0\cdot5$. Hence

$$E_i^{(0.5)} = E_i^0 + \frac{0.0591}{n} \log \frac{(2\alpha_i)^{a_i}}{(2\beta_i)^{b_i}} + \frac{0.0591(b_i - a_i)}{n} \log C_i. \quad (7)$$

3.2. O_i is a pure substance at 1 atm. pressure (gas, solid or liquid); R_i is a dissolved constituent of the aqueous phase. One then has

$$(O_i) = 1; \qquad \alpha_i(R_i) = (1 - x_i)C_i.$$

Hence

$$E_i = E_i^0 + \frac{0.0591}{n} \log \alpha_i^{a_i} - \frac{0.0591}{n} a_i \log C_i - \frac{0.0591}{n} a_i \log(1 - x_i),$$

E_i again varies in the same sense as x_i and thus remains a measure of the fraction oxidized. Putting $x_i = 0\cdot5$ we obtain

$$E_i^{(0.5)} = E_i^0 + \frac{0.0591}{n} \log(2\alpha_i)^{a_i} - \frac{0.0591}{n} a_i \log C_i. \quad (8)$$

3.3. O_i is a dissolved constituent of the aqueous phase; R_i is a pure substance at 1 atm. pressure. One then has

$$\beta_i(O_i) = x_i C_i; \qquad (R_i) = 1.$$

Hence

$$E_i = E_i^0 - \frac{0.0591}{n} \log \beta_i^{b_i} + \frac{0.0591}{n} b_i \log C_i + \frac{0.0591}{n} b_i \log x_i,$$

Once again E_i varies in the same sense as x_i and is thus still a measure of the fraction oxidized. Putting $x_i = 0\cdot5$ we obtain

$$E_i^{(0.5)} = E_i^0 - \frac{0.0591}{n} \log(2\beta_i)^{b_i} + \frac{0.0591}{n} b_i \log C_i \quad (9)$$ [2].

Suppose, therefore, that we add an oxidizing agent O_2 to a couple 1 which can act as an effective reducing agent R_1; x_1 increases, and E_1 correspondingly, but the coexistence potential $E_1^{(0\cdot5)}$ can be exceeded, i.e. the reaction can be considered to be practically significant ($x_1 > 0\cdot5$) when O_2 is introduced in the stoichiometric proportion, only if $E_2^{(0\cdot5)} > E_1^{(0\cdot5)}$. This is due to the fact that in the final equilibrium state, $\Delta G = 0$, i.e. $E_2 = E_1$. Now $x_1 > 0\cdot5$ implies that $E_1 > E_1^{(0\cdot5)}$, but also implies that $x_2 < 0\cdot5$, i.e. $E_2 < E_2^{(0\cdot5)}$. Hence

$$0 = E_1 - E_2 > E_1^{(0.5)} - E_2^{(0.5)}.$$

Since the order of addition of reagents to the system does not influence the equilibrium state obtained, the same relation $E_1^{(0\cdot5)} < E_2^{(0\cdot5)}$ is evidently appropriate for predicting a significant reaction when one adds a reducing agent R_1 to a medium containing a certain oxidizing agent O_2.

4. MIXED COUPLES

In most cases a complication arises: when the active element does not exist as a simple substance in one or the other of its two forms R_i, O_i (as in the couples $Fe^{2+}|Fe^{3+}$ and $Cl^-|Cl_2$), the couple under consideration does not involve only an ability to transfer electrons, but can involve simultaneously the release or capture of other particles. The most important case is when the only elements linked to the active element are those of the aqueous solvent, i.e. hydrogen and oxygen. Thus, the action of potassium permanganate on ferrous salts in acid solution can be interpreted as a transfer of electrons

---

(2) Between α_i, β_i, a_i, b_i, there exists the relation $\alpha_i a_i = \beta_i b_i$, but to introduce this into the preceding formulae would simplify them only in certain special cases.

on to manganese, accompanied by a capture of protons by the oxygen combined with it, while the reverse reaction can be interpreted as a transfer of electrons on to iron, accompanied by a release of protons by the solvent, which supplies the oxygen then necessary for the stability of the manganese atom deprived of electrons

$$\underset{R_1}{5\,Fe^{2+}} + \underset{O_2}{Mn\,O_4^-} + 8\,H^+ \rightleftharpoons \underset{O_1}{5\,Fe^{3+}} + \underset{R_2}{Mn^{2+}} + 4\,H_2O.$$

$5e^-$ $\qquad$ $4\,O^{2-}$

In most cases, therefore, we shall be considering half-reactions which can be represented by

(10) $$a_iR_i + q\,H_2O \rightleftharpoons b_iO_i + m\,H^+ + ne^- \quad (^3)$$

of which the free enthalpy is

$$\Delta G_i = \Delta G_i^0 + 2.3\,RT \log \frac{(O_i)^{b_i}(H^+)^m}{(R_i)^{a_i}},$$

the activity of the water being practically unity. The reversible potential which can be associated with the couple i is here

$$E_i = \frac{\Delta G_i}{nF} = \frac{\Delta G_i^0}{nF} + \frac{2.3\,RT\,m \log(H^+)}{nF} + \frac{2.3\,RT}{nF} \log \frac{(O_i)^{b_i}}{(R_i)^{a_i}}.$$

Introducing the symbol pH $= -\log(H^+)$:

(3″) $$E_i = E_i^0 - \frac{0.0591\,m}{n}\,\text{pH} + \frac{0.0591}{n} \log \frac{(O_i)^{b_i}}{(R_i)^{a_i}}.$$

In fact, (3″) differs from (3′) only in the term $E_i' = E_i^0 - 0{\cdot}0591 m/n$ pH, linear in pH, which replaces the constant term E_i^0. The prediction of redox reactions must therefore take into account the pH of the medium. In general it varies throughout such reactions, unless the medium is suitably buffered. Let us suppose that this condition is fulfilled: formulae (7), (8) and (9), which are expressions for the coexistence potentials of R_i and O_i, remain valid, provided that E_i^0 is replaced by E′. For the principal cases considered in 3.1, 3.2 and 3.3, we have the following coexistence potentials:

4.1. O_i and R_i in the aqueous phase:

(7′) $$E_i^{(0.5)} = \left[E_i^0 + \frac{0.0591}{n} \log \frac{(2\alpha_i)^{a_i}}{(2\beta_i)^{b_i}} + \frac{0.0591}{n} (b_i - a_i) \log C_i\right] - \frac{0.0591\,m}{n}\,\text{pH}.$$

4.2. O_i a pure substance at 1 atm. pressure; R_i in the aqueous phase:

(8′) $$E_i^{(0.5)} = \left[E_i^0 + \frac{0.0591}{n} \log(2\alpha_i)^{a_i} - \frac{0.0591}{n} a_i \log C_i\right] - \frac{0.0591\,m}{n}\,\text{pH}.$$

4.3. O_i in the aqueous phase; R_i a pure substance at 1 atm. pressure:

(9′) $$E_i^{(0.5)} = \left[E_i^0 - \frac{0.0591}{n} \log(2\beta_i)^{b_i} + \frac{0.0591}{n} b_i \log C_i\right] - \frac{0.0591\,m}{n}\,\text{pH}.$$

For each pH, the calculation of $E_1^{(0.5)}$ and $E_2^{(0.5)}$ by means of these formulae will once again enable us to predict the possibility (when $E_1^{(0.5)} < E_2^{(0.5)}$) of a practically significant reaction between a reducing agent R_1 and an oxidizing agent O_2.

---

(3) m and q are positive or zero in most cases; sometimes they are negative, however, as in the case for the couple NiO_2H^- | Ni_3O_4, for which the half-reaction is: $3NiO_2H^- + H^+ \rightleftharpoons Ni_3O_4 + 2H_2O + 2e^-$, where $q = -2$; $m = -1$ (*see* IV. 12).

5. GRAPHICAL REPRESENTATION

Instead of carrying out a fresh calculation for each application, it is more convenient to make a graphical representation, once and for all, of the $E_i^{(0\cdot5)}$ values for each couple (R_i, O_i). They depend on two variables, C_i and pH, and one can therefore plot a family of iso-C_i straight lines using E and pH as co-ordinates.

In general there will be several such families of lines corresponding to a given element, since its chemical properties generally involve the existence of various redox couples in which it takes part. For example, chlorine is the active element of the various couples:

$$Cl^- | Cl_2, \quad Cl_2 | ClO^-, \quad ClO^- | ClO_2^-, \quad ClO_2^- | ClO_3^-, \quad ClO_3^- | ClO_4^-.$$

The collection of families of iso-C_i lines for a given element, in terms of (E, pH) co-ordinates, constitutes the electrochemical equilibrium diagram for this element.

For a certain value of C_i, each (R_i, O_i) line of such a diagram separates the plane into two regions: below it one has $x_i < 0{\cdot}5$, i.e. the reduced form R_i predominates; above it one has $x_i > 0{\cdot}5$, i.e. the oxidized form predominates. Thus E_i has a meaning at each point of the plane; the straight lines $E = A - B\text{pH}$ represent the particular values $E_i^{(0\cdot5)}$, which one need no longer denote differently.

In order to predict the possibility of a reaction between an oxidizing agent O_2 and a reducing agent R_1, one can superimpose the corresponding two diagrams: after selecting the appropriate iso-C_i lines, it follows that, depending on whether the line (R_2, O_2) lies above or below the line (R_1, O_1) on the pH vertical considered, R_1 can be oxidized, or is practically unoxidized. In the second case, it is the reverse reaction, i.e. the reaction between the oxidizing agent O_1 and the reducing agent R_2, which becomes possible. The case of two lines intersecting at a point P (Fig. 1) is by no means exceptional: it reveals the marked influence of pH on the direction of certain reactions. For example, the coexistence potential

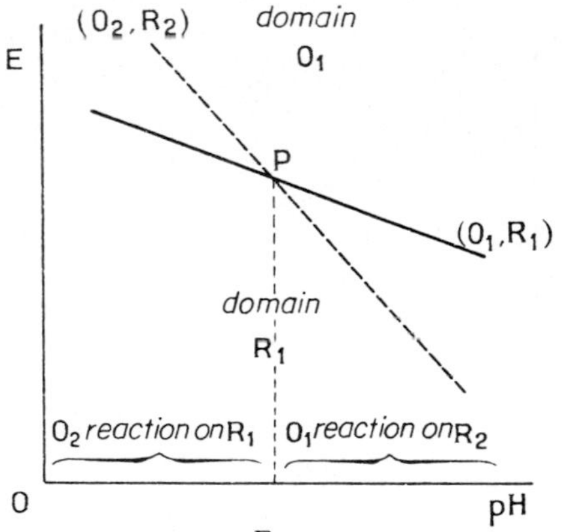

FIG. 1.

corresponding to the reference couple $H_2|H^+(E_1^0 = 0)$ at 1 atm. pressure, is $E_1 = -0{\cdot}0591$ pH. The coexistence potential corresponding to the couple $MoO_2(\text{solid})|Mo^{3+}$ is $E_2 = 0{\cdot}311 - 0{\cdot}2364$ pH $-0{\cdot}0591 \log(Mo^{3+})$, where (Mo^{3+}) represents $C_2/2$. Let us suppose that $C_2 = 0{\cdot}2$, i.e. $(Mo^{3+}) = 0{\cdot}1$. Then $E_2 = 0{\cdot}311 - 0{\cdot}2364$ pH. In an acid solution, will hydrogen at a pressure of 1 atm. reduce MoO_2 to dissolved Mo^{3+}? The condition necessary for this is

$$-0.0591\,\text{pH} < 0.370 - 0.2364\,\text{pH},$$

i.e. the reduction is possible at pH's below

$$\text{pH} = \frac{0.370}{0.1773} = 2.1,$$

whilst at higher pH's, Mo^{3+} can on the other hand decompose water with the evolution of hydrogen and the precipitation of MoO_2. These conclusions are apparent, without the necessity for calculation, on looking at the electrochemical diagram for molybdenum (IV. 10).

We call attention here to the particular importance of two couples which are involved in any aqueous system, due to the presence of the solvent: the couple $H_2|H^+$, of which the coexistence potential is $E_a = -0{\cdot}0591$ pH, and the couple $H_2O|O_2$, of which the coexistence potential is $E_b = 1{\cdot}230 - 0{\cdot}0591$ pH. The straight lines (a) and (b) representing these couples are indicated in broken lines on all the diagrams in the *Atlas*.

6. DISPROPORTIONATION

A redox *amphoter* is a state X of an element which is at the same time the reducing agent R_1 of a certain couple $R_1|O_1$ and the oxidizing agent O_2 of another couple $R_2|O_2$. Thus, the Fe^{2+} ion is an amphoter, being the reducing agent of the couple $Fe^{2+}|Fe^{3+}$ and the oxidizing agent of the couple $Fe|Fe^{2+}$. To a given amphoter therefore correspond (at a fixed concentration) two coexistence lines: $E_1 = A_1 - B_1$ pH; $E_2 = A_2 - B_2$ pH. Now, in order for the amphoter to be stable, it must not be able to react with itself according to the equation

$$\underset{R_1}{a_1 X} + q_1 H_2O + \underset{O_2}{b_2 X_2} + m_2 H^+ \rightleftarrows \underset{O_1}{b_1 O_1} + m_1 H^+ + \underset{R_2}{b_2 R_2} + q_2 H_2O.$$

It is thus necessary that

$$E_1^{(0.5)} > E_2^{(0.5)} \quad \text{or} \quad A_1 - B_1\,\text{pH} > A_2 - B_2\,\text{pH}:$$

the line representing its reducing function must lie above the line representing its oxidizing function. The three predominance domains involved are situated in the right-hand part of Fig. 2.

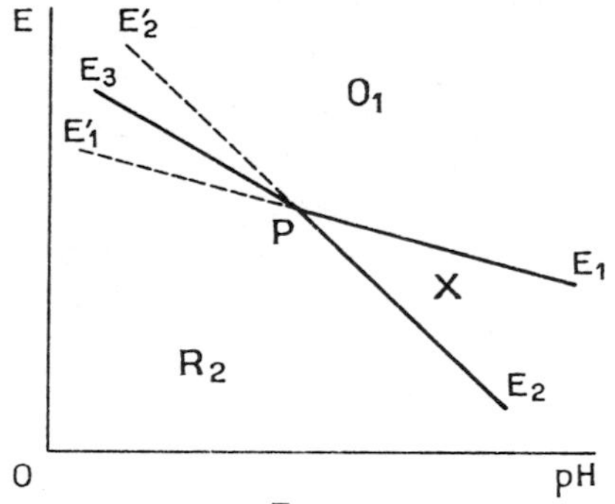

FIG. 2.

Three cases may arise:

6.1. The line E_2 lies below the line E_1 over the whole range of pH considered. The amphoter is then stable over the whole of this range. For example, the aqueous solvent is an amphoter since it is involved in the two couples $H_2O|O_2$ (couple 1) and $H_2|H^+$ (couple 2), represented by the two lines (*b*) and (*a*) mentioned above: these two lines are parallel and the first lies above the second, which explains the great stability of water at all pH's.

6.2. The line E_2 lies above the line E_1 over the whole range of pH considered. The amphoter (if it is known experimentally) is then always metastable. This is the case, for example, for the oxygen-containing compounds of sulphur, apart from those corresponding to sulphuric acid (HSO_4^-, SO_4^{2-}) and dipersulphuric acid ($S_2O_8^{2-}$), as will be seen in IV. 19. The less oxygenated compounds owe their isolation solely to the manifestly slow rate at which they *disproportionate*, which is probably a consequence of the activation energies necessary for breaking the covalent bonds. Thus, complete metastability is encountered only exceptionally amongst metal compounds, since electrovalent bonds predominate in these compounds. Each of them can be denoted on an electrochemical equilibrium diagram, but such a possibility of existence is incompatible with reality for many non-metal compounds. This difficulty can be avoided by disregarding certain very stable states (such as sulphates in the case of sulphur), for the purpose of certain narrowly defined practical applications, but this means that the number of diagrams corresponding to a given non-metal must be increased, as has been done for chlorine (IV. 20); these diagrams then correspond to different degrees of stability.

6.3. The line E_1 cuts the line E_2 in a point P. In this case, which is shown in Fig. 2, the state X is stable only in the region of pH situated to that side of P on which E_1 lies above E_2. In the opposite region X must disappear by disproportionation. The extension E'_1, E'_2 of the lines E_1, E_2 into this region do not therefore appear to have any meaning: the only couple to be considered in this region is $R_2|O_1$, spanning in a way the metastable amphoter X. A new coexistence line E_3, starting from P, separates the domains O_1 and R_2 which have become contiguous. Reasoning step by step in this way, one understands why the predominance domains of most amphoters (but not those of the extreme states, i.e. those which are richest or poorest in electrons) appear on the diagrams as closed domains. Their limits in a horizontal direction are often due to the disappearance of a state simply on account of a variation in pH, without there being oxidation or reduction of the active element. The acid function of certain hydrogen-containing compounds involves an equilibrium between the protons released and the rest of the molecule. Thus for dissolved hypochlorous acid: $HClO \rightleftharpoons ClO^- + H^+$. If, at a given temperature, k is the equilibrium constant for such a dissociation, and $pk = -\log k$, one has

$$pH = pk + \log \frac{(ClO^-)}{(HClO)}.$$

Now the above definition of coexistence requires a *vertical* boundary, of abscissa pH = pk, separating the domains HClO (*on the left*) and ClO^- (*on the right*). In this example, pk = 7·49 at 25°C. The generalization of this idea to other schemes of proton release in the absence of redox reactions, e.g.

$$Cr_2O_7^{2-} + H_2O \rightleftharpoons 2CrO_4^{2-} + 2H^+$$

creates no difficulties.

The existence of triple points P not involving a vertical boundary, as in Fig. 2, implies however the possibility of the *reversible disproportionation* of an amphoter X on change of pH of the medium. For all pH's at which X is stable, the point representing the equilibrium of its disproportionation into O_1 and R_2 lies in fact inside its predominance domain; it remains there if one changes the pH in the sense which brings it nearer to the abscissa of P. The trajectory of the equilibrium point always lies between the lines PE_1 and PE_2 and finishes up at the triple point. If one continued to change the pH in the same sense, X would cease to be stable and would be converted into $O_1 + R_2$; the active element would divide itself between these states in proportions of the same order; the trajectory would then continue in the immediate neighbourhood of PE_3, the boundary between the domains $R_2|O_1$. By way of an example, we shall discuss a diagram showing metastable states of sulphur. This diagram, which has been previously published([4]), is not incorporated among the plates of the *Atlas*, but is reproduced on a small scale in Fig. 3. It disregards the existence of thionates, which would exclude certain predominance domains, and sulphates, which would allow only the domains of sulphur and hydrogen sulphide and its ions to subsist beside their own domains (*see* IV. 19). In order not to make the representation too complicated, only one overall concentration, corresponding to 1 g-at of sulphur per kilogram of solvent, has been considered. The hydrogen sulphide is then in the gaseous state at 1 atm. pressure. Ten domains are then apparent, i.e. those for: dissolved H_2SO_3, HSO_3^-, SO_3^{2-}, $HS_2O_3^-$, $S_2O_3^{2-}$, $S_{oct.}$, S_5^{2-}, $H_2S_{gas.}$, HS^-, S^{2-}. The boundaries of the domains are numbered; each one corresponds to a half-reaction which can easily be identified; the triple points can conveniently be referred to by the numbers of the three lines which meet at them. Several reversible disproportionations, which do in fact characterize the experimental chemistry of sulphur, can be interpreted by this diagram:

([4]) G. VALENSI, *C.R. CITCE*, 2, 1950, p. 51, Tamburini, Milan, 1951.

(a) *Action of acids on thiosulphate solutions.* The representative point traverses in a north-west direction the interior of the $S_2O_3^{2-}$ domain (15–16–17–24–22–20–19) and crosses line (15), the $S_2O_3^{2-}|HS_2O_3^-$ boundary, where first of all the reaction

$$S_2O_3^{2-} + H^+ \rightleftharpoons HS_2O_3^-.$$

takes place.

It then crosses, in the same direction, the $HS_2O_3^-$ domain (13–14–15–18), going as far as the vertex (12–13–18), where the well-known disproportionation:

$$HS_2O_3^- + H^+ \rightleftharpoons S + H_2SO_3$$

takes place.

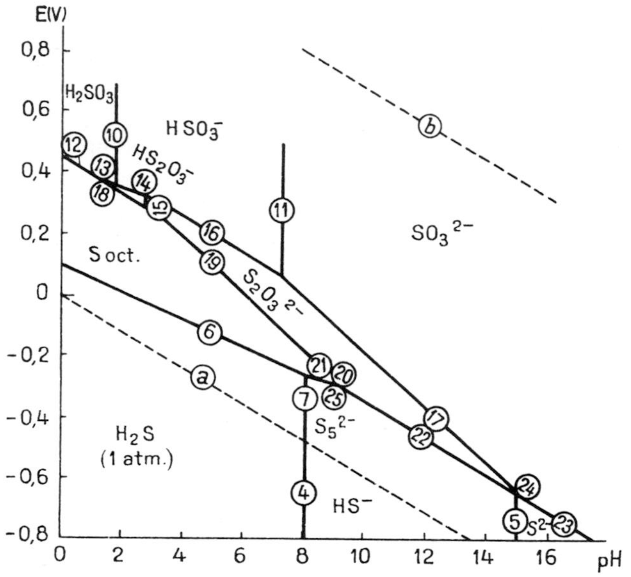

FIG. 3.

(b) *Disproportionation of sulphur in alkaline solution.* The representative point traverses in a south-east direction the interior of the $S_{oct.}$ domain (12–18–19–21–6) finishing up at the vertex (19–20–21) where the following disproportionation occurs:

$$12S + 3H_2O \rightleftharpoons S_2O_3^{2-} + 2S_5^{2-} + 6H^+,$$

Taking into account the alkalinity then acquired by the medium, whose pH reaches about 10, this can be represented as

$$12S + 6OH^- \rightleftharpoons S_2O_3^{2-} + 2S_5^{2-} + 3H_2O.$$

One can interpret in this way the industrial manufacture of polysulphides destined for agricultural uses; they are always mixed with thiosulphates. To increase the rate of reaction, one is however compelled to work at a temperature considerably greater than 25°C.

(c) *Disproportionation of polysulphides by alkalization.* The polysulphidation index of such solutions, which is 5 at the equilibrium, in the presence of an excess of solid sulphur, decreases when the final alkalinity increases, i.e. when one increases the initial proportion of alkali with respect to the sulphur used. Now, the polysulphides of index y intermediate between 5 and 1 are amphoters and can therefore disproportionate according to the equation $2S_y^{2-} \rightleftharpoons S_{y+1}^{2-} + S_{y-1}^{2-}$. The coexistence potentials of the various couples involved are very close and it would thus be somewhat arbitrary to define a separate domain for each of the intermediate polysulphides. If, starting from the pentasulphide, i.e. from the domain (21–20–25), one continues to increase the pH, one arrives finally at the vertex (20–25–7), where the ultimate disproportionation of the polysulphide sulphur takes place, giving $S_2O_3^{2-} + HS^-$, thus producing the minimum index $y = 1$. In actual fact, all the indices intermediate between 5 and 1 can be obtained by increasing the initial proportion of alkali with respect to sulphur, providing that one works at a sufficiently high temperature.

(d) *Disproportionation of polysulphides by acidification.* Under conditions in which the rate is sufficiently great, i.e. at a fairly high temperature, the disproportionations (c) and (b) are reversed if one re-acidifies the solutions obtained. This is due to the fact that in the mixtures of polysulphides and thiosulphate corresponding to such solutions, the representative point lies on line (20) and moves along it up to the vertex (19–21–20) on addition of acid; one can then move into the sulphur region, by means of the reaction of $S_2O_3^{2-}$ with S_5^{2-}, the reverse of the disproportionation (b) considered above.

This is no longer true if one starts with a polysulphide solution free from thiosulphate, which can be prepared as indicated below: its representative point then lies inside the domain (21–20–25); it moves towards the vertex (7–21–25) on acidification. At this vertex there occurs the disproportionation $S_5^{2-} + H^+ \rightleftharpoons HS^- + 4S$; line (7) is then followed as far as the vertex (6–7–4), which lies on the vertical line corresponding to the acid couple $H_2S|HS^-$; hydrogen sulphide is then produced according to the equation

$$HS^- + H^+ \rightleftharpoons H_2S.$$

It is in fact well known that the acidification of polysulphide solutions, even at ordinary temperatures, liberates hydrogen sulphide, with the deposition of sulphur. The two successive reactions involved have moreover been separated experimentally(5).

Nevertheless, at ordinary temperatures, the disproportionation of sulphur by alkalinization is a slow reaction, as is the reverse reaction, i.e. the action of acids on disproportionated solutions. Under these conditions, a different diagram for the metastable states of sulphur, neglecting all oxygen-containing sulphur compounds(6) would give a better description of certain phenomena which can be observed only at room temperature. On such an auxiliary diagram, the polysulphide domain is naturally considerably enlarged. The representative point for alkaline solutions of disproportionated sulphur no longer lies on a boundary and, at room temperature, acidification of such solutions has the same effect as if one were dealing with polysulphide solutions free from thiosulphate. Nevertheless, the thiosulphate present would no longer be inert at low pH's and would show its presence by the disproportionation (a), which produces additional sulphur $+ SO_2$ below a pH of about 2.

7. AMPHOTERIZATION

One may call the reverse reaction of a disproportionation an *amphoterization.* Returning to Fig. 2, one may imagine that, at a pH compatible with the stability of X, one causes the oxidizing agent O_1 to react with the reducing agent R_2: the reaction is possible, since the line PE_1 then lies above the line PE_2; it will give rise to the amphoter X. Hence one can derive a rule that when two states lie on either side of a given domain, they can react together to produce the state proper to this domain; this is an amphoterization. Let us return now to Fig. 3 for some examples of this:

(a) *Action of hydrogen sulphide on sulphurous acid.* The H_2SO_3 and H_2S domains, (12–13–10) and (6–4), lie on either side of the $S_{oct.}$ domain, (18–19–21–6). One can therefore have the reaction

$$SO_2 + 2H_2S \rightleftharpoons 3S + 2H_2O.$$

which does in fact constitute the second phase of the process for extracting sulphur from Lacq gases. At room temperature it is complicated by the formation of thionic compounds, which we have neglected in plotting the metastable diagram in Fig. 3.

(b) *Dissolution of sulphur in sulphite solutions.* The domains of the dissolved ions HSO_3^-, SO_3^{2-} and that of $S_{oct.}$ lie on either side of the $S_2O_3^{2-}$ domain. Sulphur can therefore react with sulphite

(5) G. VALENSI, *C.R. Acad. Sc.*, 221, 1945, p. 352.
(6) G. VALENSI, *C.R. CITCE*, 2, 1950, p. 51, Tamburini, Milan, 1951.

solutions according to the equation

$$S + SO_3^{2-} \rightleftharpoons S_2O_3^{2-}.$$

This is indeed one of the methods used for preparing alkali metal thiosulphates.

(c) *Dissolution of sulphur in sulphide solutions.* On account of the small second dissociation constant of hydrogen sulphide, an alkali metal sulphide dissolved in aqueous solution is converted largely into hydrosulphide according to the equation

$$S^{2-} + H_2O \rightleftharpoons HS^- + OH^-.$$

Now the $S_{oct.}$ and HS^- domains lie on either side of the S_5^{2-} domain (21–20–25); sulphur can therefore react with a solution of sulphide ($HS^- + OH^-$) according to the equation

$$4S + HS^- + OH^- \rightleftharpoons S_5^{2-} + H_2O.$$

This is a method for preparing polysulphide solutions free from thiosulphate, and it can be used even at room temperature. At this temperature it is not interfered with by the disproportionation of sulphur to give polysulphide + thiosulphate, which is still very slow, as we have already seen.

8. RATES OF REACTIONS WHICH ARE THERMODYNAMICALLY POSSIBLE

The preceding paragraphs show how much care is required in making use of the thermodynamic predictions embodied in the electrochemical equilibrium diagrams. For this reason they should be considered as a means of interpreting known experimental facts rather than discovering new ones. Thermodynamics cannot give information about the rates—which are often almost zero—of reactions which are compatible with the state of a given medium. If this were not the case, many substances, such as sulphites, thiosulphates, etc. would have remained unknown. In practice it is as if a double barrier were associated with each redox co-existence line, at a certain distance above it (for the reducing function) and below it (for the oxidizing function). As explained in III. 1, such divergences may be characterized by *overpotentials*, which depend on catalytic conditions. Their values (anodic or cathodic) for reactions which can be brought about by electrolysis, vary from case to case. For example the generally slow couples, whose co-existence potentials are represented by the lines (a) and (b) for water, are most often protected by overpotentials of the order of a volt. This means that gaseous oxygen does in fact oxidize only those reducing agents whose coexistence line is more than 1 V below line (*b*). Returning to Fig. 3, one can see that a stream of oxygen can oxidize a dissolved thiosulphate only with difficulty to sulphite. On the other hand it can easily oxidize dissolved hydrogen sulphide to sulphur, and likewise it can easily oxidize an alkali metal hydrosulphide to pentasulphide at pH's between 8 and 10, or to thiosulphate at pH's above 10. This explains the well known difference between the ageing of a solution of ammonium hydrosulphide used for qualitative analysis, buffered at a pH of about 9 on account of its nature, and that of a solution of potassium hydrosulphide, whose pH is nearer 14. In the same way one can interpret another industrial process for the manufacture of thiosulphates, which consists of disproportionating the sulphur first of all in an alkaline solution, thus bringing its representative point on to the boundary (20), then passing a stream of air through the solution, thus bringing the representative point inside the domain (15–16–17–22–20).

9. CONCLUSION

The few examples discussed above are sufficient to point out the usefulness of electrochemical diagrams as a means of linking up the respective features of the various compounds of a given element.

The systematic introduction of these diagrams into a text-book of descriptive inorganic chemistry would, in view of their recourse to logical arguments, help to make it more attractive than an enumeration of apparently unrelated facts. This would also enable certain chapters to be condensed, and would thus compensate to some extent the alarming increase in subject matter to be taught.(7)

(7) G. VALENSI, *Bull. Union Physiciens* (France), 45, 1950, p. 61.

Apart from their educational applications, electrochemical diagrams are of use in research, where they can enable one to dispense with a good deal of the preliminary calculation connected with determining the thermodynamic possibility of a new reaction, before tackling an experimental investigation, which would be completely futile under conditions excluded by the diagrams.

But this is all that one can ask of these electrochemical diagrams. They do not enable one to predict the kinetics of a phenomenon, although this is the decisive factor for the yield. A certain latitude must moreover be allowed with regard to the position of the domain boundaries: on the one hand, the replacement of activities by concentrations is only a rough approximation; on the other hand, the accelerating influence of a rise in temperature, which is often taken advantage of in practice, naturally modifies the boundaries valid at 25°C.

SECTION 3

ANALYTICAL CHEMISTRY

G. CHARLOT

AMONG the reactions employed by analytical chemistry, oxidation-reduction reactions, whether they be chemical or electrochemical, are the most useful. It is therefore important to the chemist to be able to predict these reactions and be able to bring them about or prevent them in order to achieve a desired result.

Among the factors that enable us to influence the properties of the majority of oxidation-reduction systems, pH is one of the most important, and undoubtedly the easiest to control. The knowledge of oxidation-reduction potentials, which enable us to predict the reactions for each pH, is also one of the primary concerns of the analyst. Potential–pH diagrams present these properties in their most useful form.

By comparing various diagrams it is possible to predict oxidation-reduction reactions; to predict the possibility of these reactions we should say, because, unlike most other reactions, oxidation-reduction reactions sometimes have very small reaction rates, and the equilibria can not therefore be attained. Now, for practical reasons, the analyst uses only fast reactions. In some cases the equilibria are reached so slowly that prediction of the reactions by means of equilibrium diagrams is of no interest. In other cases the diagrams are valuable for a first approximation. Finally, in many cases they enable quantitative predictions to be made. In these cases the diagrams summarize a large number of properties, and they do it in a manner which is more precise than previous methods.

We can quote some examples which are particularly striking, especially as far as the understanding and teaching of chemical properties is concerned. For example, the potential–pH diagram for manganese: Mn (II), Mn (II–III), Mn (III), Mn (IV), Mn (VI), Mn (VII). Starting from potential determinations in alkaline media and the solubility product of manganese (II) hydroxide, the whole of the diagram can be constructed. This diagram shows, better than calculations or descriptions, the domains of existence of the various chemical species, the various substances that can be obtained, and the various reactions that can be predicted for each pH. Making use of this diagram we can not only predict reactions, but we can also see under what conditions they can be avoided. For instance, by comparing this diagram with those of the halogens, we see that in a mixture of chloride and bromide, the bromide will be oxidized by the permanganate at pH = 3; the chloride can then be oxidized at pH = 0. We can predict those substances which will reduce permanganate to Mn (II) and also the smaller number of substances which will reduce it to manganese dioxide at pH = 0, and the very large number of substances which will reduce it to Mn (II–III), (III) and (IV) in alkaline media, etc.

The diagram for cerium, for instance, shows us that salts of Ce (IV) are very powerful oxidizing agents at pH = 0, and that salts of Ce (III), on the other hand, are very powerful reducing agents in slightly acid media.

Reduction by metals, titration of oxidizing or reducing agents using oxidation-reduction indicators, separations, etc., can be predicted and perfected by means of these diagrams.

These properties are no less important for the electrochemical reactions used in analysis. Electrochemical reactions can be dealt with in a manner analogous to chemical oxidation-reduction reactions. The knowledge of equilibrium potentials as a function of the pH is the basic piece of information in the case of so-called rapid electrochemical reactions (oxidations and reductions involving certain metals, the antimony electrode, the hydroquinone electrode, etc.). In other cases kinetic factors must be introduced, but, as in the case of chemical reactions, the knowledge of the equilibrium potential for each pH is still often a good enough first approximation to predict or distinguish between a certain number of possibilities. Electrochemical reactions are, of course, the basis of numerous electrochemical methods used in analysis: potentiometric, amperometric, coulometric methods, separation by electrolysis, etc.

To conclude: the knowledge of potential–pH equilibrium diagrams provides an important instrument for analytical chemistry, which very often involves chemical or electrochemical reactions in solution.

It seems likely that this systematic method will be used more and more widely in the future.

BIBLIOGRAPHY

G. Charlot, *Sur l'utilisation des diagrammes potentiel–pH en chimie analytique: l'analyse qualitative et les réactions en solution,* Masson, Paris, 1957; Methuen, London, 1954; Aquilar, Madrid, 1954; Kijoritsu Syuppan, Tokyo, 1958.

SECTION 4

CORROSION

M. POURBAIX

SUMMARY

1. *Theoretical corrosion, immunity and passivation conditions.*
2. *Resistance of metal to pure water.*
3. *Metals which can be passivated and activated.*
4. *Oxidizing corrosion inhibitors.*
5. *Degree of nobility of metals.*
   Thermodynamic nobility and immunity.
   Practical nobility, immunity and passivation.
6. *Experimental applications.*
7. *Note on the significance and practical implications of the potential–pH electrochemical equilibrium diagrams.*

1. THEORETICAL CORROSION, IMMUNITY AND PASSIVATION CONDITIONS

LET us assume, as a first approximation, that a metal is corrodible in the presence of an aqueous solution initially containing none of this metal according as the quantity of this metal which can be dissolved thermodynamically by the solution is lower or higher than a very small quantity which, for the sake of argument, we shall set arbitrarily at 10^{-6} g-at.wt./l; this content corresponds to 0·06 mg/l in the case of iron, copper and zinc; it corresponds to 0·03 mg/l for aluminium and to 0·2 mg/l for lead. If this hypothesis is at all correct, the lines on the potential–pH equilibrium diagrams which correspond to a solubility of 10^{-6} g-at.wt. of metal per litre (i.e. the $^{-6}$ equi-solubility lines) make a clear distinction between the domain where corrosion is possible (corrosion domain) and a domain where corrosion is impossible (non-corrosion domain). In the non-corrosion domain, two regions (or groups of regions) can be distinguished: in one of these regions, the solid stable form is the metal itself (domain of *immunity*, or *cathodic protection*), in which case, although presenting a genuine metal surface, the metal is quite incorrodible because the corrosion reaction is energetically impossible: in the other region (or regions), the solid stable form is not the metal but an oxide, a hydroxide, a hydride or a salt (*passivation* domain); the metal then tends to become coated with this oxide, hydroxide, hydride or salt which can, according to the circumstances, form on the metal either a non-porous film practically preventing all direct contact between the metal itself and the solution (in which case protection against corrosion is perfect), or a porous deposit which only partially prevents contact between the metal and the solution (in which case the protection is only imperfect). Understood in this way, *passivation thus does not necessarily imply the absence of corrosion*. Experience shows that, in the case of non-chlorinated solutions at least, the oxide films are generally perfect protectors for numerous metals, among which are aluminium, chromium, iron and tin.

In some relatively rare cases, a degradation of the metal may come about through the action, not of *dissolution*, but of gasification accompanied by the formation of a volatile hydride or oxide. If, as a rough guide, we assume that metal corrosion can take place in this way if the partial equilibrium pressure of the hydride or the oxide is equivalent to at least 10^{-6} atm., the lines of the potential–pH equilibrium diagrams which correspond to a hydride or oxide pressure equivalent to 10^{-6} atm. will enable us to establish a domain of corrosion by gasification.

It goes without saying that the concentration (10^{-6} g-at.wt./l) and pressure (10^{-6} atm.) values adopted here for the definition of the corrosion thresholds are arbitrary and that, in practice, there are good reasons for modifying these critical values. With this reservation, however, this theory can be regarded as exact as far as protection by immunity (or cathodic protection) is concerned.

As for protection by passivation, on the other hand, this theory is rather an over-simplification; although, thanks to U. R. Evans, the part played by oxides in protection by passivation received formal sanction in 1927, this role is not proved in all cases of passivation; for example, absorption phenomena can play a predominant part. On the other hand, there is a great scarcity of sufficiently precise data concerning the composition and the thermodynamic properties of protective oxide films, and such data are indispensible for an exact knowledge of their stability conditions. However this may be, in spite of these imperfections which it is well to take into account, the conclusions provided by the theoretical "corrosion, immunity and passivation" diagrams frequently coincide appreciably, quantitatively speaking, with the facts.

For further details, the reader is referred to the exposés which will be made in Chapter IV. We point particularly to three such cases of agreement concerning respectively the resistance of metals to pure water, metals which can be activated and passivated and oxidizing inhibitors of corrosion. We proceed to use these diagrams for the purpose of building up an overall picture of the degree of nobility of metals and of some non-metallic elements.

2. RESISTANCE OF METALS TO PURE WATER (See Fig. 1)

Generally speaking, the metals showing perfect resistance to pure water at a temperature in the region of 25°C will be those having an equilibrium diagram on which the perpendicular from pH = 7 crosses only the immunity or passivation domains (outside all corrosion domains) at potentials between −0·8 and +0·7 V, which are possible only in the normal conditions of use for construction metals.

With some reservations which will be pointed out later, and apart from the six metals in the platinum group, the following thirteen metals fall into this category: beryllium, aluminium, gallium, indium, tin, silver, gold, titanium, zirconium, hafnium, niobium, tantalum and chromium.

As for those of the above-mentioned metals for which a corrosion possibility exists at very low electrode potentials (tin, titanium), it will be particularly important to avoid all reducing action and to see that the surface has a good polish. As for chromium and silver, and also possibly gold and titanium, metals for which a corrosion possibility exists at high electrode potential, slight dissolution will be observed in the presence of a highly oxidizing action.

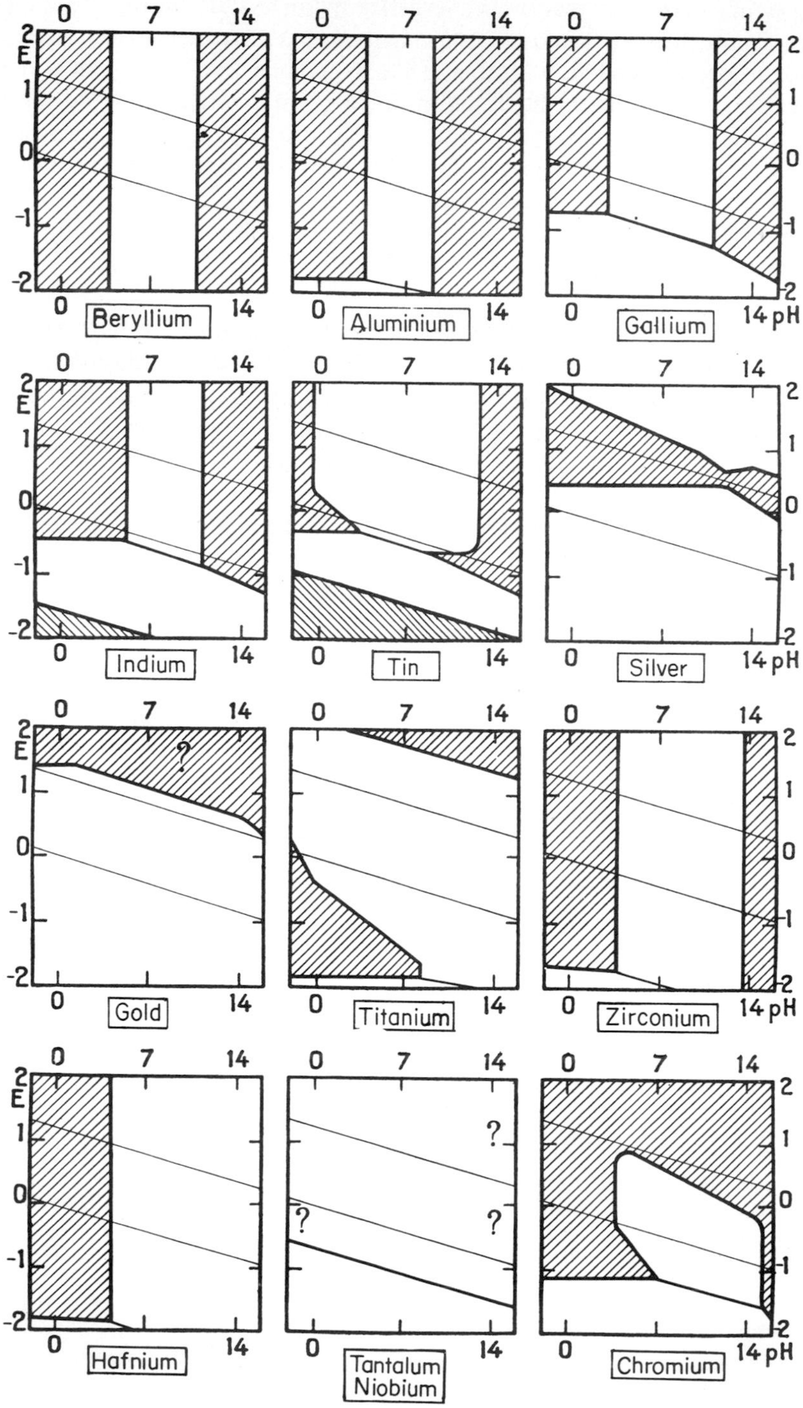

FIG. 1. Metals resistant to pure water. The hatched regions indicate theoretical corrosion domains. The non-hatched regions indicate theoretical immunity and passivation domains.

3. METALS WHICH CAN BE PASSIVATED AND ACTIVATED (See Fig. 2)

Generally speaking, the metals which can be passivated by oxidation and activated by reduction are those which have a higher oxide less soluble than a lower oxide and will thus present a triangular corrosion domain; the lower the apex of this triangle in the diagram, the easier it will be to passivate the

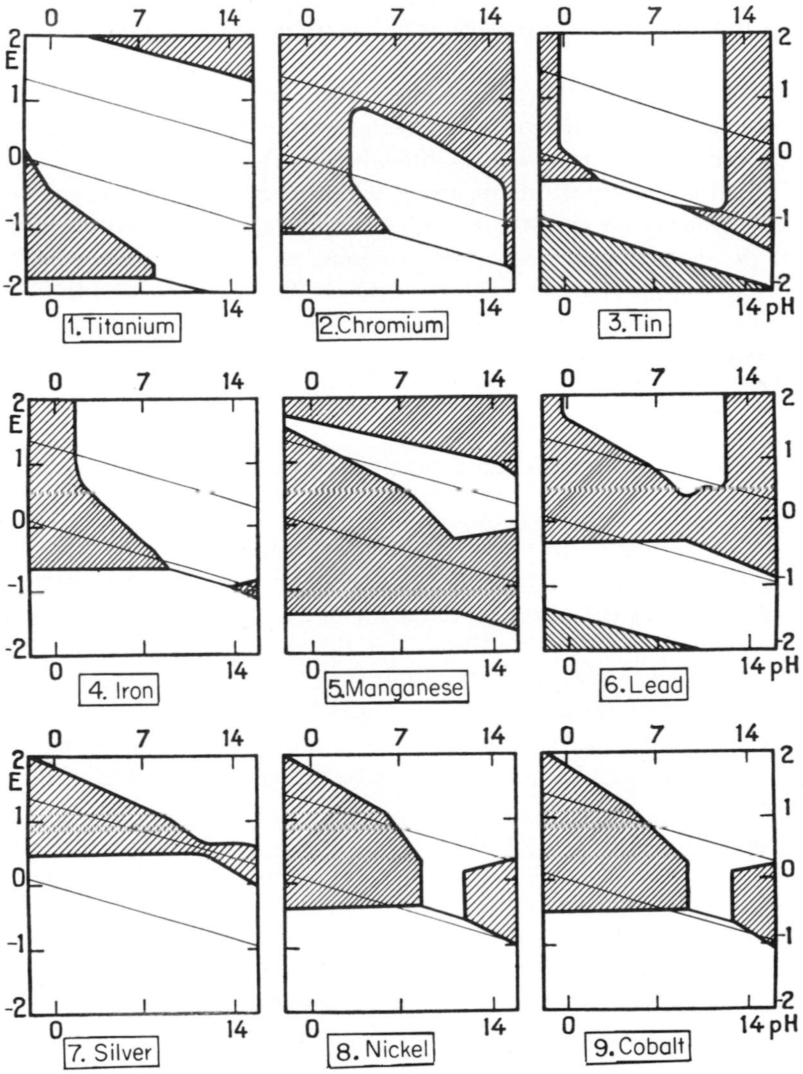

FIG. 2. Passive and active metals (as above).

metal by oxidation. This applies to the following metals, in descending order of passivability: titanium, chromium, tin, iron, manganese, lead, silver, nickel and cobalt.[1]

For the three first metals (titanium, chromium and tin), the passivation domain of which, for an extensive pH range, is situated partly below the stability domain of water, passivation will be very easy and

---

[1] Nickel and cobalt appear to be more easily passivated than the theoretical diagrams lead us to expect [see Chapter IV, sections 12.3 (nickel) and 12.2 (cobalt)].

will occur, more often than not, spontaneously, even in the absence of an oxidizing agent. Iron passivation will require an oxidizing action which, being weak for pH values between 9 and 13, will have to be relatively strong for other pH values. Passivation of the five other metals by the formation of an oxide layer will only be possible by means of a very strong oxidizing action (e.g. an anodization such as that which serves as the basis for charging lead batteries). It must however, be understood that, in spite of the difficulty of passivation, silver generally has a good corrosion resistance owing to the size of its immunity domain, and that, for reasons which have as yet been only insufficiently clarified, nickel (and perhaps cobalt too) can often be passivated at lower potentials than Fig. 2 leads us to anticipate.

Conversely, passivated titanium, chromium and tin can only be activated with relative difficulty: they generally remain passive after the oxidizing action, which would possibly have brought about passivation, has ceased. Activation of iron will be difficult for pH values between 9 and 13 and easy for other pH values. The other five metals (manganese, lead, silver, nickel and cobalt) will be very easily activated, it being nevertheless understood that whereas activation will always bring about corrosion of manganese (a by no means noble metal, the immunity domain of which exists only at very low electrode potentials), activation of the other four metals will only cause corrosion if there subsists a certain oxidizing action of variable intensity according to the metal (maintaining the electrode potential of the metal within its corrosion domain).

4. OXIDIZING CORROSION INHIBITORS (See Fig. 3)

The high susceptibility of iron to corrosion is mainly due to the existence, in the left-hand region of the part of Fig. 2 (No. 4) relating to this metal, of a large triangular domain of corrosion. In the case of solutions in presence of which the passivating iron oxide acts as an effective protector (which generally implies the absence of chloride), corrosion can be avoided by the introduction into the solution of an inhibitor having an oxidizing effect sufficient to enable the electrode potential of all the points on the surface of the iron to be high in the passivation domain of the metal. Protection will be particularly effective if, for the potential and pH conditions corresponding to the "corrosion domains" of the iron, the oxidizing inhibitor can be reduced together with formation of a solid: in becoming deposited on the "weak points" of the iron surface, this solid will improve the protective effect of the passivating oxide film.

This will thus enable us to obtain some data on the possible effectiveness of an oxidizing inhibitor by superimposing on the theoretical "corrosion, immunity and passivation" diagram for iron the potential–pH equilibrium diagram which shows the stability conditions of the solids which can be formed by reduction of this inhibitor. This has been done with Fig. 3, where consideration has been taken of 0·01 M solutions of the nine following oxidizing substances: hyperosmates, pertechnetates, chromates, molybdates, tungstates, vanadates, selenates, arsenates and antimonates.

A thick line indicates the potentials below which the inhibitor can be reduced; the shaded sections represent those parts of the corrosion domains of iron for which the products of the reduction of the oxidizing agent are not solids. If, as a first approximation, we assume that the reduction reactions of the oxidizing agent are reversible and that the solids formed in this reduction constitute a protective coating on the iron, the shaded sections in Fig. 3 show the theoretical conditions of corrosion, the non-shaded areas representing the theoretical areas of non-corrosion.

According to the first six diagrams in Fig. 3, the hyperosmates and pertechnetates are extremely effective inhibitors of iron corrosion, which coincides with Cartledge's observations(2); it is well known that the chromates, although less effective, are nevertheless very good inhibitors; the molybdates and tungstates are effective only to small extent; vanadates are hardly effective at all.

(2) See Chapter IV, sections 13.4 (osmium) and 11.2 (technetium).

On the other hand, the last three diagrams of Fig. 3 provide data on the efficacity of selenates, arsenates and antimonates.([3])

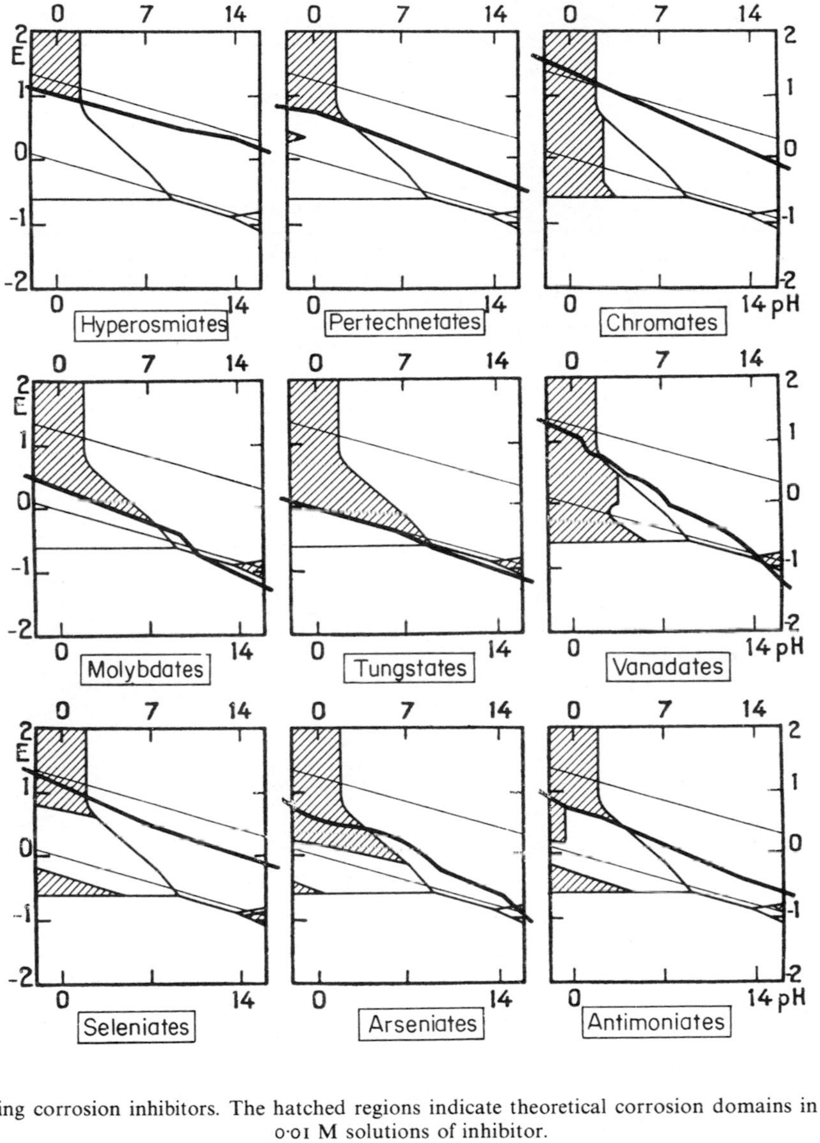

FIG. 3. Oxidizing corrosion inhibitors. The hatched regions indicate theoretical corrosion domains in the presence of 0·01 M solutions of inhibitor.

5. DEGREE OF NOBILITY OF METALS (See Fig. 4)

The Nernst scale of "solution potentials" allows us to classify the metals in order of "nobility", according to the value of the equilibrium potential of their reaction of dissolution in the form of a simple given ion considered in standard state (1 ion g/l): those metals are considered as noble which have an equilibrium potential higher than that of the standard hydrogen electrode and which,

([3]) See primarily the work done in this field by Piontelli and Fagnani, Chapter IV, section 18.4 (antimony).

therefore, cannot be corroded with release of hydrogen in a solution with a zero pH value; the non-noble metals are those for which this condition does not arise and which can thus be corroded with release of hydrogen.

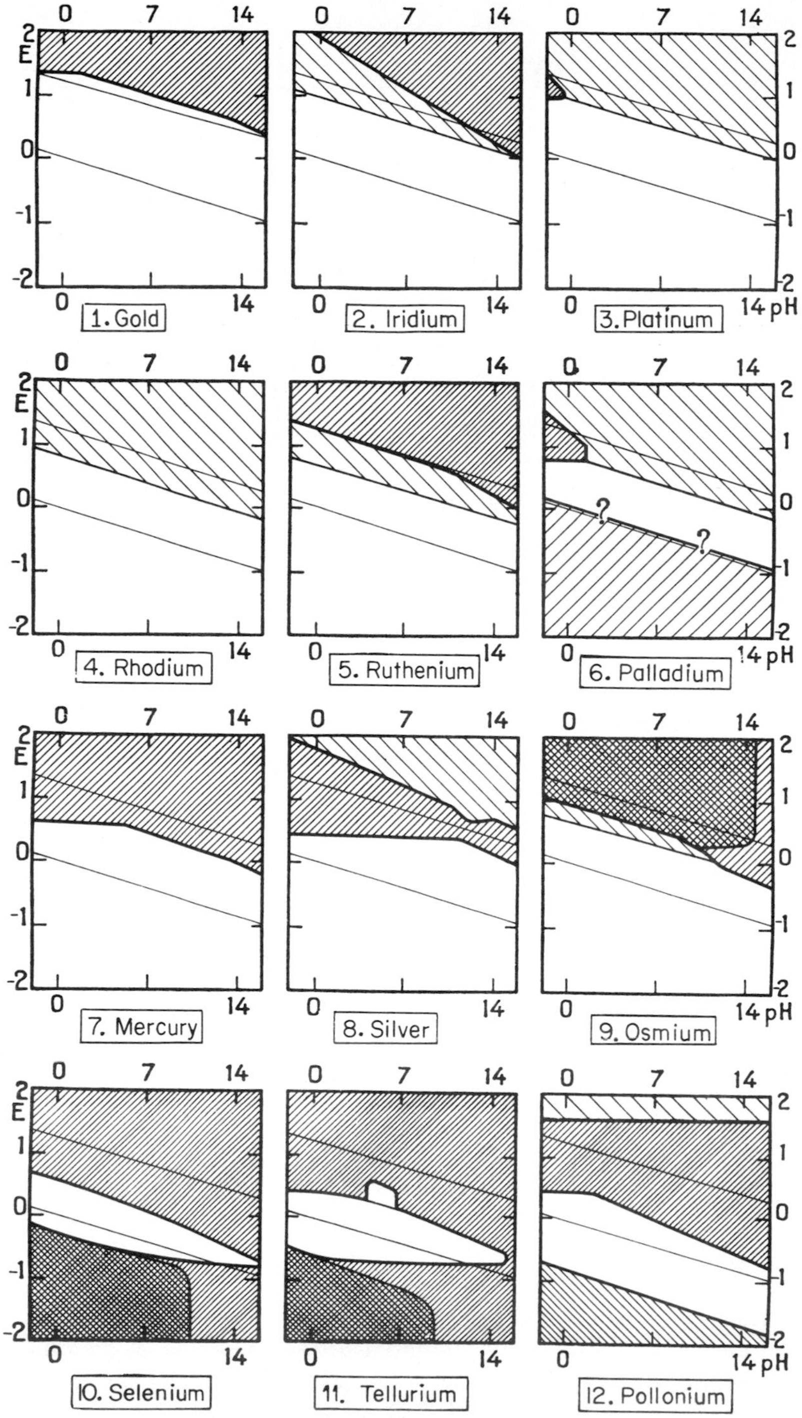

FIG. 4. Corrosion, immunity and passivation domains of metals and metalloids classified in order of thermodynamic nobility.

As R. Piontelli writes in his preface to this *Atlas*, this degree of "thermodynamic nobility" can differ appreciably from the "practical nobility" established experimentally. The divergence between these two degrees of nobility may be due to the following three facts:

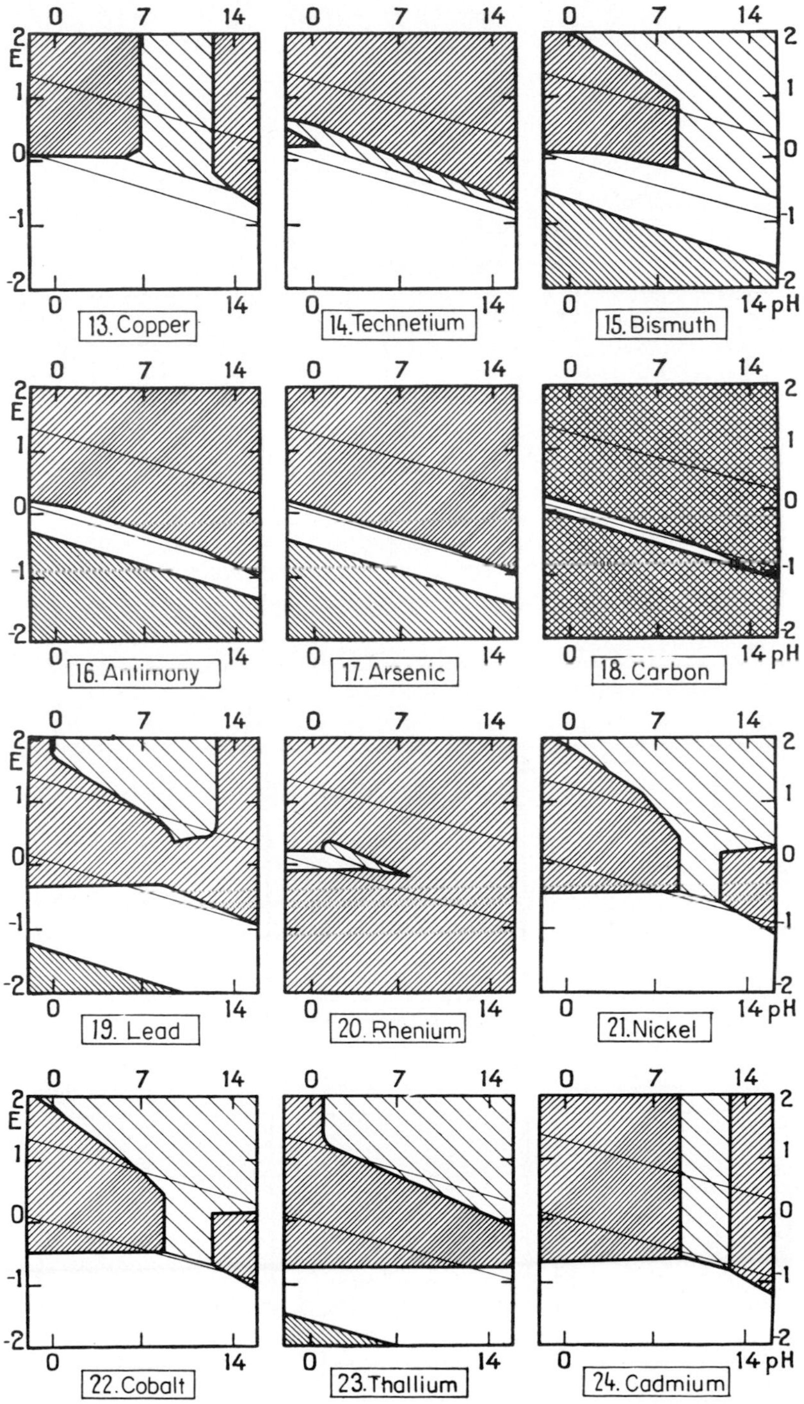

FIG. 4. (*continued*)

The metal is dissolved not in the form of a single simple ion (such as Cu^+), but in the form of two simple ions (Cu^+ and Cu^{++}) or oxygen ions (CuO_2^{--}) or in the form of complex ions [$Cu(CN)_2^-$, $CuCl_2^-$]; this results in a modification of the "solution potential" of the metal.

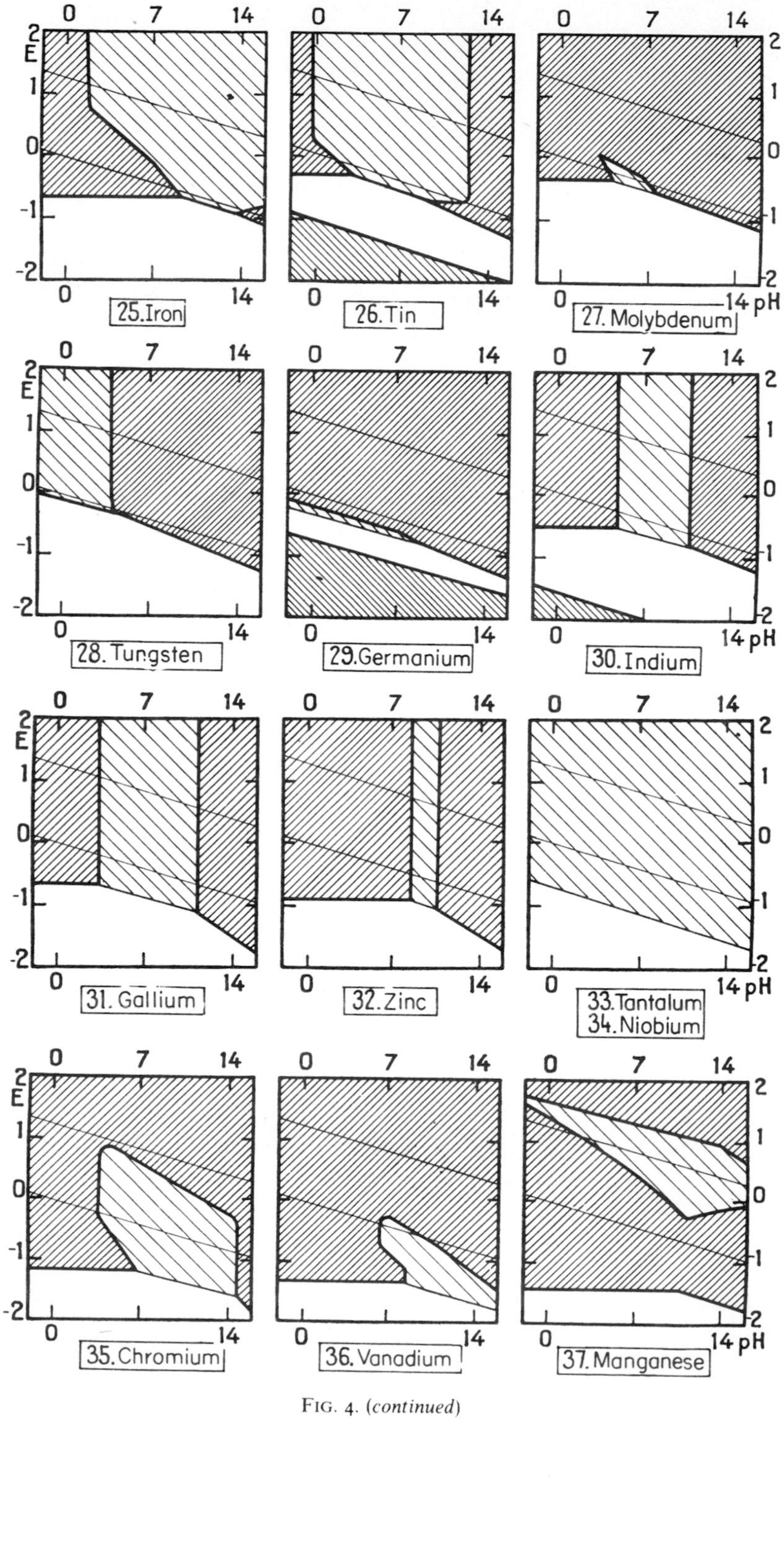

FIG. 4. (*continued*)

The metal is coated with a passivating film (oxide Fe_2O_3, hydride UH_3, salt $FePO_4$); the dissolution of the metal can thus be more or less completely braked by the interposition of a more or less protective film.

The dissolution reaction can be strongly irreversible (in the case of non-"normal" metals in the Piontelli classification, such as nickel), in which case the dissolution of the metal occurs effectively only through an appreciable potential-rise, at an electrode potential patently higher than the thermodynamic equilibrium potential.

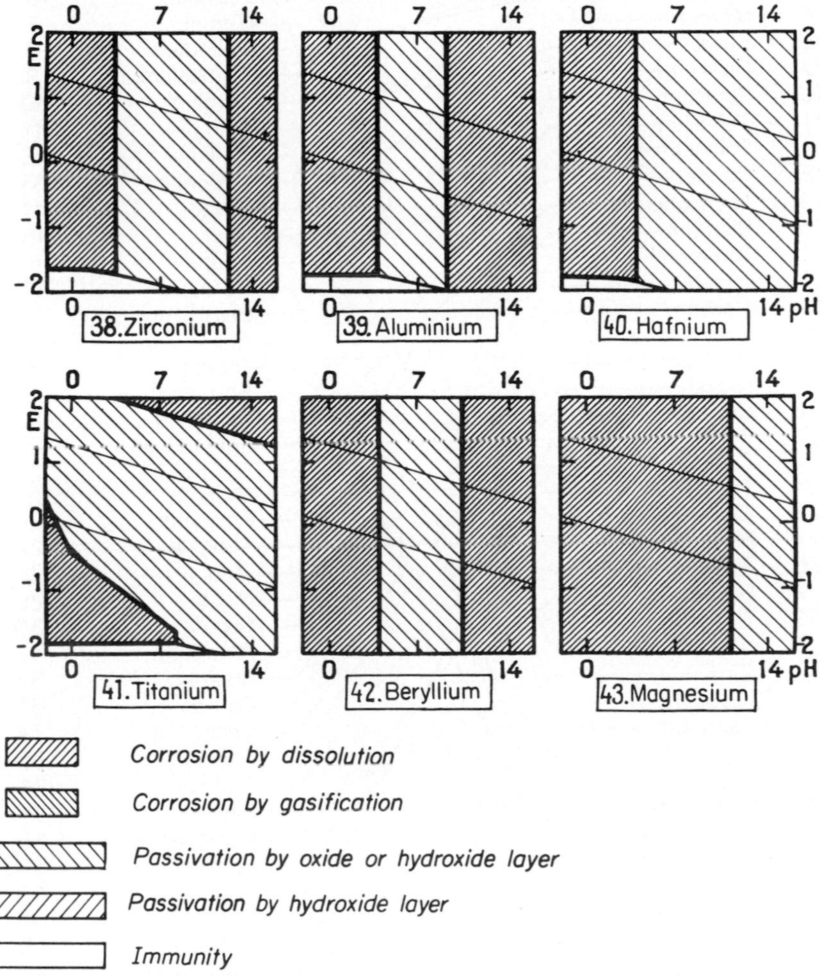

FIG. 4. (*end*)

The third cause of this divergence pertains to electrochemical kinetics and will be examined in paragraph 4.6; the first two causes can be studied on a thermodynamic basis with the aid of the potential–pH equilibrium diagrams if we adopt as the criteria of nobility, not the Nernst "solution potential", but the *immunity* conditions of the metal (in the presence of the total of the ions which this metal can produce) and the total of the *immunity* and *passivation* conditions of the metal respectively.

Thermodynamic nobility and immunity

Figure 4 gives the theoretical "corrosion, immunity and passivation" diagrams for forty-three metals and metalloids, classified in descending order of thermodynamic nobility. The shaded areas

TABLE I

	A	B	
	Noble metals		
1	Gold	Rhodium	1
2	Iridium	Niobium	2
3	Platinum	Tantalum	3
4	Rhodium	Gold	4
5	Ruthenium	Iridium	5
6	Palladium	Platinum	6
7	Mercury	Titanium	7
8	Silver	Palladium	8
9	Osmium	Ruthenium	9
10	Selenium	Osmium	10
11	Tellurium	Mercury	11
12	Polonium	Gallium	12
13	Copper	Zirconium	13
14	Technetium	Silver	14
15	Bismuth	Tin	15
16	Antimony	Copper	16
17	Arsenic	Hafnium	17
18	Carbon	Beryllium	18
19	Lead	Aluminium	19
20	Rhenium	Indium	20
21	Nickel	Chromium	21
22	Cobalt	Selenium	22
23	Thallium	Technetium	23
24	Cadmium	Tellurium	24
25	Iron	Bismuth	25
26	Tin	Polonium	26
27	Molybdenum	Tungsten	27
28	Tungsten	Iron	28
29	Germanium	Nickel	29
30	Indium	Cobalt	30
31	Gallium	Antimony	31
32	Zinc	Arsenic	32
33	{ Niobium	Carbon	33
34	{ Tantalum	Lead	34
35	Chromium	Rhenium	35
36	Vanadium	Cadmium	36
37	Manganese	Zinc	37
38	Zirconium	Moiybdenum	38
39	Aluminium	Germanium	39
40	Hafnium	Vanadium	40
41	Titanium	Magnesium	41
42	Beryllium	Thallium	42
43	Magnesium	Manganese	43
	Non-noble metals		

A
THERMODYNAMIC NOBILITY
(immunity)

B
PRACTICAL NOBILITY
(immunity and passivation)

Classification of metals and metalloids in order of nobility represent the corrosion domains and were established by lines descending from right to left in the most frequent case of corrosion by dissolution, and by lines descending from left to right in the relatively rare case of corrosion by gasification (e.g. by formation of OsO_4, H_2Se, H_2Te, CO_2, CH_4, AsH_3, SbH_3, BiH_3, GeH_4, SnH_4, PbH_2, InH, TlH). The passivation domains are lightly hatched, the hatching descending from left to right in the very frequent case of passivation by formation of oxide or hydroxide and descending from right to left in the rare case of passivation by hydride formation (Pd_2H). The white areas represent the immunity domains.

It was considered that a metal is thermodynamically noble or non-noble according as its immunity domain (i.e. its thermodynamic stability domain) shows or does not show a section in common with the thermodynamic stability domain of water at a pressure of 1 atm.; this immunity domain is situated between two lines *a* and *b* traced on the equilibrium diagrams established in Chapter IV.

It was considered that the nobility of a metal is greater, the larger the surface common both to its immunity domain and to the stability domain of the water; it was considered that the greater the surface situated between the immunity domain of a non-noble metal and the stability domain of water, the more does the non-noble metal fall short of nobility.

Practical nobility, immunity and passivation

Leaving aside, for the time being, the kinetic factors mentioned above, and assuming as a first approximation that the passivating films considered in Fig. 4 are perfectly protective, we considered that a metal is practically the more noble the greater the surface common both to the total of the immunity and passivation domains and to the stability domain of water. In the case of metals where these surfaces are preceptibly identical, it was accepted that this "practical nobility" is greater the more the immunity and passivation domains extend below and above the stability domain of water, and the more these domains overlap the section of the diagrams which corresponds to pH values between 4 and 10, which are most frequently met with in practice.

Table I shows, on the bases which have just been expounded, the classification of the forty-three elements examined on Fig. 4, on the one hand, according to "thermodynamic nobility" and, on the other, according to "practical nobility"

It must be understood that this table is to be regarded as a draft subject to considerable revision, notably because the electrochemical equilibrium diagrams on which it is based are themselves approximations and in some cases will call for drastic alteration (e.g. those for nickel and cobalt), and because the corrosion and/or passivation reactions represented are sometimes strongly irreversible (e.g. for carbon).

In its present form, this table brings out the considerable ennobling effect which passivation has on the ten following metals: niobium, tantalum, titanium, gallium, zirconium, hafnium, beryllium, aluminium, indium and chromium. According to this table, we must consider the first twenty-three items in column A as having thermodynamic nobility.

6. EXPERIMENTAL APPLICATIONS

As pointed out in section 1 (Generalities) of Chapter III, the electrochemical equilibrium diagrams cannot by themselves *solve* more than a limited number of problems. They are only one of the tools put at the disposal of the scientist, and they must almost always be employed in conjunction with other means of investigation, of which particular importance attaches to electrochemical kinetic studies, based on the judicious experimental definition of potential–current curves (e.g. by means of intensiostatic or potentiokinetic tests).

Analysis of such potential–current curves, together with the equilibrium diagrams, enables us to predetermine the theoretically possible and theoretically impossible reactions for each electrode potential value. If to this thermodynamic analysis, we add chemical, microscopic and other examinations it will generally be easy to change these theoretical possibilities into experimental certainties and thus, for example, to predetermine absolutely the conditions in which a metal alloy corrodes or does not corrode when in contact with a given aqueous solution.

Further on, the reader will find (Chapter IV, section 12.1) an exposé relating to iron, containing some examples for the application of an equilibrium diagram in the experimental study of corrosion and metal protection conditions. It would be useful: if such studies were carried out by electrochemists and metallurgists simultaneously; if they were used patiently for a systematic investigation of the effect produced by the composition of solution (pH, oxidizing agents, reducing agents, chlorides, phosphates...) and of the nature of the metal (chemical composition, structural state, heat treatment, cold working...); if they were applied progressively and thoroughly to different metals and their alloys; and if they were extended simultaneously to both the theoretical and the experimental fields to cover the behaviour of metals and alloys at high temperatures and pressures.

Such an effort would inevitably lead to better utilization of the existing metals and alloys, to new protection procedures and new alloys.

7. NOTE ON THE SIGNIFICANCE AND PRACTICAL IMPLICATIONS OF THE POTENTIAL–pH ELECTROCHEMICAL EQUILIBRIUM DIAGRAMS

In the course of "Study Sessions on the Electrochemical Behaviour and Corrosion of Metals and Stainless Steels" held in Brussels on 21 and 22 November 1957, C. Carius, C. Edeleanu and M. Pourbaix met and exchanged views on subjects of common interest. C. Edeleanu drew the attention of M. Pourbaix and C. Carius to the fact that the exact importance of the "potential–pH equilibrium diagrams" is often insufficiently realized in Great Britain and other countries, and that the interpretations made of them were therefore sometimes erroneous.

On the suggestion of C. Edeleanu, these three scientists drew up the following text, in which they express their agreement on the significance and implications of these diagrams.(4)

1. The metals having the greatest economic importance, and particularly iron, zinc and aluminium, belong, by virtue of their place in the dissolution potential scale, to the category of "non-noble" metals. The transformation of these metals into ions, forming a salt or oxide, is almost invariably accompanied by the liberation of energy, so that these metals tend to dissolve when certain favourable conditions are obtained (presence of humidity, access of atmospheric hydrogen).

   "Electrochemical equilibrium diagrams" are useful for obtaining as complete and overall a view as possible of the interface reactions thermodynamically practicable in a particular given case. Such diagrams indicate, notably as a function of the solution pH (a measure of the degree of acidity or alkalinity of that solution) and of the metal's electrode potential (which measures the reducing or oxidizing power of the interface), the thermodynamic limits of the stability of the metal in relation to its ions, to the ions of the water, and to the reaction products of these ions (hydroxides, oxides, etc.).

   These diagrams show the equilibrium potentials of the electrochemical reactions, the affinity of these reactions and the solubility of the solids for the given experimental conditions.
2. In the absence of any data indicating the contrary, the *electrochemical equilibrium diagrams* of the metals apply only to the behaviour of pure metals (pure iron, for example) in the presence of solutions not containing substances which might form soluble complexes with these metals (cyanides) or insoluble salts (phosphates). Thus these diagrams do not apply to alloys (alloy steels).

(4) See the Comptes Rendus de Séances d'Étude sur le comportement électrochimique et la corrosion des métaux et des aciers inoxydables, Brussels, 21 and 22 November 1957 (Rapport technique RT. 66 of CEBELCOR, May 1958), Appendix, pp. 9–11.

3. *The theoretical "corrosion, immunity and passivation" diagrams* which are deduced, by means of certain hypotheses, from these electrochemical equilibrium diagrams are only applicable in the cases defined under point 2 above, where the equilibrium diagrams are applied.
4. The *passivation* conditions of metals are defined as those in which the stable form of the metal in question is an insoluble oxide (or hydroxide or solid salt); if it is formed by direct contact with the metal, this oxide (or other solid product) "passivates" the metal to a greater or lesser extent and affords it a greater or lesser degree of protection against corrosion; generally speaking, protection will be complete where the film or deposit with which the metal is coated is absolutely adherent and non-porous; in all other cases, protection will be generally imperfect. Thus *passivation does not imply passivity*, if we define passivity as being the condition in which a metal does not corrode, although the metallic form is not thermodynamically stable and the metal thus tends to become transformed into another substance.

   This idea of passivity (caused by a *passivation*) differs from the idea of *immunity* (due, for example, to a *cathodic protection*), which means the condition in which a metal does not corrode because its metallic form is thermodynamically stable, thus making any transformation of the metal, and consequently corrosion, impossible.

   In the particular case of iron, for example, the oxide formed by passivation is often non-porous and thus protective in the solutions containing no chloride; it is generally porous and non-protective in chlorinated solutions.

   The pH value given in the x-axis of the electrochemical equilibrium diagrams is the pH of that fraction of the solution which is in direct contact with the surface (or with a fraction of the surface) of the metal under examination. This pH value is thus not necessarily the pH value of the bulk of the solution; the divergences between the local pH value and the bulk pH value can be considerable, particularly in cases of localized corrosion. In such cases there is generally an increase in the local pH value in the zones where reduction takes place (e.g. reduction of the dissolved oxygen) and a diminution of the local pH value in those zones where a solid oxide or hydroxide forms (e.g. rust).
5. The *electrochemical equilibrium diagrams* must be regarded primarily as patterns showing the reactions which are theoretically possible and impossible for different electrode potentials and pH conditions. If these diagrams are correctly drawn up, there can be no possibility of errors or exceptions; just as the fact that arithmetic is a formal and exact science does not prevent numerous errors in calculation from being made every day, so thermodynamics is exact, but those people who use thermodynamics may commit errors. The electrochemical equilibrium diagrams, which are of a thermodynamic character, must therefore be employed with a full realization of their significance and their conditions of validity. Essentially, these diagrams express that which is energetically *possible* or energetically *impossible*; now, numerous electrochemical reactions are irreversible, i.e. do not necessarily come about even when they are energetically possible. These diagrams, therefore, do not necessarily show what *actually* occurs; an absolute and definite reply to this point often requires *experimental kinetic studies*, consisting, for example, in the plotting of intensiostatic or potentiokinetic polarization curves.

   Electrochemical equilibrium diagrams can serve primarily as a guide in carrying out such experimental studies and in the interpretation of the results obtained.

SECTION 5

ELECTRODEPOSITION

T. P. Hoar

Information contained in potential–pH diagrams is useful in several ways for application to problems involved in electrodeposition. We consider below some representative problems associated with (a) cathodic processes, (b) anodic processes, (c) the solution.

(a) CATHODIC PROCESSES

The desired cathodic reaction in electrowinning, electrorefining, electroplating and electroforming is ordinarily metal deposition. Hydrogen deposition, oxygen reduction and oxide or hydroxide deposition are usually undesirable, although the last of these side reactions has occasional usefulness.

Consider the deposition of nickel from sulphate solution open to the air; Fig. 1 shows the germane part of the nickel potential–pH diagram. At, say, pH 4·5 and $E_H = -0{\cdot}4$ V, evidently oxygen and hydrogen ion can be reduced as well as nickelous ion; however, the overpotentials required to reduce oxygen and hydrogen ion at sensible rates are fortunately considerably higher than that required for nickelous ion reduction, and this can consequently occur at *ca.* 96–98 per cent efficiency. Decrease of pH tends to increase the relative amount of hydrogen ion reduction. Nevertheless, the "acid" type of Watts nickel bath operating at *ca.* pH 2 can give good nickel deposition even though somewhat more hydrogen is evolved, because the pH of the solution next to the cathode rises, through hydrogen ion reduction, and under steady-state deposition conditions the relative amount of hydrogen ion reduction is not unduly large. On the other hand, increase of pH of the bulk solution beyond about 5 causes the catholyte, under deposition conditions, to contain sufficient nickelous hydroxide, present as positively charged colloidal particles, to lead to co-deposition of hydroxide with metal: this gives a harder and more brittle deposit that, although suitable for rather limited purposes, is in general undesirable. Deliberate cathodic deposition of beryllia and alumina from colloidal solutions has been used for the formation of protective oxide films; the suitable electrolytes are beryllium and aluminium sulphate solutions lightly buffered to *ca.* pH 6 and 4 respectively, so that a small increase of pH caused by hydrogen ion reduction, coupled with a very small faradaic current to discharge the colloidal particles, gives the required oxide deposition on the cathode. The very small faradaic current required for hydroxide or oxide deposition, due to the small charge/mass ratio of the colloidal particles, explains why a high pH nickel bath may give almost 100 per cent cathode current efficiency and yet yield deposits containing considerable hydroxide.

In certain special cases oxide can be formed by faradaic cathodic reduction of a soluble ion: thus cathodic deposits of cuprous oxide can be made from cupric sulphate solutions buffered at *ca.* pH 3·5, as shown by the portion of the copper diagram given in Fig. 2. The conditions for the further reduction of such deposits to metal can also be obtained from potential–pH diagrams; such reduction of cuprous oxide to copper is the basis of a decorative coating with a patterned structure caused by the spread of the reduction from widely dispersed nuclei.

The conditions for cathodic deposition from alkaline solutions containing metal hydroxy- or oxy-anions are likewise to be found on the appropriate potential–pH diagrams: tin and zinc deposition

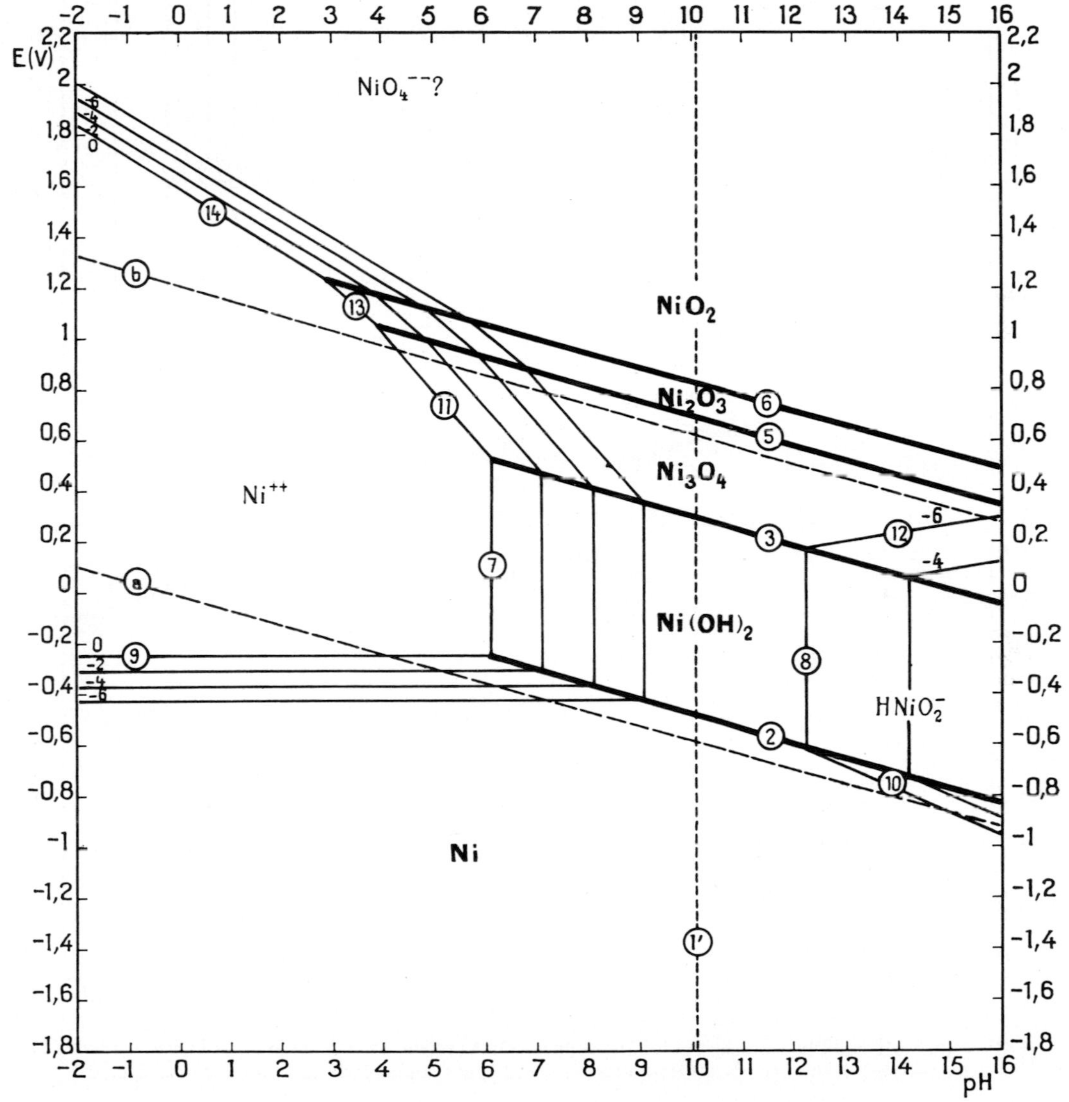

FIG. 1. Potential–pH equilibrium diagram for the nickel–water system, at 25°C.

from stannate and zincate solutions are examples (see pp. 478, 409). Furthermore, the potential–pH conditions for cathodic deposition from baths containing other complexants, such as cyanide ion, ammonia, and substituted ammonias, can readily be seen on suitable potential–pH diagrams incorporating the complex-forming reactions. It is usually convenient to calculate such diagrams for one fixed activity of complexant, just as the simple diagrams are calculated for a fixed activity of water.

Metals that form volatile hydrides, such as antimony (see p. 527), are occasionally electrodeposited.

Formation of the toxic hydride at high cathode polarization is a possible hazard, and the potential–pH conditions leading to it are easily seen on the appropriate diagram.

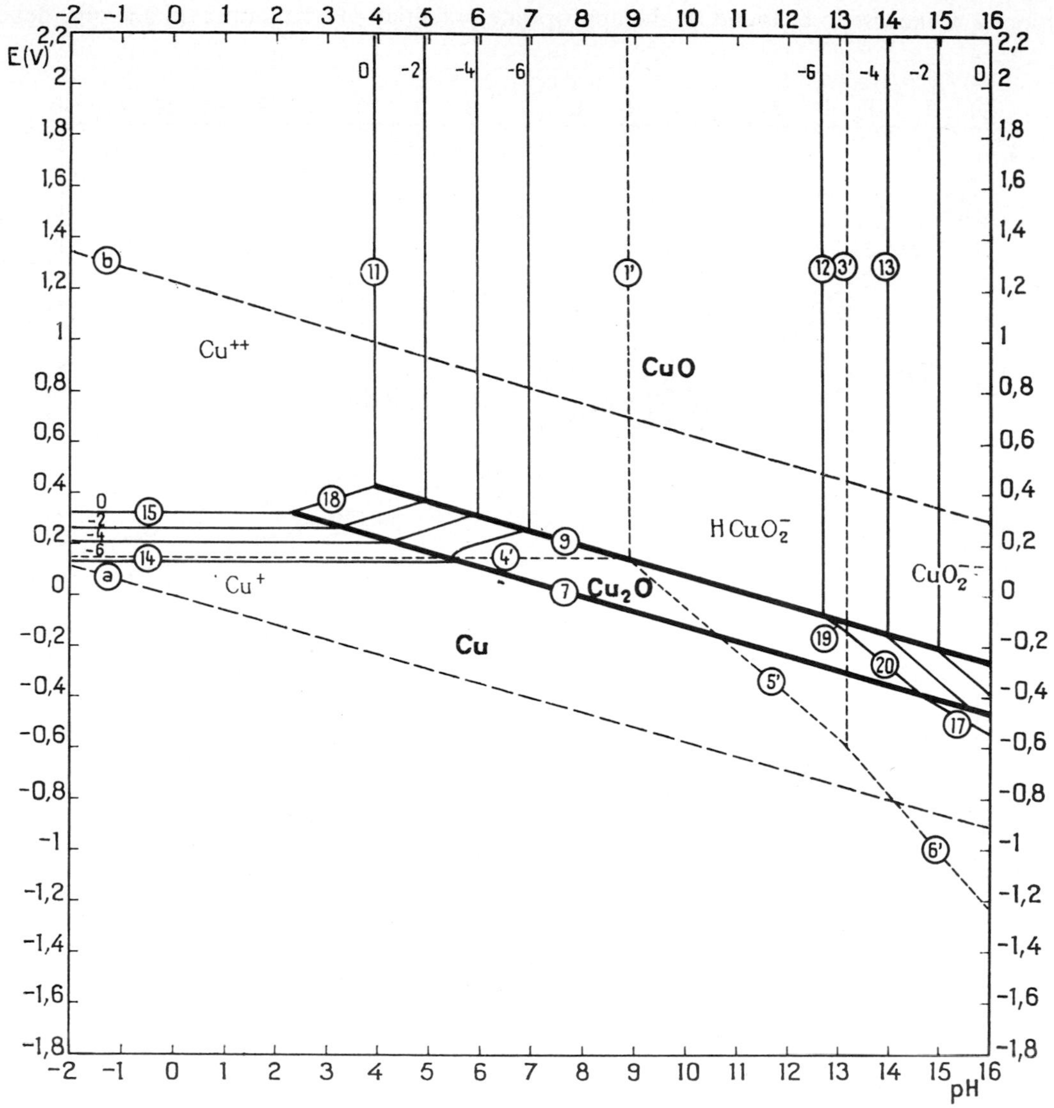

FIG. 2. Potential–pH equilibrium diagram for the copper–water system, at 25°C. [Only solid Cu, Cu_2O and CuO are considered in the figure. $Cu(OH)_2$ and trivalent copper compounds have not been considered.]

(b) ANODIC PROCESSES

In electrodeposition, it is usually desired to have either (a) an anode of the metal being deposited that dissolves at near 100 per cent current efficiency or (b) an anode that is totally insoluble and that acts merely as an inert basis for oxygen evolution. It is rarely desirable to have an anode that gives a mixture of these processes, or that operates consecutively in the dissolving and the passive states.

Again considering Fig. 1, we see, for example, that nickel dissolves to nickelous ion at unit activity at potentials more positive than −0·23 V and at pH less than about 6. At higher pH, solid nickelous hydroxide is the initial anodic product, and this is converted to higher oxides at higher anode potentials: under such conditions, passivation of a nickel anode occurs at once. However, passivation can also occur below pH 6, indeed, as low as *ca.* pH 0·5, because the anodic overpotential required to dissolve nickel to nickelous ions at the current densities required in electrodeposition process is considerable. Thus, if the polarization raises the anode potential above the broken-line extension of the $Ni/Ni(OH)_2$ line (Fig. 1), solid nickelous hydroxide may be formed at low pH; and since there is good evidence that its formation from the metal is *kinetically* easier than the formation of dissolved nickelous ion, its preferential formation is not surprising, and the tendency of nickel anodes to passivate is easily understood. In practice, this is remedied by the incorporation of a little oxide in the nickel anode and/or of chloride in the solution; the overpotential required for dissolution is thereby much reduced and the potential for passivation is not reached.

Soluble anodes operating in alkaline solution, such as tin and zinc, can also passivate at high current densities, mainly because the supply of complexing hydroxyl ions in the solution next to the anode becomes insufficient, so that insoluble hydroxides or oxides are formed. In the special case of tin anodes required to dissolve as stannate rather than stannite, a pseudo-passivation effect of this kind is advantageous; the anode is first passivated by the formation of stannic oxide at high current density, and subsequent operation at lower current density enables the stannic oxide to dissolve in the alkaline solution as stannate while being reformed anodically at the same rate. The potential–pH conditions for these transformations can be seen in the diagram for tin (p. 478).

Insoluble anodes are required in electrowinning and in some other electrodeposition processes. Lead is pre-eminently suitable owing to its easy passivation in sulphate solutions through the sparing solubility of its sulphate, and the fact that lead sulphate is readily converted anodically to the insoluble lead dioxide, which has good electron-conductivity and which is a good inert basis for hydroxyl-ion (or other anion) oxidation. Potential–pH conditions for the production and operation of lead-dioxide-coated lead anodes are shown in the diagram for the metal (p. 489). Platinum is another excellent inert anode, often used in practice for anodic oxidation processes, but usually too expensive for anodes used in electrodeposition. Chromium, on the other hand, while readily passivated like lead and platinum, enters a transpassive region at higher anode potentials and, as shown in the chromium diagram (p. 263), dissolves through the oxidation of its passivating chromic oxide film to soluble chromic acid or chromate. The same effect is found to a less extent in most of the "stainless" chromium irons and steels.

The "refractory" metals such as titanium, tantalum, etc., cannot be operated as inert anodes: although the potential–pH diagrams (pp. 217, 253) indicate the formation of oxide films over very wide ranges of pH and at very negative potentials, the films have very poor electron conductivity and the metals will not sustain any anodic reaction other than film thickening by ion transport under high-field conditions.

Anodic deposition of oxides from solution is occasionally a useful process, as in the electroanalysis of lead. As well as lead dioxide, cobaltic oxide, manganese dioxide and others can be deposited anodically by oxidation of soluble lower-valent ions; the suitable conditions of potential and pH can be readily seen in the relevant diagrams.

(c) THE SOLUTION

Solutions used in electrodeposition need primarily to be stable except during the actual reactions at the electrodes. In particular, they should normally be operated under such pH conditions that hydroxide or oxide precipitation is negligible. These conditions, both for acid and alkaline solutions, are apparent in the relevant potential–pH diagrams. Buffering the solutions to the appropriate pH is frequently adopted to minimize changes due to adventitious absorption of atmospheric carbon dioxide, or to accidental contamination from acid pickling solutions or alkaline degreasants. Buffering also helps to maintain pH in the actual layer of solution next to the cathode or anode, although, as mentioned earlier, changes caused by hydrogen ion reduction may there be appreciable.

In some circumstances, alteration of pH or potential or both can be used to advantage in the purification of a solution used for electrodeposition. The removal of iron during the electrorefining of nickel

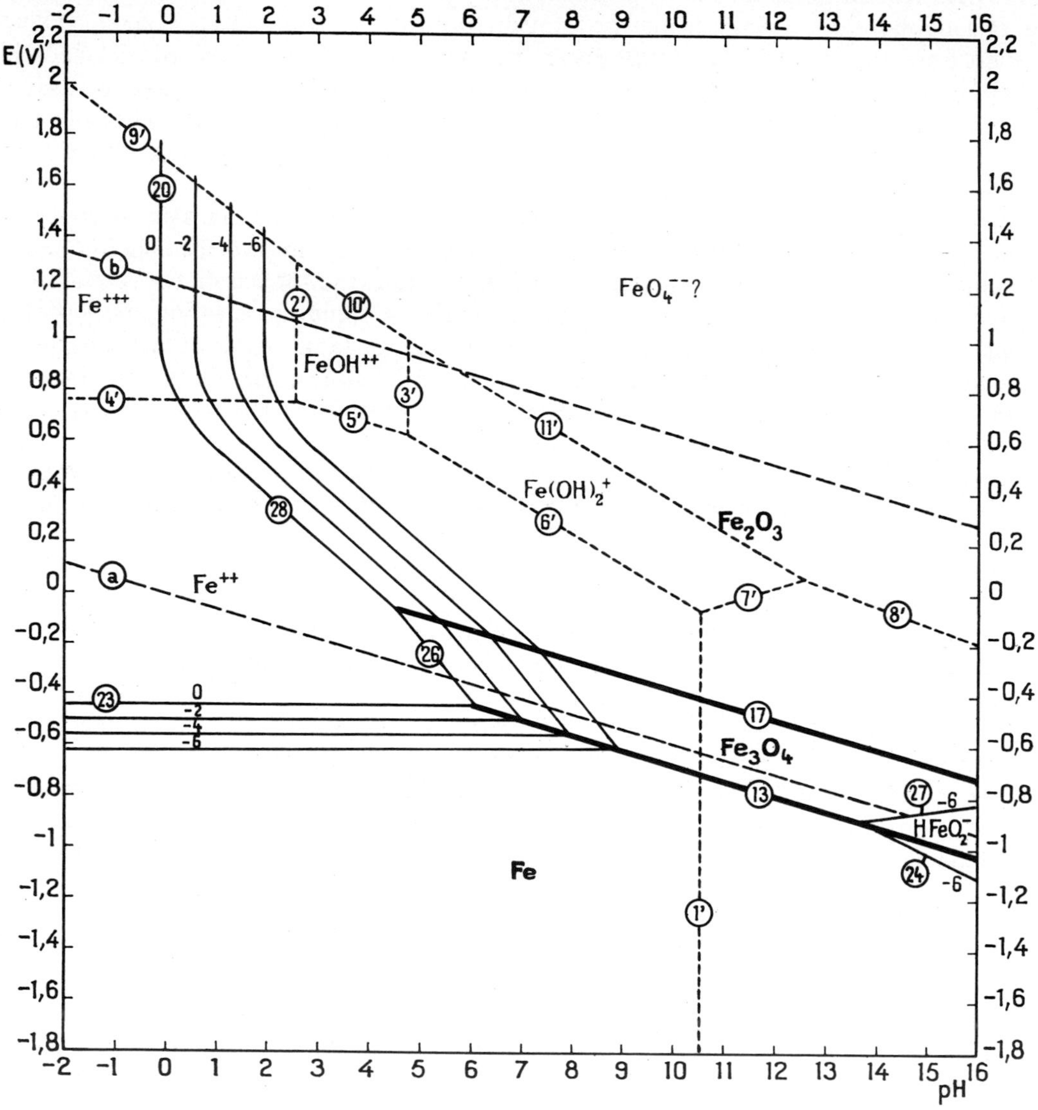

FIG. 3. Potential–pH equilibrium diagram for the iron–water system, at 25°C. (Only solid Fe, Fe_3O_4 and Fe_2O_3 are considered.)

is an example. Iron dissolves as ferrous ion from the impure nickel anodes into the fairly acid sulphate solution. The anolyte is freed from iron by raising the pH with lime and/or blowing with air, whereupon the very sparingly soluble *ferric* hydroxide is precipitated and can be removed by filtration. As can be seen in the germane part of the iron diagram (Fig. 3), both the rise of pH, and the presence of oxygen to effect oxidation and to raise the redox potential, contribute to the desired precipitation.

SECTION 6

GEOLOGY

R. M. GARRELS

THE importance of pH and potential in reactions involving minerals has been recognized by geologists for several decades, and these two variables have been widely applied in geochemical work. On the other hand, the use of pH–potential diagrams depicting stability relations among solid phases is of relatively recent vintage (Blumer [1]; Krumbein and Garrels [2]).

The greatest use to date of pH–potential diagrams has been in the application to earth environments under surface or near-surface conditions inasmuch as most of the easily available thermochemical information has been compiled for use at 25°C and 1 atm. total pressure. However, the natural realm to which such data can be applied with fair accuracy should not be underestimated; it includes almost all of the earth that we can observe directly.

One major aspect of earth chemistry to which pH–potential diagrams have been applied profitably is the weathering process. This includes the zone in which minerals, originally formed under deep-seated high-temperature, high-pressure reducing conditions, become exposed to the atmosphere as uplift and erosion continuously wear away the earth's crust. The processes of rock-weathering and soil formation are those stemming from the superimposition of the acid oxidizing dilute aqueous environment of the earth's surface upon the alkaline, oxygen-free, more concentrated aqueous subsurface environment in which the rocks had been bathed for millions of years without gross alteration. Consequently there is a direct analogy in these processes to the corrosion of metals, which also are the products of high temperature and reducing conditions, and become exposed to the varied environments at the earth's surface.

A second major area of application of pH–potential diagrams is to the process complementary to weathering—chemical sedimentation. The waters of the earth span the range of pH from zero to 12 or perhaps a little higher, and that of potential from the breakdown of water into hydrogen to its equilibration with oxygen of the atmosphere (Fig. 1). The geologist needs to know, for a system of given composition, the mineral species that should coexist at equilibrium for each kind of environment. If the extent to which modern mineral assemblages equilibrate with their environments of deposition is deciphered, then a powerful tool has been developed for inquiry into the nature of environments of the geologic past by reversing the procedure and deducing the environment from the fossil mineral assemblage.

SPECIFIC APPLICATIONS TO ROCK-WEATHERING

To date, most of the use of pH–potential diagrams in studying weathering processes has been devoted to the oxidation of mineral deposits. Attack on the major problem of the weathering of common rock minerals has been hindered by lack of thermochemical data on the silicates. The major minerals produced from mines, however, are sulphides, oxides, carbonates, hydroxycarbonates, sulphates, and hydrosulphates. Sufficient data are available to depict relations among many such mineral species. The major difficulty is related to the difference in composition between minerals and the pure chemical compounds for which thermochemical data are available.

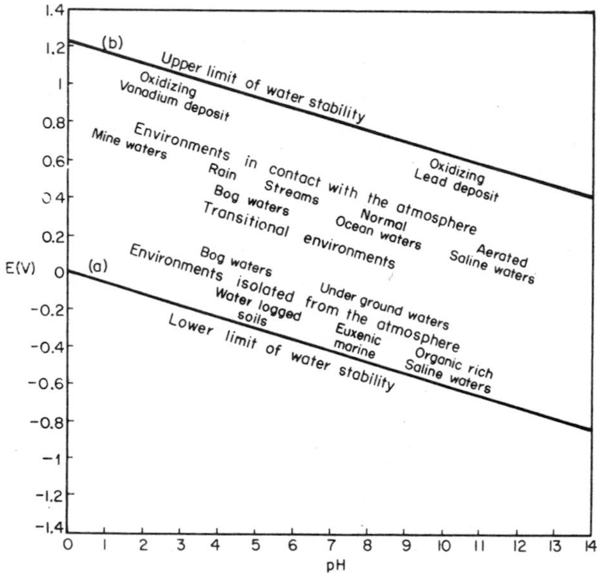

FIG. 1.

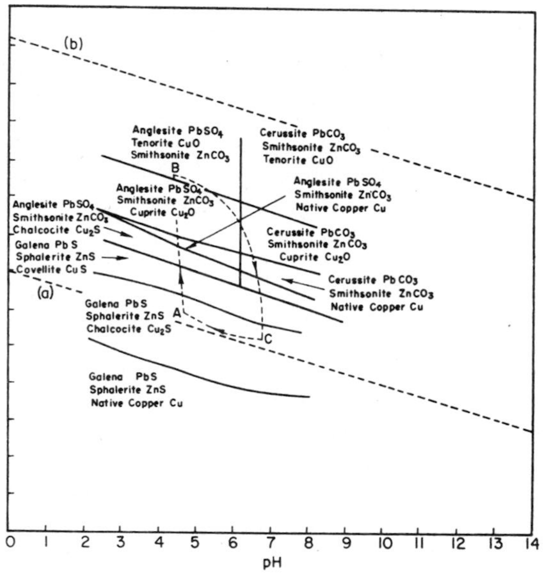

FIG. 2.

FIG. 1. Approximate positions of some natural environments as characterized by Eh and pH. (From R. M. GARRELS, *Mineral Equilibria*, Harper, New York, 1960, p. 201.)

FIG. 2. Mineral relations in an oxidizing ore body containing primary lead, zinc, and copper sulphide as functions of pH and potential. The dashed lines show deduced environmental changes with time during oxidation of a given sample of original ore. (From R. M. GARRELS, Mineral species as functions of pH and oxidation potentials, *Geochim. and Cosmochim. Acta*, **5**, 153–68 (1953).)

When sulphide ore bodies are weathered, the oxidation products are largely sulphates, oxides, and carbonates. Figure 2 shows an attempt to express mineral stability relations for an ore body containing lead, zinc, and copper sulphides as original minerals. Such a diagram can be viewed as a rough cross-section of such a deposit with the most highly oxidized compounds near the earth's surface at high potential, grading downward into the unaltered sulphides where oxygen is excluded in the zone of water saturation.

The uranium-vanadium deposits of the Colorado Plateau contain the mineral montroseite (VOOH) in the subsurface where the ores are protected from atmospheric oxygen. Evans and Garrels [3] have compared the results of oxidation as observed in nature (Fig. 3*a*) with those of the vanadium–water–

oxygen system, essentially as worked out by Deltombe *et al.* [4] (Fig. 3*b*). The remarkable correspondence between the calculated relations and those observed for the actual mineral species is apparent.

Note how the sequence of environmental changes can be followed in terms of pH and potential.

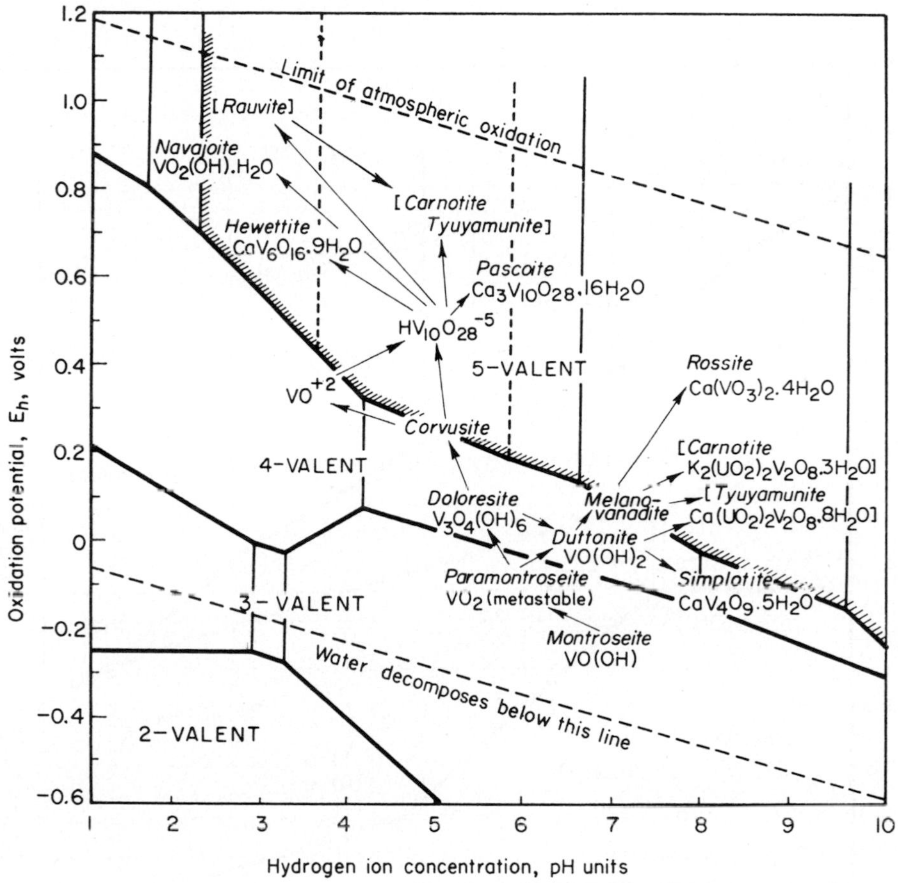

FIG. 3a. Aqueous equilibria of vanadium, showing the major aspects of relations among solids and important dissolved species. (From H. T. EVANS, Jr. and R. M. GARRELS, Thermodynamic equilibria of vanadium in aqueous systems as applied to the interpretation of the Colorado Plateau ore deposits, *Geochim. and Cosmochim.* **15**, 131–9 (1958).)

These two examples show the kind of work that is in progress, but the major job is yet to be done when data for silicates are available and it becomes possible to depict in detail the changes that occur in the weathering of ordinary rocks.

THE SPECIFIC APPLICATION TO CHEMICAL SEDIMENTATION

If the environment of a natural water changes, as where a stream enters the sea, or a portion of the sea becomes stagnant, precipitations of minerals usually occurs. The chemical sediments—those resulting from precipitation from homogeneous solution—have been classified on the basis of the pH and potential of their environment of formation (Fig. 4).

Only deposits of iron and manganese have been investigated in detail in so far as pH–potential diagrams of the important minerals are concerned (cf. Huber [5]; Krauskopf [6]).

A diagram illustrating relations among some major iron minerals is shown in Fig. 5. The use of diagrams including stability fields of sulphides and carbonates as well as those of oxides is common in the geologic literature. In many instances, the total dissolved sulphur and total dissolved carbon dioxide

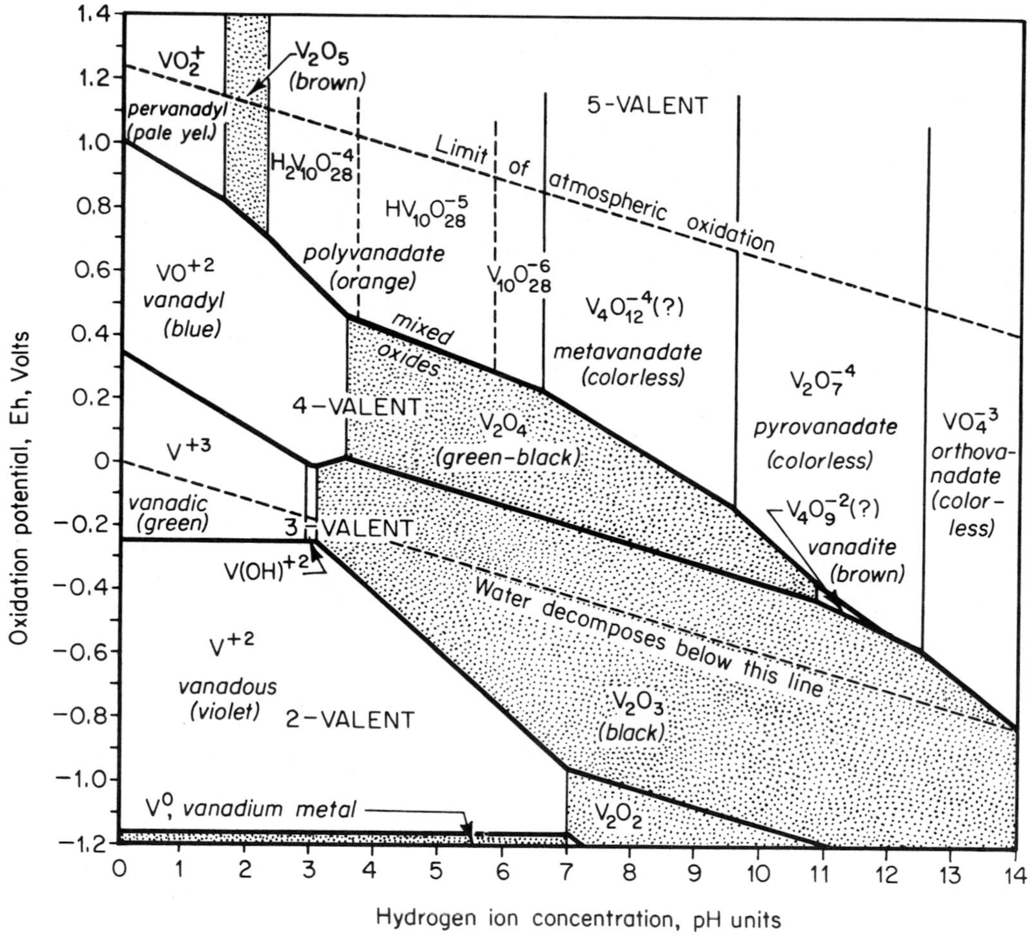

FIG. 3b. Aqueous equilibrium diagram for vanadium minerals showing stability regions for various minerals, and the paths followed during weathering. (From H. T. EVANS, Jr. and R. M. GARRELS, *loc. cit.*)

of the natural system can be estimated fairly accurately, so that the relations as depicted reflect nature without serious distortion. As shown by James [7] each mineral seen on Fig. 5 has a real counterpart in the Precambrian iron ores of the Lake Superior district of the United States. In some rocks, pyrite is the chief iron-bearing mineral; in others, siderite; in others, magnetite; and in still others, hematite. Thus the environments of deposition of these billion-and-a-half-year-old rocks can be read in terms of pH and potential.

The future undoubtedly will see the development of diagrams representing stability relations of minerals involving essentially all the elements in the periodic table.

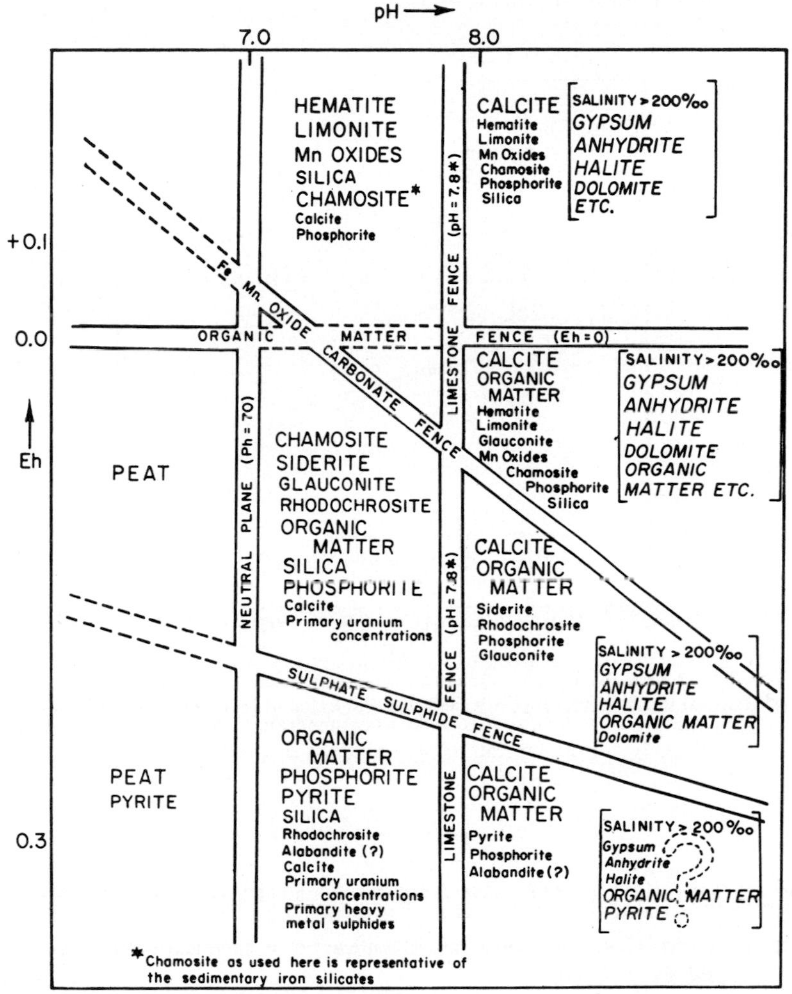

FIG. 4. Sedimentary chemical end-member associations in their relations to environmental limitations imposed by selected Eh and pH values. Associations in brackets refer to hypersaline solutions. (From W. C. KRUMBEIN and R. M. GARRELS, Origin and classification of chemical sediments in terms of pH and oxidation potentials, *J. Geol.* **60**, 1–33 (1952).)

APPLICATION TO HIGH TEMPERATURE–HIGH PRESSURE MINERAL RELATIONS

Because most rocks of the earth sooner or later are subject to high temperature and high pressure conditions, the stability relations of minerals as functions of temperature and pressure have received a great deal of attention. Pressure–temperature–composition diagrams are in widespread use. As more thermochemical data become available, equilibrium relations among minerals will be portrayed in terms of as many variables as possible, so that we can gain maximum insight into environments inaccessible to us because of time or depth. We can look forward to the development of pH–potential diagrams for elevated temperatures and pressures as well as to three-dimensional diagrams with such variables as temperature, pressure, partial pressure of a gas, or activity of a particular dissolved species as the third axis. It should be clear that the role to be played by Eh–pH diagrams in geology is an important one, and that essentially every diagram that can be constructed involving any element in the periodic table will be of interest in this domain.

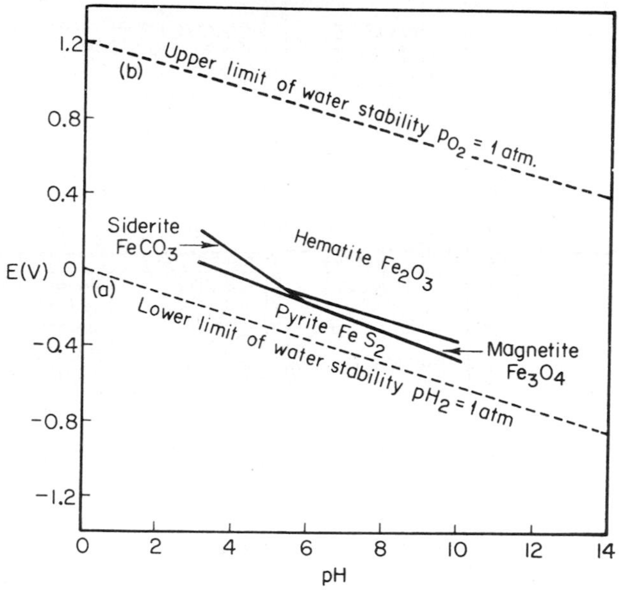

FIG. 5. Eh–pH stability fields of hematite, magnetite, siderite, and pyrite at 25°C, with carbonate equilibria as in normal sea water, and total sulphur as in average river or lake water. (Adapted from N. K. HUBER, The environmental control of iron minerals, *Econ. Geol.* **53**, 134 (1958).)

BIBLIOGRAPHY

[1] M. BLUMER, *Die Existenzgrenzen anorganischer Ionen bei der Bildung von Sedimentgesteinen, Helv. Chim. Acta,* **33**, 1568–81 (1950).

[2] W. C. KRUMBEIN and R. M. GARRELS, Origin and classification of chemical sediments in terms of pH and oxidation potentials, *J. Geol.* **60**, 1–33 (1952).

[3] H. T. EVANS, JR. and R. M. GARRELS, Thermodynamic equilibria of vanadium in aqueous systems as applied to the interpretation of the Colorado Plateau ore deposits, *Geochim. and Cosmochim. Acta,* **15**, 131–49 (1958).

[4] E. DELTOMBE, N. DE ZOUBOV and M. POURBAIX, *Comportement électrochimique du vanadium. Diagrammes d'équilibre tension–pH du système* V–H_2O à *25°C*, Rapport technique RT.29 of CEBELCOR, Brussels, 1956.

[5] N. K. HUBER, The environmental control of sedimentary iron minerals, *Econ. Geol.* **53**, 123–41 (1958).

[6] K. B. KRAUSKOPF, Separation of iron from manganese in sedimentary process, *Geochim. and Cosmochim. Acta,* **12**, 61–84 (1957).

[7] H. L. JAMES, Sedimentary facies of iron formation, *Econ. Geol.* **49**, 235–93 (1954).

[8] R. M. GARRELS, *Mineral Equilibria at Low Temperature and Pressure*, Harper, New York, 1960, p. 201.

CHAPTER IV

ESTABLISHMENT AND INTERPRETATION OF POTENTIAL–pH EQUILIBRIUM DIAGRAMS*

(*) Except where indicated, the standard free enthalpy values of formation given in this chapter are all taken from the works of W. M. Latimer (*Oxidation Potentials*, 2nd ed., Prentice-Hall, New York, 1952; *Recent References to Thermodynamic Data*, University of California, 1954).

SECTION 1.1

WATER [1]

M. POURBAIX and N. DE ZOUBOV

SUMMARY

1. *Substances considered and substances not considered.*

2. *Reactions and equilibrium formulae.*

   2.1. Two dissolved substances.

      2.1.1. Relative stability of H^+, OH^-, H^-, H_2O_2 and HO_2^-.

      2.1.2. Limits of the domains of relative predominance of H^+, OH^-, H^-, H_2O_2 and HO_2^-.

   2.2. Two gaseous substances.

      2.2.1. Relative stability of H_1, H_2, O_2 and O_3.

      2.2.2. Limits of the domains of relative predominance of H_2, O_2 and O_3.

   2.3. One dissolved substance and one gaseous substance.

3. *Equilibrium diagrams and their interpretation.*

   3.1. Establishment of the diagrams.

   3.2. Thermodynamic stability of water.

   3.3. Acid and alkaline media. Oxidizing and reducing media; rH and rO. Absolute neutrality of aqueous solutions.

   3.4. Decomposition of water. Formation of hydrogen, oxygen, ozone and hydrogen peroxide.

4. *Bibliography.*

---

[1] Extract from the Rapport CEFA/R.2 of the Commission des Études Fondamentales et Applications of CEBELCOR; see also [1], [3] and [4].

1. SUBSTANCES CONSIDERED AND SUBSTANCES NOT CONSIDERED(2)

	Considered	Not considered	μ^0(cal.)	Names
Liquid substance	$\mathbf{H_2O}$	–	— 56 690	Water
Dissolved substances	H^+	–	0	Hydrogen ion
	OH^-	–	— 37 595	Hydroxide ion
	H^-	–	31 900	Hydride ion
	H_2O_2	–	— 31 470	Hydrogen peroxide
	HO_2^-	–	— 15 610	Hydrogen peroxide ion
	–	OH	8 530	Hydroxyl
	–	HO_2	3 000	Hydrogen peroxyl
	–	O_2^-	13 000	Hyperoxide ion
	–	H_2	4 230 (*)	Natural hydrogen
	–	O_2	3 950 (*)	Natural oxygen
Gaseous substances	H_1	–	48 575	Atomic hydrogen
	H_2	–	0	Natural hydrogen
	–	O_1	54 994	Atomic oxygen
	O_2	–	0	Natural oxygen
	O_3	–	39 060	Ozone
	H_2O	–	— 54 635	Water

2. REACTIONS AND EQUILIBRIUM FORMULAE (**)

2.1. TWO DISSOLVED SUBSTANCES

2.1.1. *Relative stability of* H^+, OH^-, H^-, H_2O_2 *and* HO_2^-

1. $\mathbf{H_2O} = OH^- + H^+$ $\qquad \log(OH^-) = -14.00 + pH$

2. $H_2O_2 = HO_2^- + H^+$ $\qquad \log\frac{(HO_2^-)}{(H_2O_2)} = -11.63 + pH$

3. $H^- = H^+ + 2e^-$ $\qquad E_0 = -1.125 + 0.0295\log\frac{(H^+)}{(H^-)}$

4. $H^- + \mathbf{H_2O} = OH^- + 2H^+ + 2e^-$ $\qquad E_0 = -0.711 - 0.0591\,pH + 0.0295\log\frac{(OH^-)}{(H^-)}$

5. $2\mathbf{H_2O} = H_2O_2 + 2H^+ + 2e^-$ $\qquad E_0 = 1.776 - 0.0591\,pH + 0.0295\log(H_2O_2)$

6. $2\mathbf{H_2O} = HO_2^- + 3H^+ + 2e^-$ $\qquad E_0 = 2.119 - 0.0886\,pH + 0.0295\log(HO_2^-)$

7. $OH^- + \mathbf{H_2O} = H_2O_2 + H^+ + 2e^-$ $\qquad E_0 = 1.362 - 0.0295\,pH + 0.0295\log\frac{(H_2O_2)}{(OH^-)}$

8. $OH^- + \mathbf{H_2O} = HO_2^- + 2H^+ + 2e^-$ $\qquad E_0 = 1.706 - 0.0591\,pH + 0.0295\log\frac{(HO_2^-)}{(OH^-)}$

---

(2) The radicals OH and HO_2 which are not considered here have been dealt with in a previous study [2]. Monatomic gaseous hydrogen will be treated only very briefly here. It will be better considered when we study hydrogen (section 2). Monatomic gaseous oxygen will be considered when we study oxygen (section 19.1).

(*) We have calculated values from the solubilities of gaseous H_2 and O_2 in water.

(**) In the following general classification we have, with a view to simplification, taken water to be the solvent.

2.1.2. *Limits of the domains of relative predominance of* H^+, OH^-, H^-, H_2O_2 *and* HO_2^-

1'.	H^+ / OH^-	$pH = 7.00$
2'.	H_2O_2 / HO_2^-	$pH = 11.63$
3'.	H^- / H^+	$E_0 = -1.125$
4'.	H^- / OH^-	$E_0 = -0.711 - 0.0591\ pH$
5'.	H^+ / H_2O_2	$E_0 = 1.776 - 0.0886\ pH$
6'.	H^+ / HO_2^-	$E_0 = 2.119 - 0.1181\ pH$
7'.	OH^- / H_2O_2	$E_0 = 1.362 - 0.0295\ pH$
8'.	OH^- / HO_2^-	$E_0 = 1.706 - 0.0591\ pH$

2.2. TWO GASEOUS SUBSTANCES

2.2.1. *Relative stability of* H_1, H_2, O_2 *and* O_3

9. $H_2 = H_1 + H^+ + e^-$ $\qquad E_0 = 2.106 - 0.0591\ pH + 0.0591 \log \frac{p_{H_1}}{p_{H_2}}$

10. $H_2 + 2\mathbf{H_2O} = O_2 + 6H^+ + 6e^-$ $\qquad E_0 = 0.819 - 0.0591\ pH + 0.0098 \log \frac{p_{O_2}}{p_{H_2}}$

11. $O_2 + \mathbf{H_2O} = O_3 + 2H^+ + 2e^-$ $\qquad E_0 = 2.076 - 0.0591\ pH + 0.0295 \log \frac{p_{O_3}}{p_{O_2}}$

2.2.2. *Limits of the domains of relative predominance of* H_2, O_2 *and* O_3

9'.	H_2 / H_1	$E_0 = 2.106 - 0.0591\ pH$
10'.	H_2 / O_2	$E_0 = 0.819 - 0.0591\ pH$
11'.	O_2 / O_3	$E_0 = 2.076 - 0.0591\ pH$

2.3. ONE DISSOLVED SUBSTANCE AND ONE GASEOUS SUBSTANCE(3)

12. $\mathbf{H_2O} = H_2O$ $\qquad \log p_{H_2O} = -1.505$

13. $H_1 = H^+ + e^-$ $\qquad E_0 = -2.106 - 0.0591\ pH - 0.0591 \log p_{H_1}$

14. $H_2 = 2H^+ + 2e^-$ $\qquad E_0 = 0.000 - 0.0591\ pH - 0.0295 \log p_{H_2}$

15. $2\mathbf{H_2O} = O_2 + 4H^+ + 4e^-$ $\qquad E_0 = 1.228 - 0.0591\ pH + 0.0147 \log p_{O_2}$

16. $3\mathbf{H_2O} = O_3 + 6H^+ + 6e^-$ $\qquad E_0 = 1.501 - 0.0591\ pH + 0.0098 \log p_{O_3}$

3. EQUILIBRIUM DIAGRAMS AND THEIR INTERPRETATION (3)

3.1. ESTABLISHMENT OF THE DIAGRAMS

Using formulae (1')–(8') we have represented in Fig. 1 the domains of relative predominance of the dissolved substances H^-, H^+, OH^-, H_2O_2 and HO_2^-; using formulae (10') and (11') we have represented in Fig. 2 the domains of relative predominance of the gaseous substances H_2, O_2 and O_3 (no domain of predominance exists for H_1). Using formulae (14) and (15) we have represented, notably in Figs. 3, 4 and 5, the domain of stability of water under atmospheric pressure (Fig. 3), the acid, alkaline,

(3) For further details, see *loc. cit.* [3] and [4].

oxidizing and reducing media (Fig. 4) and the values of rH and rO for aqueous solutions (Fig. 5). Finally, using all the formulae (1)–(16) we have represented in Fig. 6 all the oxidation and reduction reactions of water that are considered in this study.

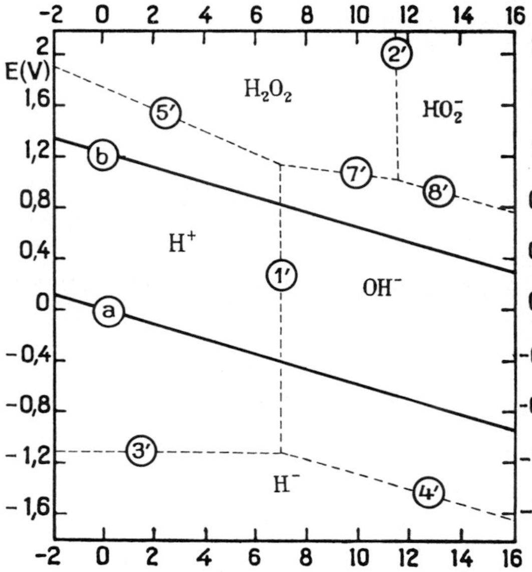

FIG. 1. Domains of relative predominance of the dissolved substances H^-, H^+, OH^-, H_2O_2 and HO_2^-.

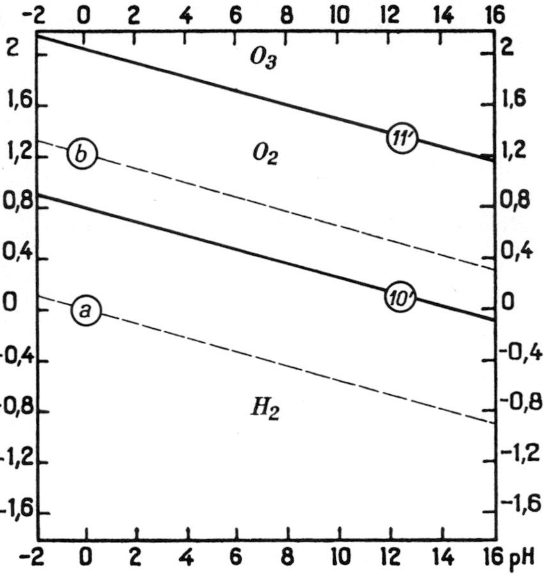

FIG. 2. Domains of relative predominance of the gaseous substances H_2, O_2 and O_3.

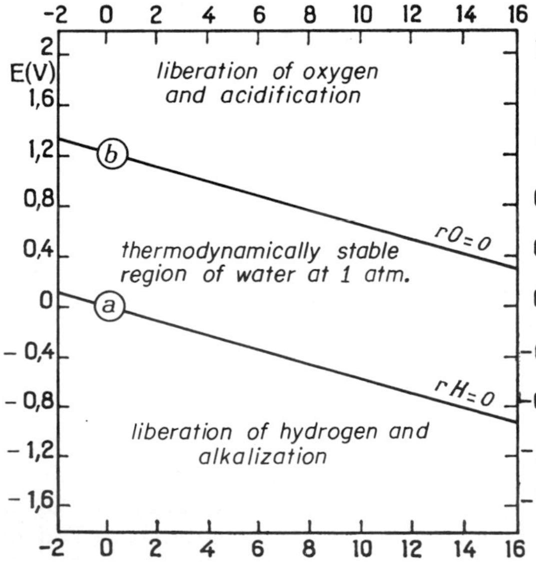

FIG. 3. Domain of thermodynamic stability of water under 1 atm. pressure.

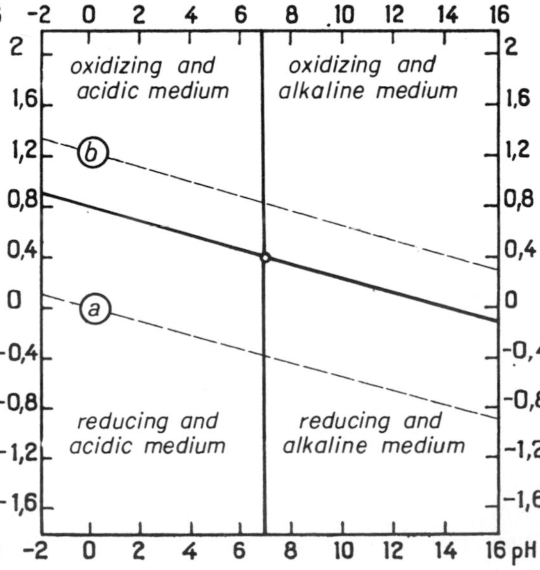

FIG. 4. Acid, alkaline, oxidizing and reducing media.

3.2. THERMODYNAMIC STABILITY OF WATER

In each of the Figs. 1–6, and notably in Fig. 3, we have drawn two parallel lines of slope −0·0591, labelled with the letters *a* and *b*, which represent respectively the equilibrium conditions of the reduction of water (or its H^+ ions) to gaseous hydrogen (reaction 14) and the oxidation of water to gaseous oxygen (reaction 15), when the partial pressure of hydrogen or oxygen is 1 atm. at 25°C.

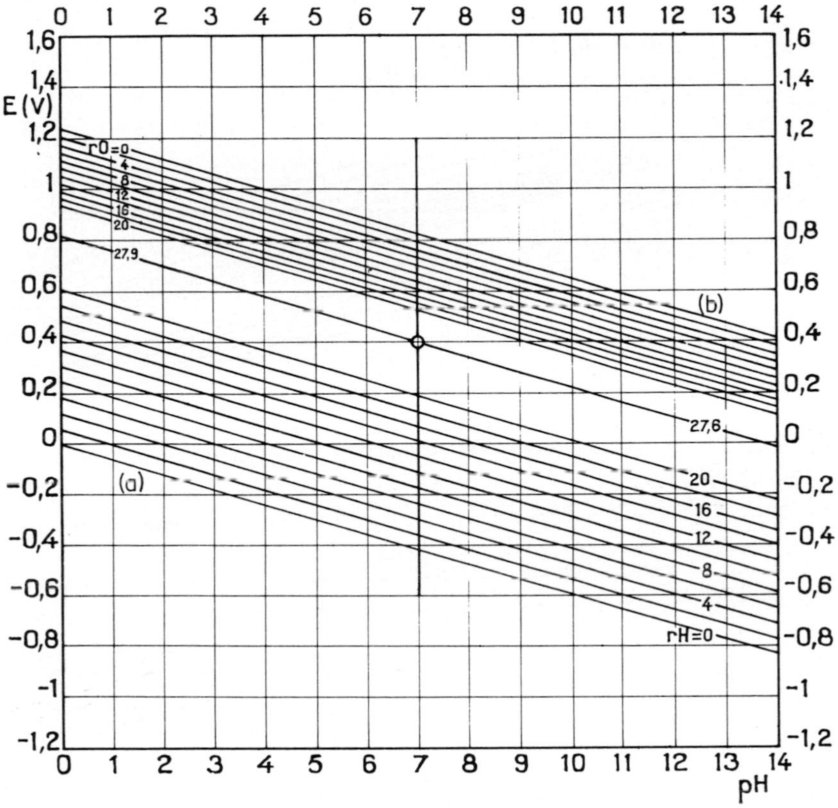

FIG. 5. rH and rO of aqueous solutions.

The equations of these two lines, obtained by equating to zero the term log p_{H_2} of relation (14) and the term log p_{O_2} of relation (15), are respectively:

(*a*) reaction $H_2 = 2H^+ + 2e^-$: $E_0 = 0.000 - 0.0591\ pH$;
(*b*) reaction $2H_2O = O_2 + 4H^+ + 4e^-$: $E_0 = 1.228 - 0.0591\ pH$.

In the portion of Fig. 3 below line (*a*), the equilibrium hydrogen pressure is above 1 atm., and water under atmospheric pressure therefore tends to be reduced with the evolution of hydrogen, becoming alkaline, according to the reaction

$$2H^+ + 2e^- \rightarrow H_2 \quad (14) \quad \text{or} \quad 2H_2O + 2e^- \rightarrow H_2 + 2OH^-.$$

In the portion of Fig. 3 above line (*b*), the equilibrium oxygen pressure is above 1 atm., and water under atmospheric pressure therefore tends to be oxidized with the evolution of oxygen, becoming acid, according to the reaction

$$2H_2O \rightarrow O_2 + 4H^+ + 4e^- \quad (15).$$

Between the two lines (*a*) and (*b*) in Fig. 3, the equilibrium pressures of hydrogen and oxygen are both below 1 atm.; the region included between these two lines is therefore the *domain of thermodynamic stability of water* under a pressure of 1 atm. Water will be thermodynamically stable in this

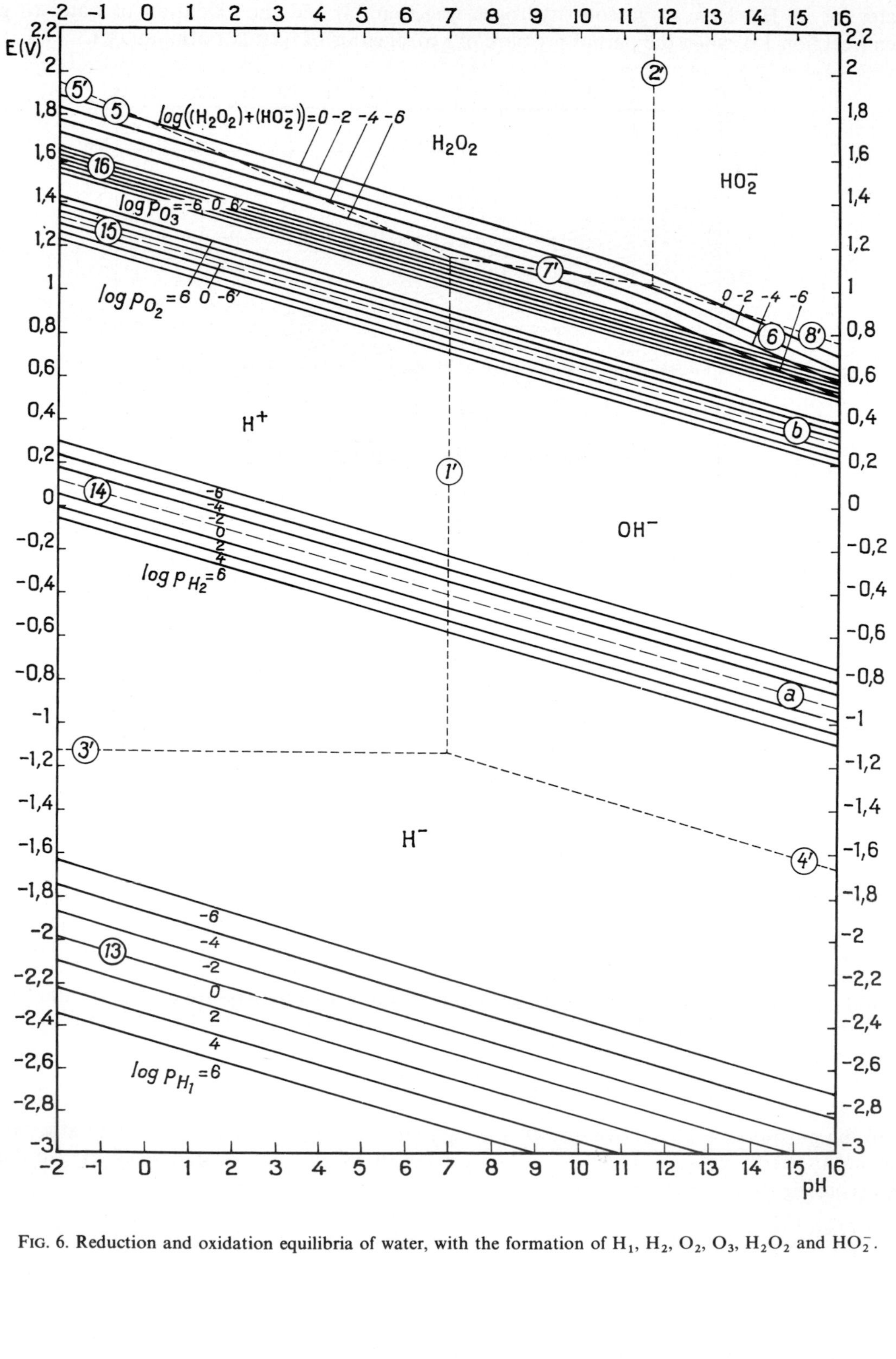

FIG. 6. Reduction and oxidation equilibria of water, with the formation of H_1, H_2, O_2, O_3, H_2O_2 and HO_2^-.

domain alone; this is true, not only for pure water, but also, to a first approximation,([4]) for the water present in dilute aqueous solutions. Since, by definition, all aqueous solutions contain water, this domain of stability of water is important for all of them; for this reason *we shall reproduce its limits (a) and (b) in all the potential–pH diagrams that we establish.*

3.3. ACID AND ALKALINE MEDIA. OXIDIZING AND REDUCING MEDIA; rH AND rO. ABSOLUTE NEUTRALITY OF AQUEOUS SOLUTIONS

As is expressed by relation (1) above, water dissociates into H^+ and OH^- ions according to the reaction $H_2O = H^+ + OH^-$ (1) whose equilibrium state, at 25°C, is

$$((H^+).(OH^-)) = 10^{-14{\cdot}00} \quad \text{or} \quad \log(H^+) + \log(OH^-) = -14{\cdot}00$$

or, by putting

$$pH = -\log(H^+), \qquad \log(OH^-) = -14{\cdot}00 + pH.$$

It will be recalled that solutions are neutral, acid or alkaline depending on whether we have

$$\begin{array}{llll} pH = 7{\cdot}00 & \text{or} & (H^+) = (OH^-) & \text{(neutral solutions),} \\ pH < 7{\cdot}00 & \text{or} & (H^+) > (OH^-) & \text{(acid solutions),} \\ pH > 7{\cdot}00 & \text{or} & (H^+) < (OH^-) & \text{(alkaline solutions).} \end{array}$$

The vertical line pH = 7 drawn in Fig. 4 therefore separates a domain in which there is a predominance of H^+ ions over OH^- ions (acid solutions) from a domain in which there is a predominance of OH^- ions over H^+ ions (alkaline solutions).

Another consideration is that water and its constituents can be reduced with the evolution of hydrogen, or oxidized with the evolution of oxygen, according to the reactions

$$2H^+ + 2e^- \rightarrow H_2 \text{ (reduction) and } 2H_2O \rightarrow O_2 + 4H^+ + 4e^- \text{ (oxidation).}$$

The equilibrium conditions of these reactions at 25°C are respectively:

$$E_0 = 0{\cdot}000 - 0{\cdot}0591\,pH - 0{\cdot}0295 \log p_{H_2}, \qquad (14)$$
$$E_0 = 1{\cdot}228 - 0{\cdot}0591\,pH + 0{\cdot}0147 \log p_{O_2}. \qquad (15)$$

If, in the same way that we have put

$$pH = -\log(H^+)$$

we put

$$rH = -\log p_{H_2} \quad \text{and} \quad rO = -\log p_{O_2},$$

the two equilibrium reactions (14) and (15) can be written respectively

$$E_0 = 0{\cdot}000 - 0{\cdot}0591\,pH + 0{\cdot}0295\,rH, \qquad (14')$$
$$E_0 = 1{\cdot}228 - 0{\cdot}0591\,pH - 0{\cdot}0147\,rO. \qquad (15')$$

Now, in the same way that water can dissociate into H^+ and OH^- ions according to the reaction $H_2O = H^+ + OH^-$ and is considered neutral from the acidity/alkalinity point of view if $(H^+) = (OH^-)$,

---

([4]) More exactly, the lines (*a*) and (*b*) are practically valid for solutions in which the free enthalpy of formation of the water μ_{H_2O} is practically equal to the free enthalpy of formation of pure water, that is −56 690 cal. at 25°C. For most aqueous solutions μ_{H_2O} is below this value; this causes an increase in the stability of the water which is shown by an enlargement of its domain of stability in Fig. 1. This increase in stability of water when certain substances are dissolved in it shows itself in an analogous way as a function of the temperature, by an elevation of the boiling point (connected with a reduction of the vapour pressure) and by a depression of the freezing-point. *Loc. cit.* [3], pp. 12 and 13.

water can decompose into gaseous hydrogen and oxygen according to the reaction $2H_2O = 2H_2 + O_2$, and may be considered neutral from the oxidation/reduction point of view if $p_{H_2} = 2p_{O_2}$, i.e. if

$$\log p_{H_2} = \log p_{O_2} + \log 2 = \log p_{O_2} + 0{\cdot}30,$$

i.e. if

$$rH = rO - 0{\cdot}30.$$

If we combine this equation with the equations

$$E_0 = 0{\cdot}000 - 0{\cdot}0591\ pH + 0{\cdot}0295\ rH, \qquad (14')$$
$$E_0 = 1{\cdot}228 - 0{\cdot}0591\ pH - 0{\cdot}0147\ rO, \qquad (15')$$

we obtain, as the condition for the neutrality of water from the oxidation/reduction point of view

$$E_0 = 0{\cdot}813 - 0{\cdot}0591\ pH \quad \text{or} \quad rH = 27{\cdot}56 \quad \text{or} \quad rO = 27{\cdot}86.$$

By combining these relations with the relation pH = 7·00 which expresses the neutrality of an aqueous solution from the acidity/alkalinity point of view, we obtain the following characteristics for the *condition of absolute neutrality* of a dilute aqueous solution, at 25°C:

$$pH = 7{\cdot}00, \quad rH = 27{\cdot}56, \quad rO = 27{\cdot}86, \quad E_0 = +0{\cdot}4\ V.$$

However, although the concept of neutrality from the acidity/alkalinity point of view has a great practical interest, the concept of neutrality from the oxidation/reduction point of view is of principally academic interest. rH, which is widely used in biological chemistry, is connected with pH and electrode potential E (calculated in volts with respect to the standard hydrogen electrode) by the following relation, valid for 25°C:

$$rH = 33{\cdot}9\ E + 2pH \qquad (14'')$$

The neutrality characteristics that we have just defined enable a potential–pH diagram to be divided into the following four regions, shown in Fig. 4:

top left: oxidizing acid media;
bottom left: reducing acid media;
bottom right: reducing alkaline media;
top right: oxidizing alkaline media.

3.4. DECOMPOSITION OF WATER. FORMATION OF HYDROGEN, OXYGEN, OZONE AND HYDROGEN PEROXIDE

In the portion of Fig. 6 below line (*a*), relating to the equilibrium of the reaction $H_2 = 2H^+ + 2e^-$ (14) for a hydrogen pressure of 1 atm., it is thermodynamically possible to reduce water with the evolution of diatomic gaseous hydrogen at atmospheric pressure. This can be done using an electrolytic cathode or by the action of sufficiently powerful reducing agents, such as metals with low electrode potentials (iron, zinc, magnesium, sodium, etc.).

For electrode potentials below those indicated by lines (3′) and (4′), negative hydrogen ions H^- can theoretically be formed; at very low potentials, below those indicated by the family of lines (13), it is theoretically possible for monatomic gaseous hydrogen to be evolved with an appreciable partial pressure, the equilibrium proportion of H_1 with respect to H_2, calculated from equation (9), remaining extremely small, however (of the order of 10^{-70}).

In the portion of Fig. 6 above line (*b*), relating to the equilibrium of the reaction $2H_2O = O_2 + 4H^+ + 4e^-$ (15) for an oxygen pressure of 1 atm., it is thermodynamically possible to oxidize water with the evolution of diatomic gaseous oxygen at atmospheric pressure. This can be done by means of an electrolytic anode or by the action of sufficiently powerful oxidizing agents (permanganate, fluorine, etc.).

For electrode potentials above those indicated by the family of lines (16), it is theoretically possible for triatomic gaseous oxygen (ozone) to be evolved with an appreciable partial pressure, the equilibrium proportion of O_3 with respect to O_2, calculated from equation (11), remaining very small, however (of the order of 10^{-21} to 10^{-14}). At potentials above those indicated by the family of lines (5–6), the evolution of gas may be accompanied by the formation of hydrogen peroxide and its ion HO_2^-.

Let us consider, as an example, the action of fluorine on water. As will be shown in section 20.1, concerning fluorine, the stable form of fluorine for potentials corresponding to the families of lines (14), (15) and (5–6) of Fig. 6 are hydrofluoric acid HF and fluoride ion F^-, with a possibility of the formation of gaseous fluorine monoxide F_2O at high potentials. Gaseous fluorine tends therefore, in the presence of water, on the one hand, to turn into fluorine monoxide and hydrofluoric acid according to the reactions

$$\begin{array}{rlcl} & F_2 + 2e^- & \rightarrow & 2F^- \\ \text{and} & F_2 + H_2O & \rightarrow & F_2O + 2H^+ + 2e^- \\ \hline \text{overall reaction} & 2F_2 + H_2O & \rightarrow & F_2O + 2F^- + 2H^+ \end{array}$$

and, on the other hand, to be reduced according to the reaction

$$F_2 + 2e^- \rightarrow 2F^-.$$

Combining this last reaction with the three oxidations

$$\begin{array}{lcll} 2H_2O & \rightarrow & O_2 + 4H^+ + 4e^- & (15), \\ 3H_2O & \rightarrow & O_3 + 6H^+ + 6e^- & (16) \end{array}$$

and

$$2H_2O \rightarrow H_2O_2 + 2H^+ + 2e^- \qquad (5),$$

this reduction of fluorine to fluoride gives rise to the following three simultaneous reactions:

$$\begin{array}{lcll} 2F_2 + 2H_2O & \rightarrow & O_2 + 4F^- + 4H^+ & \text{(formation of hydrofluoric acid and oxygen),} \\ 3F_2 + 3H_2O & \rightarrow & O_3 + 6F^- + 6H^+ & \text{(formation of hydrofluoric acid and ozone),} \\ \hline F_2 + 2H_2O & \rightarrow & H_2O_2 + 2F^- + 2H^+ & \text{(formation of hydrofluoric acid and hydrogen peroxide).} \end{array}$$

As a result of this, the action of fluorine on water can give rise to the simultaneous formation of fluorine monoxide, hydrofluoric acid, ozonized oxygen and hydrogen peroxide.

Some other considerations relating to the reduction and oxidation of water will be discussed later, when we study hydrogen peroxide (section 1.2), hydrogen (section 2) and oxygen (section 19.1).

4. BIBLIOGRAPHY

[1] M. Pourbaix, *Thermodynamique des solutions aqueuses diluées* (Thèse, Delft, 1945; Béranger, Paris and Liège, (1945). 3rd Edition, Cebelcor 1963.

[2] P. Delahay, M. Pourbaix and P. Van Rysselberghe, *Comportement électrochimique de l'oxygène, de l'eau oxygénée et des radicaux* OH *et* HO_2 (C.R. 2e Réunion du CITCE, Milan, 1950).

[3] M. Pourbaix, *Leçons sur la corrosion électrochimique* (2e fascicule) (Rapport technique RT.30, of CEBELCOR, 1956).

[4] M. Pourbaix, *Leçons sur la corrosion électrochimique* (3e fascicule) (Rapport technique RT.49, of CEBELCOR, 1957).

SECTION 1.2

HYDROGEN PEROXIDE(1)

M. POURBAIX and N. DE ZOUBOV

SUMMARY

1. *Substances considered and substances not considered.*

2. *Reactions and equilibrium formulae.*

2.1. Two dissolved substances.

2.1.1. Relative stability of water, hydrogen peroxide and the HO_2^- ion.
2.1.2. Limit of the domains of relative predominance of H_2O_2 and HO_2^-.

2.2. One dissolved substance and one gaseous substance.
Relative stability of oxygen, hydrogen peroxide and the HO_2^- ion.

3. *Equilibrium diagram and its interpretation.*

3.1. Establishment of the diagram.

3.2. Formation of hydrogen peroxide.
Oxidizing and reducing properties; decomposition of hydrogen peroxide.

3.3. Action of hydrogen peroxide on iron.

4. *Bibliography.*

(1) Extract from the Rapport CEFA/R.2 of the Commission des Études Fondamentales et Applications of CEBELCOR; see also [1], [2], [3] and [4].

1. SUBSTANCES CONSIDERED AND SUBSTANCES NOT CONSIDERED (2)

	Considered	Not considered	μ^0(cal.)	Names
Liquid substance	H_2O	–	— 56 690	Water
Dissolved substances	H^+	–	0	Hydrogen ion
	OH^-	–	— 37 595	Hydroxide ion
	H_2O_2	–	— 31 470	Hydrogen peroxide
	HO_2^-	–	— 15 610	Hydrogen peroxide ion
	–	OH	8 530	Hydroxyl
	–	HO_2	3 000	Hydrogen peroxyl
	–	O_2^-	13 000	Hyperoxide ion
Gaseous substances	O_2	–	0	Natural oxygen
	–	O_3	39 060	Ozone

These free enthalpy values are all due to W. M. Latimer.

2. REACTIONS AND EQUILIBRIUM FORMULAE

2.1. TWO DISSOLVED SUBSTANCES(*)

2.1.1. *Relative stability of water, hydrogen peroxide and the* HO_2^- *ion*

1. $H_2O_2 = HO_2^- + H^+$ $\qquad \log \frac{(HO_2^-)}{(H_2O_2)} = -11.63 + pH$

2. $2H_2O = H_2O_2 + 2H^+ + 2e^-$ $\qquad E_0 = 1.776 - 0.0591\ pH + 0.0295 \log (H_2O_2)$

3. $2H_2O = HO_2^- + 3H^+ + 2e^-$ $\qquad E_0 = 2.119 - 0.0886\ pH + 0.0295 \log (HO_2^-)$

2.1.2. *Limit of the domains of relative predominance of* H_2O_2 *and* HO_2^-

1'. H_2O_2/HO_2^- $\qquad pH = 11.63$

2.2. ONE DISSOLVED SUBSTANCE AND ONE GASEOUS SUBSTANCE

Relative stability of oxygen, hydrogen peroxide and the HO_2^- *ion*

4. $H_2O_2 = O_2 + 2H^+ + 2e^-$ $\qquad E_0 = 0.682 - 0.0591\ pH + 0.0295 \log \frac{p_{O_2}}{(H_2O_2)}$

5. $HO_2^- = O_2 + H^+ + 2e^-$ $\qquad E_0 = 0.338 - 0.0295\ pH + 0.0295 \log \frac{p_{O_2}}{(HO_2^-)}$

3. EQUILIBRIUM DIAGRAM AND ITS INTERPRETATION

3.1. ESTABLISHMENT OF THE DIAGRAM

The electrochemical equilibrium diagram I was constructed by means of equilibrium formulae 1–5. This diagram comprises two families of lines, relating respectively to certain fixed values of the concentration of hydrogen peroxide in the forms H_2O_2 and HO_2^- (2 and 3) and to certain fixed values of the ratio $\frac{p_{O_2}}{(H_2O_2) + (HO_2^-)}$ (4 and 5).

---

(2) The radicals OH and HO_2, which are not considered here, are discussed in a previous study [1].

(*) In the following equations we have, with a view to simplification, taken water to be the solvent.

3.2. FORMATION OF HYDROGEN PEROXIDE

Oxidizing and reducing properties; decomposition of hydrogen peroxide

It is well known that hydrogen peroxide can be prepared by the low temperature electrolysis of sulphuric acid solutions using a platinum anode; it is also formed, in small quantities, when certain metals (zinc, aluminium) corrode in aqueous solution.

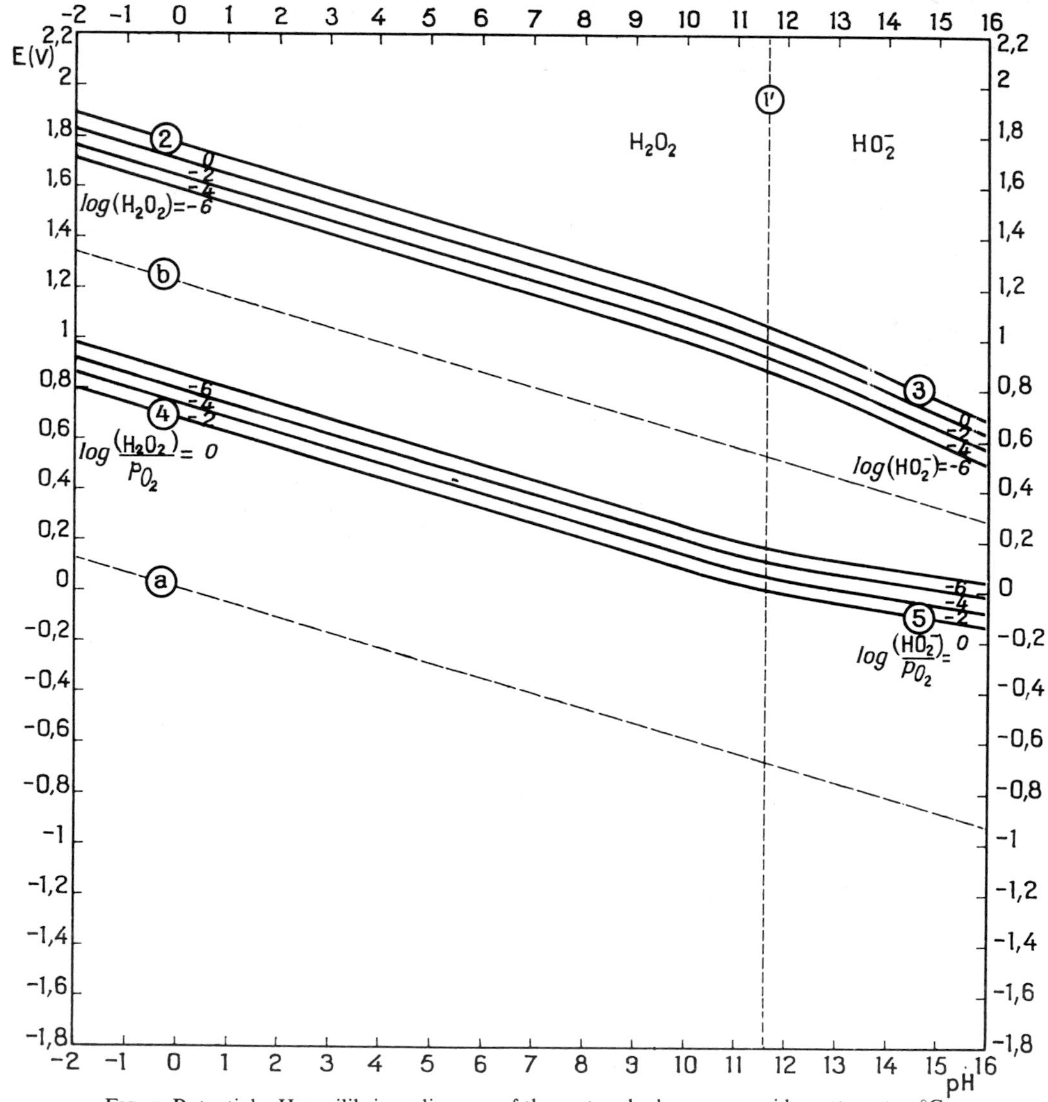

FIG. 1. Potential–pH equilibrium diagram of the system hydrogen peroxide–water, at 25°C.

In the first case, the hydrogen peroxide is formed by the oxidation of water according to the reaction $2H_2O \rightarrow H_2O_2 + 2H^+ + 2e^-$ (2) at electrode potentials corresponding to the portion of Fig. 1 above the family of lines (2–3). In the second case, it is formed by the reduction of oxygen dissolved in the solution, according to the reaction $O_2 + 2H^+ + 2e^- \rightarrow H_2O_2$ (4) at electrode potentials corresponding to the portion of Fig. 1 below the family of lines (4–5).

As shown in Figs. 2 and 3, these two families of lines enable us to represent, on the one hand, domains in which hydrogen peroxide can be formed by the oxidation of water (Fig. 2) or by the reduction of oxygen (Fig. 3), and, on the other hand, domains in which hydrogen peroxide can be reduced to water (Fig. 2), or oxidized to oxygen (Fig. 3). Below the family of lines (2–3) (Fig. 2) hydrogen peroxide can act as an oxidizing agent with the formation of water; for instance it oxidizes ferrous ions to ferric ions according to the reactions

$$
\begin{array}{lrcl}
 & H_2O_2 + 2H^+ + 2e^- & \rightarrow & 2H_2O \qquad (2) \\
\text{and} & 2Fe^{++} & \rightarrow & 2Fe^{+++} + 2e^- \\
\hline
\text{overall reaction} & H_2O_2 + 2H^+ + 2Fe^{++} & \rightarrow & 2H_2O + 2Fe^{+++}.
\end{array}
$$

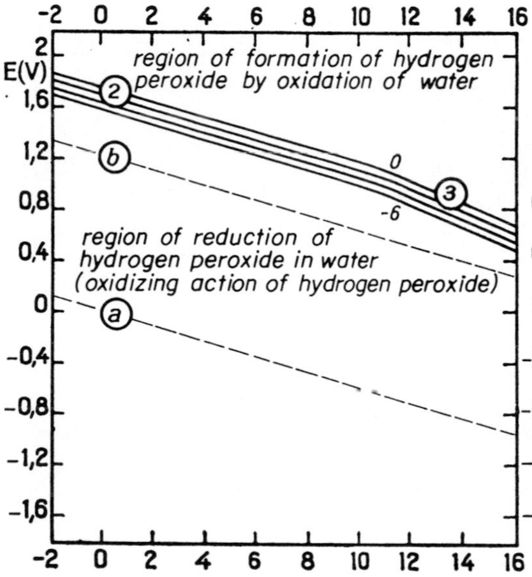

FIG. 2. Formation of hydrogen peroxide by the oxidation of water. Oxidizing action of hydrogen peroxide.

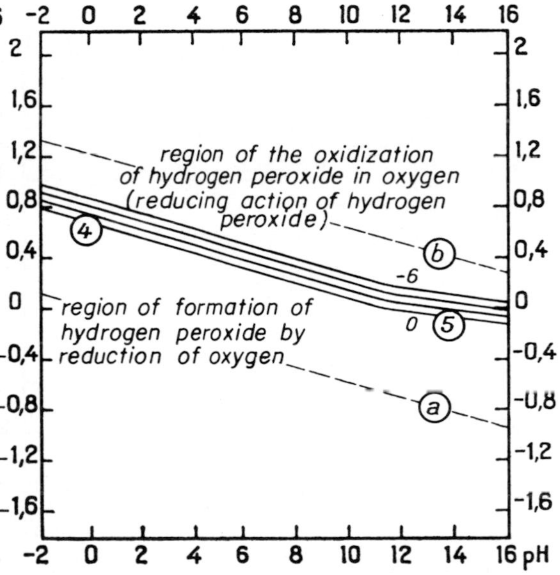

FIG. 3. Formation of hydrogen peroxide by the reduction of oxygen. Reducing action of hydrogen peroxide.

Above the family of lines (4–5) (Fig. 3) hydrogen peroxide can act as a reducing agent with the formation of oxygen; for instance it reduces permanganate to manganous ions according to the reactions:

$$
\begin{array}{lrcl}
 & 5H_2O_2 & \rightarrow & 5O_2 + 10H^+ + 10e^- \qquad (4) \\
\text{and} & 2MnO_4^- + 16H^+ + 10e^- & \rightarrow & 2Mn^{++} + 8H_2O \\
\hline
\text{overall reaction} & 5H_2O_2 + 2MnO_4^- + 6H^+ & \rightarrow & 5O_2 + 2Mn^{++} + 8H_2O.
\end{array}
$$

Hydrogen peroxide thus appears unstable and reducible to water below the family of lines (2–3) (Fig. 2); it appears unstable and oxidizable to oxygen above the family of lines (4–5) (Fig. 3). If these two families of lines are plotted on a simple diagram (Fig. 4) it is found that these two domains of instability have a common area, in which hydrogen peroxide is doubly unstable and can decompose into water and oxygen according to the reactions

$$
\begin{array}{lrcl}
 & H_2O_2 + 2H^+ + 2e^- & \rightarrow & 2H_2O \qquad (2) \\
\text{and} & H_2O_2 & \rightarrow & O_2 + 2H^+ + 2e^- \qquad (4) \\
\hline
\text{overall reaction} & 2H_2O_2 & \rightarrow & 2H_2O + O_2.
\end{array}
$$

In the domain of double instability, and only in this domain, hydrogen peroxide can decompose chemically into water and oxygen.

Consequently, if a solution of hydrogen peroxide is in contact with a metallic surface whose electrode potential is situated in this domain of double instability, the hydrogen peroxide can decompose spontaneously into water and oxygen according to the reaction $2H_2O_2 \rightarrow 2H_2 + O_2$, and, conversely, if hydrogen peroxide decomposes spontaneously into water and oxygen on a metallic surface, then this surface must necessarily exert an electrode potential whose position on the diagram is situated in the domain of double instability. We have here an example of the *electrochemical catalysis of a chemical reaction.*

On the other hand, in the presence of metallic surfaces whose condition is represented by a point not included in this domain of double instability, the decomposition of hydrogen peroxide into water and oxygen is impossible: the hydrogen peroxide will either be practically stable; or else it will be reduced to water (below this domain) *or* oxidized to oxygen (above this domain).

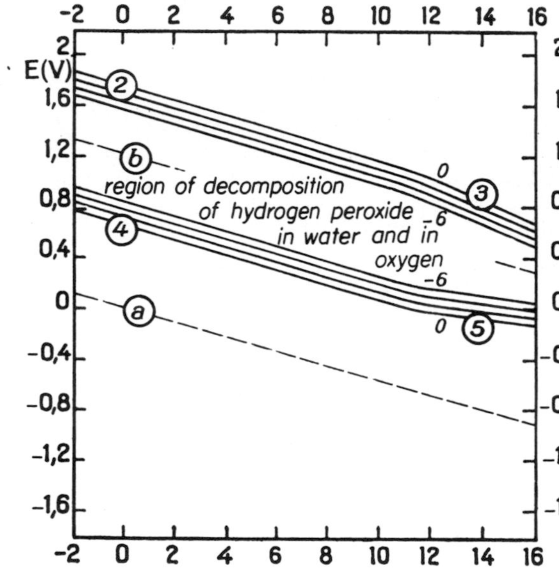

FIG. 4. Decomposition of hydrogen peroxide to water and oxygen.

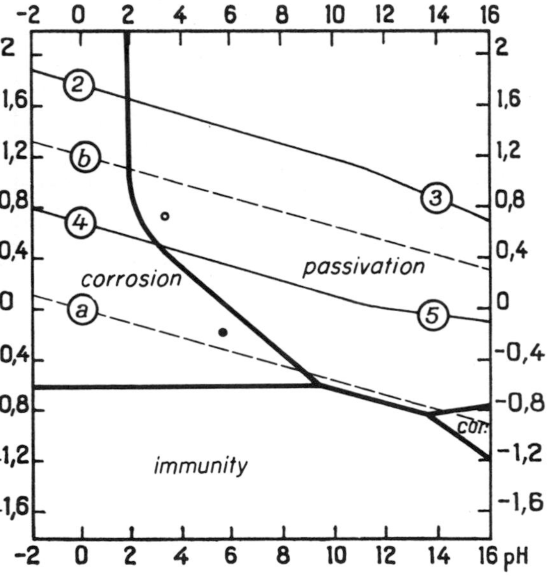

FIG. 5. Corrosion and passivation of iron by hydrogen peroxide. Reduction and decomposition of hydrogen peroxide by iron.

● Iron in the presence of a solution of H_2O_2 of 0·3 g/l. (corrosion).
○ Iron in the presence of a solution of H_2O_2 of 3·0 g/l. (passivation).

3.3. ACTION OF HYDROGEN PEROXIDE ON IRON

We have verified two of these facts in the particular case of the action of hydrogen peroxide solutions on iron ([2], [3]): some piano-wires were put into two glass flasks containing respectively a relatively dilute solution of hydrogen peroxide (0·3 g/l) and a relatively concentrated solution of hydrogen peroxide (3·0 g/l).

After a few hours the pH of the solution and the electrode potential of the iron were measured, and the state of the metal surface was noted. The conditions of pH and potential obtained were marked on Fig. 5, a potential–pH diagram representing, on the one hand, the theoretical conditions of instability and double instability of hydrogen peroxide solutions, and, on the other hand, the theoretical conditions of corrosion, immunity and passivation of iron.

We see in Fig. 5 that, for the relatively dilute solution of hydrogen peroxide, the point representing the condition of the iron (E = −0·200 V; pH = 5·7) is situated in the domain of corrosion of iron and in the domain of reduction of hydrogen peroxide; therefore corrosion of the metal without evolution of gas takes place according to the reactions:

$$\begin{array}{lrcl} & Fe & \rightarrow & Fe^{++} + 2e^- \\ \text{and} & H_2O_2 + 2H^+ + 2e^- & \rightarrow & 2H_2O \\ \hline \text{overall reaction} & Fe + H_2O_2 + 2H^+ & \rightarrow & Fe^{++} + 2H_2O. \end{array}$$

For the relatively concentrated solution of hydrogen peroxide, the point representing the condition of the iron (E = +0·720 V; pH = 3·4) is in the domain of passivation of iron and in the domain of double instability of hydrogen peroxide; therefore passivation of the iron occurs without corrosion (probably by the formation of a protective film of Fe_2O_3), and evolution of gaseous oxygen is noticed on the surface of the metal, resulting from the decomposition of hydrogen peroxide according to the reaction $2H_2O_2 \rightarrow 2H_2O + O_2$. Moreover, it is noticed, after some time, and as a result of this decomposition which causes a reduction in the concentration of hydrogen peroxide to below the critical concentration necessary to ensure passivation of the metal, that the electrode potential of the iron decreases abruptly and takes up a position, as in the previous case, in the domain of corrosion of iron and in the domain of reduction of hydrogen peroxide. The evolution of oxygen is seen to stop, passivation ceases and the metal begins to corrode.

4. BIBLIOGRAPHY

[1] P. Delahay, M. Pourbaix and P. Van Rysselberghe, *Comportement électrochimique de l'oxygène, de l'eau oxygénée et des radicaux* OH *et* HO_2 (C. R. 2e Réunion du CITCE, Milan, 1950).

[2] M. Pourbaix, *Applications de diagrammes potentiel–pH relatifs au fer et à l'eau oxygénée. Expériences de démonstration* (Rapport technique RT.2 of CEBELCOR, 1954).

[3] M. Pourbaix, *Leçons sur la corrosion électrochimique* (1er fascicule) (Rapport technique RT.57 of CEBELCOR, 1957).

[4] M. Pourbaix, *Leçons sur la corrosion électrochimique* (3e fascicule) (Rapport technique RT.49 of CEBELCOR, 1957).

SECTION 2

HYDROGEN[1]

M. POURBAIX and N. de ZOUBOV

SUMMARY

1. *Substances considered and substance not considered.*

2. *Reactions and equilibrium formulae.*
   2.1. Two dissolved substances.
      2.1.1. Relative stability of the ions H^+, OH^- and H^-.
      2.1.2. Limits of the domains of relative predominance of the ions H^+, OH^- and H^-.
   2.2. Two gaseous substances.
      2.2.1. Relative stability of H_1 and H_2.
      2.2.2. Limit of the domains of relative predominance of H_1 and H_2.
   2.3. One dissolved substance and one gaseous substance.
      Solubility of hydrogen.

3. *Equilibrium diagram and its interpretation.*
   3.1. Establishment of the diagram.
   3.2. Formation and stability of diatomic gaseous hydrogen. Hydrogen over-potential. Exchange currents.
   3.3. Hydrogen electrodes for the measurement of pH.
   3.4. Realization of powerful electrochemical reductions.
   3.5. Corrosion of metals with the evolution of hydrogen.
   3.6. Diffusion of hydrogen into iron and pickling embrittlement.
   3.7. Conditions for the formation of monatomic gaseous hydrogen.

4. *Bibliography.*

[1] Adapted version of the Rapport technique RT.69 of CEBELCOR (July 1958).
Several of the following arguments have already been published [12].

1. SUBSTANCES CONSIDERED AND SUBSTANCE NOT CONSIDERED

	Oxidation Number (Z)	Considered	Not considered	μ^0 (cal.)		Names
Liquid substance	+1	$\boldsymbol{H_2O}$	–	– 56 690		Water
Dissolved substances	–1	H^-	–	51 900		Hydride ion
	0	–	H_2	4 230	(2)	Natural hydrogen
	+1	H^+	–	0		Hydrogen ion
	»	OH^-	–	– 37 595		Hydroxide ion
Gaseous substances	0	H_1	–	48 575		Atomic hydrogen
	»	H_2	–	0		Natural hydrogen

2. REACTIONS AND EQUILIBRIUM FORMULAE

2.1. TWO DISSOLVED SUBSTANCES

2.1.1. *Relative stability of the ions* H^+, OH^- *and* H^-

$Z = +1$

1. $\boldsymbol{H_2O} = H^+ + OH^-$ $\qquad \log(OH^-) = -14.00 + pH$

$-1 \rightarrow +1$

2. $H^- = H^+ + 2e^-$ $\qquad E_0 = -1.125 + 0.0295 \log \frac{(H^+)}{(H^-)}$

3. $H^- + \boldsymbol{H_2O} = OH^- + 2H^+ + 2e^-$ $\qquad E_0 = -0.711 - 0.0591\,pH + 0.0295 \log \frac{(OH^-)}{(H^-)}$

2.1.2. *Limits of the domains of relative predominance of the ions* H^+, OH^- *and* H^-

1'. H^+/OH^- $\qquad pH = 7.00$

2'. H^-/H^+ $\qquad E_0 = -1.125$

3'. H^-/OH^- $\qquad E_0 = -0.711 - 0.0591\,pH$

2.2. TWO GASEOUS SUBSTANCES

2.2.1. *Relative stability of* H_1 *and* H_2

4. $H_2 = H_1 + H^+ + e^-$ $\qquad E_0 = 2.106 - 0.0591\,pH + 0.0591 \log \frac{p_{H_1}}{p_{H_2}}$

2.2.2. *Limit of the domains of relative predominance of* H_1 *and* H_2

4'. H_1/H_2 $\qquad E_0 = 2.106 - 0.0591\,pH$

2.3. ONE DISSOLVED SUBSTANCE AND ONE GASEOUS SUBSTANCE

Solubility of hydrogen

$0 \rightarrow +1$

5. $H_1 = H^+ + e^-$ $\qquad E_0 = -2.106 - 0.0591\,pH - 0.0591 \log p_{H_1}$

6. $H_2 = 2H^+ + 2e^-$ $\qquad E_0 = 0.000 - 0.0591\,pH - 0.0295 \log p_{H_2}$

$-1 \rightarrow 0$

7. $2H^- = H_2 + 2e^-$ $\qquad E_0 = -2.251 + 0.0295 \log \frac{p_{H_2}}{(H^-)^2}$

---

(2) Value calculated from the solubility of hydrogen in water at 25°C (17·54 cm³/l for $p_{H_2} = 1$ atm.).

3. EQUILIBRIUM DIAGRAM AND ITS INTERPRETATION

3.1. ESTABLISHMENT OF THE DIAGRAM

Using formulae (1)–(7) we have constructed the electrochemical equilibrium diagram Fig. 1.

On it we have represented the conditions of stability of the gases H_1 and H_2, as defined by equations (5) and (6) and also the domains of relative predominance of the ions H^+, OH^- and H^-, as defined by equations (1′)–(3′).

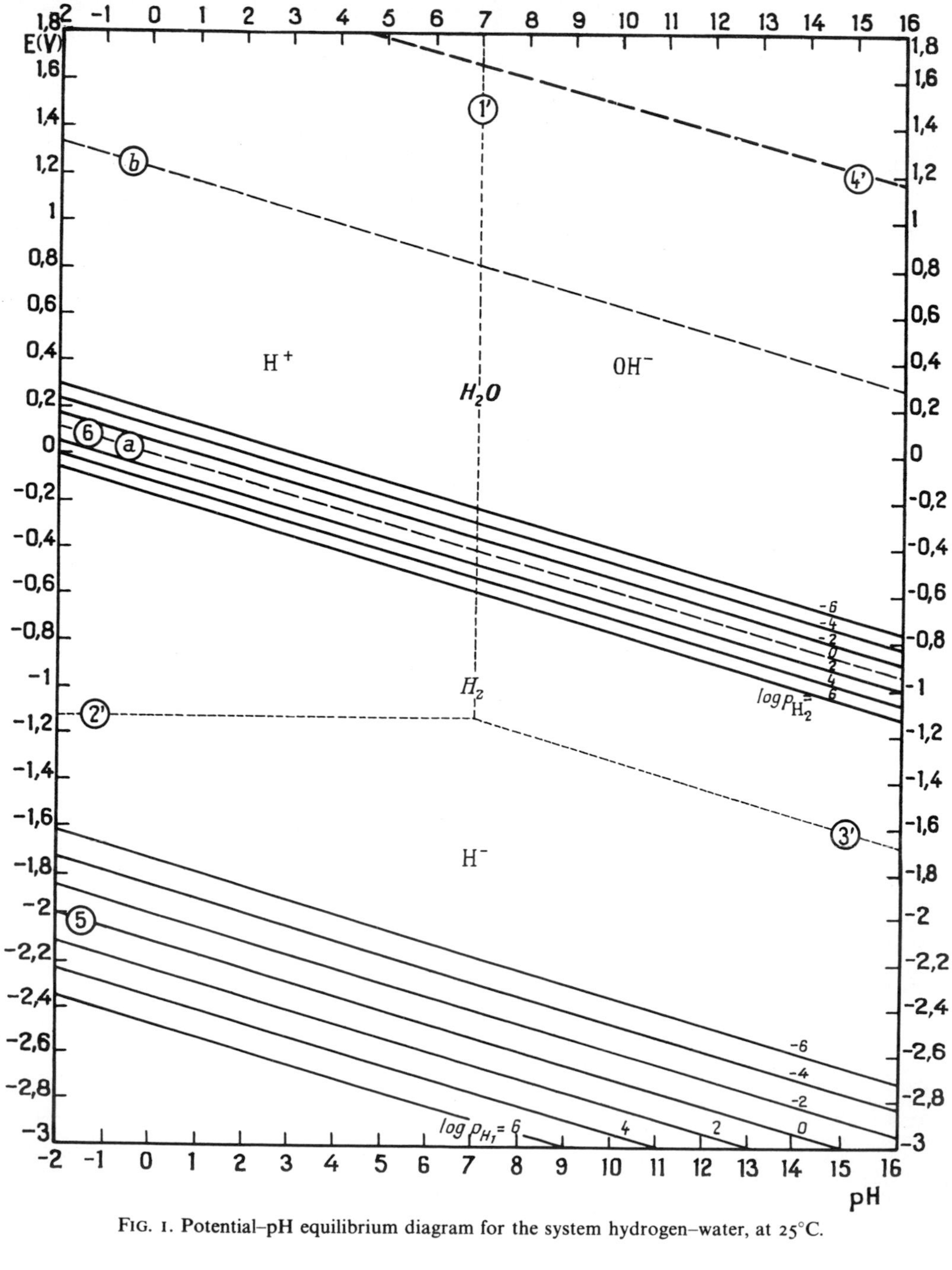

FIG. 1. Potential–pH equilibrium diagram for the system hydrogen–water, at 25°C.

3.2. FORMATION AND STABILITY OF DIATOMIC GASEOUS HYDROGEN

Diatomic gaseous hydrogen can theoretically be formed at atmospheric pressure by the reduction of water at potentials below those indicated in Fig. 1 by line (*a*), which refers to the equilibrium of reaction (6) in the particular case when $p_{H_2} = 1$ atm. These conditions of potential can be obtained either electrochemically (using appropriate cathodes), or chemically (using corrodible metals or other reducing substances).

Hydrogen overpotentials. Exchange currents. As is well known, the degree of irreversibility of the hydrogen evolution reaction $2H^+ + 2e^- \rightarrow H_2$, which can be represented by the "overpotential" of this reaction, varies greatly with the nature and condition of the metal surface (or the surface of another substance with electronic conduction) on which the reaction occurs.

As an example, some values of "hydrogen overpotentials" are given below. These values were put forward by Thiel and Hammerschmidt in 1923, for twenty-two elements in the presence of a 1M solution of H_2SO_4, at 25°C; the current densities to which these overpotentials correspond were not indicated by the investigators. The elements are given an "order number" which classifies them in order of increasing hydrogen overpotential (Table I).

TABLE I

Hydrogen overpotentials in the presence of 1 M H_2SO_4
(after Thiel and Hammerschmidt [4])

1. Pd	0.00000 V	9. V	0.1352 V	17. As	0.369 V
2. Pt	0.000002	10. Ni	0.1375	18. Bi	0.388
3. Ru	0.00043	11. W	0.157	19. Ta	0.39
4. Os	0.00148	12. Mo	0.168	20. Pb	0.402
5. Ir	0.00255	13. Cu	0.19	21. In	0.533
6. Rh	0.004	14. Si	0.192	22. Hg	0.570
7. Au	0.0165	15. Sb	0.233		
8. Ag	0.097	16. C (³)	0.335		

Shown in Fig. 2 are the values, according to various investigators (Petcherskaia and Stender [1], Ferguson [2], Knobel [3] and Iofa [13]), of the hydrogen overpotentials η of twenty-three metals and metalloids, for various current densities, in the presence of a 1 M solution of H_2SO_4, i.e. the solution considered by Thiel and Hammerschmidt, at 25°C(⁴). We have not made a critical examination of the values given in Fig. 2, which is therefore given without prejudice; however, we point out that Tafel's law $\eta = a - b \log i$, which seems to be valid generally for a given surface state, does not apply to the values given for Te and Bi, nor to some of the values for Pb; these deviations are probably due to the formation of hydrides.

For those cases in which the results of these determinations are in approximate agreement with Tafel's law, we have determined, by linear extrapolation to an overpotential of zero, the logarithm of the "exchange current" $\log i_0 = a/b$, i.e. the reaction current when the electrode potential of the metal is equal to the equilibrium potential of the reaction $H_2 = 2H^+ + 2e^-$. Now the value of the exchange current can be considered as being an absolute measure of the degree of irreversibility of this reaction on the given electrode. The table below shows, on the one hand, the values of the exchange currents deduced from Fig. 2 for nineteen metals (in the presence of 1 M H_2SO_4), and, on the other hand, values of exchange currents given by Kortüm and Bockris [5] (in the presence of various solutions of H_2SO_4 and HCl, 0·1 to 1 M). The metals considered have been classified approximately in decreasing

(³) In the form of graphite.

(⁴) The overpotentials given by Iofa for Hg are for a 0·05 M solution of H_2SO_4 at 20°C.

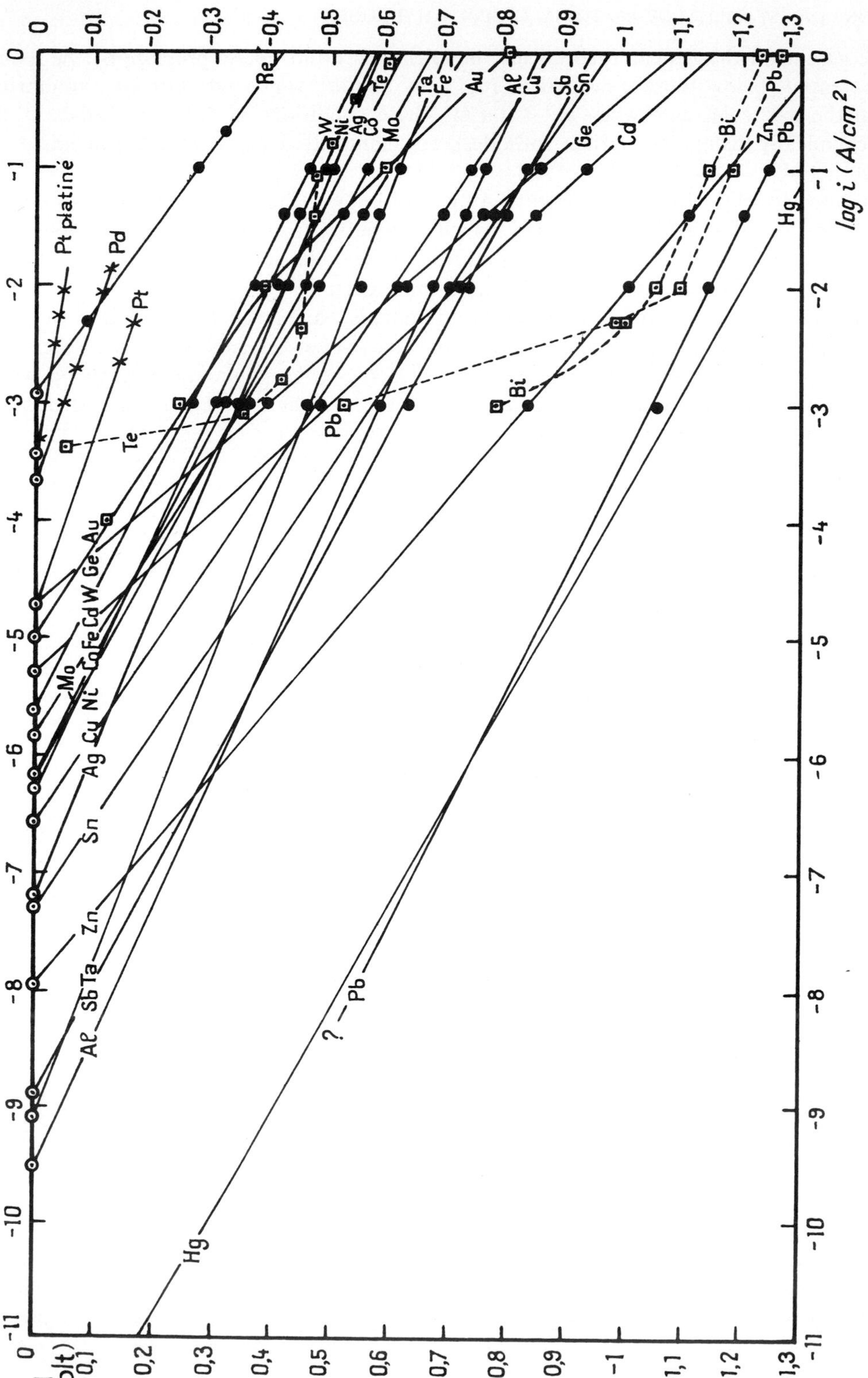

FIG. 2. Hydrogen overpotentials and exchange currents for various metals (in 1 M H_2SO_4 solution at 25°C). After Petcherskaia and Stender ●, Ferguson ×, Knobel ⊡ and Iofa (Hg in 0·05 M H_2SO_4).

order of exchange current, i.e. approximately in increasing order of hydrogen overpotential. In order to make a comparison between this classification and that of Thiel and Hammerschmidt, we have put in the "order numbers" given in Table I, for the metals considered by these investigators.

TABLE II

Logarithms of the exchange currents of the reaction $H_2 = 2H^+ + 2e^-$ (A/cm²), from Fig. 2 (1 M H_2SO_4) and after Kortüm and Bockris [5] (various solutions, 0·1 M to 1 M H_2SO_4 and HCl; 5 M for W)

		Fig. 2	KB			Fig. 2	KB
	Re	−2·9[5]	—	8.	Ag	−7·2	−3·7 to −6·3
	Pt (platinized)	−3·4	−3	18.	Bi	—	−7
1.	Pd	−3·6	—		Sn	−7·3	—
2.	Pt	−4·7	−2·8		Zn	−7·9	—
	Ge	−4·7	—	15.	Sb	−8·9	—
7.	Au	−5·0	−6		Be	—	−9
	Cd	−5·3	—	19.	Ta	−9·1	—
11.	W	−5·6	−6		Al	−9·5	—
	Fe	−5·8	—		Nb	—	−11
	Co	−6·1	—	22.	Hg	−12·6	−11·2 to −12·3
12.	Mo	−6·2	—	20.	Pb	—	−12·7
10.	Ni	−6·3	−5·4 to −6·0		Tl	—	−16
13.	Cu	−6·5	−8				

An examination of the order numbers indicated above shows that, with the exception of Ag, this classification by exchange currents is practically in agreement with the classification of Thiel and Hammerschmidt by overpotentials. Systematic studies of the exchange currents of the reaction $H_2 = 2H^+ + 2e^-$, and also of other electrochemical reactions would be of great value.

It follows from Tables I and II and Fig. 2 that the reduction of water to diatomic gaseous hydrogen H_2 takes place practically without overpotential for Re(?), platinized Pt, Pd, Pt, Ru, Os, Ir, Rh. This reduction takes place with a relatively small overpotential for Ge, Au, Cd, W, Fe; it takes place with a relatively large overpotential for Co, Mo, Ni, Cu, Bi, Sn, Zn; it takes place with a large overpotential for Sb, Be, Ta, Al, Nb, Hg, Pb and Tl.

In paragraphs 3.3, 3.4 and 3.5, we shall discuss some consequences of these important properties.

3.3. HYDROGEN ELECTRODES FOR THE MEASUREMENT OF pH

In the presence of noble metals having an overpotential of practically zero, i.e. the six metals of the platinum group (Ru, Rh, Pd, Os, Ir, Pt), the equilibrium state of the reaction $H_2 = H^+ + 2e^-$ is easily attained experimentally. If these metals are saturated with hydrogen at atmospheric pressure in a solution free from oxidizing and reducing agents, they exert an electrode potential equal to the equilibrium potential of the reaction $H_2 = 2H^+ + 2e^-$. This potential depends linearly on the pH according to the equation $E_0 = 0{\cdot}000 - 0{\cdot}0591$ pH (volt), at 25°C, and the value of the pH of the solution can therefore be deduced from the value of the potential of the hydrogen electrode (in millivolts) using the relation pH $= -16{\cdot}92$ E.

Of these metals, those in which hydrogen is very soluble (Ru, Pd, Os) can be used as electrodes for the measurement of pH without it being necessary to maintain them permanently in a current of hydrogen; it is sufficient to saturate them with hydrogen before they are put in the solution to be examined, and possibly resaturate them periodically, for them to give exact results. This is well known in the case of palladium.

(5) This exchange current value for Re seems subject to caution.

3.4. REALIZATION OF POWERFUL ELECTROCHEMICAL REDUCTIONS

If we cathodically polarize metals which have a low hydrogen overpotential (for example, metals of the platinum group) with an increasing current intensity, only a small polarization is necessary for evolution of hydrogen to occur at the metal surface. The electrode potential of the cathode is maintained at relatively high values; the reducing power of these cathodes is therefore relatively feeble.

If, on the other hand, we cathodically polarize metals which have a large hydrogen overpotential (e.g., mercury, zinc or lead) we can obtain a large polarization without evolution of hydrogen occurring. The electrode potential of the cathode can reach low values at which powerful reductions can take place. Using such cathodes, it is theoretically possible to bring about all those reductions whose "reduction potential"(6) is above the potential at which hydrogen begins to be evolved. It is this property, together with the liquid state of the metal, that enables mercury to be used in polarography.

This is true, not only for uncorrodible *noble metals* or slightly corrodible ones (mercury) in which case these reductions are the only reactions that take place, but also for corrodible *non-noble metals* (zinc, aluminium) in which case, depending on whether the potential of the metal is above or below its corrosion potential, these reductions may or may not take place simultaneously with corrosion reactions. By judicious regulation of the electrode potential of the metal used as the cathode or as the chemical reducing agent, and by the possible use of substances capable of forming oxidation-reduction systems (salts of Ti, V, Cr, Fe, Ce) or of being reduced with the formation of hydrides (As, Sb, etc.) it is possible to control the nature and yield of the reduction reactions.

Examples of such procedures are well known, for instance in the reduction of nitrobenzene ([7], pp. 184–204; [8], p. 396).

3.5. CORROSION OF METALS WITH THE EVOLUTION OF HYDROGEN

It is well known that chemical metal corrosion reactions with the evolution of hydrogen, such as

$$Fe + 2H^+ \rightarrow Fe^{++} + H_2 \qquad Zn + 2H^+ \rightarrow Zn^{++} + H_2 \qquad Pb + 2H^+ \rightarrow Pb^{++} + H_2$$

result from the combination of two electrochemical reactions

$$\begin{array}{rcl} Fe & \rightarrow & Fe^{++} + 2e^- \\ 2H^+ + 2e^- & \rightarrow & H_2 \\ \hline Fe + 2H^+ & \rightarrow & Fe^{++} + H_2 \end{array} \qquad \begin{array}{rcl} Zn & \rightarrow & Zn^{++} + 2e^- \\ 2H^+ + 2e^- & \rightarrow & H_2 \\ \hline Zn + 2H^+ & \rightarrow & Zn^{++} + H_2 \end{array} \qquad \begin{array}{rcl} Pb & \rightarrow & Pb^{++} + 2e^- \\ 2H^+ + 2e^- & \rightarrow & H_2 \\ \hline Pb + 2H^+ & \rightarrow & Pb^{++} + H_2 \end{array}$$

The rate of these corrosion reactions depends, on the one hand, on the affinity of the reaction (which can be reckoned in volts by the difference between the equilibrium potentials of the two component electrochemical reactions), and, on the other hand, on the degree of irreversibility of these two electrochemical reactions (which, for each of these reactions, can be calculated from a polarization curve, which gives overpotential values as a function of the reaction current density).

Figure 3 represents schematically such polarization "curves" for Fe, Zn and Pb, for the hypothetical case of perfect solutions of pH = 0·0 containing 0·010 g-at of dissolved metal per litre. Table III shows the characteristics assumed for the hydrogen evolution reaction $2H^+ + 2e^- \rightarrow H_2$ at the surface of these three metals(7) and for the dissolution reactions $Me \rightarrow Me^{++} + 2e^-$ of these metals(8); this table also shows the resulting characteristics for the reactions of corrosion of these metals with the

(6) It will be recalled that, on Van Rysselberghe's recommendation, we denote by the "reduction tension" of a reaction that electrode potential below which the reaction occurs in the reduction direction with an appreciable rate (e.g. 10^{-8} to 10^{-6} A/cm² [6]).

(7) The exchange currents and Tafel formulae indicated for these reactions are deduced from Fig. 2

(8) We have evaluated the exchange currents and Tafel formulae indicated for these reactions using experimental results

evolution of hydrogen, $Me + 2H^+ \rightarrow Me^{++} + H_2$. These characteristics, according to Wagner and Traud [11], are those of the points where the "curves" of cathodic polarization $2H^+ + 2e^- \rightarrow H_2$ meet those of anodic polarization $Me \rightarrow Me^{++} + 2e^-$ for a given metal.

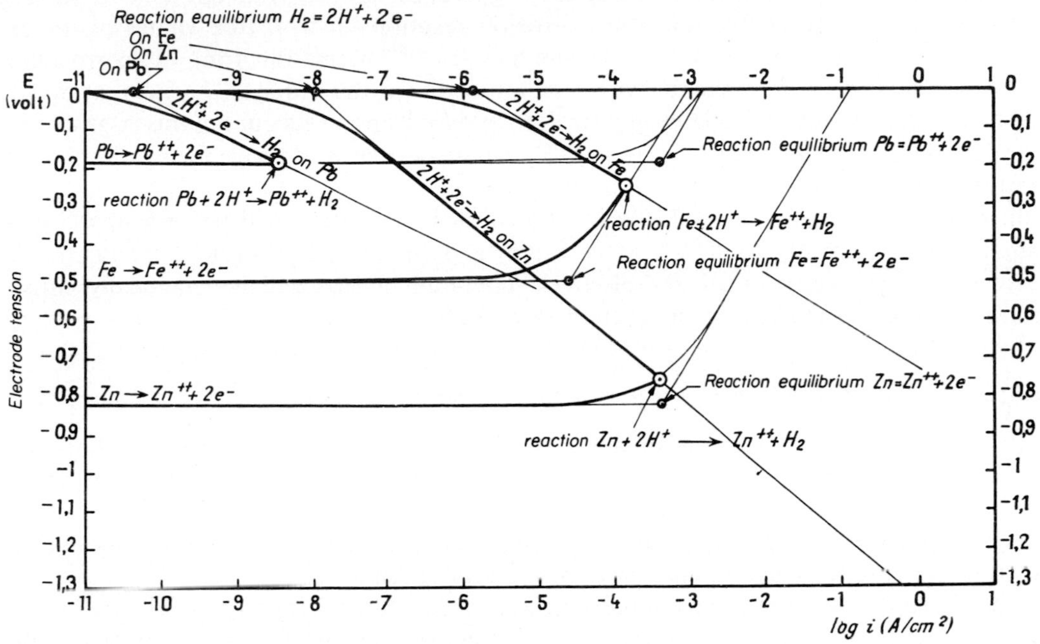

FIG. 3. Corrosion of metals with the evolution of hydrogen (Fe, Zn, Pb) in the presence of a solution of pH = 0 containing 0·01 g-at of dissolved metal per litre.

TABLE III

Characteristics of the reactions $2H^+ + 2e^- \rightarrow H_2$, $Me \rightarrow Me^{++} + 2e^-$ and $Me + 2H^+ \rightarrow Me^{++} + H_2$ relating to the behaviour of Fe, Zn and Pb in the presence of a solution of pH = 0 containing 0·01 g-at of dissolved metal per litre (from Fig. 3)

	Fe	Zn	Pb
	Characteristics of the reaction $2H^+ + 2e^- = H_2$		
Equilibrium potential (E_h volt)	0·000	0·000	0·000
Log exchange current i_0 (A/cm^2)	− 5·85	− 7·95	− 10·35
Tafel formula: value of η (volt)	$-0{\cdot}72 - 0{\cdot}123 \log i$	$-1{\cdot}34 - 0{\cdot}169 \log i$	$-0{\cdot}74 - 0{\cdot}0715 \log i$
	Characteristics of the reaction $Me \rightarrow Me^{++} + 2e^-$		
Equilibrium potential (E_h volt)	− 0·500	− 0·822	− 0·185
Log exchange current i_0 (A/cm^2)	− 4·60	− 3·40	− 3·40
Tafel formula: value of η (volt)	$1{\cdot}49 + 0{\cdot}328 \log i$	$1{\cdot}12 + 0{\cdot}340 \log i$	$0{\cdot}80 + 0{\cdot}246 \log i$
	Characteristics of the reaction $Me + 2H^+ \rightarrow Me^{++} + H_2$		
Corrosion affinity (V/g-at of metal)	0·500	0·822	0·185
Corrosion potential (E_h volt)	−0·250	−0·755	−0·185
Corrosion rate: log i (A/cm^2)	−3·83	−3·43	−8·45
Corrosion rate: (mm/year)	80	166	0·003

---

obtained by Bonhoeffer [9] concerning the behaviour of iron in 0·5 M H_2SO_4 solution and by Piontelli and Poli [10] concerning the behaviour of zinc in SO_4^{--} solution and lead in ClO_4^- solution.

The exchange currents and Tafel formulae values assumed here are given purely as a guide, without committing ourselves. Systematic research into this subject would be useful.

Figure 3 and this table show that iron will corrode rapidly in the solution considered, at an electrode potential (−0·250 V) very appreciably greater than the equilibrium potential of the corrosion reaction (−0·500 V). Although the affinity for corrosion with the evolution of hydrogen is very much greater for zinc (0·822 V/g-at of metal) than for iron (0·500 V/g-at of metal) and although the corrosion reaction for zinc is clearly less irreversible than the corrosion reaction for iron (the values of the exchange currents assumed here are $10^{-3 \cdot 40}$ A/cm^2 for zinc and $10^{-4 \cdot 60}$ A/cm^2 for iron), the corrosion rate for zinc will be only slightly greater than the corrosion rate for iron; this is due to the fact that the hydrogen overpotential for zinc is very appreciably greater than that for iron; on account of this large overpotential the electrode potential of corroding zinc (−0·755 V) will be only slightly above the equilibrium potential of the corrosion reaction (−0·822 V).

With regard to lead, Fig. 3 and Table III show that its corrosion will be very small, on account of the small reaction affinity (0·185 V/g-at of metal) and the large hydrogen overpotential for lead. Because of this large overpotential, the electrode potential of lead will be practically equal to the equilibrium potential of the corrosion reaction (−0·185 V).

3.6. DIFFUSION OF HYDROGEN INTO IRON AND PICKLING EMBRITTLEMENT

When iron corrodes in a solution of sulphuric acid whose pH is in the neighbourhood of 1 to 2, it exerts an electrode potential of about −0·25 V. Figure 1 and formula (6) show that, under these conditions, the equilibrium pressure of diatomic hydrogen reaches considerable values, of the order of $10^{5 \cdot 4}$, i.e. 250 000 atm. This pressure can be even more considerable if the iron is used as an electrolytic cathode, in which case the electrode potential is appreciably lower.

This can have the effect of greatly supersaturating the metal with hydrogen, which, if it is evolved at grain boundaries or in rifts, or underneath a protective covering (paint or galvanic deposit, for instance), can cause embrittlement of the metal as pointed out by G. Chaudron), or a lack of adherence of the covering.

3.7. CONDITIONS FOR THE FORMATION OF MONATOMIC GASEOUS HYDROGEN

Figure 1 shows that monatomic gaseous hydrogen can be formed by the reduction of water and have an appreciable partial pressure only at very low electrode potentials, in the neighbourhood of those corresponding to the family of lines (4); for these electrode potentials the equilibrium pressure of H_2 is very considerably greater than the equilibrium pressure of H_1.

Monatomic gaseous hydrogen H_1 can be predominant with respect to diatomic gaseous hydrogen H_2 only at very high electrode potentials, above those indicated by line (4′). The equilibrium partial pressures of these gases are then so small (10^{-71} atm.) that this line (4′) loses all practical interest.

4. BIBLIOGRAPHY

[1] A. G. Petcherskaia and V. V. Stender, Potentiels de dégagement d'hydrogène en solutions acides, *Zhur. Fiz. Khim.* **24**, 856–9 (1950).

[2] A. L. Ferguson, *Some Stepping Stones on the Path to the True Explanation of the Mechanism of Overvoltage* [Nat. Bur. Stand. Cir. No. 524 (*Electrochemical Constants*), 1953, pp. 227–41].

[3] M. Knobel, *Overvoltage* (International Critical Tables, VI, 1929, p. 339).

[4] A. Thiel and W. Hammerschmidt, Beiträge zur Kenntnis der Ueberspannungserscheinungen. II. Ueber den Zusammenhang zwischen der Ueberspannung des Wasserstoffs an reinen Metallen und gewissen Eigenschaften der Metalle, *Z. anorg. allgem. Chem.* **132**, 15–35 (1923).

[5] G. Kortüm and J. O'M. Bockris, *Textbook of Electrochemistry*, Vol. II, Elsevier, Amsterdam, 1951.

[6] P. Van Rysselberghe, *Rapport de la commission "Nomenclature et définitions électrochimiques" du CITCE* (C. R. 9e Reunion du CITCE, Paris, 1957, pp. 177–219).

[7] S. Glasstone and A. Hickling, *Electrolytic Oxidation and Reduction*, Chapman and Hall, London, 1935.

[8] S. SWANN, JR., *Electrolytic Reactions* (*Technique of Organic Chemistry*, Vol. II), Interscience, New York, 1956.
[9] K. F. BONHOEFFER, Ueber das elektromotorische Verhalten von Eisen, *Z. Elektrochem.* **55**, 151–4 (1951).
[10] R. PIONTELLI and G. POLI, *Vue d'ensemble sur les phénomènes de polarisation des métaux* (C. R. 2e Réunion du CITCE, Milan, September 1950).
[11] C. WAGNER and W. TRAUD, *Z. Electrochem.* **44**, 391 (1938).
[12] M. POURBAIX, Thermodynamique des solutions aqueuses diluées. Représentation graphique du rôle du pH et du potentiel (Thèse, Delft, 1945; Béranger, Paris and Liège). 3rd Edition, Cebelcor 1963.
[13] Z. A. IOFA, quoted by FROUMKINE [14].
[14] A. N. FROUMKINE, *Acta Physicochim.*, U.R.S.S., **18**, 23 (1943).

SECTIONS 3.1 to 3.5

LITHIUM, SODIUM, POTASSIUM, RUBIDIUM, CAESIUM (1)

J. Van Muylder and M. Pourbaix

SUMMARY

1. *Substances considered.*
2. *Reactions and equilibrium formulae.*
   2.1. Two solid substances.
   Limit of the domains of relative stability of the solid substances.
   2.2. One solid substance and one dissolved substance.
   Solubility of the solid substances.
3. *Equilibrium diagrams and their interpretation.*
   3.1. Establishment of the diagrams.
   3.2. Stability and formation of the alkali metals.
   3.3. Stability and formation of the hydrides of the alkali metals.
   3.4. Stability of sodium amalgams.
4. *Bibliography.*

(1) Adapted version of the Rapport technique RT.70 of CEBELCOR (July 1958).

1. SUBSTANCES CONSIDERED

	Oxidation Number (Z)	Considered	μ^0(cal.)	Name, colour, crystalline system
LITHIUM				
Solid substances	− I	**LiH**	− 16 720	Lithium hydride, grey–white, cub.
	0	**Li**	0	Lithium, silvery white, b.c. cub.
	+ I	**Li_2O**	−133 900	Lithium monoxide, white, cub.
	+ I	**LiOH**	−105 900	Lithium hydroxide, white translucent, quad.
	+ 2	**Li_2O_2**	−135 000	Lithium dioxide, white
Dissolved substance	+ I	Li^+	− 70 220	Lithium cation, colourless
SODIUM				
Solid substances	− I	**NaH**	− 9 000	Sodium hydride, grey–white, cub.
	0	**Na**	0	Sodium, silvery white, b.c. cub.
	+ I	**Na_2O**	− 90 000	Sodium monoxide, white, cub.
	+ I	**NaOH**	− 90 100	Sodium hydroxide, white, cub.
	+ 2	**Na_2O_2**	−102 800	Sodium peroxide, light yellow, quad.
Dissolved substance	+ I	Na^+	− 62 589	Sodium cation, colourless
POTASSIUM				
Solid substances	− I	**KH**	− 8 900	Potassium hydride, white, cub.
	0	**K**	0	Potassium, silvery white, b.c. cub.
	+ I	**K_2O**	− 76 200	Potassium monoxide, light yellow, cub.
	+ I	**KOH**	− 89 500	Potassium hydroxide, white, orthorh.
	+ 2	**K_2O_2**	−100 100	Potassium dioxide, white
	+ 3	**K_2O_3**	−100 000	Potassium trioxide, red
	+ 4	**K_2O_4**	− 99 600	Potassium tetroxide, yellow, quad.
Dissolved substance	+ I	K^+	− 67 460	Potassium cation, colourless
RUBIDIUM				
Solid substances	− I	**RbH**	− 7 300	Rubidium hydride, white, cub.
	0	**Rb**	0	Rubidium, silvery white, b.c. cub.
	+ I	**Rb_2O**	− 69 500	Rubidium monoxide, straw yellow, cub.
	+ I	**RbOH**	− 87 100	Rubidium hydroxide, white, rhomb.
	+ 2	**Rb_2O_2**	− 83 600	Rubidium dioxide, yellowish white, cub.
	+ 3	**Rb_2O_3**	− 92 400	Rubidium trioxide, black
	+ 4	**Rb_2O_4**	− 94 600	Rubidium tetroxide, deep orange, quad.
Dissolved substance	+ I	Rb^+	− 67 450	Rubidium cation, colourless
CAESIUM				
Solid substances	− I	**CsH**	− 7 300	Caesium hydride, white, cub.
	0	**Cs**	0	Caesium, pale yellow, b.c. cub.
	+ I	**Cs_2O**	− 65 600	Caesium monoxide, orange, rhomb.
	+ I	**CsOH**	− 84 900	Caesium hydroxide, white
	+ 2	**Cs_2O_2**	− 78 200	Caesium dioxide, yellowish white
	+ 3	**Cs_2O_3**	− 86 100	Caesium trioxide, black
	+ 4	**Cs_2O_4**	− 92 500	Caesium tetroxide, brown, quad.
Dissolved substance	+ I	Cs^+	− 67 410	Caesium cation, colourless

2. REACTIONS AND EQUILIBRIUM FORMULAE

Lithium

2.1. TWO SOLID SUBSTANCES

Limit of the domains of relative stability of the solid substances

$-I \rightarrow 0$

1. $LiH = Li + H^+ + e^-$ $E_0 = 0.726 - 0.0591\,pH$

2.2. ONE SOLID SUBSTANCE AND ONE DISSOLVED SUBSTANCE

Solubility of the solid substances

$-I \rightarrow +I$

2. $LiH = Li^+ + H^+ + 2e^-$ $E_0 = -1.161 - 0.0295\,pH + 0.0295\log(Li^+)$

$0 \rightarrow +I$

3. $Li = Li^+ + e^-$ $E_0 = -3.045 + 0.0591\log(Li^+)$

Sodium

2.1 TWO SOLID SUBSTANCES

Limit of the domains of relative stability of the solid substances

$-I \rightarrow 0$

1. $NaH = Na + H^+ + e^-$ $E_0 = 0.390 - 0.0591\,pH$

2.2. ONE SOLID SUBSTANCE AND ONE DISSOLVED SUBSTANCE

Solubility of the solid substances

$-I \rightarrow +I$

2. $NaH = Na^+ + H^+ + 2e^-$ $E_0 = -1.162 - 0.0295\,pH + 0.0295\log(Na^+)$

$0 \rightarrow +I$

3. $Na = Na^+ + e^-$ $E_0 = -2.714 + 0.0591\log(Na^+)$

Potassium

2.1. TWO SOLID SUBSTANCES

Limit of the domains of relative stability of the solid substances

$-I \rightarrow 0$

1. $KH = K + H^+ + e^-$ $E_0 = 0.386 - 0.0591\,pH$

2.2. ONE SOLID SUBSTANCE AND ONE DISSOLVED SUBSTANCE

Solubility of the solid substances

$-I \rightarrow +I$

2. $KH = K^+ + H^+ + 2e^-$ $E_0 = -1.270 - 0.0295\,pH + 0.0295\log(K^+)$

$0 \rightarrow +I$

3. $K = K^+ + e^-$ $E_0 = -2.924 + 0.0591\log(K^+)$

Rubidium

2.1. TWO SOLID SUBSTANCES

Limit of the domains of relative stability of the solid substances

$-1 \rightarrow 0$

1.　　　$\mathbf{RbH} = \mathbf{Rb} + H^+ + e^-$　　　　$E_0 = 0.317 - 0.0591 \, pH$

2.2. ONE SOLID SUBSTANCE AND ONE DISSOLVED SUBSTANCE

Solubility of the solid substances

$-1 \rightarrow +1$

2.　　　$\mathbf{RbH} = Rb^+ + H^+ + 2e^-$　　　$E_0 = -1.304 - 0.0295 \, pH + 0.0295 \log(Rb^+)$

$0 \rightarrow +1$

3:　　　$\mathbf{Rb} = Rb^+ + e^-$　　　$E_0 = -2.925 \qquad + 0.0591 \log(Rb^+)$

Caesium

2.1. TWO SOLID SUBSTANCES

Limit of the domains of relative stability of the solid substances

$-1 \rightarrow 0$

1.　　　$\mathbf{CsH} = \mathbf{Cs} + H^+ + e^-$　　　　$E_0 = 0.317 - 0.0591 \, pH$

2.2. ONE SOLID SUBSTANCE AND ONE DISSOLVED SUBSTANCE

Solubility of the solid substances

$-1 \rightarrow +1$

2.　　　$\mathbf{CsH} = Cs^+ + H^+ + 2e^-$　　　$E_0 = -1.304 - 0.0295 \, pH + 0.0295 \log(Cs^+)$

$0 \rightarrow +1$

3.　　　$\mathbf{Cs} = Cs^+ + e^-$　　　$E_0 = -2.923 \qquad + 0.0591 \log(Cs^+)$

Since the oxides, hydroxides and peroxides of the alkali metals are all very soluble in water, we have not established any formulae relating to their stability conditions in the presence of aqueous solutions.

3. EQUILIBRIUM DIAGRAMS AND THEIR INTERPRETATION

3.1. ESTABLISHMENT OF THE DIAGRAMS

Using the formulae above, we have constructed Figs. 1–5 which represent the conditions of thermodynamic equilibrium, at 25°C, of the systems lithium–water, sodium–water, potassium–water, rubidium–water and caesium–water, considering the simple ion of the metal (e.g. Li^+) as a dissolved substance; no solid oxides or hydroxides can be represented on these diagrams on account of their great solubilities. We have, however, considered the solid hydrides LiH, NaH, KH, RbH and CsH.

These figures are valid only in the absence of substances capable of forming soluble complexes or insoluble compounds with the metals. However, according to Charlot [1], these metals form practically no complexes, and very few insoluble compounds.

They are, nevertheless, soluble in mercury, with which they form amalgams; the presence of mercury therefore necessitates important modifications to these diagrams which are of considerable practical interest; an example, for sodium, is given below.

3.2. STABILITY AND FORMATION OF THE ALKALI METALS

The alkali metals, as well as the alkaline earth metals, exert extremely low solution potentials.

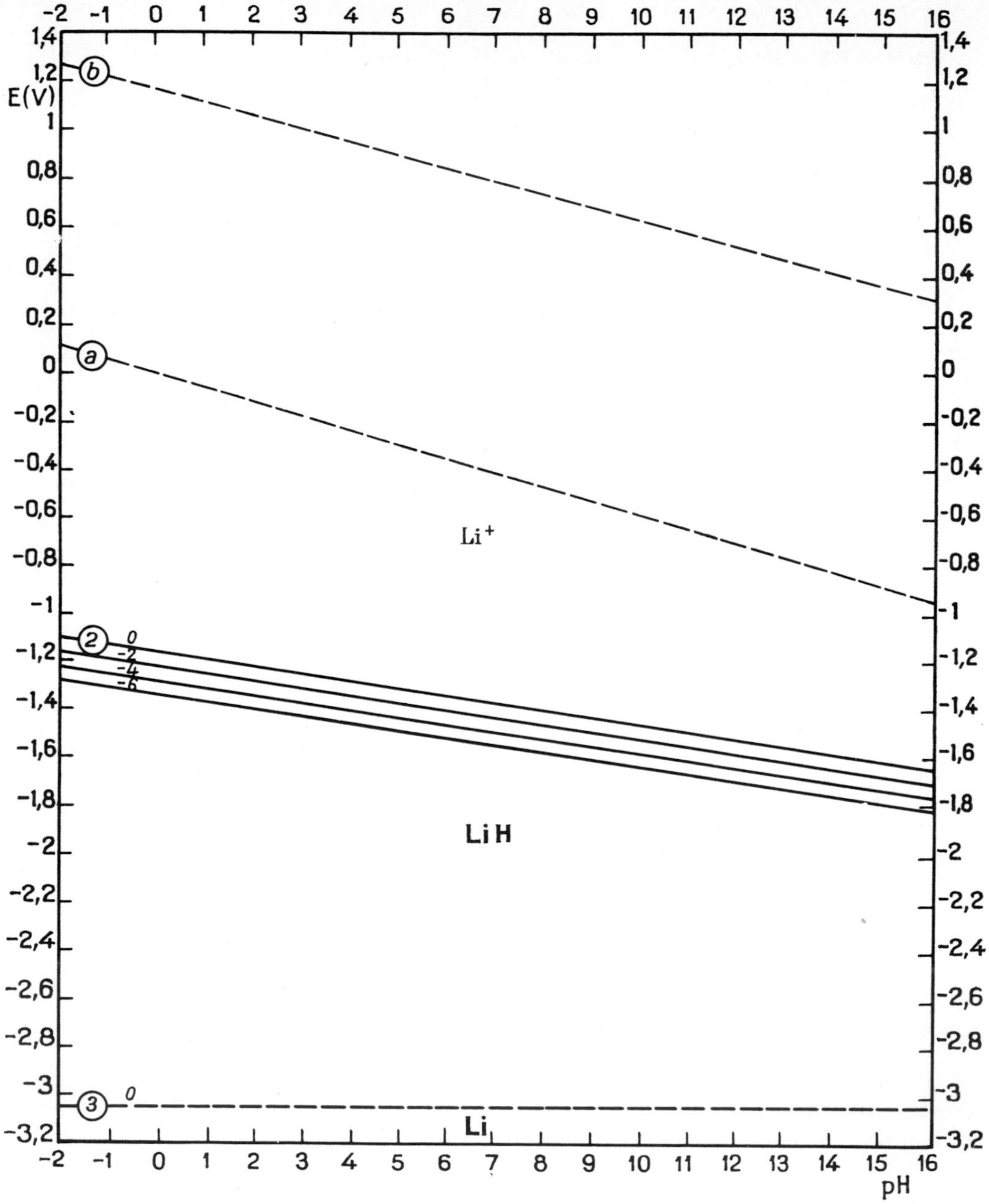

FIG. 1. Potential–pH equilibrium diagram for the system lithium–water, at 25°C.

As the whole of their domain of stability, in Figs. 1–5, is situated very much below the domain of stability of water, these metals are extremely unstable in the presence of aqueous solutions of any pH. The oxides, being very soluble, cannot produce any passivation, and the metals decompose aqueous solutions very vigorously, with the evolution of hydrogen; in the case of potassium, rubidium and caesium this decomposition is so violent that, in the presence of air, the hydrogen ignites spontaneously and an explosion often occurs.

On account of their great instability, the alkali metals cannot be separated electrolytically from aqueous solutions of their salts, except when a mercury cathode is used, in which case the metals dissolve in the mercury to form amalgams.

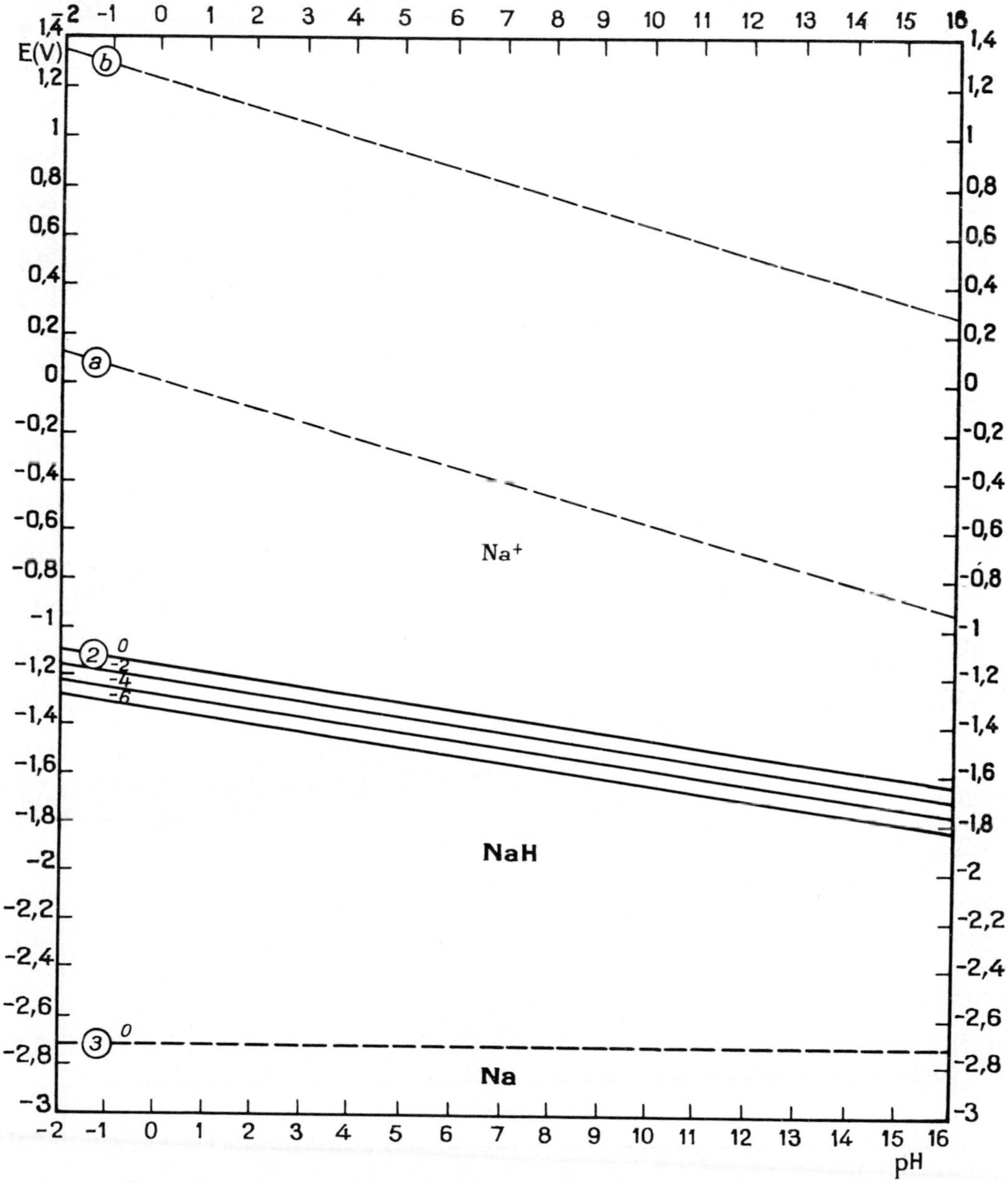

FIG. 2. Potential–pH equilibrium diagram for the system sodium–water, at 25°C.

3.3. STABILITY AND FORMATION OF THE HYDRIDES OF THE ALKALI METALS

On examination of Figs. 1–5 we notice at once that the alkali metal hydrides are much less unstable in the presence of water than are the alkali metals themselves. Although they react vigorously with water forming hydrogen, the alkali metal hydrides are perfectly stable in the absence of water and oxygen. Lithium hydride, which is a compound of two light and very easily oxidizable elements in a relatively stable form, is an extremely powerful fuel; its enthalpy of combustion to solid Li_2O and gaseous H_2O by the reaction $2LiH + O_2 = Li_2O + H_2O$, is 78 490 cal./mole, which corresponds to a calorific value of 9 900 000 cal./kg.

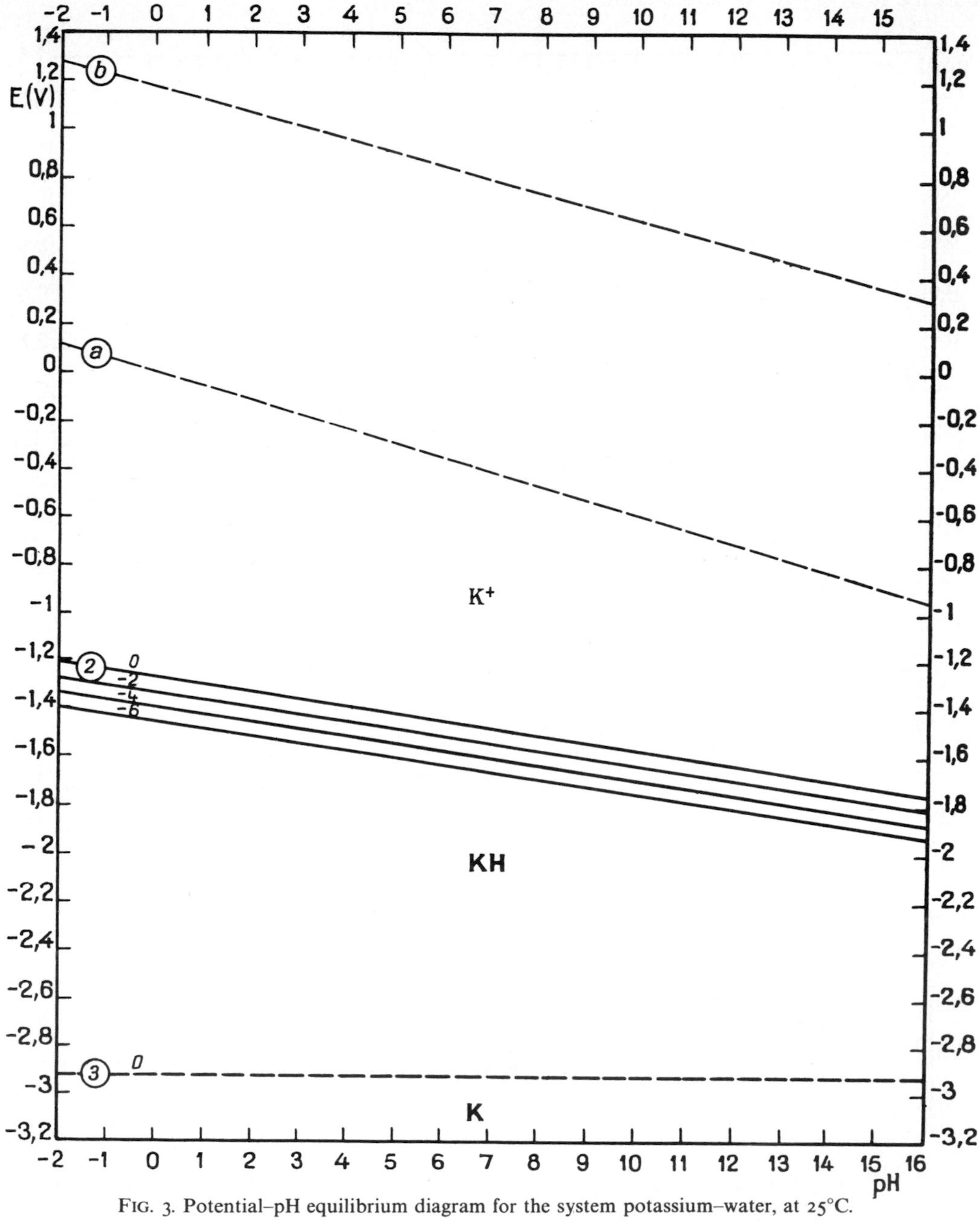

FIG. 3. Potential–pH equilibrium diagram for the system potassium–water, at 25°C.

3.4. STABILITY OF SODIUM AMALGAMS

The alkali metals are partially soluble in mercury with the formation of amalgams. Dissolution of the metals in mercury is accompanied by a reduction in free enthalpy. As this variation in enthalpy is not known with great certainty, we cannot accurately establish the equilibrium conditions relating to the oxidation of the metals dissolved in mercury to metal ions in aqueous solution.

However, M. Dodero, C. Desportes and R. Mayoud [2] have plotted, on a potential–pH diagram, a certain number of lines giving the equilibrium potential of sodium in amalgams of various concen-

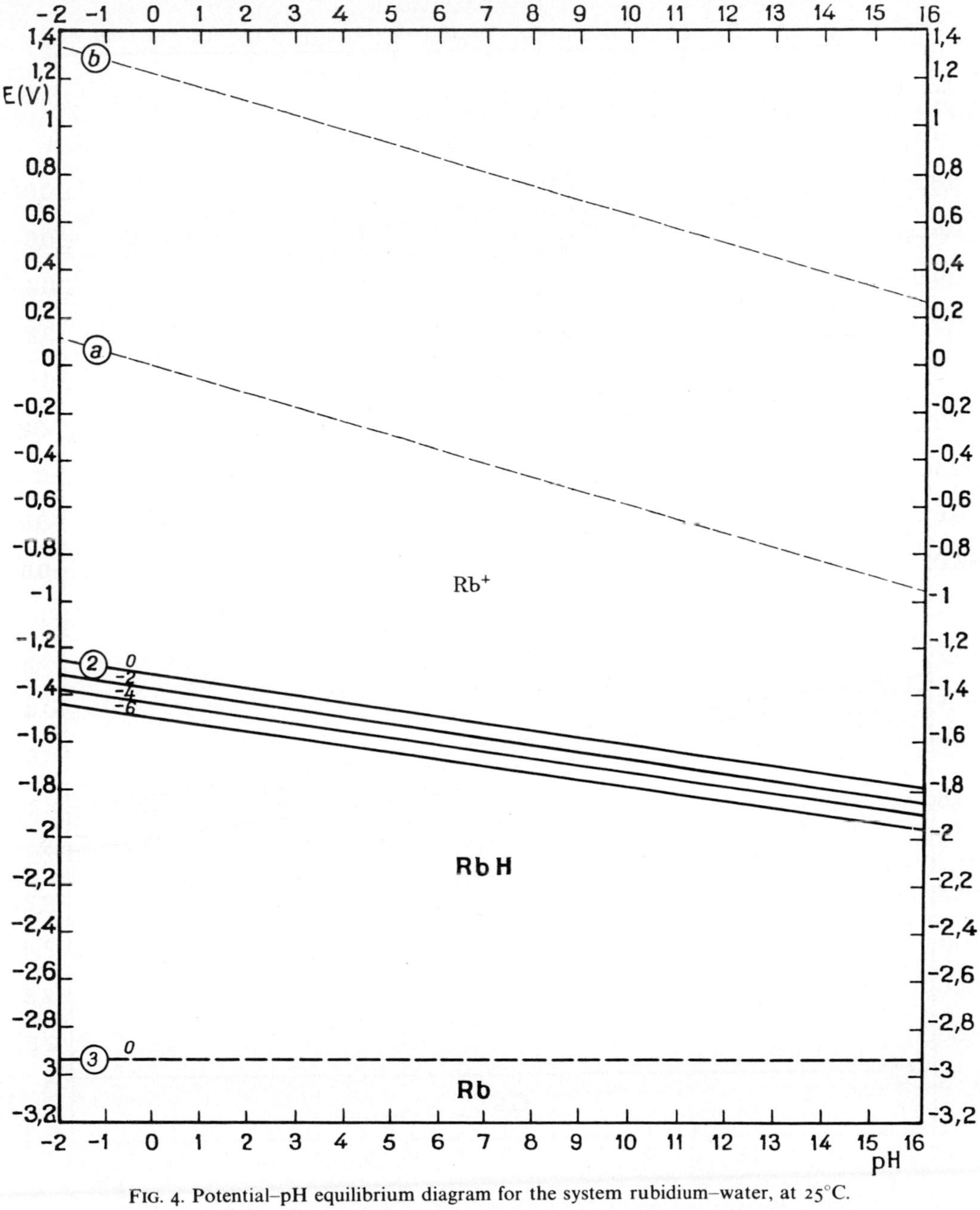

FIG. 4. Potential–pH equilibrium diagram for the system rubidium–water, at 25°C.

trations from 0·00001 to 0·74 per cent sodium (this last value corresponds to saturation with sodium). These lines, which refer to a solution of NaCl containing 1·84 g-ion Na/l (i.e. 108 g NaCl/l), were deduced from the equation

$$E_0 = -2{\cdot}71 + 0{\cdot}0591 \log a_{Na^+} - 0{\cdot}0591 \log a_{Na},$$

in which a_{Na^+} and a_{Na} represent respectively the activity of Na^+ ions in the solution and the activity of Na atoms in the mercury.

By plotting these lines on the equilibrium diagram in Fig. 2, we obtain Fig. 6 [after omitting line (3) concerning the metastable equilibrium of metallic sodium]. This shows, as a function of the pH,

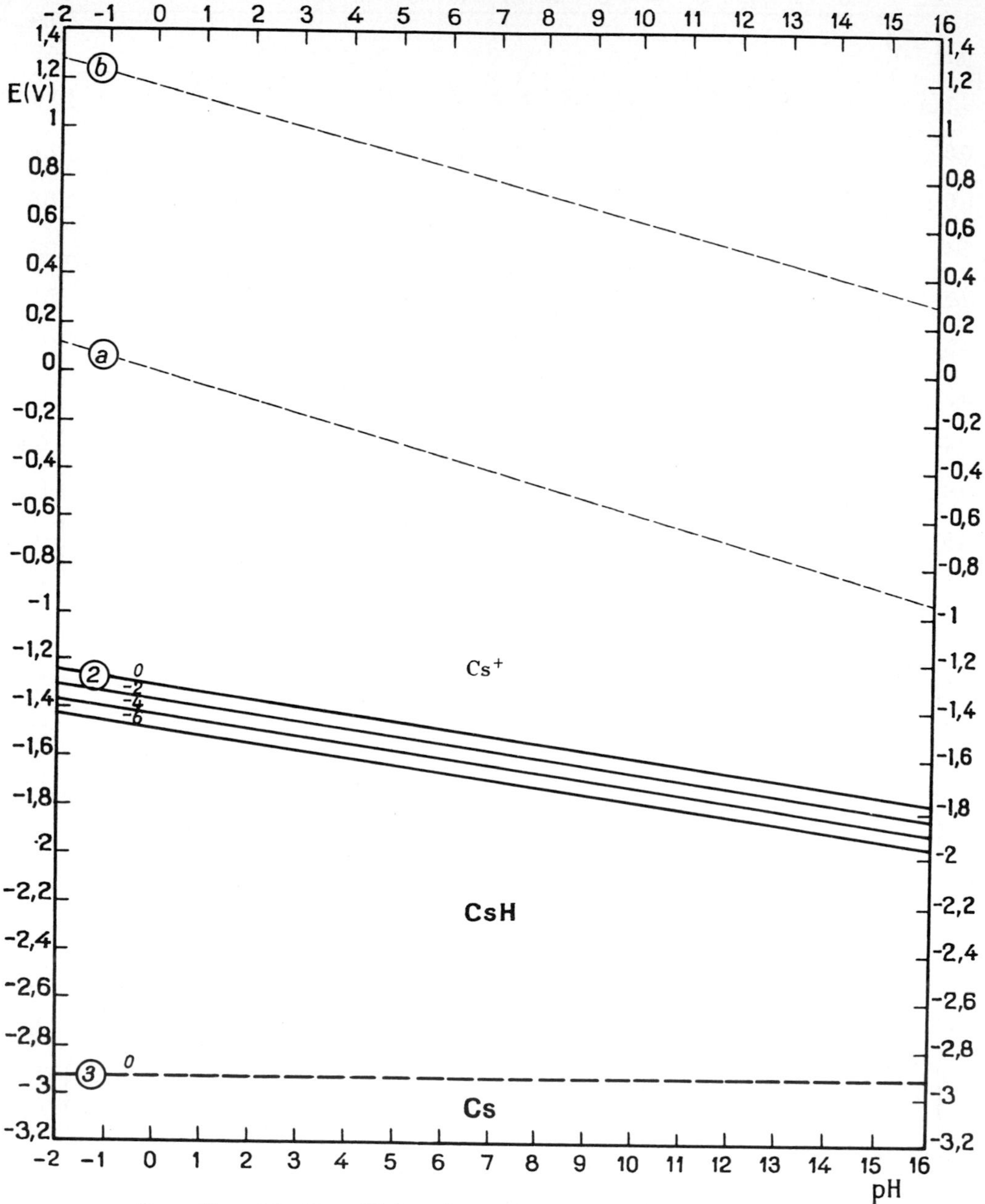

FIG. 5. Potential–pH equilibrium diagram for the system caesium–water, at 25°C.

the influence of the presence of mercury on the equilibrium potential of sodium in the presence of an aqueous solution of NaCl containing 1·84 g-ion Na^+/l.

From Fig. 6 it also follows that sodium amalgams are thermodynamically less stable than sodium hydride NaH, so that sodium hydride can theoretically be formed during the electrolysis of a sodium salt solution (e.g. NaCl), concurrently with the dissolution of sodium in the mercury and the formation of amalgams.

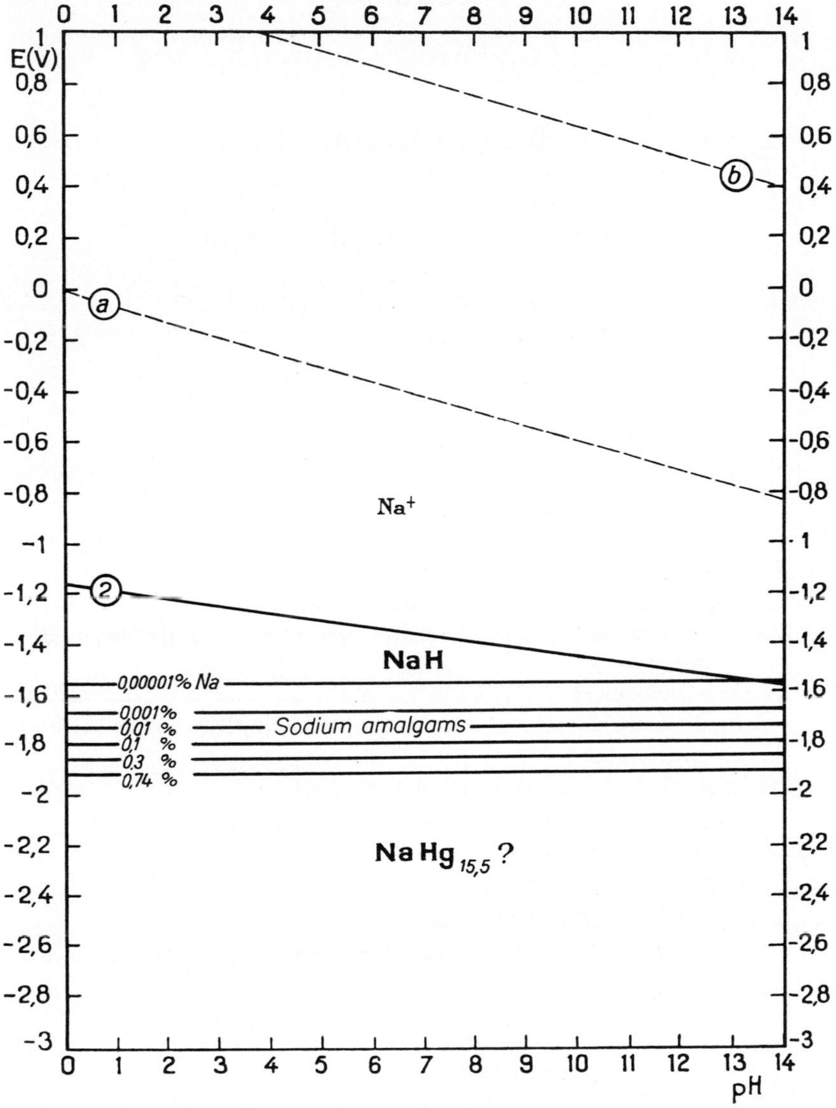

FIG. 6. Equilibrium potentials of sodium hydride and sodium amalgams (in the presence of solutions containing 108 g NaCl/l), after M. Dodero, C. Desportes and R. Mayoud [2].

4. BIBLIOGRAPHY

[1] G. CHARLOT, *L'analyse qualitative et les réactions en solution,* 4th ed., Masson, Paris, 1957.

[2] M. DODERO, C. DESPORTES and R. MAYOUD, *Sur le diagramme potentiel–pH et sur les courbes de polarisation lors de l'électrolyse de solutions de chlorure de sodium avec une cathode de mercure* (C. R. 8e Réunion du CITCE, Madrid, 1956, p. 294).

SECTION 4.1

BERYLLIUM (1)

J. VAN MUYLDER and M. POURBAIX

SUMMARY

1. *Substances considered and substance not considered.*

2. *Reactions and equilibrium formulae.*

2.1. Two dissolved substances.

2.1.1. Relative stability of the dissolved substances.

2.1.2. Limits of the domains of relative predominance of the dissolved substances.

2.2. Two solid substances.

Limits of the domains of relative stability of beryllium and its oxide and hydroxides.

2.3. One dissolved substance and one solid substance.

Solubility of beryllium and its oxide and hydroxides.

3. *Equilibrium diagram and its interpretation.*

3.1. Establishment of the diagram.

3.2. Stability and corrosion of beryllium.

3.3. Stability of the oxide and hydroxides of beryllium.

4. *Bibliography.*

---

(1) Rapport technique RT.71 of CEBELCOR (July 1958).

1. SUBSTANCES CONSIDERED AND SUBSTANCE NOT CONSIDERED

	Oxidation Number (Z)	Considered	Not considered	μ^0 (cal.)	Name, colour, crystalline system
Solid substances	−2	-	**BeH₂**	-	Beryllium hydride, white
	0	**Be**	-	0	Beryllium, steel grey, hex.
	+2	**BeO** hydr.	-	*a.* −140 650	"Precipitated" beryllium hydroxide, white (2)
	»	» hydr.	-	*b.* −139 510	β-Beryllium hydroxide, white, orthorh.
	»	» anh.	-	*c.* −139 000	Beryllium oxide, white, hex.
	»	» hydr.	-	*d.* −138 810	α-Beryllium hydroxide, white(2)
Dissolved substances	+2	Be^{++}	-	− 83 200	Beryllium ion, colourless
	»	Be_2O^{++}	-	−218 000	? , colourless
	»	$Be_2O_3^{--}$	-	−298 000	"Diberyllate" ion, colourless
	»	BeO_2^{--}	-	−153 300	Beryllate ion, colourless

2. REACTIONS AND EQUILIBRIUM FORMULAE

2.1. TWO DISSOLVED SUBSTANCES

2.1.1. *Relative stability of the dissolved substances*

$Z = +2$

1. $2Be^{++} + H_2O = Be_2O^{++} + 2H^+$ $\qquad \log\frac{(Be_2O^{++})}{(Be^{++})^2} = -6.67 + 2\,pH$

2. $2Be^{++} + 3H_2O = Be_2O_3^{--} + 6H^+$ $\qquad \log\frac{(Be_2O_3^{--})}{(Be^{++})^2} = -31.16 + 6\,pH$

3. $Be^{++} + 2H_2O = BeO_2^{--} + 4H^+$ $\qquad \log\frac{(BeO_2^{--})}{(Be^{++})} = -31.83 + 4\,pH$

4. $Be_2O^{++} + 2H_2O = Be_2O_3^{--} + 4H^+$ $\qquad \log\frac{(Be_2O_3^{--})}{(Be_2O^{++})} = -24.49 + 4\,pH$

5. $Be_2O_3^{--} + H_2O = 2BeO_2^{--} + 2H^+$ $\qquad \log\frac{(BeO_2^{--})^2}{(Be_2O_3^{--})} = -32.35 + 2\,pH$

2.1.2. *Limits of the domains of relative predominance of the dissolved substances*

$Z = +2$

1'. Be^{++} / Be_2O^{++} $\qquad pH = 3.34 - 0.500 \log C$

2'. $Be^{++} / Be_2O_3^{--}$ $\qquad pH = 5.19 - 0.167 \log C$

3'. Be^{++} / BeO_2^{--} $\qquad pH = 7.96$

4'. $Be_2O^{+} / Be_2O_3^{--}$ $\qquad pH = 6.12$

5'. $Be_2O_3^{--} / BeO_2^{--}$ $\qquad pH = 16.18 + 0.500 \log C$

2''. $Be^{++} / Be_2O_3^{--}$ and $BeO_{(s)}$ $\qquad$ *a.* $pH = 7.49$
b. $= 7.30$
c. $= 7.15$
d. $= 7.15$

2'''. $Be^{++} / Be_2O_3^{--}$ and $Be_{(s)}$ $\qquad E_0 = -0.935 - 0.1772\,pH$

5''. $Be_2O_3^{--} / BeO_2^{--}$ and $Be_{(s)}$ $\qquad E_0 = -1.873 - 0.0591\,pH$

---

(2) These values correspond to the following values for the free enthalpy of formation of $Be(OH)_2$:

a. precipitated $Be(OH)_2$ − 197 340 cal.
b. β-$Be(OH)_2$ − 196 200 cal.
d. α-$Be(OH)_2$ − 195 500 cal.

2.2. TWO SOLID SUBSTANCES

Limits of the domains of relative stability of beryllium and its oxide and hydroxides

$0 \rightarrow +2$

6. $\mathbf{Be} + H_2O = \mathbf{BeO} + 2H^+ + 2e^-$

a. E_0	$= -1.820 - 0.0591\ \mathrm{pH}$
b.	$= -1.796 - 0.0591\ \mathrm{pH}$
c.	$= -1.785 - 0.0591\ \mathrm{pH}$
d.	$= -1.781 - 0.0591\ \mathrm{pH}$

2.3. ONE DISSOLVED SUBSTANCE AND ONE SOLID SUBSTANCE(3)

Solubility of beryllium and its oxides and hydroxides

a. In gram-ions per litre

$Z = +2$

7. $Be^{++} + H_2O = \mathbf{BeO} + 2H^+$

a. $\log(Be^{++})$	$= 0.91 - 2\ \mathrm{pH}$
b.	$= 1.75 - 2\ \mathrm{pH}$
c.	$= 1.97 - 2\ \mathrm{pH}$
d.	$= 2.26 - 2\ \mathrm{pH}$

8. $2\,\mathbf{BeO} + H_2O = Be_2O_3^{--} + 2H^+$

a. $\log(Be_2O_3^{--})$	$= -29.35 + 2\ \mathrm{pH}$
b.	$= -27.67 + 2\ \mathrm{pH}$
c.	$= -26.92 + 2\ \mathrm{pH}$
d.	$= -26.64 + 2\ \mathrm{pH}$

$0 \rightarrow +2$

9. $\mathbf{Be} = Be^{++} + 2e^-$ $\quad E_0 = -1.847 + 0.0295 \log(Be^{++})$

10. $2\,\mathbf{Be} + 3H_2O = Be_2O_3^{--} + 6H^+ + 4e^-$ $\quad E_0 = -1.387 - 0.0886\ \mathrm{pH} + 0.0148 \log(Be_2O_3^{--})$

11. $\mathbf{Be} + 2H_2O = BeO_2^{--} + 4H^+ + 2e^-$ $\quad E_0 = -0.909 - 0.1182\ \mathrm{pH} + 0.0295 \log(BeO_2^{--})$

b. In gram-atoms of beryllium per litre

$Z = +2$

7'. $Be^{++}\ /\mathbf{BeO}$

a. $\log C$	$= 0.91 - 2\ \mathrm{pH}$
b.	$= 1.75 - 2\ \mathrm{pH}$
c.	$= 1.97 - 2\ \mathrm{pH}$
d.	$= 2.26 - 2\ \mathrm{pH}$

8'. $Be_2O_3^{--}\ /\mathbf{BeO}$

a. $\log C$	$= -29.05 + 2\ \mathrm{pH}$
b.	$= -27.37 + 2\ \mathrm{pH}$
c.	$= -26.62 + 2\ \mathrm{pH}$
d.	$= -26.34 + 2\ \mathrm{pH}$

$0 \rightarrow +2$

9'. $Be^{++}\ /\mathbf{Be}$ $\quad E_0 = -1.847 + 0.0295 \log C$

10'. $Be_2O_3^{--}\ /\mathbf{Be}$ $\quad E_0 = -1.391 - 0.0886\ \mathrm{pH} + 0.0148 \log C$

11'. $BeO_2^{--}\ /\mathbf{Be}$ $\quad E_0 = -0.909 - 0.1182\ \mathrm{pH} + 0.0295 \log C$

3. EQUILIBRIUM DIAGRAM AND ITS INTERPRETATION

3.1. ESTABLISHMENT OF THE DIAGRAM

Using equations (1')–(11') and (2''), (2''') and (5'') we have represented: *in Fig.* 1 the equilibrium diagram for the system beryllium–water, at 25°C, taking into account the crystalline hydroxide of variety β; *in Fig.* 2 the theoretical conditions of corrosion, immunity and passivation of beryllium in the case

(3) The letters *a*, *b*, *c* and *d* refer to the oxide and the three types of hydroxide of beryllium quoted in paragraph 1.

of passivation by a film of β-Be(OH)$_2$; and *in Fig.* 3 the influence of pH on the solubility of the oxide and the three types of hydroxide considered in paragraph 1.

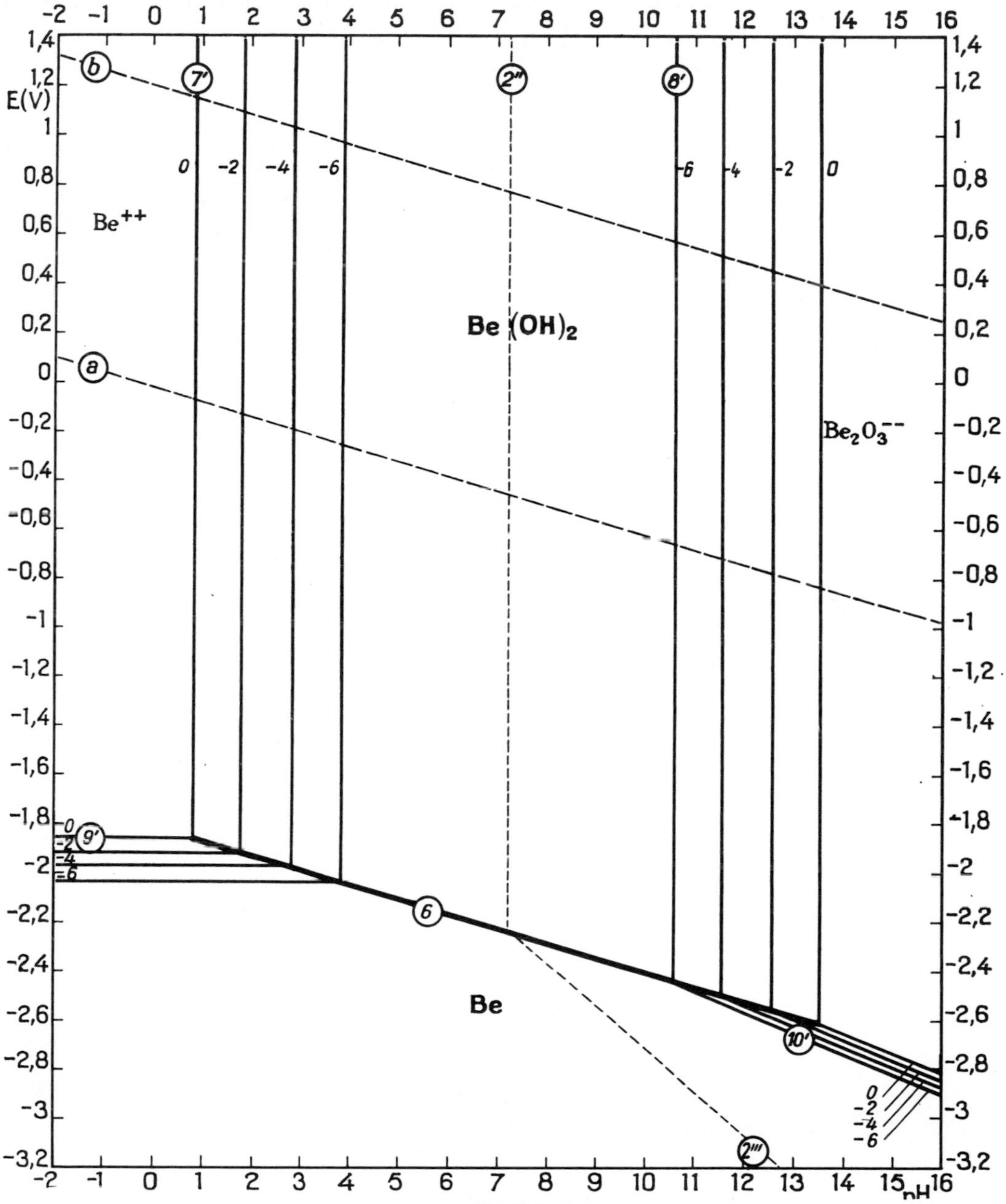

FIG. 1. Potential–pH equilibrium diagram for the system beryllium–water, at 25°C. [Diagram established considering β–Be(OH)$_2$].

These diagrams are valid only in the absence of substances with which beryllium can form soluble complexes (citric, tartaric, oxalic and fluorine complexes, the complexons, and pyro-, meta- and polyphosphoric complexes) or insoluble compounds (oxinate, beryllium ammonium phosphate, etc.) [1].

3.2. STABILITY AND CORROSION OF BERYLLIUM

As the whole of its domain of stability lies well below that of water, beryllium is theoretically a very base metal; it is clearly a reducing agent, and very unstable in the presence of water and aqueous

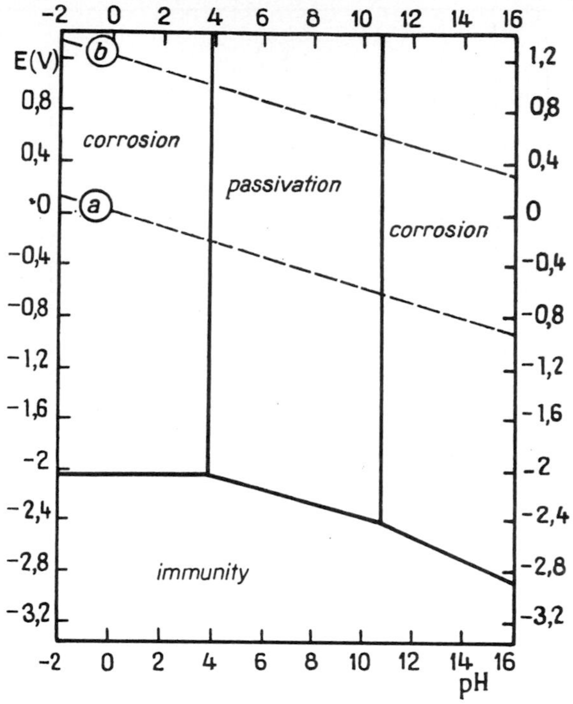

FIG. 2. Theoretical conditions of corrosion, immunity and passivation of beryllium, at 25°C [in the case of passivation by the hydroxide β-Be(OH)$_2$].

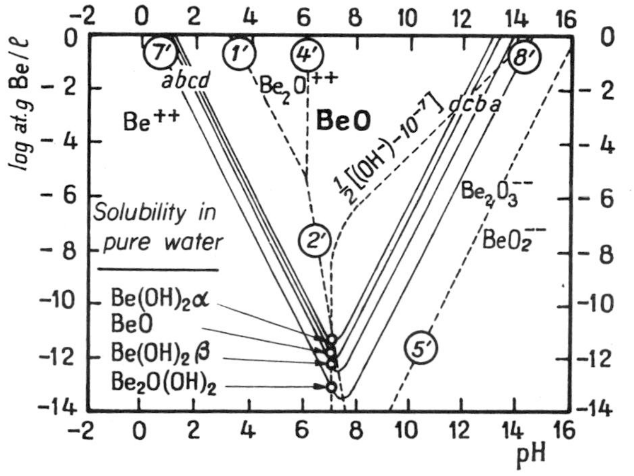

FIG. 3. Influence of pH on the solubility of BeO and its hydrates, at 25°C (approximate representation).

solutions. In the presence of acid solutions it vigorously decomposes water with the evolution of hydrogen, dissolving as beryllium ions Be^{++}; in the presence of strongly alkaline solutions, it dissolves once again with the evolution of hydrogen, but this time gives rise to diberyllate ions $Be_2O_3^{--}$ and beryllate ions BeO_2^{--}.

In the presence of water or non-complexing solutions whose pH is about 4 to 6, beryllium can theoretically become covered with a layer of oxide or hydroxide.

Figure 2, which is deduced from Fig. 1, represents the theoretical conditions of corrosion, immunity and passivation of beryllium in the presence of solutions free from complexing substances and insoluble salts.

In actual fact, the corrosion resistance of beryllium is determined by the behaviour of the layer of oxide (or hydroxide) with which it is almost invariably covered. Water has no action, even when the red-hot metal is treated with boiling water or steam, which must be due to the protective action of a layer of oxide (or hydroxide), for a freshly filed piece of metal maintained for a few hours in boiling water becomes covered with bubbles of gas, and tarnishes with increase of weight (Pascal [2]).

Dilute and concentrated solutions of hydrochloric acid and dilute solutions of sulphuric acid attack beryllium with the evolution of hydrogen; weak organic acids such as acetic, citric and tartaric acids attack beryllium initially, with the evolution of hydrogen, until a protective layer of $Be(OH)_2$ is formed (Pascal [2]).

Beryllium is a very powerful reducing agent, reducing warm concentrated sulphuric acid to SO_2, or even to S or H_2S; with nitric acid it gives NO and NH_3.

In agreement with Figs. 1 and 2, beryllium is fairly resistant to slightly alkaline solutions, of pH below about 11; but it does not generally resist the action of very alkaline solutions; a 50 per cent solution of potassium hydroxide (about $10^{1.15}$ M) reacts in the cold, but heating is necessary for evolution of hydrogen to be noticed with a 10 per cent solution (about $10^{0.18}$ M). Beryllium is clearly more resistant to alkalis than aluminium. It follows from Fig. 1 that, as is the case with all very base metals, direct determination of the equilibrium potential of the reaction $Be = Be^{++} + 2e$ using an isolated beryllium electrode dipping into an aqueous solution of its salts is not possible, as the metal corrodes with the evolution of hydrogen.

The cathodic protection of beryllium is probably impossible, because of the very low protection potential (about -2 V)*. For the same reason, its electrolytic deposition cannot be brought about in aqueous solutions; the classical process for the electrolytic separation of beryllium uses igneous electrolysis (baths of chlorides and fluorides; graphite anodes and nickel cathodes).

3.3. STABILITY OF THE OXIDE AND HYDROXIDES OF BERYLLIUM

Beryllium oxide, or glucine, BeO is a substance whose chemical properties depend to a large extent on the temperature reached during its preparation. As a general rule it becomes less reactive the longer it is calcined and the higher the temperature. If it is heated to a high temperature, glucine becomes practically insoluble in acids and bases (in the same way as Al_2O_3 and MgO).

If an alkali is added to an acid solution of a beryllium salt, a precipitate of gelatinous hydroxide is obtained, which, after thorough drying, is shown to be amorphous on X-ray examination.

Pascal [2] attributes to it the formula $Be(OH)_2 . nH_2O$, for simplicity, although this formula probably does not correspond to its constitution, particularly when the precipitate is fresh. On the other hand, Latimer [3] represents freshly precipitated beryllium hydroxide by the formula $Be_2O_3H_2$[or $Be_2O(OH)_2$].

The gelatinous (amorphous) hydroxide can be dissolved very easily in the common acids, even when they are dilute.

Its dissolution in caustic alkalis is more difficult to bring about and depends on the alkali concentration; moreover, the solubility measurements are not reproducible, as the medium favours the conversion of the amorphous hydroxide into various crystalline varieties, whose solubilities are very much lower than the solubility of the amorphous compound.

* As far as cathodic protection by putting the metal into a state of immunity is concerned. Recent work has shown that pitting of passivable metals due to chlorides may sometimes be avoided by a cathodic treatment bringing the metal into a state of perfect passivation (Cebelcor's Technical Reports RT. 103 and 120) (1962).

The amorphous hydroxide is not a stable product; in air or cold water it crystallizes slowly, passing through a succession of badly defined stages (Pascal [2]). Two crystalline varieties of the chemical species $Be(OH)_2$ exist; the so-called α-variety which is always metastable and the β-variety which is stable.

The conversion of amorphous hydroxide into crystalline α-hydroxide can be speeded up by boiling an aqueous suspension of amorphous hydroxide; if it is kept in the presence of a concentrated solution of NaOH and KOH for a sufficiently long time, the α-variety changes completely into the β-variety.

The successive crystalline varieties of beryllium hydroxide formed during this "ageing" are characterized by an increasing stability, with an accompanying variation in all their properties, notably their solubility in acids, bases and pure water. In Fig. 3 we have drawn a series of curves showing the influence of pH on the solubility of the oxide and the three hydroxides of beryllium in the four dissolved forms Be^{++}, Be_2O^{++}, $Be_2O_3^{--}$ and BeO_2^{--}; these curves are derived from equations (1′), (2′), (4′), (5′), (7′) and (8′) established in paragraph 2.

According to this figure, the most stable form of the hydroxide should be the amorphous one, but this is unacceptable in view of its experimentally established instability. The disagreement probably arises from an inaccuracy in the value of the free enthalpy of formation given by Latimer for the amorphous hydroxide [3]. Experimental data relating to the minimum solubility of the oxide and hydroxides of beryllium are practically non-existent; the literature gives only a few values, concerning the solubility of the amorphous hydroxide in pure water; these values lie between $10^{-6.85}$ and $10^{-4.10}$ moles/l (Pascal [2]), and are therefore very noticeably greater than those given by Fig. 3 ($10^{-13.6}$ to $10^{-11.4}$); an investigation into the reason for this disagreement would be valuable.

We point out, however, that the portion of Fig. 3 included between lines (7′) and (8′) (which represent the solubility of the oxide and hydroxides of beryllium) corresponds to unstable solutions, supersaturated with $Be(OH)_2$; the lines (1′) and (4′) drawn in this figure correspond therefore to non-equilibrium states; at the equilibrium no domain of predominance of the ion Be_2O^{++} exists.

4. BIBLIOGRAPHY

[1] G. CHARLOT, *L'analyse qualitative et les réactions en solution*, 4th ed., Masson, Paris, 1957.
[2] P. PASCAL, *Nouveau Traité de chimie minérale*, Vol. IV (*Glucinium*), Masson, Paris, 1958.
[3] W. M. LATIMER, *Oxidation Potentials*, Prentice-Hall, New York, 1952.

SECTION 4.2

MAGNESIUM [1]

J. Van Muylder and M. Pourbaix

SUMMARY

1. *Substances considered and substances not considered.*

2. *Reactions and equilibrium formulae.*

   2.1. Two solid substances.
   Limit of the domains of relative stability of magnesium and magnesium oxide.

   2.2. One solid substance and one dissolved substance.
   Solubility of magnesium and magnesium oxide.

3. *Equilibrium diagram and its interpretation.*

   3.1. Establishment of the diagram.

   3.2. Stability and corrosion of magnesium.

   3.3. Stability of the magnesium oxides.

   3.4. Stability of magnesium peroxide.

   3.5. Reactive anodes of magnesium.

4. *Bibliography.*

[1] This discussion is an adapted and abridged version of the Rapport technique RT.39 of CEBELCOR (March 1956) [1].

1. SUBSTANCES CONSIDERED AND SUBSTANCES NOT CONSIDERED

	Oxidation number (Z)	Considered	Not considered	μ^0 (cal.)	Name, colour, crystalline system
Solid substances	−2	-	**MgH_2**	-	Magnesium hydride, grey
	0	**Mg**	-	0	Magnesium, silvery white, hex.
	+1	-	**Mg_2O**	-	Magnesium sub-oxide, grey–black
	+2	**MgO** hydr.	-	*a*. −142 580	Magnesium hydroxide, $Mg(OH)_2$, white, rhomb.[2]
	»	» anh.	-	*b*. −136 130	Magnesium oxide, white, cub.
	+4	-	**MgO_2**	-	Magnesium peroxide
Dissolved substances	+1	-	Mg^+	-	Magnesous ion, colourless
	+2	Mg^{++}	-	−108 990	Magnesic ion, colourless

2. REACTIONS AND EQUILIBRIUM FORMULAE(3)

2.1. TWO SOLID SUBSTANCES

Limits of the domains of relative stability of magnesium and magnesium oxide

$0 \to +2$

1. $\mathbf{Mg} + H_2O = \mathbf{MgO} + 2H^+ + 2e^-$ $\quad$ *a*. $E_0 = -1.862 - 0.0591\ pH$
   b. $\quad = -1.722 - 0.0591\ pH$

2.2. ONE SOLID SUBSTANCE AND ONE DISSOLVED SUBSTANCE

Solubility of magnesium and magnesium oxide

$Z = +2$

2. $Mg^{++} + H_2O = \mathbf{MgO} + 2H^+$ $\quad$ *a*. $\log(Mg^{++}) = 16.95 - 2\ pH$
   b. $\quad = 21.68 - 2\ pH$

$0 \to +2$

3. $\mathbf{Mg} = Mg^{++} + 2e^-$ $\quad$ $E_0 = -2.363 + 0.0295 \log(Mg^{++})$

3. EQUILIBRIUM DIAGRAM AND ITS INTERPRETATION

3.1. ESTABLISHMENT OF THE DIAGRAM

Using equations (1)–(3) we have constructed Figs. 1 and 2. In Fig. 1 we have represented the potential–pH equilibrium diagram for the system magnesium–water, at 25°C, and in Fig. 2 the influence of pH on the solubility of the oxide and hydroxide of magnesium. These diagrams are valid only in the absence of substances with which magnesium can form soluble complexes (tartrate, metaphosphate, etc.) or insoluble salts (oxalate, carbonate, phosphate, fluoride, etc.).

(2) This value for μ^0_{MgO} corresponds to $\mu^0_{Mg(OH)_2} = -142\,580 - 56\,690 = -199\,270$ cal.

(3) For the reactions involving MgO, the letter *a* refers to $Mg(OH)_2$, whose free enthalpy of formation is −199 270 cal.; the letter *b* refers to anhydrous MgO, whose free enthalpy of formation is −136 130 cal.

3.2. STABILITY AND CORROSION OF MAGNESIUM

As is shown by Fig. 1, the whole of the domain of stability of magnesium is well below that of water; magnesium is therefore a very base metal and a powerful reducing agent. At all pH's it has a very great affinity to react with water, which it reduces with the evolution of hydrogen, dissolving

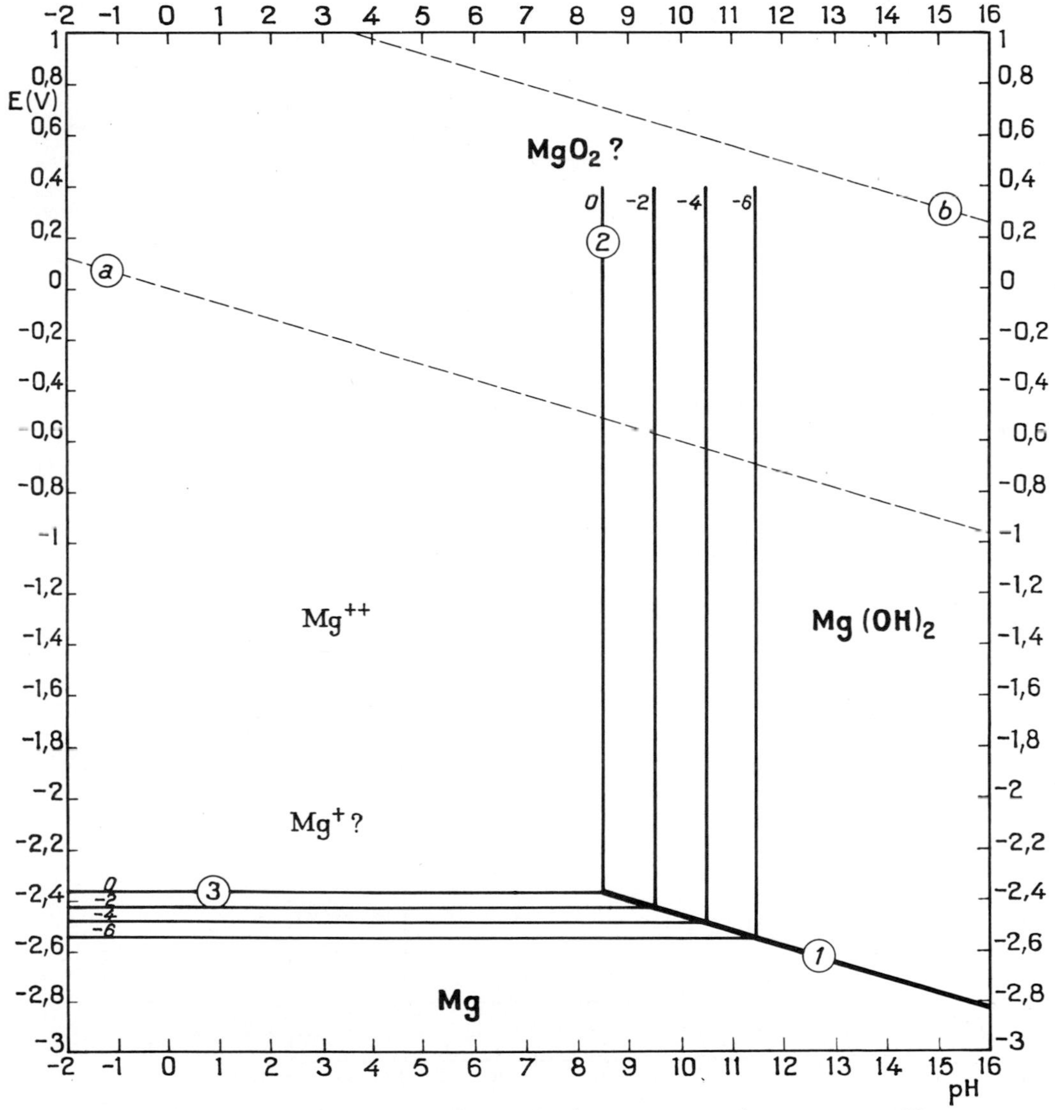

FIG. 1. Potential–pH equilibrium diagram for the system magnesium–water, at 25°C.

as Mg^+ and Mg^{++} ions; at pH's above about 8·5 and up to 11·5 it can cover itself with more or less protective oxide or hydroxide which checks the dissolution reaction.

On account of the low value of the equilibrium potential of the reaction $Mg = Mg^{++} + 2e^-$, it is impossible to prepare metallic magnesium by the electrolysis of its aqueous solutions: this would lead to the evolution of hydrogen at the cathode without the formation of magnesium.

Figure 3, which is deduced from the equilibrium diagram 1, represents the theoretical conditions of corrosion, passivation and immunity of magnesium. This figure shows that, in the presence of sufficiently alkaline solutions, magnesium can cover itself with a layer of $Mg(OH)_2$, which can protect the metal from corrosion; it will generally be corroded by acid, neutral and slightly alkaline solutions

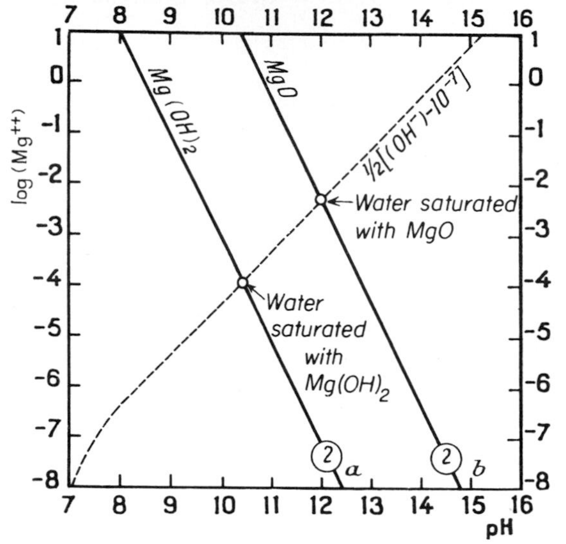

FIG. 2. Characteristics of solutions of MgO and $Mg(OH)_2$ in pure water.

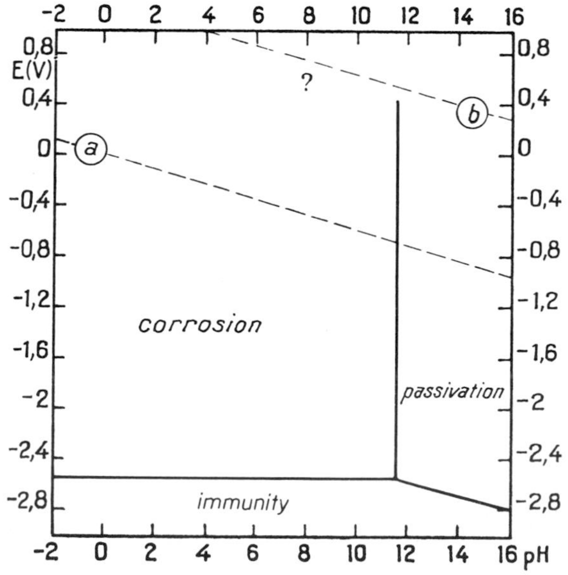

FIG. 3. Theoretical domains of corrosion, immunity and passivation of magnesium, at 25°C.

with a speed which decreases as the pH increases. The corrosion resistance of magnesium (and also that of many of its alloys) is closely connected with the formation of a protective surface film. The conditions for the formation of this film depend on the nature of the solution and on the nature of the impurities of the metal (and possibly on the nature of the elements alloyed). But when the pH of the solution exceeds that which corresponds to the appearance of the hydroxide $Mg(OH)_2$, the effect of the nature of the solution and the impurities of the metal is obliterated by the predominance of the formation of a layer of magnesium hydroxide.

3.3. STABILITY OF THE MAGNESIUM OXIDES

Figure 1 shows that the oxidation of magnesium in an alkaline solution can give rise to the formation of the oxide MgO and the hydroxide $Mg(OH)_2$, neither of which possesses any amphoteric character. Since the free enthalpy of formation of $Mg(OH)_2$ at 25°C (−142 580 cal./g-mol MgO) is below the free enthalpy of formation of anhydrous MgO (−136 130 cal.), $Mg(OH)_2$ is thermodynamically more stable than MgO in the presence of water; the oxide can therefore theoretically be hydrated according to the reaction $MgO + H_2O \rightarrow Mg(OH)_2$ whose affinity is 142 580 − 136 130 = +6 450 cal. The hydration of MgO using a water-bath is, in fact, one of the methods of preparation of the hydroxide $Mg(OH)_2$; this hydration is rapid when light magnesia is used, but is very slow for dense varieties of magnesia prepared by high temperature calcination, which are hardly attacked by water [2].

In Fig. 2 we have represented the influence of pH on the solubility of MgO and $Mg(OH)_2$. It can be seen from this figure that the "water of magnesia" obtained by saturating pure water with magnesium hydroxide has the following characteristics, at 25°C:

$$pH = 10{\cdot}45, \quad \log(Mg^{++}) = -3{\cdot}95, \quad \text{i.e. } 6{\cdot}52 \text{ mg } Mg(OH)_2/l, \quad \text{or } 1{\cdot}12 \text{ French degrees.}$$

This value for the solubility of $Mg(OH)_2$ is in very good agreement with the experimental values in *Gmelins Handbuch der anorganischen Chemie* [3] and the works of A. Seidell ([4], [5]); for some temperatures around 25°C, $\log(Mg^{++})$ lies between −3·15 and −3·95. In this respect it would be as well to point out that the solubility of $Mg(OH)_2$ in water depends on various factors which are difficult to control, and which are sufficient to explain the observed differences:

- ageing of the precipitate;
- method of preparation of the oxide MgO [when the hydroxide $Mg(OH)_2$ results from the hydration of the oxide MgO];
- presence of foreign substances.

In Gjalbaek's opinion, quoted by A. Seidell [4], magnesium hydroxide can exist in two varieties; the one which is more readily soluble is denoted "labile", and the one which is not so readily soluble is denoted "stable".

The labile form is obtained by precipitation from a solution of a magnesium salt by a base, by hydration of the oxide MgO, or by the decomposition of water by magnesium. The stable form is obtained by the ageing of the labile form in the presence of a solution containing magnesium; the conversion is rapid when the Mg^{++} concentration is large, it is slow when (Mg^{++}) is small. We give below the solubility values, according to Gjalbaek, of the hydroxide $Mg(OH)_2$ in water at 18°C, for each of these two forms:

Method	Stable form	Labile form
Direct determination	$10^{-3{\cdot}66}$ moles/l	$10^{-3{\cdot}19}$ moles/l
Conductivity	$10^{-3{\cdot}87}$ moles/l	$10^{-3{\cdot}34}$ moles/l
Electrometry	$10^{-3{\cdot}80}$ moles/l	$10^{-3{\cdot}15}$ moles/l

3.4. STABILITY OF MAGNESIUM PEROXIDE

Magnesium peroxide has not yet been prepared in the pure state. Compounds denoted by the name "magnesium peroxide" in chemical literature contain very variable percentages of active oxygen; they should be considered either as mixtures of MgO and MgO_2, or as definite compounds containing or not containing molecules of water of hydration, or even as magnesium hydroperoxide $Mg(OH)_4$.

Magnesium peroxide can be obtained by the action of hydrogen peroxide on magnesium, on the oxide MgO or on the hydroxide $Mg(OH)_2$.

We have not taken into account the existence of magnesium peroxide in establishing the equilibrium diagram for lack of thermodynamic data about it, but we have marked it approximately on Fig. 1 as a guide.

3.5. REACTIVE ANODES OF MAGNESIUM

On account of its very electronegative nature, magnesium is a metal which readily lends itself to use as a reactive anode for the sacrificial protection of iron or other metals.

The coupling of magnesium with a metal more noble than itself generally enables the potential of this metal to be reduced to a value below the equilibrium potential of its corrosion reaction. The metal is thus rendered completely immune to corrosion by the surrounding medium.

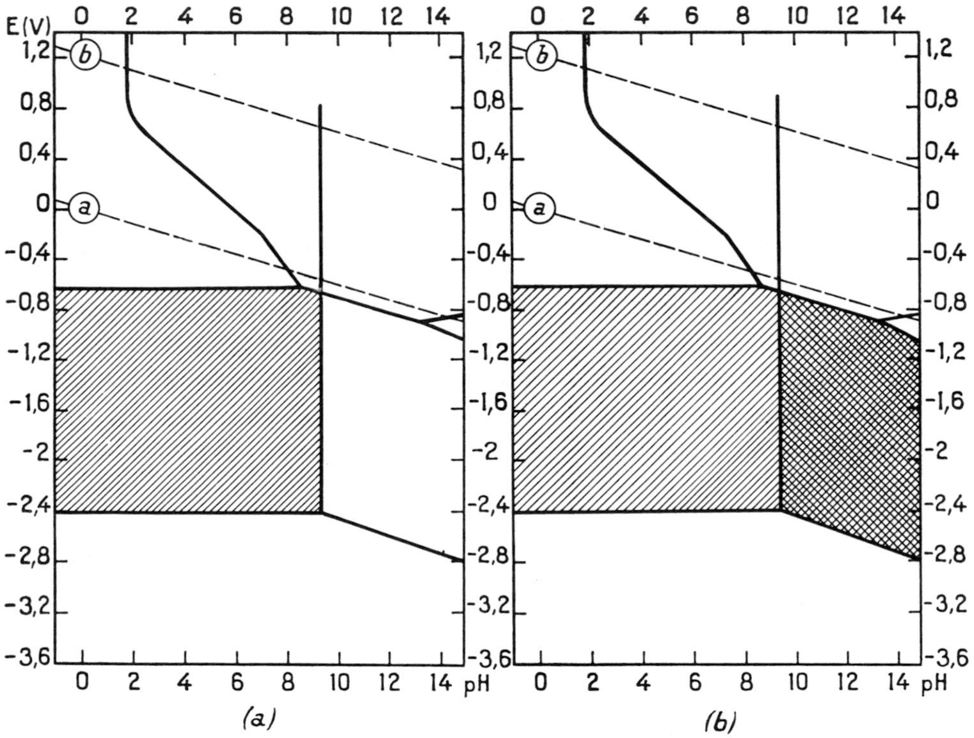

FIG. 4. Theoretical conditions for the cathodic protection of iron by magnesium (in the case of magnesium in contact with a solution containing 0·01 g-ion Mg/l).
a. Case of protective magnesium hydroxide.
b. Case of non-protective magnesium hydroxide.

The evolution of hydrogen on such anodes is quite important. Because of it, the current yield rarely exceeds 30 to 50 per cent of the theoretical yield (a yield of 100 per cent would correspond to the provision of 2 204 Ah per kilogram of magnesium dissolved).

The current yield of the reactive magnesium anodes can be improved by surrounding them with a special chemical covering (usually a mixture of gypsum and clay) and by alloying the magnesium with aluminium, zinc and manganese (the alloy Mg 6 per cent, Al 3 per cent, Zn 0·2 per cent, Mn, is particularly effective in this respect).

The result of all these precautions is to bring the practical current yield of the reactive magnesium-based anodes up to about 55–65 per cent of the theoretical yield. In Fig. 4 we have represented the theoretical conditions for the cathodic protection of iron by means of magnesium, respectively in the cases of protective magnesium hydroxide (Fig. 4a) and non-protective magnesium hydroxide (Fig. 4b).

The "backfills" employed industrially for the cathodic protection by magnesium of structures buried in the ground have the primary object of promoting the formation of non-protective hydroxide; the conditions of effectiveness of anodes covered in this way are represented by the chequered zone in Fig. 4.

4. BIBLIOGRAPHY

[1] J. Van Muylder and M. Pourbaix, *Comportement électrochimique du magnésium. Diagrammes d'équilibres tension–pH des systèmes* Mg–H_2O, Mg–CO_2–H_2O *et* Mg–H_3PO_4–H_2O, *à* 25°C (Rapport technique RT.39 of CEBELCOR, March 1956).

[2] P. Pascal, *Traité de Chimie minérale*, Vol. VII, Masson, Paris.

[3] *Gmelins Handbuch der anorganischen Chemie (Magnesium)*, Teil B. IX, Verlag Chemie G.m.b.H., 1939.

[4] A. Seidell, *Solubilities of Inorganic and Metal Organic Compounds*, D. Van Nostrand, New York, 1940.

[5] A. Seidell and W. Linke, *Solubilities of Inorganic and Organic Compounds*, Supplement to the 3rd ed., D. Van Nostrand, New York, 1951.

SECTIONS 4.3, 4.4 AND 4.5

CALCIUM, STRONTIUM, BARIUM(1)

J. VAN MUYLDER and M. POURBAIX

SUMMARY

1. *Substances considered.*

2. *Reactions and equilibrium formulae.*

   2.1. Two solid substances.
   Limits of the domains of relative stability of the solid substances.

   2.2. One solid substance and one dissolved substance.
   Solubility of the solid substances.

3. *Equilibrium diagrams and their interpretation.*

   3.1. Stability of the alkaline earth metals.

   3.2. Stability of the oxides and hydroxides of the alkaline earth metals.

   3.3. Stability of the peroxides of the alkaline earth metals.

   3.4. Stability of the hydrides of the alkaline earth metals.

4. *Bibliography.*

(1) Rapport technique RT.72 of CEBELCOR (July 1958).

1. SUBSTANCES CONSIDERED

	Oxidation number (Z)	Considered		μ^0 (cal.)	Name, colour, crystalline system
CALCIUM					
Solid substances	−2	**CaH$_2$**		−35 800	Calcium hydride, grey–white, orthorh.
	0	**Ca**		0	Calcium, silvery white, cub.
	+2	**CaO** hydr.	a.	−157 640	Hydrated calcium oxide $Ca(OH)_2$ or hydroxide, white, rhomb.
	»	» anh.	b.	−144 400	Anhydrous calcium oxide CaO, white, cub.
	+4	**CaO$_2$**		−143 000	Calcium peroxide, white
Dissolved substance	+2	Ca^{++}		−132 180	Divalent calcium ion, colourless
STRONTIUM					
Solid substances	−2	**SrH$_2$**		−33 100	Strontium hydride, grey–white, orthorh.
	0	**Sr**		0	Strontium, silvery white, cub.
	+2	**SrO** hydr.	a.	−151 110	Hydrated strontium oxide $Sr(OH)_2$ or hydroxide, white(2)
	»	» anh.	b.	−133 800	Anhydrous strontium oxide SrO, white, cub.
	+4	**SrO$_2$**		−139 000	Strontium peroxide, white
Dissolved substance	+2	Sr^{++}		−133 200	Divalent strontium ion, colourless
BARIUM					
Solid substances	−2	**BaH$_2$**		−31 600	Barium hydride, grey–white, orthorh.
	0	**Ba**		0	Barium, silvery white, cub.
	+2	**BaO** hydr.	a.	−156 590	Hydrated barium oxide $Ba(OH)_2 . 8H_2O$ or hydroxide, white, monocl.(2)
	»	» anh.	b.	−126 300	Anhydrous barium oxide BaO, white, cub.
	+4	**BaO$_2$** hydr.	c.	−138 310	Hydrated barium peroxide $BaO_2 . H_2O$, white, quad.(2)
	»	» anh.	d.	−135 800	Anhydrous barium peroxide BaO_2, white
Dissolved substance	+2	Ba^{++}		−134 000	Divalent barium ion, colourless

2. REACTIONS AND EQUILIBRIUM FORMULAE

Calcium

2.1. TWO SOLID SUBSTANCES

Limits of the domains of relative stability of the solid substances

$-2 \rightarrow 0$

1. $$CaH_2 = Ca + 2H^+ + 2e^- \qquad E_0 = 0.776 - 0.0591\,pH$$

$-2 \rightarrow +2$

2. $$CaH_2 + H_2O = CaO + 4H^+ + 4e^- \qquad a.\ E_0 = -0.706 - 0.0591\,pH$$
$$b.\ \quad = -0.563 - 0.0591\,pH$$

(2) These values correspond to the following values for the free enthalpies of formation of the hydroxides:

$\mu^0_{Ca(OH)_2} = -214\,330$ cal. $\quad \mu^0_{Ba(OH)_2 \cdot 8H_2O} = -666\,800$ cal.

$\mu^0_{Sr(OH)_2} = -207\,800$ cal. $\quad \mu^0_{BaO_2 \cdot H_2O} = -195\,000$ cal.

$0 \rightarrow +2$

3. **Ca** $+ H_2O$ $=$ **CaO** $+ 2H^+ + 2e^-$ a. $E_0 = -2.189 - 0.0591\,pH$
b. $= -1.902 - 0.0591\,pH$

$+2 \rightarrow +4$

4. **CaO** $+ H_2O$ $=$ **CaO₂** $+ 2H^+ + 2e^-$ a. $E_0 = 1.547 - 0.0591\,pH$
b. $= 1.260 - 0.0591\,pH$

2.2. ONE SOLID SUBSTANCE AND ONE DISSOLVED SUBSTANCE

Solubility of the solid substances

$Z = +2$

5. $Ca^{++} + H_2O$ $=$ **CaO** $+ 2H^+$ a. $\log(Ca^{++}) = 22.91 - 2\,pH$
b. $= 32.63 - 2\,pH$

$-2 \rightarrow +2$

6. **CaH₂** $= Ca^{++} + 2H^+ + 4e^-$ $E_0 = -1.045 - 0.0295\,pH + 0.0148 \log(Ca^{++})$

$0 \rightarrow +2$

7. **Ca** $= Ca^{++} + 2e^-$ $E_0 = -2.866 + 0.0295 \log(Ca^{++})$

$+2 \rightarrow +4$

8. $Ca^{++} + 2H_2O$ $=$ **CaO₂** $+ 4H^+ + 2e^-$ $E_0 = 2.224 - 0.1182\,pH - 0.0295 \log(Ca^{++})$

Strontium

2.1. TWO SOLID SUBSTANCES

Limits of the domains of relative stability of the solid substances

$-2 \rightarrow 0$

1. **SrH₂** $=$ **Sr** $+ 2H^+ + 2e^-$ $E_0 = 0.718 - 0.0591\,pH$

$-2 \rightarrow +2$

2. **SrH₂** $+ H_2O$ $=$ **SrO** $+ 4H^+ + 4e^-$ a. $E_0 = -0.665 - 0.0591\,pH$
b. $= -0.477 - 0.0591\,pH$

$0 \rightarrow +2$

3. **Sr** $+ H_2O$ $=$ **SrO** $+ 2H^+ + 2e^-$ a. $E_0 = -2.047 - 0.0591\,pH$
b. $= -1.672 - 0.0591\,pH$

$+2 \rightarrow +4$

4. **SrO** $+ H_2O$ $=$ **SrO₂** $+ 2H^+ + 2e^-$ a. $E_0 = 1.492 - 0.0591\,pH$
b. $= 1.116 - 0.0591\,pH$

2.2. ONE SOLID SUBSTANCE AND ONE DISSOLVED SUBSTANCE

Solubility of the solid substances

$Z = +2$

5. $Sr^{++} + H_2O$ $=$ **SrO** $+ 2H^+$ a. $\log(Sr^{++}) = 28.45 - 2\,pH$
b. $= 41.15 - 2\,pH$

$-2 \rightarrow +2$

6. **SrH₂** $= Sr^{++} + 2H^+ + 4e^-$ $E_0 = -1.085 - 0.0295\,pH + 0.0148 \log(Sr^{++})$

$0 \rightarrow +2$

7. **Sr** $= Sr^{++} + 2e^-$ $E_0 = -2.888 + 0.0295 \log(Sr^{++})$

$+2 \rightarrow +4$

8. $Sr^{++} + 2H_2O$ $=$ **SrO₂** $+ 4H^+ + 2e^-$ $E_0 = 2.333 - 0.1182\,pH - 0.0295 \log(Sr^{++})$

Barium

2.1. TWO SOLID SUBSTANCES

Limits of the domains of relative stability of the solid substances

$-2 \rightarrow 0$

1. $BaH_2 = Ba + 2H^+ + 2e^-$ $\quad E_0 = -0.685 - 0.0591\,pH$

$-2 \rightarrow +2$

2. $BaH_2 + H_2O = BaO + 4H^+ + 4e^-$
   a. $E_0 = -0.741 - 0.0591\,pH$
   b. $ = -0.412 - 0.0591\,pH$

$0 \rightarrow +2$

3. $Ba + H_2O = BaO + 2H^+ + 2e^-$
   a. $E_0 = -2.166 - 0.0591\,pH$
   b. $ = -1.509 - 0.0591\,pH$

$+2 \rightarrow +4$

4. $BaO + H_2O = BaO_2 + 2H^+ + 2e^-$
   ac. $E_0 = 1.626 - 0.0591\,pH$
   bc. $ = 1.047 - 0.0591\,pH$
   ad. $ = 1.679 - 0.0591\,pH$
   bd. $ = 1.023 - 0.0591\,pH$

2.2. ONE SOLID SUBSTANCE AND ONE DISSOLVED SUBSTANCE

Solubility of the solid substances

$Z = +2$

5. $Ba^{++} + H_2O = BaO + 2H^+$
   a. $\log(Ba^{++}) = 25.02 - 2\,pH$
   b. $\phantom{\log(Ba^{++})} = 47.24 - 2\,pH$

$-2 \rightarrow +2$

6. $BaH_2 = Ba^{++} + 2H^+ + 4e^-$ $\quad E_0 = -1.110 - 0.0295\,pH + 0.0148\log(Ba^{++})$

$0 \rightarrow +2$

7. $Ba = Ba^{++} + 2e^-$ $\quad E_0 = -2.905 + 0.0295\log(Ba^{++})$

$+2 \rightarrow +4$

8. $Ba^{++} + 2H_2O = BaO_2 + 4H^+ + 2e^-$
   c. $E_0 = 2.365 - 0.1182\,pH - 0.0295\log(Ba^{++})$
   d. $ = 2.419 - 0.1182\,pH - 0.0295\log(Ba^{++})$

3. EQUILIBRIUM DIAGRAMS AND THEIR INTERPRETATION

Using the above formulae, we have drawn Figs. 1–3, which represent the conditions of thermodynamic equilibrium for the systems calcium–water, strontium–water and barium–water, at 25°C, and Fig. 4 which shows the influence of pH on the solubility of calcium hydroxide.

These figures are valid only in the absence of substances with which the alkaline earth metals can form soluble complexes or insoluble salts. According to Charlot [1], the complexes are few in number and not very stable; they include, however, the trilons or complexons (derivatives of tetra-acetic ethylene diamine), the polymetaphosphates and the organic hydroxyl compounds (sugars, citric ions, etc.). Examples of sparingly soluble compounds are the carbonates, oxalates, sulphates, phosphates, chromates, etc.

3.1. STABILITY OF THE ALKALINE EARTH METALS

The alkaline earth metals exert an extremely low solution potential. As the whole of their domain of stability in Figs. 1–3 lies well below that of water, these metals are very unstable in the presence of aqueous solutions of any pH. They are extremely base metals and powerful reducing agents, having a large affinity to react with water, which they decompose with the evolution of hydrogen. An examination of Figs. 1–3 shows that in the presence of aqueous solutions, calcium, strontium and barium are always unstable with respect to their hydrides CaH_2, SrH_2 and BaH_2, which are themselves unstable

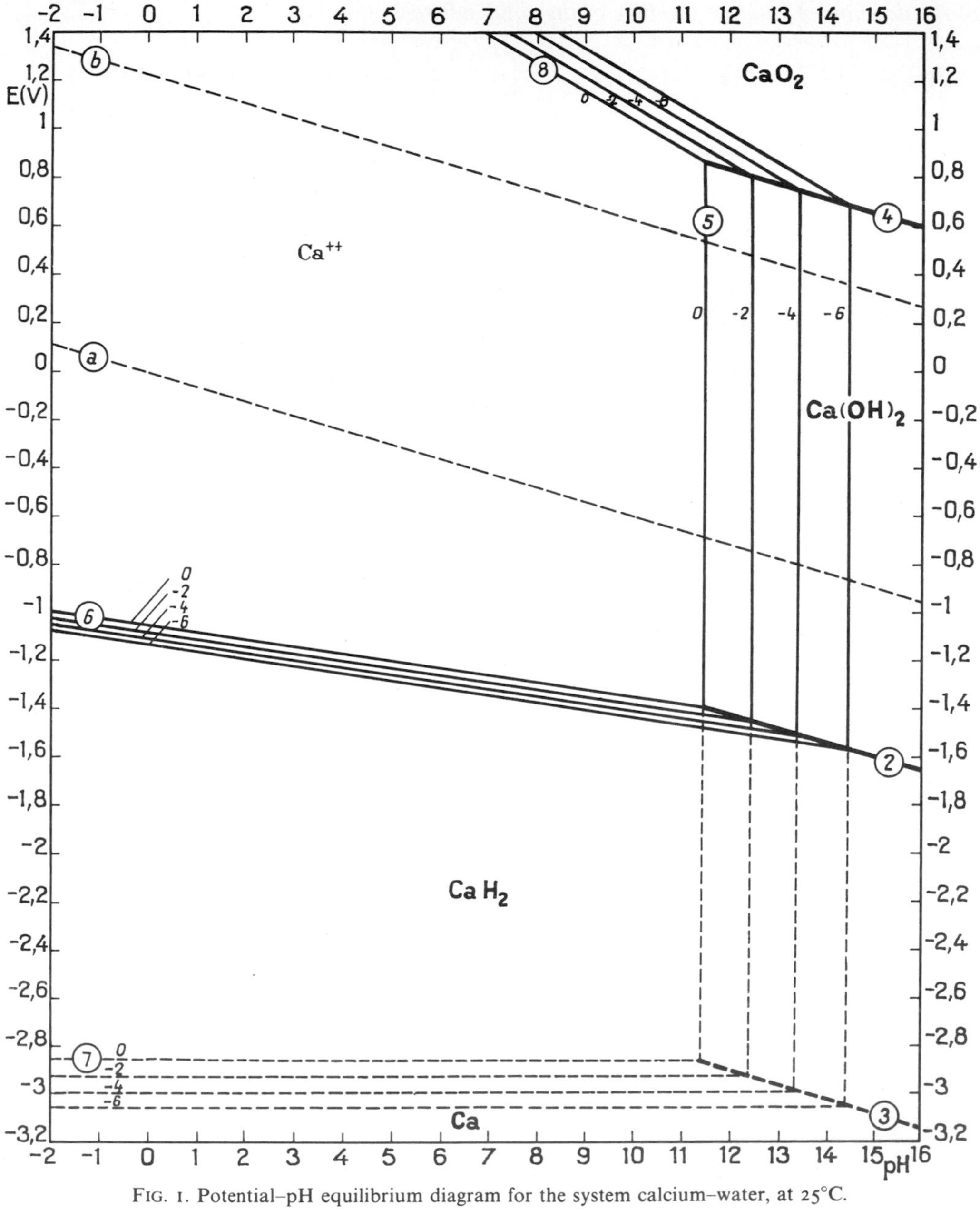

FIG. 1. Potential–pH equilibrium diagram for the system calcium–water, at 25°C.

in the presence of water. The alkaline earth metals, like the alkali metals, do not have any domain of thermodynamic stability in the presence of water. On account of their very great electronegativity, the equilibrium potentials of the reactions $M = M^{++} + 2e^-$, where M represents an alkaline earth metal, cannot be measured directly; however, using liquid amalgams, it has been possible to carry out these measurements indirectly.

For an identical reason, the electrodeposition of the alkaline earth metals cannot be brought about in aqueous solution; the electrolytic separation of these metals is possible only by the igneous electrolysis of salts such as $CaCl_2$, for example. It should be noted that the alkaline earth metals can

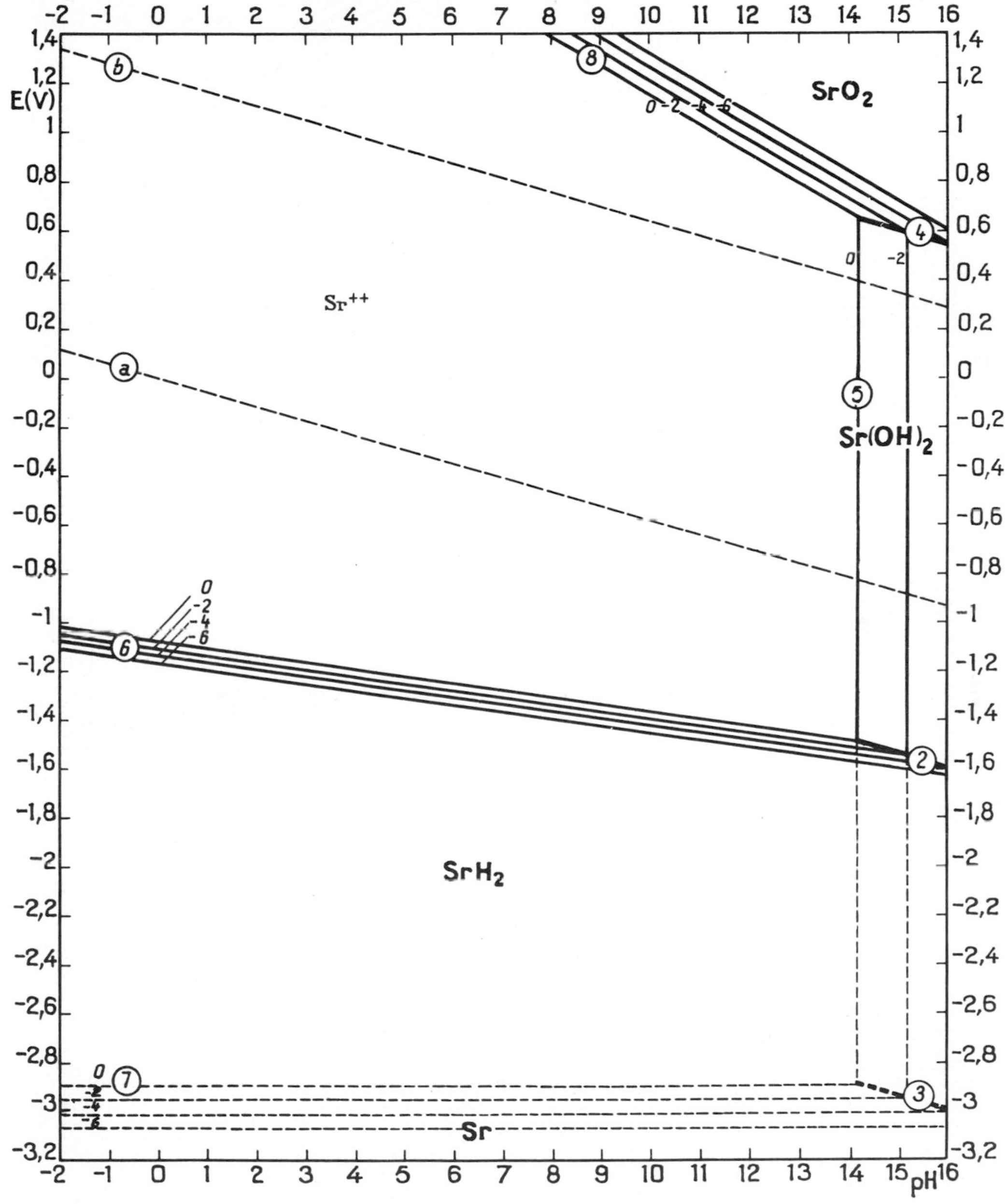

FIG. 2. Potential–pH equilibrium diagram for the system strontium–water, at 25°C.

also be obtained by the electrolysis of non-aqueous solutions of certain of their salts (e.g. calcium can be prepared by the electrolysis of a solution of $CaCl_2$ in methanol, ethanol or amyl alcohol, using a platinum cathode).

The alkaline earth metals are powerful reducing agents, and reduce fuming sulphuric acid to sulphur and sulphur dioxide. They reduce concentrated sulphuric acid to sulphur, sulphur dioxide and hydrogen sulphide. Fuming nitric acid is not attacked in the cold, but when warm it is reduced to nitrogen dioxide.

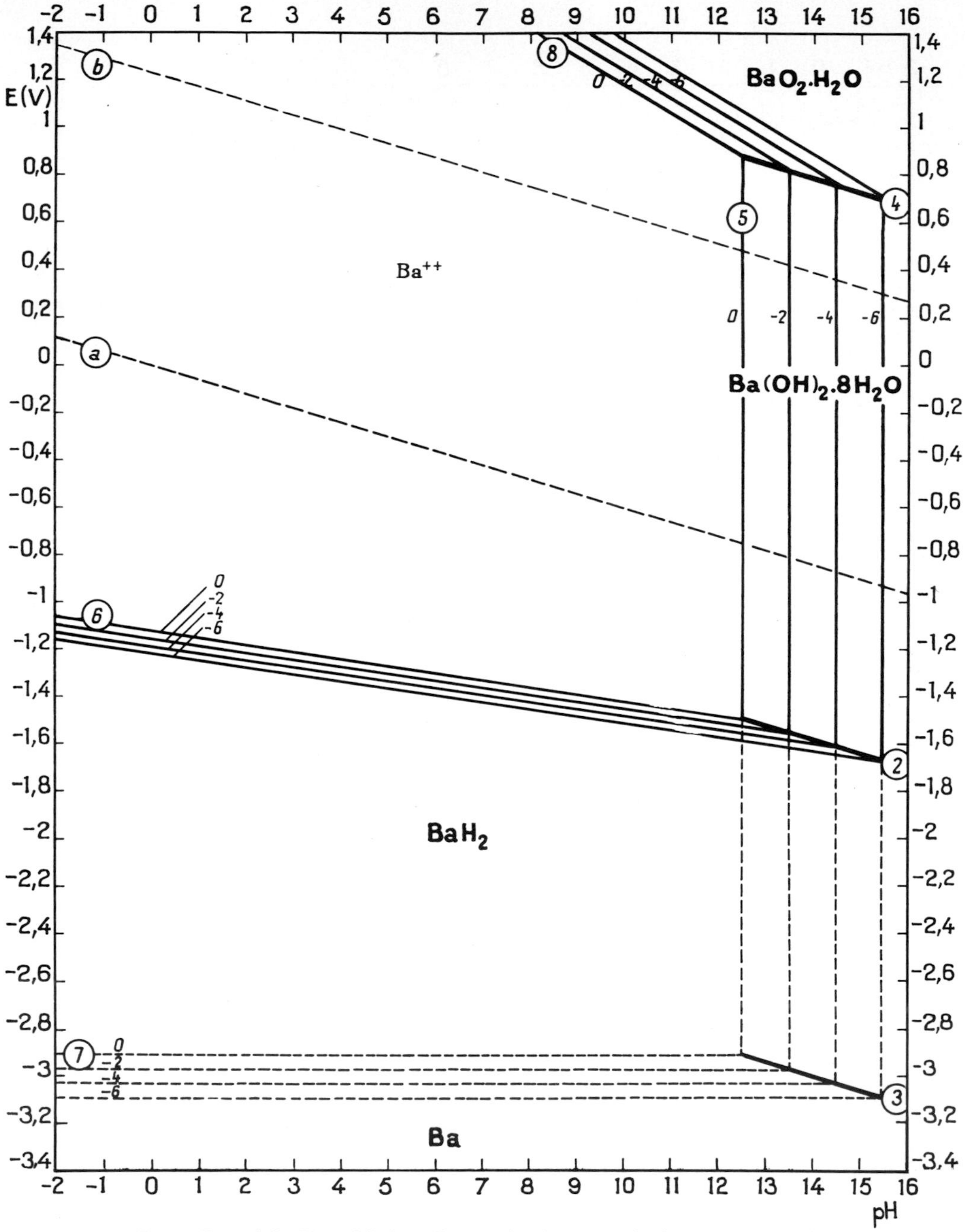

FIG. 3. Potential–pH equilibrium diagram for the system barium–water, at 25°C.

A sufficiently powerful oxidizing action can convert calcium, strontium and barium into peroxides, CaO_2, SrO_2 and BaO_2. Such a conversion occurs when the metal is treated in the cold with hydrogen peroxide (perhydrol) in ethereal solution.

3.2. STABILITY OF THE OXIDES AND HYDROXIDES OF THE ALKALINE EARTH METALS

In the presence of water, the anhydrous oxides CaO, SrO and BaO are all very unstable with respect to the corresponding hydroxides $Ca(OH)_2$, $Sr(OH)_2$ and $Ba(OH)_2 . 8H_2O$; they therefore tend to become hydrated according to the reaction $MO + H_2O \rightarrow M(OH)_2$. As is well known, this hydration reaction takes place rapidly.

In Fig. 4 we have represented the influence of pH on the solubility of calcium hydroxide. The milk of lime obtained by saturating pure water with $Ca(OH)_2$ has the following characteristics, at 25°C:

pH = 12·40, $\log(Ca^{++}) = -1{\cdot}90$, i.e. 933 mg $Ca(OH)_2$/l, or 233 French degrees.

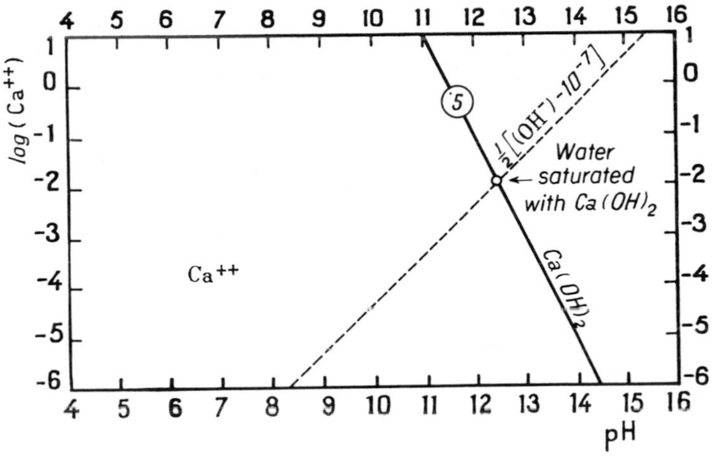

FIG. 4. Influence of pH on the solubility of calcium hydroxide, at 25°C.

Being very unstable in the presence of solutions of pH = 7, in which they tend to dissolve according to the reaction $M(OH)_2 \rightarrow M^{++} + 2OH^-$, the hydroxides of calcium, strontium and barium are relatively strong bases.

By oxidation they can be converted into peroxides MO_2; this reaction can be brought about by the action of hydrogen peroxide or Na_2O_2 on a milk of calcium, strontium or barium hydroxide.

3.3. STABILITY OF THE PEROXIDES OF THE ALKALINE EARTH METALS

The domains of stability of the peroxides lie beyond line (*b*); they are therefore oxidizing substances, thermodynamically unstable in the presence of aqueous solutions which they tend to decompose with the evolution of oxygen, being themselves reduced to the divalent state. In actual fact, the dissolution of the alkaline earth peroxides in water and in acid solutions occurs without the evolution of oxygen, but with the formation of hydrogen peroxide (Pascal [2]).

3.4. STABILITY OF THE HYDRIDES OF THE ALKALINE EARTH METALS

As is shown by Figs. 1–3, the hydrides of calcium, strontium and barium are thermodynamically unstable in the presence of water and aqueous solutions, which they decompose with the formation of hydrogen and the cations Ca^{++}, Sr^{++} and Ba^{++}

Theoretically, the hydrides of the alkaline earth metals can be obtained transitorily by the reduction of solutions containing calcium, strontium or barium at potentials below those shown respectively by the families of lines (6) and by the lines (2).

We do not know whether such a formation of hydride has been observed; in actual fact the hydrides in question are obtained only by heating the alkaline earth metals and certain of their compounds in an atmosphere of hydrogen.

4. BIBLIOGRAPHY

[1] G. Charlot, *L'analyse qualitative et les réactions en solution*, 4th ed., Masson, Paris, 1957.
[2] P. Pascal, *Traité de chimie minérale*, Vol. VI, Masson, Paris, 1934.

SECTION 4.6

RADIUM[1]

J. VAN MUYLDER and M. POURBAIX

SUMMARY

[1] Rapport technique RT.73 of CEBELCOR (July 1958).

1. SUBSTANCES CONSIDERED

	Oxidation number (Z)	Considered	μ^0 (cal.)	Name, colour
Solid substances	0	**Ra**	0	Radium, shiny white
	+2	**RaO**	−117 500	Radium oxide
Dissolved substance	+2	Ra^{++}	−134 500	Radium ion, colourless

2. REACTIONS AND EQUILIBRIUM FORMULAE

2.1. TWO SOLID SUBSTANCES

Limit of the domains of relative stability of radium and its oxide

0 → +2

1. $\mathbf{Ra} + H_2O = \mathbf{RaO} + 2H^+ + 2e^-$ $\quad E_0 = -1.319 - 0.0591\,pH$

2.2. ONE SOLID SUBSTANCE AND ONE DISSOLVED SUBSTANCE

Solubility of radium and its oxide

Z = +2

2. $Ra^{++} + H_2O = \mathbf{RaO} + 2H^+$ $\quad \log(Ra^{++}) = 34.06 - 2\,pH$

0 → +2

3. $\mathbf{Ra} = Ra^{++} + 2e^-$ $\quad E_0 = -2.916 + 0.0295 \log(Ra^{++})$

3. EQUILIBRIUM DIAGRAM AND ITS INTERPRETATION

3.1. ESTABLISHMENT OF THE DIAGRAM

Using the equilibrium formulae established in paragraph 2, we have drawn in Fig. 1 the potential–pH equilibrium diagram for the system radium–water, at 25°C. This diagram represents the conditions of thermodynamic equilibrium of the system radium–water, at 25°C, in the absence of substances with which radium can form soluble complexes (citric, sulphosalicylic, oxalacetic, fumaric, tartaric, succinic, pyranic, aspartic complexes [1]), or insoluble compounds (sulphate, carbonate, iodate, chromate).

3.2. STABILITY OF RADIUM

Radium, like the alkali and alkaline earth metals, has a very large negative equilibrium potential. As the whole of its domain of stability in Fig. 1 lies well below that of water, it is very unstable in the presence of aqueous solutions of any pH.

Being very soluble, radium oxide RaO cannot cause any passivation, and the metal decomposes water and aqueous solutions very vigorously with the evolution of hydrogen and the production of divalent cations Ra^{++}.

On account of its great electronegativity, radium cannot be separated electrolytically from aqueous solutions of its salts, except when a mercury cathode is used. Radium then dissolves in the mercury with the formation of an amalgam.

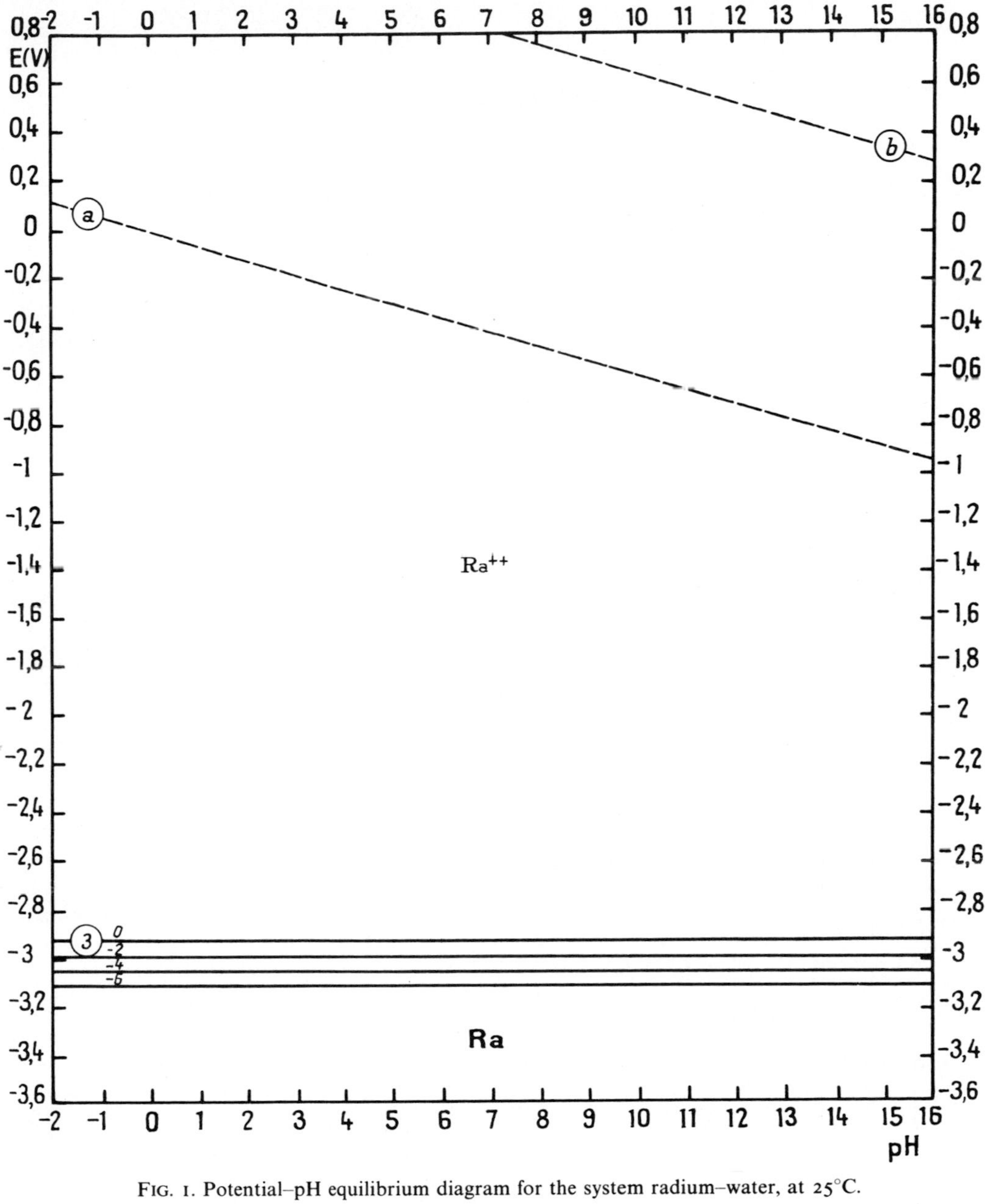

FIG. 1. Potential–pH equilibrium diagram for the system radium–water, at 25°C.

4. BIBLIOGRAPHY

[1] P. PASCAL, *Nouveau Traité de Chimie Minérale*, Vol. IV (*Radium*), Masson, Paris, 1958.

SECTION 5.1

BORON[1]

N. de Zoubov, E. Deltombe and M. Pourbaix

SUMMARY

1. *Substances considered and substances not considered.*
2. *Reactions and equilibrium formulae.*
   2.1. Two dissolved substances.
      2.1.1. Relative stability of the dissolved substances.
      2.1.2. Limits of the domains of relative predominance of the dissolved substances.
   2.2. Two solid substances.
      Limits of the domains of relative stability of the solid substances.
   2.3. One dissolved substance and one solid substance.
      Solubility of the solid substances.
   2.4. One solid substance and one gaseous substance.
      Limits of the domains of relative stability of the solid and gaseous substances.
   2.5. One dissolved substance and one gaseous substance.
      Solubility of the gaseous substances.
3. *Potential–pH equilibrium diagrams and their interpretation.*
   3.1. Establishment of the diagrams.
   3.2. Stability of boron.
   3.3. Formation and stability of the boron hydrides.
   3.4. Stability of boric acid and the borates.
      Constitution of boric solutions.
4. *Bibliography.*

---

[1] This account is an adapted and abridged version of the Rapport technique RT.47 of CEBELCOR (March 1957) [1].

1. SUBSTANCES CONSIDERED AND SUBSTANCES NOT CONSIDERED

	Oxidation number (Z)	Considered	Not considered	μ^0 (cal.)	Name, colour, crystalline system
Solid substances	− 1.4	$B_{10}H_{14}$	–	65 000 (2)	Decaborane, colourless, orthorh.
	0	B cryst.	–	0	Boron, brown–black, quad. or orthorh.
	»	–	B amorph.	–	Amorphous boron, maroon or black
	+ 0.33	–	B_6O	–	Boron sub-oxide
	+ 1	–	B_4O_2	–	Boron sub-oxide
	+ 1.5	–	B_4O_3	–	Boron sub-oxide
	+ 2	–	B_2O_2	–	Boron sub-oxide
	+ 2.5	–	B_4O_5	–	Boron sub-oxide
	+ 3	B_2O_3 hydr.	–	*a*. −290 330	Orthoboric acid H_3BO_3, white, tricl.
	»	» anh.	–	*b*. −286 430 (2)	Boric anhydride, white, cub.
	»	» hydr.	–	*c*. −284 310	Metaboric acid HBO_2 (4)
	»	» vitr.	–	*d*. −283 890 (2)	Vitreous boric anhydride, white
	»	–	B_2O_3 hydr.	–	Pyroboric acid $H_4B_2O_5$
Liquid substances	− 2.2	–	B_5H_{11}.	–	Pentaborane, colourless, (unstable)
	− 1.8	–	B_5H_9	38 800	Pentaborane, colourless, (stable)
Dissolved substances	+ 2	–	$H_4B_2O_4$	–	Hypoboric acid
	»	–	$H_3B_2O_4^-$	–	Hypoborate
	+ 3	H_3BO_3	–	−230 160 (3)	Orthoboric acid, colourless
	»	$H_2BO_3^-$	–	−217 600	Orthoborate, colourless
	»	BO_2^-	–	−169 600 (?)	Metaborate, colourless
	»	HBO_3^{--}	–	−200 290 (3)	Orthoborate, colourless
	»	BO_3^{---}	–	−181 480 (3)	Orthoborate, colourless
	»	$H_2B_4O_7$	–	−633 720 (?) (3)	Tetraboric acid, colourless
	»	$HB_4O_7^-$	–	−628 270 (?) (3)	Tetraborate, colourless
	»	$B_4O_7^{--}$	–	−616 000 (?)	Tetraborate, colourless
	»	–	$B_2O_4^{--}$	–	Diborate
	»	–	$B_6O_{10}^{--}$	–	Hexaborate
	+ 4.5	–	$B_2O_5^-$	–	Diborate
	+ 5	–	BO_3^-	–	Perborate (or $BO_2^- . H_2O_2$)
Gaseous substances	− 3	B_2H_6	–	19 780 (2)	Diborane, colourless
	− 2.5	–	B_4H_{10}	–	Tetraborane, colourless
	− 2.2	–	B_5H_{11}	–	Pentaborane
	− 1.8	B_5H_9	–	39 320 (2)	Pentaborane
	− 1.67	–	B_6H_{10}	–	Hexaborane
	− 1.4	$B_{10}H_{14}$	–	71 000 (2)	Decaborane
	− 1	BH	–	112 600 (2)	Monoborane
	+ 2	BO	–	− 19 520 (2)	Boron oxide

(2) Values of the National Bureau of Standards (July 1956).

(3) Values determined by us [1].

(4) These values for the oxides correspond to the following values for the acids:

H_3BO_3: − 230 200 cal.; HBO_2: − 170 500 cal.

2. REACTIONS AND EQUILIBRIUM FORMULAE

2.1. TWO DISSOLVED SUBSTANCES

2.1.1. *Relative stability of the dissolved substances*

$Z = +3$

1. $H_3BO_3 = H_2BO_3^- + H^+ \qquad \log\frac{(H_2BO_3^-)}{(H_3BO_3)} = -9.21 + pH$
2. $H_2BO_3^- = HBO_3^{--} + H^+ \qquad \log\frac{(HBO_3^{--})}{(H_2BO_3^-)} = -12.70 + pH$
3. $HBO_3^{--} = BO_3^{---} + H^+ \qquad \log\frac{(BO_3^{---})}{(HBO_3^{--})} = -13.80 + pH$
4. $4H_3BO_3 = H_2B_4O_7 + 5H_2O \qquad \log\frac{(H_2B_4O_7)}{(H_3BO_3)^4} = -2.55$
5. $H_2B_4O_7 = HB_4O_7^- + H^+ \qquad \log\frac{(HB_4O_7^-)}{(H_2B_4O_7)} = -4.00 + pH$
6. $4H_3BO_3 = HB_4O_7^- + H^+ + 5H_2O \qquad \log\frac{(HB_4O_7^-)}{(H_3BO_3)^4} = -6.54 + pH$
7. $HB_4O_7^- = B_4O_7^{--} + H^+ \qquad \log\frac{(B_4O_7^{--})}{(HB_4O_7^-)} = -9.00 + pH$
8. $4H_3BO_3 = B_4O_7^{--} + 2H^+ + 5H_2O \qquad \log\frac{(B_4O_7^{--})}{(H_3BO_3)^4} = -15.55 + 2\,pH$
9. $B_4O_7^{--} + 5H_2O = 4H_2BO_3^- + 2H^+ \qquad \log\frac{(H_2BO_3^-)^4}{(B_4O_7^{--})} = -21.31 + 2\,pH$
10. $B_4O_7^{--} + 5H_2O = 4HBO_3^{--} + 6H^+ \qquad \log\frac{(HBO_3^{--})^4}{(B_4O_7^{--})} = -72.11 + 6\,pH$

2.1.2. *Limits of the domains of relative predominance of the dissolved substances*

$Z = +3$

1'. $H_3BO_3\ /H_2BO_3^- \qquad pH = 9.21$
2'. $H_2BO_3^-\ /HBO_3^{--} \qquad pH = 12.70$
3'. $HBO_3^{--}\ /BO_3^{---} \qquad pH = 13.80$
4'. $H_3BO_3\ /H_2B_4O_7 \qquad 0 = 0.95 - \log C$
5'. $H_2B_4O_7\ /HB_4O_7^- \qquad pH = 4.00$
6'. $H_3BO_3\ /HB_4O_7^- \qquad pH = 6.84 - 3\log C$
7'. $HB_4O_7^-\ /B_4O_7^{--} \qquad pH = 9.00$
8'. $H_3BO_3\ /B_4O_7^{--} \qquad 2\,pH = 15.85 - 3\log C$
9'. $B_4O_7^{--}\ /H_2BO_3^- \qquad 2\,pH = 21.01 + 3\log C$
10'. $B_4O_7^{--}\ /HBO_3^{--} \qquad 2\,pH = 23.94 + \log C$

2.2. TWO SOLID SUBSTANCES

Limits of the domains of relative stability of the solid substances

$-1.4 \rightarrow 0$

11. $B_{10}H_{14} = 10\,B + 14H^+ + 14e^- \qquad E_0 = -0.201 - 0.0591\,pH$

$-1.4 \rightarrow +3$

12. $B_{10}H_{14} + 30H_2O = 10\,H_3BO_3 + 44H^+ + 44e^- \qquad E_0 = -0.657 - 0.0591\,pH$

$0 \rightarrow +3$

13. $2\,B + 3H_2O = B_2O_3 + 6H^+ + 6e^- \qquad$ *b.* $E_0 = -0.841 - 0.0591\,pH$
14. $B + 3H_2O = H_3BO_3 + 3H^+ + 3e^- \qquad$ *a.* $E_0 = -0.869 - 0.0591\,pH$

2.3. ONE DISSOLVED SUBSTANCE AND ONE SOLID SUBSTANCE

Solubility of the solid substances

a. In gram-molecules and gram-ions per litre

$Z = +3$

15.	$H_3BO_3 = H_3BO_3$	$\log(H_3BO_3) = -0.03$
16.	$4H_3BO_3 = HB_4O_7^- + H^+ + 5H_2O$	$\log(HB_4O_7^-) = -6.66 + pH$

$-1.4 \rightarrow +3$

17.	$B_{10}H_{14} + 30H_2O = 10H_3BO_3 + 44H^+ + 44e^-$	$E_0 = -0.656 - 0.0591\,pH + 0.0013\log(H_3BO_3)$
18.	$B_{10}H_{14} + 30H_2O = 10H_2BO_3^- + 54H^+ + 44e^-$	$E_0 = -0.532 - 0.0725\,pH + 0.0013\log(H_2BO_3^-)$
19.	$B_{10}H_{14} + 30H_2O = 10HBO_3^{--} + 64H^+ + 44e^-$	$E_0 = -0.362 - 0.0860\,pH + 0.0013\log(HBO_3^{--})$
20.	$B_{10}H_{14} + 30H_2O = 10BO_3^{---} + 74H^+ + 44e^-$	$E_0 = -0.176 - 0.0994\,pH + 0.0013\log(BO_3^{---})$
21.	$2B_{10}H_{14} + 35H_2O = 5HB_4O_7^- + 93H^+ + 88e^-$	$E_0 = -0.642 - 0.0623\,pH + 0.0035\log(HB_4O_7^-)$
22.	$2B_{10}H_{14} + 35H_2O = 5B_4O_7^{--} + 98H^+ + 88e^-$	$E_0 = -0.610 - 0.0637\,pH + 0.0035\log(B_4O_7^{--})$

$0 \rightarrow +3$

23.	$B + 3H_2O = H_3BO_3 + 3H^+ + 3e^-$	$E_0 = -0.869 - 0.0591\,pH + 0.0197\log(H_3BO_3)$
24.	$B + 3H_2O = H_2BO_3^- + 4H^+ + 3e^-$	$E_0 = -0.687 - 0.0788\,pH + 0.0197\log(H_2BO_3^-)$
25.	$B + 3H_2O = HBO_3^{--} + 5H^+ + 3e^-$	$E_0 = -0.437 - 0.0985\,pH + 0.0197\log(HBO_3^{--})$
26.	$B + 3H_2O = BO_3^{---} + 6H^+ + 3e^-$	$E_0 = -0.165 - 0.1182\,pH + 0.0197\log(BO_3^{---})$
27.	$4B + 7H_2O = HB_4O_7^- + 13H^+ + 12e^-$	$E_0 = -0.836 - 0.0640\,pH + 0.0049\log(HB_4O_7^-)$
28.	$4B + 7H_2O = B_4O_7^{--} + 14H^+ + 12e^-$	$E_0 = -0.792 - 0.0689\,pH + 0.0049\log(B_4O_7^{--})$

b. In gram-atoms of boron per litre

$Z = +3$

15'.	H_3BO_3/H_3BO_3	$\log C = -0.03$
16'.	$H_3BO_3/HB_4O_7^-$	$\log C = -6.06 + pH$

$-1.4 \rightarrow +3$

17'.	$B_{10}H_{14}/H_3BO_3$	$E_0 = -0.656 - 0.0591\,pH + 0.0013\log C$
18'.	$B_{10}H_{14}/H_2BO_3^-$	$E_0 = -0.532 - 0.0725\,pH + 0.0013\log C$
19'.	$B_{10}H_{14}/HBO_3^{--}$	$E_0 = -0.362 - 0.0860\,pH + 0.0013\log C$
20'.	$B_{10}H_{14}/BO_3^{---}$	$E_0 = -0.176 - 0.0994\,pH + 0.0013\log C$
21'.	$B_{10}H_{14}/HB_4O_7^-$	$E_0 = -0.644 - 0.0623\,pH + 0.0035\log C$
22'.	$B_{10}H_{14}/B_4O_7^{--}$	$E_0 = -0.612 - 0.0637\,pH + 0.0035\log C$

$0 \rightarrow +3$

23'.	B/H_3BO_3	$E_0 = -0.869 - 0.0591\,pH + 0.0197\log C$
24'.	$B/H_2BO_3^-$	$E_0 = -0.687 - 0.0788\,pH + 0.0197\log C$
25'.	B/HBO_3^{--}	$E_0 = -0.437 - 0.0985\,pH + 0.0197\log C$
26'.	B/BO_3^{---}	$E_0 = -0.165 - 0.1182\,pH + 0.0197\log C$
27'.	$B/HB_4O_7^-$	$E_0 = -0.839 - 0.0640\,pH + 0.0049\log C$
28'.	$B/B_4O_7^{--}$	$E_0 = -0.795 - 0.0689\,pH + 0.0049\log C$

2.4. ONE SOLID SUBSTANCE AND ONE GASEOUS SUBSTANCE

Limits of the domains of relative stability of the solid and gaseous substances

$-3 \rightarrow 0$

29.	$B_2H_6 = 2B + 6H^+ + 6e^-$	$E_0 = -0.143 - 0.0591\,pH - 0.0098\log p_{B_2H_6}$

$-3 \rightarrow +3$

30.	$B_2H_6 + 6H_2O = 2H_3BO_3 + 12H^+ + 12e^-$	$E_0 = -0.506 - 0.0591\,pH - 0.0049\log p_{B_2H_6}$

$-1.8 \rightarrow 0$

31.	$B_5H_9 = 5B + 9H^+ + 9e^-$	$E_0 = -0.189 - 0.0591\,pH - 0.0066\log p_{B_5H_9}$

$-1.8 \rightarrow +3$

32.	$B_5H_9 + 15H_2O = 5H_3BO_3 + 24H^+ + 24e^-$	$E_0 = -0.614 - 0.0591\,pH - 0.0025\log p_{B_5H_9}$

$-1.4 \rightarrow 0$
33. $B_{10}H_{14} = 10\,B + 14H^+ + 14e^-$ $E_0 = -0.220 - 0.0591\,pH - 0.0042 \log p_{B_{10}H_{14}}$

$-1.4 \rightarrow +3$
34. $B_{10}H_{14} + 30H_2O = 10\,H_3BO_3 + 44H^+ + 44e^-$ $E_0 = -0.662 - 0.0591\,pH - 0.0013 \log p_{B_{10}H_{14}}$

$-1 \rightarrow 0$
35. $BH = B + H^+ + e^-$ $E_0 = -4.883 - 0.0591\,pH - 0.0591 \log p_{BH}$

$-1 \rightarrow +3$
36. $BH + 3H_2O = H_3BO_3 + 4H^+ + 4e^-$ $E_0 = -1.873 - 0.0591\,pH - 0.0148 \log p_{BH}$

$0 \rightarrow +2$
37. $B + H_2O = BO + 2H^+ + 2e^-$ $E_0 = 0.806 - 0.0591\,pH + 0.0295 \log p_{BO}$

$+2 \rightarrow +3$
38. $BO + 2H_2O = H_3BO_3 + H^+ + e^-$ $E_0 = -4.219 - 0.0591\,pH - 0.0591 \log p_{BO}$

2.5. ONE DISSOLVED SUBSTANCE AND ONE GASEOUS SUBSTANCE

Solubility of the gaseous substances

a. In gram-molecules and gram-ions of boron per litre

$-3 \rightarrow +3$

39. $B_2H_6 + 6H_2O = 2H_3BO_3 + 12H^+ + 12e^-$ $E_0 = -0.506 - 0.0591\,pH + 0.0049 \log \frac{(H_3BO_3)^2}{p_{B_2H_6}}$

40. $B_2H_6 + 6H_2O = 2H_2BO_3^- + 14H^+ + 12e^-$ $E_0 = -0.415 - 0.0689\,pH + 0.0049 \log \frac{(H_2BO_3^-)^2}{p_{B_2H_6}}$

41. $B_2H_6 + 6H_2O = 2HBO_3^{--} + 16H^+ + 12e^-$ $E_0 = -0.289 - 0.0788\,pH + 0.0049 \log \frac{(HBO_3^{--})^2}{p_{B_2H_6}}$

42. $B_2H_6 + 6H_2O = 2BO_3^{---} + 18H^+ + 12e^-$ $E_0 = -0.154 - 0.0886\,pH + 0.0049 \log \frac{(BO_3^{---})^2}{p_{B_2H_6}}$

43. $2B_2H_6 + 7H_2O = HB_4O_7^- + 25H^+ + 24e^-$ $E_0 = -0.490 - 0.0616\,pH + 0.0025 \log \frac{(HB_4O_7^-)}{p^2_{B_2H_6}}$

44. $2B_2H_6 + 7H_2O = B_4O_7^{--} + 26H^+ + 24e^-$ $E_0 = -0.467 - 0.0640\,pH + 0.0025 \log \frac{(B_4O_7^{--})}{p^2_{B_2H_6}}$

As a simplification, we have not considered the similar reactions involving gaseous hydrides other than B_2H_6 (e.g. BH, B_5H_9 and $B_{10}H_{14}$).

b. For a boron concentration of 1 g-at/l

$-3 \rightarrow +3$

39'. B_2H_6 / H_3BO_3 $E_0 = -0.506 - 0.0591\,pH - 0.0049 \log p_{B_2H_6}$

40'. $B_2H_6 / H_2BO_3^-$ $E_0 = -0.415 - 0.0689\,pH - 0.0049 \log p_{B_2H_6}$

41'. B_2H_6 / HBO_3^{--} $E_0 = -0.289 - 0.0788\,pH - 0.0049 \log p_{B_2H_6}$

42'. B_2H_6 / BO_3^{---} $E_0 = -0.154 - 0.0886\,pH - 0.0049 \log p_{B_2H_6}$

43'. $B_2H_6 / HB_4O_7^-$ $E_0 = -0.490 - 0.0616\,pH - 0.0025 \log p_{B_2H_6}$

44'. $B_2H_6 / B_4O_7^{--}$ $E_0 = -0.467 - 0.0640\,pH - 0.0025 \log p_{B_2H_6}$

3. POTENTIAL–pH EQUILIBRIUM DIAGRAMS AND THEIR INTERPRETATION

3.1. ESTABLISHMENT OF THE DIAGRAMS

Using all the equations established above, we have represented in Fig. 1 the influence of pH on the solubility of orthoboric acid, and in Figs. 2 and 3 the general conditions of electrochemical equilibrium of the system boron–water, on the one hand, for solutions containing 1 g-at B/l (Fig. 2), and, on the other hand, for solutions containing respectively 10^{-2}, 10^{-4} and 10^{-6} g-at B/l (Fig. 3). In Fig. 4, we have represented the equilibrium conditions for solutions containing 1 g-at B/l, as already considered

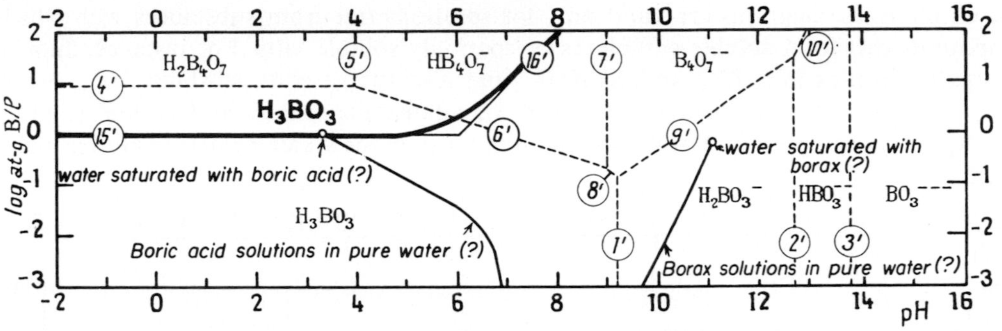

FIG. 1. Influence of pH on the solubility of boric acid, at 25°C (approximate representation).

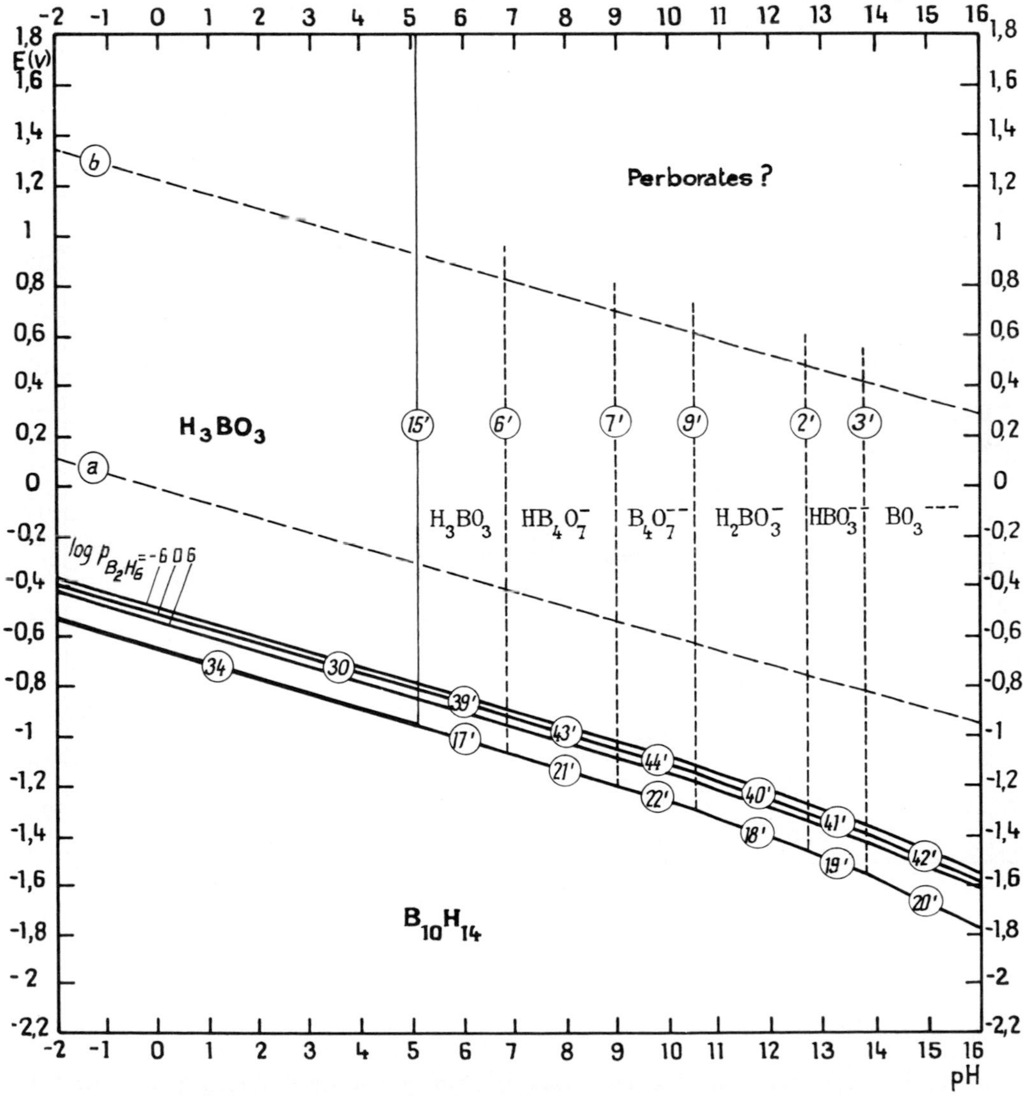

FIG. 2. Potential–pH equilibrium diagram for the system boron–water, at 25°C, for solutions containing 1 g-at B/l (10·8 g/l).

in Fig. 2, but without taking into account the solid hydride $B_{10}H_{14}$, which brings in a domain of metastability of boron.

These equilibrium diagrams are valid only for solutions free from substances with which boron or its compounds can form soluble complexes or sparingly soluble salts. For instance, fluorine forms the quite stable complex ions BF_4^- and BF_3OH^- and also the gaseous substance BF_3. Boron forms numerous complexes with molybdates, tungstates, vanadates, phosphates and arsenates, and with all the organic hydroxyl compounds. Borates of metals other than the alkali metals are all sparingly soluble in water [2].

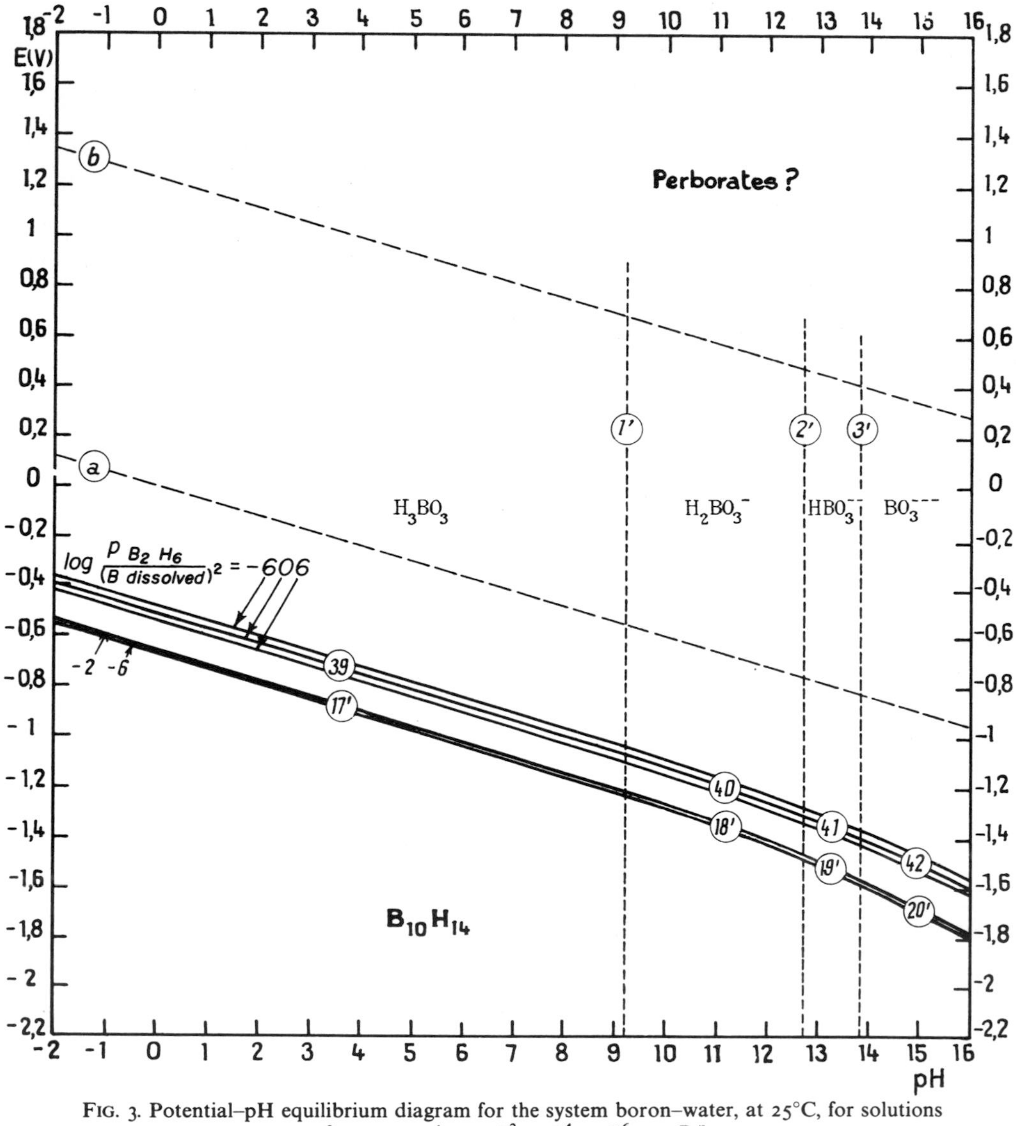

FIG. 3. Potential–pH equilibrium diagram for the system boron–water, at 25°C, for solutions of concentration 10^{-2}, 10^{-4}, 10^{-6} g-at B/l.

3.2. STABILITY OF BORON

According to Fig. 4, boron is an element which is a very powerful reducing agent, one of the most powerful reducing agents among the metalloids; it tends to decompose water with the evolution of hydrogen and gaseous boron hydride, and with the formation of boric acid or borates.

A comparison of Figs. 2 and 4 shows that boron in contact with aqueous solutions is always unstable with respect to the solid hydride $B_{10}H_{14}$, and therefore tends theoretically to cover itself with this hydride; boron has no domain of thermodynamic stability.

In actual fact, this great reactivity at ordinary temperatures is noticed experimentally only for the *amorphous variety* of boron: in sunlight, amorphous boron reacts slowly with water forming boric

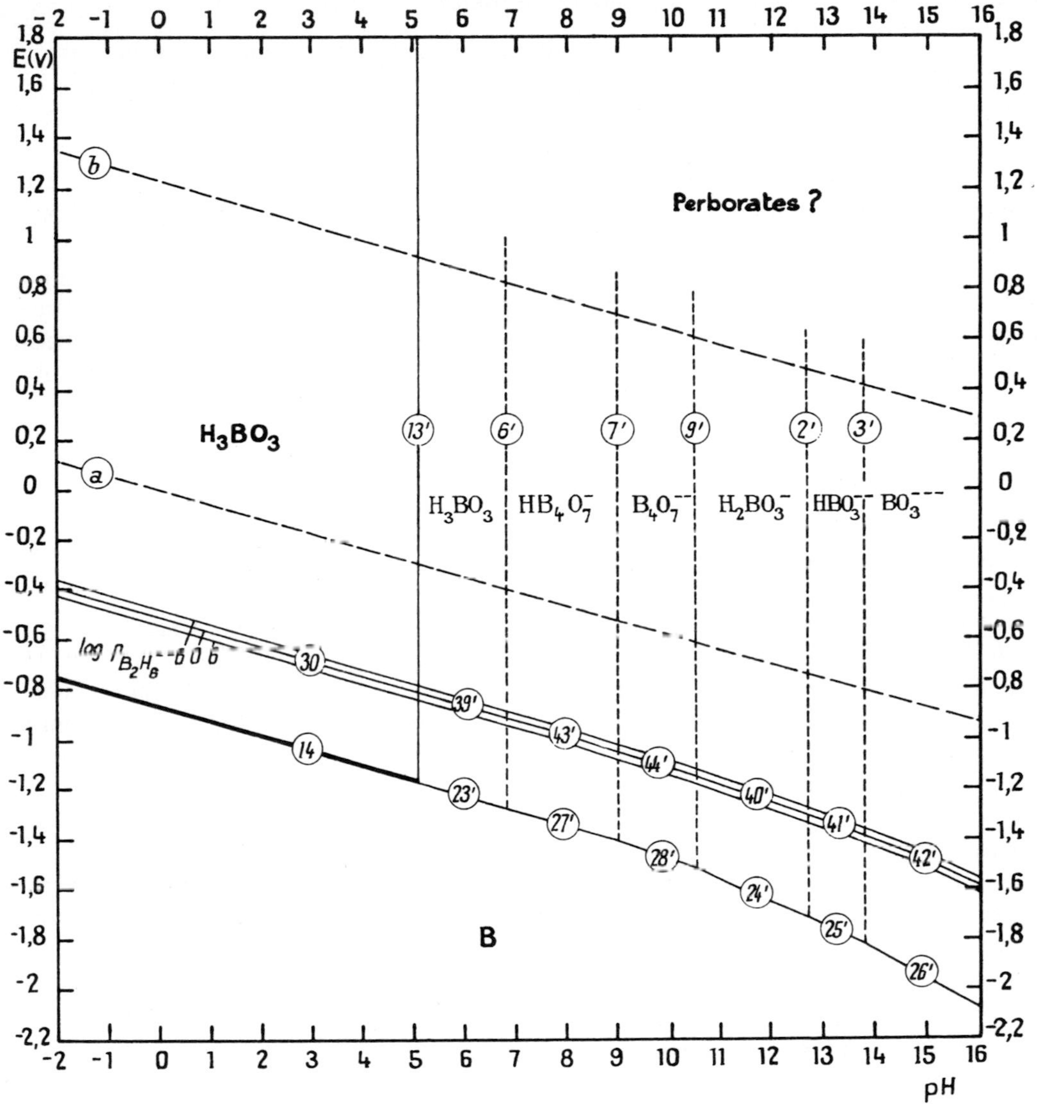

FIG. 4. Potential–pH equilibrium diagram for the system boron–water, at 25°C, not considering the solid hybride $B_{10}H_{14}$, and for solutions containing 1 g-at B/l (10·8 g/l).

acid; it is oxidized rapidly by solutions of caustic soda, nitric acid, hydrogen peroxide, permanganate, gold chloride and silver nitrate; it easily reduces chloric acid to chlorous acid, and iodic acid to iodine; it also reduces hydrocyanic acid, cynanogen, hydrogen sulphide and ammonia.

Crystalline boron is chemically much more resistant than would be predicted from the equilibrium diagrams: it is not attacked by hydrochloric acid, even when boiling, nor by hydrofluoric acid, nor by concentrated alkali solutions; it is oxidized only slowly by solutions of hydrogen peroxide and ammonium persulphate.

It has not been possible to obtain boron by the electrolysis of aqueous solutions; it has been prepared by the chemical or electrolytic reduction of boric anhydride or salts of boron at high temperatures ([3], [4]).

3.3. FORMATION AND STABILITY OF THE BORON HYDRIDES

According to the equilibrium formulae given in paragraph 2, some of which are represented graphically in Figs. 2–4, several hydrides of boron, solid and gaseous, can theoretically be obtained, together with hydrogen, by the reduction of aqueous solutions of boric acid or borates. We do not know whether these facts have been confirmed; however, by the action of B_2Mg_3 on a 4M solution of HCl at 60°, the gaseous hydrides B_2H_6, B_4H_{10}, B_5H_9, B_5H_{11}, B_6H_{10} and $B_{10}H_{14}$ are obtained, mixed with hydrogen; the quantity of boron thus obtained in the form of hydrides is about 3 per cent of the initial boron ([5]–[7]).

As the equilibrium diagrams show, the boron hydrides are unstable in the presence of water, which they tend to decompose with the formation of hydrogen and boric acid (or borate). They are rapidly oxidized to boric acid by solutions containing oxygen or other oxidizing agents (permanganate, silver nitrate, nickel or copper salts). The reducing power decreases in the order B_4H_{10}, B_2H_6, B_5H_9, $B_{10}H_{14}$; solid $B_{10}H_{14}$ is unaffected by boiling water.

3.4. STABILITY OF BORIC ACID AND THE BORATES. CONSTITUTION OF BORIC SOLUTIONS

Boric anhydride, B_2O_3, is very hygroscopic and adds on water molecules at ordinary temperatures forming successively metaboric acid HBO_2 and orthoboric acid H_3BO_3; consequently it does not appear on the equilibrium diagrams.

From Fig. 1, the solubility of orthoboric acid H_3BO_3, which is 0·933 g-mol/l, at 25°C (57·7 g/l, principally in the form of undissociated H_3BO_3) for pH's below 5, increases when the pH increases, with the formation of tetraboric ions $HB_4O_7^-$. In relatively dilute solutions, containing less than 0·01 g-at B/l, the boron exists essentially in the form of orthoboric acid H_3BO_3 or orthoborates $H_2BO_3^-$, HBO_3^{--} and BO_3^{---}; for greater concentrations, there is polymerization with the formation of tetraboric acid $H_2B_4O_7$ (a small proportion) or tetraborates $HB_4O_7^-$ and $B_4O_7^{--}$.

The portion of Fig. 1 lying above the solubility line for H_3BO_3 corresponds to unstable solutions, supersaturated with H_3BO_3; the sections of lines (4′) and (5′) drawn in this figure therefore correspond to non-equilibrium states; at the equilibrium, no domain of predominance exists for $H_2B_4O_7$.

From Fig. 1, when boric acid is dissolved in pure water, apart from undissociated H_3BO_3 a small proportion of $HB_4O_7^-$ should be formed according to the reaction $4H_3BO_3 \rightarrow HB_4O_7^- + 5H_2O + H^+$, i.e. with the formation of H^+ and $HB_4O_7^-$ ions in equal quantities.

The H_3BO_3 and $HB_4O_7^-$ concentrations of solutions obtained by the *dissolution of boric acid* H_3BO_3 *in pure water* are connected with the pH (or the H^+ ion concentration) by the following equations:

$$(HB_4O_7^-) = (H^+) - 10^{-7.00} \quad \text{and} \quad 4\log(H_3BO_3) = \log(HB_4O_7^-) + 6.54 - \text{pH} \qquad (6)$$

These two equations enable us to represent, as indicated by one of the lines in Fig. 1, the pH's of boric acid solutions of different concentrations; the pH of the solution obtained by saturating pure water with boric acid will be given by the abscissa value of the intersection of this line with the heavy line which relates to saturation with H_3PO_3; this pH is 3·3.

In the same way, the concentrations of $B_4O_7^{--}$ and $HB_4O_7^-$ ions in solutions obtained by dissolving borax ($Na_2B_4O_7$) in pure water, are connected with the pH and the OH^- ion concentration of these solutions by the following equations:

$$(HB_4O_7^-) = (OH^-) - 10^{-7.00} \quad \text{and} \quad \log(B_4O_7^{--}) = \log(HB_4O_7^-) - 9.00 + \text{pH} \qquad (7)$$

These two equations enable us to represent the pH's of borax solutions of different concentrations, as shown by one of the lines in Fig. 1; the solubility of borax in pure water being about 31 g/l, i.e. about 0·6 (or $10^{-0.22}$) g-at B/l, the pH of water saturated with borax will be given, according to these equations, by the abscissa of the point on this line whose ordinate is -0.22. We thus find the pH to be 11·1.

Given below for comparison is a table giving the experimental pH's and those calculated from the lines in Fig. 1, for solutions of boric acid and borax respectively 0·1 normal in dissolved borax, and saturated:

	Boric acid		Borax	
	exp.	calc.	exp.	calc.
Solutions containing 0·1 g-at B/l	5·2	5·2	9·2?	10·7
Saturated solutions	4·7	3·3	9·5	11·1

With the exception of that for one of the boric acid solutions, the calculated values do not agree very satisfactorily with the experimental values. These differences may be due to the fact that these solutions are not perfect, to errors in the values assumed here for the standard free enthalpies of formation, or to the existence of dissolved boron compounds not considered here.

The solutions considered in Fig. 1 can be obtained not only by dissolving orthoboric acid H_3BO_3, but also by dissolving other less hydrated acids in which boron has a valency of +3 (metaboric acid HBO_2 and pyroboric acid $H_4B_2O_5$), and also by dissolving boric anhydride B_2O_3 and tetraborates, such as borax $Na_2B_4O_7 . 10H_2O$.

Borate solutions can contain boron in forms other than those which have been considered here, for instance diboric ions $B_2O_4^{--}$ and hexaboric ions $B_6O_{10}^{--}$ (see Carpeni [8], Gode and Kechan [9], and Kechan [10]); moreover, taking into account the fact that we have assumed, as a first approximation, that the concentrations are equal to the activities, the analysis given above is obviously grossly approximate.

Concerning the electrochemical behaviour of boric solutions, Figs. 2–4 lead to the conclusion that it is energetically possible for the electrolysis of these solutions to result in the cathodic formation of boron hydrides; we do not know whether such a formation has been verified experimentally; at the anode, perborate BO_3^- can be formed, which is probably an addition compound $BO_2^- . H_2O_2$ of metaborate BO_2^- and hydrogen peroxide.

4. BIBLIOGRAPHY

[1] E. Deltombe, N. de Zoubov and M. Pourbaix, *Comportement électrochimique du bore. Diagrammes d'équilibre potentiel–pH du système* B–H_2O, *à* 25°C (Rapport technique RT.47 of CEBELCOR, 1957).

[2] G. Charlot, *L'analyse qualitative et les réactions en solution*, 4th ed., Masson, Paris, 1957.

[3] P. Pascal, *Traité de Chimie minérale*, Masson, Paris, Vol. IV, 1933, p. 517.

[4] *Gmelins Handbuch der anorganischen Chemie* (*Bor*, system nummer 13), Verlag Chemie G.m.b.H., Weinheim, 1954.

[5] A. Stock and C. Massenez, Borwasserstoffe, *Ber.* **45**, 3539–68 (1912).

[6] A. Stock and E. Kuss, Borwasserstoffe VI (1). Die einfachsten Borhydride, *Ber.* **56**, 789–808 (1923).

[7] H. I. Schlesinger and A. B. Burg, Hybrides of boron. I. An efficient new method of preparing diborane; new reactions for preparing bromodiborane and the stabler pentaborane, B_5H_9, *J. Amer. Chem. Soc.* **53**, 4321–2 (1931).

[8] G. Carpeni, *Bul. Soc. chim. Fr.*, 1949, p. 344.

[9] G. K. Gode and A. D. Kechan, Synthèses des borates en solutions aqueuses, *Chimie des borates*, Akad. Naouk Latviisk. S.S.R., Riga, 1953, pp. 29–43.

[10] A. D. Kechan, *La synthèse et l'étude des borates en solutions aqueuses*, Akad. Naouk Latviisk. S.S.R. Riga, 1955.

SECTION 5.2

ALUMINIUM (¹)

E. DELTOMBE, C. VANLEUGENHAGHE and M. POURBAIX

SUMMARY

1. *Substances considered and substances not considered.*

2. *Reactions and equilibrium formulae.*

2.1. Two dissolved substances.

2.1.1. Relative stability of Al^{+++} and AlO_2^-.

2.1.2. Limit of the domains of relative predominance of Al^{+++} and AlO_2^-.

2.2. Two solid substances.

Limits of the domains of relative stability of aluminium and its oxides.

2.3. One solid substance and one dissolved substance.

Solubility of aluminium and its oxides.

3. *Equilibrium diagram and its interpretation.*

3.1. Establishment of the diagram.

3.2. Stability and corrosion of aluminium.

3.3. Stability of aluminium oxide and its hydrates. Anodic oxidation of aluminium.

4. *Bibliography.*

(¹) Shortened and adapted version of the Rapport technique RT.42 of CEBELCOR (December 1956) [1]. A preliminary work was published by Delahay *et al.* [2]. The same method was used by Patrie [3] to study the formation of layers of oxide on aluminium in nitric acid solutions; Groot and Peekema [4] have also established a corrosion diagram for aluminium for a concentration of 3×10^{-6} g-ion Al/l.

1. SUBSTANCES CONSIDERED AND SUBSTANCES NOT CONSIDERED

	Oxidation number (Z)	Considered	Not considered	μ^0 (cal.)	Name, colour, crystalline system
Solid substances	0	**Al**	–	0	Aluminium, tin-white, f.c. cub.
	+3	**Al_2O_3** hydr.	–	*a*. −384 530 (2)	Trihydrated aluminium oxide (hydrargillite) $Al_2O_3 . 3H_2O$, white monocl.(3)
	»	» »	–	*b*. −382 400 (2)	Trihydrated aluminium oxide (bayerite) $Al_2O_3 . 3H_2O$, white, monocl.(3)
	»	» »	–	*c*. −378 310	Monohydrated aluminium oxide (böhmite) $Al_2O_3 . H_2O\gamma$, white, rhomb.
	»	» anh.	–	*d*. −376 770	Anhydrous aluminium oxide (corundum) $Al_2O_3\alpha$, white, rhomb.
	»	» hydr.	–	*e*. −373 730	Aluminium hydroxide $Al(OH)_3$, white, amorphous(3)
Dissolved substances	+1	–	Al^+	–	Aluminous ion, colourless
	+3	Al^{+++}	–	−115 000	Aluminic ion, colourless
	»	–	$AlOH^{++}$?	–	?
	»	–	AlO^+?	–	?
	»	AlO_2^-	–	−200 710 (2)	Aluminate ion, colourless

2. REACTIONS AND EQUILIBRIUM FORMULAE

2.1. TWO DISSOLVED SUBSTANCES

2.1.1. *Relative stability of* Al^{+++} *and* AlO_2^-

$Z = +3$

1. $Al^{+++} + 2H_2O = AlO_2^- + 4H^+$ $\qquad \log \frac{(AlO_2^-)}{(Al^{+++})} = -20.30 + 4\,pH$

2.1.2. *Limit of the domains of relative predominance of* Al^{+++} *and* AlO_2^-

1'. Al^{+++}/AlO_2^- $\qquad pH = 5.07$

2.2. TWO SOLID SUBSTANCES

Limits of the domains of relative stability of aluminium and its oxides

$0 \rightarrow +3$

2. **Al** $+ 3H_2O =$ **Al_2O_3** $+ 6H^+ + 6e^-$

$a.\ E_0 = -1.550 - 0.0591\,pH$
$b.\ \quad = -1.535 - 0.0591\,pH$
$c.\ \quad = -1.505 - 0.0591\,pH$
$d.\ \quad = -1.494 - 0.0591\,pH$
$e.\ \quad = -1.471 - 0.0591\,pH$

---

(2) We have calculated the standard free enthalpy of formation of hydrargillite [1] starting from the solubility product of hydrargillite $10^{-14.60}$ calculated by Fricke and Jucaitis [5]: that of bayerite starting from its solubility product $10^{-13.82}$ determined by Fricke and Meyring [6]. The standard free enthalpy of formation of the AlO_2^- ion was calculated from the solubility product of böhmite $(AlO_2^-)(H^+) = 10^{-12.32}$, given by Fricke and Meyring [6].

(3) These values of μ^0 for the oxides correspond to the following values for the hydrated oxides and hydroxide:

$Al_2O_3.3H_2O$ hydrargillite:	−554 600 cal.	$Al_2O_3.H_2O$ böhmite:	−435 000 cal.
$Al_2O_3.3H_2O$ bayerite:	−552 470 cal.	$Al(OH)_3$ hydroxide:	−271 900 cal.

2.3. ONE SOLID SUBSTANCE AND ONE DISSOLVED SUBSTANCE

Solubility of aluminium and its oxides

$Z = +3$

3. $2\,Al^{+++} + 3\,H_2O = Al_2O_3 + 6\,H^+$

a. $\log(Al^{+++})$	=	$5.70 - 3\,pH$
b.	=	$6.48 - 3\,pH$
c.	=	$7.98 - 3\,pH$
d.	=	$8.55 - 3\,pH$
e.	=	$9.66 - 3\,pH$

4. $Al_2O_3 + H_2O = 2\,AlO_2^- + 2\,H^+$

a. $\log(AlO_2^-)$	=	$-14.60 + pH$
b.	=	$-13.82 + pH$
c.	=	$-12.32 + pH$
d.	=	$-11.76 + pH$
e.	=	$-10.64 + pH$

$0 \rightarrow +3$

5. $Al = Al^{+++} + 3e^-$ $\quad E_0 = -1.663 + 0.0197 \log(Al^{+++})$

6. $Al + 2\,H_2O = AlO_2^- + 4\,H^+ + 3e^-$ $\quad E_0 = -1.262 - 0.0788\,pH + 0.0197 \log(AlO_2^-)$

3. EQUILIBRIUM DIAGRAM AND ITS INTERPRETATION

3.1. ESTABLISHMENT OF THE DIAGRAM

Using formulae (1)–(6) given in paragraph 2, we have drawn in Fig. 1 a potential–pH equilibrium diagram for the system aluminium–water at 25°C considering as the form of Al_2O_3 the most stable of the forms quoted in paragraph 1, i.e. hydrargillite.

In establishing the diagram we have not taken into account the cations $Al(OH)^{++}$ and $Al(OH)_2^+$ (or AlO^+) which seem to relate only to chloride complexes.

The equilibrium diagram in Fig. 1 is valid only in the absence of substances with which aluminium can form soluble complexes or insoluble salts. According to Charlot [7] the principal aluminium complexes are those formed with the anions of organic compounds (acetic, citric, tartaric, oxalic ions, etc.) and also the fluorine complexes. As sparingly soluble salts, the phosphate and oxinate may be mentioned. Calcium aluminate is also sparingly soluble.

3.2. STABILITY AND CORROSION OF ALUMINIUM

Figures 2*a* and 2*b* represent the theoretical conditions of corrosion, immunity and passivation of aluminium at 25°C, in the absence of substances with which aluminium forms soluble complexes or insoluble salts. Figure 2*a*, deduced from Fig. 1, refers to passivation by the formation of a layer of hydrargillite $Al_2O_3 \cdot 3H_2O$. Figure 2*b* refers to passivation by the formation of a layer of böhmite $Al_2O_3 \cdot H_2O$, which is usually the practical case, notably when the metal becomes covered with a layer of anodic oxide (see paragraph 3.3).

From Figs. 1 and 2 aluminium is seen to be a very base metal, as the whole of its domain of stability lies below that of water. In the presence of sufficiently acid solutions, it decomposes water with the evolution of hydrogen, dissolving as trivalent Al^{+++} ions; under certain conditions which are little known at present this dissolution occurs with the formation of monovalent Al^+ ions. In the presence of sufficiently alkaline solutions aluminium decomposes water with the evolution of hydrogen, dissolving as aluminate ions AlO_2^-.

In non-complexing solutions of pH roughly between 4 and 9, aluminium tends to become covered with a film of oxide; the nature of the film is generally complex (see paragraph 3.3).

In practice, the corrosion behaviour of aluminium is determined essentially by the behaviour of the oxide film with which it is almost always covered towards the corroding media to be considered. Cases of bad resistance to corrosion are often connected with a change in this oxide film, notably in its degree of hydration and porosity.

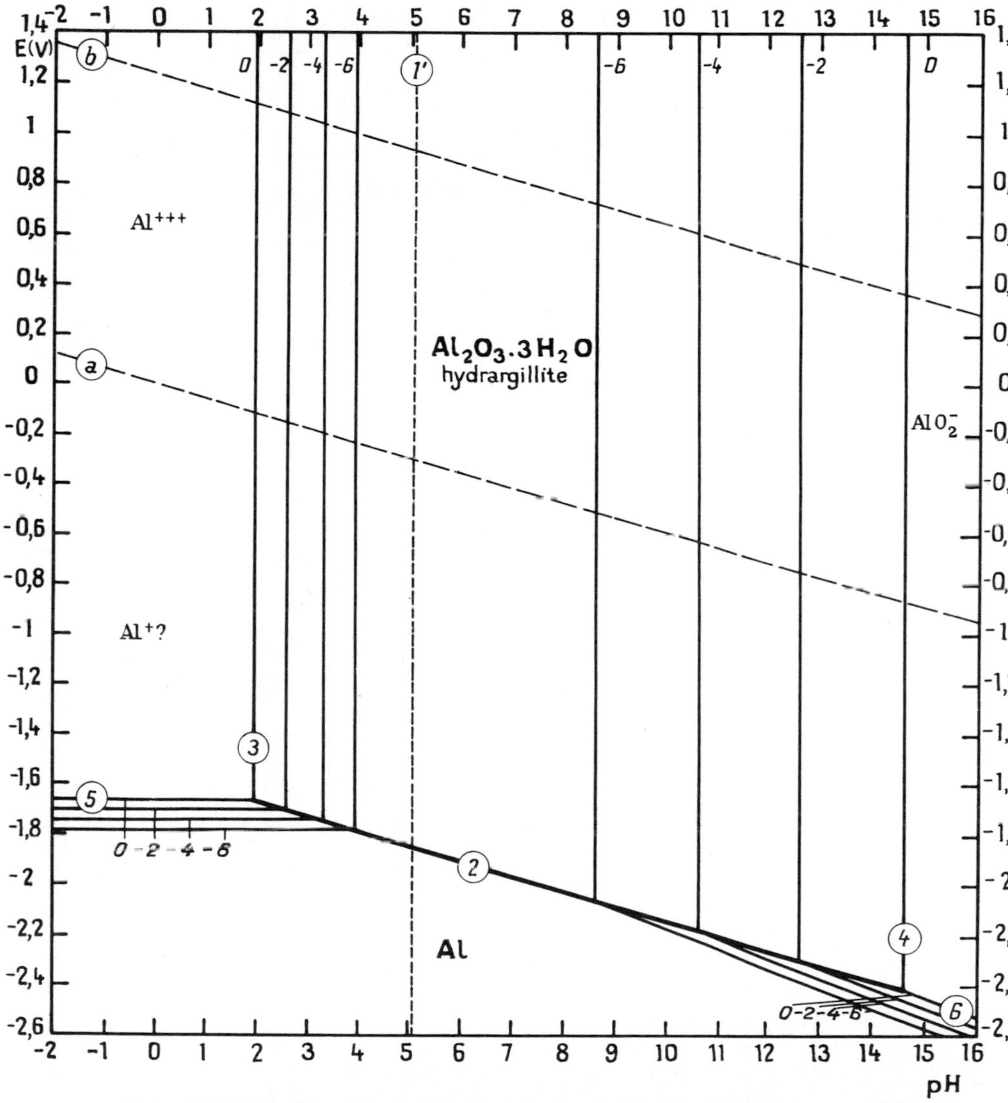

FIG. 1. Potential–pH equilibrium diagram for the system aluminium–water, at 25°C.

Chatalov [8] has studied the corrosion rate of aluminium as a function of the pH in various buffer solutions; his results are reproduced in Figs. 3*a* and 3*b*.

The equilibrium potential of the reaction $Al \rightarrow Al^{+++} + 3e^-$ (5) is practically impossible to measure directly, on account of the great tendency for hydrogen to be evolved at such low potentials; the measurements are also complicated by the great tendency of aluminium to cover itself with a layer of non-conducting oxide. Heyrovsky [9] used a liquid aluminium amalgam, enabling him to practically eliminate the secondary reaction $H_2 \rightarrow 2H^+ + 2e^-$.

As stated above (pp. 15 and 137), pitting of passivable metals (including aluminium) due to chlorides may sometimes be avoided by a cathodic treatment which brings the metal into a state of perfect passivation, by improving the quality of the protective oxide film. But cathodic protection of aluminium by bringing the metal into a state of immunity (without protective oxide) is practically impossible on

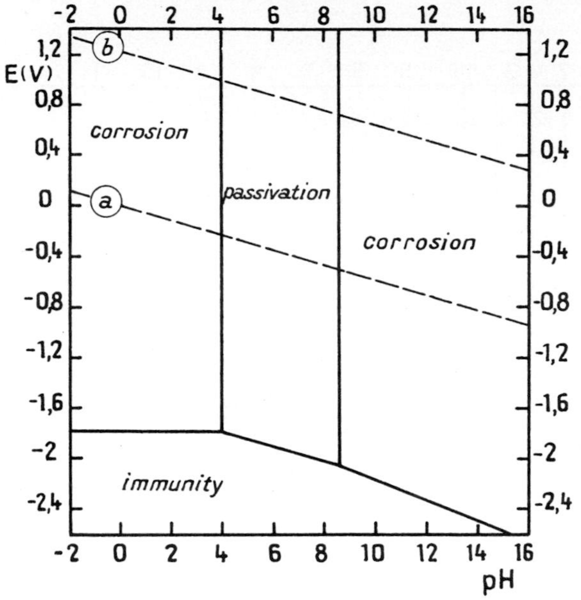

(*a*) Passivation by a film of hydrargillite $Al_2O_3.3H_2O$.

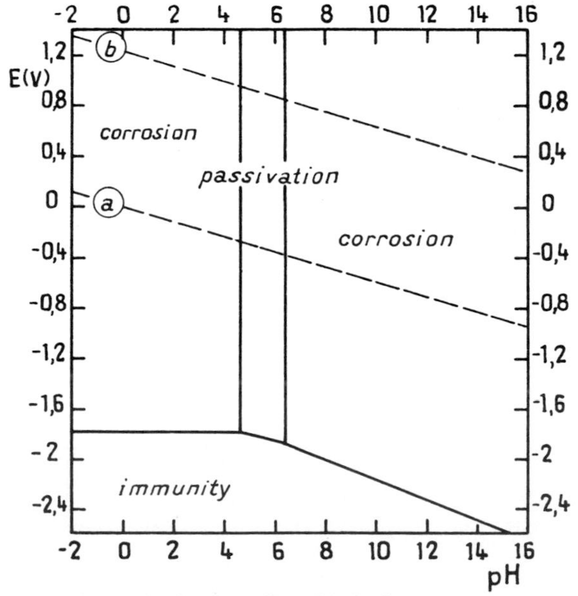

(*b*) Passivation by a film of böhmite $Al_2O_3.H_2O$.

FIG. 2. Theoretical conditions of corrosion, immunity and passivation of aluminium, at 25°C.

account of the very low equilibrium potential of the metal. For the same reason it is practically impossible to electrodeposit aluminium from aqueous solutions, although, under very special conditions, aluminium has been deposited electrochemically. The classical process for the electrolytic separation of the metal remains that of igneous electrolysis.

3.3. STABILITY OF ALUMINIUM OXIDE AND ITS HYDRATES. ANODIC OXIDATION OF ALUMINIUM

Aluminium oxide, or alumina, Al_2O_3 occurs in various forms: the ordinary variety is corundum or α-alumina, crystallizing in the rhombohedral system; the other varieties are β-alumina (hexagonal crystals), γ-alumina (cubic crystals) and δ-alumina (rhombohedral crystals). The physical and chemical properties of alumina depend to a large extent on the temperature reached during its preparation; thus, when heated to a high temperature, alumina loses its property of being a hygroscopic substance and at the same time becomes practically insoluble in acids and bases.

When alkali is added to a solution of an aluminium salt, or acid is added to an aluminate, a precipitate is obtained which is a hydroxide gel, corresponding practically to the composition $Al(OH)_3$ and amphoteric in nature.

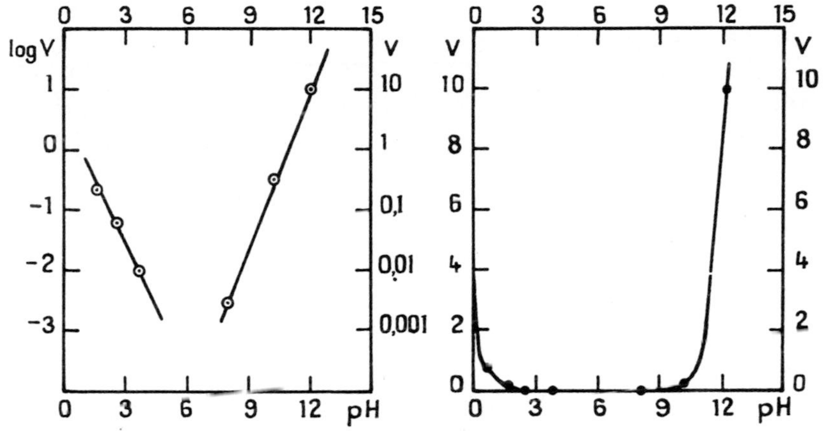

(*a*) log V as a function of pH. (*b*) log V as a function of pH.
(V, corrosion rate in mg/dm² h).

FIG. 3. Influence of pH on the corrosion rate of aluminium (Chatalov).

This aluminium hydroxide gel is not stable, however; it crystallizes in the course of time to give first the monohydrate γ-$Al_2O_3 . H_2O$ or böhmite, crystallizing in the rhombohedral system, then the trihydrate $Al_2O_3 . 3H_2O$ or bayerite, crystallizing in the monoclinic system, and, finally another trihydrate, hydrargillite, crystallizing in the same system. This development of aluminium hydroxide is known as "ageing".

The various hydrates formed during the ageing are characterized by an increasing stability and an accompanying variation in all their properties, in particular their solubility in acids, bases and pure water. In Fig. 4 we have drawn a series of curves expressing the influence of pH on the solubility of the various compounds for which we have free enthalpy values; these curves are deduced from the equilibrium relations established in paragraph 2. In Table I we give for each of these compounds the logarithm of the acid and alkaline solubility products, the logarithm of the minimum solubility which occurs at a pH of 5·1, the logarithm of the solubility in pure water, the pH obtained by dissolution in pure water and finally the crystallographic system.

In Fig. 4 we have drawn, from formulae (3) and (4), a series of curves expressing the influence of pH on the solubility of the five forms of alumina for which we know the free enthalpies of formation. We have also reproduced Kolthoff's experimental data [10] which Latimer considered to refer to the amorphous hydroxide but are much nearer to those of böhmite. This is probably due to the fact that Kolthoff gave the precipitated hydroxide time to stabilize itself. Thus when the measurements were made it is most likely that the substance in question was no longer an $Al(OH)_3$ gel.

TABLE I. Solubility of aluminium oxide and its hydrates

	Formula	log $[(Al^{+++})(OH^{-})^3]$	log $[(AlO_2^-)(H^+)]$	log (minimum solubility) (g-at Al/l)	log (solubility in pure water) (g-at Al/l)	pH on dissolution in water	Crystallographic system
Hydrargillite	$Al_2O_3 . 3H_2O$	−36·30	−14·60	−9·2	−7·8	6·8	Monocl.
Bayerite	$Al_2O_3 . 3H_2O$	−35·52	−13·82	−8·5	−7·2	6·7	Monocl.
Böhmite	γ-$Al_2O_3 . H_2O$	−34·02	−12·32	−7·0	−6·2	6·1	Tern.
Corundum	α-Al_2O_3	−33·45	−11·76	−6·4	−5·9	5·9	Tern.
Amorphous hydroxide	$Al(OH)_3$	−32·34	−10·64	−5·3	−5·3	5·3	Amorphous

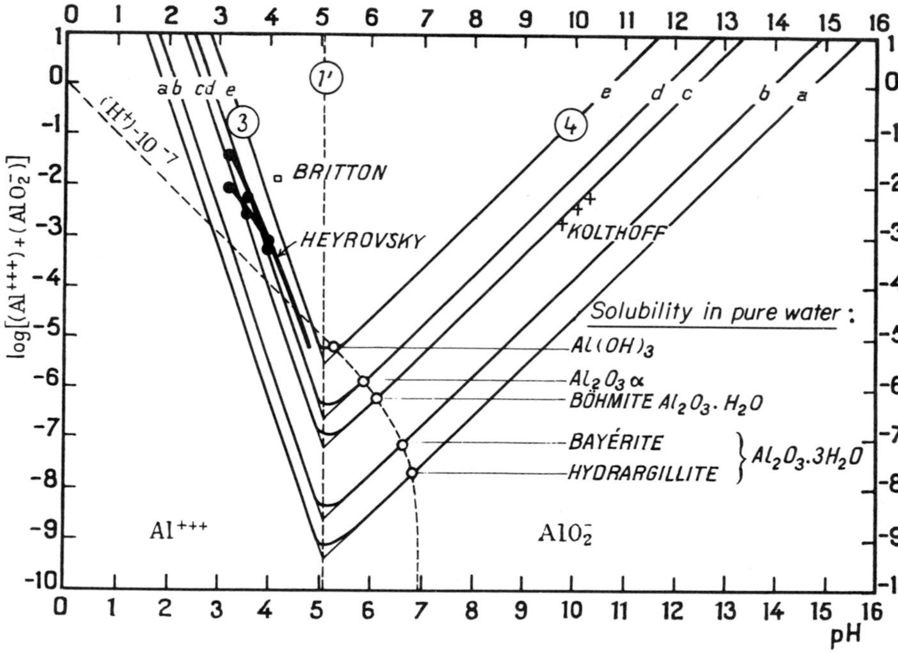

FIG. 4. Influence of pH on the solubility of Al_2O_3 and its hydrates, at 25°C.

The alkaline solubility products of böhmite, bayerite and hydrargillite are those given by Fricke and Meyring [6] and Fricke and Jucaitis [5]. They have been used to calculate the free enthalpies of these compounds [1].

The solubility product in acid solution has been calculated by Heyrovsky [11]. In Fig. 4 we have drawn the section of the straight line corresponding to Heyrovsky's solubility product $10^{-32.97}$ for concentrations below 10^{-4} M. For higher concentrations we have represented the lower and higher limits assumed by Heyrovsky for the value of (Al^{+++}) as a function of pH. We have also marked on Fig. 4 a point representing a result obtained by Britton [12], concerning freshly precipitated $Al(OH)_3$.

With regard to the minimum solubility of the hydrates, Edwards and Buswell [13] point out that, when town-water is clarified by means of aluminium compounds, the residual aluminium concentration in the treated water rarely exceeds 2 mg Al/l, i.e. $10^{-4.1}$ g-at Al/l.

Concerning the solubilities in pure water, Remy and Kuhlmann [14] calculated that of Al_2O_3 at 20°C, first by conductiometric titration ($10^{-4.74}$ g-at Al/l) and then by specific conductivity measurement ($10^{-4.69}$ g-at Al/l). Busch [15] obtained the value $10^{-4.72}$ g-at Al/l by acidimetric titration of a saturated solution at 29°C. Jander and Ruperti [16] determined analytically the percentage of Al_2O_3 in a saturated solution of $Al(OH)_3$ at 12–15°C and found it to be $10^{-5.11}$ g-at Al/l.

All these values agree well enough among themselves, but leave open the question of exactly which form of oxide or hydroxide they represent; they are all greater than the solubilities in pure water calculated from Fig. 4; the greatest one of these for amorphous $Al(OH)_3$ is $10^{-5.3}$ g-at Al/l, i.e. 0·13 mg Al/l.

The anodic behaviour of aluminium is affected by the formation of a passivating layer of oxide on the surface of the metal. Much use is made of anodically treated aluminium. This treatment covers the metal with a layer of oxide which gives it desirable properties, such as the absorption of coloured materials and resistance to chemical reagents and to the passage of electric currents.

The structure of the anodic deposit has been the object of numerous studies. The X-ray identification of alumina was carried out by Burgers *et al.* [17], in 1932. Belwe identified the same substance by electron diffraction [18].

When the oxide layer is clogged up by boiling water, the γ-oxide is converted into böhmite. It follows that the layer of oxide is made up of a thin film of anhydrous γ-Al_2O_3, directly in contact with the metal, while the part in contact with the bath consists of monohydrated alumina [19]. According to a recent study by Hart [20], the film formed on extra pure aluminium immersed in water not above 60°C develops in three stages: first of all amorphous hydroxide is formed, then orthorhombic γ-$AlO.OH$ and then bayerite $Al_2O_3 . 3H_2O$; the final film will therefore, according to Hart, be made up of three layers.

As we have said in paragraph 3.2, the corrosion resistance of aluminium is determined essentially by the behaviour of its layer of oxide. Practically neutral solutions are in general without action, except in the particular cases when there is danger of pitting, which occurs mainly in the presence of chlorides. In acid or alkaline solutions, the aluminium will be attacked as soon as the oxide film is eliminated. This dissolution is slower in acid solutions than in alkaline solutions.

4. BIBLIOGRAPHY

[1] E. Deltombe and M. Pourbaix, *Comportement électrochimique de l'aluminium. Diagrammes d'équilibres tension-pH du système* Al–H_2O *à* 25°C (Rapport technique RT.42 of CEBELCOR, December 1955).

[2] P. Delahay, M. Pourbaix and P. Van Rysselberghe, *Diagrammes d'équilibres potentiel–pH de quelques éléments* (C. R. 3e réunion du CITCE, Berne, 1951).

[3] J. Patrie, *Contribution à l'étude des phénomènes de passivation de l'aluminium immergé en milieu nitrique* (Thèse, Grenoble, 1952).

[4] C. Groot and R. M. Peekema, *The Potential-pH Diagram for Aluminium,* U.S. Atomic Energy Comm. Publ. H.W.28556, 1953, 13 pages.

[5] R. Fricke and P. Jucaitis, Untersuchungen über die Gleichgewichte in den Systemen Al_2O_3, $Na_2O . H_2O$ und Al_2O_3, $K_2O . H_2O$, *Z. anorg. allgem. Chem.* **191**, 129–49 (1930).

[6] R. Fricke and K. Meyring, Zur Älterung junger Aluminium Hydroxydgel, *Z. anorg. allgem. Chem.* **214**, 269–74 (1933).

[7] G. Charlot, *L'analyse qualitative et les réactions en solution,* 2nd ed., Masson, Paris, 1957.

[8] A. Ya. Chatalov, Effet du pH sur le comportement électrochimique des métaux et leur résistance à la corrosion, *Dokl. Akad. Naouk S.S.S.R.* **86**, 775–7 (1952).

[9] J. Heyrovsky, The Electroaffinity of Aluminium. Part II. The aluminium electrode, *J. Chem. Soc.* **117**, 27–36 (1920).

[10] I. M. Kolthoff, Die azidimetrische Bestimmung schwerer Metalle in ihren salzen, *Z. anorg. allgem. Chem.* **112**, 172–86 (1920).

[11] J. Heyrovsky, The electroaffinity of aluminium. Part I. The ionisation and hydrolysis of aluminium chloride, *J. Chem. Soc.* **117**, 11–26 (1920).

[12] H. T. S. Britton, Electrometric studies of the precipitation of hydroxides. Part II. The precipitation of hydroxides of zinc, chromium, beryllium, aluminium, bivalent tin and zirconium by use of the hydrogen electrode and their alleged atmospheric nature, *J. Chem. Soc.*, 2120–41 (1925).

[13] G. P. Edwards and A. M. Buswell, La relation entre la concentration en ion hydrogène et les propriétés de l'aluminium floculé, *Illinois State Water Surv. Bull.* **22**, 47–72 (1925); *Z.B.*, 1927, I, p. 1718.

[14] H. REMY and A. KUHLMANN, Löslichkeitsbestimmungen an schwerlöslichen Stoffen. II. Wasserlöslichkeit der Oxyde von Beryllium, Aluminium, Zink, Cadmium, Blei, Kupfer und Silber, *Z. anal. Chem.* **65**, 161–81 (1924–5).
[15] W. BUSCH, Ueber die Verwendbarkeit der electrometrischen Titration zur Löslichkeitsbestimmung schwerlöslicher Oxyde, *Z. anorg. allgem. Chem.* **161**, 161–79 (1927).
[16] G. JANDER and O. RUPERTI, Zur Fällung des Aluminiums als Oxydhydrat mittels Ammoniaks, *Z. anorg. allgem. Chem.* **153**, 253–9 (1926).
[17] W. G. BURGERS, A. CLAASEN and I. ZERNIKE, Ueber die chemische Natur des Oxydschichten welche sich bei anodischer Polarisation auf Metallen Aluminium, Zirkon, Titan und Tantal bilden, *Z. Phys.* **74**, 593–603 (1932).
[18] E. BELWE, Untersuchung von Aluminiumoxyden mittels Elektroneinterferenzen, *Z. Phys.* **100**, 192–6 (1936).
[19] J. PATRIE, Le mécanisme de l'oxydation électrolytique et la formation des couches d'oxyde d'alumine, *Rev. Aluminium*, **26**, 397–403 (1949); **27**, 3–7 (1950).
[20] R. K. HART, The formation of films on aluminium immersed in water, *Trans. Faraday Soc.* **53**, No. 7, 1020–7 (1957).

SECTIONS 5.3 AND 5.4

SCANDIUM, YTTRIUM [1]

J. Van Muylder

SUMMARY

[1] Rapport CEFA/R.9 of the Commission des Études Fondamentales et Applications of CEBELCOR.

1. SUBSTANCES CONSIDERED

	Oxidation number (Z)	Considered		μ^0 (cal.)	Name, colour, crystalline system
SCANDIUM					
Solid substances	0	**Sc**		0	Scandium, light grey, hex.
	+3	**Sc_2O_3**	hydr.	a. −416 930	Scandium hydroxide $Sc(OH)_3$, white, amorphous(3)
Dissolved substances	»	»	anh.	b. −390 000 (2)	Scandium oxide, white, cub.
	+3	Sc^{+++}		−143 700	Scandic ion, colourless
	»	$ScOH^{++}$		−193 700 (2)	Scandyl ion, colourless
YTTRIUM					
Solid substances	0	**Y**		0	Yttrium, grey, hex.
	+3	**Y_2O_3**	hydr.	a. −444 130	Yttrium hydroxide $Y(OH)_3$, light yellow(3)
Dissolved substance	»	»	anh.	b. −402 000 (2)	Yttrium oxide, white, cub.
	+3	Y^{+++}		−164 100	Yttric ion

2. REACTIONS AND EQUILIBRIUM FORMULAE

Scandium (4)

2.1. TWO DISSOLVED SUBSTANCES

2.1.1. *Relative stability of the dissolved substances*

$Z = +3$

1. $Sc^{+++} + H_2O = ScOH^{++} + H^+$ $\qquad \log\frac{(ScOH^{++})}{(Sc^{+++})} = -4.93 + pH$

2.1.2. *Limits of the domains of relative predominance of the dissolved substances*

1'. $Sc^{+++}/ScOH^{++}$ $\qquad pH = 4.93$

2.2. TWO SOLID SUBSTANCES

Limits of the domains of relative stability of the solid substances

$0 \rightarrow +3$

2. $2\,\mathbf{Sc} + 3H_2O = \mathbf{Sc_2O_3} + 6H^+ + 6e^-$
 a. $E_0 = -1.784 - 0.0591\,pH$
 b. $E_0 = -1.591 - 0.0591\,pH$

2.3. ONE DISSOLVED SUBSTANCE AND ONE SOLID SUBSTANCE

Solubility of the solid substances

$Z = +3$

3. $2Sc^{+++} + 3H_2O = \mathbf{Sc_2O_3} + 6H^+$
 a. $\log(Sc^{+++}) = 14.87 - 3pH$
 b. $\phantom{\log(Sc^{+++})} = 24.75 - 3pH$

4. $2ScOH^{++} + H_2O = \mathbf{Sc_2O_3} + 4H^+$
 a. $\log(ScOH^{++}) = 9.94 - 2pH$
 b. $\phantom{\log(ScOH^{++})} = 19.82 - 2pH$

---

(2) Values given by Brewer [1].

(3) The value for $\mu^0_{Sc_2O_3}$ corresponds to $\mu^0_{Sc(OH)_3} = -293\,500$ cal. and the value for $\mu^0_{Y_2O_3}$ corresponds to $\mu^0_{Y(OH)_3} = -307\,100$ cal.

(4) Concerning the reactions involving Sc_2O_3, the letter *a* refers to $Sc(OH)_3$, whose free enthalpy of formation is $-293\,500$ cal.; the letter *b* refers to anhydrous Sc_2O_3, whose free enthalpy of formation is $-390\,000$ cal.

$0 \rightarrow +3$

5.	**Sc**	$= Sc^{+++}$	$+ 3e^-$	$E_0 = -2.077$	$+0.0197 \log(Sc^{+++})$
6.	**Sc**	$+ H_2O = ScOH^{++} + H^+$	$+ 3e^-$	$E_0 = -1.980 - 0.0197\,pH$	$+0.0197 \log(ScOH^{++})$

Yttrium (5)

2.2. TWO SOLID SUBSTANCES

Limits of the domains of relative stability of the solid substances

$0 \rightarrow +3$

2. $2Y + 3H_2O = Y_2O_3 + 6H^+ + 6e^-$ a. $E_0 = -1.981 - 0.0591\,pH$
 b. $= -1.676 - 0.0591\,pH$

2.3. ONE DISSOLVED SUBSTANCE AND ONE SOLID SUBSTANCE

Solubility of the solid substances

$Z = +3$

3. $2Y^{+++} + 3H_2O = Y_2O_3 + 6H^+$ a. $\log(Y^{+++}) = 19.86 - 3\,pH$
 b. $= 33.32 - 3\,pH$

$0 \rightarrow +3$

3. $Y = Y^{+++} + 3e^-$ $E_0 = -2.372 + 0.0197 \log(Y^{+++})$

3. EQUILIBRIUM DIAGRAMS AND THEIR INTERPRETATION

3.1. ESTABLISHMENT OF THE DIAGRAMS

Using the equilibrium formulae given in paragraph 2, we have drawn Figs. 1–4.

Using all these formulae, we have established, in Fig. 1, an equilibrium diagram for the system scandium–water, and, in Fig. 2, an equilibrium diagram for the system yttrium–water.

In Figs. 3 and 4 we have represented, using equations (1′), (3) and (4), the influence of pH on the solubility of scandium oxide and hydroxide, and yttrium oxide and hydroxide, respectively.

These figures are valid only in the absence of substances with which scandium and yttrium can form soluble complexes or insoluble salts. According to Latimer [2], the oxalates, phosphates and carbonates of scandium and yttrium are very sparingly soluble, as is the fluoride ScF_3, which is, nevertheless, soluble in NH_4F with the formation of the complex ion ScF_6^{---}.

3.2. STABILITY OF SCANDIUM AND YTTRIUM

Scandium and yttrium both have a very large negative equilibrium potential. As the whole of their domain of stability, in Figs. 1 and 2, lies well below that of water, these metals are very unstable in the presence of aqueous solutions of any pH.

They are extremely base metals and powerful reducing agents, having a great affinity to react with water which they decompose with the evolution of hydrogen.

In the presence of acid and neutral solutions, the liberation of hydrogen is accompanied by the dissolution of scandium and yttrium respectively in the form of Sc^{+++} (scandic) and $ScOH^{++}$ ("scandyl") ions, and Y^{+++} (yttric) ions.

---

(5) Concerning the reactions involving Y_2O_3, the letter *a* refers to $Y(OH)_3$, whose free enthalpy of formation is $-444\,130$ cal.; the letter *b* refers to anhydrous Y_2O_3, whose free enthalpy of formation is $-402\,000$ cal.

In the presence of alkaline solutions, the evolution of hydrogen takes place concurrently with the formation of scandium hydroxide $Sc(OH)_3$, and yttrium hydroxide $Y(OH)_3$.

According to Figs. 1 and 2 the covering of scandium and yttrium with a layer of hydroxide takes place at pH's respectively above 5 to 8 and 6·5 to 8·5, depending on the concentration of these elements in the solution.

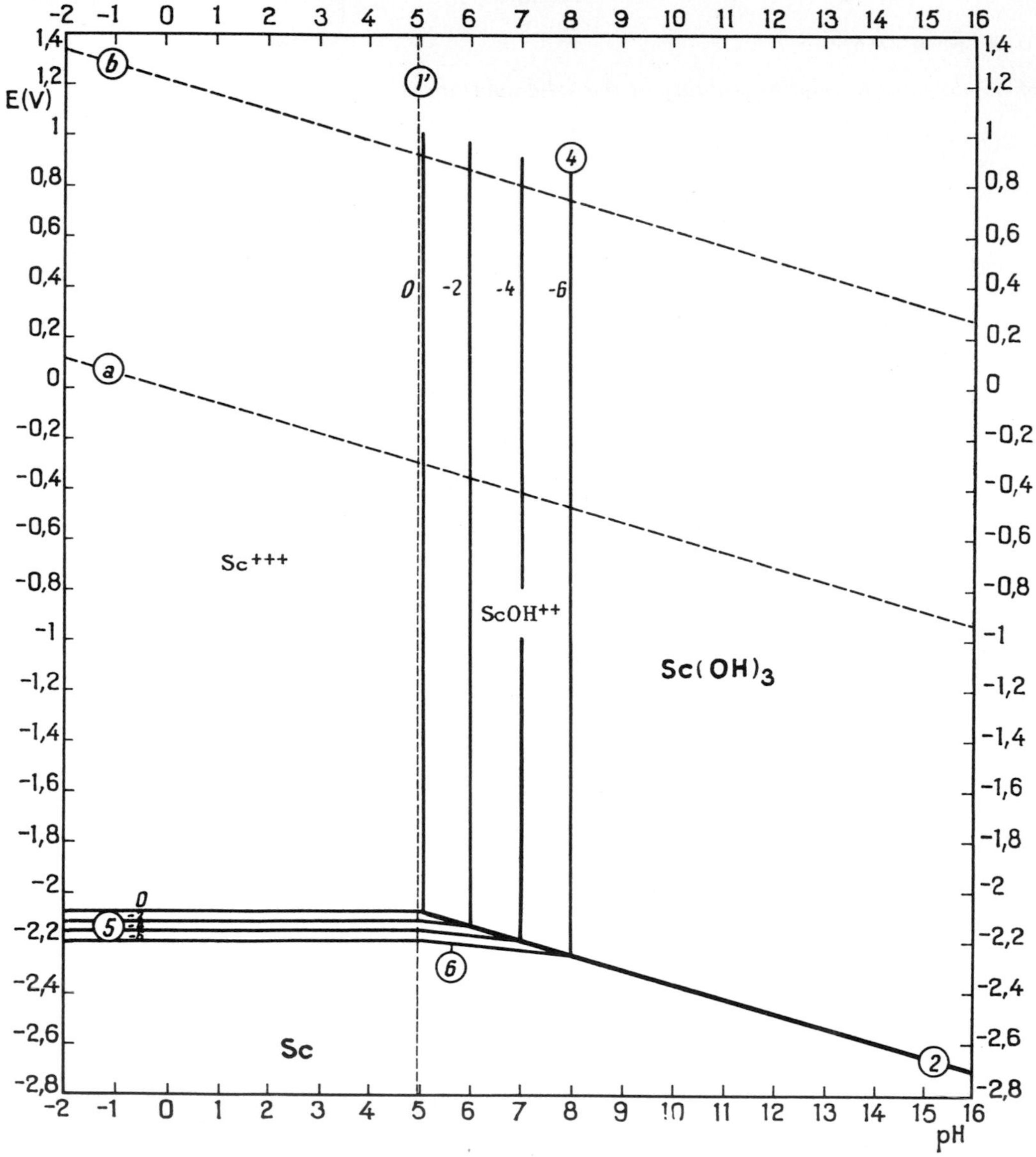

FIG. 1. Potential–pH equilibrium diagram for the system scandium–water, at 25°C.

3.3. STABILITY OF THE OXIDES AND HYDROXIDES OF SCANDIUM AND YTTRIUM

From Figs. 1 and 2 the hydroxides of scandium and yttrium, which can be obtained by treating aqueous solutions of the salts of these metals with a base, are substances which are thermodynamically stable in the presence of alkaline solutions, and unstable in the presence of acid solutions in which they dissolve as Sc^{+++} and $ScOH^{++}$ ions, and Y^{+++} ions.

From the free enthalpy of formation values given by Latimer [2] and Brewer [1], which are reproduced in paragraph 1, the oxides Sc_2O_3 and Y_2O_3 are unstable with respect to the corresponding hydroxides $Sc(OH)_3$ and $Y(OH)_3$. The oxides tend to be converted into the hydroxides by spontaneous hydration, and consequently the hydroxides alone appear in Figs. 1 and 2, in which only stable equilibria are considered.

The influence of pH on the solubility of scandium and yttrium hydroxides is represented graphically in Figs. 3 and 4.

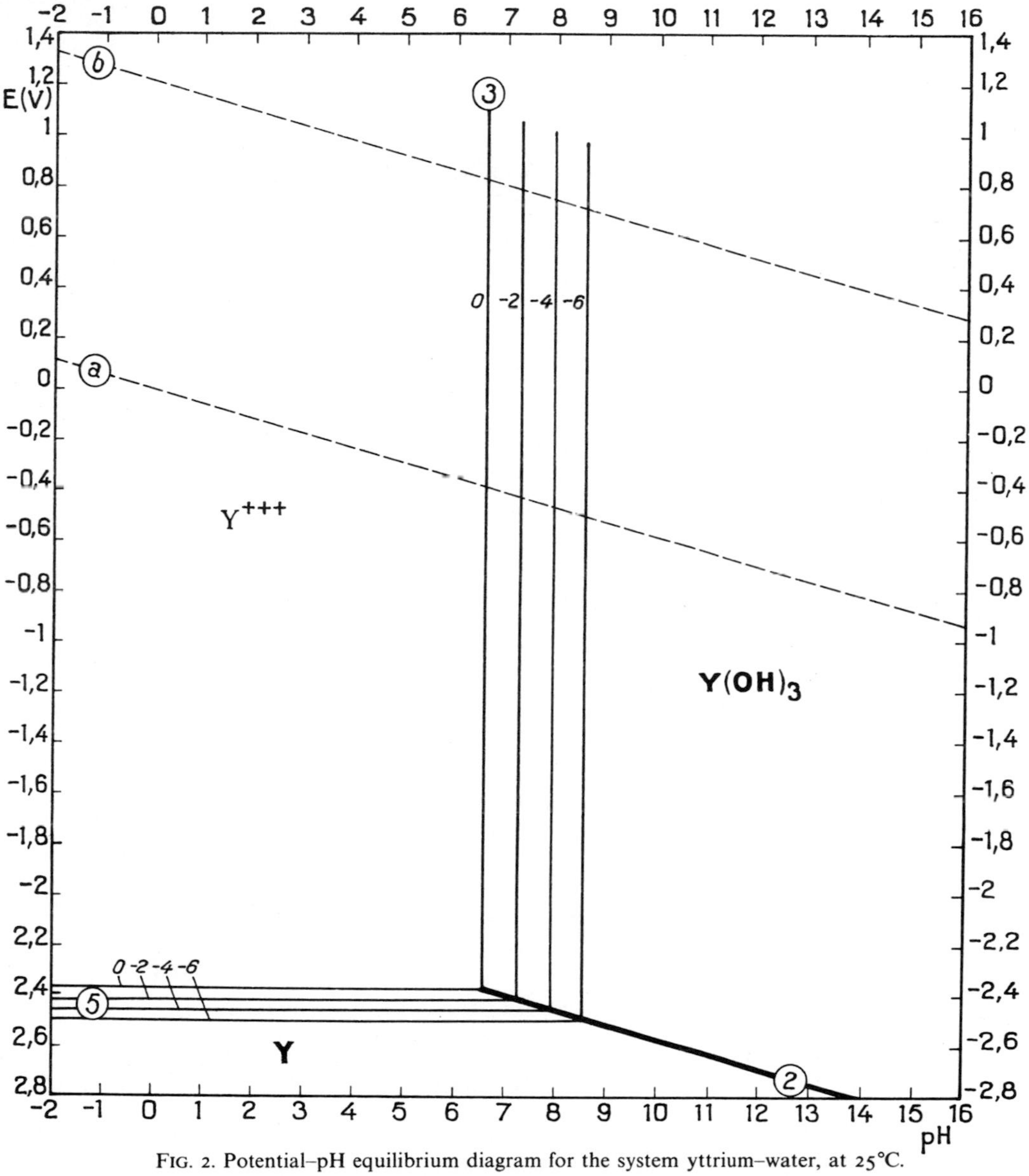

FIG. 2. Potential–pH equilibrium diagram for the system yttrium–water, at 25°C.

The solutions obtained by saturating pure water respectively with $Sc(OH)_3$ and $Y(OH)_3$ have the following characteristics, at 25°C, according to Figs. 3 and 4.

	Water saturated with $Sc(OH)_3$	Water saturated with $Y(OH)_3$
pH	8·1	8·6
log (M^{+++})	−6·2	−5·9
($M(OH)_3$) mg/l	0·06	0·14

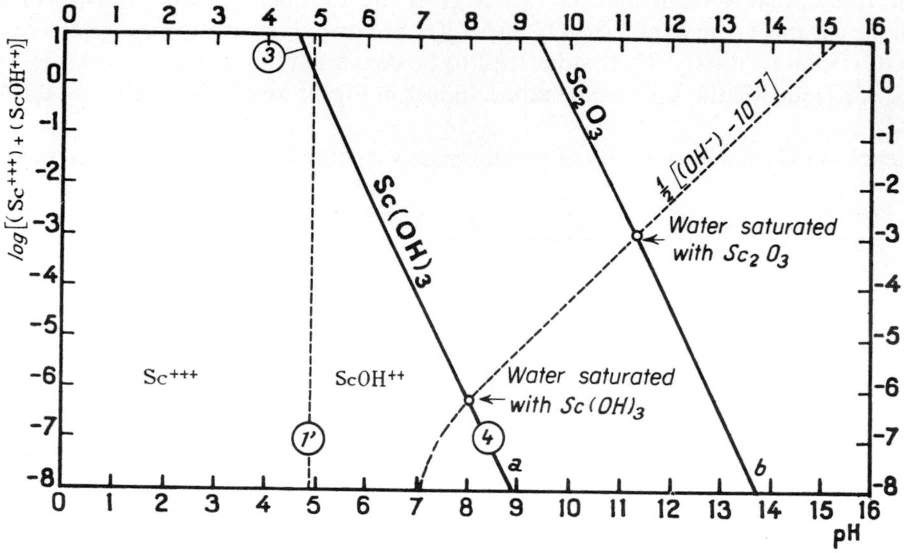

FIG. 3. Influence of pH on the solubility of scandium oxide and hydroxide, at 25°C.

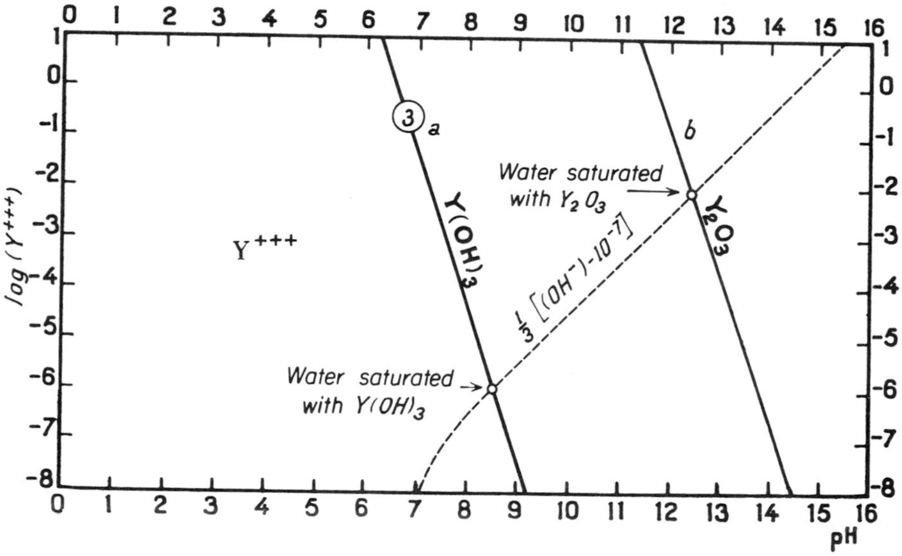

FIG. 4. Influence of pH on the solubility of yttrium oxide and hydroxide, at 25°C.

4. BIBLIOGRAPHY

[1] L. BREWER, Thermodynamic properties of the oxides and their vaporization processes, *Chem. Rev.* **52**, 1 (1953).
[2] W. LATIMER, *Oxidation Potentials*, 2nd ed., Prentice-Hall, New York, 1952.

SECTION 6

LANTHANIDES[1]

N. DE ZOUBOV and J. VAN MUYLDER

SUMMARY

[1] Adapted version of the Rapport CEFA/R.8 of the Commission des Études Fondamentales et Application of CEBELCOR.

1. SUBSTANCES CONSIDERED AND SUBSTANCES NOT CONSIDERED

	Oxidation number (Z)	Considered	Not considered	μ^0(cal.)	Name, colour, crystalline system
LANTHANUM					
Solid substances	0	**La**	–	0	Lanthanum, white, hex. or f.c. cub.
	+ 3	La_2O_3 hydr.	–	*a*. —456 330	Hydroxide, white, amorphous(2)
	»	» anh.	–	*b*. —426 900	Oxide, white, rhomb. or cub.
Dissolved substance	+ 3	La^{+++}	–	—174 500	Lanthanum ion, colourless
CERIUM					
Solid substances	0	**Ce**	–	0	Cerium, grey, hex. or f.c. cub.
	+ 3	Ce_2O_3 hydr.	–	—453 190	Cerous hydroxide, grey-green(2)
	+ 4	CeO_2	–	—219 000	Ceric oxide, light yellow, cub.
	+ 6	–	CeO_3 hydr.	–	Hydrated peroxide
Dissolved substances	+ 3	Ce^{+++}	–	—171 750	Cerous ion, colourless
	+ 4	–	Ce^{++++}	–	Ceric ion
	»	$Ce(OH)^{+++}$	–	—188 900	Ceric ion, yellow
	»	$Ce(OH)_2^{++}$	–	—245 200	Ceric ion, orange
PRASEODYMIUM					
Solid substances	0	**Pr**	–	0	Praseodymium, pale yellow, hex. or f.c. cub.
	+ 3	Pr_2O_3 hydr.	–	*a*. —449 330	Hydroxide(2)
	»	» anh.	–	*b*. —423 100	Sesquioxide, yellow-green, rhomb. or cub.
	+ 4	PrO_2	–	—220 000	Dioxide, black, cub.
Dissolved substances	+ 3	Pr^{+++}	–	—170 300	Praseodymous ion, green
	+ 4	Pr^{++++}	–	—104 350 (3)	Praseodymic ion
NEODYMIUM					
Solid substances	0	**Nd**	–	0	Neodymium, light yellow, hex.
	+ 3	Nd_2O_3 hydr.	–	*a*. —448 530	Hydroxide(2)
	»	» anh.	–	*b*. —420 600	Oxide, light blue, rhomb. or cub.
	+ 4	–	NdO_2 ?	–	Dioxide
Dissolved substance	+ 3	Nd^{+++}	–	—168 200	Neodymium ion, purplish pink

(2) These values of μ^0 for the oxides correspond to the following values for the hydroxides:

$La(OH)_3$	– 313 200 cal.	$Sm(OH)_3$	– 308 700 cal.	$Ho(OH)_3$	– 304 100 cal.
$Ce(OH)_3$	– 311 630 „	$Eu(OH)_3$	– 308 600 „	$Er(OH)_3$	– 302 800 „
$Pr(OH)_3$	– 309 700 „	$Gd(OH)_3$	– 308 000 „	$Tm(OH)_3$	– 302 400 „
$Nd(OH)_3$	– 309 300 „	$Tb(OH)_3$	– 307 800 „	$Yb(OH)_3$	– 301 700 „
$Pm(OH)_3$	– 309 000 „	$Dy(OH)_3$	– 305 400 „	$Lu(OH)_3$	– 301 000 „

(3) Value calculated considering E_0^0 of the equilibrium Pr^{+++}/Pr^{++++} to be equal to 2·86 V (Latimer).

	Oxidation number (Z)	Considered	Not considered	μ^0(cal.)	Name, colour, crystalline system
PROMETHIUM					
Solid substances	0	**Pm**	–	0	Promethium
	+3	**Pm_2O_3** hydr.	–	—447 930	Hydroxide(2)
Dissolved substance	+3	Pm^{+++}	–	—167 600	Promethium ion
SAMARIUM					
Solid substances	0	**Sm**	–	0	Samarium, light grey, rhomb. or hex.
	+3	**Sm_2O_3** hydr.	–	*a.* —447 330	Hydroxide, light yellow(2)
	»	–	**Sm_2O_3** anh.	*b.* –	Oxide, yellowish-white, cub.
Dissolved substances	+2	Sm^{++}	–	—143 940 (4)	Samarous ion
	+3	Sm^{+++}	–	—167 000	Samaric ion
EUROPIUM					
Solid substances	0	**Eu**	–	0	Europium, steel grey, b.c. cub.
	+3	**Eu_2O_3** hydr.	–	—447 130	Hydroxide, pale pink
Dissolved substances	+2	Eu^{++}	–	—156 600	Europous ion
	+3	Eu^{+++}	–	—166 500	Europic ion, pink
GADOLINIUM					
Solid substances	0	**Gd**	–	0	Gadolinium, hex.
	+3	**Gd_2O_3** hydr.	–	*a.* —445 930	Hydroxide, white, amorphous(2)
	»	–	**Gd_2O_3** anh.	*b.* –	Oxide, grey, cub.
Dissolved substance	+3	Gd^{+++}	–	—165 800	Gadolinium ion
Gaseous substance	0	–	*Gd*	77 000	Gadolinium
TERBIUM					
Solid substances	0	**Tb**	–	0	Terbium, grey–blue, hex.
	+3	**Tb_2O_3** hydr.	–	—445 530	Hydroxide, white, cub.(2)
	+4	–	**TbO_2**?	–	Peroxide, brown–black or black
Dissolved substance	+3	Tb^{+++}	–	—165 400	Terbium ion
DYSPROSIUM					
Solid substances	0	**Dy**	–	0	Dysprosium, hex.
	+3	**Dy_2O_3** hydr.	–	—440 730	Hydroxide, white, cub.(2)
Dissolved substance	+3	Dy^{+++}	–	—162 800	Dysprosium ion
HOLMIUM					
Solid substances	0	**Ho**	–	0	Holmium, hex.
	+3	**Ho_2O_3** hydr.	–	—438 130	Hydroxide(2)
Dissolved substance	+3	Ho^{+++}	–	—160 400	Holmium ion, light yellow

(4) Value calculated supposing E_0^0 of the reaction Sm^{++}/Sm^{+++} to be equal to -1.00 V (Latimer gives $E_0 > 0.9$).

	Oxidation number (Z)	Considered	Not considered	μ^0(cal.)	Name, colour, crystalline system
ERBIUM					
Solid substances	o	**Er**	–	0	Erbium, dark grey, hex.
	+3	Er_2O_3 hydr.	–	−435 530	Hydroxide, light pink, cub.
Dissolved substance	+3	Er^{+++}	–	−158 860	Erbium ion, pink(2)
THULIUM					
Solid substances	o	**Tm**	–	0	Thulium, hex.
	+3	Tm_2O_3 hydr.	–	−434 730	Hydroxide, light yellow, cub.(2)
Dissolved substances	+2	–	Tm^{++}?	–	Thulous ion
	+3	Tm^{+++}	–	−157 600	Thulic ion, light yellow
YTTERBIUM					
Solid substances	o	**Yb**		0	Ytterbium, grey, f.c.cub.
	+3	Yb_2O_3 hydr.		−433 330	Hydroxide, white, cub.(2)
Dissolved substances	+2	Yb^{++}		−129 000	Ytterbous ion
	+3	Yb^{+++}		−156 800	Ytterbic ion, colourless
LUTETIUM					
Solid substances	o	**Lu**		0	Lutetium, hex.
	+3	Lu_2O_3 hydr.		−431 930	Hydroxide(2)
Dissolved substance	+3	Lu^{+++}		−156 000	Lutetium ion

2. REACTIONS AND EQUILIBRIUM FORMULAE (5)

Lanthanum

2.2. TWO SOLID SUBSTANCES

Limits of the domains of relative stability of the solid substances

o → +3

1. $2\,La + 3H_2O = La_2O_3 + 6H^+ + 6e^-$
   a. $E_0 = -2.069 - 0.0591\,pH$
   b. $ = -1.836 - 0.0591\,pH$

2.3. ONE DISSOLVED SUBSTANCE AND ONE SOLID SUBSTANCE

Solubility of the solid substances

o → +3

2. $La = La^{+++} + 3e^-$ $\quad E_0 = -2.522 + 0{,}0197\log(La^{++\cdot}$

Z = +3

3. $2\,La^{+++} + 3H_2O = La_2O_3 + 6H^+$
   a. $\log(La^{+++}) = 23.02 - 3\,pH$
   b. $\phantom{\log(La^{+++})} = 33.81 - 3\,pH$

(5) Equilibria involving hydrated oxides or hydroxides, the more thermodynamically stable compounds, are marked with the letter *a*; those marked *b* refer to anhydrous oxides, which are less stable.

Cerium

2.1. TWO DISSOLVED SUBSTANCES

2.1.1. *Relative stability of the dissolved substances*

$Z = +4$

1. $Ce(OH)^{+++} + H_2O = Ce(OH)_2^{++} + H^+$ $\log \frac{(Ce(OH)_2^{++})}{(Ce(OH)^{+++})} = -0.29 + pH$

$+3 \rightarrow +4$

2. $Ce^{+++} + H_2O = Ce(OH)^{+++} + H^+ + e^-$ $E_0 = 1.715 - 0.0591\,pH + 0.0591 \log \frac{(Ce(OH)^{+++})}{(Ce^{+++})}$

3. $Ce^{+++} + 2H_2O = Ce(OH)_2^{++} + 2H^+ + e^-$ $E_0 = 1.731 - 0.1182\,pH + 0.0591 \log \frac{(Ce(OH)_2^{++})}{(Ce^{+++})}$

2.1.2. *Limits of the domains of relative predominance of the dissolved substances*

1'. $Ce(OH)^{+++}/Ce(OH)_2^{++}$ $pH = 0.29$

2'. $Ce^{+++}/Ce(OH)^{+++}$ $E_0 = 1.715 - 0.0591\,pH$

3'. $Ce^{+++}/Ce(OH)_2^{++}$ $E_0 = 1.731 - 0.1182\,pH$

2.2. TWO SOLID SUBSTANCES

Limits of the domains of relative stability of the solid substances

$0 \rightarrow +3$

4. $2\mathbf{Ce} + 3H_2O = \mathbf{Ce_2O_3} + 6H^+ + 6e^-$ $E_0 = 2.046 - 0.0591\,pH$

$+3 \rightarrow 4$

5. $\mathbf{Ce_2O_3} + H_2O = 2\mathbf{CeO_2} + 2H^+ + 2e^-$ $E_0 = 1.559 - 0.0591\,pH$

2.3. ONE DISSOLVED SUBSTANCE AND ONE SOLID SUBSTANCE

Solubility of the solid substances

$0 \rightarrow +3$

6. $\mathbf{Ce} = Ce^{+++} + 3e^-$ $E_0 = -2.483 + 0.0197 \log (Ce^{+++})$

$Z = +3$

7. $2Ce^{+++} + 3H_2O = \mathbf{Ce_2O_3} + 6H^+$ $\log (Ce^{+++}) = 22.15 - 3\,pH$

$+3 \rightarrow +4$

8. $\mathbf{Ce_2O_3} + H_2O + 2H^+ = 2Ce(OH)_2^{++} + 2e^-$ $E_0 = 0.422 + 0.0591\,pH + 0.0591 \log (Ce(OH)_2^{++})$

$Z = +4$

9. $\mathbf{CeO_2} + 2H^+ = Ce(OH)_2^{++}$ $\log (Ce(OH)_2^{++}) = 19.22 - 2\,pH$

Praseodymium

2.1. TWO DISSOLVED SUBSTANCES

2.1.1. *Relative stability of the dissolved substances*

$+3 \rightarrow +4$

1. $Pr^{+++} = Pr^{++++} + e^-$ $E_0 = 2.860 + 0.0591 \log \frac{(Pr^{++++})}{(Pr^{+++})}$

2.1.2. *Limits of the domains of relative predominance of the dissolved substances*

1'. Pr^{+++}/Pr^{++++} $E_0 = 2.860$

2.2. TWO SOLID SUBSTANCES

Limits of the domains of relative stability of the solid substances

$0 \rightarrow +3$

2. $2\,\mathbf{Pr} + 3H_2O = \mathbf{Pr_2O_3} + 6H^+ + 6e^-$
   a. $E_0 = -2.018 - 0.0591\,pH$
   b. $ = -1.829 - 0.0591\,pH$

$+3 \rightarrow +4$

3. $\mathbf{Pr_2O_3} + H_2O = 2\,\mathbf{PrO_2} + 2H^+ + 2e^-$
   a. $E_0 = 1.431 - 0.0591\,pH$
   b. $ = 0.863 - 0.0591\,pH$

2.3. ONE DISSOLVED SUBSTANCE AND ONE SOLID SUBSTANCE

Solubility of the solid substances

$0 \rightarrow +3$

4. $\mathbf{Pr} = Pr^{+++} + 3e^-$ $E_0 = -2.462 + 0.0197\log(Pr^{+++})$

$Z = +3$

5. $2\,Pr^{+++} + 3H_2O = \mathbf{Pr_2O_3} + 6H^+$
   a. $\log(Pr^{+++}) = 22.50 - 3\,pH$
   b. $\phantom{\log(Pr^{+++})} = 32.12 - 3\,pH$

$+3 \rightarrow +4$

6. $Pr^{+++} + 2H_2O = \mathbf{PrO_2} + 4H^+ + e^-$ $E_0 = 2.761 - 0.2364\,pH - 0.0591\log(Pr^{+++})$

$Z = +4$

7. $Pr^{++++} + 2H_2O = \mathbf{PrO_2} + 4H^+$ $\log(Pr^{++++}) = 46.72 - 4\,pH$

Neodymium

2.2. TWO SOLID SUBSTANCES

Limits of the domains of relative stability of the solid substances

$0 \rightarrow +3$

1. $2\,\mathbf{Nd} + 3H_2O = \mathbf{Nd_2O_3} + 6H^+ + 6e^-$
   a. $E_0 = -2.013 - 0.0591\,pH$
   b. $ = -1.811 - 0.0591\,pH$

2.3. ONE DISSOLVED SUBSTANCE AND ONE SOLID SUBSTANCE

Solubility of the solid substances

$0 \rightarrow +3$

2. $\mathbf{Nd} = Nd^{+++} + 3e^-$ $E_0 = -2.431 + 0.0197\log(Nd^{+++})$

$Z = +3$

3. $2\,Nd^{+++} + 3H_2O = \mathbf{Nd_2O_3} + 6H^+$
   a. $\log(Nd^{+++}) = 21.25 - 3\,pH$
   b. $\phantom{\log(Nd^{+++})} = 31.50 - 3\,pH$

Promethium

2.2. TWO SOLID SUBSTANCES

Limits of the domains of relative stability of the solid substances

$0 \rightarrow +3$

1. $2\,\mathbf{Pm} + 3H_2O = \mathbf{Pm_2O_3} + 6H^+ + 6e^-$ $E_0 = -2.008 - 0.0591\,pH$

2.3. ONE DISSOLVED SUBSTANCE AND ONE SOLID SUBSTANCE

Solubility of the solid substances

$0 \rightarrow +3$

2. $\mathbf{Pm} = Pm^{+++} + 3e^-$ $E_0 = -2.423 + 0.0197\log(Pm^{+++})$

$Z = +3$

3. $2\,Pm^{+++} + 3H_2O = \mathbf{Pm_2O_3} + 6H^+$ $\log(Pm^{+++}) = 21.03 - 3\,pH$

Samarium

2.1. TWO DISSOLVED SUBSTANCES

2.1.1. *Relative stability of the dissolved substances*

$+2 \rightarrow +3$

1. $Sm^{++} = Sm^{+++} + e^-$ $\quad E_0 = -1.000 + 0.0591 \log \frac{(Sm^{+++})}{(Sm^{++})}$

2.1.2. *Limits of the domains of relative predominance of the dissolved substances*

1'. Sm^{++}/Sm^{+++} $\quad E_0 = -1.000$

2.2. TWO SOLID SUBSTANCES

Limits of the domains of relative stability of the solid substances

$0 \rightarrow +3$

2. $2\mathbf{Sm} + 3H_2O = \mathbf{Sm_2O_3} + 6H^+ + 6e^-$ $\quad E_0 = -2.004 - 0.0591\,pH$

2.3. ONE DISSOLVED SUBSTANCE AND ONE SOLID SUBSTANCE

Solubility of the solid substances

$0 \rightarrow +2$

3. $\mathbf{Sm} = Sm^{++} + 2e^-$ $\quad E_0 = -3.121 + 0.0295 \log (Sm^{++})$

$+2 \rightarrow +3$

4. $2Sm^{++} + 3H_2O = \mathbf{Sm_2O_3} + 6H^+ + 2e^-$ $\quad E_0 = 0.230 - 0.1773\,pH - 0.0591 \log (Sm^{++})$

$Z = +3$

5. $2Sm^{+++} + 3H_2O = \mathbf{Sm_2O_3} + 6H^+$ $\quad \log (Sm^{+++}) = 20.81 - 3\,pH$

Europium

2.1. TWO DISSOLVED SUBSTANCES

2.1.1. *Relative stability of the dissolved substances*

$+2 \rightarrow +3$

1. $Eu^{++} = Eu^{+++} + e^-$ $\quad E_0 = -0.429 + 0.0591 \log \frac{(Eu^{+++})}{(Eu^{++})}$

2.1.2. *Limits of the domains of relative predominance of the dissolved substances*

1'. Eu^{++}/Eu^{+++} $\quad E_0 = -0.429$

2.2. TWO SOLID SUBSTANCES

Limits of the domains of relative stability of the solid substances

$0 \rightarrow +3$

2. $2\mathbf{Eu} + 3H_2O = \mathbf{Eu_2O_3} + 6H^+ + 6e^-$ $\quad E_0 = -2.002 - 0.0591\,pH$

2.3. ONE DISSOLVED SUBSTANCE AND ONE SOLID SUBSTANCE

Solubility of the solid substances

$0 \rightarrow +2$

3. $\mathbf{Eu} = Eu^{++} + 2e^-$ $\quad E_0 = -3.395 + 0.0295 \log (Eu^{++})$

$+2 \rightarrow 3$

4. $2Eu^{++} + 3H_2O = \mathbf{Eu_2O_3} + 6H^+ + 2e^-$ $\quad E_0 = 0.783 - 0.1773\,pH - 0.0591 \log (Eu^{++})$

$Z = +3$

5. $2Eu^{+++} + 3H_2O = \mathbf{Eu_2O_3} + 6H^+$ $\quad \log (Eu^{+++}) = 20.52 - 3\,pH$

Gadolinium

2.2. TWO DISSOLVED SUBSTANCES

Limits of the domains of relative stability of the solid substances

$0 \rightarrow +3$

1. $2\,\mathbf{Gd} + 3H_2O = \mathbf{Gd_2O_3} + 6H^+ + 6e^-$ $E_0 = -1.994 - 0.0591\,pH$

2.3. ONE DISSOLVED SUBSTANCE AND ONE SOLID SUBSTANCE

Solubility of the solid substances

$0 \rightarrow +3$

2. $\mathbf{Gd} = Gd^{+++} + 3e^-$ $E_0 = -2.397 + 0.0197 \log (Gd^{+++})$

$Z = +3$

3. $2\,Gd^{+++} + 3H_2O = \mathbf{Gd_2O_3} + 6H^+$ $\log (Gd^{+++}) = 20.45 - 3\,pH$

Terbium

2.2. TWO SOLID SUBSTANCES

Limits of the domains of relative stability of the solid substances

$0 \rightarrow +3$

1. $2\,\mathbf{Tb} + 3H_2O = \mathbf{Tb_2O_3} + 6H^+ + 6e^-$ $E_0 = -1.999 - 0.0591\,pH$

2.3. ONE DISSOLVED SUBSTANCE AND ONE SOLID SUBSTANCE

Solubility of the solid substances

$0 \rightarrow +3$

2. $\mathbf{Tb} = Tb^{+++} + 3e^-$ $E_0 = -2.391 + 0.0197 \log (Tb^{+++})$

$Z = +3$

3. $2\,Tb^{+++} + 3H_2O = \mathbf{Tb_2O_3} + 6H^+$ $\log (Tb^{+++}) = 20.30 - 3\,pH$

Dysprosium

2.2. TWO SOLID SUBSTANCES

Limits of the domains of relative stability of the solid substances

$0 \rightarrow +3$

1. $2\,\mathbf{Dy} + 3H_2O = \mathbf{Dy_2O_3} + 6H^+ + 6e^-$ $E_0 = -1.956 - 0.0591\,pH$

2.3. ONE DISSOLVED SUBSTANCE AND ONE SOLID SUBSTANCE

Solubility of the solid substances

$0 \rightarrow +3$

2. $\mathbf{Dy} = Dy^{+++} + 3e^-$ $E_0 = -2.353 + 0.0197 \log (Dy^{+++})$

$Z = +3$

3. $2\,Dy^{+++} + 3H_2O = \mathbf{Dy_2O_3} + 6H^+$ $\log (Dy^{+++}) = 20.15 - 3\,pH$

Holmium

2.2. TWO SOLID SUBSTANCES

Limits of the domains of relative stability of the solid substances

$0 \rightarrow +3$

1. $2\,\mathbf{Ho} + 3H_2O = \mathbf{Ho_2O_3} + 6H^+ + 6e^-$ $E_0 = -1.937 - 0.0591\,pH$

2.3. ONE DISSOLVED SUBSTANCE AND ONE SOLID SUBSTANCE

Solubility of the solid substances

$0 \rightarrow +3$

2. **Ho** $= Ho^{+++} + 3e^-$ $E_0 = -2.319 + 0.0197 \log(Ho^{+++})$

$Z = +3$

3. $2Ho^{+++} + 3H_2O = \mathbf{Ho_2O_3} + 6H^+$ $\log(Ho^{+++}) = 19.35 - 3\,pH$

Erbium

2.2. TWO SOLID SUBSTANCES

Limits of the domains of relative stability of the solid substances

$0 \rightarrow +3$

1. $2\mathbf{Er} + 3H_2O = \mathbf{Er_2O_3} + 6H^+ + 6e^-$ $E_0 = -1.918 - 0.0591\,pH$

2.3. ONE DISSOLVED SUBSTANCE AND ONE SOLID SUBSTANCE

Solubility of the solid substances

$0 \rightarrow +3$

2. **Er** $= Er^{+++} + 3e^-$ $E_0 = -2.296 + 0.0197 \log(Er^{+++})$

$Z = +3$

3. $2Er^{+++} + 3H_2O = \mathbf{Er_2O_3} + 6H^+$ $\log(Er^{+++}) = 19.70 - 3\,pH$

Thulium

2.2. TWO SOLID SUBSTANCES

Limits of the domains of relative stability of the solid substances

$0 \rightarrow +3$

1. $2\mathbf{Tm} + 3H_2O = \mathbf{Tm_2O_3} + 6H^+ + 6e^-$ $E_0 = -1.913 - 0.0591\,pH$

2.3. ONE DISSOLVED SUBSTANCE AND ONE SOLID SUBSTANCE

Solubility of the solid substances

$0 \rightarrow +3$

2. **Tm** $= Tm^{+++} + 3e^-$ $E_0 = -2.278 + 0.0197 \log(Tm^{+++})$

$Z = +3$

3. $2Tm^{+++} + 3H_2O = \mathbf{Tm_2O_3} + 6H^+$ $\log(Tm^{+++}) = 18.54 - 3\,pH$

Ytterbium

2.1. TWO DISSOLVED SUBSTANCES

2.1.1. *Relative stability of the dissolved substances*

$+2 \rightarrow +3$

1. $Yb^{++} = Yb^{+++} + e^-$ $E_0 = -1.205 + 0.0591 \log \frac{(Yb^{+++})}{(Yb^{++})}$

2.1.2. *Limits of the domains of relative predominance of the dissolved substances*

1'. Yb^{++} / Yb^{+++} $E_0 = -1.205$

2.2. TWO SOLID SUBSTANCES

Limits of the domains of relative stability of the solid substances

$0 \rightarrow +3$

2. $2\mathbf{Yb} + 3H_2O = \mathbf{Yb_2O_3} + 6H^+ + 6e^-$ $E_0 = -1.902 - 0.0591\,pH$

2.3. ONE DISSOLVED SUBSTANCE AND ONE SOLID SUBSTANCE

Solubility of the solid substances

$0 \rightarrow +2$

3. $\mathbf{Yb} = Yb^{++} + 2e^-$ $\quad E_0 = -2.797 + 0.0295 \log (Yb^{++})$

$+2 \rightarrow +3$

4. $2Yb^{++} + 3H_2O = \mathbf{Yb_2O_3} + 6H^+ + 2e^-$ $\quad E_0 = -0.114 - 0.1773\,pH - 0.0591 \log (Yb^{++})$

$Z = +3$

5. $2Yb^{+++} + 3H_2O = \mathbf{Yb_2O_3} + 6H^+$ $\quad \log (Yb^{+++}) = 18.47 - 3\,pH$

Lutetium

2.2. TWO SOLID SUBSTANCES

Limits of the domains of relative stability of the solid substances

$0 \rightarrow +3$

1. $2\mathbf{Lu} + 3H_2O = \mathbf{Lu_2O_3} + 6H^+ + 6e^-$ $\quad E_0 = -1.892 - 0.0591\,pH$

2.3. ONE DISSOLVED SUBSTANCE AND ONE SOLID SUBSTANCE

Solubility of the solid substances

$0 \rightarrow +3$

2. $\mathbf{Lu} = Lu^{+++} + 3e^-$ $\quad E_0 = -2.255 + 0.0197 \log (Lu^{+++})$

$Z = +3$

3. $2Lu^{+++} + 3H_2O = \mathbf{Lu_2O_3} + 6H^+$ $\quad \log (Lu^{+++}) = 18.39 - 3\,pH$

3. EQUILIBRIUM DIAGRAMS AND THEIR INTERPRETATION

3.1. ESTABLISHMENT OF THE DIAGRAMS

Using the equilibrium formulae given in paragraph 2, we have drawn Figs. 1–15 which represent the conditions for thermodynamic equilibrium of the systems lanthanides–water, at 25°C.

These figures are valid only in the absence of substances with which the metals of this group can form insoluble salts or soluble complexes, with an exception made for tetravalent cerium which exists in practice only in the form of complexes (Cl^-, SO_4^{--}, NO_3^- and ClO_4^-). According to Charlot [1], the lanthanide complexes are numerous; examples are those formed with tartaric and citric ions; examples of sparingly soluble compounds are the oxalates and fluorides.

3.2. STABILITY OF THE LANTHANIDES

The lanthanides have extremely large negative equilibrium potentials; their domains of stability in Figs. 1–15 lie well below that of water. These metals are therefore unstable in the presence of aqueous solutions of any pH. They are extremely base metals and are powerful reducing agents; they have a great affinity to react with water which they decompose with the evolution of hydrogen. In the presence of acid and neutral solutions, the reaction is accompanied by the dissolution of the metals as cations which are either divalent (Sm^{++}, Eu^{++}, Yb^{++}), or trivalent (La^{+++}, Pr^{+++}, Nd^{+++}, Pm^{+++}, Ce^{+++}, Gd^{+++}, Tb^{+++}, Dy^{+++}, Ho^{+++}, Er^{+++}, Tm^{+++}, Lu^{+++}); in the presence of alkaline solutions, the reaction gives rise to the formation of hydroxides of the general formula $M(OH)_3$, where M represents a lanthanide.

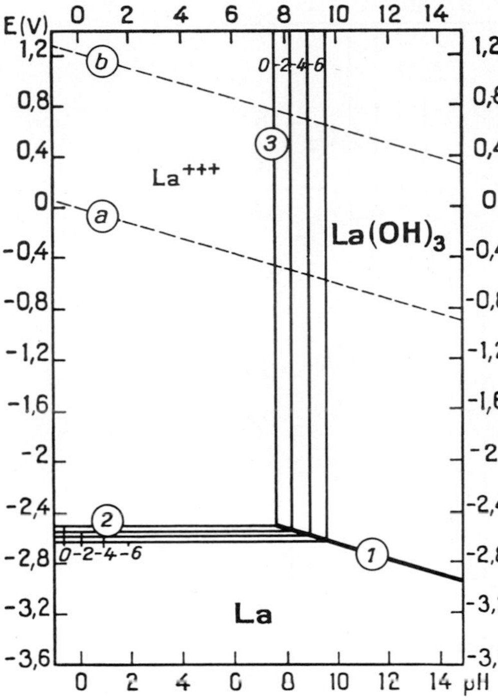

FIG. 1. Lanthanum–water.

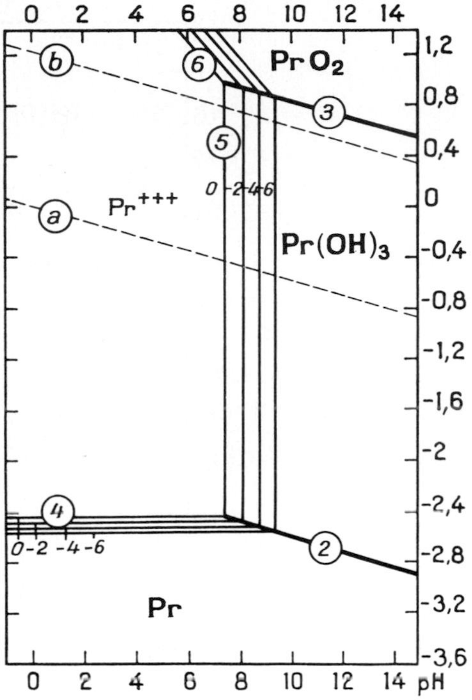

FIG. 2. Praseodymium–water.

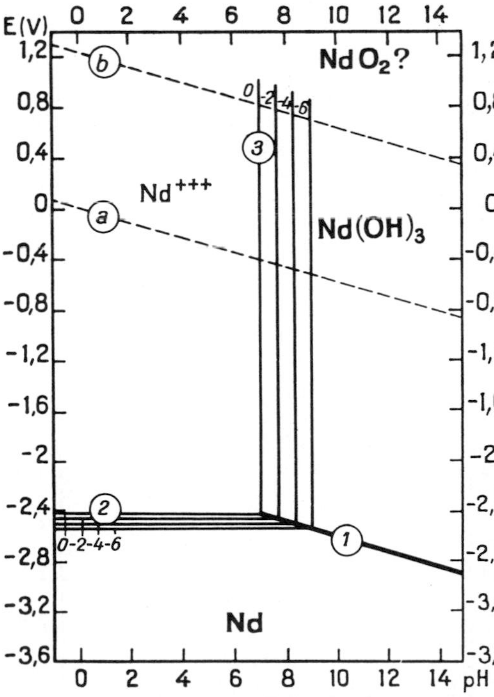

FIG. 3. Neodymium–water.

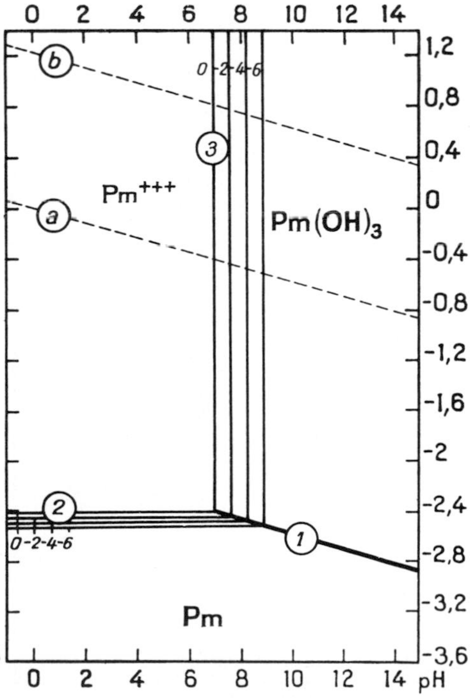

FIG. 4. Promethium–water.

FIGS. 1–15. Potential–pH equilibrium diagrams for the systems lanthanides–water, at 25 °C.

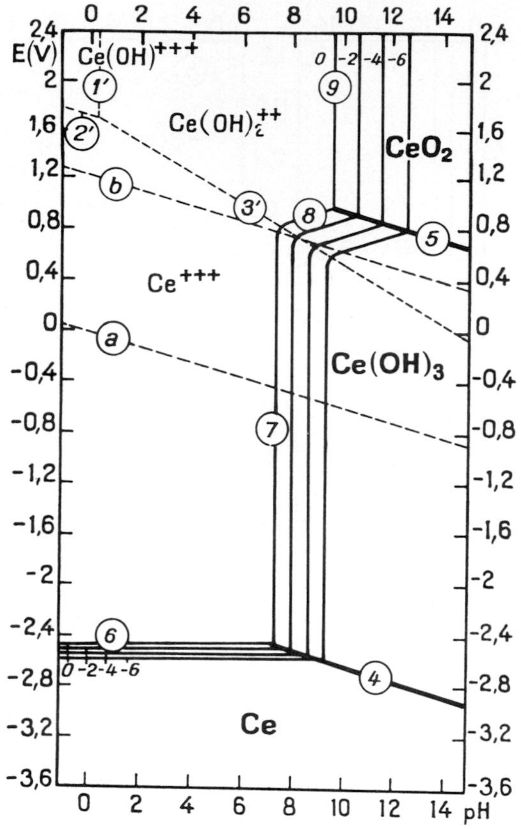

FIG. 5. Cerium–water.

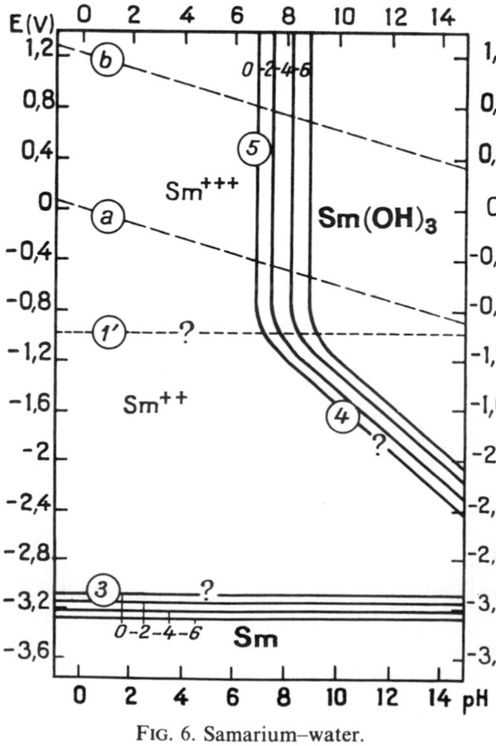

FIG. 6. Samarium–water.

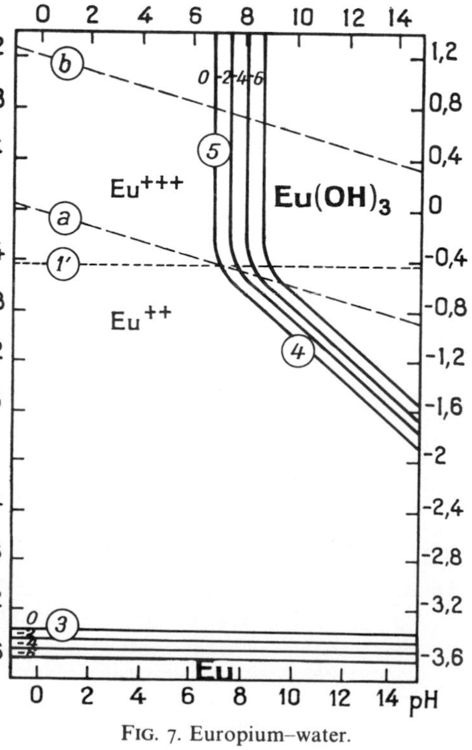

FIG. 7. Europium–water.

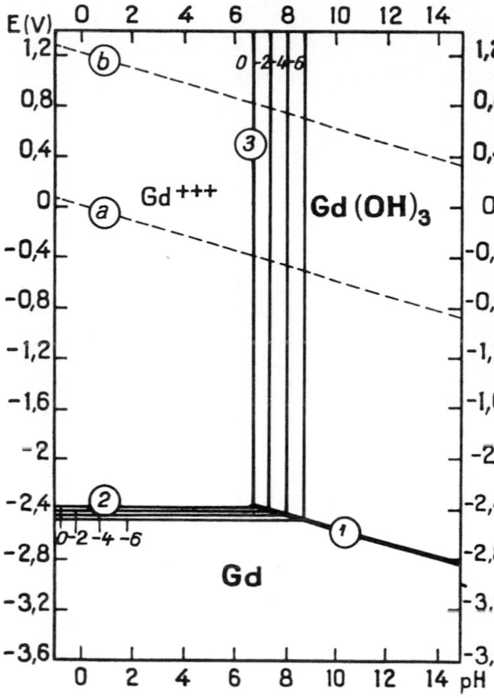

FIG. 8. Gadolinium–water.

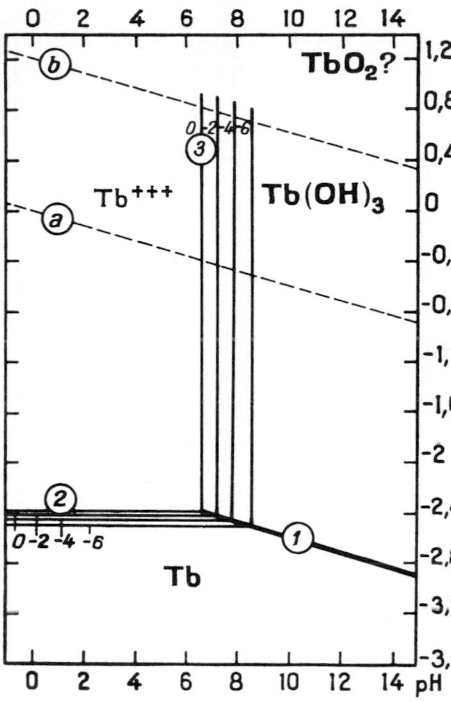

FIG. 9. Terbium–water.

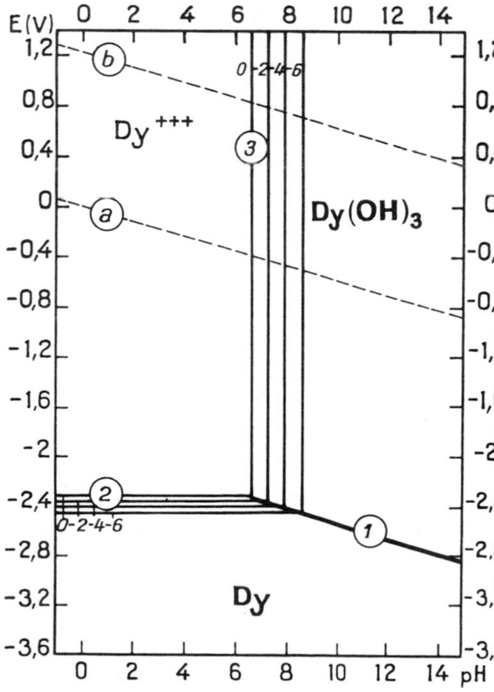

FIG. 10. Dysprosium–water.

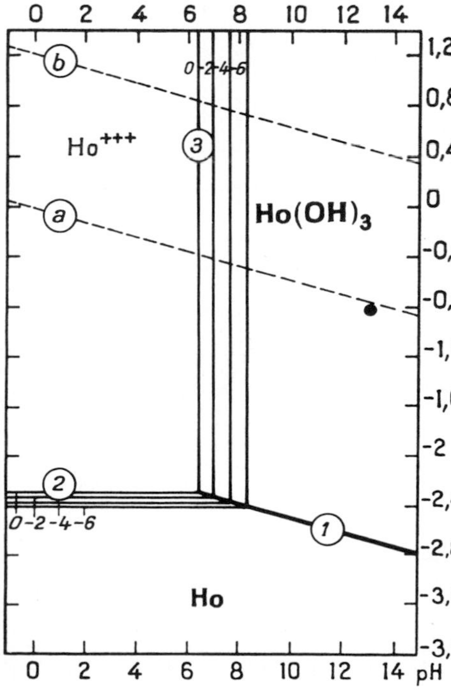

FIG. 11. Holmium–water.

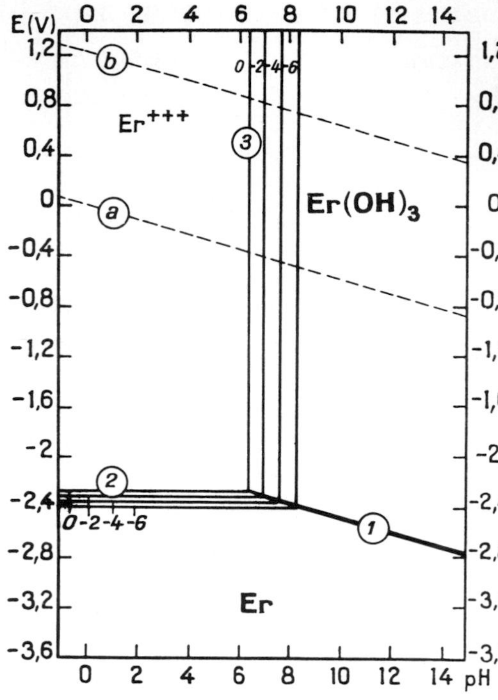

FIG. 12. Erbium–water.

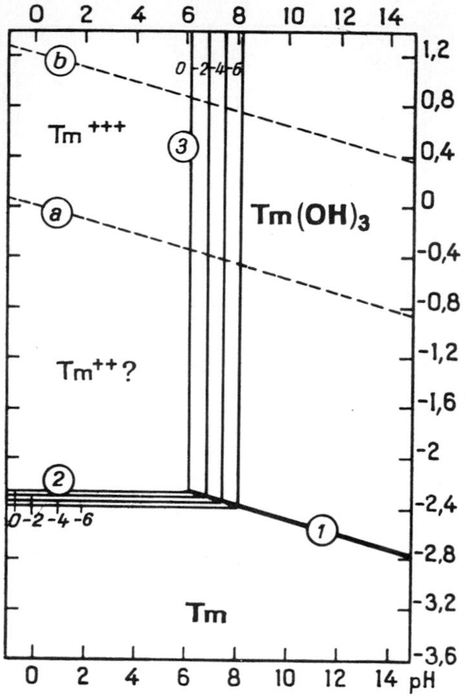

FIG. 13. Thulium–water.

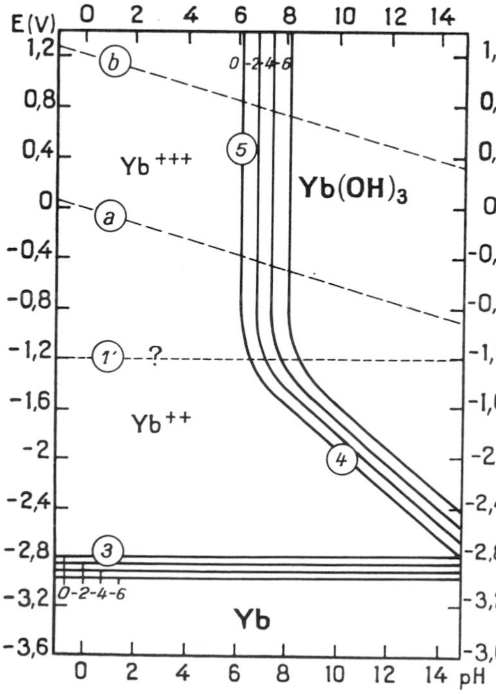

FIG. 14. Ytterbium–water.

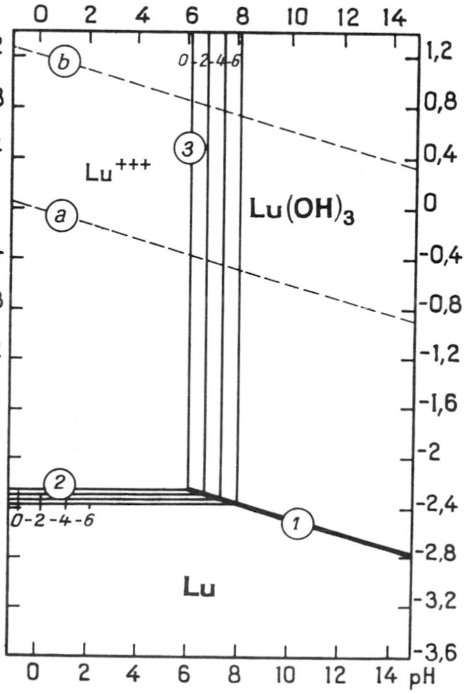

FIG. 15. Lutetium–water.

3.3. STABILITY OF THE HYDROXIDES OF THE LANTHANIDES

According to Figs. 1–15, the lanthanide hydroxides are non-amphoteric compounds, stable in alkaline solutions and unstable in acid solutions in which they dissolve as the corresponding cations. They can be obtained by the addition of alkali to acid solutions of their salts.

3.4. STABILITY OF THE PEROXIDES PrO_2, NdO_2 (?), CeO_2, TbO_2 (?)

In alkaline solution, sufficient oxidation can convert Pr, Nd, Ce and Tb into PrO_2, NdO_2 (?), CeO_2 and TbO_2 (?).

The domains of stability of these compounds lie above line (*b*), so they may be considered as being oxidizing agents, thermodynamically unstable in the presence of aqueous solutions which they decompose with the evolution of oxygen, at the same time being reduced themselves to the trivalent state.

4. BIBLIOGRAPHY

[1] G. CHARLOT, *L'analyse qualitative et les réactions en solution*, Masson, Paris, 1957.

SECTION 7

ACTINIDES([1])

N. DE ZOUBOV

SUMMARY

([1]) Adapted version of the Rapport CEFA/R.11 of the Commission des Études Fondamentales et Applications of CEBELCOR.

1. SUBSTANCES CONSIDERED AND SUBSTANCES NOT CONSIDERED

	Oxidation number (Z)	Considered	Not considered	μ^0(cal.)	Name, colour, crystalline system
ACTINIUM					
Solid substances	0	–	**Ac**	0	Actinium
	+ 3	–	**Ac_2O_3** anh.	–	Actinium sesquioxide
	»	–	» hydr.	–	Actinium hydroxide, $Ac(OH)_3$, white
Dissolved substance	+ 3	–	Ac^{+++}	−180 000 (3)	Actinic ion, colourless
THORIUM					
Solid substances	− 4	–	**ThH_4**	–	Thorium hydride, cub.
	0	**Th**	–	0	Thorium, silvery white, cub.
	+ 4	**ThO_2** anh.	–	*a*. −278 400	Thorium dioxide, cub.
	»	» hydr.	–	*b*. −265 620	Thorium hydroxide, $Th(OH)_4$ (2)
Dissolved substances	+ 4	Th^{++++}	–	−175 200	Thoric ion
	+ 6	–	ThO_3 hydr.	–	Acid peroxide
PROTOACTINIUM					
Solid substances	− 3	–	**PaH_3**	–	Protoactinium hydride, black, cub.
	0	–	**Pa**	0	Protoactinium, grey, quad.
	+ 2	–	**PaO**	–	Monoxide, black, cub.
	+ 4	–	**PaO_2**	–	Dioxide, black, cub.
	+ 4.5	–	**Pa_4O_9**	–	Nonoxide, white, cub.
	+ 5	–	**Pa_2O_5** anh.	–	Protoactinium pentoxide, white, orthorh.
	»	–	» hydr.	–	Protoactinium hydroxide
Dissolved substances	+ 4	–	Pa^{++++} (?)	–	Protoactinic ion
	+ 5	–	PaO_2^+	−229 000 (3)	Protoactinyl ion
URANIUM					
Solid substances	− 3	**UH_3**	–	−17 700 (4)	Uranium hydride, grey–brown, cub.
	0	**U**	–	0	Uranium, light grey, orthorh.
	+ 2	**UO**	–	−123 000 (5)	Uranium monoxide, grey, f.c.cub.
	+ 3	**U_2O_3** hydr.	–	−336 330	Hypouranous hydroxide, $U(OH)_3$, brown (2)

(2) These values of μ^0 for the oxides correspond to the following values for the hydroxides and hydrated oxides:

$Th(OH)_4$	−379 000 cal.	$Np(OH)_4$	−346 600 cal.	$PuO_2(OH)_2$	−278 900 cal.
$U(OH)_3$	−263 200 »	NpO_2OH	−261 800 »	$Am(OH)_3$	−300 000 »
$U(OH)_4$	−351 600 »	$NpO_2(OH)_2$	−288 300 »	$Am(OH)_4$	−347 000 »
$UO_3.H_2O$	−343 000 »	$Pu(OH)_3$	−280 200 »	AmO_2OH	−254 995 »
$UO_3.2H_2O$	−398 840 »	$Pu(OH)_4$	−340 000 »	$AmO_2(OH)_2$	−267 200 »
$Np(OH)_3$	−268 500 »	PuO_2OH	−246 700 »		

(3) Values calculated from the approximate values of E_0^0 given by Latimer [1].

(4) Value given by Seaborg and Katz [2], p. 174.

(5) Values calculated by us, according to details given in the Rapport technique RT.31 of CEBELCOR.

	Oxidation number (Z)	Considered		Not considered		μ^0(cal.)	Name, colour, crystalline system
	+ 4	UO_2	anh.	–		a. —246 600 (5)	Uranous oxide, "black oxide", brown–black, cub. or orthorh.
	»	»	hydr.	–		b. —238 220	Uranous hydroxide, $U(OH)_4$, green(2)
	+ 5.33	U_3O_8		–		—804 000 (6)	"Green oxide", olive green, orthorh.
	+ 6	UO_3	hydr.	–		c. —286 310	Monohydrated uranic oxide, $UO_3 . H_2O$, yellow–orange, amorphous or orthorh.(2)
	»	»	hydr.	–		d. —285 460 (5)	Dihydrated uranic oxide, $UO_3 . 2H_2O$, yellow–green, α f.c.quad.(2); β orthorh.
	»	»	anh.	–		e. —273 000 (6)	Uranic oxide, yellow–red, rhomb.
	+ 8	–		UO_4	hydr.	–	Dihydrated uranium peroxide $UO_4 . 2H_2O$, pale yellow, amorphous
Dissolved substances	+ 3	U^{+++}		–		—124 400	Hypouranous ion, pink or purple
	+ 4	U^{++++}		–		—138 400	Uranous ion, green
	»	UOH^{+++}		–		—193 500	Uranous ion, green
	+ 5	UO_2^+		–		—237 600	Hypouranyl ion
	+ 6	UO_2^{++}		–		—236 400	Uranyl ion, yellow with green fluorescence
	+ 8	–		HUO_5^- ?		–	Peruranate ion, orange
	»	–		UO_5^{--} ?		–	Peruranate ion, orange
NEPTUNIUM							
Solid substances	— 3.7	–		$NpH_{3.7}$?		–	Neptunium hydride, black
	0	Np		–		0	Neptunium, silvery, orthorh.
	+ 2	–		NpO		–	Neptunium monoxide, f.c.cub.
	+ 3	Np_2O_3	hydr.	–		—366 930 (7)	Hyponeptunous hydroxide $Np(OH)_3$(2)
	+ 4	NpO_2	anh.	–		a. —234 000 (6)	Neptunium dioxide brown or apple green, f.c.cub.
	»	»	hydr.	–		b. —233 220 (7)	Neptunous hydroxide $Np(OH)_4$, light brown to olive green(2)
	+ 5	Np_2O_5	hydr.	–		—466 910 (7)	Neptunium dioxyhydroxide NpO_2OH, pale green or grey–blue, amorphous or cryst.(2)
	»	–		Np_2O_5	anh.	—480 000 (6)	Neptunium pentoxide, chocolate brown, orthorh.
	+ 5.33	–		Np_3O_8 ?		–	
	+ 6	NpO_3	hydr.	–		—231 610 (7)	Neptunium dioxydihydroxide $NpO_2(OH)_2$(2)
	+ 8	–		NpO_4	hydr.	–	Dihydrated neptunium peroxide $NpO_4 . 2H_2O$, colourless

(6) Values given by Brewer [3].
(7) Values calculated by us from the values of E_B^0 given by Latimer [1].

	Oxidation number (Z)	Considered	Not considered	μ^0(cal.)	Name, colour, crystalline system
Dissolved substances(*)	+ 3	Np^{+++}	–	—128 400	Hyponeptunous ion, pale purple
	+ 4	Np^{++++}	–	—124 900	Neptunous ion
	+ 5	NpO_2^+	–	—221 000	Hyponeptunyl ion, blue–green
	+ 6	NpO_2^{++}	–	—194 500	Neptunyl ion, pale pink to yellow–green.
PLUTONIUM					
Solid substances	— 3	–	PuH_3	–	Plutonium trihydride, black
	— 2	–	PuH_2	–	Plutonium dihydride
	0	Pu	–	0	Plutonium
	+ 2	–	PuO	–	Plutonium monoxide, black, f.c.cub.
	+ 3	–	Pu_2O_3 anh.	–	Plutonium sesquioxide, silver, b.c.cub. or hex.
	»	Pu_2O_3 hydr.	–	—390 330	Hypoplutonous hydroxide $Pu(OH)_3$, pale blue to dull blue(2)
	+ 4	PuO_2 anh.	–	a. —234 000 (8)	Plutonium dioxide, yellow to yellow–green or dark brown, f.c.cub.
	»	» hydr.	–	b. —226 620	Plutonous hydroxide $Pu(OH)_4$, green(2)
	+ 5	Pu_2O_5 hydr.	–	—436 710	Plutonium dioxyhydroxide, PuO_2OH(2)
	+ 6	PuO_3 hydr.	–	—222 210	Plutonium dioxydihydroxide, $PuO_2(OH)_2$(2)
Dissolved substances	+ 3	Pu^{+++}	–	—140 500	Hypoplutonous ion, blue (violet in artificial light)
	+ 4	Pu^{++++}	–	—118 200	Plutonous ion, brown
	+ 5	PuO_2^+	–	—204 900	Hypoplutonyl ion, almost colourless
	+ 6	PuO_2^{++}	–	—183 500	Plutonyl ion, light brown
AMERICIUM					
Solid substances	— 2.7	–	$AmH_{2.7}$?	–	Americium hydride, black
	0	Am	–	0	Americium, silvery white
	+ 3	Am_2O_3 hydr.	–	a. —429 930	Hypoamericious hydroxide $Am(OH)_3$(2)
	»	» anh.	–	b. —402 000 (8)	Americium sesquioxide, orange–red, cub.
	+ 4	AmO_2 hydr.	–	c. —233 620	Americious hydroxide $Am(OH)_4$(2)
	»	» anh.	–	d. —231 000	Americium dioxide, black, f.c.cub.
	+ 5	Am_2O_5 hydr.	–	—453 300 (9)	Americium dioxyhydroxide AmO_2OH(2)
	+ 6	AmO_3 hydr.	–	—210 510 (9)	Americium dioxydihydroxide $AmO_2(OH)_2$(2)

(*) We have found in chemical literature free enthalpy values for the various dissolved neptunium substances [2], but, for the sake of homogeneity, we have adopted Latimer's values alone in drawing the diagram, more especially as there are errors in the values given.

(8) Values given by Brewer [3].

(9) Values calculated by us from tension values given by Latimer.

	Oxidation number (Z)	Considered	Not considered	μ^0(cal.)	Name, colour, crystalline system
Dissolved substances	+ 2	-	Am^{++} (?)	> —139 746 (10)	? ion
	+ 3	Am^{+++}	-	—160 500	Hypoamericious ion
	+ 4	Am^{++++}	-	—110 200	Americious ion
	+ 5	AmO_2^+	-	—194 500	Hypoamericyl ion
	+ 6	AmO_2^{++}	-	—156 700	Americyl ion
CURIUM					
Solid substances	0	-	**Cm**	0	Curium, silvery
	+ 3	-	**Cm_2O_3** hydr.	-	Curium hydroxide $Cm(OH)_3$
Dissolved substance	+ 3	-	Cm^{+++} (?)	-	Curic ion
BERKELIUM					
Solid substance	0	-	**Bk**	0	Berkelium
Dissolved substances	+ 3	-	Bk^{+++}	-	Berkelous ion
	+ 4	-	Bk^{++++} (11)	-	Berkelic ion
CALIFORNIUM					
Solid substance	0	-	**Cf**	0	Californium
Dissolved substance	+ 3	-	Cf^{+++}	-	Californous ion

2. REACTIONS AND EQUILIBRIUM FORMULAE

Thorium

2.2. TWO SOLID SUBSTANCES

Limits of the domain of relative stability of the solid substances

$0 \rightarrow +4$

1. **Th** $+ 2H_2O =$ **ThO_2** $+ 4H^+ + 4e^-$ a. $E_0 = -1.789 - 0.0591\,pH$
   b. $ = -1.650 - 0.0591\,pH$

2.3. ONE DISSOLVED SUBSTANCE AND ONE SOLID SUBSTANCE

Solubility of the solid substances

$Z = +4$

2. $Th^{++++} + 2H_2O =$ **ThO_2** $+ 4H^+$ a. $\log(Th^{++++}) = 7.47 - 4pH$
   b. $\phantom{\log(Th^{++++})} = 16.85 - 4pH$

$0 \rightarrow +4$

3. **Th** $= Th^{++++} + 4e^-$ $E_0 = -1.899 + 0.0148 \log(Th^{++++})$

(10) Cunningham and Asprey (Report AECD-2 949, 20 July, 1950) give a reduction potential Am^{+++}/Am^{++} more negative than −0·9 V.

(11) Seaborg and Katz [2] give a redox potential of about 1·6 V for the couple Bk^{+++}/Bk^{++++}.

Uranium

2.1. TWO DISSOLVED SUBSTANCES

2.1.1. *Relative stability of the dissolved substances*

$Z = +4$

1. $U^{++++} + H_2O = UOH^{+++} + H^+$ $\qquad \log\frac{(UOH^{+++})}{(U^{++++})} = -1.16 + pH$

$+3 \rightarrow +4$

2. $U^{+++} = U^{++++} + e^-$ $\qquad E_0 = -0.607 + 0.0591 \log\frac{(U^{++++})}{(U^{+++})}$

3. $U^{+++} + H_2O = UOH^{+++} + H^+ + e^-$ $\qquad E_0 = -0.538 - 0.0591\,pH + 0.0591 \log\frac{(UOH^{+++})}{(U^{+++})}$

$+4 \rightarrow +5$

4. $U^{++++} + 2H_2O = UO_2^+ + 4H^+ + e^-$ $\qquad E_0 = 0.612 - 0.2364\,pH + 0.0591 \log\frac{(UO_2^+)}{(U^{++++})}$

5. $UOH^{+++} + H_2O = UO_2^+ + 3H^+ + e^-$ $\qquad E_0 = 0.546 - 0.1773\,pH + 0.0591 \log\frac{(UO_2^+)}{(UOH^{+++})}$

$+4 \rightarrow +6$

6. $U^{++++} + 2H_2O = UO_2^{++} + 4H^+ + 2e^-$ $\qquad E_0 = 0.333 - 0.1182\,pH + 0.0295 \log\frac{(UO_2^{++})}{(U^{++++})}$

7. $UOH^{+++} + H_2O = UO_2^{++} + 3H^+ + 2e^-$ $\qquad E_0 = 0.299 - 0.0886\,pH + 0.0295 \log\frac{(UO_2^{++})}{(UOH^{+++})}$

$+5 \rightarrow +6$

8. $UO_2^+ = UO_2^{++} + e^-$ $\qquad E_0 = 0.052 + 0.0591 \log\frac{(UO_2^{++})}{(UO_2^+)}$

2.1.2. *Limits of the domains of relative predominance of the dissolved substances*

1'.	U^{++++}/UOH^{+++}	$pH = 1.16$
2'.	U^{+++}/U^{++++}	$E_0 = -0.607$
3'.	U^{+++}/UOH^{+++}	$E_0 = -0.538 - 0.0591\,pH$
4'.	U^{++++}/UO_2^+	$E_0 = 0.612 - 0.2364\,pH$
5'.	UOH^{+++}/UO_2^+	$E_0 = 0.546 - 0.1773\,pH$
6'.	U^{++++}/UO_2^{++}	$E_0 = 0.333 - 0.1182\,pH$
7'.	UOH^{+++}/UO_2^{++}	$E_0 = 0.299 - 0.0886\,pH$
8'.	UO_2^+/UO_2^{++}	$E_0 = 0.052$

2.2. TWO SOLID SUBSTANCES

Limits of the domains of relative stability of the solid substances

$-3 \rightarrow 0$

9. $\mathbf{UH_3} = \mathbf{U} + 3H^+ + 3e^-$ $\qquad E_0 = 0.256 - 0.0591\,pH$

$-3 \rightarrow +2$

10. $\mathbf{UH_3} + H_2O = \mathbf{UO} + 5H^+ + 5e^-$ $\qquad E_0 = -0.422 - 0.0591\,pH$

$-3 \rightarrow +3$

11. $2\mathbf{UH_3} + 3H_2O = \mathbf{U_2O_3} + 12H^+ + 12e^-$ $\qquad E_0 = -0.545 - 0.0591\,pH$

$-3 \rightarrow +4$

12. $\mathbf{UH_3} + 2H_2O = \mathbf{UO_2} + 7H^+ + 7e^-$ $\qquad$ *a.* $E_0 = -0.716 - 0.0591\,pH$
b. $\quad = -0.664 - 0.0591\,pH$

$0 \rightarrow +2$

13. $\mathbf{U} + H_2O = \mathbf{UO} + 2H^+ + 2e^-$ $\qquad E_0 = -1.438 - 0.0591\,pH$

$0 \rightarrow +3$

14. $2\mathbf{U} + 3H_2O = \mathbf{U_2O_3} + 6H^+ + 6e^-$ $\qquad E_0 = -1.346 - 0.0591\,pH$

$0 \rightarrow +4$

15. $\mathbf{U} + 2H_2O = \mathbf{UO_2} + 4H^+ + 4e^-$ — a. $E_0 = -1.444 - 0.0591\,pH$; b. $= -1.353 - 0.0591\,pH$

$+2 \rightarrow +3$

16. $2\mathbf{UO} + H_2O = \mathbf{U_2O_3} + 2H^+ + 2e^-$ — $E_0 = -1.163 - 0.0591\,pH$

$+3 \rightarrow +4$

17. $\mathbf{U_2O_3} + H_2O = 2\mathbf{UO_2} + 2H^+ + 2e^-$ — a. $E_0 = -1.738 - 0.0591\,pH$; b. $= -1.375 - 0.0591\,pH$

$+4 \rightarrow +5.33$

18. $3\mathbf{UO_2} + 2H_2O = \mathbf{U_3O_8} + 4H^+ + 4e^-$ — a. $E_0 = 0.533 - 0.0591\,pH$; b. $= 0.260 - 0.0591\,pH$

$+4 \rightarrow +6$

19. $\mathbf{UO_2} + H_2O = \mathbf{UO_3} + 2H^+ + 2e^-$ — ac. $E_0 = 0.368 - 0.0591\,pH$; ad. $= 0.387 - 0.0591\,pH$; ae. $= 0.657 - 0.0591\,pH$; bc. $= 0.186 - 0.0591\,pH$; bd. $= 0.204 - 0.0591\,pH$; be. $= 0.475 - 0.0591\,pH$

$+5.33 \rightarrow +6$

20. $\mathbf{U_3O_8} + H_2O = 3\mathbf{UO_3} + 2H^+ + 2e^-$ — c. $E_0 = 0.038 - 0.0591\,pH$; d. $= 0.093 - 0.0591\,pH$; e. $= 0.904 - 0.0591\,pH$

2.3. ONE DISSOLVED SUBSTANCE AND ONE SOLID SUBSTANCE

Solubility of the solid substances

$Z = +4$

21. $U^{++++} + 2H_2O = \mathbf{UO_2} + 4H^+$ — a. $\log(U^{++++}) = 3.80 - 4pH$; b. $= 9.95 - 4pH$

22. $UOH^{+++} + H_2O = \mathbf{UO_2} + 3H^+$ — a. $\log(UOH^{+++}) = 2.63 - 3pH$; b. $= 8.78 - 3pH$

$Z = +6$

23. $UO_2^{++} + H_2O = \mathbf{UO_3} + 2H^+$ — c. $\log(UO_2^{++}) = 4.97 - 2pH$; d. $= 5.60 - 2pH$; e. $= 14.74 - 2pH$

$-3 \rightarrow +3$

24. $\mathbf{UH_3} = U^{+++} + 3H^+ + 6e^-$ — $E_0 = -0.772 - 0.0295\,pH + 0.0098\log(U^{++}$

$0 \rightarrow +3$

25. $\mathbf{U} = U^{+++} + 3e^-$ — $E_0 = -1.798 + 0.0197\log(U^{++}$

$+3 \rightarrow +4$

26. $U^{+++} + 2H_2O = \mathbf{UO_2} + 4H^+ + e^-$ — a. $E_0 = -0.382 - 0.2364\,pH - 0.0591\log(U^{++}$; b. $= -0.019 - 0.2364\,pH - 0.0591\log(U^{++}$

$+4 \rightarrow +6$

27. $\mathbf{UO_2} = UO_2^{++} + 2e^-$ — a. $E_0 = 0.221 + 0.0295\log(UO_2^{+}$; b. $= 0.040 + 0.0295\log(UO_2^{+}$

$+5.33 \rightarrow +6$

28. $\mathbf{U_3O_8} + 4H^+ = 3UO_2^{++} + 2H_2O + 2e^-$ — $E_0 = -0.403 + 0.1182\,pH + 0.0886\log(UO_2^{+}$

Neptunium

2.1. TWO DISSOLVED SUBSTANCES

2.1.1. *Relative stability of the dissolved substances*

$+3 \rightarrow +4$

1. $Np^{+++} = Np^{++++} + e^-$ — $E_0 = 0.152 + 0.0591\log\frac{(Np^{+}}{(Np^{+}}$

$+3 \rightarrow +5$

2. $Np^{+++} + 2H_2O = NpO_2^+ + 4H^+ + 2e^-$ — $E_0 = 0.451 - 0.1182\,pH + 0.0295\log\frac{(NpO}{(Np^{++}}$

$+4 \rightarrow +5$

3. $Np^{++++} + 2H_2O = NpO_2^+ + 4H^+ + e^-$ $E_0 = 0.749 - 0.2364\,pH + 0.0591 \log \frac{(NpO_2^+)}{(Np^{++++})}$

$+5 \rightarrow +6$

4. $NpO_2^+ = NpO_2^{++} + e^-$ $E_0 = 1.149 + 0.0591 \log \frac{(NpO_2^{++})}{(NpO_2^+)}$

2.1.2. *Limits of the domains of relative predominance of the dissolved substances*

1'. Np^{+++}/Np^{++++} $E_0 = 0.152$
2'. Np^{+++}/NpO_2^+ $E_0 = 0.451 - 0.1182\,pH$
3'. Np^{++++}/NpO_2^+ $E_0 = 0.749 - 0.2364\,pH$
4'. NpO_2^+/NpO_2^{++} $E_0 = 1.149$

2.2. TWO SOLID SUBSTANCES

Limits of the domains of relative stability of the solid substances

$0 \rightarrow +3$

5. $2\mathbf{Np} + 3H_2O = \mathbf{Np_2O_3} + 6H^+ + 6e^-$ $E_0 = -1.420 - 0.0591\,pH$

$+3 \rightarrow +4$

6. $\mathbf{Np_2O_3} + H_2O = 2\mathbf{NpO_2} + 2H^+ + 2e^-$ a. $E_0 = -0.962 - 0.0591\,pH$
b. $= -0.928 - 0.0591\,pH$

$+4 \rightarrow +5$

7. $2\mathbf{NpO_2} + H_2O = \mathbf{Np_2O_5} + 2H^+ + 2e^-$ a. $E_0 = 1.253 - 0.0591\,pH$
b. $= 1.219 - 0.0591\,pH$

$+5 \rightarrow +6$

8. $\mathbf{Np_2O_5} + H_2O = 2\mathbf{NpO_3} + 2H^+ + 2e^-$ $E_0 = 1.310 - 0.0591\,pH$

2.3. ONE DISSOLVED SUBSTANCE AND ONE SOLID SUBSTANCE

Solubility of the solid substances

$Z = +3$

9. $2Np^{+++} + 3H_2O = \mathbf{Np_2O_3} + 6H^+$ $\log(Np^{+++}) = 21.99 - 3\,pH$

$Z = +4$

10. $Np^{++++} + 2H_2O = \mathbf{NpO_2} + 4H^+$ $\log(Np^{++++}) = 3.71 - 4\,pH$

$Z = +5$

11. $2NpO_2^+ + H_2O = \mathbf{Np_2O_5} + 2H^+$ $\log(NpO_2^+) = 11.66 - pH$

$Z = +6$

12. $NpO_2^{++} + H_2O = \mathbf{NpO_3} + 2H^+$ $\log(NpO_2^{++}) = 14.37 - 2\,pH$

$0 \rightarrow +3$

13. $\mathbf{Np} = Np^{+++} + 3e^-$ $E_0 = -1.856 + 0.0197 \log(Np^{+++})$

$+3 \rightarrow 4$

14. $Np^{+++} + 2H_2O = \mathbf{NpO_2} + 4H^+ + e^-$ a. $E_0 = 0.337 - 0.2364\,pH - 0.0591 \log(Np^{+++})$
b. $= 0.371 - 0.2364\,pH - 0.0591 \log(Np^{+++})$

$+4 \rightarrow +5$

15. $\mathbf{NpO_2} = NpO_2^+ + e^-$ a. $E_0 = 0.564 + 0.0591 \log(NpO_2^+)$
b. $= 0.530 + 0.0591 \log(NpO_2^+)$

$+5 \rightarrow +6$

16. $NpO_2^+ + H_2O = \mathbf{NpO_3} + 2H^+ + e^-$ $E_0 = 1.998 - 0.1182\,pH - 0.0591 \log(NpO_2^+)$

Plutonium

2.1. TWO DISSOLVED SUBSTANCES

2.1.1. *Relative stability of the dissolved substances*

$+3 \rightarrow +4$

1. $Pu^{+++} = Pu^{++++} + e^- \qquad E_0 = 0.967 + 0.0591 \log \frac{(Pu^{++++})}{(Pu^{+++})}$

$+3 \rightarrow +6$

2. $Pu^{+++} + 2H_2O = PuO_2^{++} + 4H^+ + 3e^- \qquad E_0 = 1.017 - 0.0788\,pH + 0.0197 \log \frac{(PuO_2^{++})}{(Pu^{+++})}$

$+4 \rightarrow +5$

3. $Pu^{++++} + 2H_2O = PuO_2^+ + 4H^+ + e^- \qquad E_0 = 1.157 - 0.2364\,pH + 0.0591 \log \frac{(PuO_2^+)}{(Pu^{++++})}$

$+4 \rightarrow +6$

4. $Pu^{++++} + 2H_2O = PuO_2^{++} + 4H^+ + 2e^- \qquad E_0 = 1.042 - 0.1182\,pH + 0.0295 \log \frac{(PuO_2^{++})}{(Pu^{++++})}$

$+5 \rightarrow +6$

5. $PuO_2^+ = PuO_2^{++} + e^- \qquad E_0 = 0.928 + 0.0591 \log \frac{(PuO_2^{++})}{(PuO_2^+)}$

2.1.2. *Limits of the domains of relative predominance of the dissolved substances*

1'. $Pu^{+++}/Pu^{++++} \qquad E_0 = 0.967$
2'. $Pu^{+++}/PuO_2^{++} \qquad E_0 = 1.017 - 0.0788\,pH$
3'. $Pu^{++++}/PuO_2^+ \qquad E_0 = 1.157 - 0.2364\,pH$
4'. $Pu^{++++}/PuO_2^{++} \qquad E_0 = 1.042 - 0.1182\,pH$
5'. $PuO_2^+/PuO_2^{++} \qquad E_0 = 0.928$

2.2. TWO SOLID SUBSTANCES

Limits of the domains of relative stability of the solid substances

$0 \rightarrow +3$

6. $2\mathbf{Pu} + 3H_2O = \mathbf{Pu_2O_3} + 6H^+ + 6e^- \qquad E_0 = -1.592 - 0.0591\,pH$

$+3 \rightarrow +4$

7. $\mathbf{Pu_2O_3} + H_2O = 2\mathbf{PuO_2} + 2H^+ + 2e^- \qquad a.\ E_0 = -0.455 - 0.0591\,pH$
$\qquad b.\ \ = -0.135 - 0.0591\,pH$

$+4 \rightarrow +5$

8. $2\mathbf{PuO_2} + H_2O = \mathbf{Pu_2O_5} + 2H^+ + 2e^- \qquad a.\ E_0 = 1.908 - 0.0591\,pH$
$\qquad b.\ \ = 1.588 - 0.0591\,pH$

$+4 \rightarrow +6$

9. $\mathbf{PuO_2} + H_2O = \mathbf{PuO_3} + 2H^+ + 2e^- \qquad a.\ E_0 = 1.485 - 0.0591\,pH$
$\qquad b.\ \ = 1.325 - 0.0591\,pH$

$+5 \rightarrow +6$

10. $\mathbf{Pu_2O_5} + H_2O = 2\mathbf{PuO_3} + 2H^+ + 2e^- \qquad E_0 = 1.062 - 0.0591\,pH$

2.3. ONE DISSOLVED SUBSTANCE AND ONE SOLID SUBSTANCE

Solubility of the solid substances

$Z = +3$

11. $2Pu^{+++} + 3H_2O = \mathbf{Pu_2O_3} + 6H^+ \qquad \log(Pu^{+++}) = 22.28 - 3\,pH$

$Z = +4$

12. $Pu^{++++} + 2H_2O = \mathbf{PuO_2} + 4H^+ \qquad a.\ \log(Pu^{++++}) = -1.78 - 4\,pH$
$\qquad b.\ \ = 3.64 - 4\,pH$

$Z = +6$

13. $PuO_2^{++} + H_2O = \mathbf{PuO_3} + 2H^+ \qquad \log(PuO_2^{++}) = 13.19 - 2\,pH$

$0 \rightarrow +3$

14. **Pu** $= Pu^{+++} + 3e^-$ $E_0 = -2.031 + 0.0197 \log (Pu^{+++})$

$+3 \rightarrow +4$

15. $Pu^{+++} + 2H_2O =$ **PuO_2** $+ 4H^+ + e^-$
 a. $E_0 = 0.862 - 0.2364\,pH - 0.0591 \log (Pu^{+++})$
 b. $= 1.182 - 0\;2364\,pH - 0.0591 \log (Pu^{+++})$

$+4 \rightarrow +6$

16. **PuO_2** $= PuO_2^{++} + 2e^-$
 a. $E_0 = 1.095 + 0.0295 \log (PuO_2^{++})$
 b. $= 0.935 + 0.0295 \log (PuO_2^{++})$

Americium

2.1. TWO DISSOLVED SUBSTANCES

2.1.1. *Relative stability of the dissolved substances*

$+3 \rightarrow +4$

1. $Am^{+++} = Am^{++++} + e^-$ $E_0 = 2.181 + 0.0591 \log \frac{(Am^{++++})}{(Am^{+++})}$

$+3 \rightarrow +5$

2. $Am^{+++} + 2H_2O = AmO_2^{+} + 4H^+ + 2e^-$ $E_0 = 1.721 - 0.1182\,pH + 0.0295 \log \frac{(AmO_2^{+})}{(Am^{+++})}$

$+3 \rightarrow +6$

3. $Am^{+++} + 2H_2O = AmO_2^{++} + 4H^+ + 3e^-$ $E_0 = 1.694 - 0.0788\,pH + 0.0197 \log \frac{(AmO_2^{++})}{(Am^{+++})}$

$+4 \rightarrow +5$

4. $Am^{++++} + 2H_2O = AmO_2^{+} + 4H^+ + e^-$ $E_0 = 1.261 - 0.2364\,pH + 0.0591 \log \frac{(AmO_2^{+})}{(Am^{++++})}$

$+5 \rightarrow +6$

5. $AmO_2^{+} = AmO_2^{++} + e^-$ $E_0 = 1.639 + 0.0591 \log \frac{(AmO_2^{++})}{(AmO_2^{+})}$

2.1.2. *Limits of the domains of relative predominance of the dissolved substances*

1'. Am^{+++}/Am^{++++} $E_0 = 2.181$
2'. Am^{+++}/AmO_2^{+} $E_0 = 1.721 - 0.1182\,pH$
3'. Am^{+++}/AmO_2^{++} $E_0 = 1.694 - 0.0788\,pH$
4'. Am^{++++}/AmO_2^{+} $E_0 = 1.261 - 0.2364\,pH$
5'. AmO_2^{+}/AmO_2^{++} $E_0 = 1.639$

2.2. TWO SOLID SUBSTANCES

Limits of the domains of relative stability of the solid substances

$0 \rightarrow +3$

6. 2**Am** $+ 3H_2O =$ **Am_2O_3** $+ 6H^+ + 6e^-$
 a. $E_0 = -1.878 - 0.0591\,pH$
 b. $= -1.676 - 0.0591\,pH$

$+3 \rightarrow +4$

7. **Am_2O_3** $+ H_2O = 2$**AmO_2** $+ 2H^+ + 2e^-$
 ac. $E_0 = 0.420 - 0.0591\,pH$
 ad. $= 0.533 - 0.0591\,pH$
 bc. $= -0.185 - 0.0591\,pH$
 bd. $= -0.072 - 0.0591\,pH$

$+4 \rightarrow +5$

8. 2**AmO_2** $+ H_2O =$ **Am_2O_5** $+ 2H^+ + 2e^-$
 c. $E_0 = 1.530 - 0.0591\,pH$
 d. $= 1.418 - 0.0591\,pH$

$+5 \rightarrow +6$

9. **Am_2O_5** $+ H_2O = 2$**AmO_3** $+ 2H^+ + 2e^-$ $E_0 = 1.930 - 0.0591\,pH$

2.3. ONE DISSOLVED SUBSTANCE AND ONE SOLID SUBSTANCE

Solubility of the solid substances

$Z = +3$

10. $2\,Am^{+++} + 3\,H_2O = \mathbf{Am_2O_3} + 6\,H^+$ — a. $\log(Am^{+++}) = 22.43 - 3\,pH$; b. $= 32.68 - 3\,pH$

$Z = +5$

11. $2\,AmO_2^{+} + H_2O = \mathbf{Am_2O_5} + 2\,H^+$ — $\log(AmO_2^{+}) = -2.80 - pH$

$Z = +6$

12. $AmO_2^{++} + H_2O = \mathbf{AmO_3} + 2\,H^+$ — $\log(AmO_2^{++}) = 2.26 - 2\,pH$

$0 \rightarrow +3$

13. $\mathbf{Am} = Am^{+++} + 3e^-$ — $E_0 = -2.320 + 0.0197 \log(Am^{+}$

$+3 \rightarrow +4$

14. $Am^{+++} + 2\,H_2O = \mathbf{AmO_2} + 4\,H^+ + e^-$ — c. $E_0 = 1.746 - 0.2364\,pH - 0.0591 \log(Am^{+}$; d. $= 1.856 - 0.2364\,pH - 0.0591 \log(Am^{+}$

$+3 \rightarrow +5$

15. $2\,Am^{+++} + 5\,H_2O = \mathbf{Am_2O_5} + 10\,H^+ + 4e^-$ — $E_0 = 1.639 - 0.1477\,pH - 0.0295 \log(Am^{+}$

$+5 \rightarrow +6$

16. $\mathbf{Am_2O_5} + 2\,H^+ = 2\,AmO_2^{++} + H_2O + 2e^-$ — $E_0 = 1.804 + 0.0591\,pH + 0.0591 \log(Am($

3. EQUILIBRIUM DIAGRAMS AND THEIR INTERPRETATION

3.1. ESTABLISHMENT OF THE DIAGRAMS

Using the equilibrium formulae given in paragraph 2, we have drawn Figs. 1–5 which represent the conditions of thermodynamic equilibrium of the systems thorium–, uranium–, neptunium–, plutonium– and americium–water, at 25°C.

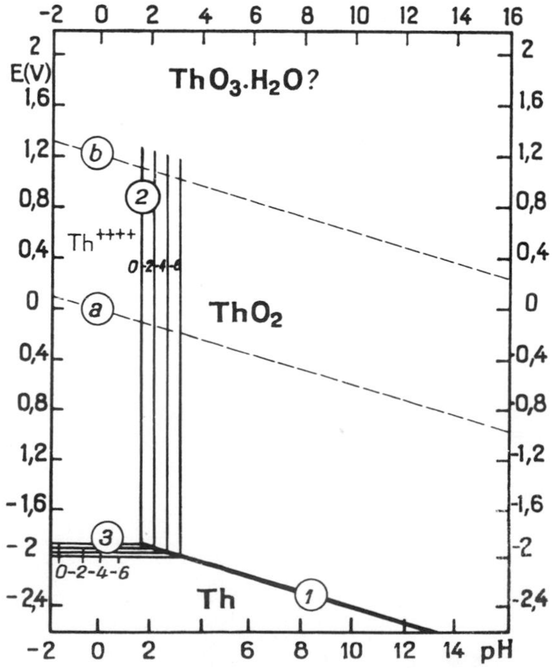

FIG. 1. Thorium–water.

FIGS. 1–5. Potential–pH equilibrium diagrams for the systems actinides–water, at 25°C.

The diagrams for the systems actinium–, protoactinium–, curium–, berkelium– and californium–water have not been drawn on account of the lack of thermodynamic data concerning them. We have, however, given in paragraph 1, purely as a guide, the compounds of these elements which are known at present.

In this account we give two potential–pH equilibrium diagrams for the system uranium–water, at 25°C (Fig. 2). Figure 2*a* was established by considering as solid substances U, UO, U_2O_3, UO_2, U_3O_8 and anhydrous UO_3, and shows the domains of stability of the metal and the "green oxide" U_3O_8, the principal constituent of pitchblende; Fig. 2*b* was established considering the following solid substances: UH_3, U, UO, U_2O_3, UO_2, U_3O_8, and $UO_3 . 2H_2O$, and is the potential–pH diagram for the stable equilibria of the system uranium–water.

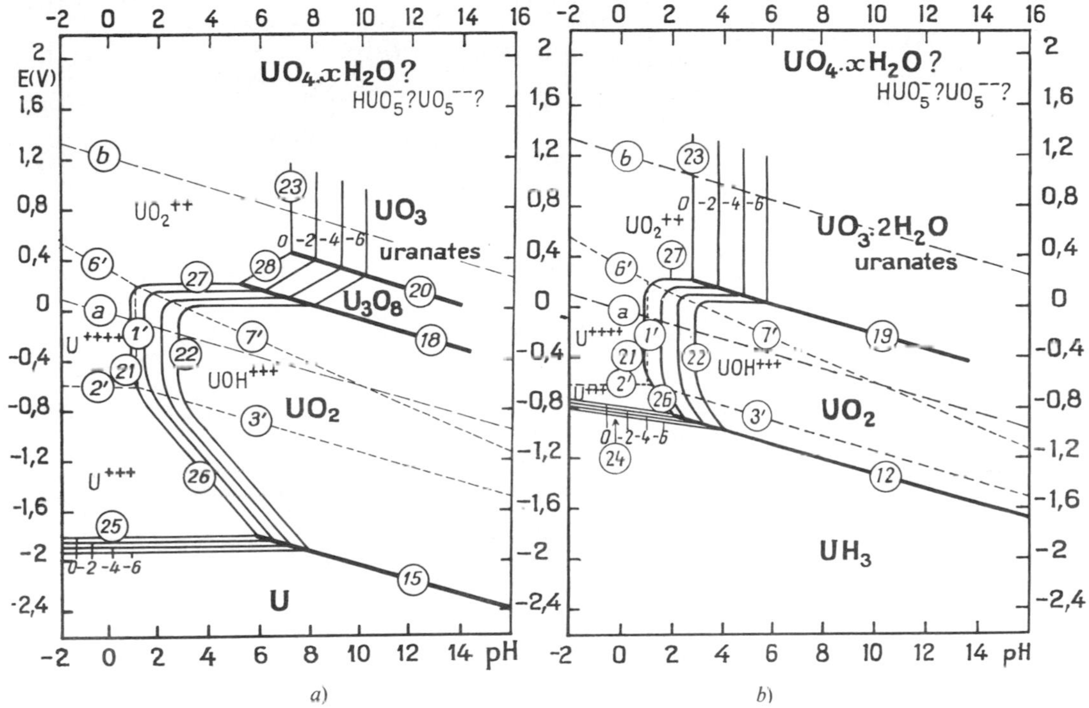

FIG. 2. Uranium–water.

A detailed study of uranium has been made previously [4] and Sillén [5] has published some redox diagrams for uranium, neptunium and plutonium.

Figures 1–5 are valid only in the absence of substances with which the metals of this group can form insoluble salts and soluble complexes.

The *sparingly soluble compounds* of actinium are the same as those for lanthanum: the hydroxide, the fluoride, the oxalate, the carbonate, the phosphate and the hydrofluosilicate; the yellow alkaline uranates are sparingly soluble; the fluoride UF_4 and the red–brown uranyl ferrocyanide are very sparingly soluble; AmF_3 and americium oxalate (the latter in acid solution), the fluorides of curium and berkelium, and curium hydroxide, are also sparingly soluble salts.

With regard to *complex ions* we point out the very marked tendency of tetravalent *thorium* to form complexes with the following anions: fluoride, iodate, bromate, nitrate, chlorate, and chloride, formate, acetate and chloroacetates, sulphate and sulphite, carbonate, oxalate, tartrate, malate, citrate, salicylate, sulphosalicylate.

Protoactinium forms soluble complexes with fluorides, oxalates and tartrates. Tetravalent *uranium* U^{++++} and UOH^{+++} forms complexes with the acids HCl, H_2SO_4, H_3PO_4 and $(COOH)_2$, and with the acetates, while hexavalent uranium UO_2^{++} forms complexes with oxalic, citric, malonic, tartaric, hydrofluoric and carbonic acids. The trivalent ions of the rare earth elements have, in general, only a

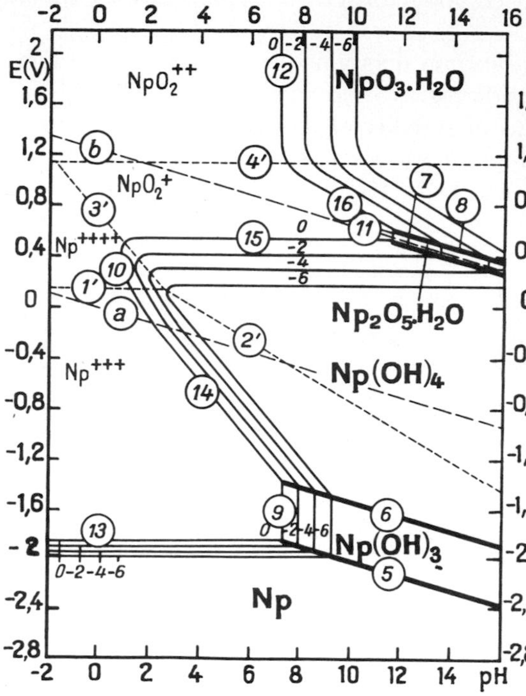

FIG. 3. Neptunium–water.

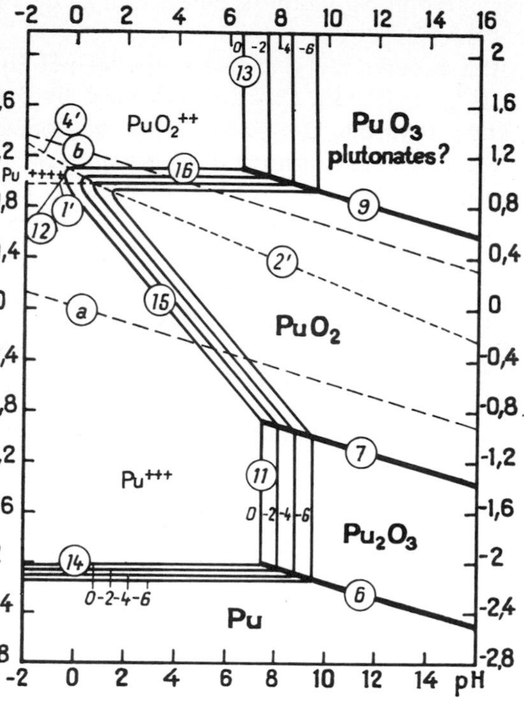

FIG. 4. Plutonium–water.

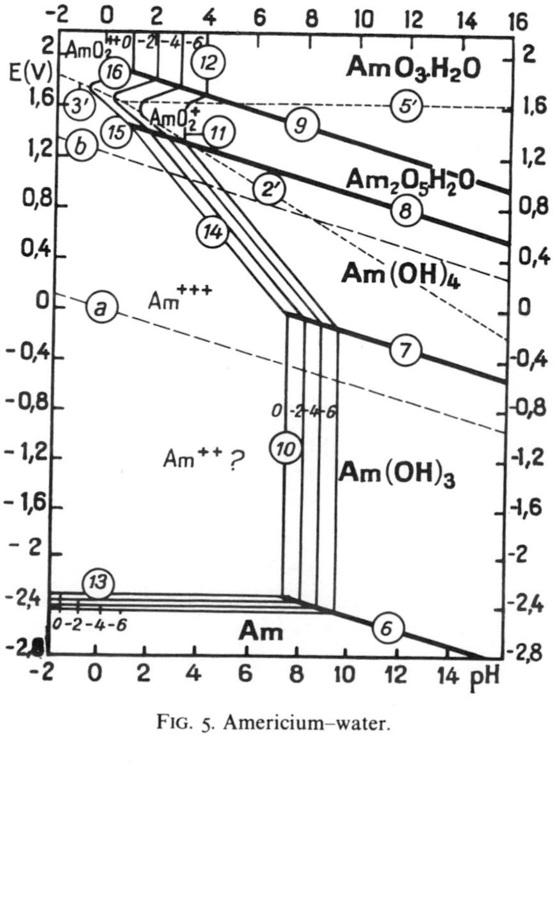

FIG. 5. Americium–water.

very slight tendency to form complex ions; such is the case with *plutonium* which forms only trivalent carbonated complexes. We point out the following: the tetravalent complexes of *neptunium* and *plutonium* with the anions: fluoride, sulphate, phosphate, oxalate and acetate; the complexes of *plutonium* with the anions: nitrate, chloride, sulphite, carbonate, citrate and peroxygenated complexes; the hexavalent complexes of *neptunium* and *plutonium* with NO_3^-, Cl^-, SO_4^{--} and CO_3^{--}. Trivalent *americium* forms soluble complexes with the oxalates in alkaline media.

3.2. STABILITY OF THE ACTINIDES AND URANIUM HYDRIDE UH_3

The actinides all exert large negative equilibrium potentials and their domains of stability in the respective potential–pH equilibrium diagrams lie well below the domain of stability of water. The actinides are therefore very base metals and very powerful reducing agents, unstable in the presence of water and aqueous solutions of any pH. They have a great affinity to react with water which they decompose with the evolution of hydrogen; they dissolve in the presence of solutions which are strongly acid, in the case of thorium, and acid or neutral in the case of uranium, neptunium, plutonium and americium, with the formation of trivalent cations (U^{+++}, Np^{+++}, Pu^{+++}, Am^{+++}) or tetravalent cations (Th^{++++}, U^{++++} and Np^{++++}).

In the presence of alkaline solutions, the reaction gives rise to the formation of hydroxides (or hydrated oxides) forming a passivating layer on the metal. This has been verified experimentally for thorium, uranium and plutonium.

Solid *uranium hydride* UH_3, thermodynamically more stable than uranium, is obtained by the action of hydrogen on the metal at temperatures between 250° and 350°C, by the action of steam on uranium and by the dehydrogenation of certain organic compounds by uranium. According to the equilibrium diagram Fig. 2*b*, it is a very unstable compound which ignites spontaneously in air, and violently reduces water with the formation of UO_2 and H_2; the acids H_2SO_4, HNO_3, and hydrogen peroxide react violently with the hydride forming uranyl salts; numerous oxidizing agents, for example manganates, bromates, chlorates and dichromates catalyse the decomposition of UH_3. Alkalis, on the other hand, have little or no action on the hydride [6].

On account of their instability the actinides do not exist in the elementary state in nature, and cannot be obtained by the electrolysis of aqueous solutions of their salts.

However, the metals in the elementary state can be obtained by electrolytic reduction in a non-aqueous phase, such as anhydrous alcoholic solutions of actinium and uranium salts, or molten solutions of thorium chlorides or fluorides in the presence of NaCl or KCl.

The actinides displace metals less electronegative than themselves from their solutions; for instance uranium and its hydride displace Hg, Ag, Cu, Sn, Bi, Pt and Au from their solutions [6].

3.3. STABILITY OF THE OXIDES AND HYDROXIDES OF THE ACTINIDES

According to Figs. 1–5, the anhydrous and hydrated oxides of the actinides are mostly non-amphoteric compounds, stable in alkaline solutions and unstable in acid solutions in which they dissolve as trivalent cations (U^{+++} and Np^{+++} in the presence of very powerful reducing agents; Am^{+++} both in reducing solutions and weakly oxidizing solutions) or tetravalent cations (Th^{++++}, in reducing or oxidizing solutions; U^{++++} and Np^{++++}, in the absence of reducing or oxidizing agents and in a sufficiently acid medium to avoid the formation of a more oxidized hydroxide; Pu^{++++} in a very strongly acid oxidizing media).

In the presence of powerful oxidizing agents the dissolution of almost all the actinide oxides in acid solutions will give rise to the formation of ions of the hexavalent metals: UO_2^{++}, NpO_2^{++}, PuO_2^{++} and AmO_2^{++}. The cations of the metals in the pentavalent state, of general formula MO_2^+ (where M represents an actinide) are mostly very unstable and do not therefore appear on the potential–pH diagrams. They become transformed by the reactions

$$\begin{array}{lll} & M^{V} + M^{III} & = 2\,M^{IV} \\ \text{and} & 2\,M^{V} + 2\,M^{IV} & = 2\,M^{VI} + 2\,M^{III} \\ \hline \text{overall reaction} & 3\,M^{V} & = 2\,M^{VI} + M^{III}. \end{array}$$

However, the hyponeptunyl ion NpO_2^+ is stable in acid aqueous solution and the cation AmO_2^+ has a small domain of existence in Fig. 5. The latter is unstable in aqueous solution and undergoes the following dichotomy:

$$3\,AmO_2^+ + 4\,H^+ = 2\,AmO_2^{++} + Am^{+++} + 2\,H_2O.$$

The progressive oxidation of neptunium, plutonium and americium in acid solution takes place according to the scheme

$$M^0 \rightarrow M^{3+} \rightarrow M^{4+} \rightarrow MO_2^+ \rightarrow MO_2^{++};$$

plutonium hydroxide, of oxidation number +5, is unstable with respect to the oxidation states immediately above and below it, and does not therefore appear on the diagram.

Thorium possesses only two oxidation states in aqueous solution: +4, corresponding to the formation of thoric oxide ThO_2, and +6, corresponding to the formation of a peroxyacid H_2ThO_4 which is slightly soluble.

The oxides UO and U_2O_3 are thermodynamically unstable with respect to UH_3, U and UO_2 and have not therefore any domain of existence in the potential–pH diagrams in Figs. 2*a* and *b*; only the oxides UO_2 and $UO_3.2H_2O$ are stable in the presence of aqueous solutions; uranium peroxide $UO_4.xH_2O$ is an oxidizing agent.

The actinide hydroxides are almost all insoluble in alkaline solutions and even in molten alkalis. We nevertheless point out the formation of peruranates of simplified formulae HUO_5^- and UO_5^{--}, and plutonates which are more soluble than the corresponding yellow uranates.

In accordance with Figs. 1–5, only the oxides ThO_2, UO_2 and $UO_3.2H_2O$, PuO_2, Am_2O_3 and AmO_2 have a domain of stability in common with that of water, and are stable in the presence of water and non-acid aqueous solutions; they form a passivating protective layer on the metal. The "sesquioxides" Np_2O_3 and Pu_2O_3 are reducing agents while the higher hydrated oxides corresponding to anhydrous oxides such as NpO_3, PuO_3, Am_2O_5 and AmO_3 are powerful oxidizing agents.

4. BIBLIOGRAPHY

[1] W. M. LATIMER, *Oxidation Potentials*, 2nd ed., Prentice-Hall, New York, 1952.
[2] G. T. SEABORG and J. J. KATZ, *The Actinide Elements*, McGraw-Hill, U.S.A., 1954, 870 pp.
[3] L. BREWER, Thermodynamic properties of the oxides and their vaporization processes, *Chem. Rev.* **52**, 1 (1953).
[4] E. DELTOMBE, N. DE ZOUBOV and M. POURBAIX, *Comportement électrochimique de l'uranium. Diagrammes d'équilibres tension–pH du système* U-H_2O, *à* 25°C (Rapport technique RT.31 of CEBELCOR, 1956).
[5] L. G. SILLÉN, Redox diagrams, *J. Chem. Ed.* **29**, 600 (1952).
[6] D. T. HURD, *An Introduction to the chemistry of the hydrides*, John Wiley, New York, 1952, pp. 178–81.

SECTION 8.1

TITANIUM (1)

J. SCHMETS, J. VAN MUYLDER and M. POURBAIX

SUMMARY

1. *Substances considered and substances not considered.*

2. *Reactions and equilibrium formulae.*

2.1. Two dissolved substances.

2.1.1. Relative stability of the dissolved substances.

2.1.2. Limits of the domains of relative predominance of the dissolved substances.

2.2. Two solid substances.

Relative stability of the solid substances.

2.3. One solid substance and one dissolved substance.

Solubility of the solid substances.

3. *Equilibrium diagrams and their interpretation.*

3.1. Establishment of the diagrams.

3.2. Stability and corrosion of titanium.

3.3. Stability of the oxide TiO.

3.4. Stability of the sesquioxide Ti_2O_3 and the hydroxide $Ti(OH)_3$.

3.5. Stability of the oxide Ti_3O_5.

3.6. Stability of the dioxide TiO_2 and its hydrate $TiO_2 . H_2O$.

3.7. Stability of the peroxide $TiO_3 . 2H_2O$.

4. *Bibliography.*

(1) Shortened and adapted version of the Rapport technique RT.4 of CEBELCOR [1].

1. SUBSTANCES CONSIDERED AND SUBSTANCES NOT CONSIDERED

	Oxidation number (Z)	Considered	Not considered	μ^0 (cal.)	Name, colour, crystalline system
Solid substances	0	**Ti**	–	0	Titanium, silvery grey, hex.
	+2	**TiO**	–	−116 920 (2)	Titanium monoxide, black
	»	–	**TiO** hydr.	–	Hypotitanous hydroxide $Ti(OH)_2$, black
	+3	**Ti_2O_3** anh.	–	a. −342 310 (2)	Titanium sesquioxide, violet, rhomb.
	»	» hydr.	–	b. −331 740 (2)	Titanium hydroxide $Ti(OH)_3$, violet–black(3)
	+3.33	**Ti_3O_5**	–	−553 120 (2)	Blue oxide
	+4	**TiO_2** anh.	–	c. −212 330 (2)	Titanium dioxide or rutile, blue, rhomb.
	»	» hydr.	–	d. −196 300	Hydrated dioxide $TiO_2.H_2O$ or metatitanic acid, white(3)
	»	–	**TiO_2** hydr.		Orthotitanic acid $Ti(OH)_4$
	+6	**TiO_3** hydr.	–	–	Hydrated peroxide $TiO_3.2H_2O$, yellow
Dissolved substances	+2	Ti^{++}	–	− 75 100	Hypotitanous ion, greenish brown
	+3	Ti^{+++}	–	− 83 600	Titanous ion, violet
	+4	TiO^{++}	–	−138 000	Titanyl ion, colourless
	»	$HTiO_3^-$	–	−228 460 (2)	Titanate ion, colourless
	+6	TiO_2^{++}	–	−111 670 (2)	Pertitanyl ion, orange
	»	–	$HTiO_4^-$	–	Acid pertitanate ion, colourless
	»	–	TiO_4^{--}	–	Pertitanate ion, colourless

2. REACTIONS AND EQUILIBRIUM FORMULAE(4)

2.1. TWO DISSOLVED SUBSTANCES

2.1.1. *Relative stability of the dissolved substances*

$Z = +4$

1. $TiO^{++} + 2H_2O = HTiO_3^- + 3H^+$ $\qquad \log \frac{(HTiO_3^-)}{(TiO^{++})} = -16.82 + 3pH$

$+2 \rightarrow +3$

2. $Ti^{++} = Ti^{+++} + e^-$ $\qquad E_0 = -0.368 + 0.0591 \log \frac{(Ti^{+++})}{(Ti^{++})}$

$+2 \rightarrow +4$

3. $Ti^{++} + H_2O = TiO^{++} + 2H^+ + 2e^-$ $\qquad E_0 = -0.135 - 0.0591\,pH + 0.0295 \log \frac{(TiO^{++})}{(Ti^{++})}$

4. $Ti^{++} + 3H_2O = HTiO_3^- + 5H^+ + 2e^-$ $\qquad E_0 = 0.362 - 0.1475\,pH + 0.0295 \log \frac{(HTiO_3^-)}{(Ti^{++})}$

$+3 \rightarrow +4$

5. $Ti^{+++} + H_2O = TiO^{++} + 2H^+ + e^-$ $\qquad E_0 = 0.100 - 0.1182\,pH + 0.0591 \log \frac{(TiO^{++})}{(Ti^{+++})}$

---

(2) These values have either been calculated or justified by other means [1].

(3) These values of μ^0 for the oxides correspond to the following values for the hydroxides and hydrated oxides:

$Ti(OH)_3$: −250 905 cal., $TiO_2.H_2O$: −252 990 cal.

(4) In reactions involving Ti_2O_3, the letter *a* refers to anhydrous Ti_2O_3, whose free enthalpy of formation is −342 310 cal.; the letter *b* refers to $Ti(OH)_3$, whose free enthalpy of formation is −501 940 cal. In reactions involving TiO_2, the letter *c* corresponds to anhydrous TiO_2, whose free enthalpy of formation is −212 330 cal.; the letter *d* refers to $TiO_2 . H_2O$, whose free enthalpy of formation is −252 990 cal.

$+4 \rightarrow +6$

6. $TiO^{++} + H_2O = TiO_2^{++} + 2H^+ + 2e^-$ $\quad E_0 = 1.800 - 0.0591\,pH + 0.0295 \log \frac{(TiO_2^{++})}{(TiO^{++})}$

7. $HTiO_3^- + H^+ = TiO_2^{++} + H_2O + 2e^-$ $\quad E_0 = 1.303 + 0.0295\,pH + 0.0295 \log \frac{(TiO_2^{++})}{(HTiO_3^-)}$

2.1.2. *Limits of the domains of relative predominance of the dissolved substances*

1'. $TiO^{++}/HTiO_3^-$ $\quad pH = 5.61$

2'. Ti^{++}/Ti^{+++} $\quad E_0 = -0.368$

3'. Ti^{++}/TiO^{++} $\quad E_0 = -0.135 - 0.0591\,pH$

4'. $Ti^{++}/HTiO_3^-$ $\quad E_0 = 0.362 - 0.1475\,pH$

5'. Ti^{+++}/TiO^{++} $\quad E_0 = 0.100 - 0.1182\,pH$

6'. TiO^{++}/TiO_2^{++} $\quad E_0 = 1.800 - 0.0591\,pH$

7'. $HTiO_3^-/TiO_2^{++}$ $\quad E_0 = 1.303 + 0.0295\,pH$

2.2. TWO SOLID SUBSTANCES

Relative stability of the solid substances

$0 \rightarrow +2$

8. $\mathbf{Ti} + H_2O = \mathbf{TiO} + 2H^+ + 2e^-$ $\quad E_0 = -1.306 - 0.0591\,pH$

$+2 \rightarrow +3$

9. $2\mathbf{TiO} + H_2O = \mathbf{Ti_2O_3} + 2H^+ + 2e^-$ $\quad$ a. $E_0 = -1.123 - 0.0591\,pH$
b. $= -0.894 - 0.0591\,pH$

$+3 \rightarrow +3.33$

10. $3\mathbf{Ti_2O_3} + H_2O = 2\mathbf{Ti_3O_5} + 2H^+ + 2e^-$ $\quad$ a. $E_0 = -0.490 - 0.0591\,pH$
b. $= -1.178 - 0.0591\,pH$

$+3 \rightarrow +4$

11. $\mathbf{Ti_2O_3} + H_2O = 2\mathbf{TiO_2} + 2H^+ + 2e^-$ $\quad$ ac. $E_0 = -0.556 - 0.0591\,pH$
ad. $= -0.139 - 0.0591\,pH$
bc. $= -0.786 - 0.0591\,pH$
bd. $= -0.091 - 0.0591\,pH$

$+3.33 \rightarrow +4$

12. $\mathbf{Ti_3O_5} + H_2O = 3\mathbf{TiO_2} + 2H^+ + 2e^-$ $\quad$ c. $E_0 = -0.589 - 0.0591\,pH$
d. $= -0.453 - 0.0591\,pH$

2.3. ONE SOLID SUBSTANCE AND ONE DISSOLVED SUBSTANCE

Solubility of the solid substances

$Z = +2$

13. $Ti^{++} + H_2O = \mathbf{TiO} + 2H^+$ $\quad \log(Ti^{++}) = 10.91 - 2pH$

$Z = +3$

14. $2Ti^{+++} + 3H_2O = \mathbf{Ti_2O_3} + 6H^+$ $\quad$ a. $\log(Ti^{+++}) = -8.09 - 3pH$
b. $= 2.03 - 3pH$

$Z = +4$

15. $TiO^{++} + H_2O = \mathbf{TiO_2} + 2H^+$ $\quad$ c. $\log(TiO^{++}) = -12.94 - 2pH$
d. $= -1.18 - 2pH$

16. $HTiO_3^- + H^+ = \mathbf{TiO_2} + H_2O$ $\quad$ c. $\log(HTiO_3^-) = -29.76 + pH$
d. $= -18.00 + pH$

$0 \rightarrow +2$

17. $\mathbf{Ti} = Ti^{++} + 2e^-$ $\quad E_0 = -1.630 + 0.0295 \log(Ti^{++})$

$+2 \rightarrow +3$

18. $2Ti^{++} + 3H_2O = \mathbf{Ti_2O_3} + 6H^+ + 2e^-$ $\quad$ a. $E_0 = -0.478 - 0.1773\,pH - 0.0591 \log(Ti^{++})$
b. $= -0.248 - 0.1773\,pH - 0.0591 \log(Ti^{++})$

$+2 \rightarrow +4$

19. $Ti^{++} + 2H_2O = \mathbf{TiO_2} + 4H^+ + 2e^-$ $\quad$ c. $E_0 = -0.502 - 0.1182\,pH - 0.0295 \log(Ti^{++})$
d. $= -0.169 - 0.1182\,pH - 0.0295 \log(Ti^{++})$

$+3 \rightarrow +4$

20. $Ti^{+++} + 2H_2O = \mathbf{TiO_2} + 4H^+ + e^-$

c. $E_0 = -0.666 - 0.2364\,pH - 0.0591\log(Ti^{+++})$

d. $ = \ \ 0.029 - 0.2364\,pH - 0.0591\log(Ti^{+++})$

21. $\mathbf{Ti_2O_3} + 3H_2O = 2HTiO_3^- + 4H^+ + 2e^-$

a. $E_0 = -0.601 - 0.1182\,pH + 0.0591\log(HTiO_3^-)$

b. $ = \ \ 0.973 - 0.1182\,pH + 0.0591\log(HTiO_3^-)$

$+4 \rightarrow +6$

22. $\mathbf{TiO_2} = TiO_2^{++} + 2e^-$

c. $E_0 = 2.182 + 0.0295\log(TiO_2^{++})$

d. $ = 1.835 + 0.0295\log(TiO_2^{++})$

3. EQUILIBRIUM DIAGRAMS AND THEIR INTERPRETATION

3.1. ESTABLISHMENT OF THE DIAGRAMS

Using relations (1)–(22) we have drawn two potential–pH equilibrium diagrams for the system titanium–water. In Fig. 1 we have considered the oxides Ti_2O_3 and TiO_2 in the anhydrous state; in Fig. 2, we have considered these oxides in the hydrated state.

These two diagrams show the conditions of thermodynamic stability of titanium and those derivatives of it which can exist in the presence of water and aqueous solutions free from substances with which titanium can form soluble complexes or insoluble salts.

Among the principal titanium complexes, we point out, according to Charlot [2], the citric complexes, the tartaric complexes (very stable), and the carbonic complexes (not very stable), and the complexes with hydrogen peroxide (orange complexes TiO_2^{++}).

The thermodynamic data collected in paragraph 1 are in part subject to caution, in particular with regard to the free enthalpies of formation of the ions $HTiO_3^-$ and TiO_2^{++}, and also that of the hydroxide $Ti(OH)_3$. Consequently, Figs. 1 and 2 do not claim to represent exactly the equilibrium conditions of the system titanium–water, particularly in the regions marked with question marks.

From Figs. 1 and 2, we have deduced, according to the convention that we have previously adopted, Figs. 3 and 4 which represent the theoretical conditions for corrosion, immunity and passivation of titanium, at 25°C.

These figures differ mainly in the fact that the oxide of tetravalent titanium considered in Fig. 4 is the hydrated oxide $TiO_2 . H_2O$, while in Fig. 3 we have considered the anhydrous oxide TiO_2, in the form of rutile whose domain of thermodynamic stability is much larger.

3.2. STABILITY AND CORROSION OF TITANIUM

Bearing in mind the reservations which have just been pointed out, Figs. 1–4 illustrate the following facts:

Titanium is not a noble metal; in actual fact its domain of thermodynamic stability does not have any portion in common with the domain of thermodynamic stability of water, and it lies well below the latter. If this metal generally exerts a high electrode potential, it is because a passivating film of oxide is formed on its surface; the stability of this covering protects the metal from further deterioration. In the presence of water, therefore, titanium will not react in the same way as potassium or sodium, but will behave similarly to aluminium, which is also a base metal which is easily rendered passive.

It is this passivation by an oxide film in an oxidizing medium free from complexing anions that is responsible for the resistance to deterioration of titanium in the presence of water, as pointed out by various investigators (notably Fontana [3], Haissinsky and Emmanuel-Zavizziano [4]) and also the absence of a metal displacement reaction when titanium is put into a copper sulphate solution. (See Botts and Krauskopf [5]). On the other hand, as Straumanis and Chen have shown [17], concentrated non-oxidizing acids (hydrochloric acid and sulphuric acid) cause a lowering of the potential of the metal, probably on account of the greater solubility of the oxides and hydroxides of titanium in the reducing medium (Fig. 1); F^- ions, through their complexing action, cause the dissolution of the protective film, enabling displacement reactions to be obtained (for instance titanium in the presence of a solution of cupric fluoride) (*loc. cit.* [5]).

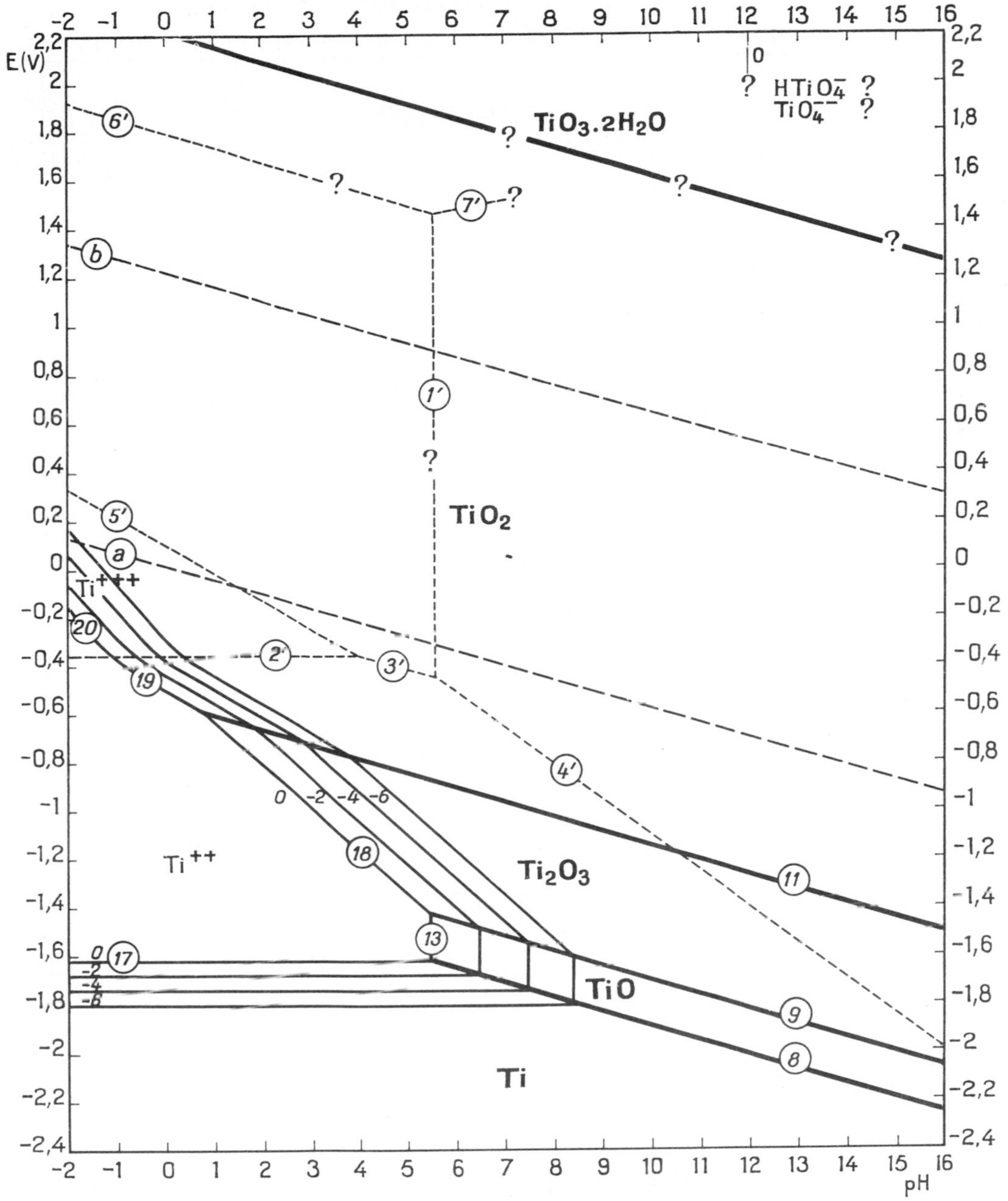

FIG. I. Potential–pH equilibrium diagram for the system titanium–water, at 25°C. [Figure established by considering, as derivatives of tri- and tetravalent titanium, the anhydrous oxides Ti_2O_3 and TiO_2 (rutile).]

Titanium dissolves, with difficulty, in concentrated non-oxidizing strong acids; titanous ions Ti^{+++} (violet) and titanyl TiO^{++} (colourless) are formed. Nitric acid causes passivation of the metal (see Gee *et al.* [6]).

Hydrofluoric acid, which is both non-oxidizing and complexing, can attack the metal even when its concentration is small, as is shown notably in Gee's works [7]; other details will be found in Gmelin

([8], p. 287); a systematic study of the action of F^- ions and titanium–fluorine complexes on the electrochemical behaviour of titanium would be of great interest.

Alkalis, in particular caustic soda, have only a slight action on titanium.

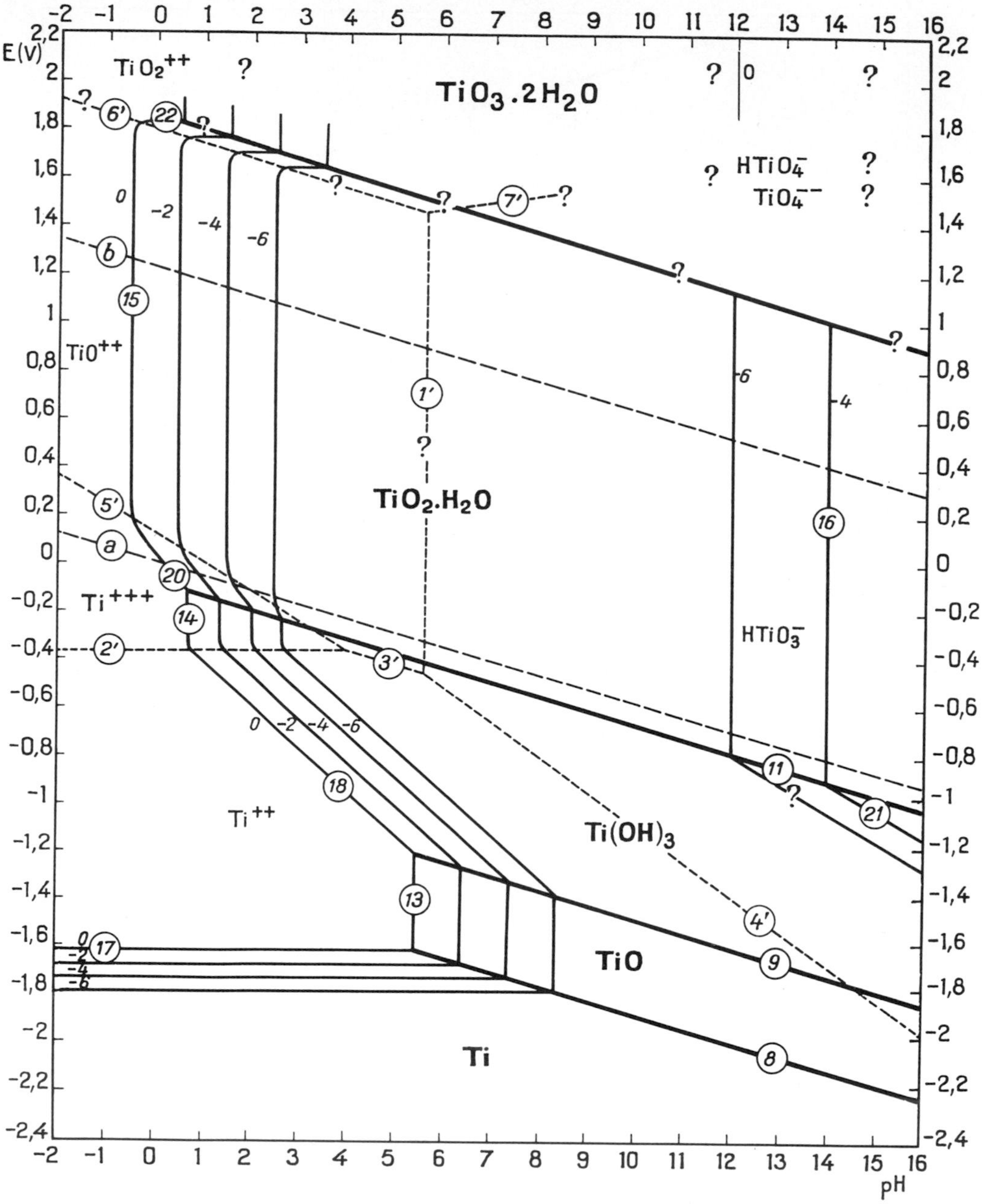

FIG. 2. Potential–pH equilibrium diagram for the system titanium–water, at 25°C. [Figure established considering, as derivatives of tri- and tetravalent titanium, the hydroxide $Ti(OH)_3$ and the hydrated oxide $TiO_2.H_2O$.]

An analysis of the experimental facts known at present concerning the conditions for corrosion and non-corrosion of titanium [1] leads to the conclusion that these conditions are represented almost exactly in Fig. 3; it will be recalled that this figure, relating to the behaviour of titanium in the absence of complexing substances (such as fluorides) at 25°C, was established by assuming passivation to be due to a film of rutile TiO_2. Taking into account the excellent protective properties of such a film, titanium appears in this figure to be resistant to corrosion in the presence of any non-complexing solutions, with the exception of acid reducing solutions and very oxidizing solutions.

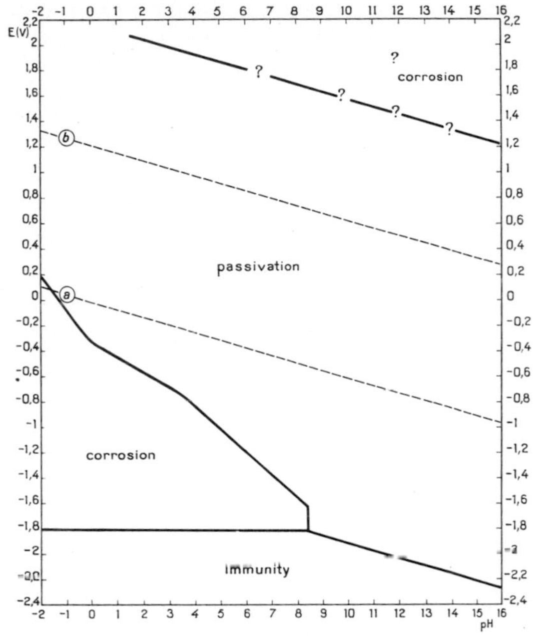

FIG. 3. Theoretical domains of corrosion, immunity and passivation of titanium, at 25°C. [Deduced from Fig. 1, assuming passivation by the anhydrous oxide TiO_2 (rutile).]

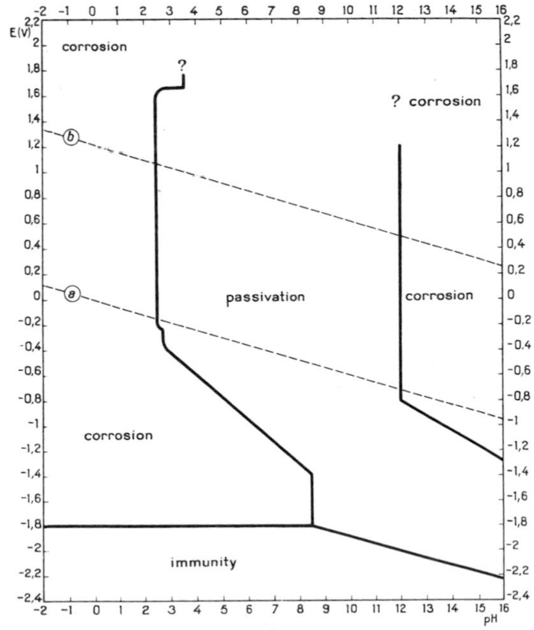

FIG. 4. Theoretical domains of corrosion, immunity and passivation of titanium, at 25°C. [Deduced from Fig. 2, assuming passivation by the hydrated oxide $TiO_2 . H_2O$.]

In actual fact titanium is particularly stable in the presence of the majority of non-fluorinated aqueous solutions; if the solution is moderately oxidizing, the metal can be considered to be safe from corrosion. The systematic study of the corrosion of titanium carried out by Hutchinson and Permar [16] shows this to be the case, in fact; in sea-water, for example, which is a particularly dangerous medium for most metals, titanium resists corrosion. In the presence of very oxidizing solutions, such as hydrogen peroxide solutions, titanium will be corroded; although, in agreement with the probable domain of corrosion which appears in Fig. 3 at very high electrode potentials, titanium generally corrodes if one attempts to use it as an electrolytic anode, it no longer corrodes if it is partially covered with a noble metal of relatively small oxygen overpotential (e.g. platinum [18]), which lowers its electrode potential from the domain of corrosion situated in the upper part of Fig. 3 into the domain of passivation. This important property enables titanium to be used for the manufacture of uncorrodible electrodes for industrial use as electrolytic anodes and as ground beds for cathodic protection.

3.3. STABILITY OF THE OXIDE TiO

As shown in Fig. 1, the black monoxide TiO [and also the black hydroxide $Ti(OH)_2$ not considered in this figure] is a reducing substance, unstable in the presence of water. In the presence of acid solutions free from oxidizing agents, it dissolves with the evolution of hydrogen (as shown by Dawihl and Schröter [10], with the formation of brown green hypotitanous ions Ti^{++} and violet titanous ions Ti^{+++} (according to Portcheke and Scheller [9]).

This oxide is converted into TiO_2 by the action of nitric acid, as Dawihl and Schröter have shown [10]. In Figs. 1 and 2 the domain of predominance of the hypotitanous ion Ti^{++} lies entirely below line (*a*) corresponding to the equilibrium of the reaction of the reduction of water to gaseous hydrogen at atmospheric pressure; this ion is therefore unstable and tends to be oxidized to titanous ions Ti^{+++} reducing the water with the evolution of hydrogen. Caustic soda does not react with TiO.

3.4. STABILITY OF THE SESQUIOXIDE Ti_2O_3 AND THE HYDROXIDE $Ti(OH)_3$

In agreement with Fig. 1, titanous oxide Ti_2O_3 (violet ?, metallic in appearance) is a feeble reducing agent; it dissolves in concentrated sulphuric acid with the formation of violet titanous ions Ti^{+++}; when it is dissolved in warm sulphuric acid the dissolution is accompanied by the reduction of the acid to elementary sulphur. Caustic soda has no action on Ti_2O_3.

Only a small amount of information is available for $Ti(OH)_3$; even its colour is uncertain. In neutral or ammoniacal media, it reduces NO_3^- to NH_3.

3.5. STABILITY OF THE OXIDE Ti_3O_5

From the free enthalpy of formation values assumed in paragraph 1, the blue oxide Ti_3O_5 is thermodynamically unstable with respect to titanous oxide Ti_2O_3 and rutile TiO_2, and tends to decompose to give a mixture of these two oxides. Ti_3O_5 does not therefore appear in Fig. 1, which refers to the thermodynamically stable anhydrous oxides, although this oxide can actually be stable and present a characteristic X-ray spectrum. In fact, Ti_3O_5, together with TiO_2, is the oxidized form of titanium which is the most resistant to acids and bases; it is not impossible that Ti_3O_5 may play a part in the formation of passivating layers on titanium.

3.6. STABILITY OF THE DIOXIDE TiO_2 AND ITS HYDRATE $TiO_2 . H_2O$

By increasing the pH of strongly acid solutions of titanyl ions TiO^{++}, a precipitate of orthotitanic acid $Ti(OH)_4$ is formed, whose free enthalpy of formation is unknown; it is an unstable substance which changes gradually, by dehydration, into metatitanic acid $TiO_2 . H_2O$, considered in Fig. 2.([5]) As this figure shows, $TiO_2 . H_2O$ is appreciably soluble in strongly acid solutions (10^{-4} g-at Ti/l for pH = 1·4) and in strongly alkaline solutions (10^{-4} g-at Ti/l for pH = 14); on the other hand, as Fig. 1 shows, anhydrous TiO_2 (rutile, whose formation is at present certain only at high temperatures) is practically insoluble in acid and alkaline media (see Gmelin [8], p. 255).

Figures 1 and 2 show that the domain of stability of anhydrous TiO_2 (rutile) and that of $TiO_2 . H_2O$ cover the domain of stability of water. The tetravalent oxide is therefore the oxide which is thermodynamically stable in the presence of water or aqueous solutions. Rutile, which is the form of the tetravalent oxide having the least free energy (−212 330 cal. for TiO_2 in the form of rutile and −196 300 cal. for TiO_2 in the form of $TiO_2 . H_2O$), is the most stable of the oxides of tetravalent titanium; it is probable that it is a film of TiO_2 which assures the protection of titanium in aqueous solutions.

Nevertheless, we have no knowledge of any experimental work proving definitely that this passivation is due to the formation of an oxide film. Uhlig and Geary [13] think that the primary stage of passivation consists of an absorption of oxygen or other substances. Hall and Hackerman [14] consider that, during the anodic passivation of titanium in neutral NaCl solution, a monatomic layer of oxygen is formed, fixed by covalent bonds; in the case of polarization with the evolution of oxygen a film of TiO_2 would be formed.

Hickman and Gulbransen [15] have shown that titanium covers itself with rutile when it is heated to 300 to 700°C in the presence of air.

3.7. STABILITY OF THE PEROXIDE $TiO_3 . 2H_2O$

The yellow peroxide $TiO_3 . 2H_2O$, whose conditions of thermodynamic stability have been represented diagrammatically in Figs. 1 and 2, is an oxidizing substance, unstable in the presence of water and much more soluble than TiO_2 or $TiO_2 . H_2O$; it dissolves in acid solutions with the formation of yellow to red pertitanyl ions TiO_2^{++}, and in alkaline solution with the formation of titanate ions $HTiO_3^-$ and/or colourless pertitanate ions $HTiO_4^-$ and TiO_4^{--} (?). From approximate experiments that we have carried out in the laboratory, the solubility of $TiO_3 . 2H_2O$ seems to be around 1 g-mol/l for pH = 0·5 (on the acid side) and for pH = 12 (on the alkaline side).

By the action of hydrogen peroxide on very acid solutions of tri- or tetravalent titanium, a solution of peroxidized TiO_2^{++} ions is obtained, which deposits a precipitate of peroxide, $TiO_3 . 2H_2O$, on increase in pH. The oxidizing power of $TiO_3 . 2H_2O$ is similar to that of hydrogen peroxide. This peroxide can also be formed by the action of hydrogen peroxide on the oxide $TiO_2 . H_2O$. We emphasize the fact that the representation of the stability of titanium peroxide and its dissolution products in acid and alkaline media given in Figs. 1 and 2 is grossly approximate.

4. BIBLIOGRAPHY

[1] J. SCHMETS and M. POURBAIX, *Comportement électrochimique du titane. Diagramme d'équilibres tension–pH du système* Ti–H_2O. *Corrosion du titane* (Rapport technique RT.4 of CEBELCOR, 1953).
[2] G. CHARLOT, *Théorie et méthode nouvelles d'analyse qualitative*, 3rd ed., Masson, 1949.
[3] M. G. FONTANA, *Ind. Eng. Chem.* **40**, 99 A (1948).
[4] M. HAISSINSKY and H. EMMANUEL-ZAVIZZIANO, *C. R. Acad. Sc.* **204**, 759 (1937).
[5] E. D. BOTTS and F. C. KRAUSKOPF, *J. Phys. Chem.* **31**, 1416 (1927).
[6] E. A. GEE, L. B. GOLDEN and W. E. LUSBEY, *Ind. Eng. Chem.* **41**, 1668 (1949).
[7] E. A. GEE, *J. Electrochem. Soc.* **96**, 19 C (1949).
[8] *Gmelins Handbuch der anorganischen Chemie*, **41** (*Titan*).
[9] G. PORTCHEKE and W. SCHELLER, *Z. anorg. allgem. Chem.* **235**, 264 (1938).
[10] W. DAWIHL and K. SCHRÖTER, *Z. anorg. allgem. Chem.* **233**, 178 (1937).

(5) According to Klimenko and Sirokomsky [11] some $Ti(OH)_4$ is precipitated at a pH of about 1·5 by the addition of alkali to a solution of titanic sulphate $TiO(SO_4)_2$. According to Askenasy and Heise [12], metatitanic acid is precipitated by heating acid solutions of $TiO(SO_4)_2$.

[11] N. G. Klimenko and V. S. Sirokomsky, *Zavodskaya Labor.* **13**, 1029 (1947).
[12] P. Askenasy and K. Heise, *Z. anorg. allgem. Chem.* **196**, 269 (1931).
[13] H. H. Uhlig and A. Geary, *Publication of the Corrosion Laboratory*, Department of Metallurgy, Massachusetts Institute of Technology, Cambridge, Massachusetts (U.S.A.).
[14] C. D. Hall, Jr. and N. Hackerman, *J. Phys. Chem.* **57**, 262 (1953).
[15] J. W. Hickman and E. A. Gulbransen, *Anal. Chem.* **20**, 158 (1948).
[16] G. E. Hutchinson and P. H. Permar, *Corrosion* **5**, 319 (1949).
[17] M. Straumanis and P. Chen, *Corrosion*, **7**, 229 (1951).
[18] H. Preiser, *Platinum Met. Rev.* **3**, 38–43 (1953).

SECTION 8.2

ZIRCONIUM (1)

M. MARAGHINI, E. DELTOMBE, N. DE ZOUBOV, P. VAN RYSSELBERGHE and M. POURBAIX

SUMMARY

(1) Shortened and adapted version of the Rapport technique RT.45 of CEBELCOR [1].

1. SUBSTANCES CONSIDERED AND SUBSTANCES NOT CONSIDERED

	Oxidation number (Z)	Considered	Not considered	μ^0 (cal.)	Name, colour, crystalline system
Solid substances	0	**Zr**	-	0	Zirconium, grey–white, cub.
	+2	-	**ZrO** ?	-	Zirconium monoxide
	+4	**ZrO_2** hydr.	-	*a.* −256 620	Hydrated oxide $ZrO_2.2H_2O$ or $Zr(OH)_4$, white, amorphous(2)
	»	» hydr.	-	*b.* −254 810	Hydrated oxide $ZrO(OH)_2$ or $ZrO_2.H_2O$, white(2)
	»	» anh.	-	*c.* −247 700 (3)	Anhydrous oxide ZrO_2 or zirconia, white, monocl.
	+5	-	**Zr_2O_5** ?	-	Zirconium pentoxide
	+6	-	**ZrO_3** ?	-	Zirconium peroxide
	+7	-	**Zr_2O_7** ?	-	Zirconium heptoxide
Dissolved substances	+4	Zr^{++++}	-	−142 000 (3)	Zirconic ion, colourless
	»	ZrO^{++}	-	−201 500 (3)	Zirconyl ion, colourless
	»	$HZrO_3^-$	-	−287 700	Zirconate ion, colourless

2. REACTIONS AND EQUILIBRIUM FORMULAE (4)

2.1. TWO DISSOLVED SUBSTANCES

2.1.1. *Relative stability of the dissolved substances*

Z = +4

1. $Zr^{++++} + H_2O = ZrO^{++} + 2H^+$ $\qquad \log\frac{(ZrO^{++})}{(Zr^{++++})} = 2.06 + 2\,pH$

2. $ZrO^{++} + 2H_2O = HZrO_3^- + 3H^+$ $\qquad \log\frac{(HZrO_3^-)}{(ZrO^{++})} = -19.95 + 3\,pH$

2.1.2. *Limits of the domains of relative predominance of the dissolved substances*

1'. Zr^{++++}/ZrO^{++} $\qquad pH = -1.03$

2'. $ZrO^{++}/HZrO_3^-$ $\qquad pH = 6.65$

2.2. TWO SOLID SUBSTANCES

Limits of the domains of relative stability of the solid substances

$0 \rightarrow +4$

3. **Zr** $+ 2H_2O =$ **ZrO_2** $+ 4H^+ + 4e^-$ $\qquad$ *a.* $E_0 = -1.553 - 0.0591\,pH$
b. $\quad = -1.533 - 0.0591\,pH$
c. $\quad = -1.456 - 0.0591\,pH$

---

(2) The values of μ^0 for the oxides correspond to the following values for the hydroxides or hydrated oxides:
$ZrO_2.2H_2O$ or $Zr(OH)_4$: −370 000 cal. $\qquad ZrO_2.H_2O$ or $ZrO(OH)_2$: −311 500 cal.

(3) These values have been confirmed elsewhere [1].

(4) For the reactions involving ZrO_2, the letter *a* refers to $ZrO_2.2H_2O$, whose free enthalpy of formation is −370 000 cal., the letter *b* refers to $ZrO_2.H_2O$, whose free enthalpy of formation is −311 500 cal., and the letter *c* refers to anhydrous ZrO_2, whose free enthalpy of formation is −247 700 cal.

2.3. ONE SOLID SUBSTANCE AND ONE DISSOLVED SUBSTANCE

Solubility of the solid substances

$Z = +4$

4.	$Zr^{++++} + 2H_2O = \mathbf{ZrO_2} + 4H^+$	a. $\log(Zr^{++++}) = -0.91 - 4\,pH$
		b. $= 0.79 - 4\,pH$
		c. $= 5.64 - 4\,pH$
5.	$ZrO^{++} + H_2O = \mathbf{ZrO_2} + 2H^+$	a. $\log(ZrO^{++}) = 1.15 - 2\,pH$
		b. $= 2.48 - 2\,pH$
		c. $= 7.70 - 2\,pH$
6.	$\mathbf{ZrO_2} + H_2O = HZrO_3^- + H^+$	a. $\log(HZrO_3^-) = -18.78 + pH$
		b. $= -17.46 + pH$
		c. $= -12.25 + pH$

$0 \rightarrow +4$

7.	$\mathbf{Zr} = Zr^{++++} + 4e^-$	$E_0 = -1.539 + 0.0148 \log(Zr^{++++})$
8.	$\mathbf{Zr} + H_2O = ZrO^{++} + 2H^+ + 4e^-$	$E_0 = -1.570 - 0.0295\,pH + 0.0148 \log(ZrO^{++})$
9.	$\mathbf{Zr} + 3H_2O = HZrO_3^- + 5H^+ + 4e^-$	$E_0 = -1.276 - 0.0740\,pH + 0.0148 \log(HZrO_3^-)$

3. EQUILIBRIUM DIAGRAM AND ITS INTERPRETATION

3.1. ESTABLISHMENT OF THE DIAGRAM

Using the equilibrium formulae established in paragraph 2, we have drawn Figs. 1, 2 and 3.

Figure 1 represents the conditions of thermodynamic equilibrium of the system zirconium–water, at 25°C. Figure 2, which is deduced from Fig. 1 after making certain assumptions, shows the theoretical conditions of corrosion, immunity and passivation of zirconium.

Figure 3 shows the influence of pH on the solubility of ZrO_2, $ZrO_2 . H_2O$ and $ZrO_2 . 2H_2O$, at 25°C.

Recent research ([2], [3], [4], [5]) on aqueous solutions of zirconium salts has brought to light the existence of complicated phenomena of hydrolysis, polymerization and the formation of colloidal solutions and complexes. The ion Zr^{++++}, which has been identified only in concentrated solutions of very low pH, seems to be converted, on dilution of its solutions or on increasing their pH, into a continuous series of polymers each one of which is hydrolysed to a different degree. In view of the impossibility of representing such complex phenomena in an equilibrium diagram, we have assumed arbitrarily that the ion ZrO^{++} of zirconyl salts represents all the various stages of polymerization and hydrolysis of the Zr^{++++} ion.

It will be recalled that the equilibrium diagram is valid only in the absence of substances with which zirconium can form soluble complexes or insoluble salts. According to Charlot [6] the ions Zr^{++++} and ZrO^{++} form numerous complexes: relatively stable sulphuric ones, not very stable hydrochloric ones, very stable hydrofluoric and oxalic ones, and very slightly stable carbonic ones. Hydrogen peroxide gives solid white complex compounds which are attributed the formulae Zr_2O_5, ZrO_3 or Zr_2O_7, slightly soluble in very dilute acid media and soluble in alkaline media. The polyhydric alcohols also form complexes with zirconium. Insoluble salts of zirconium are also numerous; we point out the phosphate $ZrH_2(PO_4)_2$, the arsenate and the iodate.

3.2. STABILITY AND CORROSION OF ZIRCONIUM

From Fig. 1 zirconium shows itself to be a very base metal, as its domain of stability lie well below that of water. It should have a great tendency to decompose water with the evolution of hydrogen, dissolving as zirconic ions Zr^{++++} and zirconyl ions ZrO^{++} in very acid solutions, and as zirconate ions $HZrO_3^-$ in very alkaline solutions; in moderately acid, neutral and moderately alkaline solutions, the metal should cover itself with a film of oxide.

On account of the very low value of the potential of the reduction of Zr^{++++}, ZrO^{++} and $HZrO_3^-$ ions to metallic zirconium, the electrolytic separation of zirconium from aqueous solutions cannot

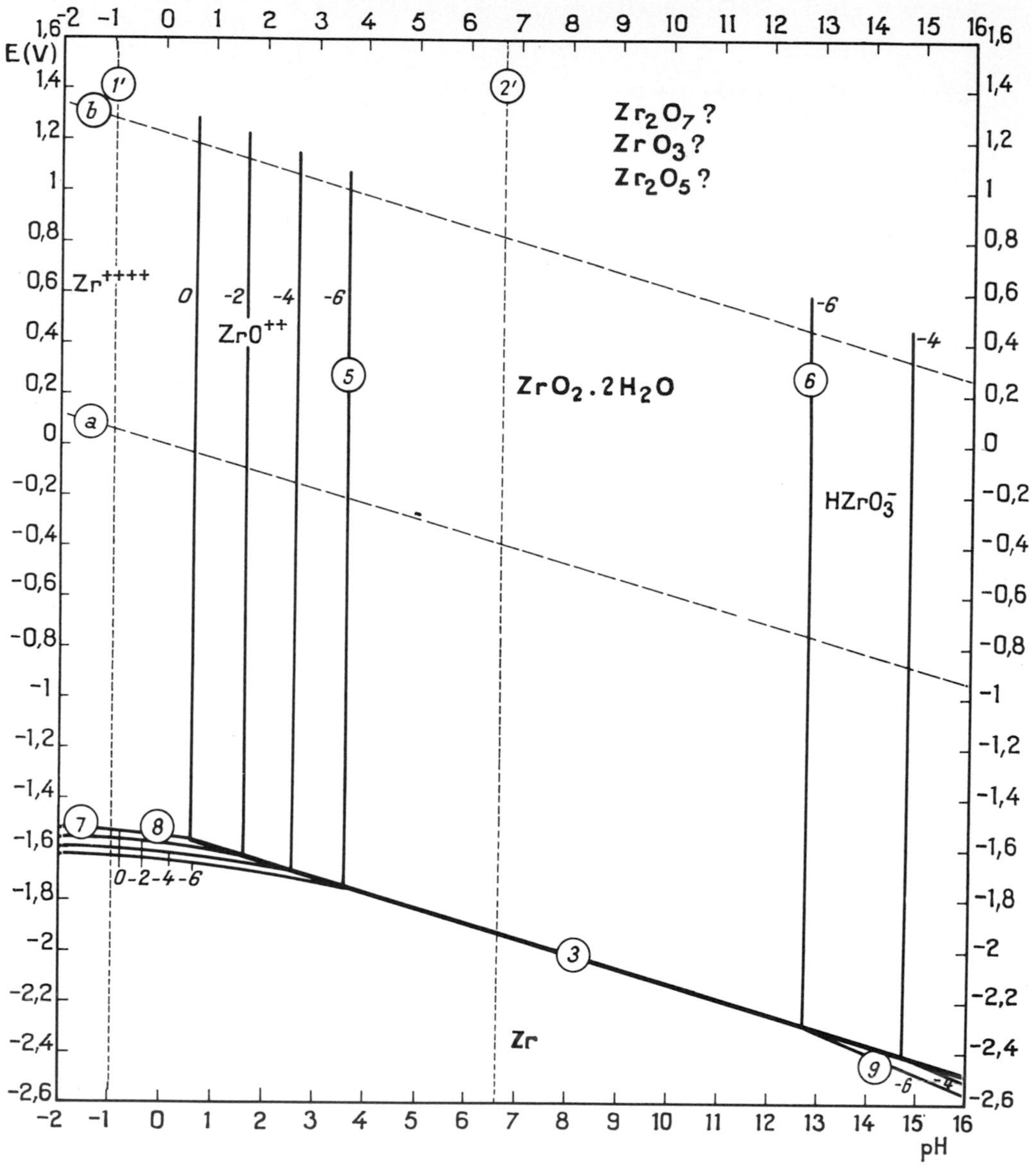

FIG. 1. Potential–pH equilibrium diagram for the system zirconium–water, at 25°C. (Considering $ZrO_2.2H_2O$.)

be carried out in practice; the only electrolytic deposits so far obtained have been those produced by the electrolysis of molten salts (potassium zirconifluoride or a mixture of zirconium and sodium chlorides), which gives an impure powdery metal.

It is worth noting that, according to Gable [7], zirconium is displaced by zinc from solutions of anhydrous zirconium sulphate in methyl alcohol.

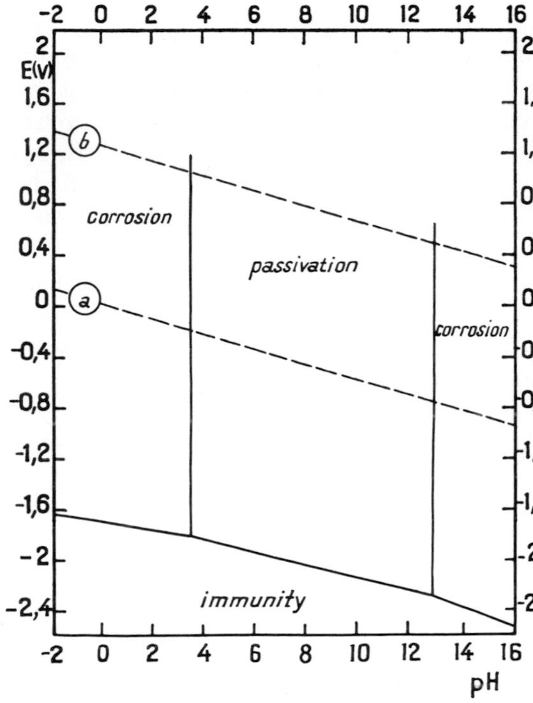

FIG. 2. Theoretical conditions of corrosion, immunity and passivation of zirconium, at 25°C. [Assuming passivation by $ZrO_2.2H_2O$ or by an anhydrous oxide ZrO_2 of equivalent free enthalpy of formation (−256 620 cal.).]

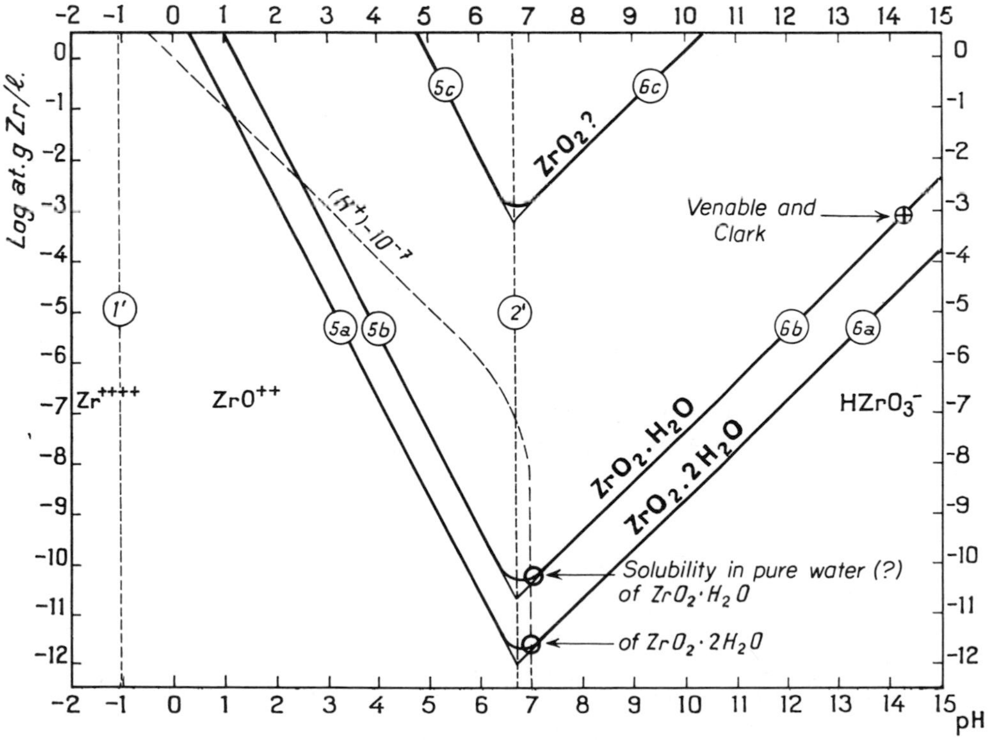

FIG. 3. Influence of pH on the solubility of ZrO_2, $ZrO_2.H_2O$ and $ZrO_2.2H_2O$, at 25°C.

Figure 2, which is deduced from Fig. 1, represents (subject to certain assumptions, principally that passivation is due to a film of $ZrO_2 . 2H_2O$) the theoretical conditions for corrosion, immunity and passivation of zirconium in the presence of solutions free from substances with which this metal can form soluble complexes or insoluble salts. This figure shows domains of corrosion in very acid and very alkaline solutions, which contradicts the observed facts; this is probably due to the formation of an oxide film of greater stability than the oxide considered here. It should also be pointed out that the alkaline zirconates are sparingly soluble and can, on account of this, take part in the formation of a protective film in alkaline solutions.

It is well known that at ordinary temperatures zirconium is particularly resistant to many powerful acid and alkaline reagents, and in particular sulphuric acid, hydrochloric acid, phosphoric acid and nitric acid at various concentrations [8]; it is attacked only by aqua regia and hydrofluoric acid, probably with the formation of soluble complexes.

It is generally acknowledged that this excellent resistance to corrosion is due to the metal being covered with a layer of oxide; according to Burgers *et al.* [9], during anodic polarization in a solution of phosphoric acid, zirconium covers itself with a film of monoclinic ZrO_2, identical to the natural zirconia called "baddeleyite". According to Charlesby [10] the anodic passivation film is made up of cubic ZrO_2 in the case of polarization in 0·1 N HNO_3; in dilute H_2SO_4 or a borate solution, the film is mainly amorphous, but contains some crystals of cubic ZrO_2.

Having found no value for the free enthalpy of formation of cubic ZrO_2 in chemical literature, we have not been able to draw an equilibrium diagram for it, nor a corresponding corrosion diagram.

The corrosion resistance of zirconium in the presence of pure water, which is excellent at ordinary temperatures, is defective at very high temperatures; this has been connected with the formation of zirconium hydride.

3.3. STABILITY OF THE ZIRCONIUM OXIDES

The existence of oxygen derivatives of zirconium in valency states other than 4 is doubtful; thus the so-called monoxide ZrO may be a mixture of Zr and ZrO_2, and the existence of Zr_2O_3 is also contested; as for the peroxides Zr_2O_5, ZrO_3 or Zr_2O_7 obtained by the action of hydrogen peroxide on zirconium salts, these should be considered as being complexes of ZrO_2 with H_2O_2.

The only well-defined oxide is zirconia ZrO_2, which is monoclinic in the natural state (baddeleyite); this variety, which is stable at ordinary temperatures, changes into a denser quadratic variety at about 1 000°C. We have seen, in paragraph 3.2, that during the anodic polarization of the metal it is possible for the monoclinic variety, an amorphous variety or a cubic variety to be formed, depending on the operating conditions.

The chemical properties of zirconia depend also on the method used to prepare it; thus, if it is strongly calcined, it is practically insoluble in all acids except hydrofluoric acid; the conversion of zirconia into zirconates takes place only at high temperatures, for instance by fusing it with alkaline carbonates or oxides and chlorides of the alkaline earth metals.

When solutions of zirconium salts are diluted a hydroxide gel is obtained which is subject to the phenomenon of ageing. Although attempts have been made to identify the products obtained, their exact nature is still unconfirmed. Among the various hydrates put forward, we should mention $ZrO_2 . H_2O$ and $ZrO_2 . 2H_2O$ which are the only ones considered in paragraph 2. By drying the precipitate over H_2SO_4 in a vacuum at room temperature, Van Bemmelen [11] obtained a product having the composition $ZrO_2 . H_2O$, and by drying at 100°C, he obtained a product corresponding to $ZrO_2 . 0{\cdot}66 H_2O$ (or $3ZrO_2 . 2H_2O$). The hydrate precipitated in the cold dissolves in HCl and HBr when it is fresh, but after ageing it becomes rapidly less soluble; it is insoluble in caustic soda solutions and sparingly soluble in concentrated solutions of caustic potash giving rise to the formation of zirconates. Of the latter, it is the metazirconates in particular which appear to be well defined; these are derived from H_2ZrO_3; metazirconates of the alkali and alkaline earth metals are known. In Fig. 3

we have represented, using the formula established in paragraph 2, the influence of pH on the solubility of $ZrO_2 . H_2O$ and $ZrO_2 . 2H_2O$; as a guide we have also represented the solubility of monoclinic ZrO_2, but we draw attention to the fact that the free enthalpy of this compound seems incompatible with those of the ions Zr^{++++} and ZrO^{++}; according to this figure the solubility of each of these three forms in pure water is:

for ZrO_2 : $10^{-2.9}$ moles ZrO_2/l, i.e. 155 mg ZrO_2/l
for $ZrO_2 . H_2O$: $10^{-10.4}$ moles ZrO_2/l, i.e. $5 \cdot 10^{-7}$ mg ZrO_2/l
for $ZrO_2 . 2H_2O$: $10^{-11.8}$ moles ZrO_2/l, i.e. $2 \cdot 10^{-8}$ mg ZrO_2/l

This solubility for ZrO_2 is quite obviously much too great; D'Ans and Eick [12] give for $ZrO_2 . 2H_2O$ a solubility of 10^{-6} g ZrO_2 in 100 g of water, i.e. 10^{-7} mole of ZrO_2/l. In Fig. 3 we have also marked the solubility of hydrated ZrO_2 in 12 per cent potash (i.e. about 2·38 M, pH ~ 14·3) as measured by Venable and Clark [13]: 0·09 g ZrO_2/l, i.e. $10^{-3.14}$ mole/l.

4. BIBLIOGRAPHY

[1] M. Maraghin, P. Van Rysselberghe, E. Deltombe, N. de Zoubov and M. Pourbaix, *Comportement électrochimique du zirconium. Diagramme d'équilibre tension–pH du système* Zr–H_2O, *à* 25°C (Rapport technique RT.45 of CEBELCOR, January 1957).

[2] R. E. Connick and W. H. McVey, The aqueous chemistry of zirconium, *J. Amer. Chem. Soc.* **71**, 3182–91 (1949).

[3] E. M. Larsen and A. M. Gammil, Electrometric titrations of zirconium and hafnium solutions, *J. Amer. Chem. Soc.* **72**, 3615–19 (1950).

[4] R. E. Connick and W. H. Reas, The hydrolysis and polymerization of zirconium in perchloric acid solution, *J. Amer. Chem. Soc.* **73**, 1171–6 (1951).

[5] B. A. J. Lister and L. A. McDonald, Some aspects of the solution chemistry of zirconium, *J. Chem. Soc.* (*London*), 1952, pp. 4315–30.

[6] G. Charlot, *Théorie et méthode nouvelles d'analyse qualitative*, 3rd ed., Masson, Paris, 1949.

[7] H. S. Gable, The metallic precipitation of zirconium, *J. Amer. Chem. Soc.* **52**, 3741 (1930).

[8] L. B. Golden, J. R. Lane and W. L. Acherman, Corrosion resistance of titanium, zirconium and stainless steel, *Ind. Eng. Chem.* **44**, 1930–9 (1952).

[9] W. G. Burgers, A. Claasen and I. Zernike, The chemical nature of oxide layers that are formed by anodic polarization on the metals aluminium, zirconium, titanium and tantalum, *Z. Physik*, **74**, 593–603 (1932).

[10] A. Charlesby, Ionic currents in thin films of zirconium oxide, *Acta Met.* **1**, 340–7 (1953).

[11] J. M. Van Bemmelen, Die Metazinnsaürc und Metazirkonsaüre, *Z. anorg. allgem. Chem.* **45**, 83–5 (1905).

[12] J. D'Ans and H. Eick, Basic zirconium sulfates, *Z. Elektrochem.* **55**, 19 28 (1951).

[13] F. P. Venable and T. Clark, A study of the zirconates, *J. Amer. Chem. Soc.* **18**, 434–44 (1896).

SECTION 8.3

HAFNIUM (1)

J. VAN MUYLDER

SUMMARY

(1) Rapport CEFA/R.10 of the Commission des Études Fondamentales et Applications of CEBELCOR.

1. SUBSTANCES CONSIDERED AND SUBSTANCES NOT CONSIDERED

	Oxidation number (Z)	Considered	Not considered	μ^0(cal.)	Name, colour, crystalline system
Solid substances	0	**Hf**	-	0	Hafnium, grey, hex.
	+4	**HfO_2** hydr.	-	a. −268 800	Hafnium oxide $HfO_2.H_2O$ or $HfO(OH)_2$ (3)
	»	» anh.	-	b. −252 200 (2)	Hafnium oxide, white, monol., quad.
	+6	-	**HfO_3** hydr.	-	Hafnium peroxide HfO_32H_2O, white
Dissolved substances	+4	Hf^{++++}	-	−156 800 (4)	Hafnic ion, colourless
	»	HfO^{++}	-	−215 700 (4)	Hafnyl ion, colourless

2. REACTIONS AND EQUILIBRIUM FORMULAE

2.1. TWO DISSOLVED SUBSTANCES

2.1.1. *Relative stability of the dissolved substances*

$Z = +4$

1. $Hf^{++++} + H_2O = HfO^{++} + 2H^+$ $\qquad \log \frac{(HfO^{++})}{(Hf^{++++})} = 1.61 + 2\,pH$

2.1.2. *Limits of the domains of relative predominance of the dissolved substances*

1'. Hf^{++++}/HfO^{++} $\qquad pH = 0.80$

2.2. TWO SOLID SUBSTANCES

Limits of the domains of relative stability of the solid substances

$0 \rightarrow +4$

2. $\mathbf{Hf} + 2H_2O = \mathbf{HfO_2} + 4H^+ + 4e^-$ $\qquad$ a. $E_0 = -1.685 - 0.0591\,pH$; b. $= -1.505 - 0.0591\,pH$

2.3. ONE DISSOLVED SUBSTANCE AND ONE SOLID SUBSTANCE

Solubility of the solid substances

$Z = +4$

3. $Hf^{++++} + 2H_2O = \mathbf{HfO_2} + 4H^+$ $\qquad$ a. $\log(Hf^{++++}) = 1.01 - 4\,pH$; b. $= 13.19 - 4\,pH$

4. $HfO^{++} + H_2O = \mathbf{HfO_2} + 2H^+$ $\qquad$ a. $\log(HfO^{++}) = 2.62 - 2\,pH$; b. $= 14.81 - 2\,pH$

$0 \rightarrow +4$

5. $\mathbf{Hf} = Hf^{++++} + 4e^-$ $\qquad E_0 = -1.700 + 0.0148 \log(Hf^{++++})$

6. $\mathbf{Hf} + H_2O = HfO^{++} + 2H^+ + 4e^-$ $\qquad E_0 = -1.724 - 0.0295\,pH + 0.0148 \log(HfO^{++})$

---

(2) Value given by Brewer [1].

(3) This value of $\mu^0_{HfO_2}$ corresponds to $\mu^0_{HfO_2.H_2O} = -325\,500$ cal.

(4) Values calculated from those given by Latimer.

3. EQUILIBRIUM DIAGRAM AND ITS INTERPRETATION

3.1. ESTABLISHMENT OF THE DIAGRAM

Using the equilibrium formulae given in paragraph 2, we have constructed Fig. 1 which represents the equilibrium diagram for the system hafnium–water, at 25°C.

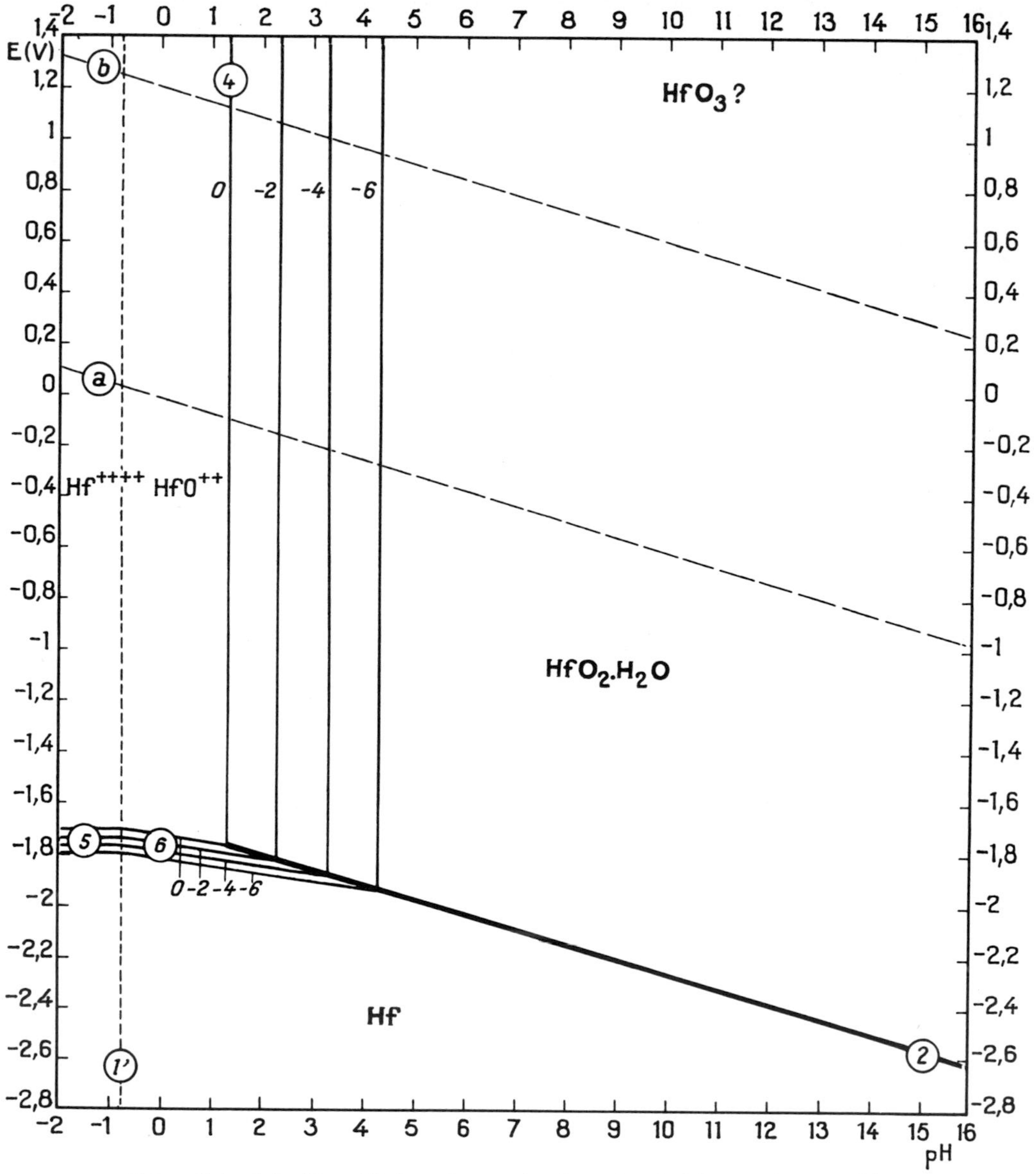

FIG. 1. Potential–pH equilibrium diagram for the system hafnium–water, at 25°C.

This figure is valid only in the absence of substances with which hafnium can form soluble complexes or insoluble salts; in this respect, we point out in particular the existence of fluorinated, oxalic and salicylic complexes.

3.2. STABILITY OF HAFNIUM

From Fig. 1 hafnium appears to be a very base metal, as its domain of thermodynamic stability lies at potentials clearly below those which correspond to the stability of water. Hafnium has a strong tendency to decompose water with the evolution of hydrogen, dissolving in acid solutions as hafnic ions Hf^{++++} and hafnyl ions HfO^{++}; in moderately acid, neutral and alkaline solutions the metal tends to become covered with a film of oxide, HfO_2. It is generally accepted that hafnium's good corrosion resistance is due to the presence of this layer of oxide, which is thin and protective [2].

As a result of the very low value of the reduction potential of Hf^{++++} and HfO^{++} ions to hafnium, the electrolytic separation of the latter from its aqueous solutions cannot be carried out in practice.

3.3. STABILITY OF HAFNIUM OXIDE

According to Fig. 1, hafnium oxide, which can be obtained by treating aqueous solutions of hafnium salts with a base, and also by the hydrolysis of such solutions, is a substance which is thermodynamically stable in the presence of neutral and alkaline solutions, and unstable in acid solutions in which it is soluble in the form of hafnyl ions HfO^{++} and hafnic ions Hf^{++++}

From the free enthalpy of formation values given in paragraph 1, the hydrated oxide HfO_2, $HfO_2 . H_2O$ or $HfO(OH)_2$, is more stable than the anhydrous oxide; for this reason it is the oxide $HfO_2 . H_2O$ that we have considered in establishing Fig. 1.

By treating HfO_2 in the cold with hydrogen peroxide in the presence of an alkaline solution, a peroxide $HfO_3 . 2H_2O$ should be formed, which, through lack of data, is indicated only approximately in Fig. 1.

4. BIBLIOGRAPHY

[1] L. BREWER, Thermodynamic properties of the oxides and their vaporization processes, *Chem. Rev.* **52**, 1 (1953).

[2] *Gmelins Handbuch der anorganischen Chemie.* (*Hafnium*, S.N. 43), Verlag Chemie, Berlin, 1941 and Weinheim, 1958.

SECTION 9.1

VANADIUM(1)

E. Deltombe, N. de Zoubov and M. Pourbaix

SUMMARY

(1) Adapted and shortened version of the Rapport technique RT.29 of CEBELCOR [1].

1. SUBSTANCES CONSIDERED AND SUBSTANCES NOT CONSIDERED

	Oxidation number (Z)	Considered	Not considered	μ^0 (cal.)	Name, colour, crystalline system
Solid substances	0	**V**	-	0	Vanadium, light grey, b.c.cub.
	+2	**V_2O_2**	-	—189 000	Hypovanadous oxide, light grey, f.c.cub.
	+3	**V_2O_3**	-	—271 000	Vanadous oxide, black, rhomb.
	+4	**V_2O_4**	-	—318 000	Vanadic oxide, blue, quad.
	»	-	V_2O_4 hydr.	-	Hydrated vanadic oxide $V_2O_4 . 7H_2O$
	»	-	» »	-	Hydrated vanadic oxide $V_2O_4 . 2H_2O$ or $VO(OH)_2$
	+5	**V_2O_5**	-	*a.* —344 000	"Developed" vanadium pentoxide, red, orthorh.
	»	»	-	*b.* —342 036 (2)	"Non-developed", vanadium pentoxide, red
	»		V_2O_5 hydr.	-	Hydrated pentoxide $V_2O_5 . 2H_2O$ or pyrovanadic acid $H_4V_2O_7$
	»	-	» »	-	Hydrated pentoxide $V_2O_5 . H_2O$ or metavanadic acid HVO_3
	»	-	» »	-	Hydrated pentoxide $3V_2O_5 . 2H_2O$ or hexavanadic acid $H_4V_6O_{17}$
Dissolved substances	+2	V^{++}	-	— 54 200 (2)	Hypovanadous ion, violet
	+3	V^{+++}	-	— 60 080 (2)	Vanadous ion, green
	»	VOH^{++}	-	—112 790 (2)	Vanadous ion, green
	»	VO^{+}	-	—107 990 (2)	Vanadous ion, green
	+4	VO^{++}	-	—109 000	Vanadyl ion, blue
	»	HVO_2^{+}	-	—158 380 (2)	? ion
	»	$HV_2O_5^{-}$	-	—360 650 (2)	Hypovanadate ion, red–brown
	+5	VO_2^{+}	-	—142 550 (2)	Vanadic ion, light yellow
	»	$H_3V_2O_7^{-}$	-	—450 918 (2)	Pyrovanadate ion, orange
	»	$H_2VO_4^{-}$	-	—248 775 (2)	Orthovanadate or metavanadic ion VO_3^-, colourless
	»	HVO_4^{--}	-	—235 800 (2)	Orthovanadate ion, colourless
	»	VO_4^{---}	-	—220 125 (2)	Orthovanadate ion, colourless
	+7	-	VO_4^{-}	—203 900	Pervanadate ion, colourless
	+9	-	VO_5^{-}	-	Hypervanadate ion

2. REACTIONS AND EQUILIBRIUM FORMULAE (3)

2.1. TWO DISSOLVED SUBSTANCES

2.1.1. *Relative stability of the dissolved substances*

Z = +3

1. $V^{+++} + H_2O = VOH^{++} + H^+$ $\qquad \log \frac{(VOH^{++})}{(V^{+++})} = -\ 2.92 + \ pH$

2. $VOH^{++} = VO^{+} + H^+$ $\qquad \log \frac{(VO^{+})}{(VOH^{++})} = -\ 3.52 + \ pH$

(2) These enthalpy values have been calculated elsewhere [1] by means of various data (solubility products, equilibrium constants, oxidation-reduction potentials) given by the following investigators: Ducret [2], Charlot [3], Meites [4] and Jones and Colvin [5].

(3) Concerning the reactions involving V_2O_5, the letter *a* refers to "developed" V_2O_5 whose free enthalpy of formation is −344 000 cal.; the letter *b* refers to "non-developed" V_2O_5 whose free enthalpy of formation is −342 036 cal.

$Z = +4$

3. $VO^{++} + H_2O = HVO_2^{+} + H^{+}$ $\qquad \log \frac{(HVO_2^{+})}{(VO^{++})} = -5.36 + pH$

4. $2HVO_2^{+} + H_2O = HV_2O_5^{-} + 3H^{+}$ $\qquad \log \frac{(HV_2O_5^{-})}{(HVO_2^{+})^2} = -9.39 + 3pH$

5. $2VO^{++} + 3H_2O = HV_2O_5^{-} + 5H^{+}$ $\qquad \log \frac{(HV_2O_5^{-})}{(VO^{++})^2} = -20.12 + 5pH$

$Z = +5$

6. $2VO_2^{+} + 3H_2O = H_3V_2O_7^{-} + 3H^{+}$ $\qquad \log \frac{(H_3V_2O_7^{-})}{(VO_2^{+})^2} = -3.10 + 3pH$

7. $VO_2^{+} + 2H_2O = H_2VO_4^{-} + 2H^{+}$ $\qquad \log \frac{(H_2VO_4^{-})}{(VO_2^{+})} = -5.24 + 2pH$

8. $H_3V_2O_7^{-} + H_2O = 2H_2VO_4^{-} + H^{+}$ $\qquad \log \frac{(H_2VO_4^{-})^2}{(H_3V_2O_7^{-})} = -7.38 + pH$

9. $H_2VO_4^{-} = HVO_4^{--} + H^{+}$ $\qquad \log \frac{(HVO_4^{--})}{(H_2VO_4^{-})} = -9.52 + pH$

10. $HVO_4^{--} = VO_4^{---} + H^{+}$ $\qquad \log \frac{(VO_4^{---})}{(HVO_4^{--})} = -11.50 + pH$

$+2 \rightarrow +3$

11. $V^{++} = V^{+++} + e^{-}$ $\qquad E_0 = -0.255 + 0.0591 \log \frac{(V^{+++})}{(V^{++})}$

12. $V^{++} + H_2O = VOH^{++} + H^{+} + e^{-}$ $\qquad E_0 = -0.082 - 0.0591\,pH + 0.0591 \log \frac{(VOH^{++})}{(V^{++})}$

13. $V^{++} + H_2O = VO^{+} + 2H^{+} + e^{-}$ $\qquad E_0 = 0.126 - 0.1182\,pH + 0.0591 \log \frac{(VO^{+})}{(V^{++})}$

$+2 \rightarrow +4$

14. $2V^{++} + 5H_2O = HV_2O_5^{-} + 9H^{+} + 4e^{-}$ $\qquad E_0 = 0.338 - 0.1329\,pH + 0.0148 \log \frac{(HV_2O_5^{-})}{(V^{++})^2}$

$+3 \rightarrow +4$

15. $VO^{+} = VO^{++} + e^{-}$ $\qquad E_0 = -0.044 + 0.0591 \log \frac{(VO^{++})}{(VO^{+})}$

16. $V^{+++} + H_2O = VO^{++} + 2H^{+} + e^{-}$ $\qquad E_0 = 0.337 - 0.1182\,pH + 0.0591 \log \frac{(VO^{++})}{(V^{+++})}$

17. $VOH^{++} = VO^{++} + H^{+} + e^{-}$ $\qquad E_0 = 0.164 - 0.0591\,pH + 0.0591 \log \frac{(VO^{++})}{(VOH^{++})}$

18. $2VO^{+} + 3H_2O = HV_2O_5^{-} + 5H^{+} + 2e^{-}$ $\qquad E_0 = 0.551 - 0.1477\,pH + 0.0295 \log \frac{(HV_2O_5^{-})}{(VO^{+})^2}$

$+3 \rightarrow +5$

19. $VO^{+} + 3H_2O = VO_4^{---} + 6H^{+} + 2e^{-}$ $\qquad E_0 = 1.256 - 0.1773\,pH + 0.0295 \log \frac{(VO_4^{---})}{(VO^{+})}$

$+4 \rightarrow +5$

20. $VO^{++} + H_2O = VO_2^{+} + 2H^{+} + e^{-}$ $\qquad E_0 = 1.004 - 0.1182\,pH + 0.0591 \log \frac{(VO_2^{+})}{(VO^{++})}$

21. $2VO^{++} + 5H_2O = H_3V_2O_7^{-} + 7H^{+} + 2e^{-}$ $\qquad E_0 = 1.096 - 0.2068\,pH + 0.0295 \log \frac{(H_3V_2O_7^{-})}{(VO^{++})^2}$

22. $VO^{++} + 3H_2O = H_2VO_4^{-} + 4H^{+} + e^{-}$ $\qquad E_0 = 1.314 - 0.2364\,pH + 0.0591 \log \frac{(H_2VO_4^{-})}{(VO^{++})}$

23. $HV_2O_5^{-} + 2H_2O = H_3V_2O_7^{-} + 2H^{+} + 2e^{-}$ $\qquad E_0 = 0.501 - 0.0591\,pH + 0.0295 \log \frac{(H_3V_2O_7^{-})}{(HV_2O_5^{-})}$

24. $HV_2O_5^{-} + 3H_2O = 2H_2VO_4^{-} + 3H^{+} + 2e^{-}$ $\qquad E_0 = 0.719 - 0.0886\,pH + 0.0295 \log \frac{(H_2VO_4^{-})^2}{(HV_2O_5^{-})}$

25. $HV_2O_5^{-} + 3H_2O = 2HVO_4^{--} + 5H^{+} + 2e^{-}$ $\qquad E_0 = 1.281 - 0.1477\,pH + 0.0295 \log \frac{(HVO_4^{--})^2}{(HV_2O_5^{-})}$

26. $HV_2O_5^{-} + 3H_2O = 2VO_4^{---} + 7H^{+} + 2e^{-}$ $\qquad E_0 = 1.962 - 0.2068\,pH + 0.0295 \log \frac{(VO_4^{---})^2}{(HV_2O_5^{-})}$

2.1.2. *Limits of the domains of relative predominance of the dissolved substances*

$Z = +3$

1'.	V^{+++}/VOH^{++}	$pH = 2.92$
2'.	VOH^{++}/VO^{+}	$pH = 3.52$

$Z = +4$

3'.	VO^{++}/HVO_2^{+}	$pH = 5.36$
4'.	$HVO_2^{+}/HV_2O_5^{-}$	$pH = 3.13 - 0.333 \log C$
5'.	$VO^{++}/HV_2O_5^{-}$	$pH = 4.02 - 0.200 \log C$

$Z = +5$

6'.	$VO_2^{+}/H_3V_2O_7^{-}$	$pH = 1.03 - 0.333 \log C$
7'.	$VO_2^{+}/H_2VO_4^{-}$	$pH = 2.62$
8'.	$H_3V_2O_7^{-}/H_2VO_4^{-}$	$pH = 7.38 + \log C$
9'.	$H_2VO_4^{-}/HVO_4^{--}$	$pH = 9.52$
10'.	HVO_4^{--}/VO_4^{---}	$pH = 11.50$

$+2 \rightarrow +3$

11'.	V^{++}/V^{+++}	$E_0 = -0.255$
12'.	V^{++}/VOH^{++}	$E_0 = -0.082 - 0.0591\ pH$
13'.	V^{++}/VO^{+}	$E_0 = 0.126 - 0.1182\ pH$

$+2 \rightarrow +4$

14'.	$V^{++}/HV_2O_5^{-}$	$E_0 = 0.338 - 0.1329\ pH - 0.0148 \log C$

$+3 \rightarrow +4$

15'.	VO^{+}/VO^{++}	$E_0 = -0.044$
16'.	V^{+++}/VO^{++}	$E_0 = 0.337 - 0.1182\ pH$
17'.	VOH^{++}/VO^{++}	$E_0 = 0.164 - 0.0591\ pH$
18'.	$VO^{+}/HV_2O_5^{-}$	$E_0 = 0.551 - 0.1477\ pH - 0.0295 \log C$

$+3 \rightarrow +5$

19'.	VO^{+}/VO_4^{---}	$E_0 = 1.256 - 0.1773\ pH$

$+4 \rightarrow +5$

20'.	VO^{++}/VO_2^{+}	$E_0 = 1.004 - 0.1182\ pH$
21'.	$VO^{++}/H_3V_2O_7^{-}$	$E_0 = 1.096 - 0.2068\ pH - 0.0295 \log C$
22'.	$VO^{++}/H_2VO_4^{-}$	$E_0 = 1.314 - 0.2364\ pH$
23'.	$HV_2O_5^{-}/H_3V_2O_7^{-}$	$E_0 = 0.501 - 0.0591\ pH$
24'.	$HV_2O_5^{-}/H_2VO_4^{-}$	$E_0 = 0.719 - 0.0886\ pH + 0.0295 \log C$
25'.	$HV_2O_5^{-}/HVO_4^{--}$	$E_0 = 1.281 - 0.1477\ pH + 0.0295 \log C$
26'.	$HV_2O_5^{-}/VO_4^{---}$	$E_0 = 1.962 - 0.2068\ pH + 0.0295 \log C$

$Z = +4$

5'' (35' and 36').	$VO^{++}/HV_2O_5^{-}$ and $\mathbf{V_2O_4}$	$pH = 4.97$

$Z = +5$

6'' (37' and 38').	$VO_2^{+}/H_3V_2O_7^{-}$ and $\mathbf{V_2O_5}$	*a.* $pH = 1.81$
		b. $= 1.45$
8'' (45' and 46').	$H_3V_2O_7^{-}/H_2VO_4^{-}$ and $\mathbf{V_2O_4}$	$E_0 = 0.572 - 0.0591\ pH$

$+3 \rightarrow +4$

18'' (34' and 42').	$VO^{+}/HV_2O_5^{-}$ and $\mathbf{V_2O_3}$	$E_0 = 0.524 - 0.1182\ pH$
18''' (43' and 36').	$VO^{+}/HV_2O_5^{-}$ and $\mathbf{V_2O_4}$	$E_0 = 0.837 - 0.1773\ pH$

$+4 \rightarrow +5$

21'' (35' and 45').	$VO^{++}/H_3V_2O_7^{-}$ and $\mathbf{V_2O_4}$	$E_0 = 0.941 - 0.1477\ pH$
21''' (48' and 38').	$VO^{++}/H_3V_2O_7^{-}$ and $\mathbf{V_2O_5}$	*a.* $E_0 = 1.220 - 0.2363\ pH$
		b. $= 1.175 - 0.2363\ pH$
24'' (36' and 46').	$HV_2O_5^{-}/H_2VO_4^{-}$ and $\mathbf{V_2O_4}$	$E_0 = 0.431 - 0.0591\ pH$
25'' (36' and 47').	$HV_2O_5^{-}/HVO_4^{--}$ and $\mathbf{V_2O_4}$	$E_0 = 0.995 - 0.1182\ pH$
26'' (42' and 44').	$HV_2O_5^{-}/VO_4^{---}$ and $\mathbf{V_2O_3}$	$pH = 12.40$

2.2. TWO SOLID SUBSTANCES

Limits of the domains of relative stability of the solid substances

$0 \rightarrow +2$

27. $2\,\mathbf{V} \quad\quad + 2\,H_2O = \mathbf{V_2O_2} + 4\,H^+ + 4\,e^- \quad\quad E_0 = -0.820 - 0.0591\ pH$

$+2 \rightarrow +3$

28. $\mathbf{V_2O_2} + H_2O = \mathbf{V_2O_3} + 2\,H^+ + 2\,e^- \quad\quad E_0 = -0.549 - 0.0591\ pH$

$+3 \rightarrow +4$

29. $\mathbf{V_2O_3} + H_2O = \mathbf{V_2O_4} + 2\,H^+ + 2\,e^- \quad\quad E_0 = 0.210 - 0.0591\ pH$

$+4 \rightarrow +5$

30. $\mathbf{V_2O_4} + H_2O = \mathbf{V_2O_5} + 2\,H^+ + 2\,e^- \quad a.\ E_0 = 0.666 - 0.0591\ pH$
                                                      $b.\ \ \ \ = 0.708 - 0.0591\ pH$

2.3. ONE SOLID SUBSTANCE AND ONE DISSOLVED SUBSTANCE

Solubility of the solid substances

a. In gram-ions per litre

$Z = +2$

31. $2\,V^{++} + 2\,H_2O = \mathbf{V_2O_2} + 4\,H^+ \quad\quad \log(V^{++}) = 12.02 - 2\ pH$

$Z = +3$

32. $2\,V^{+++} + 3\,H_2O = \mathbf{V_2O_3} + 6\,H^+ \quad\quad \log(V^{+++}) = 7.05 - 3\ pH$

33. $2\,VOH^{++} + H_2O = \mathbf{V_2O_3} + 4\,H^+ \quad\quad \log(VOH^{++}) = 4.13 - 2\ pH$

34. $2\,VO^+ + H_2O = \mathbf{V_2O_3} + 2\,H^+ \quad\quad \log(VO^+) = 0.61 - pH$

$Z = +4$

35. $2\,VO^{++} + 2\,H_2O = \mathbf{V_2O_4} + 4\,H^+ \quad\quad \log(VO^{++}) = 4.90 - 2\ pH$

36. $\mathbf{V_2O_4} + H_2O = HV_2O_5^- + H^+ \quad\quad \log(HV_2O_5^-) = -10.30 + pH$

$Z = +5$

37. $2\,VO_2^+ + H_2O = \mathbf{V_2O_5} + 2\,H^+ \quad a.\ \log(VO_2^+) = -\ 0.82 - pH$
                                                      $b.\ \ \ \ \ = -\ 0.10 - pH$

38. $\mathbf{V_2O_5} + 2\,H_2O = H_3V_2O_7^- + H^+ \quad a.\ \log(H_3V_2O_7^-) = -\ 4.74 + pH$
                                                       $b.\ \ \ \ \ = -\ 3.30 + pH$

$0 \rightarrow +2$

39. $\mathbf{V} \quad\quad = V^{++} \quad\quad + 2\,e^- \quad\quad E_0 = -1.175 \quad\quad +0.0295\log(V^{++})$

$+2 \rightarrow +3$

40. $2\,V^{++} + 3\,H_2O = \mathbf{V_2O_3} + 6\,H^+ + 2\,e^- \quad\quad E_0 = 0.161 - 0.1773\ pH - 0.0591\log(V^{++})$

$+3 \rightarrow +4$

41. $\mathbf{V_2O_3} + 2\,H^+ = 2\,VO^{++} + H_2O + 2\,e^- \quad\quad E_0 = -0.080 + 0.0591\ pH + 0.0591\log(VO^{++})$

42. $\mathbf{V_2O_3} + 2\,H_2O = HV_2O_5^- + 3\,H^+ + 2\,e^- \quad\quad E_0 = 0.515 - 0.0886\ pH + 0.0295\log(HV_2O_5^-)$

43. $2\,VO^+ + 2\,H_2O = \mathbf{V_2O_4} + 4\,H^+ + 2\,e^- \quad\quad E_0 = 0.246 - 0.1182\ pH - 0.0591\log(VO^+)$

$+3 \rightarrow +5$

44. $\mathbf{V_2O_3} + 5\,H_2O = 2\,VO_4^{---} + 10\,H^+ + 4\,e^- \quad\quad E_0 = 1.238 - 0.1477\ pH + 0.0295\log(VO_4^{---})$

$+4 \rightarrow +5$

45. $\mathbf{V_2O_4} + 3\,H_2O = H_3V_2O_7^- + 3\,H^+ + 2\,e^- \quad\quad E_0 = 0.806 - 0.0886\ pH + 0.0295\log(H_3V_2O_7^-)$

46. $\mathbf{V_2O_4} + 4\,H_2O = 2\,H_2VO_4^- + 4\,H^+ + 2\,e^- \quad\quad E_0 = 1.022 - 0.1182\ pH + 0.0591\log(H_2VO_4^-)$

47. $\mathbf{V_2O_4} + 4\,H_2O = 2\,HVO_4^{--} + 6\,H^+ + 2\,e^- \quad\quad E_0 = 1.586 - 0.1773\ pH + 0.0591\log(HVO_4^{--})$

48. $2\,VO^{++} + 3\,H_2O = \mathbf{V_2O_5} + 6\,H^+ + 2\,e^- \quad a.\ E_0 = 0.958 - 0.1773\ pH - 0.0591\log(VO^{++})$
                                                             $b.\ \ \ \ = 0.998 - 0.1773\ pH - 0.0591\log(VO^{++})$

b. In gram-atoms of vanadium per litre

$Z=+2$			
31'.	V_2O_2	$/V^{++}$	$\log C = 12.02 - 2\,pH$
$Z=+3$			
32'.	V_2O_3	$/V^{+++}$	$\log C = 7.05 - 3\,pH$
33'.	V_2O_3	$/VOH^{++}$	$\log C = 4.13 - 2\,pH$
34'.	V_2O_3	$/VO^{+}$	$\log C = 0.61 - pH$
$Z=+4$			
35'.	V_2O_4	$/VO^{++}$	$\log C = 4.90 - 2\,pH$
36'.	V_2O_4	$/HV_2O_5^-$	$\log C = -10.00 + pH$
$Z=+5$			
37'.	V_2O_5	$/VO_2^+$	a. $\log C = -0.82 - pH$
			b. $= -0.10 - pH$
38'.	V_2O_5	$/H_3V_2O_7^-$	a. $\log C = -4.44 + pH$
			b. $= -3.00 + pH$
$0 \rightarrow +2$			
39'.	V	$/V^{++}$	$E_0 = -1.175 + 0.0295 \log C$
$+2 \rightarrow +3$			
40'.	V_2O_3	$/V^{++}$	$E_0 = 0.161 - 0.1773\,pH - 0.0591 \log C$
$+3 \rightarrow +4$			
41'.	V_2O_3	$/VO^{++}$	$E_0 = -0.080 + 0.0591\,pH + 0.0591 \log C$
42'.	V_2O_3	$/HV_2O_5^-$	$E_0 = 0.506 - 0.0886\,pH + 0.0295 \log C$
43'.	V_2O_4	$/VO^{+}$	$E_0 = 0.246 - 0.1182\,pH - 0.0591 \log C$
$+3 \rightarrow +5$			
44'.	V_2O_3	$/VO_4^{---}$	$E_0 = 1.238 - 0.1477\,pH + 0.0295 \log C$
$+4 \rightarrow +5$			
45'.	V_2O_4	$/H_3V_2O_7^-$	$E_0 = 0.797 - 0.0886\,pH + 0.0295 \log C$
46'.	V_2O_4	$/H_2VO_4^-$	$E_0 = 1.022 - 0.1182\,pH + 0.0591 \log C$
47'.	V_2O_4	$/HVO_4^{--}$	$E_0 = 1.586 - 0.1773\,pH + 0.0591 \log C$
48'.	V_2O_5	$/VO^{++}$	a. $E_0 = 0.958 - 0.1773\,pH - 0.0591 \log C$
			b. $= 0.998 - 0.1773\,pH - 0.0591 \log C$

3. EQUILIBRIUM DIAGRAM AND ITS INTERPRETATION

3.1. ESTABLISHMENT OF THE DIAGRAM

Using the equilibrium formulae (1)–(48) established in paragraph 2, we have drawn Figs. 1, 2, 3, 4 and 5.

Figure 1, established using relations (1')–(26'), represents, for various total dissolved vanadium concentrations C (in gram-atoms per litre), the domains of relative predominance of vanadium in each of the dissolved forms considered.

This figure shows, in particular, how the domains of relative predominance of the ions containing two vanadium atoms ($HV_2O_5^-$ and $H_3V_2O_7^-$) vary with the total concentration of dissolved vanadium.

These variations can also be seen in Fig. 3 (for the ion $HV_2O_5^-$) and in Fig. 4 (for the ion $H_3V_2O_7^-$); it can be seen, for instance, in Fig. 3, which relates to solutions of tetravalent vanadium, that the ion HVO_2^+ can be predominant with respect to the two other ions considered (VO^{++} and $HV_2O_5^-$) only for total dissolved vanadium concentrations below $10^{-6.6}$ g-at/l. This ion does not therefore appear in Fig. 1 in which solutions of tetravalent vanadium containing less than $10^{-4.8}$ g-at/l are not considered (this value being the minimum solubility of V_2O_4).

Likewise, Fig. 4, which relates to solutions of pentavalent vanadium, shows that the ion $H_3V_2O_7^-$ can be predominant with respect to the ions VO_2^+ and $H_2VO_4^-$ only for total dissolved vanadium concentrations above $10^{-4.7}$ g-at/l.

Figure 2 is a diagram showing all the equilibria of the system vanadium–water. It was obtained by superimposing in Fig. 1 the lines (27)–(30) (which separate the domain of stability of the condensed substances) and the lines (31')–(48') (which represent the solubilities of each of these condensed substances in all of the dissolved forms). The two parts of this figure lying outside the lines log C = 0 relate to solutions which are not saturated with any of the five solid substances considered (V, V_2O_2, V_2O_3,

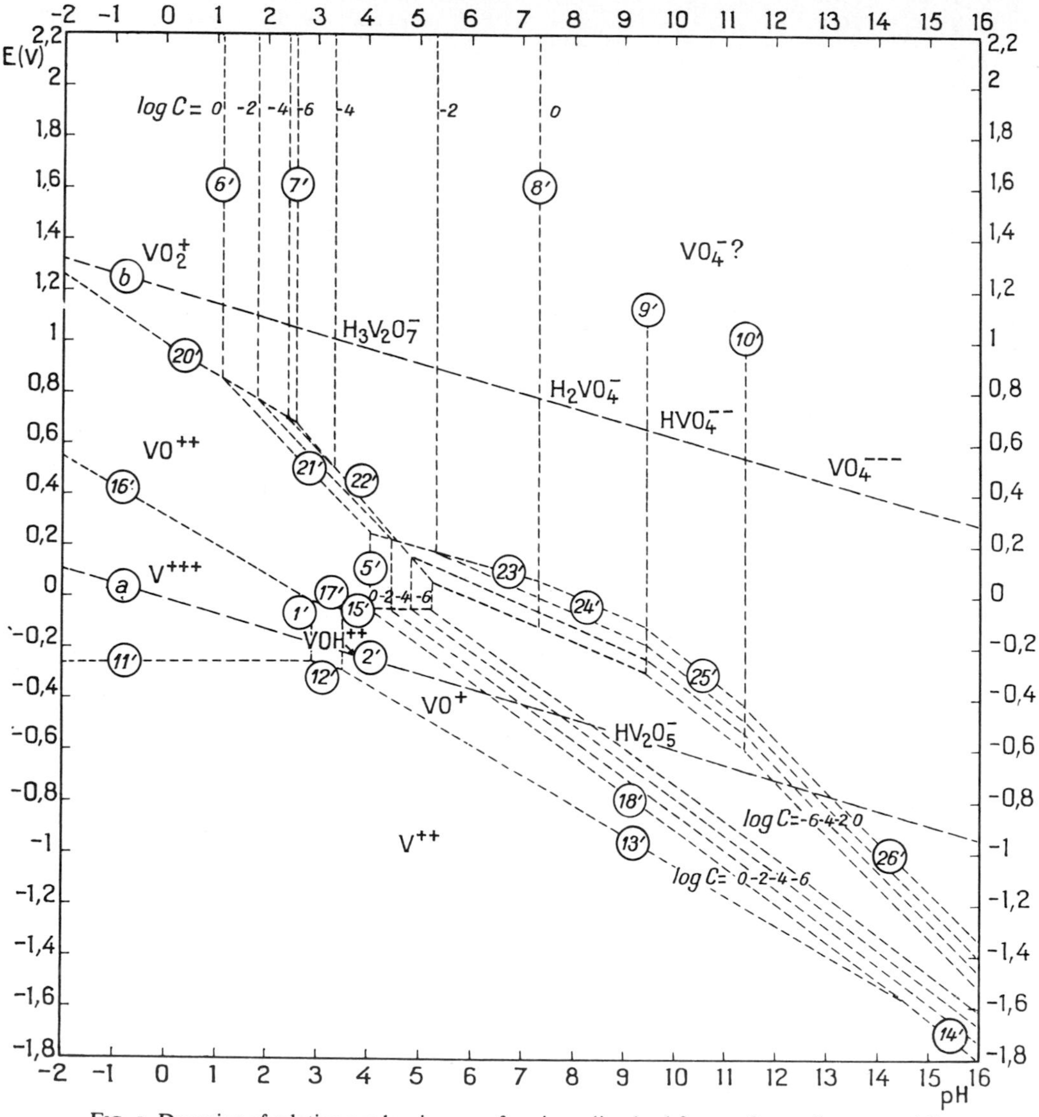

FIG. 1. Domains of relative predominance of various dissolved forms of vanadium, at 25°C.

V_2O_4 or V_2O_5), and containing a total of 1 g at V/l in the twelve dissolved forms considered (V^{++}, V^{+++}, VOH^{++}, VO^+, VO^{++}, HVO_2^+, $HV_2O_5^-$, VO_2^+, $H_3V_2O_7^-$, $H_2VO_4^-$, HVO_4^{--}, VO_4^{---}). The part of Fig. 2 lying inside these lines relates to solutions saturated with one of the five solid substances considered.

From Fig. 2 we have derived Fig. 5, which shows the theoretical conditions for corrosion, immunity and passivation of vanadium, at 25°C.

These figures are valid only in the absence of substances with which vanadium can form soluble complexes or insoluble salt. The ion V^{+++} is complexed by the ions CN^-, SCN^-, $C_2O_4^{--}$ and F^-;

the ion VO^{++} is complexed by the ions F^-, SCN^- and $C_2O_4^{--}$, and the tartrate ion; the ion VO_2^+ is complexed by phosphoric and tungstic acids and hydrogen sulphide. The majority of the vanadates of metals other than the alkali metals are insoluble; the brown sulphide V_2S_5 is sparingly soluble in very dilute acid media.

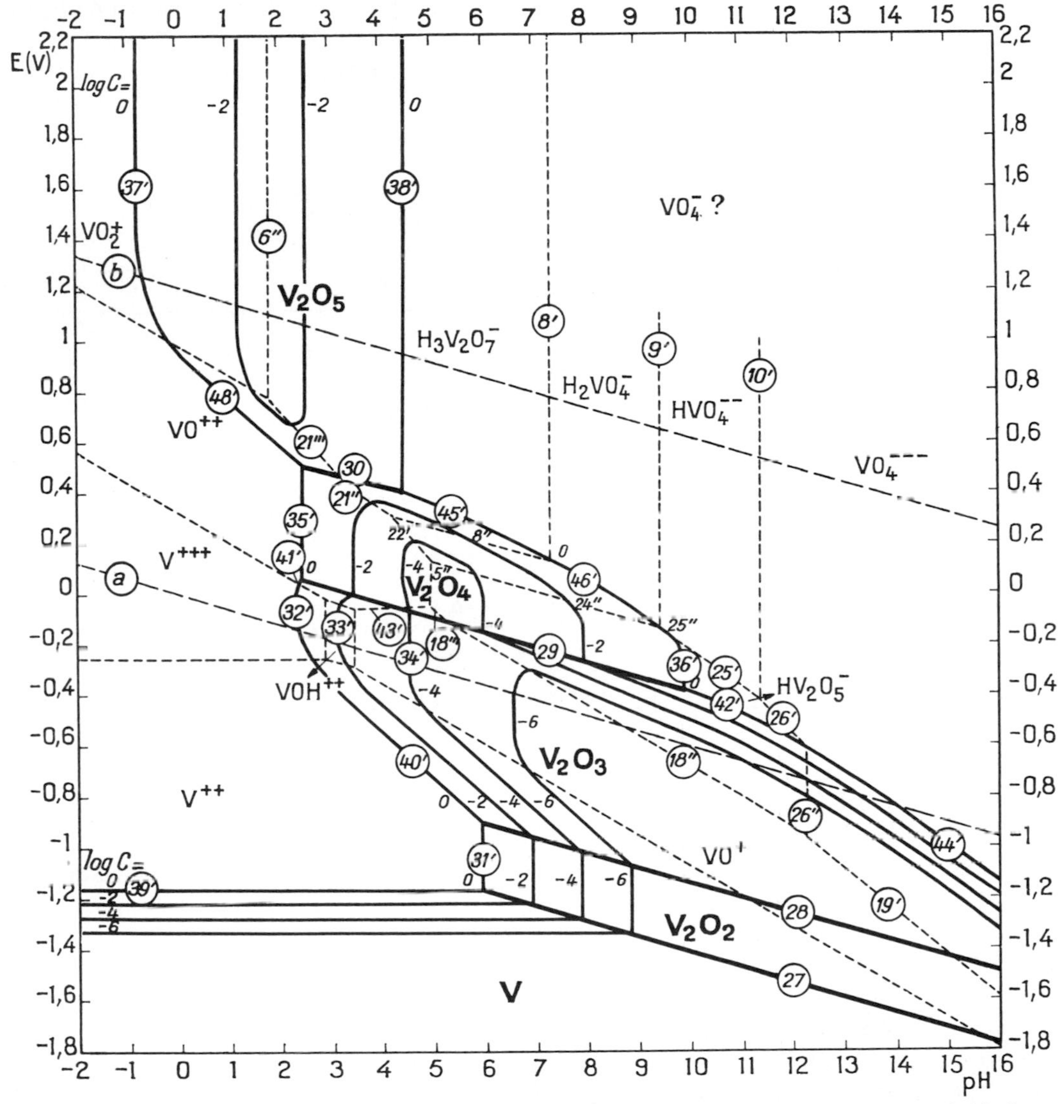

FIG. 2. Potential–pH equilibrium diagram for the system vanadium–water, at 25°C. The portions of this figure lying outside the lines log C = 0 relate to unsaturated solutions (of V, V_2O_2, V_2O_3, V_2O_4 or V_2O_5) containing a total of 1 g-at. of dissolved vanadium per litre (51 g/l) in the twelve dissolved forms considered here. The portion of the figure inside the lines log C = 0 relates to solutions saturated with V, V_2O_2, V_2O_3, V_2O_4 or V_2O_5.

3.2. STABILITY AND CORROSION OF VANADIUM

According to Figs. 2 and 5, vanadium is a very base metal, its domain of thermodynamic stability lying at potentials clearly below those which correspond to the stability of water; vanadium can therefore theoretically dissolve with the evolution of hydrogen, both in alkaline solutions and acid solutions. The electrochemical behaviour of vanadium is still not very well known; as far as the standard electrode potential is concerned, this has a value of $-1{\cdot}175$ V (formula 39′), according to Fig. 2; but it is as well to note here that this value is deduced from a free enthalpy value for the ion V^{++} which was calculated step by step, starting from the free enthalpy value for V_2O_5 and passing through those of the ions VO_2^+, VO^{++}, V^{+++}, deriving each one from the one before; it is evident, under these conditions, that this calculated value $-1{\cdot}175$ V can represent only an order of magnitude. Experimentally, we have hardly any values at all, except those of Marino [6] who, by determining the electromotive force of cells of the type $V/MX/NaNO_3/AgNO_3/Ag$ (where M = Na, K, Zn, Mg, etc., and X = Cl, Br, OH), calculated the following electrode potentials for vanadium (with respect to the standard hydrogen electrode):

for 1N KCl and KBr	approx. $-0{\cdot}31$V
for 1N HNO_3	approx. $-0{\cdot}52$V
for 1N KOH	approx. $+0{\cdot}19$V
for 1N NaOH	approx. $-0{\cdot}23$V

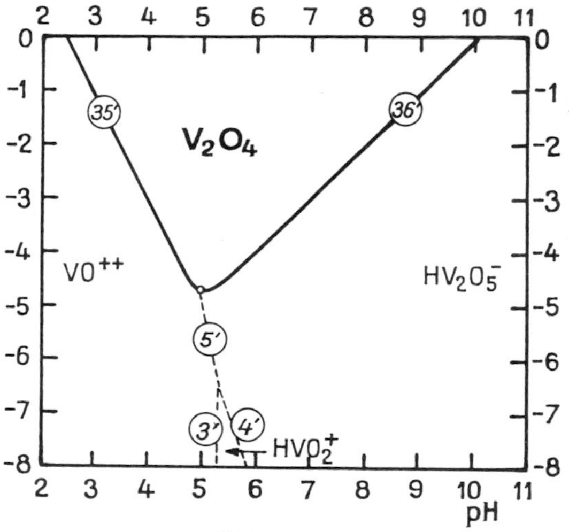

FIG. 3.

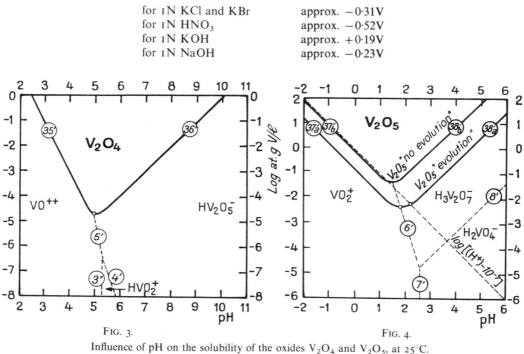

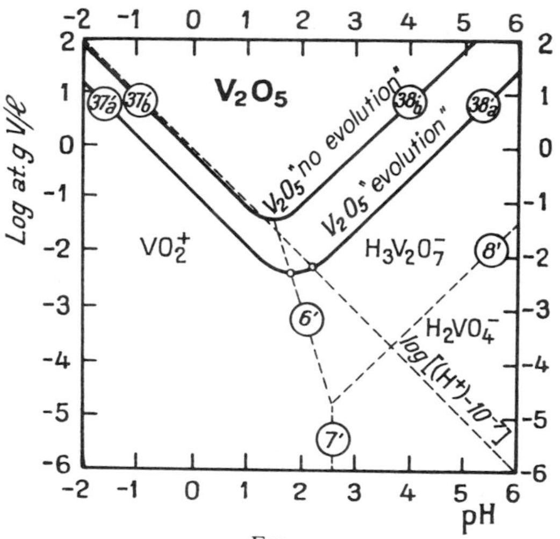

FIG. 4.

Influence of pH on the solubility of the oxides V_2O_4 and V_2O_5, at 25°C.

By setting up galvanic cells of the type $V/KCl/H_2CrO_4/Pt$, Marino obtained e.m.f. values between 1·25 and 1·37 V; the electromotive forces were around 2 V for the cell $V/KOH/H_2CrO_4/Pt$; in no case did Marino establish the existence of passivation.

Marino also studied the anodic behaviour of vanadium in solutions of acids, neutral salts and bases, with current densities from 2 to 3 mA/cm^2; in the acids (HCl, H_2SO_4, HNO_3) and the neutral salts (K_2SO_4, KCl, KBr, KNO_3) he obtained in every case a dissolution of the vanadium in the tetravalent state (probably, if one refers to the equilibrium diagram, in the form of the ion VO^{++}), while in the alkalis (5, 8 and 10 per cent KOH) he obtained only vanadates derived from pentavalent vanadium (dissolution as VO_4^{---}, for instance).

Muthman and Fraunberger [7] showed that vanadium immersed in an electrolyte experienced a decrease in electrode potential when it was scraped, and an increase in this potential in the presence of traces of oxygen; this behaviour, similar to that of numerous other metals was considered by these investigators to be characteristic of metals which can be passivated. Schmidt [8] measured the electrode potential of vanadium in a 1N solution of KCl, in the presence of hydrogen or nitrogen, giving the metal a scraping from time to time; he observed thus that the potential decreased after each scraping, and then increased progressively, both in the presence of hydrogen and also in the presence of nitrogen; the same experiments carried out on numerous other metals led Schmidt to interpret the passivation phenomena as resulting from the presence of a gaseous film.

Contrary to the theoretical predictions and the electrochemical behaviour discussed above, the corrosion behaviour of vanadium is, in actual fact, comparable to that of a noble metal; it seems that this discrepancy may be due to a passive state of the metal caused, for instance, by chemisorption of oxygen; dry or moist air does not tarnish the polished surface of vanadium, and water has no action. Hydracids do not react at room temperature, except for HF which reacts slowly. The oxidizing acids (hot concentrated H_2SO_4, concentrated chloric acid and HNO_3) convert it into vanadic acid.

3.3. STABILITY OF THE VANADIUM OXIDES

An examination of Fig. 2 shows that, of the four oxides V_2O_2 (grey), V_2O_3 (black), V_2O_4 (blue–black) and V_2O_5 (brick red), it is V_2O_4 which has the greatest stability from the oxidation and reduction points of view, since its domain of stability lies entirely within the limits of that of water;

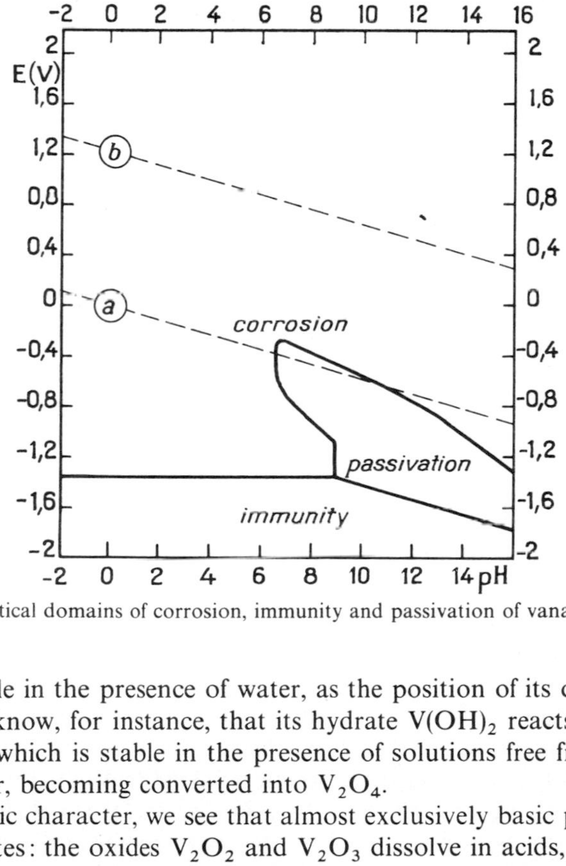

FIG. 5. Theoretical domains of corrosion, immunity and passivation of vanadium, at 25°C.

the oxide V_2O_2 is unstable in the presence of water, as the position of its domain of stability is clearly below that of water; we know, for instance, that its hydrate $V(OH)_2$ reacts with water with the evolution of hydrogen. V_2O_3, which is stable in the presence of solutions free from oxidizing agents, reacts with the oxygen in the air, becoming converted into V_2O_4.

Concerning acidobasic character, we see that almost exclusively basic properties correspond to the divalent and trivalent states: the oxides V_2O_2 and V_2O_3 dissolve in acids, but not in bases; it is to be noticed, however, that V_2O_3 can dissolve in alkaline media by oxidation, principally in the form of vanadate ions VO_4^{---}. V_2O_4, which is relatively soluble in water, is amphoteric; it dissolves easily in acid solutions and in alkaline solutions.

The oxide V_2O_5 which is also amphoteric, is clearly acid; it has a minimum solubility for pH's around 2; very soluble in neutral and alkaline solutions, it also dissolves easily in very acid solutions, with the formation of VO_2^+ ions.

Using the equilibrium formulae established above, we have represented in Figs. 3 and 4 the influence of pH on the solubility of V_2O_4 and the two varieties of V_2O_5 whose free enthalpy values are given in paragraph 1. In these figures we have also marked the limits of the domains of relative predominance of the various dissolved forms of vanadium considered.

It can be seen, for example, from Fig. 3, that V_2O_4 has a minimum solubility for a pH of about 5·0: the amount of vanadium dissolved is then about $10^{-4.8}$ g-at/l (that is 0·8 mg/l), and is divided equally between the two forms VO^{++} and $HV_2O_5^-$; this is in agreement with relation (5″).

Then again, according to Fig. 4, "developed" V_2O_5 will have a minimum solubility for a pH of about 1·8; the amount of vanadium dissolved will then be about $10^{-2.35}$ g-at/l (i.e. 230 mg/l), and will be divided equally between the two forms VO_2^+ and $H_3V_2O_7^-$; this is in agreement with relation (6″). The characteristics of the solution obtained by dissolving "developed" V_2O_5 in pure water until a saturated solution is obtained are given by the coordinates of the point of intersection of the line giving the value of $\log[(H^+) - 10^{-7}]$ with the line relating to the solubility of V_2O_5; these characteristics are:

$$pH = 2.15, \qquad (V) = 10^{-2.15}, \qquad \text{i.e. } 360\ \text{mgV/l}.$$

Meyer and Aulich [9] obtained experimentally the value 0·7 g/l for the solubility of V_2O_5 (i.e. 392 mg V/l) in pure water, which corresponds satisfactorily with the calculated value.

Of the vanadium oxides, only V_2O_5 has any technical importance; as the potential–pH diagram shows, it is the oxide which is thermodynamically stable in the presence of oxygen at atmospheric pressure: it can actually be obtained by the oxidation of V_2O_4 or other lower oxides by air or other oxidizing agents such as nitric acid. Industrially, it is separated from sodium vanadate solutions arising from the treatment of minerals with soda, by precipitating vanadic acid by means of nitric or sulphuric acid (avoiding an excess of acid which would redissolve the vanadic acid); by drying the separated vanadic acid, the oxide is obtained. One can also treat alkaline vanadate lyes with ammonia; sparingly soluble ammonium vanadate is precipitated, which is then separated off and calcined in air to obtain the anhydride V_2O_5 in the form of a brick-red powder. It is this method which is used, for instance, in preparing the catalytic mass for the manufacture of sulphuric acid by the contact process: a granulated mixture made up of ammonium vanadate and powdered pumice stone is roasted to about 440°C.

The thermal decomposition of V_2O_5 gives V_2O_4 and an equilibrium is set up: $2V_2O_5 = 2V_2O_4 + O_2$. Reducing agents reduce it to V_2O_4, V_2O_3 or even V_2O_2, depending on their reducing power and also on the operating conditions. Thus hydrogen at normal pressure gives V_2O_3 which is, according to Fig. 2, the oxide which is thermodynamically stable in the presence of hydrogen at 25°C, whilst, at 150 atm. pressure at 2 000°C, it gives V_2O_2; hot sulphur and white hot carbon give V_2O_3; the halogen hydracids reduce V_2O_5 to V_2O_4 with the liberation of halogens, for example, according to the reaction $V_2O_5 + 2HCl = V_2O_4 + H_2O + Cl_2$; the alkali metals, calcium and aluminium reduce V_2O_5 to different degrees. Other substances which will reduce V_2O_5 are: CO, HCN, HNO_2, HPO_2, $HAsO_2$, tartaric acid, sugars, formaldehyde, etc.

The oxide V_2O_3 is a black powder obtained by reducing V_2O_5 (by melting in a charcoal crucible of the pentoxide, by oxidation of V_2O_3 or by heating a mixture of V_2O_5 and V_2O_3. It is also obtained by roasting ammonium vanadate, but cut off from the air this time, to avoid the formation of V_2O_5. Hot V_2O_4 is reduced to V_2O_3 by hydrogen; it can be oxidized to V_2O_5 by air or nitric acid.

The oxide V_2O_3 is a black powder obtained by reducing V_2O_5 (by melting in a charcoal crucible or by hydrogen at red heat); it is also obtained by thermal decomposition of V_2O_5 at 1 750° and by roasting ammonium vanadate in the absence of air. It slowly absorbs oxygen from the air, being converted into V_2O_4; when heated it burns like tinder to give V_2O_4.

Finally, the oxide V_2O_2 which is a metallic grey powder, is obtained by the reduction of the higher oxides by potassium; we have already drawn attention to the instability of this substance, and the ease of its oxidation to V_2O_3.

Corresponding to the oxides considered above are a certain number of more or less well-defined hydrates: $V_2O_47H_2O$, $V_2O_42H_2O$ or $VO(OH)_2$, $V_2O_4 . H_2O$, more readily soluble in acids and alkalis than the oxide V_2O_4; $V_2O_5 . 2H_2O$, or pyrovanadic acid, $H_4V_2O_7$, is sparingly soluble in water;

$V_2O_5.H_2O$, or metavanadic acid HVO_3, is slightly more soluble in water than V_2O_5; $3V_2O_5.2H_2O$, or hexavanadic acid $H_4V_6O_{17}$, exists only in solution. Garrels [10] established potential–pH equilibrium diagrams between the hydroxides $V(OH)_2$, $V(OH)_3$, $VO(OH)_2$ and the ions V^{++}, V^{+++} and VO^{++} assuming, for the hydroxides, free enthalpies equal to the sums of the free enthalpies of the corresponding oxides and water, which, basing our ideas on the known data relating to $Pb(OH)_2$ and PbO, $Cu(OH)_2$ and CuO, $Ni(OH)_2$ and NiO, $Al_2O_3.H_2O$ and Al_2O_3, $Al_2O_3.3H_2O$ and Al_2O_3, does not involve an error of more than 2 000 cal; Garrels' diagrams relating to the hydroxides are therefore identical to those which we have drawn, considering the oxides. Garrels draws some conclusions of geological interest from his diagrams of which we should like to mention in particular the impossibility of the existence of $V(OH)_2$ in nature, as its domain of stability lies considerably below that of water.

4. BIBLIOGRAPHY

[1] E. Deltombe, N. de Zoubov and M. Pourbaix, *Comportement électrochimique du vanadium. Diagramme d' équilibre tension–pH du système* V–H_2O, *à* 25°C (Rapport technique RT.29 of CEBELCOR, 1956).

[2] I. P. Ducret, Contribution à l'étude des ions des valences 4 et 5 du vanadium, *Ann. Chim.* **6**, 705–73 (1951).

[3] G. Charlot, *Théorie et méthode nouvelles d'analyse qualitative*, 3rd ed., Masson, Paris, 1949, p. 225.

[4] L. Meites, Equilibria in solutions of +3 and +4 vanadium, *J. Amer. Chem. Soc.* **75**, 6059–60 (1953).

[5] G. Jones and J. H. Colvin, Electrochemical studies on vanadium salts. I. The vanadyl-vanadic oxidation-reduction potential, *J. Amer. Chem. Soc.* **66**, 1563–71 (1944).

[6] L. Marino, Comportement électrochimique du vanadium, *Gazz. Chim. Ital.* **34**, 230–47 (1904).

[7] W. Muthman and F. Fraunberger, Passivität der Metalle, *Sitzb. Bayr. Akad. Wiss.* 1904, pp. 201–41.

[8] G. C. Schmidt, Ueber Passivität, *Z. Phys. Chem.* **106**, 105–54 (1923).

[9] J. Meyer and M. Aulich, Zur Kenntnis der Vanadosalze, *Z. anorg. allgem. Chem.* **194**, 278–92 (1930).

[10] R. M. Garrels, Some thermodynamic relations among the vanadium oxides and their relation to the oxidation states of the uranium ores of the Colorado Plateaus, *Amer. Min.* **38**, 1251–65 (1953).

SECTION 9.2

NIOBIUM([1])

J. Van Muylder, N. de Zoubov and M. Pourbaix

SUMMARY

1. *Substances considered and substances not considered.*

2. *Reactions and equilibrium formulae.*

3. *Equilibrium diagram and its interpretation.*
   - 3.1. Establishment of the diagram.
   - 3.2. Stability and corrosion of niobium.
   - 3.3. Stability of niobium monoxide NbO.
   - 3.4. Stability of niobium dioxide NbO_2.
   - 3.5. Stability of niobium pentoxide Nb_2O_5.

4. *Bibliography.*

([1]) Adapted and shortened version of the Rapport technique RT.53 of CEBELCOR [1].

1. SUBSTANCES CONSIDERED AND SUBSTANCES NOT CONSIDERED

	Oxidation number (Z)	Considered	Not considered	μ^0(cal.)[2]	Name, colour, crystalline system
Solid substances	-1	-	NbH	-	Niobium hydride
	0	Nb	-	0	Niobium, steel grey, rhomb.
	$+1$	-	Nb_2O ?	-	Niobium sub-oxide
	$+2$	NbO	-	$-90\,500$	Niobium monoxide, grey–black, cub.
	$+3$	-	Nb_2O_3 ?	-	Niobium sesquioxide
	$+4$	NbO_2	-	$-176\,000$	Niobium dioxide, grey–black, quad.
	$+5$	Nb_2O_5	-	$-422\,000$	Niobium pentoxide, white
	»	-	Nb_2O_5 hydr.	-	Hydrated niobium pentoxide or niobic acid $Nb_2O_5.nH_2O$, white
	$+7$	-	Nb_2O_7 hydr.	-	Hydrated perniobic oxide or perniobic acid $HNbO_4.nH_2O$, yellow–green
Dissolved substances	$+5$	-	NbO_3^-	-	"Metaniobate" ion
	»	-	NbO_4^{---}	-	"Orthoniobate" ion
	$+7$	-	?	-	Perniobate ion

2. REACTIONS AND EQUILIBRIUM FORMULAE

TWO SOLID SUBSTANCES

Relative stability of niobium and its oxides

$0 \rightarrow +2$

1. $$Nb + H_2O = NbO + 2H^+ + 2e^- \qquad E_0 = -0.733 - 0.0591\,pH$$

$+2 \rightarrow +4$

2. $$NbO + H_2O = NbO_2 + 2H^+ + 2e^- \qquad E_0 = -0.625 - 0.0591\,pH$$

$+4 \rightarrow +5$

3. $$2NbO_2 + H_2O = Nb_2O_5 + 2H^+ + 2e^- \qquad E_0 = -0.289 - 0.0591\,pH$$

3. EQUILIBRIUM DIAGRAM AND ITS INTERPRETATION

3.1. ESTABLISHMENT OF THE DIAGRAM

Using relations (1)–(3), we have drawn in Fig. 1 a potential–pH equilibrium diagram for the system niobium–water at 25°C.

This diagram represents the conditions of thermodynamic stability of niobium and those derivatives of it which can exist in the presence of water and aqueous solutions free from substances capable of forming soluble complexes or insoluble compounds with niobium.

Through lack of thermodynamic data, the hydride, niobic acid and perniobic acid (solid substances), and also the niobates and perniobates (dissolved substances) have been indicated in Fig. 1 purely as a rough guide.

Niobium can form numerous complexes; of these we point out the following, according to Charlot [2]: fluorinated, oxyfluorinated, tartaric and oxalic complexes, and complexes with hydrogen peroxide and the polyhydric alcohols.

Figure 2, derived from Fig. 1, represents the theoretical conditions for immunity and passivation of niobium.

([2]) All free enthalpy values are from Brewer (*Chem. Rev.* **52**, 1953).

3.2. STABILITY AND CORROSION OF NIOBIUM

From Fig. 1, niobium appears to be a base metal, as its domain of thermodynamic stability lies at potentials well below those which correspond to the stability of water.

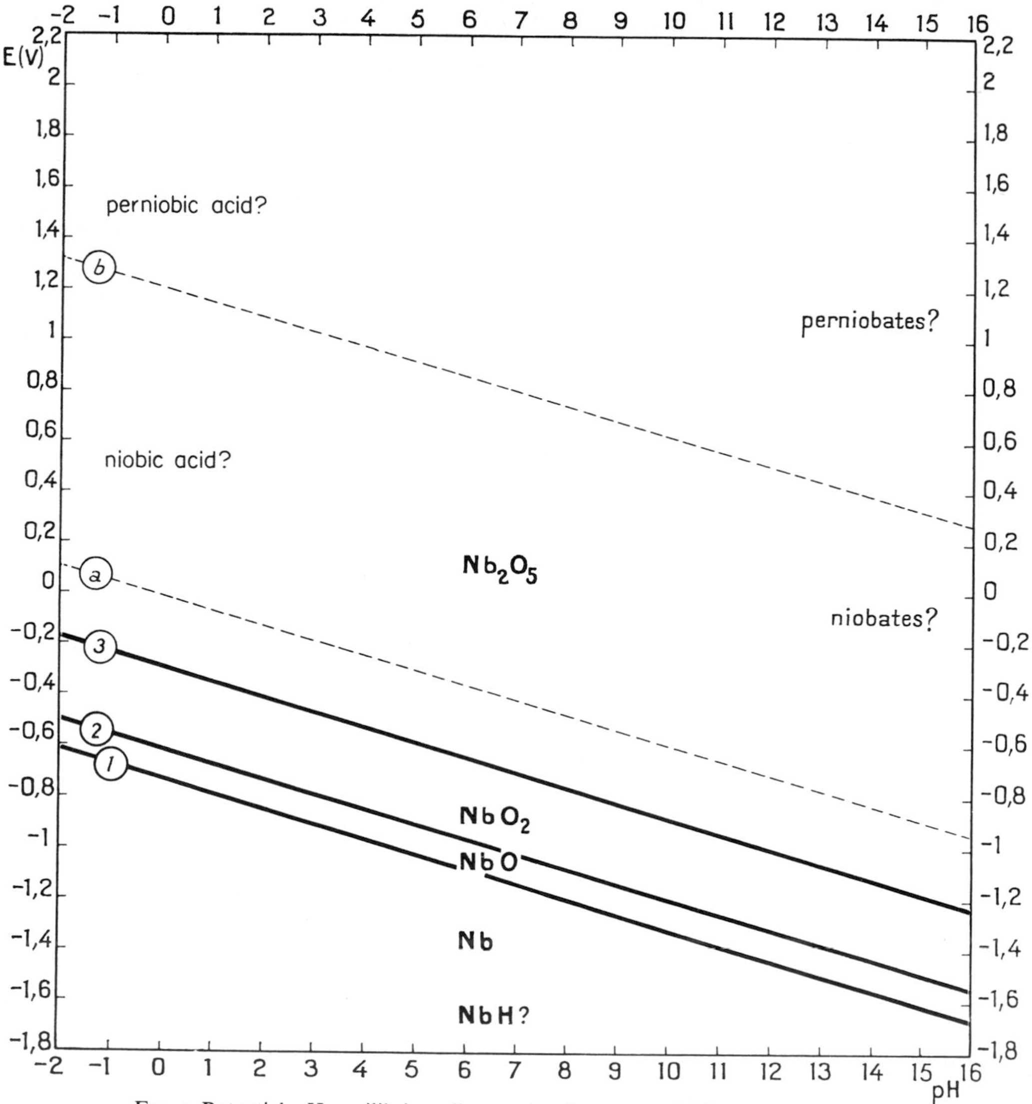

FIG. 1. Potential–pH equilibrium diagram for the system niobium–water, at 25°C.

For all pH's it tends to cover itself with a layer of oxide. Consequently the electrochemical behaviour of niobium and its corrosion resistance will depend on the intrinsic properties of the layer of oxide formed and the stability of the latter with respect to the solutions considered. Depending on whether this layer is, or is not, of good quality (compactness, imperviousness, continuity, etc.) and thermodynamically stable or unstable in the surrounding medium, niobium will behave as a noble metal (uncorrodible) or as a base metal (corrodible).

In Fig. 2, the domain of immunity corresponds to the domain of stability of metallic niobium, and the domain of passivation corresponds to the domain of stability of the niobium oxides; in the absence of complexing substances the domain of corrosion of the metal is non-existent.

In actual fact, niobium is a metal which is resistant to corrosion: unaffected by air, oxygen and water, it is not attacked by the common acids such as HCl, H_2SO_4 and HNO_3 and their mixtures; aqua regia and the caustic alkalis are without action. To overcome its unreactivity towards chemical reagents, it is necessary to use fused caustic alkalis or alkaline carbonates, or complexing substances.

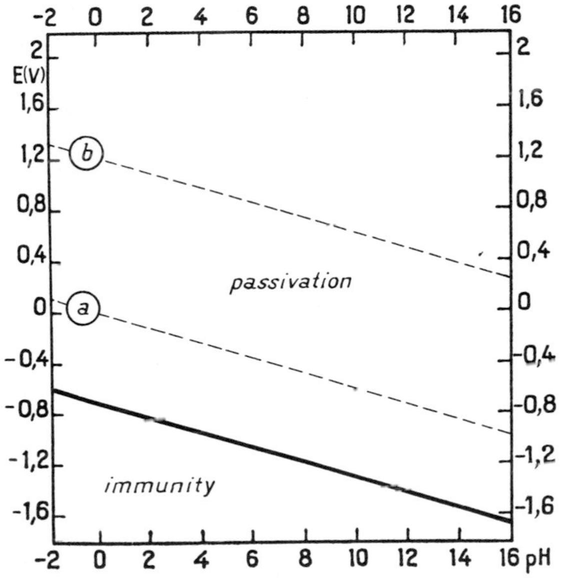

FIG. 2. Theoretical domains of immunity and passivation of niobium, at 25°C.

Hydrofluoric acid reacts slowly with niobium, but the attack is made rapid if the metal is put in contact with platinum (von Bolton [3]) or if nitric acid is added to the hydrofluoric acid; probably fluorinated or oxyfluorinated complexes of niobium are then formed.

The behaviour of niobium towards chemical reagents and its ability to be rendered passive lead to the conclusion that the niobium pentoxide Nb_2O_5 formed on the metal is in actual fact a protective oxide.

3.3. STABILITY OF NIOBIUM MONOXIDE NbO

The position of niobium monoxide on the equilibrium diagram for the system niobium–water, at 25°C, shows it to be a thermodynamically unstable substance in the presence of water or acid, neutral and basic solutions. In solutions of any pH it tends theoretically to decompose the water with the evolution of hydrogen, becoming oxidized to a higher oxide.

3.4. STABILITY OF NIOBIUM DIOXIDE NbO_2

As the domain of stability of niobium dioxide is situated below line (*a*), this compound is thermodynamically unstable in the presence of water and aqueous solutions of any pH; theoretically it tends to decompose water with the evolution of hydrogen, becoming oxidized to niobium pentoxide.

3.5. STABILITY OF NIOBIUM PENTOXIDE Nb_2O_5

The position of the domain of stability of niobium pentoxide on the equilibrium diagram for the system niobium–water, at 25°C, shows it to be a substance which is thermodynamically stable in the presence of water and non-complexing acid, alkaline and neutral solutions. It can be attacked by concentrated hydrofluoric acid with the formation of fluorinated or oxyfluorinated complexes.

When treated at high temperatures with molten alkalis and alkaline carbonates, niobium pentoxide is converted into niobates of general formula $MNbO_3$ (where M represents a monovalent metal radical).

Hydrogen peroxide oxidizes niobates to perniobates of the general formula M_3NbO_8.

Niobium pentoxide can exist in the hydrated state; it is then a white solid usually called niobic acid. According to P. Sue [4], dehydration at gradually increasing temperatures displays the formation of a hydrate $3Nb_2O_5.H_2O$, stable between 400° and 540°, and the less evident formation of a compound $2Nb_2O_5.H_2O$, which appears to be stable between 195° and 296°C.

According to Fig. 1, niobium pentoxide can be reduced to a lower oxide and to metallic niobium; however, it does not seem possible to bring about this operation by electrochemical means, at least, not in the presence of non-complexing solutions.

4. BIBLIOGRAPHY

[1] J. VAN MUYLDER, N. DE ZOUBOV and M. POURBAIX, *Comportement électrochimique du niobium. Diagramme d'équilibres tension–pH du système* Nb–H_2O, *à* 25°C. (Rapport technique RT.53 of CEBELCOR, June 1957).
[2] G. CHARLOT, *L'analyse qualitative et les réactions en solution*, 4th ed., Masson, Paris, 1957.
[3] W. VON BOLTON, Das Niob, seine Darstellung und seine Eigenschaften, *Z. Elektrochem.* **13**, 145 (1907).
[4] P. SUE, Sur la déshydratation de l'acide niobique, *C. R. Acad. Sc.* **194**, 1745 (1932).

SECTION 9.3

TANTALUM[1]

J. VAN MUYLDER and M. POURBAIX

SUMMARY

1. *Substances considered and substances not considered.*

2. *Reaction and equilibrium formula.*

3. *Equilibrium diagram and its interpretation.*

  3.1. Establishment of the diagram.

  3.2. Stability and corrosion of tantalum.

  3.3. Formation and stability of tantalum pentoxide.

4. *Bibliography.*

---

(1) Shortened and adapted version of the Rapport technique RT.52 of CEBELCOR [1].

1. SUBSTANCES CONSIDERED AND SUBSTANCES NOT CONSIDERED

	Oxidation number (Z)	Considered	Not considered	μ^0(cal.)	Name, colour, crystalline system
Solid substances	−1	–	**TaH**	–	Tantalum hydride, ?, orthorh.
	0	**Ta**	–	0	Tantalum, silvery white, b.c.cub.
	+1	–	Ta_2O	–	Oxide of monovalent tantalum, ?., orthorh.
	+2	–	**TaO**	–	Tantalum monoxide
	+4	–	TaO_2	–	Tantalum dioxide
	+5	Ta_2O_5	–	−456 500	Tantalum pentoxide, white, orthorh.
	»	–	Ta_2O_5 hydr.	–	Hydrated tantalum pentoxide or hydroxide $Ta(OH)_5$, or tantalic acid $HTaO_3$, white
	+7	–	Ta_2O_7 hydr.	–	Hydrated pertantalic oxide or pertantalic acid $HTaO_4$ hydr., white
Dissolved substances	+5	–	TaO_3^-	–	"Metatantalate" ion
	»	–	TaO_4^{---}	–	"Orthotantalate" ion
	+7	–	?	–	Pertantalate ion

2. REACTION AND EQUILIBRIUM FORMULA

TWO SOLID SUBSTANCES

Relative stability of **Ta** *and* Ta_2O_5

$0 \rightarrow +5$

1. $2Ta + 5H_2O = Ta_2O_5 + 10H^+ + 10e^-$ $\quad E_0 = -0.750 - 0.0591\,pH$

3. EQUILIBRIUM DIAGRAM AND ITS INTERPRETATION

3.1. ESTABLISHMENT OF THE DIAGRAM

Using relation (1), we have drawn in Fig. 1 a potential–pH equilibrium diagram for the system tantalum–water at 25°C.

This diagram represents the conditions of thermodynamic stability of tantalum and those derivatives of it which can exist in the presence of water and aqueous solutions free from substances capable of forming with tantalum soluble complexes or insoluble compounds.

Through lack of thermodynamic data, tantalic acid and pertantalic acid (solid substances), and also the tantalates and pertantalates (dissolved substances) are marked in Fig. 1 purely as a guide.

Tantalum can give rise to numerous complexes; we point out, according to Charlot [2], the following: fluorinated, oxyfluorinated, tartaric and oxalic complexes, and complexes with hydrogen peroxide and the polyhydric alcohols.

Figure 2, which is deduced from Fig. 1, represents the theoretical conditions of immunity and passivation of tantalum.

3.2. STABILITY AND CORROSION OF TANTALUM

From Figs. 1 and 2, tantalum appears to be a theoretically base metal, as its domain of stability lies at potentials well below those which correspond to the stability of water.

For all pH's it tends to cover itself with a layer of oxide, so that its behaviour in the presence of aqueous solutions will depend essentially on the behaviour of this layer of oxide towards the solutions considered. Depending on whether this layer is, or is not, of good quality (compactness, imperviousness, continuity, etc.) and thermodynamically stable or unstable in the surrounding medium, tantalum will behave as an uncorrodible metal or as a corrodible one.

The equilibrium potential of the reaction $2Ta + 5H_2O = Ta_2O_5 + 10H^+ + 10e^-$ is impossible to measure directly in practice on account of the great protective power of the layer of oxide which screens the metal from contact with the solution, at least in the absence of complexing substances.

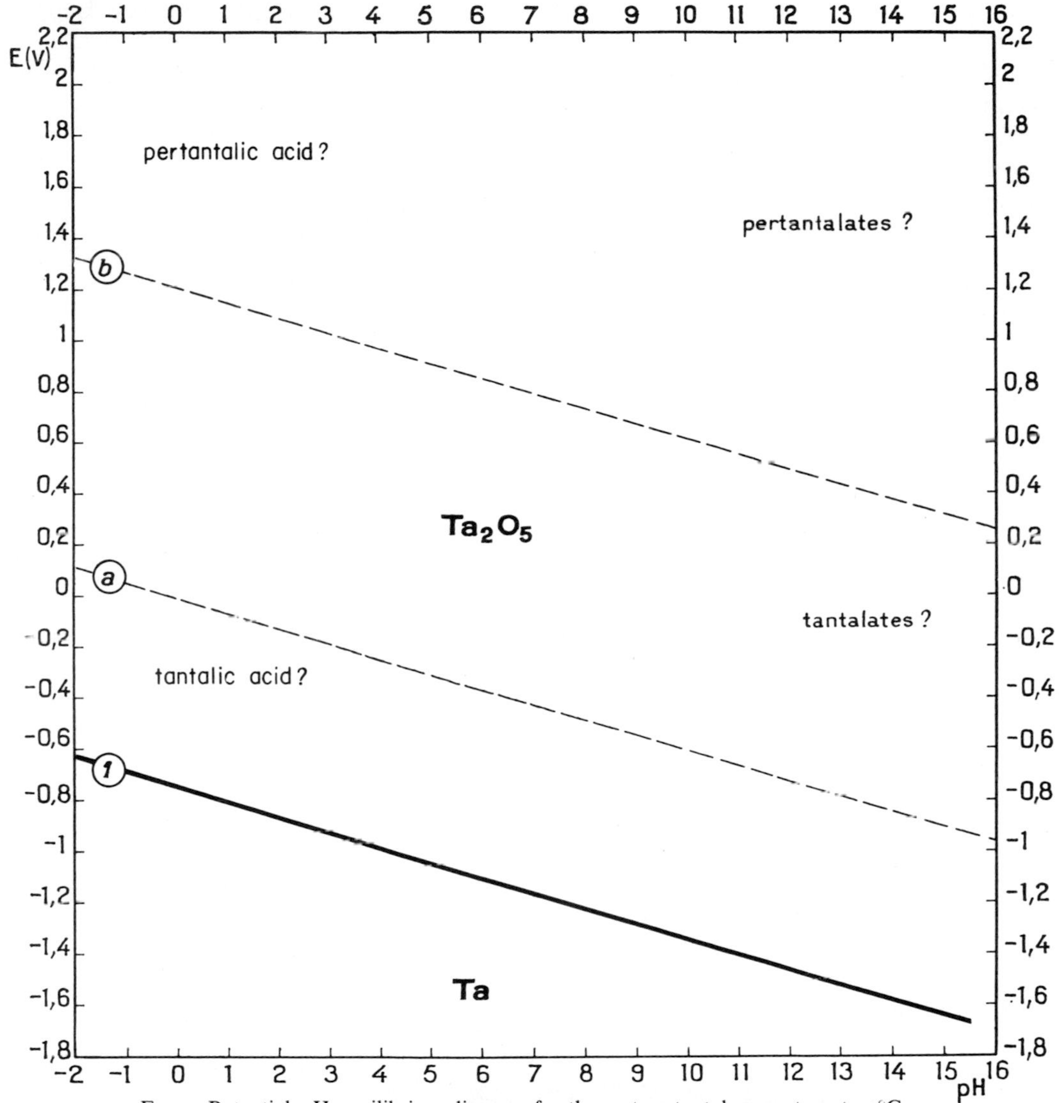

FIG. 1. Potential–pH equilibrium diagram for the system tantalum–water, at 25°C.

The values obtained by those experimenters who have attempted to measure this potential are, in fact, always higher than the theoretically calculated value ($E_0^0 = -0{\cdot}75$ V).

In Fig. 2 the domain of immunity corresponds to the domain of stability of metallic tantalum, and the domain of passivation corresponds to the domain of stability of tantalum pentoxide; the domain of corrosion is non-existent in the absence of complexing substances.

In actual fact, under these conditions, the behaviour of tantalum is that of a very noble metal: unaffected by air, oxygen and water, it is not attacked by any of the common acids such as HCl, H_2SO_4,

HNO_3 and their mixtures; even aqua regia has no action; tantalum is also resistant to caustic alkali solutions. To overcome this chemical resistance, it is necessary to use fused caustic alkalis or complexing solutions.

Pure hydrofluoric acid reacts with difficulty with pure tantalum; however, the attack can be speeded up by putting the metal in contact with platinum (von Bolton [3]), or by addition of nitric acid (Balke [4]); probably fluorinated or oxyfluorinated tantalum complexes are then formed. The behaviour of tantalum towards chemical reagents and its marked ability to be passivated lead to the conclusion that the tantalum pentoxide Ta_2O_5 which is formed on the metal is in actual fact a protective oxide.

By anodic polarization tantalum becomes covered with a film of Ta_2O_5; when used as an anode in a concentrated solution of KOH, it dissolves.

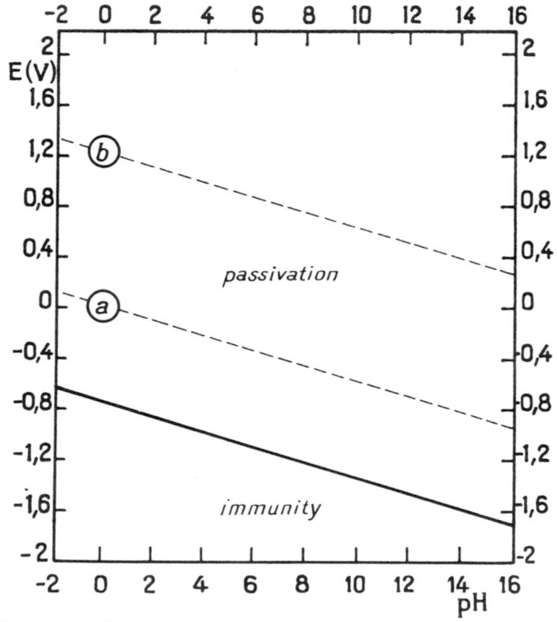

FIG. 2. Theoretical domains of immunity and passivation of tantalum, at 25°C.

There exists a solid hydride TaH, which is stable in the absence of water and unstable in the presence of water. This hydride has been obtained by the action of hydrogen on tantalum and by the electrolysis of a dilute solution of sulphuric acid with a tantalum cathode [5].

Through lack of thermodynamic data, we have not been able to take this hydride into account when establishing the equilibrium diagram.

3.3. FORMATION AND STABILITY OF TANTALUM PENTOXIDE Ta_2O_5

The position of the domain of stability of tantalum pentoxide in the equilibrium diagram of the system tantalum–water, at 25°C, shows it to be a substance which is thermodynamically stable in the presence of water and also acid, neutral and alkaline non-complexing solutions. Like tantalum, tantalum pentoxide can be attacked by concentrated hydrofluoric acid, with the formation of fluorinated or oxyfluorinated complexes.

Tantalum pentoxide can be converted into insoluble tantalates of general formula $MTaO_3$ (where M represents a monovalent metallic radical) by treatment at high temperatures with alkali or alkaline earth oxides or carbonates.

The tantalates $MTaO_3$ can be oxidized by hydrogen peroxide to pertantalates, of general formula M_3TaO_8, which are soluble in water forming stable solutions.

Tantalum pentoxide can exist in the hydrated state; it is then a white solid, more or less amorphous, generally called tantalic acid; it has a variable percentage of water of crystallization and is attributed the formula $Ta_2O_5.H_2O$ or $HTaO_3$.

According to Fig. 1, tantalum pentoxide can be reduced to metallic tantalum; nevertheless, it does not seem possible to bring about this reduction by electrolytic means starting directly from the oxide, but, according to Bouhard [6], it is possible to deposit tantalum on a carbon or platinum cathode by electrolysis of oxalic solutions of tantalic acid acidulated with 3 per cent of HCl or H_2SO_4.

4. BIBLIOGRAPHY

[1] J. Van Muylder and M. Pourbaix, *Comportement électrochimique du tantale. Diagramme d'équilibres tension–pH du système* Ta–H_2O, *à* 25°C (Rapport technique RT.52 of CEBELCOR, 1957).
[2] G. Charlot, *L'analyse qualitative et les réactions en solution,* 4th ed., Masson, Paris, 1957.
[3] W. von Bolton, Das Tantal, seine Darstellung und seine Eigenschaften, *Z. Elektrochem.* **11**, 45 (1905).
[4] C. Balke, Ductile Tantalum, *Ind. Eng. Chem.* **15**, 560 (1923).
[5] P. Pascal, *Nouveau Traité de Chimie minérale,* Vol. XII, Masson, Paris, 1958.
[6] G. C. Bouhard, *Préparation du niobium et du tantale, et application de ces métaux à la manufacture de filaments pour lampes à incandescence* (French patent No. 377931, 30 April, 1907).

SECTION 10.1

CHROMIUM[1]

E. Deltombe, N. de Zoubov and M. Pourbaix

SUMMARY

(1) Shortened and adapted version of the Rapport technique RT.41 of CEBELCOR [1].

1. SUBSTANCES CONSIDERED AND SUBSTANCES NOT CONSIDERED

	Oxidation number (Z)	Considered	Not considered	μ^0(cal.)	Name, colour, crystalline system
Solid substances	0	**Cr**	–	0	Chromium, white, cub.
	+ 2	–	**CrO**	–	Oxide of divalent chromium, black, hex.
	»	**CrO** hydr.	–	– 83 810	Hydroxide of divalent chromium, $Cr(OH)_2$, yellow(2)
	+ 2.67	–	**Cr_3O_4**	–	Chromo-chromic oxide, brown
	+ 3	**Cr_2O_3** hydr.	–	*a*. −260 530	Chromic hydroxide $Cr(OH)_3$, green, hex.(2)
	»	»	–	*b*. −250 200	Chromic oxide, green, orthorh.
	»	» hydr.	–	*c*. −240 930	Chromic hydroxide $Cr(OH)_3 . nH_2O$(2)
	+ 3.6	–	**Cr_5O_9**	–	? , violet, orthorh.
	+ 4	**CrO_2** hydr.	–	−129 000 (3)	Hydrated chromium dixodide or hydroxide $Cr(OH)_4$, brown(2)
	+ 6	**CrO_3**	–	−120 000 (3)	Chromium trioxide or chromic anhydride, deep red, orthorh.
	+ 8	–	**CrO_4**	–	Chromium tetroxide
	+ 10	–	**CrO_5**	–	Chromium pentoxide
Dissolved substances	+ 2	Cr^{++}	–	– 42 100	Chromous ion, blue–green
	+ 3	Cr^{+++}	–	– 51 500	Chromic ion, green
	»	$CrOH^{++}$	–	−103 000	Chromyl ion, green or violet
	»	$Cr(OH)_2^+$	–	−151 210 (3)	Chromyl ion
	»	CrO_2^-	–	−128 090 (3)	Chromite ion, green
	»	CrO_3^{---}	–	−144 220 (3)	Chromite ion, green
	+ 6	H_2CrO_4	–	−185 920 (3)	Chromic acid, orange–red
	»	$HCrO_4^-$	–	−184 900	Acid chromate ion, orange
	»	CrO_4^{--}	–	−176 100	Chromate ion, yellow
	»	$Cr_2O_7^{--}$	–	−315 400	Dichromate ion, orange
	»	–	$Cr_3O_{10}^{--}$	–	? , red
	»	–	$Cr_4O_{13}^{--}$	–	? , brown
	»	–	CrO^{++++}	–	?
	»	–	CrO_2^{++}	–	?

2. REACTIONS AND EQUILIBRIUM FORMULAE(4)

2.1 TWO DISSOLVED SUBSTANCES

2.1.1. *Relative stability of the dissolved substances*

$Z = +3$

1. $Cr^{+++} + 2H_2O = CrO_2^- + 4H^+$ $\qquad \log\frac{(CrO_2^-)}{(Cr^{+++})} = -26.99 + 4\,pH$

2. $Cr^{+++} + H_2O = CrOH^{++} + H^+$ $\qquad \log\frac{(CrOH^{++})}{(Cr^{+++})} = -\ 3.81 + pH$

---

(2) These values of μ^0 for the oxides correspond to the following values for the hydrated oxides or hydroxides:

$Cr(OH)_2$:	−140 500 cal.,	$Cr(OH)_3 . nH_2O$:	−205 500 cal.,
$Cr(OH)_3$:	−215 300 cal.	$Cr(OH)_4$:	−242 380 cal.

(3) The value of the free enthalpy of CrO_3 was calculated by Brewer [2] from thermal data. The other values marked with the sign (3) were calculated by us [1].

(4) In the reactions involving Cr_2O_3 the letter *a* relates to $Cr(OH)_3$ whose free enthalpy of formation is −215 300 cal.; the letter *b* relates to anhydrous Cr_2O_3 whose free enthalpy of formation is −250 200 cal., and the letter *c* to $Cr(OH)_3 . nH_2O$ whose free enthalpy of formation is −205 500 cal.

3. $CrOH^{++} + H_2O = Cr(OH)_2^+ + H^+$ $\qquad \log \frac{(Cr(OH)_2^+)}{(CrOH^{++})} = -6.22 + pH$

4. $Cr(OH)_2^+ = CrO_2^- + 2H^+$ $\qquad \log \frac{(CrO_2^-)}{(Cr(OH)_2^+)} = -16.96 + 2\,pH$

5. $CrO_2^- + H_2O = CrO_3^{---} + 2H^+$ $\qquad \log \frac{(CrO_3^{---})}{(CrO_2^-)} = -29.76 + 2\,pH$

$Z = +6$

6. $H_2CrO_4 = HCrO_4^- + H^+$ $\qquad \log \frac{(HCrO_4^-)}{(H_2CrO_4)} = -0.75 + pH$

7. $2H_2CrO_4 = Cr_2O_7^{--} + H_2O + 2H^+$ $\qquad \log \frac{(Cr_2O_7^{--})}{(H_2CrO_4)^2} = 0.18 + 2\,pH$

8. $H_2CrO_4 = CrO_4^{--} + 2H^+$ $\qquad \log \frac{(CrO_4^{--})}{(H_2CrO_4)} = -7.20 + 2\,pH$

9. $HCrO_4^- = CrO_4^{--} + H^+$ $\qquad \log \frac{(CrO_4^{--})}{(HCrO_4^-)} = -6.45 + pH$

10. $Cr_2O_7^{--} + H_2O = 2HCrO_4^-$ $\qquad \log \frac{(HCrO_4^-)^2}{(Cr_2O_7^{--})} = -1.68$

11. $Cr_2O_7^{--} + H_2O = 2CrO_4^{--} + 2H^+$ $\qquad \log \frac{(CrO_4^{--})^2}{(Cr_2O_7^{--})} = -14.59 + 2\,pH$

$+2 \rightarrow +3$

12. $Cr^{++} = Cr^{+++} + e^-$ $\qquad E_0 = -0.407 + 0.0591 \log \frac{(Cr^{+++})}{(Cr^{++})}$

13. $Cr^{++} + H_2O = CrOH^{++} + H^+ + e^-$ $\qquad E_0 = -0.182 - 0.0591\,pH + 0.0591 \log \frac{(CrOH^{++})}{(Cr^{++})}$

14. $Cr^{++} + 2H_2O = Cr(OH)_2^+ + 2H^+ + e^-$ $\qquad E_0 = 0.185 - 0.1182\,pH + 0.0591 \log \frac{(Cr(OH)_2^+)}{(Cr^{++})}$

15. $Cr^{++} + 2H_2O = CrO_2^- + 4H^+ + e^-$ $\qquad E_0 = 1.188 - 0.2364\,pH + 0.0591 \log \frac{(CrO_2^-)}{(Cr^{++})}$

$+3 \rightarrow +6$

16. $Cr^{+++} + 4H_2O = H_2CrO_4 + 6H^+ + 3e^-$ $\qquad E_0 = 1.335 - 0.1182\,pH + 0.0197 \log \frac{(H_2CrO_4)}{(Cr^{+++})}$

17. $Cr^{+++} + 4H_2O = HCrO_4^- + 7H^+ + 3e^-$ $\qquad E_0 = 1.350 - 0.1379\,pH + 0.0197 \log \frac{(HCrO_4^-)}{(Cr^{+++})}$

18. $2Cr^{+++} + 7H_2O = Cr_2O_7^{--} + 14H^+ + 6e^-$ $\qquad E_0 = 1.333 - 0.1379\,pH + 0.0098 \log \frac{(Cr_2O_7^{--})}{(Cr^{+++})^2}$

19. $Cr^{+++} + 4H_2O = CrO_4^{--} + 8H^+ + 3e^-$ $\qquad E_0 = 1.477 - 0.1576\,pH + 0.0197 \log \frac{(CrO_4^{--})}{(Cr^{+++})}$

20. $CrOH^{++} + 3H_2O = HCrO_4^- + 6H^+ + 3e^-$ $\qquad E_0 = 1.275 - 0.1182\,pH + 0.0197 \log \frac{(HCrO_4^-)}{(CrOH^{++})}$

21. $2CrOH^{++} + 5H_2O = Cr_2O_7^{--} + 12H^+ + 6e^-$ $\qquad E_0 = 1.258 - 0.1182\,pH + 0.0098 \log \frac{(Cr_2O_7^{--})}{(CrOH^{++})^2}$

22. $CrOH^{++} + 3H_2O = CrO_4^{--} + 7H^+ + 3e^-$ $\qquad E_0 = 1.402 - 0.1379\,pH + 0.0197 \log \frac{(CrO_4^{--})}{(CrOH^{++})}$

23. $Cr(OH)_2^+ + 2H_2O = HCrO_4^- + 5H^+ + 3e^-$ $\qquad E_0 = 1.152 - 0.0985\,pH + 0.0197 \log \frac{(HCrO_4^-)}{(Cr(OH)_2^+)}$

24. $2Cr(OH)_2^+ + 3H_2O = Cr_2O_7^{--} + 10H^+ + 6e^-$ $\qquad E_0 = 1.135 - 0.0985\,pH + 0.0098 \log \frac{(Cr_2O_7^{--})}{(Cr(OH)_2^+)^2}$

25. $Cr(OH)_2^+ + 2H_2O = CrO_4^{--} + 6H^+ + 3e^-$ $\qquad E_0 = 1.279 - 0.1182\,pH + 0.0197 \log \frac{(CrO_4^{--})}{(Cr(OH)_2^+)}$

26. $CrO_2^- + 2H_2O = CrO_4^{--} + 4H^+ + 3e^-$ $\qquad E_0 = 0.945 - 0.0788\,pH + 0.0197 \log \frac{(CrO_4^{--})}{(CrO_2^-)}$

27. $2CrO_2^- + 3H_2O = Cr_2O_7^{--} + 6H^+ + 6e^-$ $\qquad E_0 = 0.801 - 0.0591\,pH + 0.0098 \log \frac{(Cr_2O_7^{--})}{(CrO_2^-)^2}$

28. $CrO_3^{---} + H_2O = CrO_4^{--} + 2H^+ + 3e^-$ $\qquad E_0 = 0.359 - 0.0394\,pH + 0.0197 \log \frac{(CrO_4^{--})}{(CrO_3^{---})}$

2.1.2. *Limits of the domains of relative predominance of the dissolved substances*

$Z = +3$

1′.	Cr^{+++} / CrO_2^-	$pH = 6.75$
2′.	Cr^{+++} / $CrOH^{++}$	$pH = 3.81$
3′.	$CrOH^{++}$ / $Cr(OH)_2^+$	$pH = 6.22$
4′.	$Cr(OH)_2^+$ / CrO_2^-	$pH = 8.48$
5′.	CrO_2^- / CrO_3^{---}	$pH = 14.88$

$Z = +6$

6′.	H_2CrO_4 / $HCrO_4^-$	$pH = 0.75$
7′.	H_2CrO_4 / $Cr_2O_7^{--}$	$pH = -0.09 - \frac{1}{2}\log C$
8′.	H_2CrO_4 / CrO_4^{--}	$pH = 3.60$
9′.	$HCrO_4^-$ / CrO_4^{--}	$pH = 6.45$
10′.	$Cr_2O_7^{--}$ / $HCrO_4^-$	$0 = 1.68 + \log C$
11′.	$Cr_2O_7^{--}$ / CrO_4^{--}	$pH = 7.29 + \frac{1}{2}\log C$

$+2 \rightarrow +3$

12′.	Cr^{++} / Cr^{+++}	$E_0 = -0.407$
13′.	Cr^{++} / $CrOH^{++}$	$E_0 = -0.182 - 0.0591\,pH$
14′.	Cr^{++} / $Cr(OH)_2^+$	$E_0 = 0.185 - 0.1182\,pH$
15′.	Cr^{++} / CrO_2^-	$E_0 = 1.188 - 0.2364\,pH$

$+3 \rightarrow +6$

16′.	Cr^{+++} / H_2CrO_4	$E_0 = 1.335 - 0.1182\,pH$
17′.	Cr^{+++} / $HCrO_4^-$	$E_0 = 1.350 - 0.1379\,pH$
18′.	Cr^{+++} / $Cr_2O_7^{--}$	$E_0 = 1.333 - 0.1379\,pH - 0.0098\log C$
19′.	Cr^{+++} / CrO_4^{--}	$E_0 = 1.477 - 0.1576\,pH$
20′.	$CrOH^{++}$ / $HCrO_4^-$	$E_0 = 1.275 - 0.1182\,pH$
21′.	$CrOH^{++}$ / $Cr_2O_7^{--}$	$E_0 = 1.258 - 0.1182\,pH - 0.0098\log C$
22′.	$CrOH^{++}$ / CrO_4^{--}	$E_0 = 1.402 - 0.1379\,pH$
23′.	$Cr(OH)_2^+$ / $HCrO_4^-$	$E_0 = 1.152 - 0.0985\,pH$
24′.	$Cr(OH)_2^+$ / $Cr_2O_7^{--}$	$E_0 = 1.135 - 0.0985\,pH - 0.0098\log C$
25′.	$Cr(OH)_2^+$ / CrO_4^{--}	$E_0 = 1.279 - 0.1182\,pH$
26′.	CrO_2^- / CrO_4^{--}	$E_0 = 0.945 - 0.0788\,pH$
27′.	CrO_2^- / $Cr_2O_7^{--}$	$E_0 = 0.801 - 0.0591\,pH - 0.0098\log C$
28′.	CrO_3^{---} / CrO_4^{--}	$E_0 = 0.359 - 0.0394\,pH$

2.2. TWO SOLID SUBSTANCES

Relative stability of chromium and its oxides

$0 \rightarrow +2$

29. $\mathbf{Cr} + H_2O = \mathbf{CrO} + 2H^+ + 2e^-$ $\quad E_0 = -0.588 - 0.0591\,pH$

$0 \rightarrow +3$

30. $2\mathbf{Cr} + 3H_2O = \mathbf{Cr_2O_3} + 6H^+ + 6e^-$
 - *a.* $E_0 = -0.654 - 0.0591\,pH$
 - *b.* $= -0.579 - 0.0591\,pH$
 - *c.* $= -0.512 - 0.0591\,pH$

$+2 \rightarrow +3$

31. $2\mathbf{CrO} + H_2O = \mathbf{Cr_2O_3} + 2H^+ + 2e^-$
 - *a.* $E_0 = -0.785 - 0.0591\,pH$
 - *b.* $= -0.561 - 0.0591\,pH$
 - *c.* $= -0.360 - 0.0591\,pH$

$+3 \rightarrow +4$

32. $\mathbf{Cr_2O_3} + H_2O = 2\mathbf{CrO_2} + 2H^+ + 2e^-$
 - *a.* $E_0 = 1.284 - 0.0591\,pH$
 - *b.* $= 1.060 - 0.0591\,pH$
 - *c.* $= 0.859 - 0.0591\,pH$

2.3. ONE SOLID SUBSTANCE AND ONE DISSOLVED SUBSTANCE

Solubility of chromium and its oxides

a. Solubility in gram-ions or gram-molecules per litre

$Z = +2$			
33.	$Cr^{++} + H_2O = \mathbf{CrO} + 2H^+$		$\log(Cr^{++}) = 10.99 - 2\,pH$
$Z = +3$			
34.	$2Cr^{+++} + 3H_2O = \mathbf{Cr_2O_3} + 6H^+$	*a.*	$\log(Cr^{+++}) = 4.60 - 3\,pH$
		b.	$= 8.39 - 3\,pH$
		c.	$= 11.79 - 3\,pH$
35.	$2CrOH^{++} + H_2O = \mathbf{Cr_2O_3} + 4H^+$	*a.*	$\log(CrOH^{++}) = 1.58 - 2\,pH$
		b.	$= 4.58 - 2\,pH$
		c.	$= 7.98 - 2\,pH$
36.	$2Cr(OH)_2^+ = \mathbf{Cr_2O_3} + H_2O + 2H^+$	*a.*	$\log(Cr(OH)_2^+) = -5.43 - pH$
		b.	$= -1.64 - pH$
		c.	$= 1.76 - pH$
37.	$\mathbf{Cr_2O_3} + H_2O = 2CrO_2^- + 2H^+$	*a.*	$\log(CrO_2^-) = -22.36 + pH$
		b.	$= -18.60 + pH$
		c.	$= -15.20 + pH$
38.	$\mathbf{Cr_2O_3} + 3H_2O = 2CrO_3^{---} + 6H^+$	*a.*	$\log(CrO_3^{---}) = -52.15 + 3\,pH$
		b.	$= -48.36 + 3\,pH$
		c.	$= -44.96 + 3\,pH$
$0 \rightarrow +2$			
39.	$\mathbf{Cr} = Cr^{++} + 2e^-$		$E_0 = -0.913 + 0.0295 \log(Cr^{++})$
$0 \rightarrow +3$			
40.	$\mathbf{Cr} = Cr^{+++} + 3e^-$		$E_0 = -0.744 + 0.0197 \log(Cr^{+++})$
41.	$\mathbf{Cr} + 2H_2O = CrO_2^- + 4H^+ + 3e^-$		$E_0 = -0.213 - 0.0788\,pH + 0.0197 \log(CrO_2^-)$
42.	$\mathbf{Cr} + 3H_2O = CrO_3^{---} + 6H^+ + 3e^-$		$E_0 = 0.374 - 0.1182\,pH + 0.0197 \log(CrO_3^{---})$
$0 \rightarrow +6$			
43.	$\mathbf{Cr} + 4H_2O = H_2CrO_4 + 6H^+ + 6e^-$		$E_0 = 0.295 - 0.0591\,pH + 0.0098 \log(H_2CrO_4)$
44.	$\mathbf{Cr} + 4H_2O = HCrO_4^- + 7H^+ + 6e^-$		$E_0 = 0.303 - 0.0689\,pH + 0.0098 \log(HCrO_4^-)$
45.	$2\mathbf{Cr} + 7H_2O = Cr_2O_7^{--} + 14H^+ + 12e^-$		$E_0 = 0.294 - 0.0689\,pH + 0.0049 \log(Cr_2O_7^{--})$
46.	$\mathbf{Cr} + 4H_2O = CrO_4^{--} + 8H^+ + 6e^-$		$E_0 = 0.366 - 0.0788\,pH + 0.0098 \log(CrO_4^{--})$
$+2 \rightarrow +3$			
47.	$2Cr^{++} + 3H_2O = \mathbf{Cr_2O_3} + 6H^+ + 2e^-$	*a.*	$E_0 = -0.136 - 0.1773\,pH - 0.0591 \log(Cr^{++})$
		b.	$= 0.088 - 0.1773\,pH - 0.0591 \log(Cr^{++})$
		c.	$= 0.289 - 0.1773\,pH - 0.0591 \log(Cr^{++})$
48.	$\mathbf{CrO} + H_2O = CrO_2^- + 2H^+ + e^-$		$E_0 = 0.538 - 0.1182\,pH + 0.0591 \log(CrO_2^-)$
49.	$\mathbf{CrO} + 2H_2O = CrO_3^{---} + 4H^+ + e^-$		$E_0 = 0.297 - 0.2364\,pH + 0.0591 \log(CrO_3^{---})$
$+3 \rightarrow +4$			
50.	$Cr^{+++} + 2H_2O = \mathbf{CrO_2} + 4H^+ + e^-$		$E_0 = 1.556 - 0.2364\,pH - 0.0591 \log(Cr^{+++})$
51.	$CrOH^{++} + H_2O = \mathbf{CrO_2} + 3H^+ + e^-$		$E_0 = 1.331 - 0.1773\,pH - 0.0591 \log(CrOH^{++})$
$+3 \rightarrow +6$			
52.	$\mathbf{Cr_2O_3} + 5H_2O = 2HCrO_4^- + 8H^+ + 6e^-$	*a.*	$E_0 = 1.259 - 0.0788\,pH + 0.0197 \log(HCrO_4^-)$
		b.	$= 1.184 - 0.0788\,pH + 0.0197 \log(HCrO_4^-)$
		c.	$= 1.117 - 0.0788\,pH + 0.0197 \log(HCrO_4^-)$
53.	$\mathbf{Cr_2O_3} + 4H_2O = Cr_2O_7^{--} + 8H^+ + 6e^-$	*a.*	$E_0 = 1.242 - 0.0788\,pH + 0.0098 \log(Cr_2O_7^{--})$
		b.	$= 1.168 - 0.0788\,pH + 0.0098 \log(Cr_2O_7^{--})$
		c.	$= 1.101 - 0.0788\,pH + 0.0098 \log(Cr_2O_7^{--})$
54.	$\mathbf{Cr_2O_3} + 5H_2O = 2CrO_4^{--} + 10H^+ + 6e^-$	*a.*	$E_0 = 1.386 - 0.0985\,pH + 0.0197 \log(CrO_4^{--})$
		b.	$= 1.311 - 0.0985\,pH + 0.0197 \log(CrO_4^{--})$
		c.	$= 1.244 - 0.0985\,pH + 0.0197 \log(CrO_4^{--})$

$+4 \rightarrow +6$

55.	$\mathbf{CrO_2}$	$+2H_2O = HCrO_4^- + 3H^+ + 2e^-$		$E_0 = 1.246 - 0.0886\,pH + 0.0295 \log (HCrO_4^-)$
56.	$2\,\mathbf{CrO_2}$	$+3H_2O = Cr_2O_7^{--} + 6H^+ + 4e^-$		$E_0 = 1.221 - 0.0886\,pH + 0.0148 \log (Cr_2O_7^{--})$
57.	$\mathbf{CrO_2}$	$+2H_2O = CrO_4^{--} + 4H^+ + 2e^-$		$E_0 = 1.437 - 0.1182\,pH + 0.0295 \log (CrO_4^{--})$

b. Solubility in gram-atoms of chromium per litre

45'.	$\mathbf{Cr}$	$/Cr_2O_7^{--}$		$E_0 = 0.293 - 0.0689\,pH + 0.0049 \log C$
53'.	$\mathbf{Cr_2O_3}$	$/Cr_2O_7^{--}$	a.	$E_0 = 1.239 - 0.0788\,pH + 0.0098 \log C$
			b.	$= 1.165 - 0.0788\,pH + 0.0098 \log C$
			c.	$= 1.098 - 0.0788\,pH + 0.0098 \log C$
56'.	$\mathbf{CrO_2}$	$/Cr_2O_7^{--}$		$E_0 = 1.217 - 0.0886\,pH + 0.0148 \log C$

3. EQUILIBRIUM DIAGRAMS AND THEIR INTERPRETATION

3.1. ESTABLISHMENT OF THE DIAGRAMS

In Fig. 1 we have drawn a diagram representing, as a function of the pH and the concentration of dissolved chromium in the solutions, the domains of predominance of chromium in the various dissolved forms of hexavalent chromium.

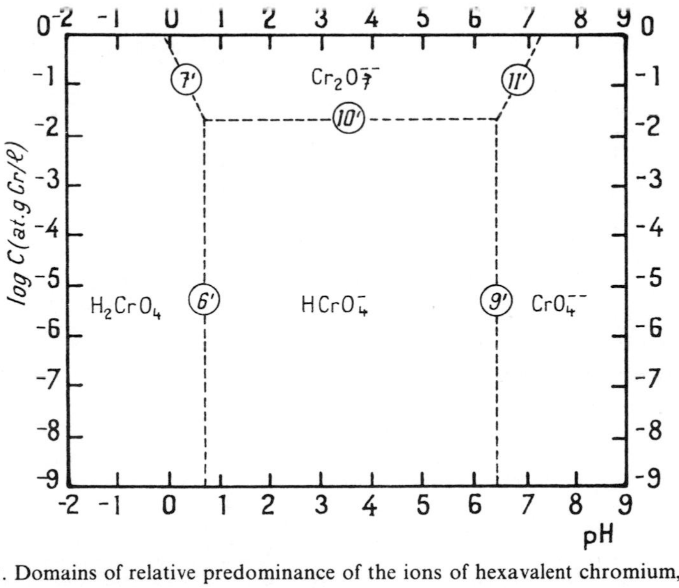

FIG. 1. Domains of relative predominance of the ions of hexavalent chromium, at 25°C.

On account of the complexity of the system chromium–water, we have drawn in Figs. 2, 3 and 4 three general equilibrium diagrams in which we have considered respectively the three forms of chromium oxide (anhydrous and hydrated) which are mentioned in paragraph 1. For the least stable of these forms (Fig. 4) which is a $Cr(OH)_3 . nH_2O$ obtained by precipitation in solutions containing chloride, we have also considered ions represented by the formulae $CrOH^{++}$ and $Cr(OH)_2^+$ which seem in actual fact to be complex ions containing chlorine.

We point out that, mainly on account of approximations made concerning these complex ions, Fig. 4 should be considered only as a fairly rough representation.

Figures 5*a*, *b* and *c*, deduced respectively from Figs. 2, 3 and 4, represent the theoretical conditions of corrosion, immunity and passivation of chromium at 25°C.

It will be recalled that Figs. 2 and 3 are valid only in the absence of substances with which chromium can form soluble complexes or insoluble salts; according to Charlot [3], Cr^{++} ions form ammine and cyanide complexes; Cr^{+++} ions form complexes not only with chlorides, but also with fluorides, sulphates, ammonium salts, cyanides, sulphocyanides, oxalates and citrates; chromates are complexed

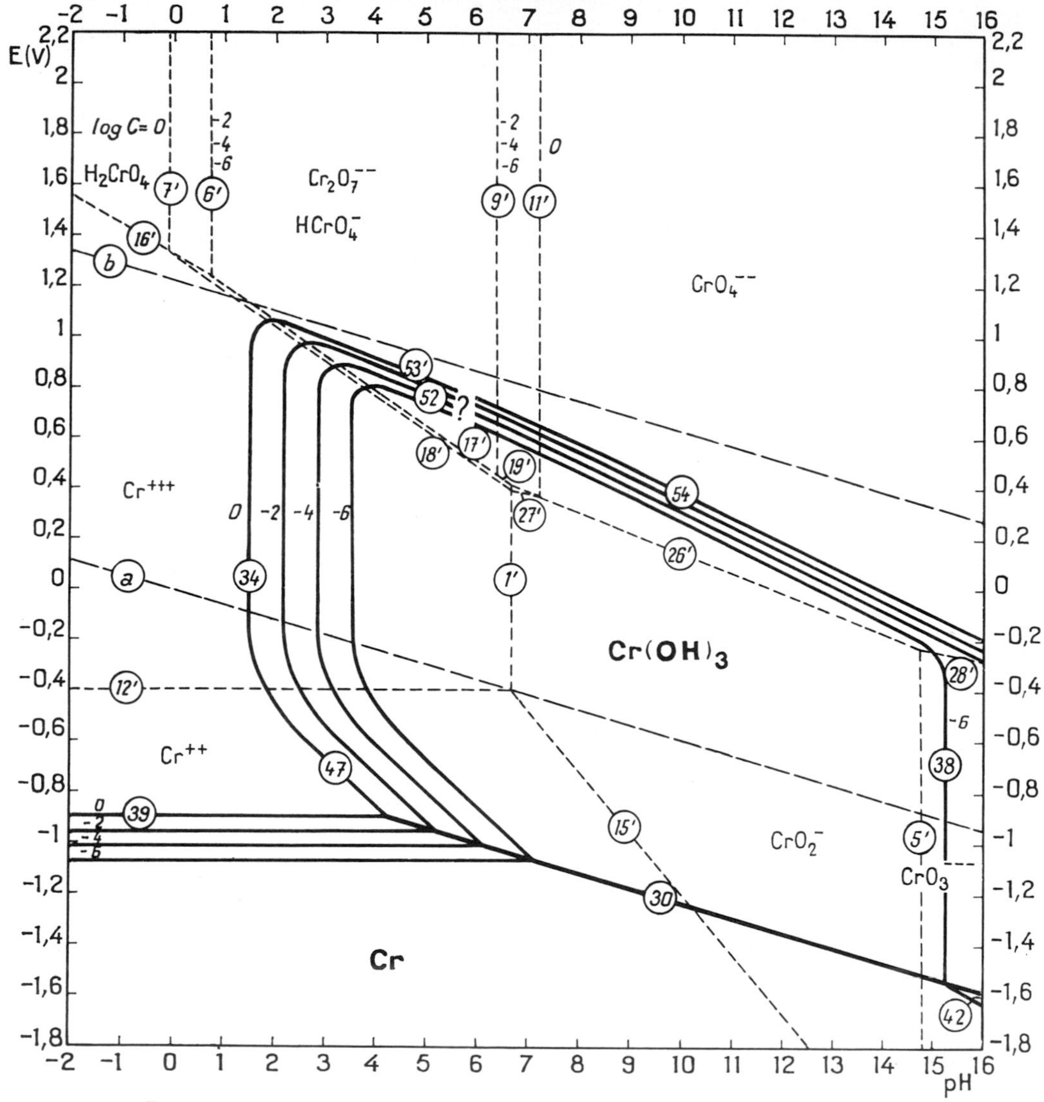

FIG. 2. Potential–pH equilibrium diagram for the system chromium–water, at 25°C.
In solutions not containing chloride.
[Figure established considering $Cr(OH)_3$.]

by hydrogen peroxide; the chromates of the alkali metals and also ferric, cupric, manganous and magnesium chromates are soluble, but most of the other chromates are insoluble.

3.2. STABILITY, CORROSION AND ELECTRO-DEPOSITION OF CHROMIUM

From Figs. 2, 3 and 4, chromium is seen to be a very base metal, as its domain of stability lies considerably below that of water; from this point of view, it appears to be less noble than zinc whose standard dissolution potential is $-0{\cdot}763$ V, compared with $-0{\cdot}913$ V for chromium. In the presence of acid solutions it tends to decompose the water with the evolution of hydrogen, dissolving as chromous ions Cr^{++}. In the presence of neutral and slightly alkaline solutions not containing chloride, it tends to

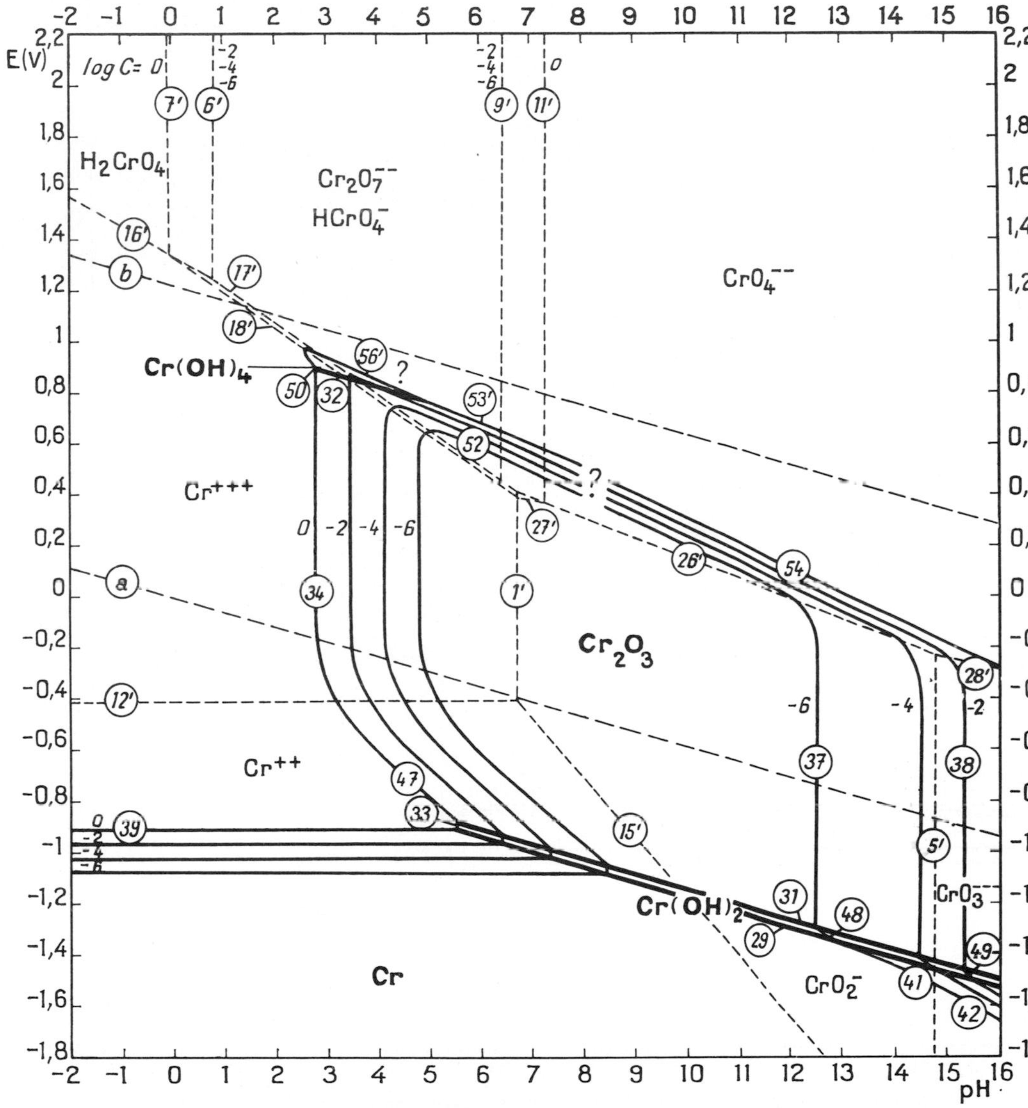

FIG. 3. Potential–pH equilibrium diagram for the system chromium–water, at 25°C.
In solutions not containing chloride.
(Figure established considering anhydrous Cr_2O_3.)

become covered with chromic oxide or hydroxide; in the presence of very alkaline non-oxidant solutions, it tends to dissolve as chromite ions CrO_2^- and CrO_3^{---}.

Figure 4 shows that in solutions containing chloride, chromium is more easily attacked by both acid solutions and alkaline solutions, on account of the increased solubility of the hydroxide.

Figure 5*c*, which is deduced from Fig. 4, represents very approximately, assuming passivation by a film of chromic hydroxide, the theoretical conditions of corrosion, immunity and passivation of chromium in the presence of solutions containing chloride. Likewise Figs. 5*a* and *b*, deduced respectively from Figs. 2 and 3, represent these conditions in the presence of solutions which do not contain chloride.

Examination of the chemical and electrochemical properties of chromium brings out the essential point that the metal behaves as if it existed in two clearly different states: the active state in which it

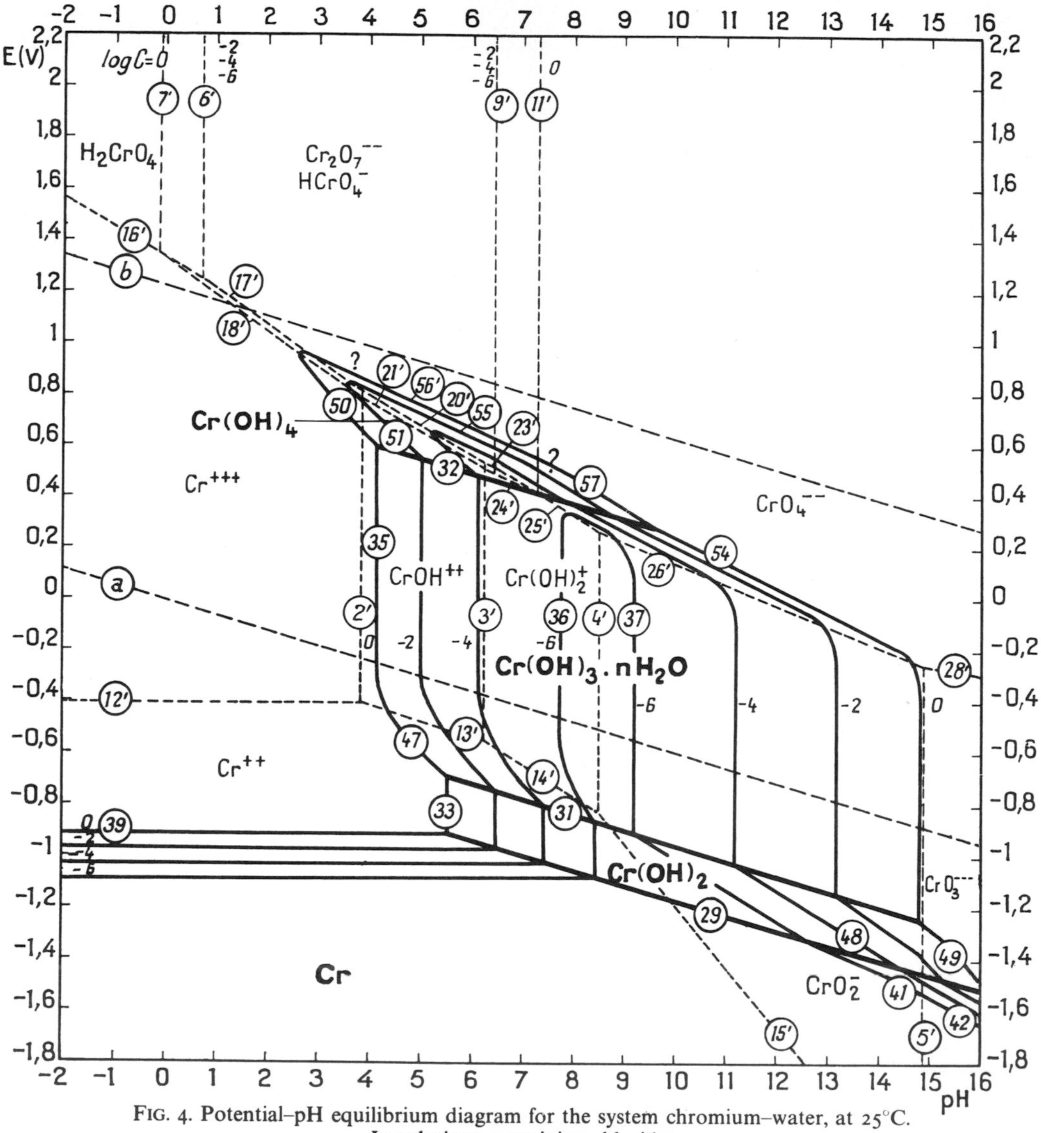

FIG. 4. Potential–pH equilibrium diagram for the system chromium–water, at 25°C.
In solutions containing chloride.
[Approximate representation made by considering $Cr(OH)_3 . nH_2O$.]

appears to be an extremely corrodible metal, and the passive state in which it behaves as a noble metal. The active state is produced by contact of the metal with reducing solutions, HCl or H_2SO_4, or by cathodic polarization; the passive state, on the other hand, is produced by contact with oxidizing solutions or by anodic polarization in solutions not containing chloride. A change from one state to the other can be effected by modifying the oxidizing-reducing properties of the solutions or by reversing the polarization; the oxidizing action of the air is often sufficient to make chromium pass from the active state to the passive state.

The phenomena observed during the electrochemical polarization of the metal illustrate particularly well this passage from the active state to the passive state and vice versa. Grube *et al.* [4] characterized its anodic behaviour as follows: in acid solutions of pH around 1 to 2 (0·01 and 0·1 M H_2SO_4 and 0·01 M HCl) the polarization curves display at first a section corresponding to the dissolution of the metal as chromous ions Cr^{++} for potentials around $-0{\cdot}5$ to $-0{\cdot}6$ V; an increase in the current

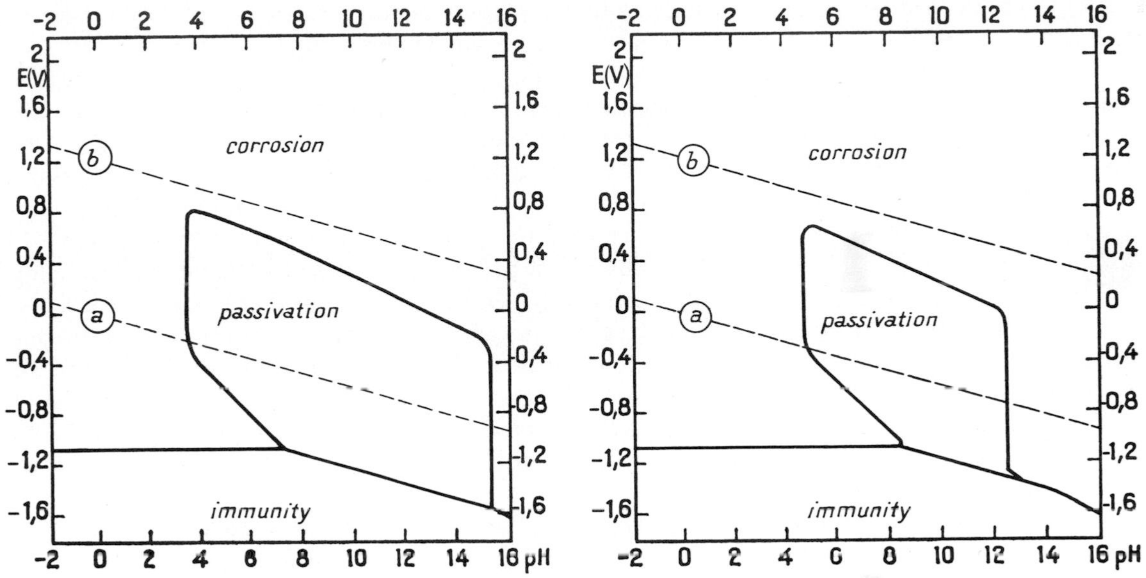

(*a*) Figure established considering $Cr(OH)_3$. (*b*) Figure established considering Cr_2O_3.
In solutions not containing chloride.

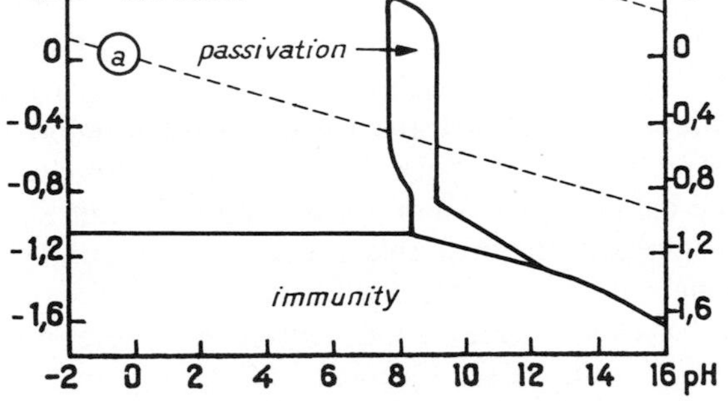

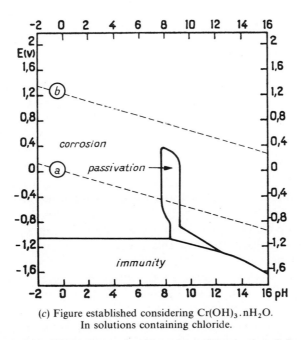

(*c*) Figure established considering $Cr(OH)_3 . nH_2O$.
In solutions containing chloride.

FIG. 5. Theoretical conditions of corrosion, immunity and passivation of chromium, at 25°C.

density then produces a sharp increase in the potential to a value above +1·2 V; this abrupt increase in the potential corresponds to a change from the active state of the metal to the passive state; on increasing the current density further, a new section of activity is encountered, also corresponding to the dissolution of the electrode, but this time in the form of chromic acid. In neutral solutions (1 M KCl) one observes the disappearance of the first active period in which chromium passes into solution as chromous ions Cr^{++} and, in this case, the potential increases steadily to a high value corresponding to the dissolution of the passivated chromium as chromic acid. In alkaline solutions of pH around 14 (1 M KOH) the potential increases steadily, within the limits of current density employed, from about 0·57 V to about 0·90 V, and the electrode dissolves as chromate ions CrO_4^{--}.

This peculiar behaviour of chromium has been interpreted in various ways and some of the theories put forward present the passivity phenomenon as being characteristic of a state of the metal different from that for which we have thermodynamic data and which would correspond to the so-called "active" chromium. Up to what point can the so-called "passive" state be explained by the formation of a passivating film of oxide? If we refer to Fig. 3 in which we have considered a film of anhydrous Cr_2O_3, we see that although this interpretation may be valid for neutral solutions, it is no longer valid for acid solutions of pH = 1 to 2, or for alkaline solutions of pH = 14. On the other hand, by imagining the existence of an oxide or a hydroxide whose solubility is much lower than that of Cr_2O_3 even, such as the hypothetical $Cr(OH)_3$ considered in Fig. 2, for instance, we arrive at an interpretation which is correct for acid and alkaline solutions as well as for neutral solutions. Thus, in Fig. 2, the first period of activity when chromium passes into solution as chromous ions Cr^{++} during anodic polarization in acid solution, would correspond to the space between lines (39) and (47); the sharp jump of the potential which starts at about −0·5 to −0·6 V, would correspond to the electrode being covered with a protective film of oxide or hydroxide; the second period of activity of the electrode, around 1·2 V, would correspond to the lines (52) characterizing the dissolution of this oxide or hydroxide as $HCrO_4^-$ ions; likewise, according to Fig. 2, for alkaline solutions, the electrode would initially be covered with the oxide or hydroxide considered and would be capable of dissolving only as chromate ions CrO_4^{--} and only at high potentials (lines 54).

The oxidizing-reducing properties of the "passive" state of chromium, just as the anodic behaviour of the metal, are well explained by considering this passive state to correspond to a covering of the metal with an oxide or hydroxide of very small solubility. Thus while the so-called *active* chromium has an electrochemical behaviour intermediate between those of zinc and cadmium (it dissolves in non-oxidizing acids to give Cr^{++} ions, it is capable of reducing a certain number of salts, such as the chlorides of copper, silver and lead, and also cadmium chloride, bromide and iodide) the so-called *passive* chromium shows itself to be more noble than copper, silver and mercury and is not soluble in acids (Pascal [5]).

Preparation of electrolytic chromium. According to Figs. 2 and 3, chromium can be obtained electrolytically from acid solutions of chromates, chromic salts or chromous salts, and these possibilities are actually applied in practice. However, electrodeposition from solutions of chromic and chromous salts is hardly used in chromium plating operations on account of certain operational difficulties brought about for instance by the ease with which chromous solutions are oxidized, by the undesirable influence of impurities or variations in the pH and by an abundant evolution of hydrogen. This technique is used only in the extraction of the metal from its ores; thus, in a process developed by the U.S. Bureau of Mines [6], the bath is made up of a mixture of chromic sulphate $Cr_2(SO_4)_3$, chromous sulphate $CrSO_4$ and sodium sulphate; the insoluble anodes are surrounded by a diaphragm to prevent the oxidation of the chromous salt. The cathodic current yield is around 50 per cent (calculated for trivalent chromium); the deposits of chromium thus obtained are grey and may contain up to 4 per cent of Cr_2O_3. According to Figs. 2 and 3, the formation of oxide or hydroxide can be avoided only by maintaining a high degree of acidity in the catholyte.

Electro-plating of chromium. The baths used for chromium plating are generally based on chromic acid (in which the chromium is hexavalent) and sulphuric acid; these are preferred to baths of trivalent chromium salts although they theoretically require a greater amount of current for the same amount of chromium deposited on account of the higher valency of chromium in chromic acid. At present, two types of bath are used: "concentrated" baths containing about 400 g CrO_3/l giving brilliant platings, and "dilute" baths containing about 250 g CrO_3/l giving industrial platings called "hard platings"; in each case the amount of sulphuric acid added to the baths is 1 part of SO_4 for 100 parts of CrO_3; the chromium deposits thus obtained are very pure. According to Dubpernell [7], the acidity of these baths is very high and corresponds to a negative pH; from the equilibrium diagrams in Figs. 2 and 3, it is therefore essentially a question of a solution of H_2CrO_4. In this process, the deposition of chromium is also accompanied by evolution of hydrogen and the current yield is not very high (of the order of 15 per cent). We also point out here that, in accordance with the equilibrium diagram, and taking into account the relatively small hydrogen overpotential of chromium,(5) it seems difficult to electro-deposit chromium from solutions of chromous salts without at the same time causing considerable quantities of hydrogen to separate out; this would explain the undesirable influence of impurities of metals having small hydrogen overpotentials. In the possibility of a direct reduction of chromic acid to metallic chromium without passing through the intermediate stages Cr^{+++} and Cr^{++}, chromium could theoretically be formed starting at potentials given by formula (43): $E_0 = 0.295 - 0.0591\text{ pH} + 0.0098 \log(H_2CrO_4)$ (see § 2); i.e. at potentials above the equilibrium potential of the reaction $H_2 = 2H^+ + 2e^-(a)$; in this case it could be possible for chromium to be formed without any evolution of hydrogen. Experimental research in this connection would be useful.

3.3. STABILITY OF THE COMPOUNDS OF DIVALENT CHROMIUM

From Figs. 2, 3 and 4, the blue–green chromous ion Cr^{++} and the corresponding hydroxide $Cr(OH)_2$ both show themselves to be compounds which are unstable in water, as their domains of predominance or stability lie below that of water.

Chromous salt solutions are in fact strongly reducing and are very easily oxidized to the chromic state, for instance by the oxygen of the air. In acid media chromous solutions decompose the water with the evolution of hydrogen. They displace tin, platinum and gold from solutions of their salts; they precipitate cuprous and mercurous salts from solutions of cupric and mercuric salts.

On increasing their pH, chromous salt solutions precipitate the yellow hydrate $Cr(OH)_2$ at pH = 5·5 for molar solutions, at pH = 6·5 for 10^{-2} M solutions (Charlot indicates a pH around 6). This hydroxide can be oxidized by the air to chromic oxide or hydroxide; this probably explains why its colour changes quickly from yellow to brown, and then to black. The corresponding anhydrous oxide CrO is a black powder, which can also be easily oxidized to chromic oxide.

3.4. STABILITY OF THE COMPOUNDS OF TRIVALENT CHROMIUM

As can be predicted from the equilibrium diagram, the compounds of trivalent chromium are very stable. The green chromic ion Cr^{+++} can be reduced to the blue–green chromous ion Cr^{++} and oxidized to orange chromic acid; in acid solution this oxidation can be carried out by boiling chromic solutions with nitric acid or potassium chlorate; in slightly acid or neutral media, it can be carried out by boiling with freshly precipitated manganese dioxide or potassium permanganate. We also point out here the oxidation, according to Yost [9], of Cr^{+++} to $Cr_2O_7^{--}$ by the action of $H_2S_2O_8$ in the presence of Ag^+ as a catalyst.

On addition of an alkali to Cr^{+++} solutions, chromic oxide Cr_2O_3 is precipitated in a badly defined state of hydration; in the presence of an excess of alkali, the hydrate redissolves as chromite (green CrO_2^- and CrO_3^{---} ions); it can be oxidized to chromate by the halogens, hypochlorite, lead

(5) We have no precise data concerning this hydrogen overpotential, but, according to Blum and Hogaboom [8], the metals of the group chromium, molybdenum and tungsten are considered to be metals with low hydrogen overpotentials.

peroxide and hydrogen peroxide. The physical and chemical properties of chromic hydroxide vary greatly with the way in which it is precipitated, and the product obtained shows very noticeably ageing phenomena, which also have the effect of modifying its physical and chemical properties. On calcining, chromic hydroxide becomes converted into green chromic oxide Cr_2O_3 which, when prepared at high temperatures, is practically insoluble in acids; however, it can be oxidized to chromate by fusion at high temperatures with sodium carbonate and sodium nitrate or potassium chlorate.

In Fig. 6 we have represented, from formulae (34), (37) and (38), the influence of pH on the solubility of chromic oxide Cr_2O_3 as Cr^{+++}, CrO_2^- and CrO_3^{---} ions. According to this figure the characteristics

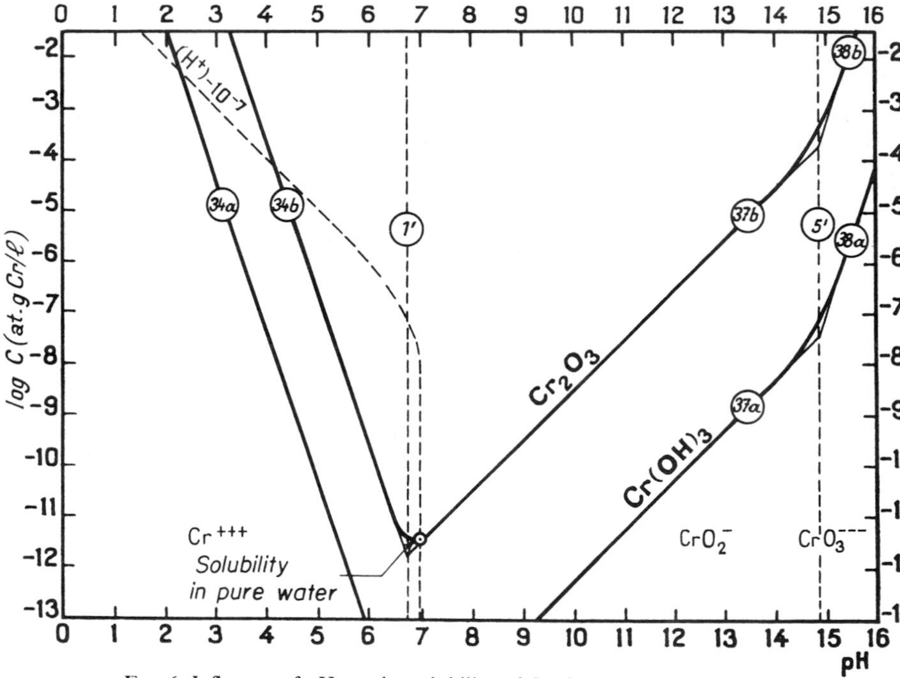

FIG. 6. Influence of pH on the solubility of Cr_2O_3 and $Cr(OH)_3$, at 25°C. In solutions not containing chloride.

of a solution obtained by dissolving Cr_2O_3 in pure water until saturation is reached are given by the coordinates of the point of intersection of the solubility curve with the line giving the values of $(H^+) - 10^{-7}$; these characteristics are:

$$pH = 7{\cdot}0, \quad (Cr) = 10^{-11{\cdot}6}, \quad \text{i.e. } 0{\cdot}24 \times 10^{-7} \text{ mg } Cr_2O_3/l.$$

We have not found in chemical literature any precise data concerning the experimental value of this solubility.

A similar curve has been drawn on the same figure for the hypothetical hydroxide $Cr(OH)_3$ and the characteristics that would be obtained by dissolving such a hydroxide until saturation are:

$$pH = 7{\cdot}0, \quad (Cr) = 10^{-14{\cdot}3}, \quad \text{i.e. } 0{\cdot}38 \times 10^{-10} \text{ mg } Cr_2O_3/l.$$

In Fig. 7 we have drawn the solubility curve for freshly precipitated $Cr(OH)_3.nH_2O$; in this case, as the solubility product in acid solutions, determined by Bjerrum [10], relates to solutions containing chloride, we have taken into account the ions $CrOH^{++}$ and $Cr(OH)_2^+$; for this hydroxide the saturation conditions are:

$$pH = 7{\cdot}9, \quad (Cr) = 10^{-6{\cdot}1}, \quad \text{i.e. } 0{\cdot}06 \text{ mg } Cr_2O_3/l.$$

We have also given in this figure some experimental values of Bjerrum relating to acid solutions containing chloride and of Fricke and Windhausen [11] relating to alkaline solutions not containing chloride, and also the pH = 4·6 assumed by Charlot for the precipitation of chromic hydroxide in 10^{-2} M solution; this pH corresponds to the solubility of $Cr(OH)_3 . nH_2O$ as Cr^{+++} ions, when the ions $CrOH^{++}$ and $Cr(OH)_2^+$ are not taken into account; we have not found in chemical literature any experimental data concerning the solubility of chromic hydroxide in pure water.

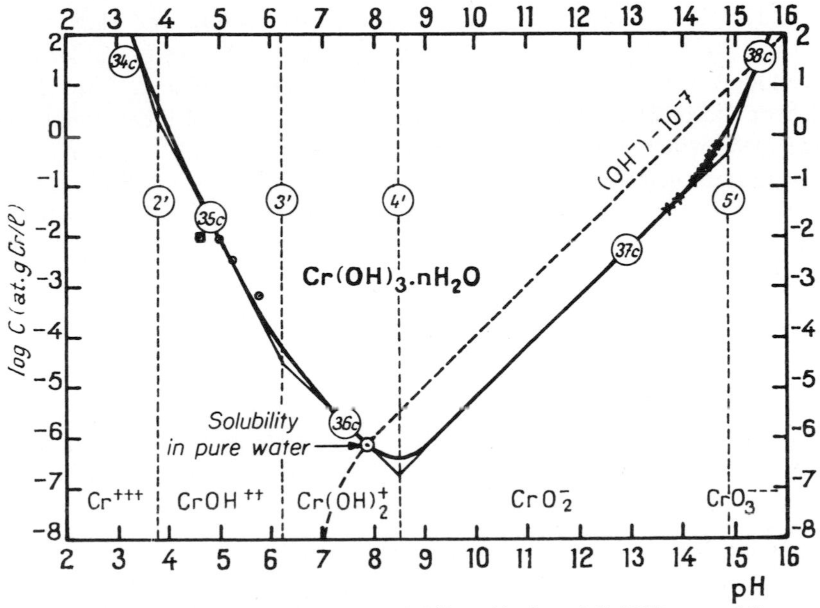

FIG. 7. Influence of pH on the solubility of hydrated $Cr(OH)_3$, at 25°C.
In solutions containing chloride.
(Values of Bjerrum ⊙, Charlot ⊡, Fricke and Windhausen ×.)

3.5. STABILITY OF THE COMPOUNDS OF QUADRIVALENT CHROMIUM

In this valency state the only known compound is hydrated chromic dioxide which we have represented by the formula $Cr(OH)_4$. It can be obtained in solution by the action of the hydroxide $Cr(OH)_3$ on chromic anhydride CrO_3, or by the action of a salt of trivalent chromium on a chromate, and also by the reduction of chromates with various reducing agents, such as hyposulphite, Ag_2O and KI. When prepared in solution it is a brown powder whose amount of water of crystallization depends on the method of preparation. Boiling water, alkalis and alkaline carbonates convert it into trivalent chromium hydroxide, which seems to indicate the constitution of a salt, the dioxide CrO_2 being considered sometimes as a chromate of trivalent chromium $Cr_2O_3 . CrO_3$.

It will be recalled that oxides of chromium of intermediate valency also exist, but we have not taken these into account for want of thermodynamic data about them. Of these oxides we point out Cr_5O_9 which is obtained by the decomposition of chromyl chloride at 300°C and which consists of small purple rhombic crystals, insoluble in acids and decomposed slowly by alkalis to give Cr_2O_3 and chromate. A hydrate $Cr_5O_9.9H_2O$ is known. Cr_3O_4 is obtained as a hydrate $Cr_3O_4.H_2O$ by heating $Cr(OH)_2$. It is a brownish powder, which has a powerful reducing action.

3.6. STABILITY OF THE COMPOUNDS OF HEXAVALENT CHROMIUM

Chromic anhydride CrO_3, crystallizing as red rhombic needles, is very soluble in water; its solutions are strongly oxidizing. Equilibrium diagrams Figs. 2, 3 and 4 show the domains of relative predominance of its dissolved forms H_2CrO_4, $HCrO_4^-$ and CrO_4^{--} as a function of pH and potential; Fig. 1 shows the domains of these same dissolved forms as a function of pH and concentration of dissolved chromium.

It can be seen from the equilibrium diagrams in Figs. 2, 3 and 4 that the reduction of chromic acid or chromates can lead, depending on the pH of the solution, to the formation either of chromic salts, chromous salts or metallic chromium in acid media, or the oxide Cr_2O_3 or hydroxide $Cr(OH)_3$ in neutral or slightly alkaline media, or chromite in very alkaline solutions. It can also be seen that the oxidizing action is greatest in very acid solutions; of the various oxidation reactions that are easily brought about by chromates in acid media, we point out the following: the oxidation of HI, HCl and HBr respectively to I_2, Cl_2 and Br_2; the oxidation of SO_2 to H_2SO_4, and H_2S to elemental sulphur; the oxidation of numerous organic substances such as ethyl alcohol to acetaldehyde and oxalic acid to CO_2. All these oxidation reactions are accompanied by a colour change from the orange or yellow of the original dichromate or chromate solution to the green colour of the chromic ion.

Lines (53′) and (18′), which express the conditions of equilibrium of dichromates with Cr_2O_3 and chromic solutions, lie completely below line (*b*) which expresses the equilibrium of the oxidation of water to oxygen at atmospheric pressure. Consequently, unlike potassium permanganate solutions, potassium dichromate solutions are perfectly stable and can retain their titre indefinitely, which is important in analytical chemistry.

3.7. PASSIVATING ACTION OF THE CHROMATES

The passivating action of chromates with respect to iron is a property of which much practical use is made. One of us [12] has already described how, if one assumes according to Hoar and Evans [13] that this passivating action is due to the formation of a mixture of hydrated Fe_2O_3 and Cr_2O_3 in every important in analytical chemistry.

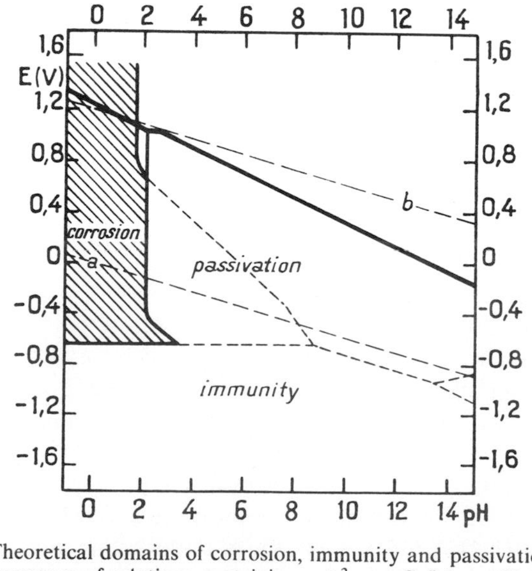

FIG. 8. Theoretical domains of corrosion, immunity and passivation of iron in the presence of solutions containing 10^{-2} g-at Cr/l (1·9 g K_2CrO_4/l).

crack in the oxide film with which the surface of the iron is previously covered, it is possible to obtain a graphical representation of the phenomenon by superimposing the corrosion diagram for iron on the equilibrium diagram for chromium for a given chromate concentration. Such a representation is made in Fig. 8 for iron in the presence of a solution containing 0·01 g-at of chromium per litre dissolved as chromate or dichromate. The theoretical conditions for passivation of iron are represented in such a diagram by that part of the domain of stability of chromic hydroxide not in common with the domain of immunity of iron. Under these conditions, the chromate or dichromate can theoretically be reduced by the iron with the formation of passivating chromic hydroxide [14].

4. BIBLIOGRAPHY

[1] E. DELTOMBE, N. DE ZOUBOV and M. POURBAIX, *Comportement électrochimique du chrome. Diagrammes d'équilibres tension–pH du système* Cr-H_2O *à* 25°C (Rapport technique RT.41 of CEBELCOR, 1956).

[2] L. BREWER, The thermodynamic properties of the oxides and their vaporization processes, *Chem. Rev.* **52**, 1-75 (1953).

[3] G. CHARLOT, *L'analyse qualitative et les réactions en solution*, 4th ed., Masson, Paris, 1957.

[4] G. GRUBE, R. HEIDINGER and L. SCHLECHT, Ueber das elektrochemische Verhalten des Chroms, *Z. Elektrochem.* **32**, 70–9 (1926).

[5] P. PASCAL, *Traité de Chimie minérale*, Vol. X, Masson, Paris, 1933, pp. 439–596.

[6] R. R. LLOYD, W. T. RAWLES and R. G. FEENEY, The electrowinning of chromium from trivalent salt solutions, *Trans. Electrochem. Soc.* **89**, 443–55 (1946).

[7] G. DUBPERNELL, Chromium plating, *Trans. Electrochem. Soc.* **80**, 589–615 (1941).

[8] W. BLUM and G. B. HOGABOOM, *Principles of Electroplating and Electroforming*, 3rd ed., McGraw–Hill, New York, 1949, p. 336.

[9] D. M. YOST, Catalysis by silver ion of the oxidation of chromic salts by peroxysulfuric acid. The existence of trivalent silver compounds, *J. Amer. Chem. Soc.* **48**, 152–64 (1926).

[10] J. BJERRUM, Studien über Chromichlorid. III. Hydroxoaquochromichloride, *Z. Phys. Chem* **73**, 724–59 (1910).

[11] R. FRICKE and O. WINDHAUSEN, Ueber die Aelterung des Chromhydroxydes sowie über Alkalichromite und ihre Lösungen, *Z. anorg. allgem. Chem.* **132**, 273–88 (1924).

[12] M. POURBAIX, *Thermodynamique des solutions aqueuses diluées. Représentation graphique du rôle du pH et du potentiel*. (Thèse, Delft, 1945, pref. F. SCHEFFER, Béranger, Paris and Liège, 1945).

[13] T. HOAR and U. EVANS, The passivity of metals. Part VII. The specific function of chromates, *J. Chem. Soc.* 2476–481 (1932).

[14] M. POURBAIX and N. DE ZOUBOV, *Sur les conditions de passivation du fer par les chromates, molybdates, tungstates et vanadates* (Rapport technique RT.43 of CEBELCOR, 1957).

SECTION 10.2

MOLYBDENUM([1])

E. DELTOMBE, N. DE ZOUBOV and M. POURBAIX

SUMMARY

1. *Substances considered and substances not considered.*

2. *Reactions and equilibrium formulae.*

2.1. Two dissolved substances.

2.1.1. Relative stability of the dissolved substances.

2.1.2. Limits of the domains of relative predominance of the dissolved substances.

2.2. Two solid substances.

Limits of the domains of relative stability of the solid substances.

2.3. One dissolved substance and one solid substance.

Solubility of the solid substances.

3. *Equilibrium diagram and its interpretation.*

3.1. Establishment of the diagram.

3.2. Stability, corrosion and electro-deposition of molybdenum.

3.3. Stability of the compounds of trivalent molybdenum.

3.4. Stability of the compounds of tetravalent molybdenum.

3.5. Stability of the compounds of pentavalent molybdenum; molybdenum blue.

3.6. Stability of the compounds of hexavalent molybdenum.

4. *Bibliography.*

([1]) Adapted and abridged version of the Rapport technique RT. 35 of CEBELCOR [1].

1. SUBSTANCES CONSIDERED AND SUBSTANCES NOT CONSIDERED

	Oxidation number (Z)	Considered	Not considered	μ^0(cal.)	Name, colour, crystalline system
Solid substances	0	**Mo**	–	0	Molybdenum, silvery white, b.c.cub.
	+2	–	**MoO** hydr.	–	Hypomolybdenous hydroxide $Mo(OH)_2$
	+3	–	$\mathbf{Mo_2O_3}$ hydr.	–	Molybdenous hydroxide $Mo(OH)_3$, black
	+4	$\mathbf{MoO_2}$	–	–120 000 (2)	Molybdenum dioxide, brown–purple, quad.
	»	–	$\mathbf{MoO_2}$ hydr.	–	Dihydrated molybdenum dioxide or hydroxide $Mo(OH)_4$, brown–black
	»	–	» »	–	Monohydrated molybdenum dioxide or $MoO(OH)_2$
	+5	–	$\mathbf{Mo_2O_5}$	–	"Molybdenum pentoxide", purple–black
	»	–	» hydr.	–	Molybdenyl hydrate $MoO(OH)_3$, light brown, amorphous
	+5.33	–	$\mathbf{Mo_3O_8}$	–	"Molybdenum blue", dark blue
	+6	$\mathbf{MoO_3}$ hydr.	–	*a*. –227 000 ?	Molybdic acid H_2MoO_4?, white or yellowish, hex.(3)
	»	»	–	*b*. –161 950	Molybdic trioxide or anhydride, white, orthorh.
	»	–	$\mathbf{MoO_3}$ hydr.	–	Hydrated molybdic acid $H_2MoO_4 . H_2O$, yellow, monocl.
	»	–	» »	–	Hydrated molybdic acid $H_2Mo_2O_7$
Dissolved substances	+3	Mo^{+++}	–	– 13 800	Molybdenous ion, dark olive–green
	+6	$HMoO_4^-$?	–	–213 600 (2)	Acid molybdate ion, colourless
	»	MoO_4^{--}	–	–205 420 (2)	Molybdate ion, colourless
	+7	–	MoO_4^- ?	–	Permolybdate ion, yellow to red
		–	$Mo_6O_{13}^{--}$?	–	Condensed molybdenum ion
		–	$Mo_7O_{24}^{--}$?	–	Condensed molybdenum ion

2. REACTIONS AND EQUILIBRIUM FORMULAE (4)

2.1. TWO DISSOLVED SUBSTANCES

2.1.1. *Relative stability of the dissolved substances*

Z = +6

1. $HMoO_4^- = MoO_4^{--} + H^+$ $\qquad \log\frac{(MoO_4^{--})}{(HMoO_4^-)} = -6.00 + pH$

+3 → +6

2. $Mo^{+++} + 4H_2O = HMoO_4^- + 7H^+ + 3e^-$ $\qquad E_0 = 0.390 - 0.1379\,pH + 0.0197\log\frac{(HMoO_4^-)}{(Mo^{+++})}$

3. $Mo^{+++} + 4H_2O = MoO_4^{--} + 8H^+ + 3e^-$ $\qquad E_0 = 0.508 - 0.1576\,pH + 0.0197\log\frac{(MoO_4^{--})}{(Mo^{+++})}$

---

(2) Values calculated by Brewer [2] and by us [1] starting from the solubility of MoO_3 in water and the pK of molybdic acid given by Charlot [3].

(3) This value of $\mu^0_{MoO_3} = -227\,000$ cal. corresponds to $\mu^0_{H_2MoO_4} = -283\,690$ cal.

(4) In the reactions involving MoO_3, the letter *a* relates to H_2MoO_4, whose free enthalpy of formation is –283 690 cal.; the letter *b* relates to anhydrous MoO_3, whose free enthalpy of formation is –161 950 cal.

2.1.2. *Limits of the domains of relative predominance of the dissolved substances*

1'.	$HMoO_4^-/MoO_4^{--}$	$pH = 6.00$
2'.	$Mo^{+++}/HMoO_4^-$	$E_0 = 0.390 - 0.1379\,pH$
3'.	Mo^{+++}/MoO_4^{--}	$E_0 = 0.508 - 0.1576\,pH$

2.2. TWO SOLID SUBSTANCES

Limits of the domains of relative stability of the solid substances

$0 \rightarrow +4$

4. $Mo + 2H_2O = \mathbf{MoO_2} + 4H^+ + 4e^-$ $\quad E_0 = -0.072 - 0.0591\,pH$

$+4 \rightarrow +6$

5. $\mathbf{MoO_2} + H_2O = \mathbf{MoO_3} + 2H^+ + 2e^-$ $\quad$ a. $E_0 = -1.091 - 0.0591\,pH$
   b. $= 0.320 - 0.0591\,pH$

2.3. ONE DISSOLVED SUBSTANCE AND ONE SOLID SUBSTANCE

Solubility of the solid substances

$Z = +6$

6. $\mathbf{MoO_3} + H_2O = HMoO_4^- + H^+$ $\quad$ a. $\log(HMoO_4^-) = -51.42 + pH$
   b. $= -3.70 + pH$

$0 \rightarrow +3$

7. $Mo = Mo^{+++} + 3e^-$ $\quad E_0 = -0.200 + 0.0197\log(Mo^{+++})$

$0 \rightarrow +6$

8. $Mo + 4H_2O = MoO_4^{--} + 8H^+ + 6e^-$ $\quad E_0 = 0.154 - 0.0788\,pH + 0.0098\log(MoO_4^{--})$

$+3 \rightarrow +4$

9. $Mo^{+++} + 2H_2O = \mathbf{MoO_2} + 4H^+ + e^-$ $\quad E_0 = 0.311 - 0.2364\,pH - 0.0591\log(Mo^{+++})$

$+3 \rightarrow +6$

10. $Mo^{+++} + 3H_2O = \mathbf{MoO_3} + 6H^+ + 3e^-$ $\quad$ a. $E_0 = -0.623 - 0.1182\,pH - 0.0197\log(Mo^{+++})$
    b. $= 0.317 - 0.1182\,pH - 0.0197\log(Mo^{+++})$

$+4 \rightarrow +6$

11. $\mathbf{MoO_2} + 2H_2O = HMoO_4^- + 3H^+ + 2e^-$ $\quad E_0 = 0.429 - 0.0886\,pH + 0.0295\log(HMoO_4^-)$
12. $\mathbf{MoO_2} + 2H_2O = MoO_4^{--} + 4H^+ + 2e^-$ $\quad E_0 = 0.606 - 0.1182\,pH + 0.0295\log(MoO_4^{--})$

3. EQUILIBRIUM DIAGRAM AND ITS INTERPRETATION

3.1. ESTABLISHMENT OF THE DIAGRAM

Using the equilibrium relations established in paragraph 2, we have drawn Fig. 1 which represents the conditions of thermodynamic equilibrium of the system molybdenum–water at 25°C, in the absence of complexing substances and substances forming insoluble salts. Molybdenum forms a large number of complexes: hydrochloric, oxalic, thiocyanic and other complexes of trivalent molybdenum; hydrocyanic complexes of tetravalent molybdenum; hydrochloric, hydrocyanic, thiocyanic and phosphoric complexes of pentavalent molybdenum; hydrochloric complexes of hexalent molybdenum with phosphoric, arsenic and vanadic ions, and with hydrofluoric, citric, tartaric and oxalic ions all of which prevent the precipitation of oxide (Charlot [3]).

Molybdenum bromide, chloride and sulphide are sparingly soluble, as are the molybdates of the majority of metals other than the alkali metals.

Figure 2, which is deduced from Fig. 1, represents the theoretical conditions of corrosion, immunity and passivation of molybdenum in the presence of solutions free from substances with which this metal can form soluble complexes or insoluble salts.

In Fig. 3 we have represented the influence of pH on the solubility of MoO_3, from the formulae established in paragraph 2.

3.2. STABILITY, CORROSION AND ELECTRO-DEPOSITION OF MOLYBDENUM

From Figs. 1 and 2 molybdenum is seen to be a base metal, as its domain of stability lies completely below that of water. It is not found in nature in the native state.

In the presence of alkaline solutions, it has a slight tendency to decompose water with the evolution of hydrogen, dissolving in the hexavalent state as molybdate ions MoO_4^{--}. In the presence of non-complexing acid solutions, it tends to dissolve in the trivalent state with the formation of Mo^{+++} ions

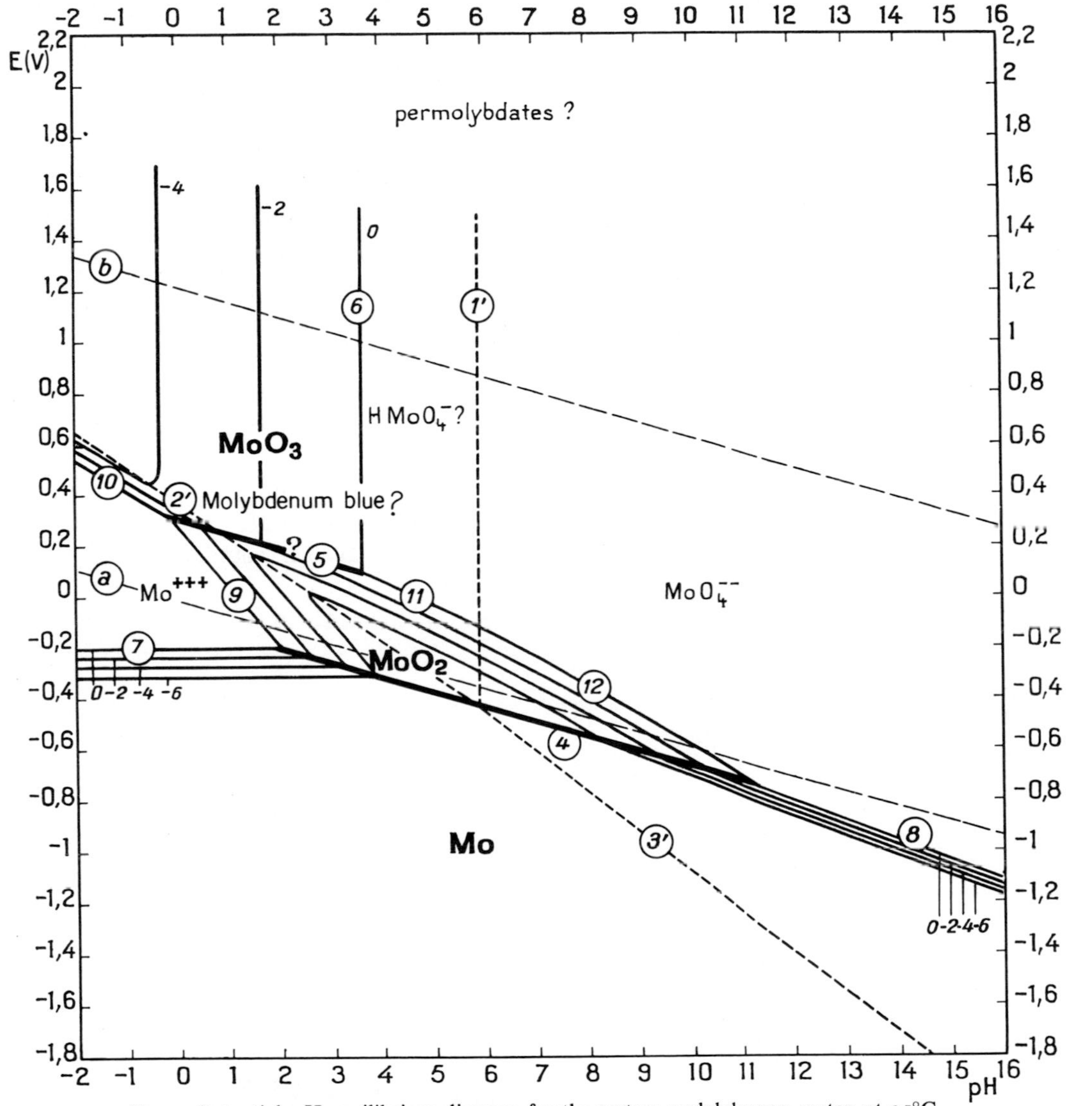

FIG. 1. Potential–pH equilibrium diagram for the system molybdenum–water, at 25°C.

and the evolution of hydrogen. In the presence of neutral or slightly acid or alkaline solutions, it tends to cover itself with tetravalent dioxide MoO_2.

In practice it is noticed that molybdenum is attacked only slightly by dilute non-complexing acids; only dilute nitric acid acting as an oxidizing agent attacks it appreciably, while concentrated nitric acid covers it with a layer of oxide MoO_3 which protects the metal from further attack. The fact that molybdenum does not dissolve appreciably in non-oxidizing acids is probably due to the value of the hydrogen overpotential on molybdenum, which is not negligible; according to the data of Petcherskaia and Stender [4] this hydrogen overpotential in M H_2SO_4 at 25°C is approximately of the same order of magnitude as that of iron:

Current density (mA/cm²)	1	5	10	20	40	60	100	200
Hydrogen overpotential (V)	0·35	0·42	0·45	0·48	0·52	0·53	0·56	0·59

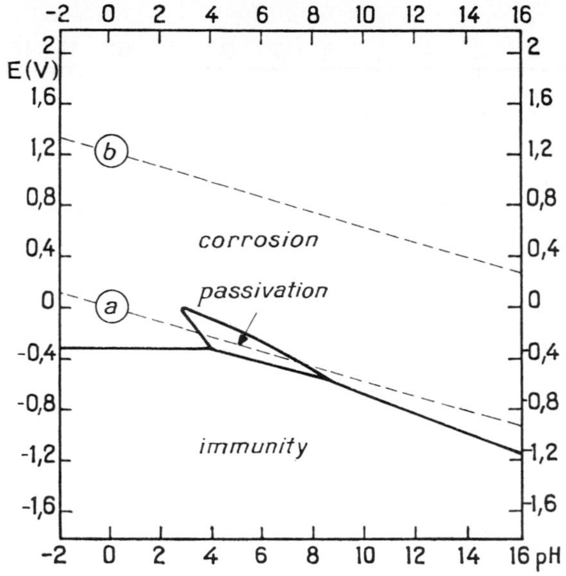

FIG. 2. Theoretical conditions of corrosion, immunity and passivation of molybdenum, at 25°C.

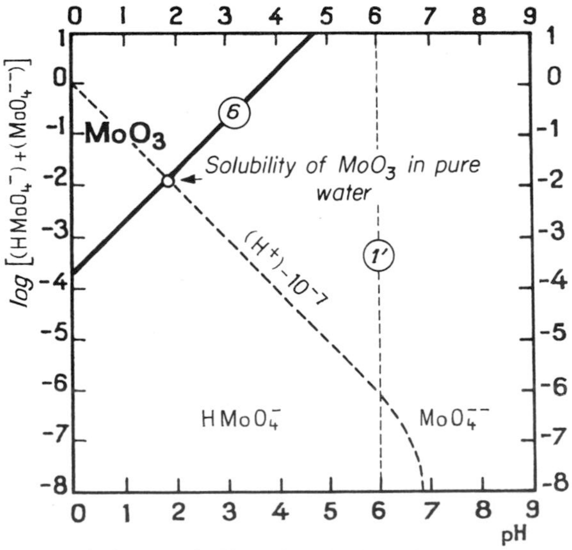

FIG. 3. Influence of pH on the solubility of MoO_3, at 25°C.

When the metal is attacked by hydrochloric acid, it is probable that a film of insoluble chloride is formed which passivates the metal. Water is generally considered to be without action on molybdenum; but, according to Malowan's experiments [5] the metal in the form of powder or foil is oxidized by tap water and distilled water (free from CO_2); water in contact with molybdenum turns blue in colour.

According to Marino [6], molybdenum dissolves in the hexavalent state by anodic polarization in solutions of HCl, KOH and neutral salts.

It would be valuable to examine if, in accordance with what is to be predicted from Fig. 1, the formation of trivalent molybdenum can be brought about by anodic polarization at low electrode potentials.

Molybdenum is distinguished by a peculiar behaviour with regard to passivation: depending on the pretreatment of the metal it is either active or passive; chemically passivating reagents are not only oxidizing agents such as nitric acid, concentrated chromic acid and ferric chloride, but also dilute hydrochloric and sulphuric acids; the highest degree of passivity is, however, obtained by anodic polarization under certain conditions of current density. Activation of the metal is produced either chemically, by bases such as KOH or NH_3 and reducing agents, or electrochemically, by cathodic polarization in a solution of KOH. This behaviour peculiar to molybdenum seems to be in agreement with the equilibrium diagram, according to which, in alkaline media, the metal is constantly active and dissolves as molybdate ions MoO_4^{--} by oxidation, while in acid media it is liable to dissolve at first as molybdenous ions Mo^{+++} at relatively low electrode potentials and cover itself with a passivating layer of MoO_2 or MoO_3 [lines (9) and (10) of Fig. 1] at higher potentials; this behaviour of molybdenum in acid media is analogous to that of iron. As already pointed out, the passivation of molybdenum in acid media may also be due to the formation of a film of insoluble salt.

On account of the ease with which "active" molybdenum can pass into the passive state, the experimental data that we possess concerning the equilibrium potential of the reaction of dissolution of the metal are very much subject to caution, and values varying between +0·66 and −0·74 V can be found in chemical literature.

According to Fig. 1, molybdenum can be obtained electrolytically from acid solutions of molybdenum salts or alkaline solutions of molybdates. In practice, the electrolytic reduction of the molybdenum chlorides gives a positive result only in non-aqueous solutions, for instance solutions of $MoCl_2$ and anhydrous HCl in absolute alcohol (according to Wolf [7]) or solutions of $MoCl_6$ in acetone (according to Wolfram Lampen A.G. [8]).

The most usual processes for the electrolytic separation of molybdenum are based, however, on the electrolysis of molten salts (a mixture of calcium molybdenate and molybdenum carbide in molten bauxite, or a molten mixture of sodium and molybdenum chlorides).

3.3. STABILITY OF THE COMPOUNDS OF TRIVALENT MOLYBDENUM

As is shown in Fig. 1, the molybdenous ion Mo^{+++} is stable only in strongly acid reducing media; on being oxidized, the Mo^{+++} ions are slowly converted into a red compound whose composition is unknown; according to equilibrium diagram Fig. 1, the principal oxidation product should be the purple-brown oxide MoO_2.

Halides treated with alkalis give a brown–black precipitate of hydroxide $Mo(OH)_3$, which can be oxidized by the air to white MoO_3. Older chemical literature mentions a "sesquioxide" Mo_2O_3 obtained by careful dehydration of $Mo(OH)_3$. However, as Guichard [9] has shown, the dehydration of $Mo(OH)_3$ by warming always gives rise to oxidation to MoO_3, even in a current of hydrogen; according to Guichard, it is most probable that the water contained in the hydroxide acts as an oxidizing agent at the temperature necessary for the dehydration.

3.4. STABILITY OF THE COMPOUNDS OF TETRAVALENT MOLYBDENUM

Tetravalent molybdenum is known in solution only in the form of complex ions which are not considered here.

By reducing ammonium molybdate solutions with hydrogen at ordinary temperature and pressure in the presence of colloidal palladium, Paal and Büttner [10] obtained the brown–black hydroxide $Mo(OH)_4$ (or $MoO_2 . 2H_2O$); by drying this hydroxide carefully in the cold the monohydrate $MoO_2 . H_2O$ [or $MoO(OH)_2$] is obtained; if the hydroxide is dried by warming the brown–purple anhydrous oxide MoO_2 is obtained, which, of these three forms of oxide, is the only one that we have been able to consider here. This oxide MoO_2 can be obtained by other means, for example by heating molybdenum in air, or in water vapour, by reducing solutions of MoO_3 with metals such as Zn, Cd, Mg, and by the electrolytic reduction of molten MoO_3.

From Fig. 1, strong non-oxidizing acids should cause MoO_2 to split up into molybdenous ions Mo^{+++} and acid molybdate ions $HMoO_4^-$ [according to the family of lines (9) and (11)] with the possible formation of molybdenum blue and MoO_3 [according to line (5)]; oxidizing acids should convert it into molybdenum blue and MoO_3. Non-oxidizing alkalis should cause MoO_2 to split up into molybdate MoO_4^{--} and metallic molybdenum [according to the family of lines (12) and line (4)], which would react with water to form molybdate and hydrogen; oxidizing alkalis should convert it into molybdate.

In actual fact, MoO_2 is oxidized by nitric acid to MoO_3, but it is, in general, insoluble in non-oxidizing acids. In the presence of aerated water $Mo(OH)_4$ is easily oxidized by forming a solution of "molybdenum blue"; it is soluble in concentrated acids, forming solutions which are red to purplish brown and are feebly reducing; we do not know whether this reducing property is actually due to the formation of trivalent Mo^{+++}, or to the existence of complexes of tetravalent molybdenum.

3.5. STABILITY OF THE COMPOUNDS OF PENTAVALENT MOLYBDENUM; MOLYBDENUM BLUE

Like tetravalent molybdenum, pentavalent molybdenum is known in solution only in the form of complexes. The hydroxide $MoO(OH)_3$ or $Mo_2O_5 . 3H_2O$, molybdenyl hydrate, is obtained as a dark-brown precipitate by treating a solution of ammonium molybdenum oxychloride $(NH_4)_2(MoOCl_5)$ with NH_3. Through lack of thermodynamic data, no derivative of pentavalent molybdenum could be considered quantitatively in Fig. 1. We point out that $Mo_2O_5 . 3H_2O$ is easily oxidized by the air, and seems liable to decompose into compounds of tri- and hexavalent molybdenum: according to Jakób and Turkievicz [11], when it is treated with KOH in an atmosphere of hydrogen, it is partially converted into $Mo(OH)_3$ and the solution contains molybdenum in the hexavalent state.

The dehydration product of $MoO(OH)_3$ is the oxide Mo_2O_5, which can also be obtained by the reduction of MoO_3; it is a purplish-black powder which is very sparingly soluble in acids.

Together with the compounds of pentavalent molybdenum we can consider molybdenum blue, a compound containing oxygen whose percentages of oxygen and molybdenum approximately fit the formula Mo_3O_8, an oxide in which molybdenum would have a valency between +5 and +6; however, it is usually considered to be a molybdenyl molybdate $Mo_2O_5 . xMoO_3$. It is a blue compound which is very soluble in water and easily forms colloidal solutions; it is obtained either by the reduction of molybdate solutions or by the oxidation of lower oxides such as MoO_2.

3.6. STABILITY OF THE COMPOUNDS OF HEXAVALENT MOLYBDENUM

The compounds of hexavalent molybdenum are the most important ones; they are illustrated by molybdenum trioxide or molybdic anhydride MoO_3, by its hydrates (molybdic acids) and by its dissolved forms, principally the molybdate ion MoO_4^{--} obtained by the action of alkalis on MoO_3. By varying the relative quantities of MoO_3 and alkalis a whole series of salts can be obtained: the di-, trimolybdates, etc.; to these various salts there should correspond various condensed ions. According to Jander *et al.* [12] who have studied molybdate solutions by diffusion measurements and conductometric titrations, the nature of the ions varies with the pH in such a way that a domain of stability can be attributed to each of them; for example:

$6 < pH < 14$	MoO_4^{2-}	$0{\cdot}9 < pH < 1{\cdot}5$	$Mo_{12}O_{41}^{10-}$
$4{\cdot}5 < pH < 6$	$Mo_3O_{11}^{4-}$	pH = approx. 0·9	$Mo_{24}O_{78}^{12-}$
$1{\cdot}5 < pH < 4{\cdot}5$	$Mo_6O_{21}^{6-}$		

It is this complex range of substances that we have symbolized by the ion $HMoO_4^-$ in establishing the equilibrium diagram.

The oxide MoO_3, prepared by roasting ammonium molybdate, is a white powder; its solubility in water is about 2 g/l (Bucholz [13] and Hattchett [14]; see also Travers and Malaprade [15]), i.e. $10^{-1.85}$ mole/l, which is in agreement with Fig. 3. It does not combine directly with water to give hydrates; these are obtained only from molybdates; there exist two well-defined hydrates $MoO_3 . H_2O$ and $MoO_3 . 2H_2O$.

As we have pointed out in an earlier work [1], the fairly close solubility values for MoO_3 and its two hydrates show that these three compounds have stabilities which are practically equal; the domain of stability attributed to MoO_3 in the equilibrium diagram in Fig. 1 can therefore also be attributed to one of its hydrates. In Fig. 3 we have represented, by means of the formulae established in paragraph 2, the influence of pH on the solubility of MoO_3; the characteristics of the solution obtained by dissolving this oxide in pure water until a saturated solution is obtained are given in this figure by the coordinates of the point of intersection of this solubility line with the line showing the values of $[(H^+)-10^{-7}]$; these characteristics are:

$$pH = 1.85, \quad (HMoO_4^-) = 10^{-1.85}, \quad \text{i.e. } 2\text{g } MoO_3/l.$$

Molybdic solutions treated with hydrogen peroxide give rise to the formation of the so-called permolybdates, which are yellow–orange in acid media and intense red in alkaline media. On account of a lack of precise data relating to these compounds, in which molybdenum would have a valency of +7, we have not taken them into account in establishing the equilibrium diagram in which they appear purely as a guide.

4. BIBLIOGRAPHY

[1] E. Deltombe, N. de Zoubov and M. Pourbaix, *Comportement électrochimique du molybdène. Diagramme d'équilibres tension–pH du système* Mo–H_2O *à* 25 °C (*Rapport technique* RT.35 of CEBELCOR, 1956).

[2] L. Brewer, The thermodynamic properties of the oxides and their vaporization processes, *Chem. Rev.* **52**, 1–75 (1953).

[3] G. Charlot, *L'analyse qualitative et les réactions en solution*, 4th ed., Masson, Paris, 1957.

[4] A. G. Petcherskaia and V. V. Stender, Potentiels de dégagement d'hydrogène dans les solutions acides, *J. Fiz. Khim.* **24**, 856–9 (1950).

[5] S. L. Malowan, Ueber die Korrosion des Molybdäns und Wolframs, *Z. Metallk.* **23**, 69–70 (1931); *Z.B.* II, 763 (1931).

[6] L. Marino, Comportement électrochimique du molybdène; analogies avec le chrome, *Gazz. Ital.* **35**, II 193–224 (1905); *Z.B.* II, 1158 (1905).

[7] K. Wolf, Das elektrochemische Verhalten des Molybdäns und einiger Molybdänverbindungen, *Dissert, Aachen T.H.*, 1917; *Z.B.* I, 608 (1918).

[8] Wolfram Lampen A.G., D.R.P. 237.014, 1910; Verfahren zur elektrolytischen Abscheidung von Wolfram oder chemisch ähnlichen Metallen, *Z.B.* II, 410 (1911).

[9] M. Guichard, Recherches sur les oxydes, les sulfures et les iodures de molybdène, *Ann. Chim. Phys.* 7th series **23**, 498–574 (1901).

[10] C. Paal and H. Büttner, Ueber katalytische Wirkungen kolloïdaler Metalle der Platingruppe. XI. Die Reduktion der Molybdänsäure, *Ber.* **48**, 220–3 (1915).

[11] W. F. Jakób and E. Turkievicz, Untersuchungen ueber die vierte Oxydationsstufe des Molybdäns, *Roczniki Chemji.* **11**, 569–76 (1931); *Z.B.* II, 3589 (1931).

[12] G. Jander, K. F. Jahr and W. Heukeshoven, Ueber amphotere Oxydhydrate, deren wässrige Lösungen und Kristallisierende Verbindungen. XI. Mitteilung, *Z. anorg. allgem. Chem.* **194**, 383–428 (1930).

[13] C. F. Bucholz, *Scherer J.* **9**, 489 (1802); Pascal, XI, p. 49.

[14] Hattchett, *Phil. Trans.* **85**, 323 (1795); Pascal, XI, p. 49.

[15] A. Travers and L. Malaprade, Contribution à l'étude de l'acide molybdique et des molybdates, *Bull. Soc. Chim. Fr.*, 4th series, **39**, 1408–20 (1926).

SECTION 10.3

TUNGSTEN[1]

E. Deltombe, N. de Zoubov and M. Pourbaix

SUMMARY

[1] Shortened and adapted version of the Rapport technique RT.32 of CEBELCOR [1].

1. SUBSTANCES CONSIDERED AND SUBSTANCES NOT CONSIDERED

	Oxidation number (Z)	Considered	Not considered	μ^0(cal.)	Name, colour, crystalline system
Solid substances	0	**W**	–	0	Tungsten, grey, b.c.cub. and cub.
	+4	$\mathbf{WO_2}$	–	−124 400	Tungsten dioxide, brown, quad.
	»	–	$\mathbf{WO_2}$ hydr.	–	Hydrated tungsten dioxide WO_22H_2O
	+5	$\mathbf{W_2O_5}$	–	−306 900	"Pentoxide", blue
	+6	$\mathbf{WO_3}$	–	−182 470	Tungstic anhydride or trioxide, yellow, monocl.
	»	–	$\mathbf{WO_3}$ hydr.	–	Tungstic acid H_2WO_4 or WO_3H_2O, yellow
	»	–	» »	–	Dihydrated trioxide WO_32H_2O, pale yellow
	»	–	» »	–	Trihydrated trioxide WO_33H_2O or the acid H_6WO_6, white
	+8	–	$\mathbf{WO_4}$ hydr.	–	Pertungstic acid $H_2WO_5H_2O$ or $WO_3H_2O_2H_2O$
Dissolved substances	+6	WO_4^{--}	–	−220 000	Tungstic ion, colourless
	+8	–	WO_5^{--}	–	"Pertungstic" ion

2. REACTIONS AND EQUILIBRIUM FORMULAE

2.1. TWO SOLID SUBSTANCES

Limits of the domains of relative stability of the solid substances

$0 \rightarrow +4$

1. $\mathbf{W} + 2H_2O = \mathbf{WO_2} + 4H^+ + 4e^-$ $\qquad E_0 = -0.119 - 0.0591\,pH$

$+4 \rightarrow +5$

2. $2\mathbf{WO_2} + H_2O = \mathbf{W_2O_5} + 2H^+ + 2e^-$ $\qquad E_0 = -0.031 - 0.0591\,pH$

$+5 \rightarrow +6$

3. $\mathbf{W_2O_5} + H_2O = 2\mathbf{WO_3} + 2H^+ + 2e^-$ $\qquad E_0 = -0.029 - 0.0591\,pH$

2.2. ONE DISSOLVED SUBSTANCE AND ONE SOLID SUBSTANCE

Solubility of the solid substances

$Z = +6$

4. $\mathbf{WO_3} + H_2O = WO_4^{--} + 2H^+$ $\qquad \log(WO_4^{--}) = -14.05 + 2\,pH$

$0 \rightarrow +6$

5. $\mathbf{W} + 4H_2O = WO_4^{--} + 8H^+ + 6e^-$ $\qquad E_0 = 0.049 - 0.0788\,pH + 0.0098\log(WO_4^{--})$

$+4 \rightarrow +6$

6. $\mathbf{WO_2} + 2H_2O = WO_4^{--} + 4H^+ + 2e^-$ $\qquad E_0 = 0.386 - 0.1182\,pH + 0.0295\log(WO_4^{--})$

$+5 \rightarrow +6$

7. $\mathbf{W_2O_5} + 3H_2O = 2WO_4^{--} + 6H^+ + 2e^-$ $\qquad E_0 = 0.801 - 0.1773\,pH + 0.0591\log(WO_4^{--})$

3. EQUILIBRIUM DIAGRAM AND ITS INTERPRETATION

3.1. ESTABLISHMENT OF THE DIAGRAM

Using the equilibrium relations established in paragraph 2, we have drawn in Fig. 1 a potential–pH equilibrium diagram, taking into account the tungstic ion WO_4^{--} and the solid substances W, WO_2, W_2O_5 and anhydrous WO_3. This figure represents the conditions of thermodynamic equilibrium of the

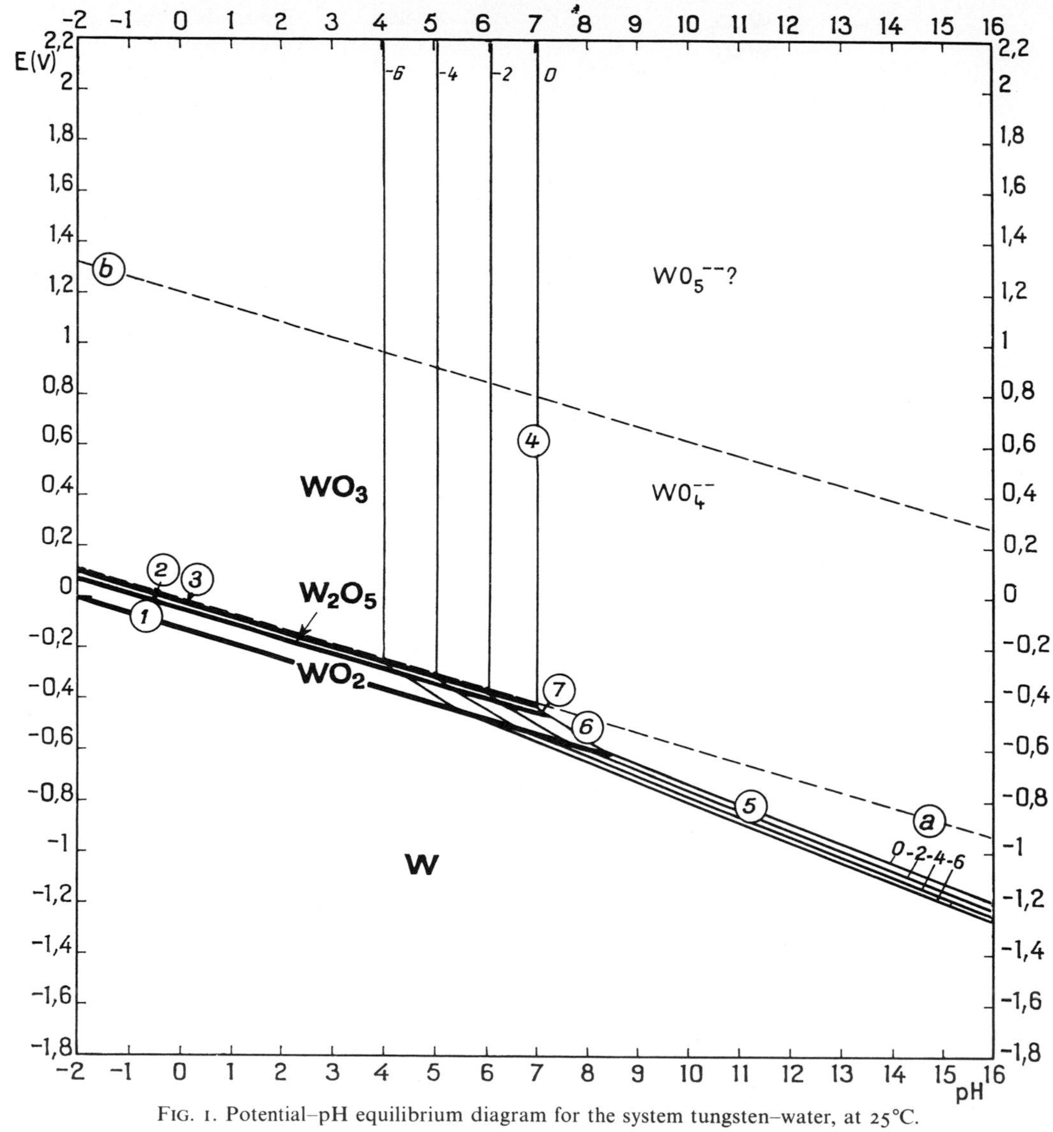

FIG. 1. Potential–pH equilibrium diagram for the system tungsten–water, at 25°C.

system tungsten–water, at 25°C, in the absence of complexing substances and substances forming insoluble salts.

Tungsten forms numerous complexes; we point out the following, according to Charlot [2]: the hydrochloric complexes of trivalent tungsten, the hydrofluoric and oxalic complexes of tetravalent tungsten, the cyanide complexes of pentavalent tungsten and in particular the hydrochloric complexes with phosphoric, arsenic and vanadic ions, and with hydrofluoric, citric, tartaric and oxalic ions. The tungstates of the alkali metals are soluble; the other tungstates are insoluble.

Figure 2, which is deduced from Fig. 1 after making certain assumptions, represents the theoretical conditions of corrosion, immunity and passivation of tungsten at 25°C.

Figure 3 shows the influence of pH on the solubility of yellow tungstic anhydride at ordinary temperatures.

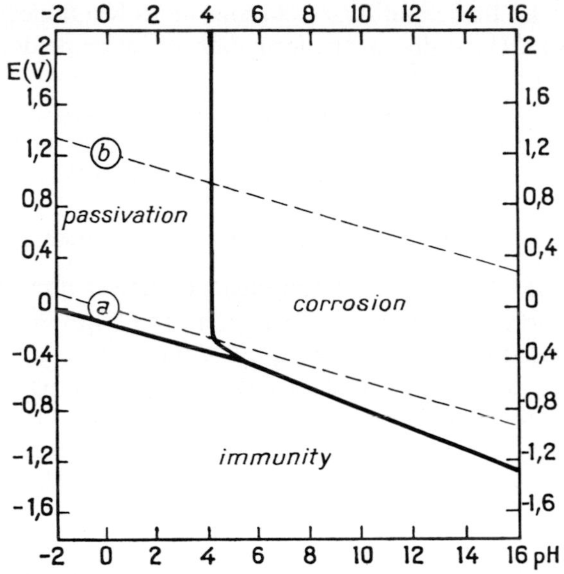

FIG. 2. Theoretical conditions of corrosion, immunity and passivation of tungsten, at 25°C.

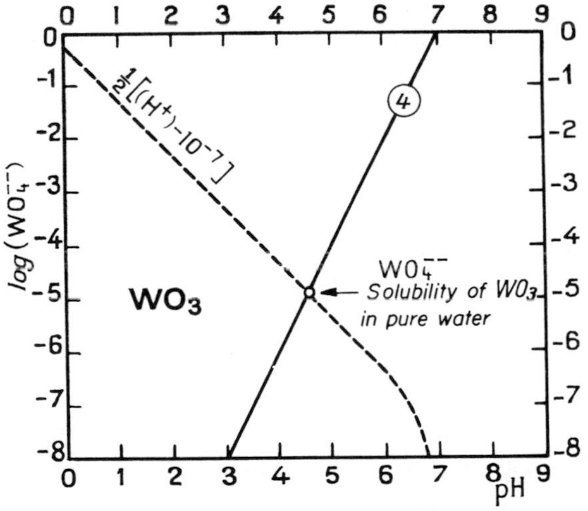

FIG. 3. Influence of pH on the solubility of anhydrous WO_3, at 25°C.

3.2. STABILITY, CORROSION AND ELECTRO-DEPOSITION OF TUNGSTEN

From Figs. 1 and 2, tungsten is seen to be a base metal, as its domain of stability lies completely below that of water. In the presence of alkaline solutions it has a slight tendency to decompose water with the evolution of hydrogen, dissolving as tungstic ions WO_4^{--}. In the presence of non-complexing acid solutions, it tends to become covered with dioxide WO_2 or a higher oxide.

Experiment shows that, in accordance with Fig. 1, tungsten is hardly corroded by most acid solutions; only the complexing acids (hydrofluoric, phosphoric and oxalic acids) attack it. Gmelin [3] quotes various pieces of research work according to which tungsten does not dissolve if it is anodically polarized in the presence of solutions of hydrochloric, sulphuric and nitric acids (Le Blanc and Byers [4]).

In contrast, the hexavalent state dissolves by anodic polarization in alkaline solutions of KOH and NaOH (Pirani and Schröter [5]); however, in these solutions it becomes passive at high current densities (800 to 1 750 mA/cm^2) (Le Blanc and Byers). According to Katalinič [6], the anodic passivation in solutions of NaOH and Na_2CO_3 is due to the formation of lower oxides which, for potentials above 60 V, are oxidized to WO_3, emitting light.

According to Fig. 1 it should be possible to obtain tungsten electrolytically from alkaline solutions of tungstates, nevertheless, experiments carried out in this connection, notably by Smith [7] and Koerner [8], have led to the formation only of the oxides W_2O_5 (blue) and WO_2 (brown).

3.3. STABILITY AND FORMATION OF THE TUNGSTEN OXIDES AND TUNGSTIC SOLUTIONS

According to Fig. 1 only the hexavalent tungsten derivatives (tungstic anhydride WO_3 and the tungstates WO_4^{--}) are stable in the presence of water, at 25°C. Indeed, tungsten is not found in the native state; it occurs in nature essentially in the form of tungstates.

The lower oxides WO_2 and W_2O_5 tend to decompose water with the evolution of hydrogen, according to Fig. 1. The *brown dioxide* WO_2, obtained by the reduction of WO_3 with hydrogen, is oxidized to tungstic acid by concentrated nitric acid; if it is in the amorphous state, it is attacked by hot concentrated alkaline solutions, which oxidize it to tungstate with the evolution of hydrogen. WO_2 can form a dihydrate $WO_2.2H_2O$ (or H_4WO_4) which, through lack of thermodynamic data, has not been considered in Fig. 1.

The *blue oxide* W_2O_5, obtained principally by the hydrolysis of the pentachloride WCl_5, is also oxidized to tungstate by boiling alkaline solutions; it can be obtained by the electrolytic or chemical reduction of tungstate solutions (for instance by means of $SnCl_2$, $TiCl_3$, HI).

Yellow tungstic anhydride WO_3, which is generally prepared by roasting ammonium tungstate or by the oxidation of the metal or its lower oxides, exists in two varieties: the product obtained by roasting is an inpalpable powder; on fusing and solidifying this powder one obtains well-defined crystals of the rhombohedral system. Only the WO_3 obtained as a powder and denoted by the name "yellow WO_3" has been considered in Fig. 1. As shown in this figure, WO_3 is insoluble in acids, except for hydrofluoric acid with which it forms complexes; it is soluble in alkalis, forming tungstates. In Fig. 3 we have represented the influence of pH on the solubility of yellow WO_3. The characteristics of the solution obtained by dissolving this oxide in pure water until saturation is reached are given in this diagram by the co-ordinates of the point of intersection of this solubility line with the line giving the values of $\frac{1}{2}[(H^+) - 10^{-7}]$; these characteristics are:

$$pH = 4{\cdot}6, \quad (WO_4^{--}) = 10^{-4{\cdot}9}, \quad \text{i.e. } 2{\cdot}9 \text{ mg } WO_3/l.$$

Rabinovitch and Kargin [9], by studying the influence of dilution on the behaviour of WO_3 hydrosols, observed that these sols turn into real solutions when the pH reaches 4·8; as the dissolution of WO_3 in water occurs according to the reaction $WO_3 + H_2O \rightarrow WO_4^{--} + 2H^+$, i.e. with the formation of one WO_4^{--} ion for two H^+ ions, this pH must correspond to a WO_4^{--} concentration of $0{\cdot}5 \times 10^{-4{\cdot}8}$, i.e. $10^{-5{\cdot}1}$ g-ions/l. These values of pH and tungsten concentration correspond fairly well with the values given above.

By acidifying alkaline tungstate solutions, a precipitate of white trihydrate $WO_3.3H_2O$ (or H_6WO_6) is obtained which, on drying, loses water and is converted into pale yellow dihydrate $WO_3.2H_2O$, then into yellow monohydrate $WO_3.H_2O$ or tungstic acid H_2WO_4. These various hydrates are not formed by direct hydration of the anhydride WO_3. Through lack of thermodynamic data about them, we have not been able to consider them in Fig. 1.

We point out, finally, that the action of hydrogen peroxide on tungstic hydrate and the tungstates gives rise to a compound which is soluble in water and has the composition $WO_3.H_2O_2.H_2O$ or $H_2WO_5.H_2O$; it is called *pertungstic acid*. Solutions of pertungstates are decomposed in the air evolving oxygen; on treating them with dilute acids H_2O_2 is liberated. These substances have been represented symbolically in the equilibrium diagram by the ion WO_5^{--}.

4. BIBLIOGRAPHY

[1] E. Deltombe, N. de Zoubov and M. Pourbaix, *Comportement électrochimique du tungstène. Diagramme d'équilibres tension–pH du système* W–H_2O *à* 25°C (Rapport technique RT.32 of CEBELCOR, 1956).

[2] G. Charlot, *L'analyse qualitative et les réactions en solution,* 4th ed., Masson, Paris, 1957, p. 210.

[3] *Gmelins Handbuch der anorganischen Chemie,* S.N., 54, Vol. XVII, Berlin, 1933.

[4] M. Le Blanc and H. G. Byers, Das anodische Verhalten von Wolfram, *Z. Phys. Chem.* **69**, 19–25 (1909).

[5] M. Pirani and K. Schröter, Elektrolytische Formgebung von harten metallischen Gegenständen, *Z. Metallk.* **16**, 132–3 (1924).

[6] M. Katalinič, Ueber eine Leuchterscheinung am Wolframanoden, *Z. Phys.* **14**, 14–18 (1922).

[7] E. F. Smith, Neue elektrolytische Resultate, *Ber.* **13**, 751–54 (1880).

[8] W. E. Koerner, The electrolytic behaviour of tungsten, *Trans. Amer. Electrochem. Soc.* **31**, 221–55 (1917).

[9] A. J. Rabinovitch and V. A. Kargin, Auflösung der Kolloïdteilchen bei Verdünnung der Sole, *Z. Phys. Chem.* A, **152**, 24–35 (1931).

SECTION 11.1

MANGANESE(¹)

A. MOUSSARD, J. BRENET, F. JOLAS, M. POURBAIX and J. VAN MUYLDER

SUMMARY

(¹) Adapted and shortened version of the Rapport technique RT.18 of CEBELCOR [1].

1. SUBSTANCES CONSIDERED AND SUBSTANCES NOT CONSIDERED

	Oxidation number (Z)	Considered	Not considered	μ^0(cal.)	Name, colour, crystalline system
Solid substances	0	**Mn**	–	0	α-manganese, light grey, cub.
	»	–	**Mn**	330	γ-manganese, light grey, f.c.quad.
	+2	**MnO** hydr.	–	a. – 90 210	Manganous hydroxide $Mn(OH)_2$, light pink, rhomb.(2)
	»	»	–	b. – 86 800	Manganous oxide, green, cub.
	+2.67	Mn_3O_4	–	–306 000	Mangano-manganic oxide, brown–black, def. quad.
	+3	Mn_2O_3	–	c. –212 300	α-manganic oxide, black, cub.
	»	» hydr.	–	d. –191 930	Manganic hydroxide $Mn(OH)_3$, brown–black, monocl.(2)
	»	–	Mn_2O_3	–	γ-manganic oxide, black
	+4	–	MnO_2	–	α-manganese dioxide, brown–black
	»	MnO_2	–	–111 100	β-manganese dioxide "pyrolusite", brown–black, quad.
	»	–	MnO_2		γ-manganese dioxide, brown–black
Dissolved substances	+2	Mn^{++}	–	– 54 400	Manganous ion, pale pink
	»	$HMnO_2^-$	–	–120 900	Dimanganite ion
	+3	Mn^{+++}	–	– 19 600	Manganic ion
	+5	–	MnO_4^{---}	–	? ion, blue
	+6	MnO_4^{--}	–	–120 400	Manganate ion, green
	+7	MnO_4^-	–	–107 400	Permanganate ion, purple

2. REACTIONS AND EQUILIBRIUM FORMULAE (3)

2.1. TWO DISSOLVED SUBSTANCES

2.1.1. *Relative stability of the dissolved substances*

$Z = +2$

1. $Mn^{++} + 2H_2O = HMnO_2^- + 3H^+$ $\qquad \log\frac{(HMnO_2^-)}{(Mn^{++})} = -34.39 + 3\,pH$

$+2 \rightarrow +3$

2. $Mn^{++} = Mn^{+++} + e^-$ $\qquad E_0 = 1.509 + 0.0591 \log\frac{(Mn^{+++})}{(Mn^{++})}$

$+2 \rightarrow +6$

3. $Mn^{++} + 4H_2O = MnO_4^{--} + 8H^+ + 4e^-$ $\qquad E_0 = 1.742 - 0.1182\,pH + 0.0148 \log\frac{(MnO_4^{--})}{(Mn^{++})}$

4. $HMnO_2^- + 2H_2O = MnO_4^{--} + 5H^+ + 4e^-$ $\qquad E_0 = 1.234 - 0.0738\,pH + 0.0148 \log\frac{(MnO_4^{--})}{(HMnO_2^-)}$

$+2 \rightarrow +7$

5. $Mn^{++} + 4H_2O = MnO_4^- + 8H^+ + 5e^-$ $\qquad E_0 = 1.507 - 0.0945\,pH + 0.0118 \log\frac{(MnO_4^-)}{(Mn^{++})}$

---

(2) These values of μ^0 for the oxides correspond to the following values for the hydrated oxides or hydroxides:

$Mn(OH)_2$: – 146 900 cal., $\qquad$ $Mn(OH)_3$: – 181 000 cal.

(3) In the reactions involving MnO the letter *a* relates to $Mn(OH)_2$, whose free enthalpy of formation is – 146 900 cal.; the letter *b* relates to anhydrous MnO, whose free enthalpy of formation is – 86 800 cal.

In the reactions involving Mn_2O_3, the letter *c* corresponds to anhydrous Mn_2O_3, whose free enthalpy of formation is – 212 300 cal.; the letter *d* indicates $Mn(OH)_3$, whose free enthalpy of formation is – 181 000 cal.

$+3 \rightarrow +7$

6. $Mn^{+++} + 4H_2O = MnO_4^- + 8H^+ + 4e^-$ $E_0 = 1.506 - 0.1182\,pH + 0.0148 \log \frac{(MnO_4^-)}{(Mn^{+++})}$

$+6 \rightarrow +7$

7. $MnO_4^{--} = MnO_4^- + e^-$ $E_0 = 0.564 + 0.0591 \log \frac{(MnO_4^-)}{(MnO_4^{--})}$

2.1.2. *Limits of the domains of relative predominance of the dissolved substances*

$Z = +2$

1'. $Mn^{++}/HMnO_2^-$ $pH = 11.46$

$+2 \rightarrow +3$

2'. Mn^{++}/Mn^{+++} $E_0 = 1.509$

$+2 \rightarrow +6$

3'. Mn^{++}/MnO_4^{--} $E_0 = 1.742 - 0.1182\,pH$

4'. $HMnO_2^-/MnO_4^{--}$ $E_0 = 1.234 - 0.0738\,pH$

$+2 \rightarrow +7$

5'. Mn^{++}/MnO_4^- $E_0 = 1.507 - 0.0945\,pH$

$+3 \rightarrow +7$

6'. Mn^{+++}/MnO_4^- $E_0 = 1.506 - 0.1182\,pH$

$+6 \rightarrow +7$

7'. MnO_4^{--}/MnO_4^- $E_0 = 0.564$

2.2. TWO SOLID SUBSTANCES

Limits of the domains of relative stability of the solid substances

$0 \rightarrow +2$

8. $\mathbf{Mn} + H_2O = \mathbf{MnO} + 2H^+ + 2e^-$
 a. $E_0 = -0.727 - 0.0591\,pH$
 b. $= -0.652 - 0.0591\,pH$

$+2 \rightarrow +2.67$

9. $3\mathbf{MnO} + H_2O = \mathbf{Mn_3O_4} + 2H^+ + 2e^-$
 a. $E_0 = 0.462 - 0.0591\,pH$
 b. $= 0.240 - 0.0591\,pH$

$+2.67 \rightarrow +3$

10. $2\mathbf{Mn_3O_4} + H_2O = 3\mathbf{Mn_2O_3} + 2H^+ + 2e^-$
 c. $E_0 = 0.689 - 0.0591\,pH$
 d. $= 2.014 - 0.0591\,pH$

$+3 \rightarrow +4$

11. $\mathbf{Mn_2O_3} + H_2O = 2\mathbf{MnO_2} + 2H^+ + 2e^-$
 c. $E_0 = 1.014 - 0.0591\,pH$
 d. $= 0.573 - 0.0591\,pH$

2.3. ONE SOLID SUBSTANCE AND ONE DISSOLVED SUBSTANCE

Solubility of the solid substances

$Z = +2$

12. $Mn^{++} + H_2O = \mathbf{MnO} + 2H^+$
 a. $\log(Mn^{++}) = 15.31 - 2\,pH$
 b. $= 17.82 - 2\,pH$

13. $\mathbf{MnO} + H_2O = HMnO_2^- + H^+$
 a. $\log(HMnO_2^-) = -19.08 + pH$
 b. $= -16.57 + pH$

$0 \rightarrow +2$

14. $\mathbf{Mn} = Mn^{++} + 2e^-$ $E_0 = -1.179 + 0.0295 \log(Mn^{++})$

15. $\mathbf{Mn} + 2H_2O = HMnO_2^- + 3H^+ + 2e^-$ $E_0 = -0.163 - 0.0886\,pH + 0.0295 \log(HMnO_2^-)$

$+2 \rightarrow +2.67$

16. $3Mn^{++} + 4H_2O = \mathbf{Mn_3O_4} + 8H^+ + 2e^-$ $E_0 = 1.824 - 0.2364\,pH - 0.0886 \log(Mn^{++})$

17. $3HMnO_2^- + H^+ = \mathbf{Mn_3O_4} + 2H_2O + 2e^-$ $E_0 = 1.228 + 0.0295\,pH - 0.0886 \log(HMnO_2^-)$

$+2 \rightarrow +3$

18.	$2Mn^{++} + 3H_2O = \mathbf{Mn_2O_3} + 6H^+ + 2e^-$	c. $E_0 =$	$1.443 - 0.1773\,pH - 0.0591 \log (Mn^{++})$
		d. $=$	$1.900 - 0.1773\,pH - 0.0591 \log (Mn^{++})$
19.	$2HMnO_2^- = \mathbf{Mn_2O_3} + H_2O + 2e^-$	c. $E_0 = -0.590$	$-0.0591 \log (HMnO_2^-)$
		d. $= -0.148$	$-0.0591 \log (HMnO_2^-)$

$+2 \rightarrow +4$

20. $Mn^{++} + 2H_2O = \mathbf{MnO_2} + 4H^+ + 2e^-$ $\quad E_0 = 1.228 - 0.1182\,pH - 0.0295 \log (Mn^{++})$

$+3 \rightarrow +4$

21. $Mn^{+++} + 2H_2O = \mathbf{MnO_2} + 4H^+ + e^-$ $\quad E_0 = 0.948 - 0.2364\,pH - 0.0591 \log (Mn^{+++})$

$+4 \rightarrow +6$

22. $\mathbf{MnO_2} + 2H_2O = MnO_4^{--} + 4H^+ + 2e^-$ $\quad E_0 = 2.257 - 0.1182\,pH + 0.0295 \log (MnO_4^{--})$

$+4 \rightarrow +7$

23. $\mathbf{MnO_2} + 2H_2O = MnO_4^- + 4H^+ + 3e^-$ $\quad E_0 = 1.692 - 0.0788\,pH + 0.0197 \log (MnO_4^-)$

3. EQUILIBRIUM DIAGRAM AND ITS INTERPRETATION

3.1. ESTABLISHMENT OF THE DIAGRAM

Figure 1, established from formulae (1)–(23), represents the conditions of thermodynamic equilibrium of the system manganese–water, at 25°C, in the absence of substances with which manganese can form soluble complexes or insoluble salts.

According to Charlot [2], manganese gives rise in particular to the following complexes:

Divalent Mn: fluorine, phosphoric, oxalic and ammine complexes;

Trivalent Mn: hydrochloric, phosphoric, sulphur, cyanide, oxalic complexes, etc.;

Quadrivalent Mn: hydrochloric, hydrofluoric and cyanide complexes.

3.2. STABILITY OF MANGANESE AND ITS OXIDES AND HYDROXIDES

The whole of the domain of thermodynamic stability of manganese lies well below the domain of stability of water, whose lower limit is indicated by line (*a*), valid for a hydrogen pressure of 1 atm. Manganese, a very base reducing metal, is therefore thermodynamically very unstable in the presence of water, and tends to react with it with the evolution of hydrogen. In practice this reaction is slow (Charlot [2]) probably on account of the large hydrogen overpotential of the metal.

Manganese can easily be dissolved by acid or neutral oxidizing solutions with the formation of pale pink manganous ions Mn^{++}. A slight oxidizing action, such as that of oxygen, can oxidize manganous solutions, with the formation of solid oxides: brown–black Mn_3O_4, black Mn_2O_3 or various varieties of anhydrous or hydrated MnO_2, which are brown or black. A more powerful oxidizing action, for instance one which is produced electrolytically, can oxidize these solutions of divalent manganese to the hexavalent or heptavalent state, with the formation of green manganate ions MnO_4^{--} (at very high pH's) or purple permanganate ions MnO_4^-.

The domain of stability of the permanganate ion MnO_4^- covers the whole of the upper part of the diagram and is situated, whatever the pH, above line (*b*) relating to the equilibrium of the oxidation of water to oxygen at atmospheric pressure. This accounts for the very pronounced oxidizing character of permanganate solutions and explains why this oxidizing character persists all along the pH scale, despite the fact that the potential of a platinum electrode immersed in the solution decreases when the pH increases; it also illustrates the fact that, unlike potassium dichromate solutions, potassium permanganate solutions are not perfectly stable at 25°C; it is, in fact, generally MnO_2 and not MnO_4^-, that is the form of manganese which is stable in the presence of water: permanganate therefore tends to oxidize water with the evolution of oxygen and separation of MnO_2 according to the reactions:

$$4\,MnO_4^- + 16\,H^+ + 12\,e^- \rightarrow 4\,MnO_2 + 8\,H_2O \qquad (23)$$

and

$$6\,H_2O \rightarrow 3\,O_2 + 12\,H^+ + 12\,e^- \qquad (b)$$

overall reaction

$$4\,MnO_4^- + 4\,H^+ \rightarrow 4\,MnO_2 + 3\,O_2\nearrow + 2\,H_2O.$$

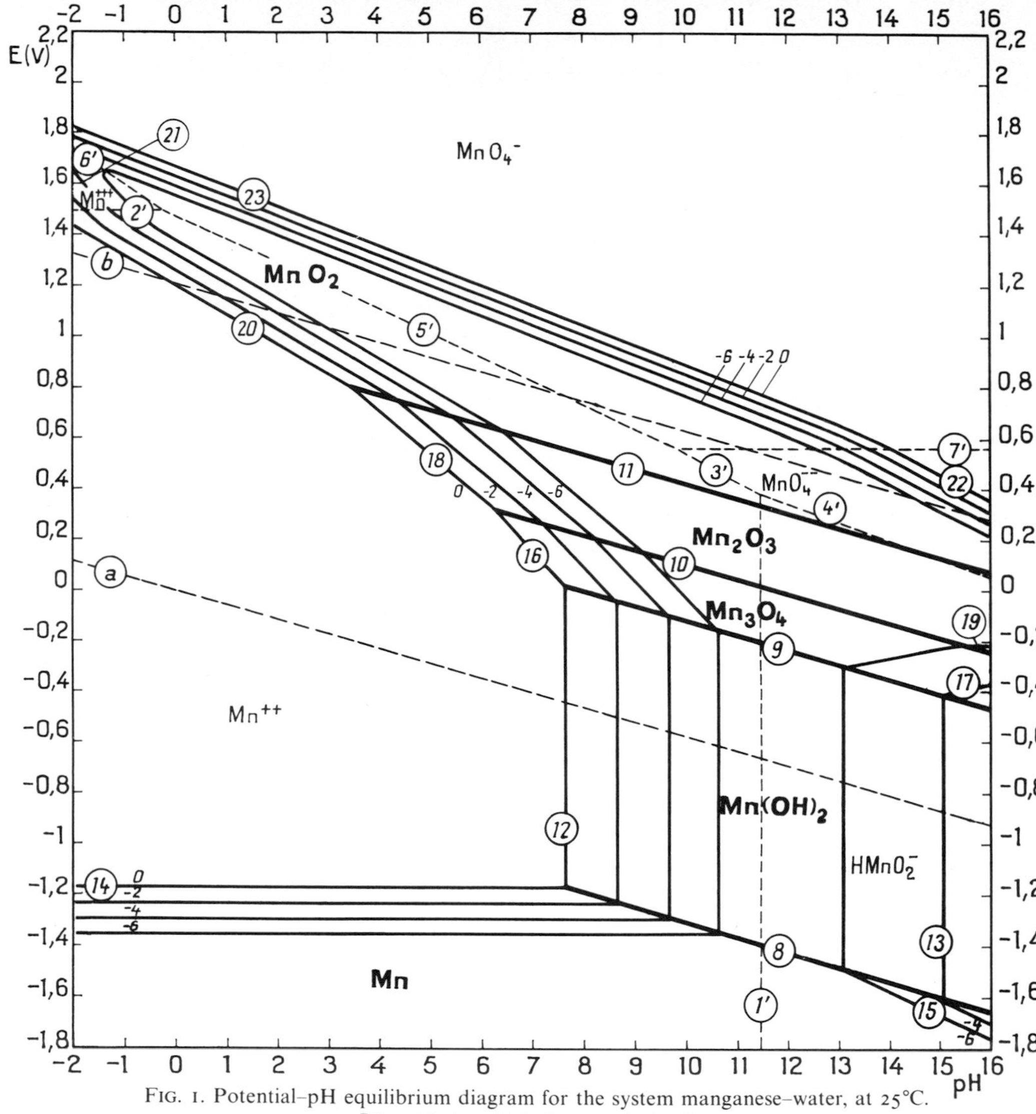

FIG. 1. Potential–pH equilibrium diagram for the system manganese–water, at 25°C. [Considering β-MnO_2 (pyrolusite).]

As Valensi [3] has shown, Fig. 1 also illustrates the conditions under which permanganate oxidizes sulphites to sulphates and chlorides to chlorine (in sufficiently acid solutions), and also the conditions under which permanganate can be obtained by the oxidation of manganous salts by means of chlorine (at high pH's), lead peroxide PbO_2 (at low pH's) or persulphate (in the presence of silver nitrate as a catalyst).

The domains of stability of the manganous ion Mn^{++} and the permanganate ion MnO_4^- are separated by a domain of stability of various oxides which, although very important in neutral or slightly acid solutions, is considerably smaller in strongly acid solutions. Thus the direct reduction of MnO_4^- to Mn^{++} is possible only in sufficiently acid solutions; in slightly acid, neutral or alkaline solutions, the reduction generally ceases at MnO_2 or at a mixture of lower oxides.

The domain of stability of Mn_2O_3 exists only for slightly acid, neutral or alkaline solutions; consequently if one introduces some Mn_2O_3 into a definitely acid solution, it probably splits up into Mn^{++} ions and an oxide which has, to a good approximation, the formula MnO_2. However, this reaction is complex and it should be noted that it always leads to the formation of non-stoichiometric varieties α-MnO_2 and γ-MnO_2 and never the stoichiometric variety β-MnO_2 or pyrolusite (Brenet and Grund [4], Brenet [5]).

The diagram also shows that on alkalinization of a reducing medium containing Mn^{++} ions, a white precipitate of manganous hydroxide $Mn(OH)_2$ will be formed which is very slightly soluble in very alkaline solutions to give dimanganite ions $HMnO_2^-$. In the case of a 0·01 M solution, precipitation will begin at pH = 8·65, and will reach a maximum at a pH in the region of 11·5; redissolution in a strongly alkaline solution is very slight [2]. In the presence of oxygen, a white suspension of manganous hydroxide will become brown, as the result of the formation of higher oxides which are known; this fact constitutes the basis of a process for checking the absence of oxygen in hydrogen or other gases (Thiesse [6]). In the presence of more vigorous oxidizing agents, such as H_2O_2 and ClO^-, the oxidation may go as far as the dioxide MnO_2 (Charlot [2]). However, it should be noted that the dioxide thus formed is again a non-stoichiometric dioxide, α- or γ-MnO_2, and never the stoichiometric variety β-MnO_2 (Brenet [7]).

With regard to the green anhydrous oxide MnO, it is, at 25°C, thermodynamically unstable with respect to $Mn(OH)_2$ and therefore tends to be converted into this hydroxide.

We point out that the diagram is in fairly good agreement with a diagram established by Charlot [2] using the results of experimental measurements.

More recently it has become evident that the equilibrium states of reactions involving manganese oxides can be realized experimentally only in fairly narrow domains of pH.

Outside these pH domains the reactions are practically irreversible, probably owing to the existence of complex reactions or kinetically very slow reactions. But in the case of β-MnO_2, the potentials of the equilibria between MnO_2 and Mn^{++} (reaction 20) and between MnO_2 and MnO_4^- (reaction 23) can be determined for certain pH domains. For instance, in the case of the equilibrium between β-MnO_2 and Mn^{++}, the domain of reversibility lies approximately between pH = 3 and pH = 4, with an Mn^{++} ion activity such that $-\log[Mn^{++}] = p_{Mn} = 3$ approximately.

For this domain it has been possible to verify a good agreement between the lines (20) of the diagram and the potentials presented by a β-MnO_2 (pyrolusite) electrode [8].

3.3. ELECTROLYTIC PRODUCTION OF MANGANESE

The electrolytic production of manganese will be possible, in neutral or acid solutions free from complexing substances on cathodes whose potential is below the potentials shown by the lines (14). In the case of solutions containing, for example, 1 g-ion Mn/l (55 g/l), this potential will have to be below approximately −1·2 V.

As the lines (14) lie well below line (*a*), the electrolytic separation of the metal will be accompanied by the evolution of hydrogen, and consequently the current yield will be below 100 per cent. The affinity to evolve hydrogen is measured by the difference between the potentials of the cathode and the potential relating to line (*a*) of the diagram; as this line goes upwards as the pH increases, the affinity (and the rate) of hydrogen evolution will be larger the smaller the pH of the solution, all other conditions remaining constant. The current yield will therefore be improved by an increase in the cathodic pH. However, this pH cannot exceed a certain limit, beyond which there is a risk that the manganese will contain some hydroxide $Mn(OH)_2$. The best conditions of yield and metal purity will therefore be obtained at cathodic pH's slightly below the pH of $Mn(OH)_2$ saturation which is, for example, 7·4 in the case of solutions containing 1 g-ion Mn/l (55 g/l). This opinion is in agreement with the results of research carried out by Jogarao and Prasada Rao [9] who, for cathodic solutions of pH = 7·2 containing 32 to 37 g Mn/l (0·6M), recorded a current yield of 62·7 per cent at about 33°C.

3.4. MANGANESE DIOXIDE CELLS

Leclanché type cells are made up of a zinc anode and an electrolyte which is usually basically ammonium chloride and zinc chloride. The cathode consists of a mixture of manganese dioxide and carbon (graphite, acetylene black).

The operation of the cell results from the fact that when the two electrodes are joined through a resistance, the zinc is oxidized and the manganese dioxide reduced. The mechanism of the reactions, is, however, very complex and is not yet very well known.

Nevertheless it appears, as Brenet [10] has shown by means of X-ray diagrams, that the change in the dioxide differs depending on whether one is dealing with β-MnO_2 (pyrolusite), or with the non-stoichiometric "active" varieties, α- or γ-MnO_2.

The calculation of the e.m.f. of such a cell has therefore to be made by means of different reactions, depending on the variety of dioxide used.

In the case of β-MnO_2, one can consider either the reaction $2MnO_2 + 2H^+ + 2e^- \rightarrow Mn_2O_3 + H_2O$ (11), or the reaction $MnO_2 + 4H^+ + 2e^- \rightarrow Mn^{++} + 2H_2O$ (20) depending on the pH of the solution. The calculated e.m.f.'s thus obtained are fairly close to those observed industrially (Walkley [11]).

In the case of α- or γ-MnO_2, reaction (20) no longer agrees absolutely; but in this case we can base our calculations on experimentally verified reactions (Gabano and Brenet [12]). We can thus justify the e.m.f.'s observed in practice which are of the order of 1·75 to 1·80 V for cells using these "active" varieties as a depolarizer.

Moreover it is interesting to notice that the free enthalpies of formation of the varieties α- and γ-MnO_2 are of the same order of magnitude as that of β-MnO_2, but that, on the other hand, the electrochemical reactions involving these varieties α- and γ-MnO_2 are often very different [12].

It would probably be necessary to take into account the fact that the electrolytes actually used are very concentrated salt solutions for which the formulae relating to dilute solutions are not applicable without correction.

Finally, for the reactions considered in Leclanché cells, one must also take into account the presence of Cl^-, NH_4^+ ions and NH_3, which can form complex ions with zinc.

4. BIBLIOGRAPHY

[1] A. MOUSSARD, J. BRENET, F. JOLAS, M. POURBAIX and J. VAN MUYLDER, *Comportement électrochimique du manganèse. Diagramme d'équilibres tension–pH du système* Mn–H_2O, *à 25°C* (Rapport technique RT.18 of CEBELCOR, December 1954).

[2] G. CHARLOT, *Théorie et méthodes nouvelles d'analyse qualitative*, 3rd ed., Masson, Paris, 1949.

[3] G. VALENSI, Nouvelle méthode d'enseignement de la Chimie minérale, *Bull. Union des Physiciens*, No. 394, October 1950, p. 61.

[4] J. BRENET and A. GRUND, Sur l'obtention de diverses variétés de bioxydes de manganèse, *C.R. Acad, Sc.* **242**, 2343–44 (1956).

[5] J. BRENET, Sur le mécanisme de la dismutation du sesquioxide en bioxyde de manganèse et en ions manganeux, *C.R. Acad. Sc.* **243**, 1310–11 (1956).

[6] X. THIESSE, *De la prévision des réactions d'oxydo-réduction en Chimie minérale* (Thèse, Nancy, G. Thomas, Nancy, p. 54).

[7] J. BRENET, Private lecture.

[8] J. BRENET and A. MOUSSARD, Problème sur le potentiel des électrodes à bioxyde de manganèse, *C.R. 6e Réunion du CITCE*, Poitiers, 1954.

[9] A. JOGARAO and Y. PRASADA RAO, Operating cell characteristics in electrowinning of manganese, *Currents Sc.* **23**, No. 8, 260–61 (1954).

[10] J. BRENET, Influence de divers facteurs sur l'évolution du bioxyde de manganèse au cours de la dépolarisation, *C.R.* 8e *Réunion du CITCE*, Madrid, 1956, pp. 394–401.

[11] A. WALKLEY, The suitability of manganese dioxides and graphites for use in Leclanché-type dry cells, *Austr. J. Appl. Sc.* **3**, No. 4, 324–37 (1952).

[12] J. GABANO and J. BRENET, Les équilibres électrochimiques de différentes variétés de bioxyde de manganèse, *Z. Elektrochem.* **62**, No. 5, 497–500 (1958).

SECTION 11.2

TECHNETIUM[1]

N. DE ZOUBOV and M. POURBAIX

SUMMARY

(1) Shortened and adapted version of the Rapport technique RT.50 of CEBELCOR [1].

1. SUBSTANCES CONSIDERED AND SUBSTANCES NOT CONSIDERED

	Oxidation number (Z)	Considered	Not considered	μ^0(cal.)(2)	Name, colour, crystalline system
Solid substances	0	**Tc**	–	0	Technetium, silvery grey, hex.
	+4	**TcO_2**	–	— 88 290	Technetium dioxide, brown–black
	+6	**TcO_3**	–	—110 070	Technetium trioxide
	+7	**Tc_2O_7**	–	—222 540	Technetium heptoxide, pale yellow
	»	» hydr.	–	—282 540	Pertechnetic acid $HTcO_4$ or hydrated heptoxide $Tc_2O_7H_2O$, dark red
Dissolved substances	—1	–	Tc^-	–	Technetide ion
	+2	Tc^{++}	–	18 450	Technetous ion
	+7	$HTcO_4$	–	—150 455	Pertechnetic acid, yellow, pink or red
	»	TcO_4^-	–	—150 615	Pertechnetate ion, colourless

2. REACTIONS AND EQUILIBRIUM FORMULAE

2.1. TWO DISSOLVED SUBSTANCES

2.1.1. *Relative stability of the dissolved substances*

$Z = +7$

1. $HTcO_4 = TcO_4^- + H^+$ $\qquad \log\frac{(TcO_4^-)}{(HTcO_4)} = 0.12 + pH$

$+2 \rightarrow +7$

2. $Tc^{++} + 4H_2O = HTcO_4 + 7H^+ + 5e^-$ $\qquad E_0 = 0.501 - 0.0827\ pH + 0.0118 \log\frac{(HTcO_4)}{(Tc^{++})}$

3. $Tc^{++} + 4H_2O = TcO_4^- + 8H^+ + 5e^-$ $\qquad E_0 = 0.500 - 0.0945\ pH + 0.0118 \log\frac{(TcO_4^-)}{(Tc^{++})}$

2.1.2. *Limits of the domains of relative predominance of the dissolved substances*

1'. $HTcO_4/TcO_4^-$ $\qquad pH = -0.12$

2'. $Tc^{++}/HTcO_4$ $\qquad E_0 = 0.501 - 0.0827\ pH$

3'. Tc^{++}/TcO_4^- $\qquad E_0 = 0.500 - 0.0945\ pH$

2.2. TWO SOLID SUBSTANCES

Limits of the domains of relative stability of the solid substances

$0 \rightarrow +4$

4. **Tc** $+ 2H_2O =$ **TcO_2** $+ 4H^+ + 4e^-$ $\qquad E_0 = 0.272 - 0.0591\ pH$

$+4 \rightarrow +6$

5. **TcO_2** $+ H_2O =$ **TcO_3** $+ 2H^+ + 2e^-$ $\qquad E_0 = 0.757 - 0.0591\ pH$

---

(2) All these enthalpy values were calculated from new data given by Cartledge and Smith [2], Latimer [3] and Cobble *et al.* [4].

2.3. ONE DISSOLVED SUBSTANCE AND ONE SOLID SUBSTANCE

Solubility of the solid substances

$0 \to +2$

6. $\mathbf{Tc} = Tc^{++} + 2e^-$ $E_0 = 0.400 + 0.0295 \log (Tc^{++})$

$0 \to +7$

7. $\mathbf{Tc} + 4H_2O = TcO_4^- + 8H^+ + 7e^-$ $E_0 = 0.472 - 0.0675\,pH + 0.0084 \log (TcO_4^-)$

$+2 \to +4$

8. $Tc^{++} + 2H_2O = \mathbf{TcO_2} + 4H^+ + 2e^-$ $E_0 = 0.144 - 0.1182\,pH - 0.0295 \log (Tc^{++})$

$+4 \to +7$

9. $\mathbf{TcO_2} + 2H_2O = HTcO_4 + 3H^+ + 3e^-$ $E_0 = 0.740 - 0.0591\,pH + 0.0197 \log (HTcO_4)$
10. $\mathbf{TcO_2} + 2H_2O = TcO_4^- + 4H^+ + 3e^-$ $E_0 = 0.738 - 0.0788\,pH + 0.0197 \log (TcO_4^-)$

$+6 \to +7$

11. $\mathbf{TcO_3} + H_2O = HTcO_4 + H^+ + e^-$ $E_0 = 0.707 - 0.0591\,pH + 0.0591 \log (HTcO_4)$
12. $\mathbf{TcO_3} + H_2O = TcO_4^- + 2H^+ + e^-$ $E_0 = 0.700 - 0.1182\,pH + 0.0591 \log (TcO_4^-)$

3. EQUILIBRIUM DIAGRAM AND ITS INTERPRETATION

3.1. ESTABLISHMENT OF THE DIAGRAM

Using formulae (1)–(12), we have drawn Fig. 1 representing the potential–pH equilibrium diagram for the system technetium–water, at 25°C. From this diagram we have derived Fig. 2 representing the theoretical conditions of corrosion, immunity and passivation of technetium, at 25°C.

These diagrams are valid only in the absence of substances with which technetium can form soluble complexes or insoluble salts. We have not found any information in chemical literature concerning the complexes of technetium or the solubility of its salts.

3.2. FORMATION, STABILITY AND CORROSION OF TECHNETIUM

Metallic technetium, which is silvery grey, is seen from Figs. 1 and 2 to be a relatively noble metal, as it has a zone of stability in common with that of water.

As shown by Fig. 1, technetium can be obtained, possibly mixed with the oxide TcO_2, by the reduction of pertechnetate solutions; metallic zinc, tin, nickel, lead and copper, and mercurous salts reduce acid solutions of pertechnetates to technetium.

According to the equilibrium diagram (Fig. 1) and the corresponding theoretical corrosion diagram (Fig. 2) (valid in the presence of solutions containing 10^{-6} g-at Tc/l, i.e. 0·1 mg/l) technetium remains practically unchanged in the presence of all non-complexing aqueous solutions free from oxidizing agents, except for very strongly acid solutions. Slightly oxidizing solutions of all pH's can cover technetium with insoluble oxide TcO_2; very oxidizing solutions of all pH's can dissolve it with the formation of pertechnetate.

In actual fact, technetium tarnishes slowly in moist air; it is not attacked appreciably by alkaline solutions of hydrogen peroxide; it is dissolved easily by nitric acid, aqua regia and a mixture of nitric acid and hydrogen peroxide, which convert it to soluble Tc_2O_7; it is not dissolved by concentrated hydrochloric acid, even when hot.

In Figs. 1 and 2 we have represented by a question mark, and purely as a guide, the conditions of the possible existence of the technetide ion Tc^- mentioned by Cobble *et al.* [4] and the domain of corrosion corresponding to this ion. We point out, however, that we have not found any proof of the real existence of this ion, nor of the possibilities of corrosion by reduction that would correspond to it.

3.3. FORMATION AND STABILITY OF THE TECHNETIUM OXIDES

According to Fig. 1 the oxidation of technetium in solutions of all pH's can give rise to the formation of brown-black dioxide TcO_2, which can be oxidized itself to pertechnetate and pertechnetic acid; in very strongly acid solutions some trioxide TcO_3 and heptoxide Tc_2O_7 can be formed, which are very soluble and do not appear in the equilibrium diagram.

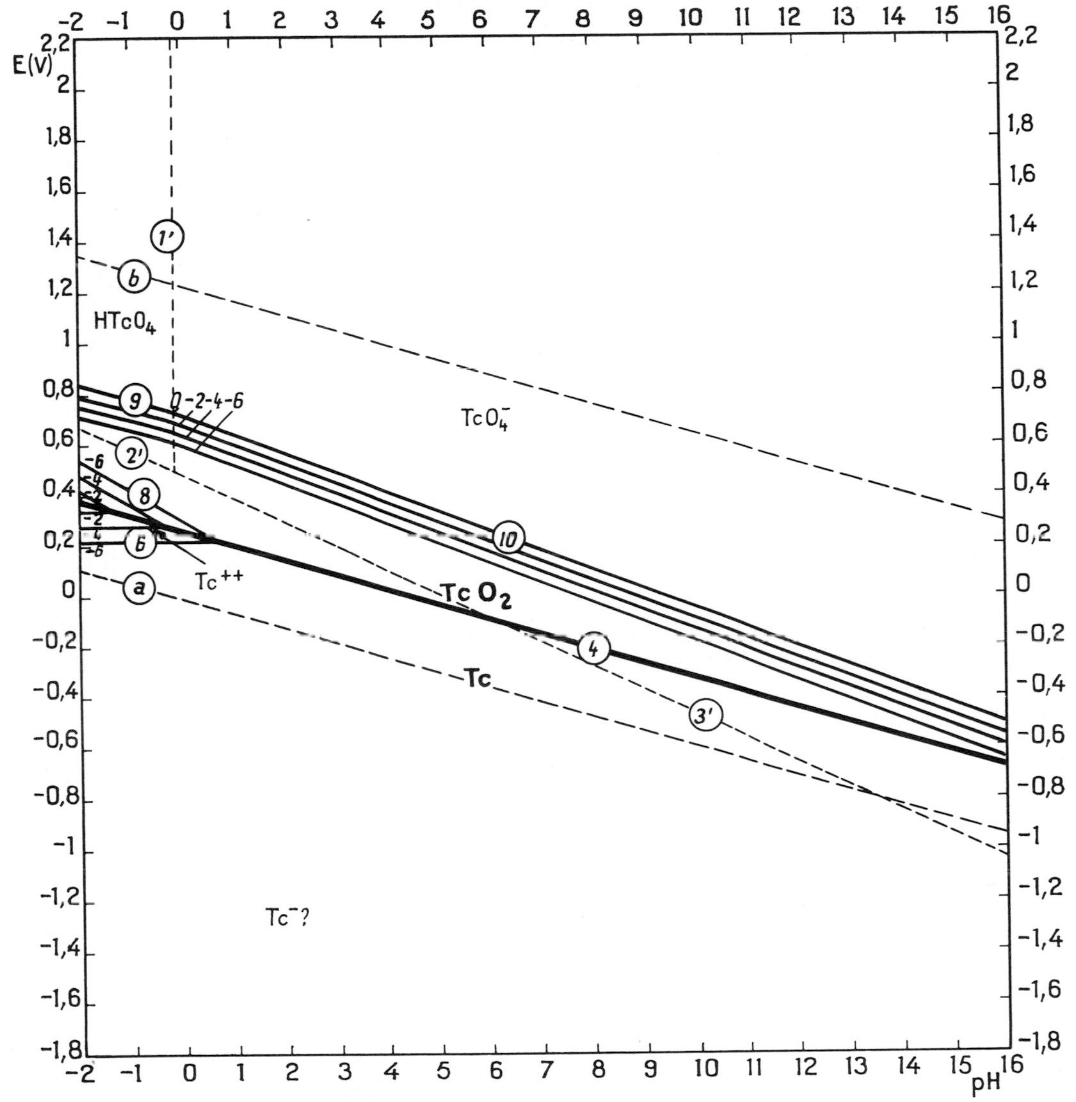

FIG. 1. Potential–pH equilibrium diagram for the system technetium–water, at 25°C.

The dioxide TcO_2, stable in moderately oxidizing solutions of any pH, can be prepared by the direct oxidation of technetium or by the reduction of a hydrochloric solution of ammonium pertechnetate with zinc. It is also obtained by the electrolytic reduction of a pertechnetate solution using a gold or platinum cathode.

Figure 1 does not show any predominance domains for dissolved forms of hexavalent technetium; in solutions, the trioxide TcO_3 disproportionates according to reactions (11) and (12) into pertechnetic acid or pertechnetate in which the technetium is heptavalent and by reaction (5) into the dioxide in which the technetium is tetravalent [4], according to the overall chemical reaction

$$3TcO_3 + H_2O \rightarrow 2TcO_4^- + TcO_2 + 2H^+.$$

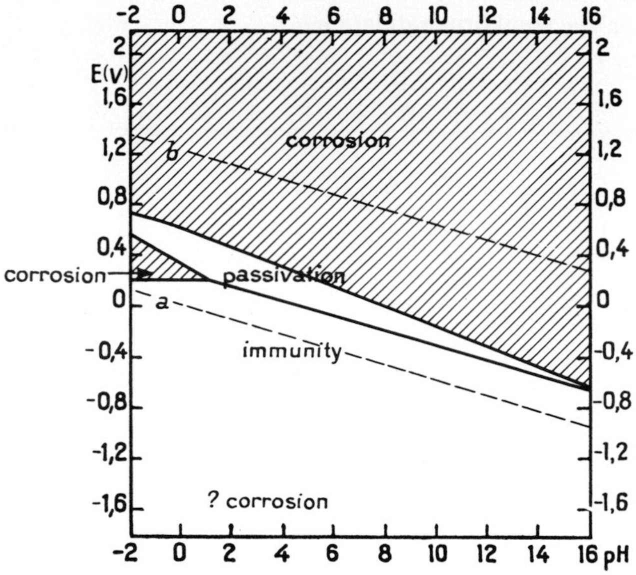

FIG. 2. Theoretical domains of corrosion, immunity and passivation of technetium, at 25°C.

3.4. STABILITY AND PASSIVATING ACTION OF THE PERTECHNETATES

The pertechnetates TcO_4^- are the stable form of technetium in oxygen-saturated solutions of any pH. In hydrochloric solutions they can be reduced by stannous chloride to the divalent state; as shown above they can be reduced in acid solutions to metallic technetium by metallic zinc, tin, nickel, lead and copper, and by mercurous salts.

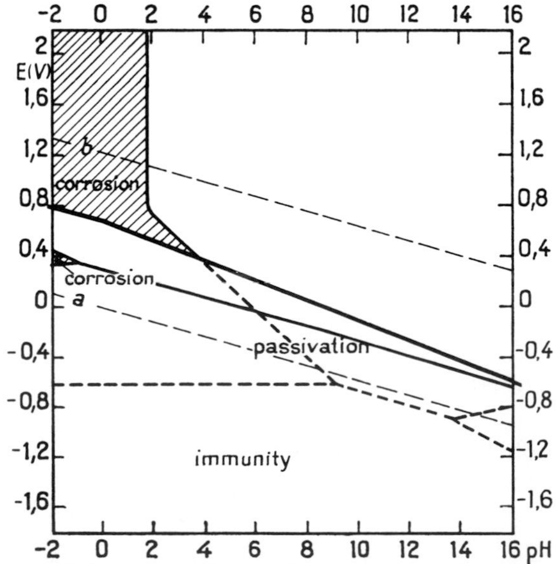

FIG. 3. Theoretical conditions of corrosion, immunity and passivation of iron in the presence of solutions containing 10^{-2} g-mol of pertechnetate per litre (1 g Tc/l).

The pertechnetates, even in very low concentrations, have remarkable inhibitive properties for the corrosion of electrolytic iron, soft steel and cast iron in contact with water or neutral, alkaline, or slightly acid solutions of chlorides or other salts.

Cartledge attributes this passivating action, on the one hand to a feeble reversible adsorption of the inhibitor on to the anodic areas of the metal, and on the other hand to a reduction of pertechnetate to insoluble TcO_2. This interpretation is in agreement with Fig. 3, established by us during a previous study [1], which represents the theoretical conditions of corrosion, immunity and passivation of iron in the presence of solutions containing 0·01 g-mol of pertechnetate per litre (1 g Tc/l). According to this figure the pertechnetates possess excellent passivating properties, which is in agreement with the facts. According to Cartledge, the reduction of pertechnetates does not occur at the cathodic areas.

4. BIBLIOGRAPHY

[1] N. de Zoubov and M. Pourbaix, *Comportement électrochimique du technétium. Diagramme d'équilibres tension–pH du système* Tc–H_2O, *à* 25°C (Rapport technique RT.50 of CEBELCOR, 1957).

[2] G. H. Cartledge and Wm. T. Smith, Jr., Revision of the electrode-potential diagram for technetium, *J. Phys. Chem.* **59**, 1111–12 (1955).

[3] W. M. Latimer, *Oxidation Potentials*, 2nd ed., Prentice-Hall, New York, 1952; *Recent References to Thermodynamic Data*, August 1954, University of California.

[4] J. W. Cobble, Wm. T. Smith, Jr. and G. E. Boyd, Thermodynamic properties of technetium and rhenium compounds. II. Heats of formation of technetium heptoxide and pertechnic acid, potential of the technetium (IV)–technetium (VIII) couple, and a potential diagram for technetium, *J. Amer. Chem. Soc.* **75**, 5777–82 (1953).

SECTION 11.3

RHENIUM (1)

N. DE ZOUBOV and M. POURBAIX

SUMMARY

(1) Shortened and adapted version of the Rapport technique RT.51 of CEBELCOR [1].

1. SUBSTANCES CONSIDERED AND SUBSTANCES NOT CONSIDERED

	Oxidation number (Z)	Considered	Not considered	$\mu°$(cal.)(2)	Name, colour, crystalline system
Solid substances	0	**Re**	–	0	Rhenium, grey–white, hex.
	+1	–	**Re_2O** hydr.	–	Hydrated rhenium suboxide ($Re_2O.2H_2O$?)
	+2	–	**ReO** hydr.	–	Hydrated rhenium monoxide ($ReO.H_2O$?)
	+3	**Re_2O_3** hydr.	–	–138 610	Hydrated sesquioxide, dark brown to black
	+4	**ReO_2**	–	– 89 000	Dioxide, grey–black or dark brown
	+5	–	**Re_2O_5** hydr.	–	Hydrated rhenium pentoxide, red
	+6	**ReO_3**	–	–127 300	Trioxide or rhenic anhydride, red or blue, cubic
	+7	**Re_2O_7**	–	–252 700	Perrhenic anhydride, yellow, monocl.
	+8	–	**Re_2O_8**	–	Rhenium peroxide, white
Dissolved substances	–1	Re^-	–	9 200	Rhenide ion, colourless
	+1	–	Re^+	–	?
	»	–	$HReO$	–	?
	+2	–	Re^{++}	–	Hyporhenous ion
	+3	Re^{+++}	–	20 755	Rhenous ion, red
	+4	–	Re^{++++}	–	Hyporhenic ion
	+5	–	Re^{+++++}	–	Rhenic ion, green
	+6	–	H_2ReO_4	–	Rhenic acid, yellow
	»	ReO_4^{--}	–	–150 960	Rhenate ion, yellow–red
	+7	–	$HReO_4$	–	Perrhenic acid, colourless
	»	ReO_4^-	–	–167 100	Perrhenate ion, colourless

2. REACTIONS AND EQUILIBRIUM FORMULAE

2.1. TWO DISSOLVED SUBSTANCES

2.1.1. *Relative stability of the dissolved substances*

$-1 \rightarrow +3$

1. $Re^- = Re^{+++} + 4e^-$ $\quad E_0 = 0.125 + 0.0148 \log \frac{(Re^{+++})}{(Re^-)}$

$-1 \rightarrow +6$

2. $Re^- + 4H_2O = ReO_4^{--} + 8H^+ + 7e^-$ $\quad E_0 = 0.412 - 0.0675\,pH + 0.0084 \log \frac{(ReO_4^{--})}{(Re^-)}$

$-1 \rightarrow +7$

3. $Re^- + 4H_2O = ReO_4^- + 8H^+ + 8e^-$ $\quad E_0 = 0.273 - 0.0591\,pH + 0.0074 \log \frac{(ReO_4^-)}{(Re^-)}$

$+3 \rightarrow +6$

4. $Re^{+++} + 4H_2O = ReO_4^{--} + 8H^+ + 3e^-$ $\quad E_0 = 0.795 - 0.1576\,pH + 0.0197 \log \frac{(ReO_4^{--})}{(Re^{+++})}$

$+3 \rightarrow +7$

5. $Re^{+++} + 4H_2O = ReO_4^- + 8H^+ + 4e^-$ $\quad E_0 = 0.422 - 0.1182\,pH + 0.0148 \log \frac{(ReO_4^-)}{(Re^{+++})}$

$+6 \rightarrow +7$

6. $ReO_4^{--} = ReO_4^- + e^-$ $\quad E_0 = -0.700 + 0.0591 \log \frac{(ReO_4^-)}{(ReO_4^{--})}$

---

(2) The free enthalpy values of Re, Re_2O_3, Re^-, Re^{+++}, ReO_4^{--} and ReO_4^- were indicated by Latimer [2] or calculated by us from data given by Latimer.

The free enthalpy values of ReO_2, ReO_3 and Re_2O_7 were calculated by Boyd *et al.* [3] or calculated by us from data given by these investigators.

2.1.2. *Limits of the domains of relative predominance of the dissolved substances*

1'.	Re^{-}/Re^{+++}	$E_0 = 0.125$
2'.	Re^{-}/ReO_4^{--}	$E_0 = 0.412 - 0.0675\ pH$
3'.	Re^{-}/ReO_4^{-}	$E_0 = 0.273 - 0.0591\ pH$
4'.	Re^{+++}/ReO_4^{--}	$E_0 = 0.795 - 0.1576\ pH$
5'.	Re^{+++}/ReO_4^{-}	$E_0 = 0.422 - 0.1182\ pH$
6'.	ReO_4^{--}/ReO_4^{-}	$E_0 = -0.700$

2.2. TWO SOLID SUBSTANCES

Limits of the domains of relative stability of the solid substances

$0 \rightarrow +3$

7. $2\,\mathbf{Re} + 3H_2O = \mathbf{Re_2O_3} + 6H^+ + 6e^-$ $\quad E_0 = 0.227 - 0.0591\ pH$

$+3 \rightarrow +4$

8. $\mathbf{Re_2O_3} + H_2O = 2\,\mathbf{ReO_2} + 2H^+ + 2e^-$ $\quad E_0 = 0.375 - 0.0591\ pH$

$+4 \rightarrow +6$

9. $\mathbf{ReO_2} + H_2O = \mathbf{ReO_3} + 2H^+ + 2e^-$ $\quad E_0 = 0.399 - 0.0591\ pH$

2.3. ONE DISSOLVED SUBSTANCE AND ONE SOLID SUBSTANCE

Solubility of the solid substances

$Z = +3$

10. $2Re^{+++} + 3H_2O = \mathbf{Re_2O_3} + 6H^+$ $\quad \log(Re^{+++}) = -3.69 - 3\ pH$

$-1 \rightarrow 0$

11. $Re^{-} = \mathbf{Re} + e^-$ $\quad E_0 = -0.400 - 0.0591 \log(Re^-)$

$-1 \rightarrow +3$

12. $2Re^{-} + 3H_2O = \mathbf{Re_2O_3} + 6H^+ + 8e^-$ $\quad E_0 = 0.070 - 0.0443\ pH - 0.0148 \log(Re^-)$

$0 \rightarrow +3$

13. $\mathbf{Re} = Re^{+++} + 3e^-$ $\quad E_0 = 0.300 + 0.0197 \log(Re^{+++})$

$0 \rightarrow +7$

14. $\mathbf{Re} + 4H_2O = ReO_4^- + 8H^+ + 7e^-$ $\quad E_0 = 0.369 - 0.0675\ pH + 0.0084 \log(ReO_4^-)$

$+3 \rightarrow +4$

15. $Re^{+++} + 2H_2O = \mathbf{ReO_2} + 4H^+ + e^-$ $\quad E_0 = 0.157 - 0.2364\ pH - 0.0591 \log(Re^{+++})$

$+3 \rightarrow +6$

16. $Re^{+++} + 3H_2O = \mathbf{ReO_3} + 6H^+ + 3e^-$ $\quad E_0 = 0.318 - 0.1182\ pH - 0.0197 \log(Re^{+++})$

$+3 \rightarrow +7$

17. $\mathbf{Re_2O_3} + 5H_2O = 2ReO_4^- + 10H^+ + 8e^-$ $\quad E_0 = 0.476 - 0.0739\ pH + 0.0148 \log(ReO_4^-)$

$+4 \rightarrow +7$

18. $\mathbf{ReO_2} + 2H_2O = ReO_4^- + 4H^+ + 3e^-$ $\quad E_0 = 0.510 - 0.0788\ pH + 0.0197 \log(ReO_4^-)$

$+6 \rightarrow +7$

19. $\mathbf{ReO_3} + H_2O = ReO_4^- + 2H^+ + e^-$ $\quad E_0 = 0.732 - 0.1182\ pH + 0.0591 \log(ReO_4^-)$

3. EQUILIBRIUM DIAGRAM AND ITS INTERPRETATION

3.1. ESTABLISHMENT OF THE DIAGRAM

Figure 1, established from relations (1)–(19), represents the conditions of thermodynamic equilibrium of the system rhenium–water, at 25°C. Figure 2 is derived from Fig. 1 after making certain assumptions and shows the theoretical conditions of corrosion, immunity and passivation of rhenium.

These figures are valid only in the absence of substances with which rhenium can form soluble complexes or insoluble salts; for the complexes, Charlot [4] gives the following information:

at valency +4: there exist hydrochloric complexes;
at valency +5: there exist oxalic and tartaric complexes, blue to green;

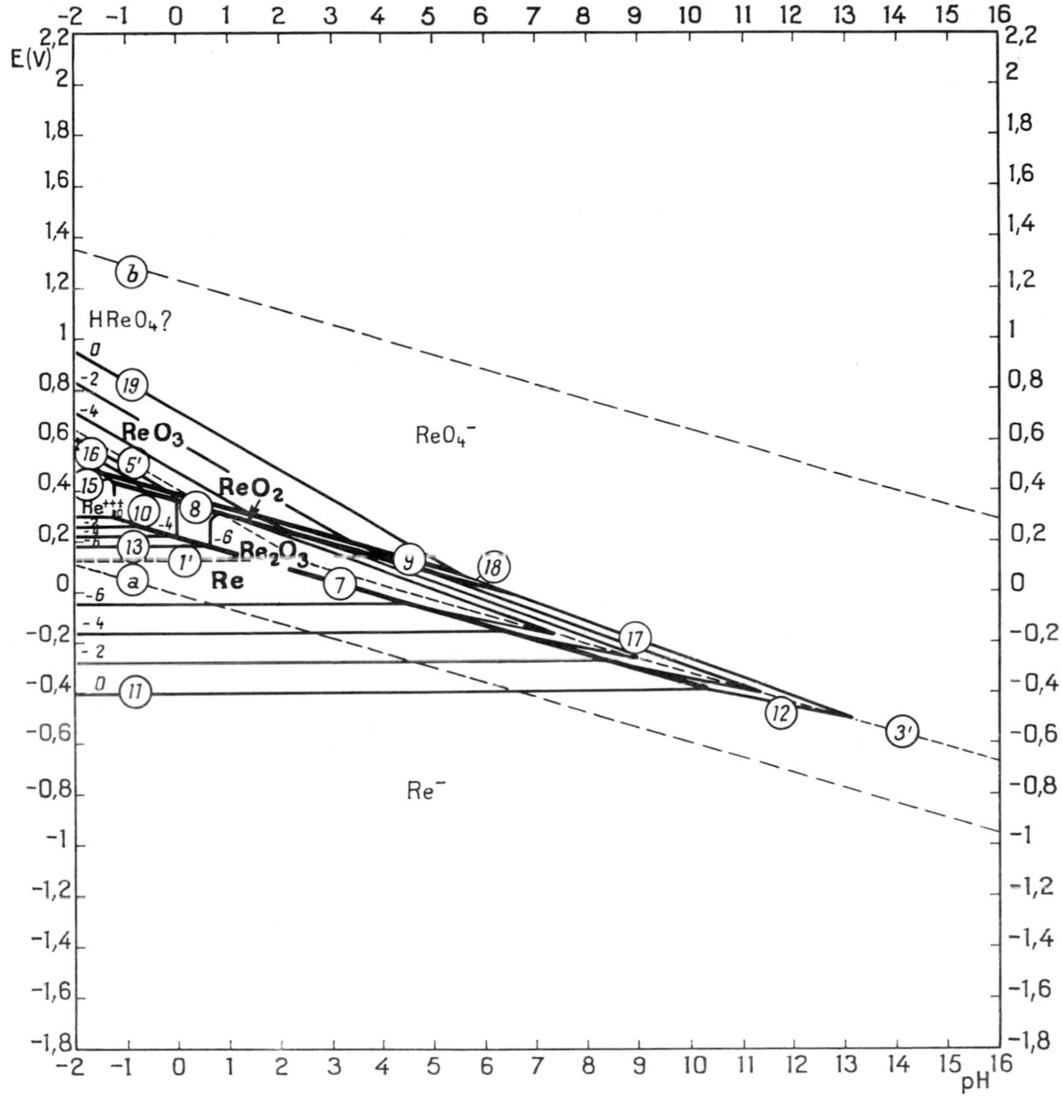

FIG. 1. Potential–pH equilibrium diagram for the system rhenium–water, at 25°C.

for the insoluble salts he indicates:

at valency +4: the rhenites of the type ReO_3Me^{II} are insoluble in water and alkaline solutions;
at valency +7: the perrhenates of Ag^+, Tl^+, Cs^+, Rb^+ are quite sparingly soluble; they also form sparingly soluble salts with certain organic bases.

3.2. FORMATION, STABILITY AND CORROSION OF RHENIUM

Metallic rhenium, shiny white in the compact state and grey–black in the divided state shows itself in Figs. 1 and 2 to be a relatively base metal, having a very small zone of stability in common with that of water.

Like most other metals, rhenium is not affected by oxygen or dry air.

As is shown by Fig. 1, rhenium can be obtained, possibly mixed with some lower oxides, by the electrolysis of neutral or acid solutions of perrhenates or perrhenic acid.

It is obtained in a finely divided grey–black form using current densities between 0·01 and 0·1 A/cm^2; with high current densities lead-coloured tree-like growths are formed at the cathode; these are compounds of metallic rhenium with brown hydrated lower oxides.

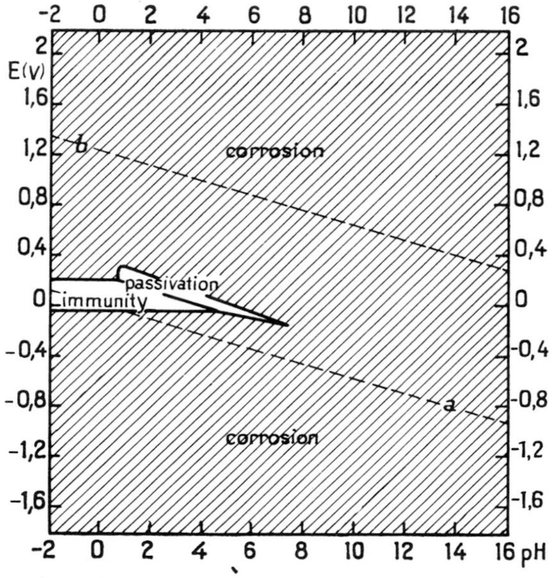

FIG. 2. Theoretical domains of corrosion, immunity and passivation of rhenium, at 25°C.

Rhenium can also be obtained by chemical reduction, but only with difficulty: more powerful reducing agents than zinc, such as stannous chloride and hydriodic acid, reduce heptavalent rhenium only as far as the valency state of +4.

In agreement with the equilibrium diagram in Fig. 1 and the theoretical corrosion diagram in Fig. 2 (valid in the presence of solutions containing 10^{-6} g-at Re/l, i.e. 0·19 mg/l), rhenium remains unchanged only within narrow limits of pH and electrode potential, corresponding to acid solutions free from oxidizing and reducing substances; it is very easily oxidized, in alkaline solution, with the formation of various oxides (Re_2O_3, ReO_2, ReO_3), as well as perrhenic acid and soluble perrhenates; it is very easily reduced with the formation of soluble rhenide.

In the presence of moist air, rhenium is oxidized to perrhenic acid, even at room temperature; this oxidation is very rapid in the case of finely divided rhenium, which is occasionally pyrophoric. The oxidation of rhenium, even when compact, is rapid in the presence of solutions of hydrogen peroxide or alkaline or acid oxidizing solutions; solutions of nitrites, nitrates or alkali metal peroxides; nitric acid solutions. Concentrated sulphuric acid also dissolves rhenium, but more slowly.

We do not know of any data concerning the reduction of rhenium, but it is known from the works of Lundell and Knowles [5] that some rhenide (or hydrorhenic acid HRe) can be prepared by the reduction of a sulphuric acid solution of perrhenate free from air using zinc amalgam, for example according to the reaction (3) $ReO_4^- + 8H^+ + 8e^- \rightarrow Re^- + 4H_2O$.

The corrosion diagram for rhenium (Fig. 2) comprises an anodic domain of corrosion (corresponding to the formation of ReO_4^-) and a cathodic one (corresponding to the formation of Re^-) and a domain of passivation (corresponding to the formation of more or less hydrated Re_2O_3).

3.3. FORMATION AND STABILITY OF THE RHENIUM OXIDES

According to Fig. 1, the oxidation of rhenium in acid, neutral or slightly alkaline solutions can give rise to the formation of various oxides: the dark brown to black "sesquioxide" $Re_2O_3 . xH_2O$ (which we have represented by the formula Re_2O_3), the grey–black or dark brown dioxide ReO_2 or $ReO_2 . xH_2O$, the red or blue trioxide or rhenic anhydride ReO_3, and the yellow heptoxide Re_2O_7, which is very soluble with the formation of perrhenic acid $HReO_4$ or perrhenate ReO_4^-.

The families of lines (10), (12), (17) and (3') illustrate the amphoteric character of the *sesquioxide* Re_2O_3: solubility in very acid solution (line 10) with the formation of red Re^{+++} ions and ability to disproportionate in alkaline solutions to form perrhenates ReO_4^- and colourless rhenides Re^- [lines (12), (17) and (3')]. Re_2O_3 can be oxidized to the dioxide ReO_2 in acid or neutral solution and to perrhenate ReO_4^- in alkaline solution. Hydrated Re_2O_3 can be obtained by the treatment of very acid solutions of $ReCl_3$ with NaOH or by electrolysis; however, as this substance can be oxidized, it is best to work in the absence of air or other oxidant.

The *dioxide* ReO_2, in which rhenium is quadrivalent, can disproportionate in very acid solution or in neutral or alkali solution, respectively with the formation of trivalent Re^{+++} ions and of the trioxide ReO_3 according to lines (15) and (9), or with the formation of heptavalent rhenium ReO_4^- ions and sesquioxide Re_2O_3 according to lines (18) and (8). ReO_2 can be oxidized to ReO_3 or perrhenic acid $HReO_4$ in very acid solution and to perrhenate in less acid solution.

Anhydrous or hydrated ReO_2 can be obtained by the hydrolysis of fluoride- or chloride-containing solutions of quadrivalent rhenium (K_2ReF_6) or pentavalent rhenium (K_2ReOCl_5), or by the chemical or electrochemical reduction of solutions of perrhenic acid or perrhenates.

The *trioxide* ReO_3 or rhenic anhydride, in which rhenium is hexavalent, is more stable than technetium trioxide; it dissociates with the formation of perrhenate ReO_4^-, in which rhenium is heptavalent, and trivalent Re^{+++} ions [according to lines (19), (16) and (5')] or dioxide ReO_2 [according to lines (19) and (9)] with the transient formation of unstable reddish-yellow rhenic acid H_2ReO_4 or rhenate ReO_4^{--}. This disproportionation of the rhenates according to the reaction

$$3\,ReO_4^{--} + 2\,H_2O \rightarrow 2\,ReO_4^- + ReO_2 + 4\,OH^-$$

is analogous to the disproportionation of the manganates according to the reaction

$$3\,MnO_4^{--} + 2\,H_2O \rightarrow 2\,MnO_4^- + MnO_2 + 4\,OH^-,$$

but in the case of the rhenates it is much easier and more complete.

ReO_3 can be oxidized to perrhenates according to line (19), for example by concentrated nitric acid. It can be reduced below lines (16) and (9), for instance, in the cold, by stannous chloride or the iodides.

Yellow perrhenic anhydride Re_2O_7, in which rhenium is heptavalent, can be obtained by the evaporation of an aqueous solution of perrhenic acid or by the oxidation of rhenium with 30 per cent nitric acid using a water-bath; it is very hygroscopic and very soluble in water with the formation of perrhenic acid $HReO_4$.

Through lack of thermodynamic data or the uncertainty of their existence, we have not taken into account the pentoxide Re_2O_5, the peroxide Re_2O_8 or the lower oxides hydrated Re_2O and ReO.

3.4. STABILITY AND PASSIVATING ACTION OF THE PERRHENATES

As is shown by Fig. 1, perrhenic acid and the perrhenates are the stable forms of rhenium in the presence of aqueous solutions containing oxygen; their solutions are only slightly oxidizing; hydriodic acid and the iodides reduce them to the tetravalent state.

A study of the action of the perrhenates with regard to the passivation of electrolytic iron was made by Cartledge [6] under various experimental conditions. From this study it appears that the perrhenate ion ReO_4^- which, according to many reports, is similar to the pertechnetate ion TcO_4^-, is completely different to the latter regarding its inhibitive action towards the corrosion of iron and steels.

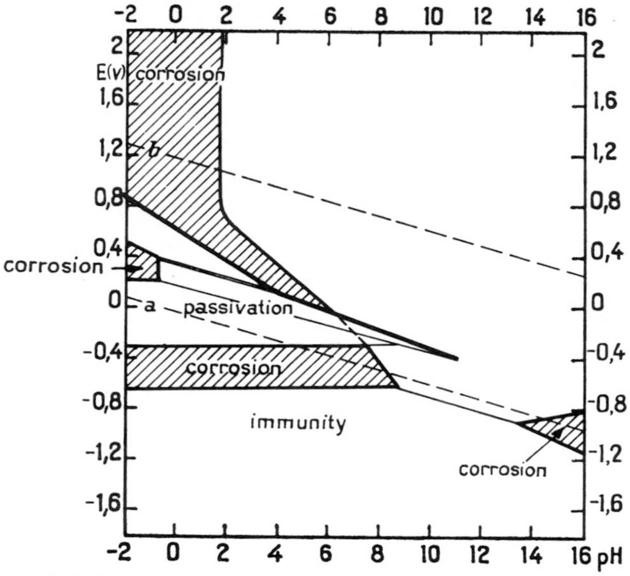

FIG. 3. Theoretical circumstances of corrosion, immunity and passivation of iron in the presence of solutions of 10^{-2} g-mol of perrhenate per litre (1·9 g Re/l).

Measurements of the electrode potential of electrolytic iron in the presence of potassium perrhenate and sodium sulphate show that the passivation is absolutely zero in non-aerated solutions and small in aerated solutions; the corrosion rate is substantially the same in pure water as in a perrhenate solution, even if hydrogen peroxide is added to the latter; this is in agreement with Fig. 3, established previously by us [1], which shows the theoretical conditions of corrosion, immunity and passivation of iron in the presence of solutions containing 10^{-2} g-mol of perrhenate per litre (i.e. 1·9 g Re/l).

4. BIBLIOGRAPHY

[1] N. DE ZOUBOV and M. POURBAIX, *Comportement électrochimique du rhénium. Diagramme d'équilibres tension–pH du système* Re–H_2O, *à* 25°C (Rapport technique RT.51 of CEBELCOR, 1957).

[2] W. M. LATIMER, *Oxidation Potentials,* 2nd ed., Prentice-Hall, New York, 1952, pp. 12 and 243, and *Recent References to Thermodynamic Data,* University of California, August 1954.

[3] G. E. BOYD, J. W. COBBLE and WM. T. SMITH, JR., Thermodynamic properties of technetium and rhenium compounds. III. Heats of formation of rhenium heptoxide and trioxide, and a revised potential diagram for rhenium, *J. Amer. Chem. Soc.* **75**, 5783–4 (1953).

[4] G. CHARLOT, *L'analyse qualitative et les réactions en solution*, 4th ed., Masson, Paris, 1957, p. 210.

[5] G. E. F. LUNDELL and H. B. KNOWLES, *U.S. Bur. Stand. J. Res.* **18**, 629 (1937).

[6] G. H. CARTLEDGE, The mechanism of the inhibition of corrosion by the pertechnetate ion. III. Studies on the perrhenate ion, *J. Phys. Chem.* **60**, 32–36 (1956).

SECTION 12.1

IRON[1]

M. POURBAIX and N. DE ZOUBOV

SUMMARY

1. *Substances considered and substances not considered.*

2. *Reactions and equilibrium formulae.*

  2.1. Two dissolved substances.

    2.1.1. Relative stability of the dissolved substances.

    2.1.2. Limits of the domains of relative predominance of the dissolved substances.

  2.2. Two solid substances.

    Limits of the domains of relative stability of iron and its oxides and hydroxides.

  2.3. One solid substance and one dissolved substance.

    Solubility of iron and its oxides and hydroxides.

3. *Equilibrium diagrams and their interpretation.*

  3.1. Establishment of the diagrams.

  3.2. Formation, stability and corrosion of iron.

    3.2.1. Theoretical considerations.

    3.2.2. Experimental verification and detailed investigation.

    3.2.3. Processes for the protection of iron against corrosion.

  3.3. Significance and practical importance of the electrochemical equilibrium diagrams for iron.

4. *Bibliography.*

---

[1] Adapted version of the Rapport CEFA/R.13 of the Commission des Études Fondamentales et Applications of CEBELCOR.

1. SUBSTANCES CONSIDERED AND SUBSTANCES NOT CONSIDERED

	Oxidation number (Z)	Considered	Not considered	μ^0(cal.)	Name, colour, crystalline system
Solid substances	0	Fe	–	0	α-Iron, light grey, f.c.cub.
	+2	FeO hydr.	–	– 58 880 (2)	Ferrous hydroxide $Fe(OH)_2$, white, rhomb.
	»	–	FeO anh.	–	Ferrous oxide, black, cub.
	+2.67	Fe_3O_4 anh.	–	–242 400	Magnetite, black, cub.
	»	–	$Fe_3O_4.xH_2O$	–	Hydrated magnetite, green–black
	+3	Fe_2O_3 anh.	–	*a.* –177 100	Haematite, red–brown, rhomb. or cub.
	»	» hydr.	–	*b.* –161 930 (3)	Ferric hydroxide $Fe(OH)_3$, red–brown, f.c.cub.
Dissolved substances	+2	Fe^{++}	–	– 20 300	Ferrous ion, green
	»	$HFeO_2^-$	–	– 90 627 (*)	Dihypoferrite ion, green
	»	–	FeO_2^{--}	–	Hypoferrite ion
	+3	Fe^{+++}	–	– 2 530	Ferric ion, colourless
	»	$FeOH^{++}$	–	– 55 910	Ferric ion, colourless
	»	$Fe(OH)_2^+$	–	–106 200	Ferric ion, colourless
	»	–	FeO_2^-	–	Ferrite ion
	+4	–	FeO^{++}	–	Ferryl ion
	»	–	FeO_3^{--}	–	Perferrite ion
	+5	–	FeO_2^+	–	Perferryl ion
	+6	FeO_4^{--}?	–	–111 685 ? (*)	Ferrate ion, violet

These values are indicated by W. M. Latimer, except for the two values given below which were calculated by us as follows (see [1], pp. 83 and 84):

(*) for $HFeO_2^-$: We have assumed, as the solubility product $(HFeO_2^-).(H^+)$ relating to the reaction $Fe(OH)_2 = HFeO_2^- + H^+$, the value $10^{-18.3}$ (Schrager [2]);

(*) for FeO_4^{--} : for want of more precise data we have provisionally assumed, for the standard equilibrium potential of the reaction $Fe^{+++} + 4H_2O = FeO_4^{--} + 8H^+ + 3e^-$, the approximate value $E_0^0 = +1{\cdot}7$ V given by Hodgmann ([3], p. 951), whose origin we have not been able to find.(4)

2. REACTIONS AND EQUILIBRIUM FORMULAE

2.1. TWO DISSOLVED SUBSTANCES

2.1.1. *Relative stability of the dissolved substances*

$Z = +2$

1. $Fe^{++} + 2H_2O = HFeO_2^- + 3H^+$ $\qquad \log\frac{(HFeO_2^-)}{(Fe^{++})} = -31.58 + 3\,pH$

$Z = +3$

2. $Fe^{+++} + H_2O = FeOH^{++} + H^+$ $\qquad \log\frac{(FeOH^{++})}{(Fe^{+++})} = -\ 2.43 + pH$

3. $FeOH^{++} + H_2O = Fe(OH)_2^+ + H^+$ $\qquad \log\frac{(Fe(OH)_2^+)}{(FeOH^{++})} = -\ 4.69 + pH$

---

(2) This value of $\mu^0_{FeO\,hydr.}$ corresponds to $\mu^0_{Fe(OH)_2} = -115\,570$ cal.

(3) This value of $\mu^0_{Fe_2O_3\,hydr.}$ corresponds to $\mu^0_{Fe(OH)_3} = -166\,000$ cal.

(4) We point out that Latimer gives two approximate values for the equilibrium potentials of the oxidation-reduction reactions: $FeO_2^-/FeO_4^{--} = V^0 > +0{\cdot}9$ V at pH 14 and $Fe^{+++}/FeO_4^{--} = V^0 > +1{\cdot}9$ V at pH 0.

$+2 \rightarrow +3$

4. $Fe^{++} = Fe^{+++} + e^-$ $\quad E_0 = 0.771 + 0.0591 \log \frac{(Fe^{+++})}{(Fe^{++})}$

5. $Fe^{++} + H_2O = FeOH^{++} + H^+ + e^-$ $\quad E_0 = 0.914 - 0.0591\,pH + 0.0591 \log \frac{(FeOH^{++})}{(Fe^{++})}$

6. $Fe^{++} + 2H_2O = Fe(OH)_2^+ + 2H^+ + e^-$ $\quad E_0 = 1.191 - 0.1182\,pH + 0.0591 \log \frac{(Fe(OH)_2^+)}{(Fe^{++})}$

7. $HFeO_2^- + H^+ = Fe(OH)_2^+ + e^-$ $\quad E_0 = -0.675 + 0.0591\,pH + 0.0591 \log \frac{(Fe(OH)_2^+)}{(HFeO_2^-)}$

$+2 \rightarrow +6$

8. $HFeO_2^- + 2H_2O = FeO_4^{--} + 5H^+ + 4e^-$ $\quad E_0 = 1.001 - 0.0738\,pH + 0.0148 \log \frac{(FeO_4^{--})}{(HFeO_2^-)}$

$+3 \rightarrow +6$

9. $Fe^{+++} + 4H_2O = FeO_4^{--} + 8H^+ + 3e^-$ $\quad E_0 = 1.700 - 0.1580\,pH + 0.0197 \log \frac{(FeO_4^{--})}{(Fe^{+++})}$

10. $FeOH^{++} + 3H_2O = FeO_4^{--} + 7H^+ + 3e^-$ $\quad E_0 = 1.652 - 0.1379\,pH + 0.0197 \log \frac{(FeO_4^{--})}{(FeOH^{++})}$

11. $Fe(OH)_2^+ + 2H_2O = FeO_4^{--} + 6H^+ + 3e^-$ $\quad E_0 = 1.559 - 0.1182\,pH + 0.0197 \log \frac{(FeO_4^{--})}{(Fe(OH)_2^+)}$

2.1.2. *Limits of the domains of relative predominance of the dissolved substances*

1′.	$Fe^{++}/HFeO_2^-$	$pH = 10.53$
2′.	$Fe^{+++}/FeOH^{++}$	$pH = 2.43$
3′.	$FeOH^{++}/Fe(OH)_2^+$	$pH = 4.69$
4′.	Fe^{++}/Fe^{+++}	$E_0 = 0.771$
5′.	$Fe^{++}/FeOH^{++}$	$E_0 = 0.914 - 0.0591\,pH$
6′.	$Fe^{++}/Fe(OH)_2^+$	$E_0 = 1.191 - 0.1182\,pH$
7′.	$HFeO_2^-/Fe(OH)_2^+$	$E_0 = -0.675 + 0.0591\,pH$
8′.	$HFeO_2^-/FeO_4^{--}$	$E_0 = 1.001 - 0.0738\,pH$
9′.	Fe^{+++}/FeO_4^{--}	$E_0 = 1.700 - 0.1580\,pH$
10′.	$FeOH^{++}/FeO_4^{--}$	$E_0 = 1.652 - 0.1379\,pH$
11′.	$Fe(OH)_2^+/FeO_4^{--}$	$E_0 = 1.559 - 0.1182\,pH$

2.2. TWO SOLID SUBSTANCES (5)

Limits of the domains of relative stability of iron and its oxides and hydroxides

$0 \rightarrow +2$

12. $\mathbf{Fe} + H_2O = \mathbf{FeO} + 2H^+ + 2e^-$ $\quad E_0 = -0.047 - 0.0591\,pH$

$0 \rightarrow +2.67$

13. $3\mathbf{Fe} + 4H_2O = \mathbf{Fe_3O_4} + 8H^+ + 8e^-$ $\quad E_0 = -0.085 - 0.0591\,pH$

$0 \rightarrow +3$

14. $2\mathbf{Fe} + 3H_2O = \mathbf{Fe_2O_3} + 6H^+ + 6e^-$ $\quad$ a. $E_0 = -0.051 - 0.0591\,pH$
b. $= 0.059 - 0.0591\,pH$

$+2 \rightarrow 2.67$

15. $3\mathbf{FeO} + H_2O = \mathbf{Fe_3O_4} + 2H^+ + 2e^-$ $\quad E_0 = -0.197 - 0.0591\,pH$

$+2 \rightarrow +3$

16. $2\mathbf{FeO} + H_2O = \mathbf{Fe_2O_3} + 2H^+ + 2e^-$ $\quad$ a. $E_0 = -0.057 - 0.0591\,pH$
b. $= 0.271 - 0.0591\,pH$

$+2.67 \rightarrow +3$

17. $2\mathbf{Fe_3O_4} + H_2O = 3\mathbf{Fe_2O_3} + 2H^+ + 2e^-$ $\quad$ a. $E_0 = 0.221 - 0.0591\,pH$
b. $= 1.208 - 0.0591\,pH$

---

(5) For the reactions involving Fe_2O_3, the letter *a* relates to anhydrous Fe_2O_3, whose free enthalpy of formation is $-177\,100$ cal.; the letter *b* relates to $Fe(OH)_3$, whose free enthalpy of formation is $-166\,000$ cal.

2.3. ONE SOLID SUBSTANCE AND ONE DISSOLVED SUBSTANCE (5)

Solubility of iron and its oxides and hydroxides

$Z = +2$		
18.	$Fe^{++} + H_2O = \mathbf{FeO} + 2H^+$	$\log(Fe^{++}) = 13.29 - 2\,pH$
19.	$\mathbf{FeO} + H_2O = HFeO_2^- + H^+$	$\log(HFeO_2^-) = -18.30 + pH$
$Z = +3$		
20.	$2Fe^{+++} + 3H_2O = \mathbf{Fe_2O_3} + 6H^+$	a. $\log(Fe^{+++}) = -0.72 - 3\,pH$ b. $= 4.84 - 3\,pH$
21.	$2FeOH^{++} + H_2O = \mathbf{Fe_2O_3} + 4H^+$	a. $\log(FeOH^{++}) = -3.15 - 2\,pH$ b. $= 2.41 - 2\,pH$
22.	$2Fe(OH)_2^+ = \mathbf{Fe_2O_3} + H_2O + 2H^+$	a. $\log(Fe(OH)_2^+) = -7.84 - pH$ b. $= -2.28 - pH$
$0 \rightarrow +2$		
23.	$\mathbf{Fe} = Fe^{++} + 2e^-$	$E_0 = -0.440 + 0.0295 \log(Fe^{++})$
24.	$\mathbf{Fe} + 2H_2O = HFeO_2^- + 3H^+ + 2e^-$	$E_0 = 0.493 - 0.0886\,pH + 0.0295 \log(HFeO_2^-)$
$0 \rightarrow +3$		
25.	$\mathbf{Fe} = Fe^{+++} + 3e^-$	$E_0 = -0.037 + 0.0197 \log(Fe^{+++})$
$+2 \rightarrow +2.67$		
26.	$3Fe^{++} + 4H_2O = \mathbf{Fe_3O_4} + 8H^+ + 2e^-$	$E_0 = 0.980 - 0.2364\,pH - 0.0886 \log(Fe^{++})$
27.	$3HFeO_2^- + H^+ = \mathbf{Fe_3O_4} + 2H_2O + 2e^-$	$E_0 = -1.819 + 0.0295\,pH - 0.0886 \log(HFeO_2^-)$
$+2 \rightarrow +3$		
28.	$2Fe^{++} + 3H_2O = \mathbf{Fe_2O_3} + 6H^+ + 2e^-$	a. $E_0 = 0.728 - 0.1773\,pH - 0.0591 \log(Fe^{++})$ b. $= 1.057 - 0.1773\,pH - 0.0591 \log(Fe^{++})$
29.	$2HFeO_2^- = \mathbf{Fe_2O_3} + H_2O + 2e^-$	a. $E_0 = -1.139 - 0.0591 \log(HFeO_2^-)$ b. $= -0.810 - 0.0591 \log(HFeO_2^-)$

3. EQUILIBRIUM DIAGRAMS AND THEIR INTERPRETATION

3.1. ESTABLISHMENT OF THE DIAGRAMS

Using formulae (1′)–(11′) we have represented in Fig. 1 the domains of relative predominance of the dissolved substances Fe^{++}, $HFeO_2^-$, Fe^{+++}, $FeOH^{++}$, $Fe(OH)_2^+$ and FeO_4^{--}. Using formulae (18)–(29) we have represented in Figs. 2 and 3 the influence of pH on the solubility of $Fe(OH)_2$ (Fig. 2) and on the solubility of Fe_2O_3 and $Fe(OH)_3$ (Fig. 3).

Using all the formulae (1)–(29) we have given in Figs. 4 and 5 two general equilibrium diagrams for the system iron–water, on the one hand considering as solid substances only Fe, Fe_3O_4 and Fe_2O_3 (Fig. 4), and, on the other hand considering as solid substances only Fe, $Fe(OH)_2$ and $Fe(OH)_3$ (Fig. 5).

From Fig. 4 we have derived two theoretical diagrams, Figs. 6*a* and *b*, of "corrosion, immunity and passivation" of iron, on the one hand assuming passivation by Fe_2O_3 alone (Fig. 6*a*), and on the other hand assuming passivation by Fe_2O_3 and Fe_3O_4 (Fig. 6*b*). These figures are valid only in the absence of substances which can form soluble complexes or insoluble salts with iron. According to Charlot [4], divalent iron forms the following complexes: ammine complexes, complexes with organic hydroxyl compounds and with hypophosphite, oxalate and cyanide ions. Trivalent iron forms numerous complexes: hydrochloric (lemon–yellow), sulphuric (yellow), thiocyanic (deep red) and acetic, which are not very stable; hydrofluoric (colourless), pyrophosphoric, phosphoric, organic hydroxyl and oxalic (green), which are more stable, and the very stable orange–yellow ferricyanide $Fe(CN)_6^{---}$ and ferrinitrosocyanide complexes.

The following compounds are sparingly soluble [4]: carbonates, cyanides, oxalates, phosphates, sulphides, etc. of divalent iron; phosphates and sulphides (in alkaline media) of trivalent iron.

3.2. FORMATION, STABILITY AND CORROSION OF IRON

3.2.1. *Theoretical considerations*

From Figs. 4 and 5 iron appears to be a base metal, as its domain of thermodynamic stability, at 25°C and atmospheric pressure, has no portion in common with that of water.

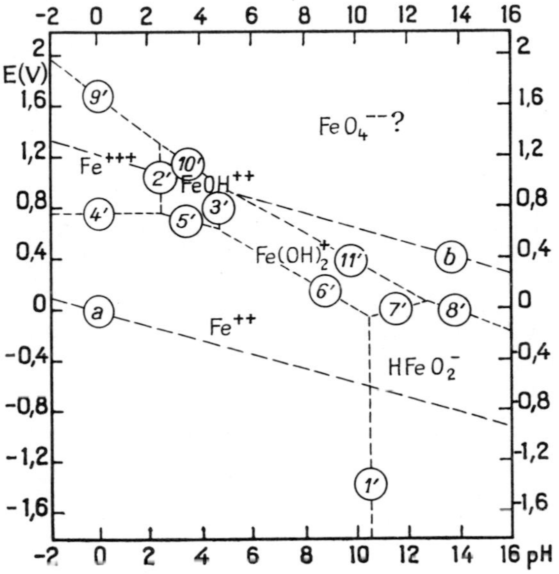

FIG. 1. Domains of relative predominance of the dissolved substances Fe^{++}, $HFeO_2^-$, Fe^{+++}, $FeOH^{++}$, $Fe(OH)_2^+$ and FeO_4^{--}.

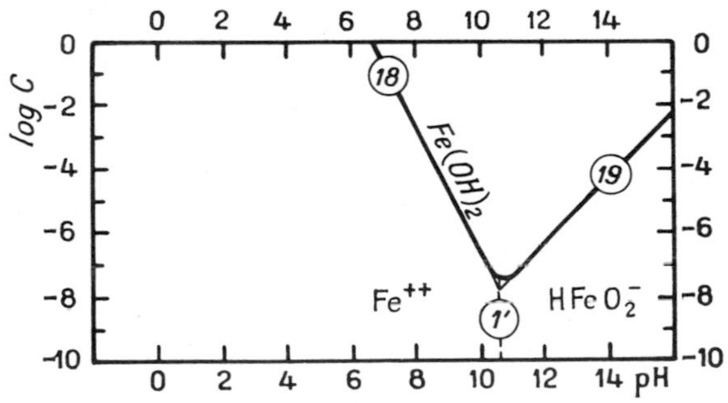

FIG. 2. Influence of pH on the solubility of $Fe(OH)_2$.

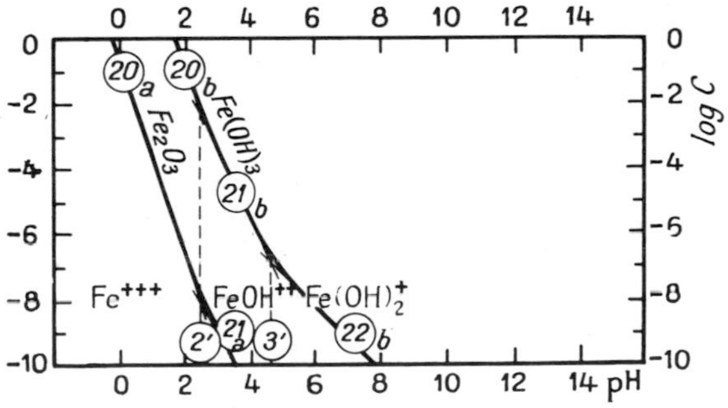

FIG. 3. Influence of pH on the solubility of Fe_2O_3 and $Fe(OH)_3$.

Unstable in the presence of water and a large number of aqueous *non-oxidizing* solutions, iron will therefore corrode in such solutions with the evolution of hydrogen; this reaction, which will be very vigorous in acid solutions, will become progressively less vigorous as the pH of the solution increases, and will almost cease at pH's around 10–13 when the iron wiil become covered with a film of oxide; at very high pH's, above about 13, solutions free from oxidizing agents will be corrosive.

The electrode potential of iron immersed in a solution is increased by the presence of oxidizing agents. The addition of such compounds will therefore have the effect either of passivating the metal more or less perfectly, or, on the other hand, of increasing its corrosion rate, depending on whether or not the increase in potential is sufficient to bring the metal into the passivation domain. The ease with which iron is passivated by oxidizing agents will therefore be the greater the smaller the range of electrode potentials at which corrosion is possible. From Fig. 6*a* passivation will therefore be relatively difficult, or even impossible, at pH's below about 8; it will be relatively easy at pH's above about 8, and very easy at pH's between about 10 and 12.

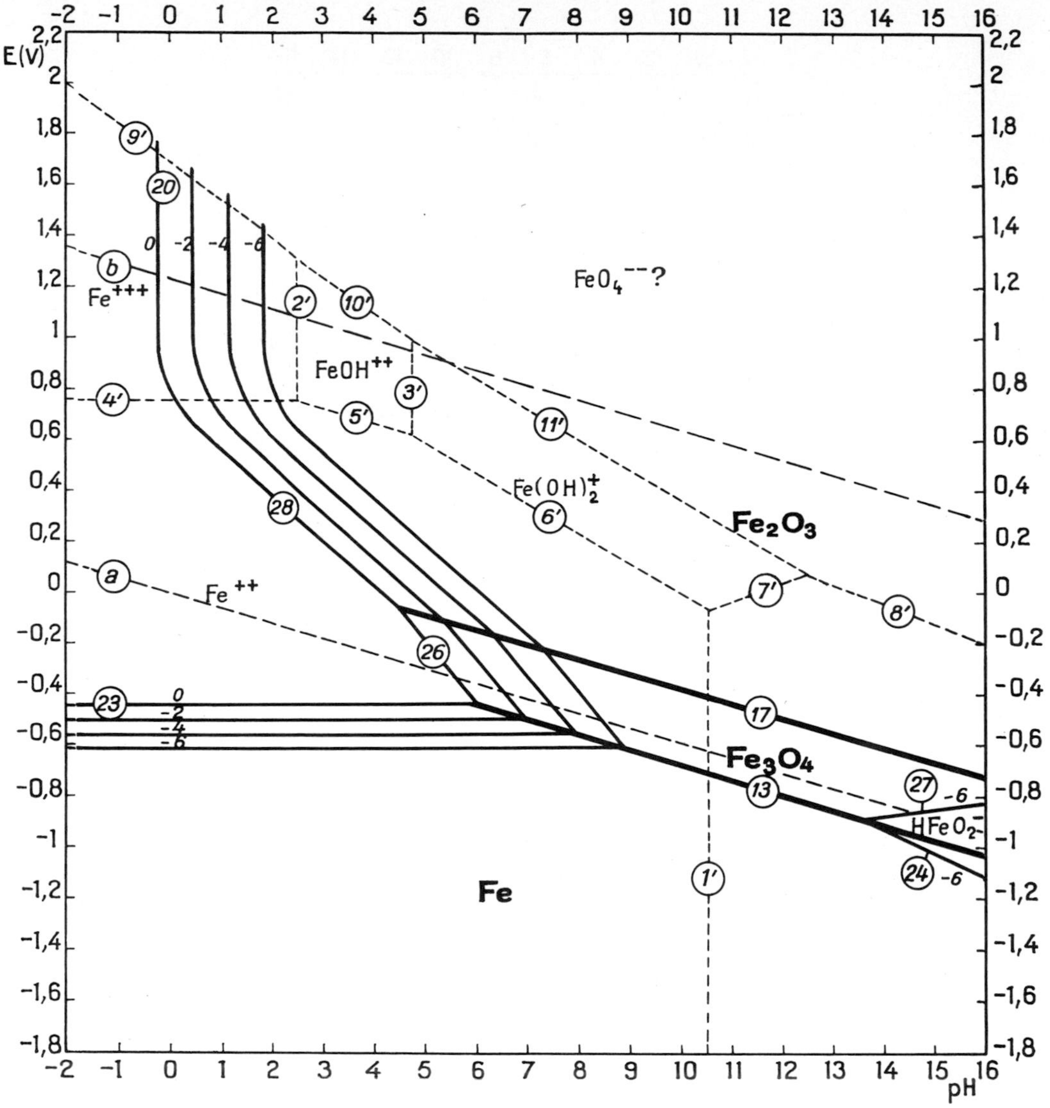

FIG. 4. Potential–pH equilibrium diagram for the system iron–water, at 25°C (considering as solid substances only Fe, Fe_3O_4 and Fe_2O_3).

This, however, concerns the behaviour of iron at 25°C and atmospheric pressure. When the pressure is above 1 atm. the domain of stability of water extends beyond lines (*a*) and (*b*) in Fig. 4; when the hydrogen pressure reaches 740 atm. (i.e. rH = −2·87) the lower limit of the domain of stability of water merges with the line $E_0 = -0{\cdot}085 - 0{\cdot}0591$ pH (volt) which represents the conditions of the equilibrium between Fe and Fe_3O_4 according to reaction (13) (see § 2). At these pressures and within certain limits of pH (between about 10 and 12), iron can therefore be thermodynamically stable in the presence of water, without necessarily being covered with a film of oxide; at pressures above 740 atm. (at 25°C) the domain of stability of iron and that of water have a portion in common, which confers upon iron the characteristics of a noble metal, within very narrow limits however.

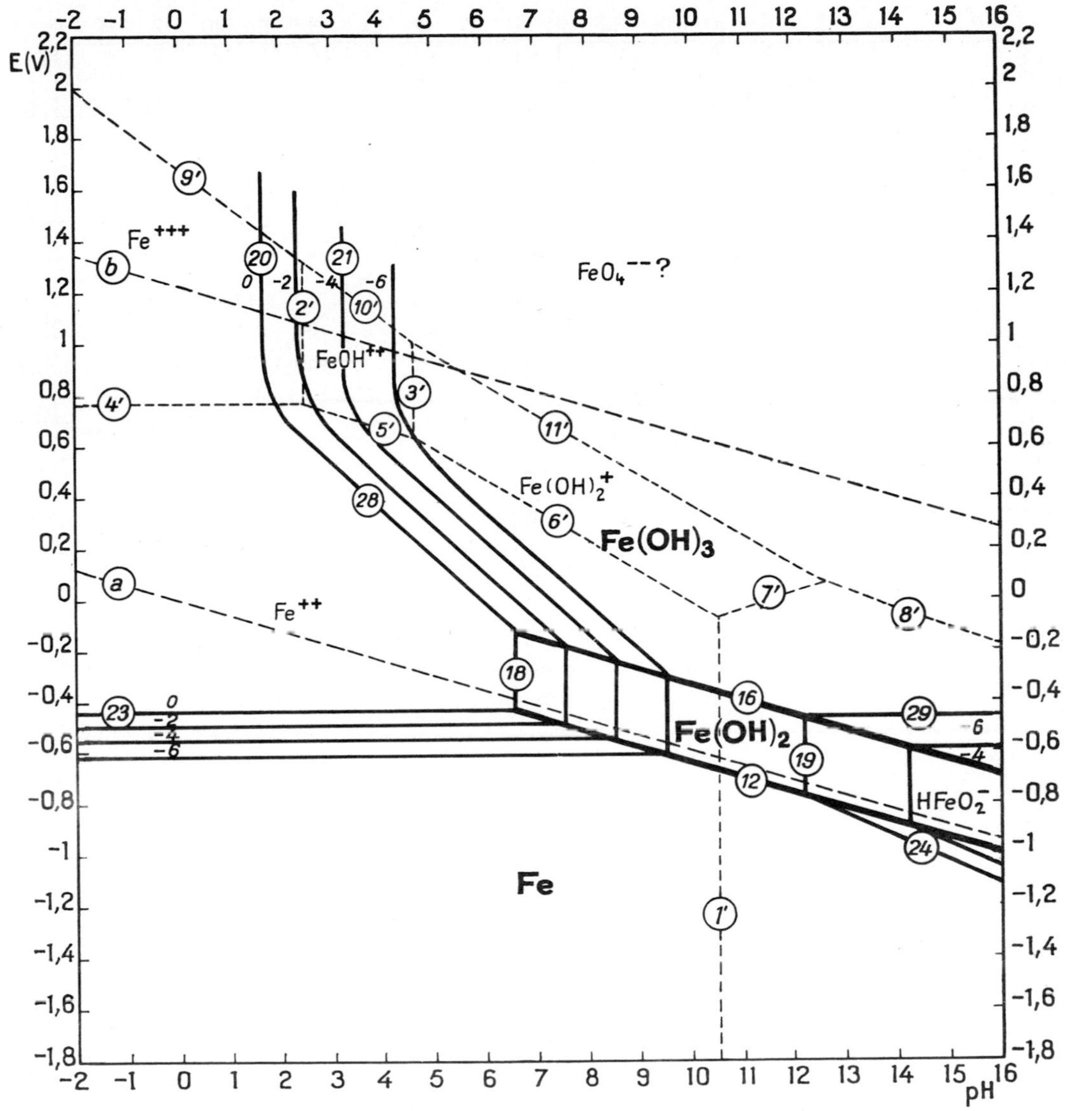

FIG. 5. Potential–pH equilibrium diagram for the system iron–water, at 25°C [considering as solid substances only Fe, $Fe(OH)_2$ and $Fe(OH)_3$].

In agreement with Figs. 4 and 5, metallic iron can be obtained, together with some hydrogen, by the reduction of acid solutions of ferrous salts.

3.2.2. *Experimental verification and detailed investigation*

(*a*) *General conditions of corrosion, immunity and passivation.* In order to verify and make a detailed investigation of these conclusions, we have performed several series of experiments since 1937 in order to examine the behaviour of iron in the presence of various aqueous solutions and under various conditions of pH and electrode potential.

First of all, in order to verify experimentally the possible existence of the domains of corrosion, immunity and passivation shown in the theoretical Figs. 6*a* and *b*, we determined polarization curves

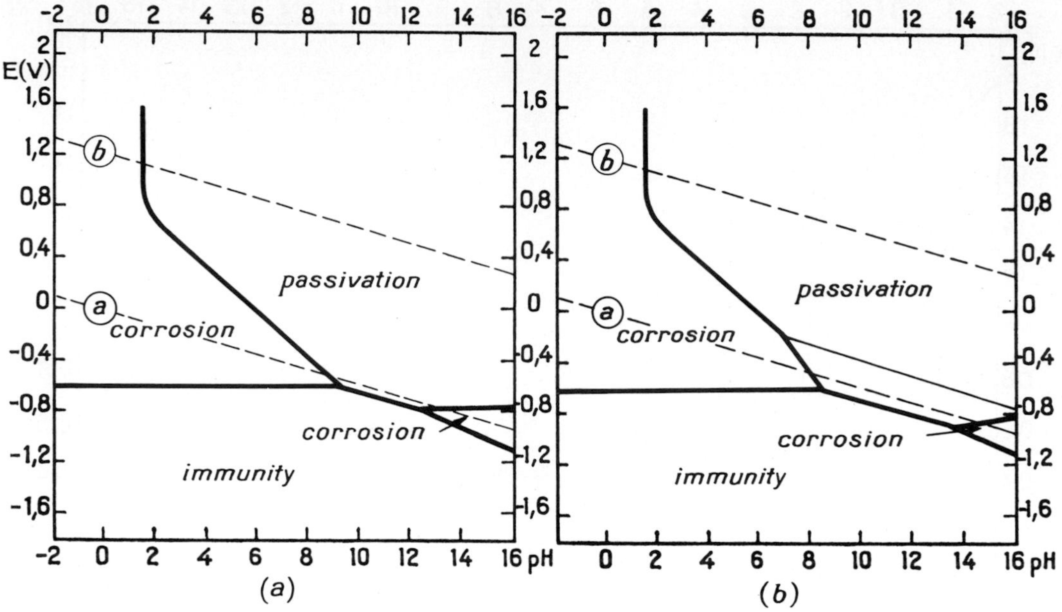

(*a*) Assuming passivation by a film of Fe_2O_3.

(*b*) Assuming passivation by films of Fe_2O_3 and Fe_3O_4.

FIG. 6. Theoretical conditions of corrosion, immunity and passivation of iron.

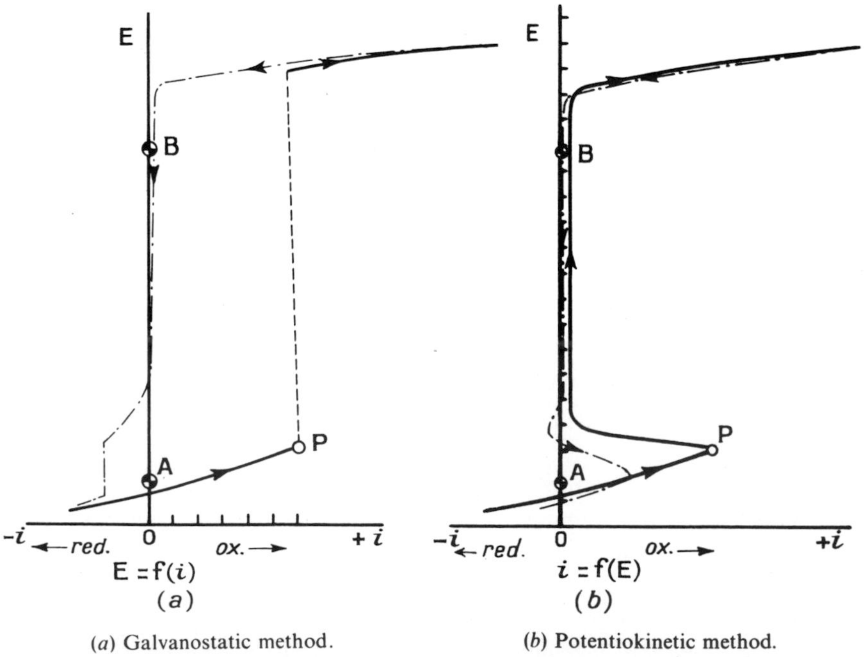

(*a*) Galvanostatic method.

(*b*) Potentiokinetic method.

FIG. 7. Polarization curves for iron in 0·10 M $NaHCO_3$ solutions (pH = 8·4).

for iron in various agitated buffer solutions of pH between 1 and 15, using a method that has been described elsewhere (*loc. cit.* [1]; stelling No. 7; [5], [6]). Figures 7*a* and *b* show two examples of such polarization curves, determined respectively by a manual galvanostatic method and an automatic potentiokinetic method ([7], [8]). These experiments showed that iron is actually passivated under definite conditions of electrode potential and current density; the passivation potential and passivation current density depend on the pH as indicated in Figs. 8*a* and *b*. These experiments also enabled us to establish Figs. 9*a* and *b* which represent diagrammatically the *experimental* conditions of corrosion, immunity and passivation of iron in agitated solutions, with a schematic indication of the corrosion rates of the metal.

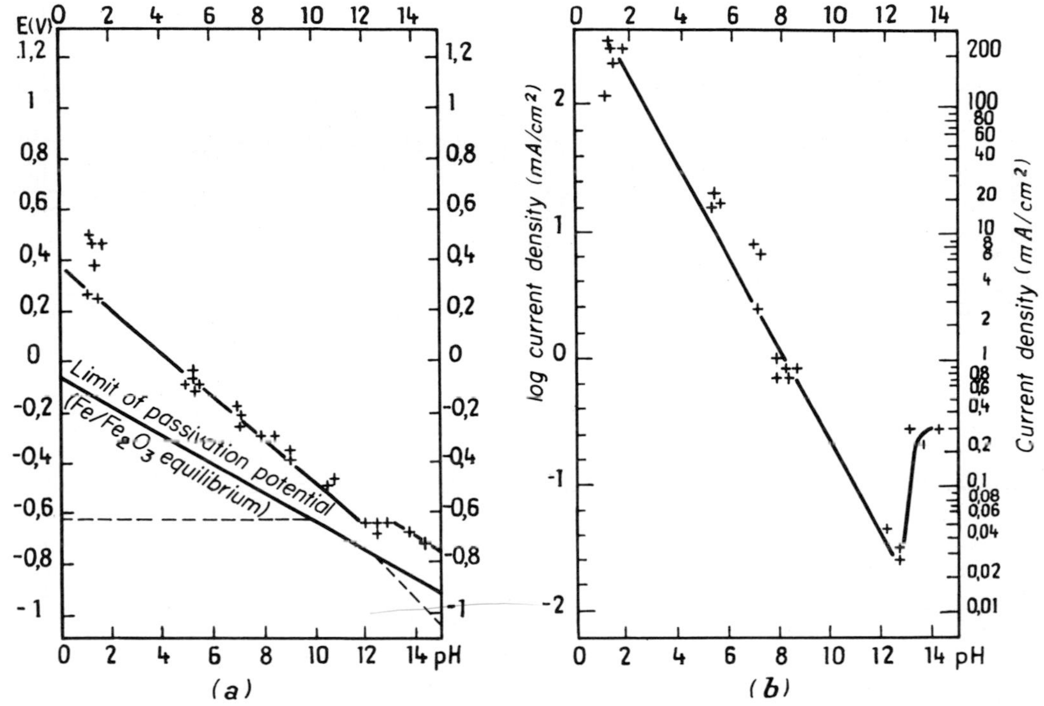

(*a*) Passivation potentials. (*b*) Passivation current densities.

FIG. 8. Influence of pH on the conditions of anodic passivation of iron.

By comparing the experimental diagrams Figs. 8*a* and *b* with the theoretical diagrams Figs. 6*a* and *b*, it can be seen that the theoretical predictions are verified as far as the principal lines are concerned: there actually exist two domains of corrosion (connected, nevertheless, by a narrow domain in which a slight amount of corrosion is possible), one domain of immunity and one domain of passivation; the line separating the domain of passivation from the domains of corrosion does not, however, correspond exactly with the line predicted theoretically.(6) From the above it appears most probable that the thermodynamic method used in this *Atlas* to predict the general conditions of corrosion, immunity and passivation is practically exact, in the particular case of iron at least; more especially this implies the validity of the theory of passivation by an oxide film. This theory was suspected towards 1836 by Michael Faraday and contested for a long time, receiving formal ratification in 1930 when Evans [9] isolated the film formed on iron passivated by anodic treatment in a dilute solution of sulphuric acid,

(6) The limits of the theoretical domains of passivation represented in Figs. 6*a* and *b* relate to solutions containing 10^{-6} g-at Fe/l (i.e. 0·06 mg/l). This, of course, does not necessarily correspond to the experimental cases practically experienced.

thus making visible a film that was invisible when in contact with the metal; Mayne and Pryor in 1949 and 1950 produced some important information in support of this theory, namely that in the presence of an aerated caustic soda solution iron covers itself with a protective film of γ-Fe_2O_3 [10].

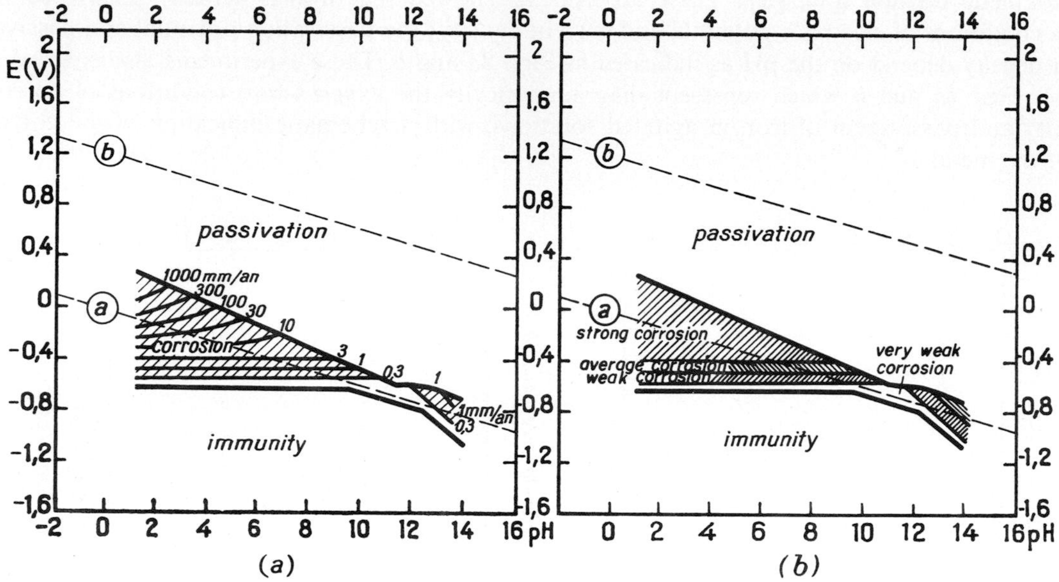

(*a*) Corrosion rates. (*b*) Corrosion intensities.

FIG. 9. Experimental conditions of corrosion, immunity and passivation of iron in the presence of agitated aqueous solutions.

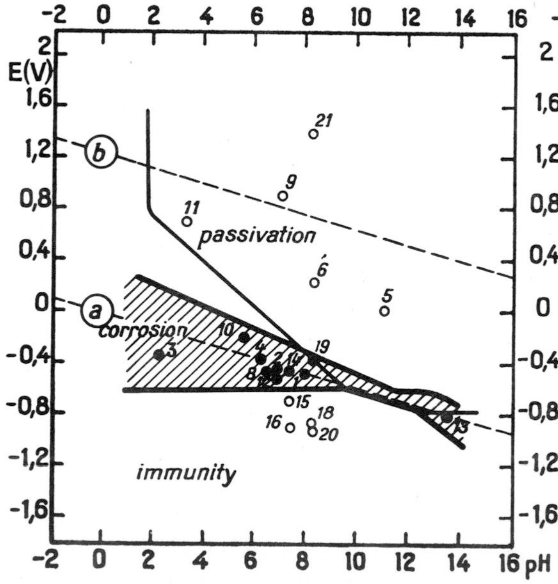

FIG. 10. Theoretical and experimental conditions of corrosion and non-corrosion of iron.

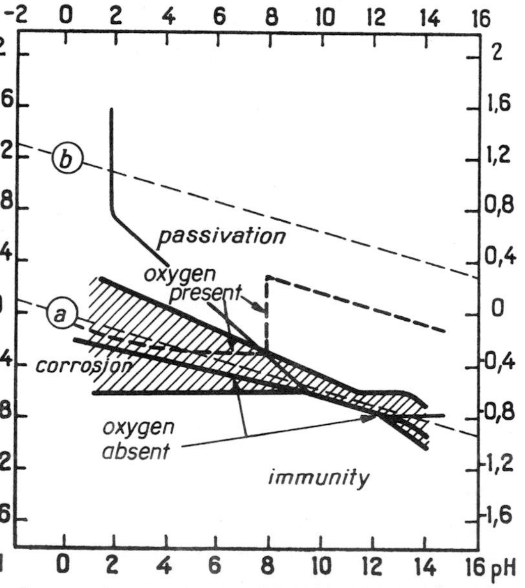

FIG. 11. Electrode-potentials of iron in the absence and in the presence of oxygen.

We also point out that Fig. 8*b* indicates the critical oxidation rate, one side of which an oxidation is passivating and the other side of which it is activating. From this figure it results that iron is most easily passivated at pH's around 12: a very mild oxidizing action is then sufficient to produce passivation.

In Fig. 10 we have reproduced the theoretical and experimental boundaries of the domains of corrosion, immunity and passivation of iron, already represented respectively in Figs. 6*a* and 9*a*. Also shown are the results of various experiments relating to the behaviour of iron in the presence of aqueous solutions. We give below some information concerning these experiments, already shown in previous publications ([11], [12], [13], [14]). Marked in Fig. 10 are the electrode potentials exerted by specimens of iron immersed in solutions of various pH's, these specimens of iron being either electrically insulated, or coupled to another metal, or used as an electrolytic anode or cathode. The cases in which corrosion took place are represented by a black disc ●, and the cases in which there was no corrosion are represented by a white disc ○. The characteristics of the specimens of iron and the solutions were as follows:

No.	pH	E (volt)	
Insulated iron			
1. Distilled water	8·1	−0·486	●
2. NaCl, 1 g/l	6·9	−0·445	●
3. H_2SO_4, 1 ,,	2·3	−0·351	●
4. $NaHSO_3$, 1 ,,	6·4	−0·372	●
5. NaOH, 1 ,,	11·2	+0·026	○
6. K_2CrO_4, 1 ,,	8·5	+0·235	○
8. $KMnO_4$, 0·3 ,,	6·7	−0·460	●
9. $KMnO_4$, 1 ,,	7·1	+0·900	○
10. H_2O_2, 0·3 ,,	5·7	−0·200	●
11. H_2O_2, 3 ,,	3·4	+0·720	○
12. Brussels tap-water	7·0	−0·450	●
13. Air-free NaOH, 40 g/l	13·7	−0·810	●
Iron coupled to another metal			
14. Tap-water, iron–copper	7·5	−0·445	●
15. ,, iron–zinc	7·5	−0·690	○
16. ,, iron–magnesium	7·5	−0·910	○
Iron used as an electrode			
18. 0·10 M $NaHCO_3$, $-^{ve}$ pole	8·4	−0·860	○
19. ,, $+^{ve}$ pole	8·4	−0·350	●
20. ,, $-^{ve}$ pole	8·4	−0·885	○
21. ,, $+^{ve}$ pole	8·4	+1·380	○

It can be seen that, without exception, there is actually corrosion or non-corrosion of the iron depending on whether the point representing the condition of the metal lies in the domain of corrosion, in Fig. 10, or in the domains of immunity or passivation; this agreement holds good not only for the experimental corrosion–immunity–passivation diagram drawn in Fig. 9*a*, but also for the theoretical diagrams in Figs. 6*a* and *b*.

(*b*) *Activating or passivating action of oxygen and other oxidizing agents.* In Fig. 11 we have represented the influence of pH on the electrode potential of electrically insulated iron, on the one hand, in the presence of solutions free from oxygen and other oxidizing agents, and, on the other hand, in the presence of solutions saturated with oxygen at atmospheric pressure.

It can be seen from this figure that, *for solutions free from oxygen*, the potential of the iron is always below line *a*, which implies the possibility of hydrogen evolution. At pH's below about 9·5 or above about 12·5 the potential lies inside the corrosion domains, which means that iron is corroded with the evolution of hydrogen. The corrosion will progressively increase in intensity as the pH decreases below 9·5 or increases above 12·5. At pH's between about 9·5 and 12·5, the potential is near the boundary of the immunity domain and is practically the same as the equilibrium potential of the system Fe–Fe_3O_4, the value of which depends on the pH as shown by relation (13) in paragraph 2.2; under these pH conditions iron will tend to be converted into magnetite with the evolution of hydrogen; however, this conversion will be slow, and will stop completely if the magnetite thus produced forms a protective film on the metal.

The *presence of oxygen* in the solution will have the effect of increasing the electrode potential of the metal. At pH's below about 8 this increase will be insufficient to bring about passivation of the iron; oxygen will therefore increase the corrosion rate. At pH's above about 8 oxygen will bring about passivation by forming a film on the metal, most probably made up of γ-Fe_2O_3 (Mayne and Pryor [10]), which will, in general, be protective in the case of solutions not containing chloride.

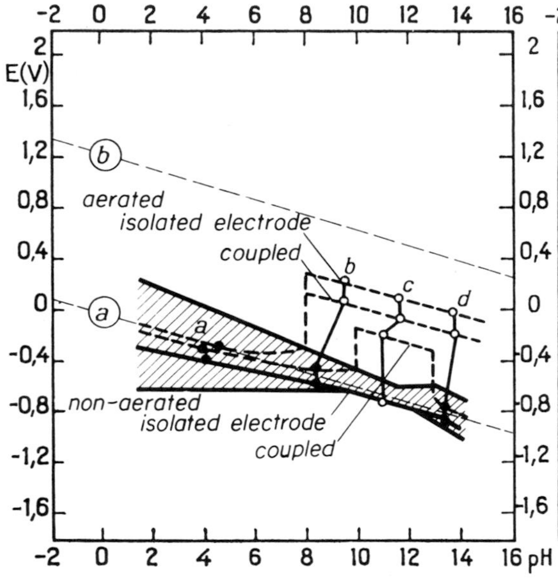

FIG. 12. Differential aeration of iron (Evans cells).

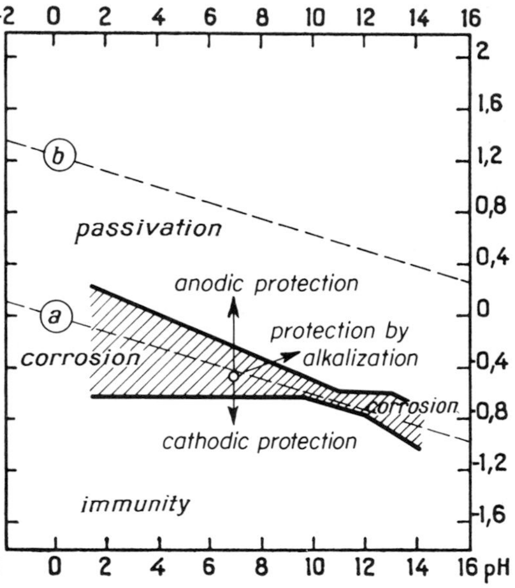

FIG. 13. Protection of iron against corrosion.

(*c*) *Differential aeration.* Figure 11 leads to the following interpretation of the differential aeration phenomena discovered in 1923 by Evans [15]: when a piece of iron is immersed in a practically neutral non-buffered solution, which is aerated in one region and not aerated in another, it is noticed that this "differential aeration" produces an increase in the corrosion rate in the non-aerated regions, and a decrease in the corrosion rate in the aerated regions, with a flow of electric current between these regions. It results from Fig. 11 that, on account of the increase of the pH above 8 due to the reduction of oxygen by the reaction $O_2+2H_2O+4e^- \rightarrow 4OH^-$, the aerated regions will be passivated and the non-aerated regions will not be passivated (Fig. 12); the short-circuiting of aerated regions of high electrode potential and non-aerated regions of low electrode potential will cause electric currents to flow with the reduction of oxygen in the aerated regions and an increase in corrosion in the non-aerated regions. Figure 11 also shows that, for solutions of various pH's, the mode of operation of these "Evans differential aeration cells" will in general vary with the pH as follows:

(*a*) pH below 7: "abnormal" operation: aeration will cause an *increase* in the corrosion rate of the aerated zones with a *small* flow of current between the aerated and non-aerated zones and a *small* increase in the corrosion rate of the non-aerated zones.

(*b*) pH approximately 7–10: "normal" operation: passivation of the aerated zones, a large current and a large corrosion rate in the non-aerated zones;

(*c*) pH approximately 10–13: "abnormal" operation: passivation of the aerated and non-aerated zones without a flow of current;

(*d*) pH above 13: "normal" operation, qualitatively the same as for pH's of approximately 7–10, but less vigorous.

3.2.3. *Processes for the protection of iron against corrosion*

The corrosion of iron by natural waters, and by a large number of moist materials, is due to the existence in Figs. 6*a* and *b* of a large "dangerous triangle" in which the electrode potential of the metal very often is situated.

In order to protect iron against corrosion, therefore, three groups of processes are theoretically possible([7]): as shown in Fig. 13, the point representing the condition of the metal can be displaced downwards (*cathodic protection*), upwards (*anodic protection or protection by passivation*) or to the right (*protection by passivating alkalinization*).

A detailed account of this is beyond the scope of the present book. We shall content ourselves with giving a brief description of each of the three groups of processes.

Cathodic protection is based on the fact that the potential of iron is lowered, on reduction, into the domain of immunity in which the corrosion of iron is theoretically impossible, i.e. appreciably below the following values (Fig. 6):

for pH's below about 10:	$E_0 = -0{\cdot}62$	(volt)
" between about 10 and 13:	$E_0 = -0{\cdot}08-0{\cdot}059$ pH	"
" above about 13:	$E_0 = +0{\cdot}31-0{\cdot}088$ pH	"

Cathodic protection can be brought about either by making the structure to be protected the negative electrode of a source of direct current, or by connecting the structure to a "reactive anode" of zinc or magnesium which corrodes sacrificially; cathodic protection is *generally* free from dangers and affords *perfect* protection of structures in permanent contact with water or a moist medium (soil, porous concrete, etc.) even if the water or other medium is strongly corrosive.

Anodic protection or *protection by passivation* is based on the fact that the potential of iron is raised, on oxidation, into the domain of passivation in which the metal can become covered with a more or less protective film of oxide, i.e. appreciably above the following values (Fig. 8*a*):

for pH's below about 12:	$E_0 = +0{\cdot}40-0{\cdot}085$ pH	(volt)
" between 12 and 13:	$E_0 = -0{\cdot}63$	"
" above 13:	$E_0 = +0{\cdot}20-0{\cdot}062$ pH	"

Anodic protection or protection by passivation can be brought about either by making the structure to be protected the positive electrode of a source of direct current, or by the use of oxidizing substances (which are introduced into the corrosive medium or applied to the surface of the metal); the latter method is sometimes dangerous for the following two reasons: firstly, if the oxidizing action is insufficient there is a generalized increase in corrosion instead of passivation; secondly, if the passivating film is porous and insufficiently protective (which is frequently the case with media containing chloride), the protection is imperfect and corrosion takes place in the form of localized "pitting" at certain points of the structure. Based upon this method of protection is the action of a large number of "anodic" inhibitors (chromates, nitrites, oxygen, etc.) which are added to the corrosive medium or used as constituents of a primary coat of paint, for satisfactory results to be obtained the method must be used with care and with a perfect knowledge of the problem to be solved.

([7]) We shall not consider here protection by the application of coatings (paints, galvanization, electro-plating, etc.) which are intended to prevent completely any direct contact between the metal and the solution.

Finally, *protection by alkalinization*, which is a variation of protection by passivation, consists of the addition of alkaline substances to the water or corrosive medium, producing a pH at which passivation is particularly easy (for instance 10–13). This method is used principally in the treatment of waters with trisodium phosphate or caustic soda, and also in protection by cement coatings. It must also be used with care. It is as well to make sure that the medium treated in this way is oxidizing, in particular if the pH is very high, in order to avoid the metal taking up a position in the small corrosion domain which is shown in Figs. 6 and 9 for alkaline reducing media, and which is one of the principal causes of the caustic embrittlement of boilers.

3.3. SIGNIFICANCE AND PRACTICAL IMPORTANCE OF THE ELECTROCHEMICAL EQUILIBRIUM DIAGRAMS FOR IRON

At this stage we should like to emphasize the fact that potential–pH electrochemical equilibrium diagrams, such as those given in Figs. 4 and 5 of this section of the *Atlas*, represent essentially the conditions under which the reactions considered for their establishment are theoretically possible or impossible, from the thermodynamic point of view. However, a large number of electrochemical reactions are irreversible, which means that although they are thermodynamically possible they do not necessarily take place; in order for them to take place a certain overpotential is required; while these diagrams may show definitely that a reaction cannot take place, they do not show definitely whether or not a thermodynamically possible reaction *will* take place.

In spite of these limitations, the equilibrium diagrams (Figs. 4 and 5), and the "corrosion, immunity and passivation" diagrams derived from them, have proved to be useful and in good agreement with the facts. They have enabled us to specify, predict and control the conditions of cathodic protection of iron and non-alloyed steels in various surrounding media (waters, acid solutions, alkaline solutions, soils and concretes). Moreover, as Evans pointed out in his preface to the English translation of our Delft thesis, by enabling us to predetermine the theoretical conditions of the formation of oxide films, the diagrams have provided explanations of certain controversial phenomena connected with the passivation of metals by film formation; in particular they have enabled us to elucidate the conditions under which oxygen and other oxidizing agents act as activating or passivating substances.

Nevertheless, it should be realized that such equilibrium diagrams cannot, by themselves, provide the *complete* solution to any problem. They should be considered primarily as a tool which, in the hands of those who fully understand the meaning of electrode potentials, can assist in the understanding of facts, guide research and lead to the development of near-perfect techniques in fields involving electrochemistry, in particular concerning the protection of metals against corrosion. Such research must involve not only thermodynamic studies but also kinetic studies and chemical, microscopic and structural examination.

By way of an example we draw the reader's attention to Figs. 7*a* and *b*, which represent potential–current curves for the successive anodic and cathodic polarization of iron in a 0·1 M sodium bicarbonate solution, firstly using a galvanostatic method (Fig. 7*a*), and, secondly, using a potentiokinetic method (Fig. 7*b*). Diagrams such as that in Fig. 7*a* have enabled us to determine the passivation potentials and passivation current densities represented in Figs. 8 and also in Figs. 9*a* and *b* which are derived from them: these potentials and current densities are respectively the ordinates and abscissae of the points P, for which passivation appears.

The curves in Fig. 7 reveal that, contrary to a still widespread opinion, the passivation is, to all intents and purposes, reversible, at least in the case of bicarbonate solutions: just as "active" iron becomes passive if, by oxidation, its potential is raised above the passivation potential corresponding to the point P, so also "passivated" iron becomes active if, by reduction, its potential is lowered below this value. This gives a quantitative aspect to Evans' theory of the *reductive dissolution* of the passivation film formed on iron.

Recent work by de Zoubov [16] and Clerbois [17] working independently of each other, has shown that for sodium bicarbonate solutions, the passivation potential of iron is exactly that at which ferrous carbonate $FeCO_3$ is in thermodynamic equilibrium with an oxide of iron Fe_2O_3 or Fe_3O_4; these equilibrium conditions have been indicated in the construction of potential–pH equilibrium diagrams for the ternary system $Fe–CO_2–H_2O$ [18]. The passivation of iron therefore seems to be due to the formation of a film of Fe_2O_3 or Fe_3O_4 in contact with the metal in a solution saturated with $FeCO_3$, and this passivation would therefore appear when the solid substance formed by corrosion ceases to be non-protective ferrous carbonate and becomes protective oxide.

4. BIBLIOGRAPHY

[1] M. Pourbaix, *Thermodynamique des solutions aqueuses diluées. Représentation graphique du rôle du pH et du potentiel* (Thèse, Delft, 1945; Béranger, Paris and Liège). *Thermodynamics of Dilute Aqueous Solutions,* Arnold, London.

[2] B. Schrager, *Chem. News.*, 138, 1929, p. 354.

[3] Ch. D. Hodgmann, *Handbook of Chemistry and Physics,* 26, Chemical Rubber Publ. Co., Cleveland, 1936.

[4] G. Charlot, *L'analyse qualitative et les réactions en solution,* 4th ed., Masson, Paris, 1957, pp. 180–185.

[5] M. Pourbaix, *Corrosion, passivité et passivation du fer; le rôle du pH et du potentiel* [Thèse, Brussels, 1945; *Mémoires Soc. Roy. Belge Ingénieurs et Industriels,* No. 1, March 1951, pp. 1–40].

[6] M. Pourbaix, *Sur l'interprétation thermodynamique des courbes de polarisation* (Rapport technique RT.1 of CEBELCOR, 1952).

[7] M. Pourbaix, *Compte rendu d'une séance d'étude sur des recherches fondamentales en électrochimie et en corrosion* (Brussels, 15 July 1958) (Rapport technique RT.67 of CEBELCOR, 1958).

[8] M. Pourbaix, J. Laureys and L. Neelemans, *Méthode de prédétermination des circonstances de non corrosion et de corrosion des métaux et alliages* (Rapport CEFA/R.1 of the Commission des Études Fondamentales et Applications of CEBELCOR, 1958).

[9] U. R. Evans, *Nature,* **126**, 130 (1930). See also U. R. Evans and M. J. Pryor, *J. Chem. Soc.*, 1949, p. 3330; 1950, pp. 1259, 1266 and 1274.
A more recent description of the method of isolation of the protective film and a discussion of the important phenomenon of "reductive dissolution" of the oxide can be found in U. R. Evans, *The Corrosion and Oxidation of Metals,* pp. 222–8 (Ed. Arnold, London, 1960).

[10] J. E. O. Mayne and M. J. Pryor, The mechanism of inhibitors of corrosion of iron; I. by chromic acid and potassium chromate, *J. Chem. Soc.*, 1949, pp. 1831–5; II. by sodium hydroxide solution (in collaboration with J. W. Menter), *J. Chem. Soc.*, 1950, p. 3229.

[11] M. Pourbaix, *Applications de diagrammes tension–pH relatifs au fer et à l'eau oxygénée. Expériences de démonstration* (Rapport technique RT.2 of CEBELCOR, 1954).

[12] M. Pourbaix, *Leçons sur la corrosion électrochimique* (1er fascicule) (Rapport technique RT.57 of CEBELCOR, 1957).

[13] M. Pourbaix, Deux expériences de cours en thermodynamique électrochimique, *C. R.* 2e *Réunion du CITCE,* Milan, 1950, Tamburini, Milan, 1951.

[14] J. Feron and M. Pourbaix, Potentiels de passivation et d'activation du fer. Corrosion cathodique du fer en présence d'oxygène, *C.R.* 3e *Réunion du CITCE,* Berne, 1951; Manfredi, Milan, 1952.

[15] U. R. Evans, *J. Inst. Metals,* **30**, 267 (1923).

[16] N. de Zoubov, *Sur le comportement électrochimique du fer en solution bicarbonique.* Lecture delivered in Brussels on 30 August 1960 at the reunion of Commission 5 "corrosion" of the Comité International de Thermodynamique et de Cinétique Électrochimiques CITCE.

[17] F. Clerbois, *Contribution à l'étude du comportement anodique des métaux en milieu aqueux,* Grenoble Thesis, 1960.

[18] E. Deltombe and M. Pourbaix, *Comportement électrochimique du fer en solution carbonique. Diagrammes d'équilibres tension–pH du système* $Fe–CO_2–H_2O$, at 25°C (Rapport technique RT.8 of CEBELCOR, 1954).

SECTION 12.2

COBALT([1])

E. DELTOMBE and M. POURBAIX

SUMMARY

([1]) Shortened and adapted version of the Rapport technique RT.6 of CEBELCOR [1].

1. SUBSTANCES CONSIDERED AND SUBSTANCES NOT CONSIDERED

	Oxidation number (Z)	Considered	Not considered	μ^0(cal.)	Name, colour, crystalline system
Solid substances	0	Co	–	0	Cobalt, grey, hex.
	+2	CoO hydr.	–	a. – 52 310	Hydrated cobaltous oxide or cobaltous hydroxide $Co(OH)_2$, blue (red), rhomb.(2)
	»	»	–	b. – 49 000	Cobaltous oxide, grey–green, cub.
	+2.67	Co_3O_4	–	–167 835 (3)	Cobalto-cobaltic oxide, grey–black, cub.
	»	–	Co_3O_4 hydr.	–	Hydrated cobalto-cobaltic oxide.
	+3	Co_2O_3 hydr.	–	–115 130	Hydrated cobaltic oxide or cobaltic hydroxide $Co(OH)_3$, yellow–brown(2)
	»	–	Co_2O_3	–	Anhydrous cobaltic oxide, brown, rhomb.
	+4	CoO_2	–	– 51 840 (3)	Cobaltic peroxide
	»	–	CoO_2 hydr.	–	Monohydrated cobaltic hydroxide $CoO_2.H_2O$ or cobaltic acid H_2CoO_3
Dissolved substances	+2	Co^{++}	–	– 12 800	Cobaltous ion, pink
	»	$HCoO_2^-$	–	– 82 970 (3)	Dicobaltite ion, blue
	+3	Co^{+++}	–	28 900	Cobaltic ion

2. REACTIONS AND EQUILIBRIUM FORMULAE(4)

2.1. TWO DISSOLVED SUBSTANCES

2.1.1. *Relative stability of the dissolved substances*

Z = +2

1. $Co^{++} + 2H_2O = HCoO_2^- + 3H^+$ $\qquad \log\frac{(HCoO_2^-)}{(Co^{++})} = -31.70 + 3\,pH$

+2 → +3

2. $Co^{++} = Co^{+++} + e^-$ $\qquad E_0 = 1.808 + 0.0591 \log\frac{(Co^{+++})}{(Co^{++})}$

3. $HCoO_2^- + 3H^+ = Co^{+++} + 2H_2O + e^-$ $\qquad E_0 = -0.065 + 0.1773\,pH + 0.0591 \log\frac{(Co^{+++})}{(HCoO_2^-)}$

2.1.2. *Limits of the domains of relative predominance of the dissolved substances*

1'. $Co^{++}/HCoO_2^-$ $\qquad pH = 10.57$

2'. Co^{++}/Co^{+++} $\qquad E_0 = 1.808$

3'. $HCoO_2^-/Co^{+++}$ $\qquad E_0 = -0.065 + 0.1773\,pH$

---

(2) These values of μ^0 for the oxides correspond to the following values for the hydroxides:

$Co(OH)_2$: – 109 000 cal., $\qquad Co(OH)_3$: – 142 600 cal.

(3) Values calculated from data given by Besson [4], Gayer and Garrett (*J. Amer. Chem. Soc.* **72**, 3921 (1950)).

(4) For the reactions involving CoO, the letter *a* relates to $Co(OH)_2$, whose free enthalpy of formation is – 109 000 cal.; the letter *b* relates to anhydrous CoO, whose free enthalpy of formation is – 49 000 cal.

2.2. TWO SOLID SUBSTANCES

Limits of the domains of relative stability of the solid substances

$0 \to +2$

4. $\quad$ **Co** $\; + \; H_2O = \;$ **CoO** $\; +2\,H^+ \; +2\,e^-$ $\qquad$ $a.\; E_0 = \quad 0.095 - 0.0591\; pH$
$\qquad\qquad\qquad\qquad\qquad\qquad\qquad\qquad\qquad\qquad$ $b.\; = \quad 0.166 - 0.0591\; pH$

$+2 \to +2.67$

5. $\quad$ $3\,$**CoO** $\; + \; H_2O = \;$ **Co$_3$O$_4$** $\;+2\,H^+ \; +2\,e^-$ $\qquad$ $a.\; E_0 = \quad 0.993 - 0.0591\; pH$
$\qquad\qquad\qquad\qquad\qquad\qquad\qquad\qquad\qquad\qquad$ $b.\; = \quad 0.777 - 0.0591\; pH$

$+2.67 \to +3$

6. $\quad$ $2\,$**Co$_3$O$_4$** $\; + \; H_2O = 3\,$**Co$_2$O$_3$** $\;+2\,H^+ \; +2\,e^-$ $\qquad$ $E_0 = \quad 1.018 - 0.0591\; pH$

$+3 \to +4$

7. $\quad$ **Co$_2$O$_3$** $\; + \; H_2O = 2\,$**CoO$_2$** $\;+2\,H^+ \; +2\,e^-$ $\qquad$ $E_0 = \quad 1.477 - 0.0591\; pH$

2.3. ONE DISSOLVED SUBSTANCE AND ONE SOLID SUBSTANCE

Solubility of the solid substances

$Z = +2$

8. $\quad$ $Co^{++} \; + \; H_2O = \;$ **CoO** $\; +2\,H^+$ $\qquad\qquad$ $a.\; \log(Co^{++}) \; = \quad 12.60 - 2\; pH$
$\qquad\qquad\qquad\qquad\qquad\qquad\qquad\qquad\qquad$ $b.\; \qquad\qquad = \quad 15.03 - 2\; pH$

9. $\quad$ **CoO** $\; + \; H_2O = \; HCoO_2^- + \; H^+$ $\qquad\qquad$ $a.\; \log(HCoO_2^-) = -19.10 + \; pH$
$\qquad\qquad\qquad\qquad\qquad\qquad\qquad\qquad\qquad$ $b.\; \qquad\qquad = -16.67 + \; pH$

$Z = +3$

10. $\quad$ $2\,Co^{+++} + 3\,H_2O = \;$ **Co$_2$O$_3$** $+6\,H^+$ $\qquad\qquad$ $\log(Co^{+++}) = -1.05 - 3\; pH$

$0 \to +2$

11. $\quad$ **Co** $\qquad\qquad = \; Co^{++} \qquad\qquad +2\,e^-$ $\qquad$ $E_0 = -0.277 \qquad\qquad +0.0295\; \log(Co^{++})$

12. $\quad$ **Co** $\; +2\,H_2O = \; HCoO_2^- +3\,H^+ +2\,e^-$ $\qquad$ $E_0 = \quad 0.659 - 0.0886\; pH +0.0295\; \log(HCoO_2^-)$

$+2 \to +2.67$

13. $\quad$ $3\,Co^{++} \; +4\,H_2O = \;$ **Co$_3$O$_4$** $+8\,H^+ \; +2\,e^-$ $\qquad$ $E_0 = \quad 2.112 - 0.2364\; pH -0.0886\; \log(Co^{++})$

14. $\quad$ $3\,HCoO_2^- + \; H^+ = \;$ **Co$_3$O$_4$** $+2\,H_2O +2\,e^-$ $\qquad$ $E_0 = -0.700 + 0.0295\; pH -0.0886\; \log(HCoO_2^-)$

$+2 \to +3$

15. $\quad$ $2\,Co^{++} \; +3\,H_2O = \;$ **Co$_2$O$_3$** $+6\,H^+ \; +2\,e^-$ $\qquad$ $E_0 = \quad 1.746 - 0.1773\; pH -0.0591\; \log(Co^{++})$

16. $\quad$ $2\,HCoO_2^- \qquad = \;$ **Co$_2$O$_3$** $+ \; H_2O +2\,e^-$ $\qquad$ $E_0 = -0.128 \qquad\qquad -0.0591\; \log(HCoO_2^-)$

$+2 \to +4$

17. $\quad$ $Co^{++} \; +2\,H_2O = \;$ **CoO$_2$** $\;+4\,H^+ \; +2\,e^-$ $\qquad$ $E_0 = \quad 1.612 - 0.1182\; pH -0.0295\; \log(Co^{++})$

$+3 \to +4$

18. $\quad$ $Co^{+++} +2\,H_2O = \;$ **CoO$_2$** $\;+4\,H^+ \; + \; e^-$ $\qquad$ $E_0 = \quad 1.416 - 0.2364\; pH -0.0591\; \log(Co^{+++})$

3. EQUILIBRIUM DIAGRAM AND ITS INTERPRETATION

3.1. ESTABLISHMENT OF THE DIAGRAM

Using relations (1)–(18), we have constructed a potential–pH equilibrium diagram for the system cobalt–water at 25°C (Fig. 1).

This diagram indicates the conditions of thermodynamic stability of cobalt and those derivatives of it which can exist in the presence of water or aqueous solutions free from substances with which cobalt can form soluble complexes or insoluble salts.

Cobalt forms soluble complexes with ammonia, chlorides, cyanides and sulphocyanides; it forms insoluble salts with sulphides, carbonates, oxalates and cyanides (Charlot [2]).

Figure 2, derived from Fig. 1, represents the theoretical conditions of corrosion, immunity and passivation of cobalt.

3.2. STABILITY, FORMATION AND CORROSION OF COBALT

The domain of thermodynamic stability of cobalt, in Fig. 1, has a small area in common with that of water. Cobalt therefore appears to be a slightly noble metal; in this respect and many other respects it is very similar to nickel, being appreciably more noble than iron but slightly less noble than lead. Like nickel and other more noble metals, cobalt can theoretically be obtained in the metallic state,

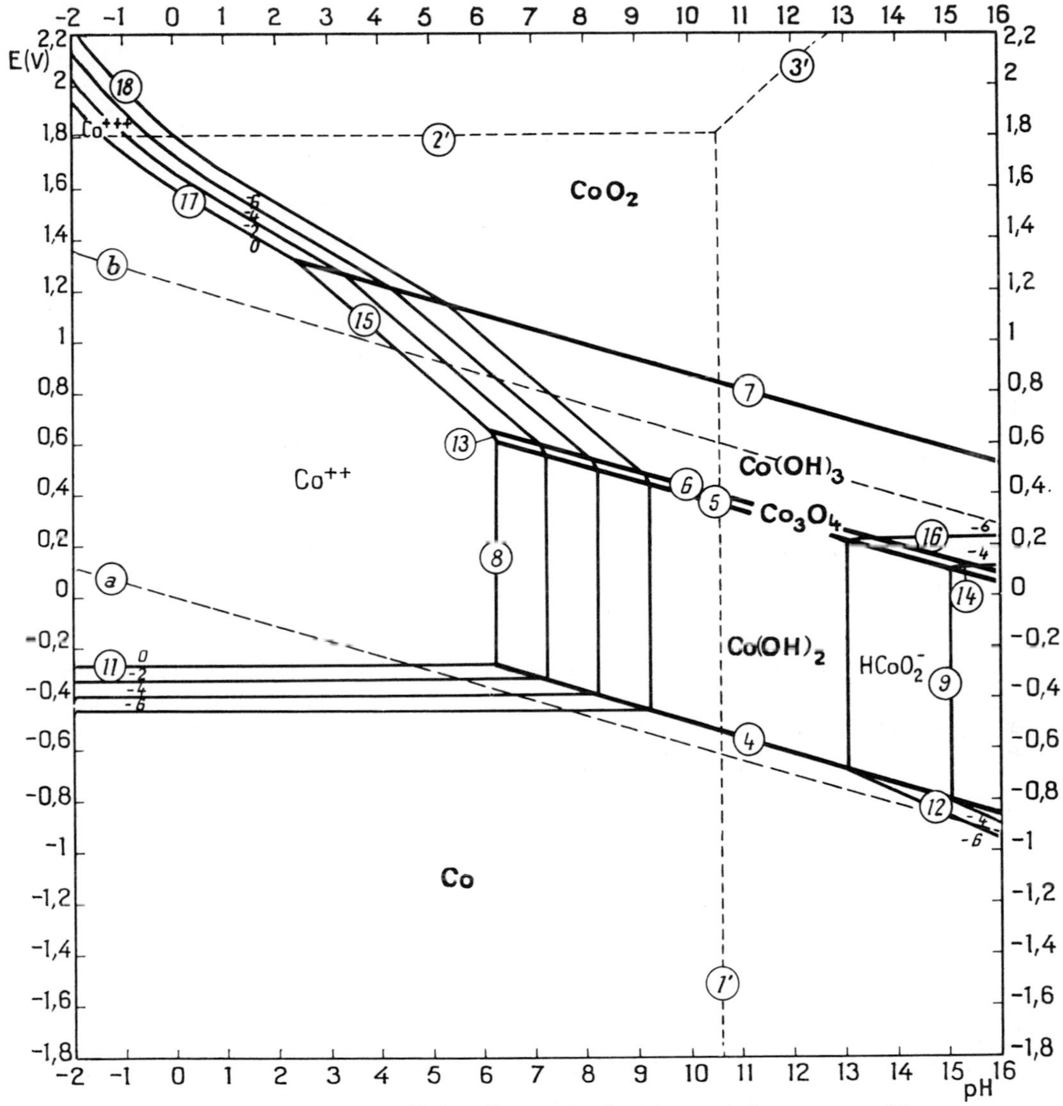

FIG. 1. Potential–pH equilibrium diagram for the system cobalt–water, at 25°C.

according to Fig. 1, by the action of hydrogen on practically neutral solutions of its salts; in actual fact this reaction is extremely slow at room temperature, but can be brought about at a high temperature and pressure, by the Forward process, for example.

Native cobalt is very rare in nature (it is present in the native irons of Greenland, together with platinum in the River Ural, and with native silver in the River Ontario, etc.). It usually occurs as sulphide, arsenide, antimonide, arsenate, oxide, etc.

According to the theoretical Figs. 1 and 2, the corrosion resistance of cobalt in non-complexing solutions depends as follows on the pH and the presence of oxidizing agents: cobalt is uncorrodible in neutral or alkaline solutions free from oxidizing agents, slightly corrodible in acid solutions free from oxidizing agents and very corrodible in acid or very alkaline solutions containing oxidizing agents. Neutral or slightly alkaline oxidizing solutions cover it with a layer of oxide. Cobalt is easily protected cathodically for instance by lowering its electrode potential to a value below −0·5 V in acid or neutral solution.

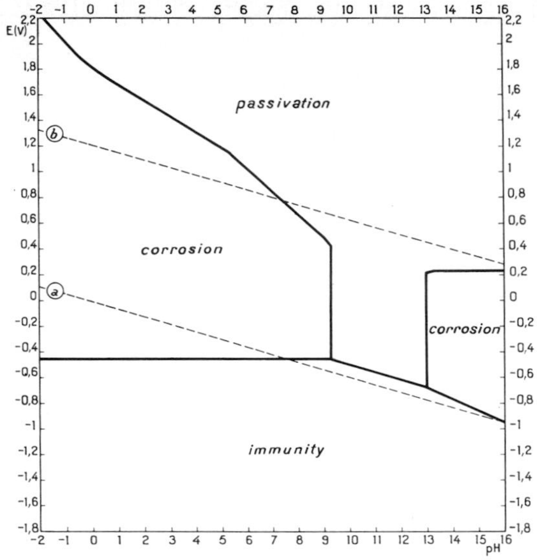

FIG. 2. Theoretical domains of corrosion, immunity and passivation of cobalt, at 25°C.

These predictions are in good agreement with the experimental results, except for the fact that on account of the large hydrogen overpotential of cobalt, it is practically uncorroded by non-oxidizing acids: cobalt is one of the metals least attacked by non-oxidizing acids; however, if it is put in contact with a substance of low hydrogen overpotential such as platinum, corrosion will take place with the evolution of hydrogen. In the presence of water the metal covers itself with a layer of oxide and becomes passive [3]; it can also be passivated in neutral or alkaline aqueous solutions by anodic oxidation.

On account of this good corrosion resistance, electro-plating with cobalt is of considerable practical interest.

3.3. STABILITY OF THE OXIDES AND HYDROXIDES OF COBALT

Besson [4] has shown that the oxidation of cobaltous hydroxide in an alkaline medium by various oxidizing agents can give rise to the formation of various oxides, which can also be obtained by anodic oxidation: thus, air oxidizes $Co(OH)_2$ to Co_2O_3, the reaction being rapid up to the stage Co_3O_4. Persulphate, permanganate, hypochlorite and hypobromite form CO_2O_3; when used in excess they also produce some CoO_2. Hydrogen peroxide can act as an oxidizing agent, converting CoO into Co_2O_3, and as a reducing agent, bringing about the reverse process: a state of equilibrium between CoO and Co_2O_3 is thus reached.

The results of numerous studies on the various oxides and hydroxides of cobalt have been published, but, in most of them, the conclusions concerning the composition of the various compounds are rendered inaccurate by the ability of CoO and Co_3O_4 to absorb oxygen; it was thus thought possible to define oxides of very varied compositions. As Gmelin describes [5], the oxides which can ultimately be considered to have a real existence are CoO and Co_3O_4 and the hydrate $Co_2O_3H_2O$. CoO is difficult to obtain in the pure state, since on cooling it easily absorbs oxygen to give Co_3O_4; it can be prepared only by roasting the carbonate or hydroxide in a vacuum.

On considering an aqueous system, we notice that the standard free enthalpy of formation of $Co(OH)_2$ at 25°C (−109 000 cal.) is below that of the system $CoO + H_2O$ (−49 000 − 56 690 = −105 690 cal.); the hydroxide is therefore the most stable form and for this reason we have considered it in establishing Fig. 1.

Co_3O_4 also forms an indefinite hydrate $Co_3O_4 . nH_2O$, whose free enthalpy of formation we do not know, which means that we cannot compare the relative stability of the two substances. Co_3O_4, unlike CoO, is stable in air.

It appears that the oxide Co_2O_3 cannot be obtained in the pure state from the hydrate $Co(OH)_3$, as the dehydration of the latter almost invariably takes place with the evolution of oxygen. In aqueous media it is therefore logical to refer to the stable form $Co(OH)_3$, as we have done in establishing Fig. 1, more especially as we do not know the free enthalpy of formation of Co_2O_3.

The peroxide CoO_2 (or its hydrate $CoO_2 . nH_2O$) which can be formed by the action of excess oxidizing agent on cobaltous hydroxide $Co(OH)_2$, is highly unstable, decomposing water with the formation of cobaltic hydroxide $Co(OH)_3$ and the evolution of oxygen. As described above, it is certain that some CoO_2 is formed during the anodic oxidation of cobalt in alkaline solution, and for this reason we have considered it in establishing Fig. 1. We have not considered the hypothetical "cobaltic acid" H_2CoO_3 or $CoO_2 . H_2O$, in which cobalt is tetravalent, as the data given in chemical literature concerning its existence are contradictory.

As shown by Fig. 1, cobaltous hydroxide $Co(OH)_2$ is precipitated when a solution of cobaltous ions is made alkaline: for a molar solution of Co^{++} ions precipitation begins at pH = 6·3, and for a 10^{-6} M solution it begins at pH = 9·3. At higher pH's than 10·6 $Co(OH)_2$ redissolves as dicobaltite ions $HCoO_2^-$.

The cobaltous ion Co^{++} is oxidized in very acid media to the cobaltic ion Co^{+++} at a potential of about +1·81 V. This oxidation can be brought about both electrolytically and by the action of fluorine or ozone, but the cobaltic salts thus formed are usually unstable, and only the fluoride and sulphate have been isolated. On the other hand, complexes of cobaltic salts with ammonia are very stable, but a discussion of them is beyond the scope of the present study. At higher pH's cobaltous salts can be oxidized to cobaltic hydroxide $Co(OH)_3$.

3.4. ELECTROLYTIC PRODUCTION OF COBALT

The actual processes used in practice for the electrolytic extraction of cobalt illustrate the requirement of producing working conditions which enable a compromise to be made between the danger of hydroxide separation, which would give a metal contaminated with oxide, and the danger of hydrogen evolution, which would reduce the current yield and modify the structure of the metal; in general, slightly acid or almost neutral electrolytic baths are used. These baths either have diaphragms or forced electrolyte circulation.

It is obvious from Fig. 1 that, in order to reduce the hydrogen evolution, it is necessary to work at as high a pH as possible, but, to avoid precipitation of the hydroxide $Co(OH)_2$, the pH must remain below 6·3 for a solution molar in Co^{++} ions (7·3 for a 0·01 M solution); a pH around neutrality must therefore be maintained.

We must point out, in particular, the harmful influence of acidity on the yield: as Udy [6] describes, for a solution of $CoSO_4$ with 0·3 to 1 per cent H_2SO_4, the yield is 80 to 95 per cent; it falls to 8 per cent with 5 per cent H_2SO_4; in a neutral solution (in the absence of oxygen) the yield can reach 100 per cent, but there is a tendency for oxide to separate out.

Here is a summary of one of the processes used by the Union Minière du Haut-Katanga described by L. Theys [7]: a constant pH is maintained by feeding the electrolytic cells with a solution of cobalt sulphate saturated with excess precipitated cobalt hydrate; the sulphuric acid liberated at the anodes is immediately neutralized by the cobalt hydrate which is converted into soluble sulphate, and the pH of the bath is thus maintained automatically around 7. The danger of oxide occlusion at the cathode is avoided by churning the electrolyte vigorously with compressed air led in through pipes which form part of the cathodes, emerging at their lower edges; the bubbles of air so produced sweep over the two faces of the cathodes. Ammonium sulphate is added to the electrolyte to maintain a high conductivity. The current yield is as large as 90–93 per cent. The deposits are removed from the steel cathodes and subjected to thermal refining; they contain 93·5 to 95 per cent cobalt.

Recently the Union Minière du Haut-Katanga have opened up a factory (Kolwezi, June 1961) where cobalt is separated electrolytically from a clear concentrated solution, from which copper, zinc and nickel have previously been removed. The electrolysis is carried out without a diaphragm at 60°C, the solution being kept at a pH of about 1·5 by stirring. Under these conditions precipitation of manganese at the cathode is prevented.

The current efficiency of the process is only of the order of 75 per cent (instead of 90–93 per cent under the conditions given above), but high purity deposits are obtained: about 99·8 per cent of cobalt (instead of 90–93 per cent) and 0·1 per cent of nickel [8].

On account of the possibility of formation of complex ions between cobalt and ammonia, the diagrams established in this account are inadequate for a thermodynamic study of the behaviour of solutions containing both cobalt sulphate and ammonium sulphate; such a study requires a knowledge of the thermodynamic characteristics of the ternary system $Co–NH_3–H_2O$.

The process is often carried out at a temperature above room temperature. The favourable influence of raising the temperature has been pointed out by several investigators, notably by Raessler [9] who showed that the electrolytic yield, in electrolytes of various acidities, increases as the temperature increases; moreover, the separation of hydrogen decreases as the temperature increases, enabling cobalt with a smaller hydrogen content to be obtained.

3.5. ELECTROLYTIC AND CHEMICAL COBALT-PLATING

Although cobalt can be deposited on iron and other common metals, very little electro-plating of cobalt is carried out at present. Cobalt deposits differ from those of nickel in that they have a slightly bluer tint.

The physico-chemical principles of the process are the same as those which have just been described for the electrolytic production of cobalt.

Schildbach [10] has pointed out the various advantages of cobalt-plating over nickel-plating: smaller polarization, the possibility of obtaining hydroxide-free deposits at normal temperatures with concentrated slightly acid solutions, the more difficult passivation of the anodes which dissolve uniformly, etc.

The disadvantage of cobalt deposits is that they tend to peel off and curl up, especially when they are thin; the object of most of the processes under study is to avoid this inconvenience.

In the older processes, the electrolytic baths were made up either of chloride, with or without addition of NH_4Cl, NaCl, H_3BO_3, etc., or of sulphate, also with or without addition of $MgSO_4$, $(NH_4)_2SO_4$, citric acid, H_3BO_3, etc.

From the systematic research carried out by Kalmus *et al.* [11] it appears that the baths of greatest interest are made up of a solution of roughly 200 g of the double salt $CoSO_4 . (NH_4)_2SO_4 . 6H_2O$ per litre of water, or, even better, of a solution of 312·5 g $CoSO_4$, 19·6 g NaCl and boric acid to saturation, per litre of water; the bath is acid to litmus and has a good conductivity; it gives an adherent deposit on copper, brass, iron and steel, whatever the thickness; this deposit is hard and easily polished. The current yield is practically 100 per cent.

The deposition of cobalt on certain metals such as iron can also be carried out without using electric current, by simple chemical reduction. A description of this is given in Section 18.2 (phosphorus) of Chapter IV of this *Atlas*.

4. BIBLIOGRAPHY

[1] E. DELTOMBE and M. POURBAIX, *Comportement électrochimique du cobalt. Diagramme d'équilibres potentiel–pH du système* Co–H_2O, *à* 25°C (Rapport technique RT.6 of CEBELCOR, 1954).

[2] G. CHARLOT, *L'analyse qualitative et les réactions en solution*, 4th ed., Masson, Paris, 1957.

[3] W. BILTZ, Ueber die Bildungswärmen intermetallischer Verbindungen V. Kobalt-Aluminiumlegierungen; Kupferlegierungen, *Z. anorg. allgem. Chem.* **134**, 26 (1924).

[4] J. BESSON, *Étude comparée de l'oxydation par voie humide des hydroxydes nickeleux, cobalteux, manganeux et ferreux* (Thesis Paris, 1947).

[5] *Gmelins Handbuch der anorganischen Chemie*, S.N. 58, vol. XVIII.

[6] M. J. UDY (Haynes Stellite Co.), A. P. No. 1336765, 1909; Gmelin, XVIII, p. 81.

[7] L. THEYS, *La métallurgie du cobalt à l'Union Minière du Haut-Katanga* (Comméм. 50e Anniv. du Comité Spéc. du Haut-Katanga, Scientific Congress, Elisabethville, 13–19 August 1950), vol. I, pp. 249–267.

[8] L. THEYS, private communication.
C. PIEDBOEUF and F. SUYS, *Introduction du "process control" et de l'automation dans une nouvelle usine hydrométallurgique du Katanga* (C.R. XXXIst Industrial Chemistry Congress, Liège, Belgium, September, 1958).
M. BOUCHAT and J. SAQUET, Electrolytic cobalt in Katanga, *J. of Metals*, October 1960, pp. 801–8.

[9] M. M. RAESSLER, *Dissert.*, Dresden, vol. II, 1913; Gmelin, XVIII, p. 81.

[10] R. SCHILDBACH, Ueber das elektrochemische Verhalten des Kobalts, *Z. Elektrochem.* **16**, 967–79 (1910).

[11] H. T. KALMUS, C. H. HARPER and W. L. SAVELL, *Researches on Cobalt and Cobalt Alloys.* Part III, *Electro-plating with Cobalt*, Canada Department of Mines, 1915, Report No. 334; *J. Ind. Eng. Chem.* **7**, 379–99 (1915).

SECTION 12.3

NICKEL([1])

E. DELTOMBE, N. DE ZOUBOV and M. POURBAIX

SUMMARY

([1]) Adapted and shortened version of the Rapport technique RT.23 of CEBELCOR [1].

1. SUBSTANCES CONSIDERED AND SUBSTANCES NOT CONSIDERED

	Oxidation number (Z)	Considered	Not considered	μ^0(cal.)	Name, colour, crystalline system
Solid substances	0	**Ni**	-	0	Nickel, silvery white, f.c.cub.
	+2	**NiO** hydr.	-	a. — 51 610	Hydrated oxide or nickelous hydroxide $Ni(OH)_2$, green, rhomb.(2)
	»	»	-	b. — 51 300	Nickelous oxide, grey, cub.
	+2.67	Ni_3O_4 hydr.	-	—170 150 (3)	Dihydrated nickelo-nickelic oxide $Ni_3O_4 . 2H_2O$(2)
	+3	Ni_2O_3 hydr.	-	—112 270 (3)	Monohydrated nickelic oxide $Ni_2O_3 . H_2O$, black(2)
	+4	NiO_2 hydr.	-	— 51 420 (3)	Dihydrated nickel peroxide $NiO_2 . 2H_2O$, black(2)
Dissolved substances	+2	Ni^{++}	-	— 11 530	Nickelous ion, green
	»	-	$NiOH^+$	-	?
	»	$HNiO_2^-$	-	— 83 465 (3)	Dinickelite ion
	»	-	NiO_2^{--}	-	Nickelite ion
	+3	-	Ni^{+++}	-	Nickelic ion
	+6	-	NiO_4^{--}	-	Nickelate ion

2. REACTIONS AND EQUILIBRIUM FORMULAE(4)

2.1. TWO DISSOLVED SUBSTANCES

2.1.1. *Relative stability of the dissolved substances*

$Z = +2$

1. $Ni^{++} + 2H_2O = HNiO_2^- + 3H^+$ $\quad \log \frac{(HNiO_2^-)}{(Ni^{++})} = -30.40 + 3\,pH$

2.1.2. *Limits of the domains of relative predominance of the dissolved substances*

1'. $Ni^{++} / HNiO_2^-$ $\quad pH = 10.13$

2.2. TWO SOLID SUBSTANCES

Limits of the domains of relative stability of the solid substances

$0 \rightarrow +2$

2. $Ni + H_2O = NiO + 2H^+ + 2e^-$
   a. $E_0 = 0.110 - 0.0591\,pH$
   b. $ = 0.116 - 0.0591\,pH$

$+2 \rightarrow +2.67$

3. $3NiO + H_2O = Ni_3O_4 + 2H^+ + 2e^-$
   a. $E_0 = 0.897 - 0.0591\,pH$
   b. $ = 0.876 - 0.0591\,pH$

$+2 \rightarrow +3$

4. $2NiO + H_2O = Ni_2O_3 + 2H^+ + 2e^-$
   a. $E_0 = 1.032 - 0.0591\,pH$
   b. $ = 1.020 - 0.0591\,pH$

---

(2) These values of μ° for the oxides correspond to the following values for the hydroxides and hydrated oxides:

$Ni(OH)_2$: −108 300 cal., $\quad Ni_2O_3.H_2O$: −168 960 cal.,
$Ni_3O_4.2H_2O$: −283 530 cal., $\quad NiO_2.2H_2O$: −164 800 cal.

(3) All these values have been justified elsewhere [1].

(4) In reactions in which NiO takes part, the letter *a* refers to $Ni(OH)_2$ whose free enthalpy of formation is −108 300 cal.; the letter *b* refers to anhydrous NiO whose free enthalpy of formation is −51 300 cal.

$+2.67 \rightarrow +3$

5. $2\,Ni_3O_4 + H_2O = 3\,Ni_2O_3 + 2H^+ + 2e^-$ $\quad E_0 = 1.305 - 0.0591\,pH$

$+3 \rightarrow +4$

6. $Ni_2O_3 + H_2O = 2\,NiO_2 + 2H^+ + 2e^-$ $\quad E_0 = 1.434 - 0.0591\,pH$

2.3. ONE SOLID SUBSTANCE AND ONE DISSOLVED SUBSTANCE

Solubility of the solid substances

$Z = +2$

7. $Ni^{++} + H_2O = NiO + 2H^+$ $\quad$ a. $\log(Ni^{++}) = 12.18 - 2\,pH$ $\quad$ b. $= 12.41 - 2\,pH$

8. $NiO + H_2O = HNiO_2^- + H^+$ $\quad$ a. $\log(HNiO_2^-) = -18.22 + pH$ $\quad$ b. $= -17.99 + pH$

$0 \rightarrow +2$

9. $Ni = Ni^{++} + 2e^-$ $\quad E_0 = -0.250 + 0.0295 \log(Ni^{++})$

10. $Ni + 2H_2O = HNiO_2^- + 3H^+ + 2e^-$ $\quad E_0 = 0.648 - 0.0886\,pH + 0.0295 \log(HNiO_2^-)$

$+2 \rightarrow +2.67$

11. $3Ni^{++} + 4H_2O = Ni_3O_4 + 8H^+ + 2e^-$ $\quad E_0 = 1.977 - 0.2364\,pH - 0.0886 \log(Ni^{++})$

12. $3HNiO_2^- + H^+ = Ni_3O_4 + 2H_2O + 2e^-$ $\quad E_0 = -0.718 + 0.0295\,pH - 0.0886 \log(HNiO_2^-)$

$+2 \rightarrow +3$

13. $2Ni^{++} + 3H_2O = Ni_2O_3 + 6H^+ + 2e^-$ $\quad E_0 = 1.753 - 0.1773\,pH - 0.0591 \log(Ni^{++})$

$+2 \rightarrow +4$

14. $Ni^{++} + 2H_2O = NiO_2 + 4H^+ + 2e^-$ $\quad E_0 = 1.593 - 0.1182\,pH - 0.0295 \log(Ni^{++})$

3. EQUILIBRIUM DIAGRAM AND ITS INTERPRETATION

3.1. ESTABLISHMENT OF THE DIAGRAMS

Using relations (1)–(14) we have constructed, in Fig. 1, a potential–pH equilibrium diagram for the system nickel–water at 25°C.

From Fig. 1 we have derived Fig. 2, representing the theoretical conditions of corrosion, immunity and passivation of nickel at 25°C.

In Fig. 3, Fig. 2 has been reproduced, and the experimental results of various investigators have been added to it.

Figure 4, deduced from Fig. 3, shows the probable experimental conditions of corrosion, immunity and passivation of nickel in solutions not containing chloride.

Using relations (1'), (7) and (8) we have represented, in Fig. 5, the influence of pH on the solubility of nickelous hydroxide $Ni(OH)_2$.

Figure 6 shows the equilibrium conditions of the principal reactions liable to take place at the iron and nickel electrodes of iron–nickel accumulators, during their charging and discharging.

It should be remembered that most of these diagrams are valid only in the absence of substances with which nickel can form soluble complexes or insoluble salts.

Charlot [2] mentions the existence of the following complexes: hydrochloric and sulphuric (very unstable), ammine (fairly unstable), oxalic, thiocyanide, metaphosphoric, pyrophosphoric and cyanide.

There is a large number of sparingly soluble compounds: the least soluble ones are the ferri- and ferrocyanides, and in particular the black sulphide NiS and the red nickel dimethylglyoxime.

3.2. STABILITY AND CORROSION OF NICKEL

Nickel can be considered to be a slightly noble metal, as its domain of thermodynamic stability has a small zone in common with that of water (Fig. 1). It is distinctly more noble than iron which has no zone of stability in common with that of water, and is slightly more noble than cobalt.

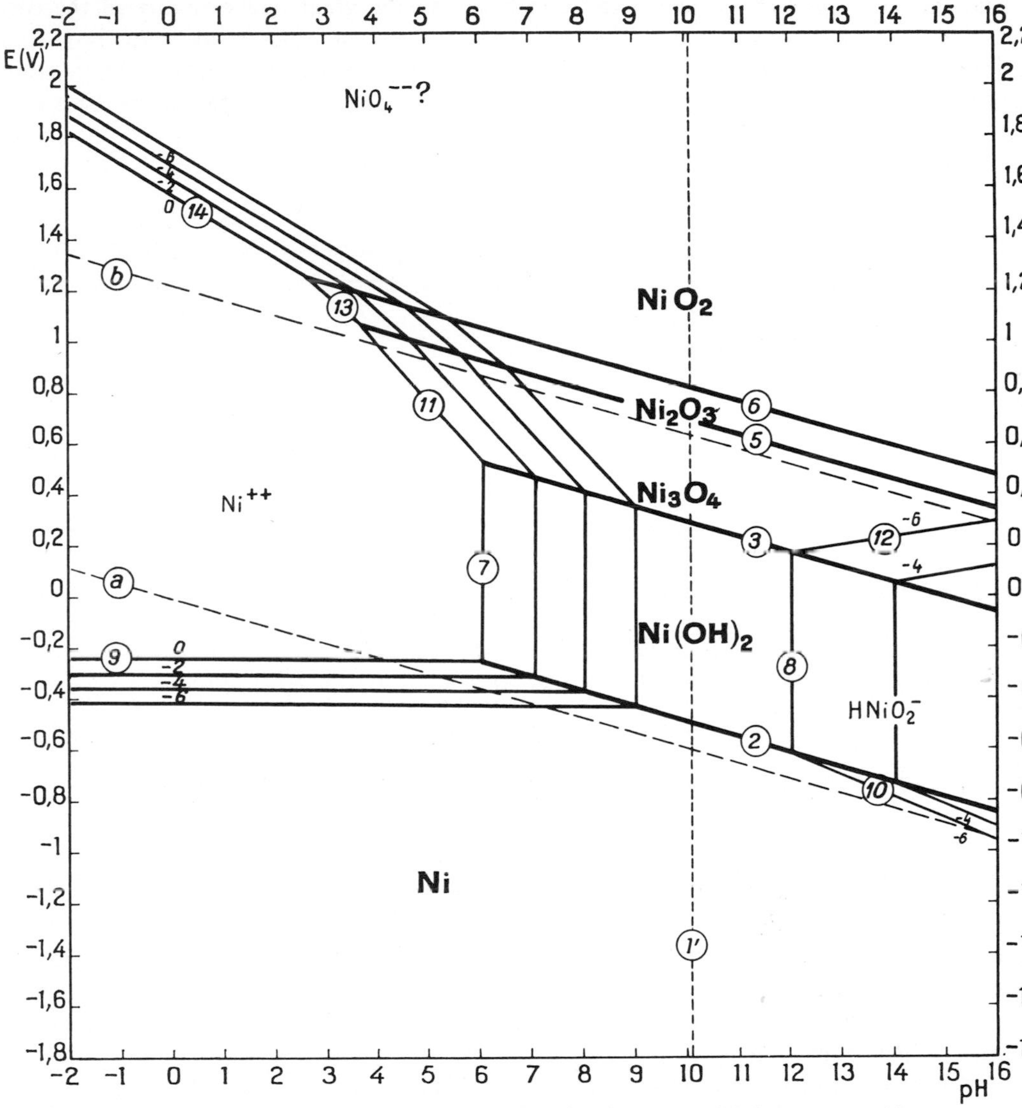

FIG. 1. Potential–pH equilibrium diagram for the system nickel–water, at 25°C.

According to the theoretical diagrams Figs. 1 and 2 which are very similar to the corresponding diagrams for cobalt, the corrosion resistance of nickel should depend as follows on the pH and the presence of oxidizing agents, for non-complexing solutions: it should be uncorrodible in neutral or alkaline solutions free from oxidizing agents, slightly corrodible in acid solutions free from oxidizing agents, and very corrodible in acid or very alkaline solutions containing oxidizing agents. Neutral or slightly alkaline oxidizing solutions should cover it with a layer of oxide. The cathodic protection of nickel is easily brought about, for instance by lowering its electrode potential to a value below −0·4 V in an acid or neutral solution.

These predictions are only partly in agreement with the experimental facts. When there is no oxidizing action, i.e. notably in the case of solutions not containing oxidizing agents and in the absence of any anodic polarization, nickel is hardly corroded at all, not only in neutral or alkaline solutions, but also in many acid solutions. This favourable behaviour in non-oxidizing acid media is probably due, on the one hand, to the great irreversibility of the corrosion reaction $Ni \rightarrow Ni^{++} + 2e^-$ (pointed out by Piontelli [3]), and, on the other hand, to the large hydrogen overpotential of nickel (Petcherskaia and Stender [4]); but it is known that nickel behaves sometimes as a reversible hydrogen electrode, implying a very small hydrogen overpotential in these cases: for

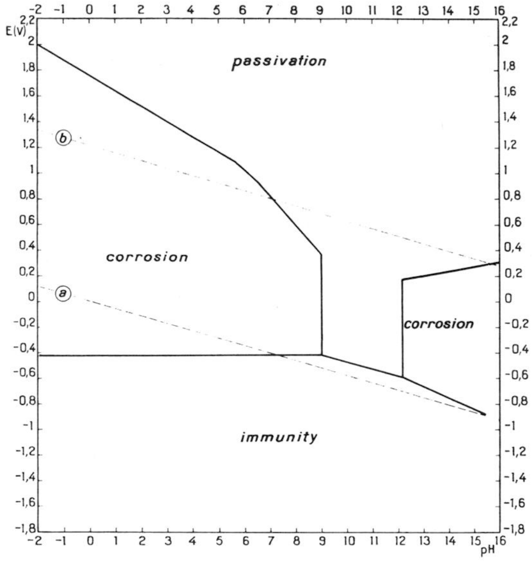

FIG. 2. Theoretical domains of corrosion, immunity and passivation of nickel, at 25°C.

example, Foresti [5] describes an electrolytic process for obtaining "active" nickel, which behaves as a reversible hydrogen electrode like platinized platinum, for pH's above 4·5; Berezina [6] prepared electrolytically a nickel electrode exerting the same potential as a reversible platinized platinum electrode for pH's between 3·0 and 12·8. It would be valuable to investigate the cause of this behaviour.

Figure 3 shows the results of various experimenters concerning the conditions of pH and electrode potential under which corrosion takes place or does not take place; the white circles correspond to conditions under which no corrosion was observed; the black circles correspond to generalized corrosion; the heavy lines correspond to anodic passivation. From this figure it can be seen that in all the cases for which passivation is predicted there is in fact no corrosion, and in the lower parts of the two theoretical corrosion domains corrosion actually occurs. However, in the upper parts of these two theoretical corrosion domains, several experimenters have observed an absence of corrosion. In agreement with the theoretical diagram Fig. 2, MacGillavry ([7], [8]) confirms that nickel does not generally corrode in neutral or alkaline solutions free from air (e.g. Na_2CO_3, NaOH); in the presence of air MacGillavry did not observe any corrosion in slightly alkaline solutions (Na_2CO_3), but records corrosion in neutral solutions (K_2SO_4) and acid solutions (HCl). In accordance with this figure, the International Nickel Company [9] considers that nickel corrodes slightly in very alkaline solutions containing oxygen; for 4 per cent NaOH solutions (pH = 12·7), the corrosion rate at room temperature varies from 0·001 mm/year (permanent immersion) to 0·01 mm/year (intermittent immersion).

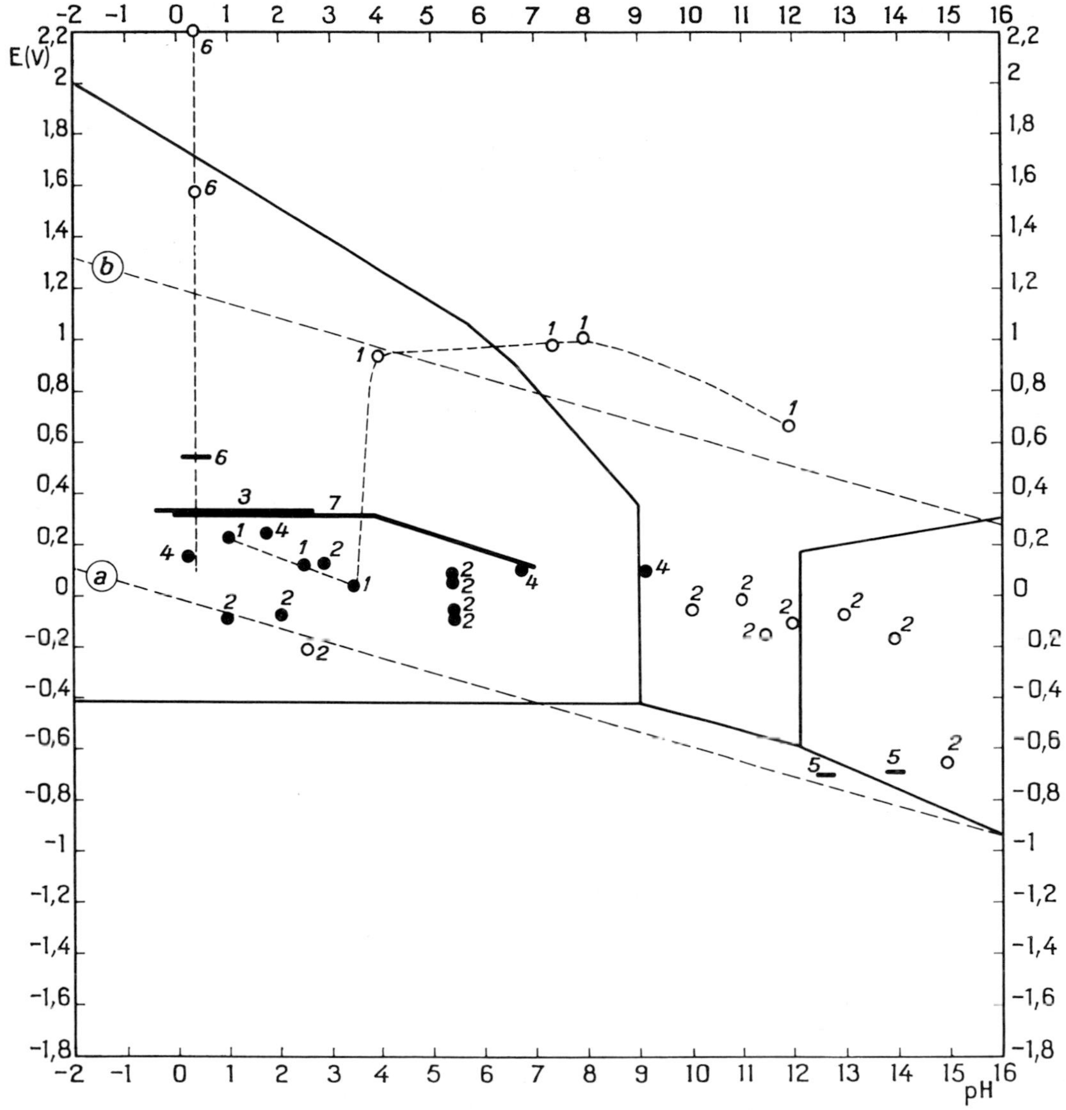

FIG. 3. Experimental conditions of corrosion and passivation of nickel.
○ no corrosion; ● generalised corrosion; — passivation.

1, Colombier [13]; 2, MacGillavry and Swenson [7], [8]; 3, Rothmund [10]; 4, Hickling and Spice [22]; 5, Voltchkova *et al.* [12]; 6, Turner [23]; 7, Pourbaix [24].

However, there are other experimental facts which are not in agreement with the theoretical Fig. 2: it is known that in general nickel has a good resistance to corrosion by tap water, whose pH is usually about 7·5 to 8·0; although dilute phosphoric acid and dilute nitric acid rapidly corrode nickel, dilute sulphuric acid and dilute hydrochloric acid corrode it relatively slowly; concentrated nitric acid does not corrode it at all; it is only occasionally that the nickel anodes do not dissolve with difficulty in the neutral baths used for the electro-plating of nickel. Research on the anodic polarization of nickel carried out by Rothmund [10], Pourbaix [11] and Voltchkova [12] leads to the conclusion that in acid or very alkaline solutions nickel is passivated at certain definite potentials, by a mechanism which is still uncertain. This is true at least in the presence of solutions not containing chloride. These actual passivation potentials are appreciably lower than the theoretical ones shown in Fig. 2. Figure 4, although still very approximate, expresses better than Fig. 2 the actual conditions of corrosion or non-corrosion of nickel in solutions not containing chloride.

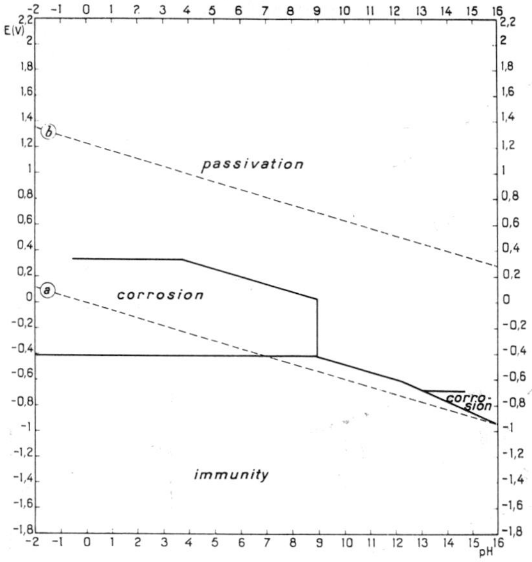

FIG. 4. Probable experimental conditions of corrosion, immunity and passivation of nickel, in solutions not containing chloride.

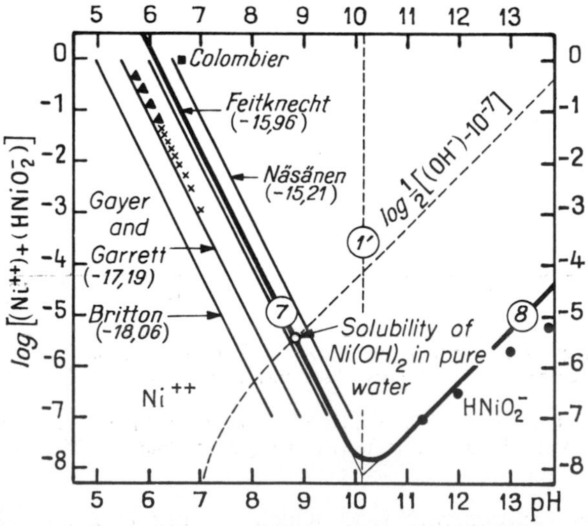

FIG. 5. Influence of pH on the stability of $Ni(OH)_2$.
Experimental results and values assumed for the solubility product $(Ni^{++})(OH^-)^2$.

× Solubility of $Ni(OH)_2$ in HCl solutions (Gayer and Garrett [16]);
▲ pH of $NiCl_2$ solutions of various concentrations (Gayer and Woontner [17]);
■ pH of the equilibrium between a 1 M $NiSO_4$ solution and $Ni(OH)_2$ (Colombier [13]);
● Solubility of $Ni(OH)_2$ in NaOH solutions (Gayer and Garrett [16]).
Feitknecht [25], Näsänen [26], Britton [27].

A detailed investigation of this, and also of the influence of various factors on the electrochemical behaviour of nickel (presence of chloride in the solution; presence of sulphur or other elements or impurities in the nickel) would be valuable.

In 1936, during an investigation of the influence of pH on the behaviour of various solutions containing ammonium persulphate, Colombier [13] observed that the electrode potential of the metal

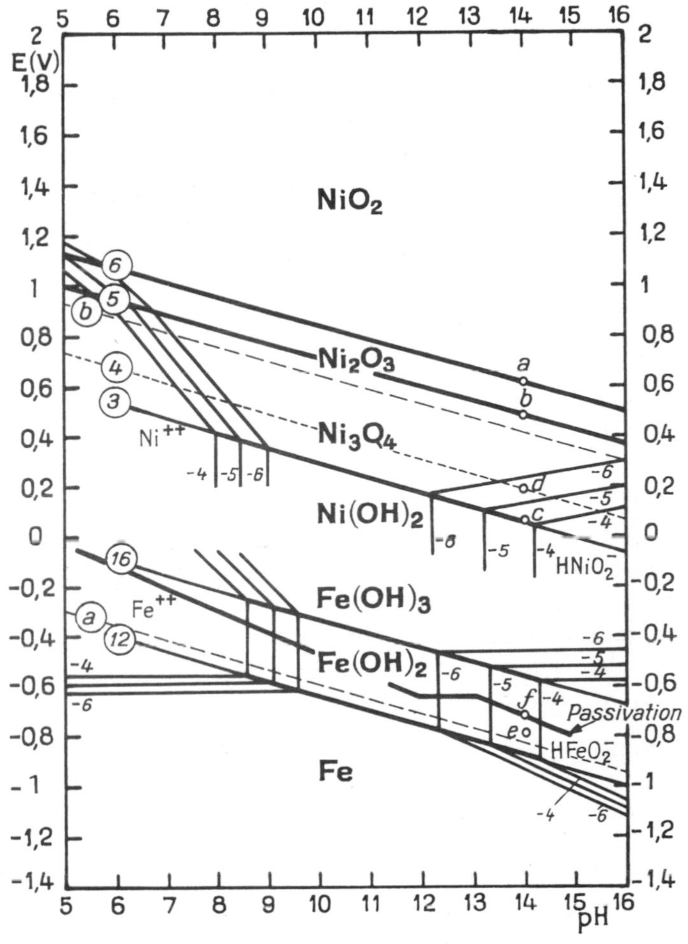

FIG. 6. Iron–nickel accumulators.

is small at pH's between 1 and 3·5 and high at pH's between 4 and 12. Figure 3 shows that these two groups of values correspond respectively to conditions of corrosion and to conditions of passivation, separated from each other by the anodic passivation potentials (line 7). We have published elsewhere [1] a fairly detailed analysis of work carried out on the electrochemical behaviour of nickel.

3.3. STABILITY OF NICKELOUS HYDROXIDE $Ni(OH)_2$

The position of its domain of stability in the equilibrium diagram (Fig. 1) shows that $Ni(OH)_2$ is a thermodynamically stable substance in the presence of water or neutral or slightly alkaline solutions free from oxidizing or reducing agents.

It readily dissolves in acid solutions with the formation of nickelous ions Ni^{++}; in very alkaline solutions it dissolves as nickelite ions $HNiO_2^-$. According to Fig. 1 the oxidation of nickelous hydroxide in alkaline media can give rise to the formation of Ni_3O_4, Ni_2O_3 and NiO_2.

This conversion can be brought about by the usual oxidizing agents (persulphate, hypochlorite, hypobromite, hypoiodite, hydrogen peroxide, ozone, etc.). Besson [14] makes the observation that all these oxidizing agents convert $Ni(OH)_2$ into Ni_3O_4 or Ni_2O_3 depending on the amount used.

The peroxide NiO_2 seems to be formed when the oxidizing agent is in large excess, but it is then difficult to know if one is dealing with a well-defined peroxide NiO_2 or with Ni_2O_3 or Ni_3O_4 containing occluded oxygen.

The free enthalpy of formation of $Ni(OH)_2$ ($-108\,300$ cal.) is only slightly less than the sum of the free enthalpies of formation of NiO and H_2O which is $-51\,300 - 56\,690 = -107\,990$ cal.; $Ni(OH)_2$ is therefore more stable than NiO at 25°C, but the affinity of the hydration reaction $NiO + H_2O \rightarrow Ni(OH)_2$ is very small (310 cal.). Hüttig and Peter [15] have actually shown that NiO is practically unconverted to $Ni(OH)_2$ at ordinary temperatures; even after 5 days of heating in an autoclave at 150°C no reaction is noticed.

In Fig. 5 we have represented the influence of pH on the solubility of $Ni(OH)_2$, according to reactions (7) and (8). Also shown in this figure are some experimental results obtained by various experimenters, for the following solutions:

Colombier [13]: 1 M $NiSO_4$ solution;
Gayer and Garret [16]: HCl and NaOH solutions;
Gayer and Woontner [17]: $NiCl_2$ solutions (pH = 5·6 to 6·3).

3.4. STABILITY OF NICKELO-NICKELIC OXIDE Ni_3O_4

The domain of stability of the saline oxide Ni_3O_4 has a large zone in common with that of water; it is the nickel oxide which is thermodynamically stable in the presence of aerated water. It is soluble in acid solutions with the formation of nickelous ions Ni^{++}, and slightly soluble in very alkaline solutions with the formation of nickelite ions $HNiO_2^-$.

3.5. STABILITY OF NICKELIC OXIDE Ni_2O_3

The domain of stability of nickelic oxide Ni_2O_3 lies completely above line (*b*). It is therefore an oxidizing agent, unstable in the presence of water which it tends to decompose with the evolution of oxygen. It dissolves in acid solutions with the formation of Ni^{++} ions and the evolution of oxygen; it is insoluble in alkaline solutions.

It can be prepared by the oxidation of the hydroxide $Ni(OH)_2$ in the presence of excess oxidizing agents, without which one generally obtains the oxide Ni_3O_4.

3.6. STABILITY OF NICKEL PEROXIDE NiO_2

Nickel peroxide NiO_2 is obtained by the vigorous oxidation of $Ni(OH)_2$, Ni_3O_4 or Ni_2O_3, either by chemical means, or by electrolytic means. As is shown by Fig. 1, NiO_2 is an unstable substance which decomposes rapidly into Ni_2O_3, Ni_3O_4 and oxygen.

3.7. ELECTROLYTIC PRODUCTION OF NICKEL

The electro-deposition of nickel is a process currently used in the electro-metallurgy of the metal to separate it from other metals such as iron or cobalt. A chloride or sulphate solution is generally used; the anodic and cathodic compartments are separated by a diaphragm and the electrolytic bath is heated (to about 70°C).

In order to determine the working conditions appropriate to each particular case, one can refer to the potential–pH equilibrium diagram (Fig. 1). This shows, among other things, the pH domains in which to work if one wants, on the one hand, to avoid simultaneous deposition of hydroxide (possible for cathodic pH's above about 6·1 in a molar solution), and, on the other hand, to obtain a better yield by reducing the amount of hydrogen simultaneously evolved; the diagram does indeed show the increasing proportion of hydrogen evolved in relation to metal as the pH decreases; this is represented by the increasing divergence between the equilibrium potential of a hydrogen electrode (line *a*) and that of a nickel electrode (line 9).

Reducing the Ni^{++} ion concentration will have a similar effect, also on account of the divergence between these two equilibrium potentials. As an example we quote the process for the extraction of nickel from sulphur-free copper mattes,(5) in which one uses a bath of sulphate containing about 40 g Ni/l, i.e. a concentration 0·68 M, to which one adds 20 g of boric acid per litre in order to maintain a pH of about 5; the current yield is said to be 94 per cent.

3.8. ELECTRO-PLATING OF NICKEL

Nickel-plating is the most widespread application of electro-deposition; it is obvious that the physico-chemical principles of the process of nickel-plating by electrolytic means are the same as those just described for the production of nickel by electrolysis. Usually one employs a bath of nickel sulphate containing a certain amount of nickel chloride and boric acid; nickel chloride is to prevent the anodes from becoming passivated; we have already mentioned this passivation when dealing with the conditions of corrosion of nickel; boric acid is used here as a buffer substance, to ensure that the pH remains fairly constant. Indeed, one of the most important factors in nickel-plating is to maintain a suitable pH in the bath; in general the deposits obtained in solutions of pH above 6·2 (for solutions approximately molar in nickel) are very fragile, not very adherent and dark in colour, as a result of the simultaneous deposition of hydroxide.

3.9. CHEMICAL NICKEL-PLATING

The deposition of nickel on certain metals such as iron can also be carried out without using any electric current, by simple chemical reduction. A. Brenner and G. Riddell [18] have perfected a process of nickel-plating by dipping pieces of metal in baths of nickel chloride to which hypophosphite has been added: the Ni^{++} ions are reduced to metallic nickel and the hypophosphite oxidized to phosphite, according to the reaction

$$Ni^{++} + H_2PO_2^- + H_2O \rightarrow Ni + H_2PO_3^- + 2H^+.$$

An ammoniacal alkaline medium or an acid medium can be used. The detailed mechanism of the reaction is unknown, but appears to be different depending on whether the medium is acid or alkaline; in both cases the reaction takes place only if certain metals are present to act as catalysts.

It is very probable that the overall chemical reaction shown above results from the combination of the following two electrochemical reactions:

	$Ni^{++} + 2e^-$	$\rightarrow$	Ni	(reduction)
and	$H_2PO_2^- + H_2O$	$\rightarrow$	$H_2PO_3^- + 2H^+ + 2e^-$	(oxidation)
overall reaction	$Ni^{++} + H_2PO_2^- + H_2O$	$\rightarrow$	$Ni + H_2PO_3^- + 2H^+$.	

A description of this is given in section 18.2 (phosphorus) of this *Atlas*.

(5) See *Ullmans Enzyklopädie der technischen Chemie*, vol. 8, 1931, p. 125; E. Jimeno and F. R. Morral, *Metalurgia General*, Madrid, 1955, p. 320.

3.10. NICKEL ACCUMULATORS

Edison accumulators are made up of a nickel peroxide electrode (+ve pole) and an iron electrode (−ve pole) immersed in a 20 per cent KOH solution (Kremann and Müller [19]), whose pH is around 14·0.

In Fig. 6 we have represented the equilibrium conditions of the principal reactions liable to take place at the two electrodes. This figure enables us to interpret the phenomena which take place during the charging and discharging of the accumulator.(6)

During the charging of the accumulator, the potential of the nickel electrode rises to about +0·6 V (point *a*), at which the electrode becomes covered with peroxide NiO_2. When the charging current is broken this NiO_2, which is highly unstable, decomposes fairly quickly into Ni_2O_3 and oxygen, and the electrode potential decreases progressively, becoming eventually +0·48 V (point *b*); when the NiO_2 is completely decomposed the anode is covered with a mixture of Ni_2O_3 and Ni_3O_4. The operation of the nickel accumulator is based essentially for a slow discharge on the reduction of Ni_2O_3 (or $Ni_2O_3 . H_2O$) to Ni_3O_4 (or $Ni_3O_4 . 2H_2O$) at a potential of about +0·48 V, with the liberation of 0·15 Ah for every gram of nickel that changes from the one degree of oxidation to the other. If the discharge is carried sufficiently far for the Ni_2O_3 to be reduced completely to Ni_3O_4, this Ni_3O_4 is then reduced to $HNiO_2^-$ ions of divalent nickel; the potential ceases to be practically stable and decreases as the concentration of nickel in the electrolyte increases; when this concentration reaches about $10^{-4.2}$ g-ions/l (i.e. about 40 mg Ni/l), the reduction of Ni_3O_4 takes place with the formation of solid $Ni(OH)_2$, and the potential becomes steady at about +0·07 V (point *c*), and remains almost at this value until the Ni_3O_4 is completely converted into $Ni(OH)_2$, i.e. until the battery is completely exhausted. For a quicker discharge, the saline oxide Ni_3O_4 no longer appears in the various reduction stages of the NiO_2 and the operation of the accumulator in this case is based upon the direct reduction of the Ni_2O_3 (or $Ni_2O_3 . H_2O$) to $Ni(OH)_2$, which causes the potential to be lowered from +0·48 V corresponding to a slow discharge to +0·20 V relating to the Ni_2O_3–$Ni(OH)_2$ equilibrium (point *d*); the reduction should therefore take place with the liberation of 0·45 Ah for every gram of nickel changing from the one degree of oxidation to the other in the presence of an electrolyte containing $10^{-5.6}$ g-ions Ni/l [i.e. about 0·23 mg $Ni(OH)_2$].

The operation of the iron electrode is probably based on a change from the metallic state to the state of divalent hydroxide $Fe(OH)_2$ (or magnetite Fe_3O_4) in the presence of a solution containing dihypoferrite $HFeO_2^-$.

During experiments carried out in 1938 and 1942 ([11], [20]), one of us (M. P.) observed that, in the presence of NaOH solutions free from oxidizing agents and containing 200 g NaOH/l, iron exerts a potential of −0·78 V if it is electrically insulated (point *e* of Fig. 6). Anodic polarization of the iron, with a low current density (below about 30 mA/dm^2), causes a slight increase in the potential of the iron and its dissolution in the divalent state, at the rate of 1·04 g Fe/Ah; when the current density reaches about 30 mA/dm^2, the metal is passivated at a potential of about −0·72 V (point *f*) and there follows an increase in the potential of the metal with suppression of corrosion. According to the lower part of Fig. 6, where we have indicated the experimental values of the passivation potential of iron [20] and the theoretical conditions of equilibrium of iron and its hydroxides in the presence of ferrous solutions [21], the solubility of $Fe(OH)_2$ in solutions of pH = 14 should be about $10^{-4.3}$ g-ions/l (i.e. about 30 mg/l).

It follows from this figure that, in the case of an iron–nickel accumulator whose positive electrode is made up of a mixture of Ni_2O_3 and Ni_3O_4, the electromotive force is theoretically about 0·48+0·78 = 1·26 V; for a mixture of Ni_2O_3 and $Ni(OH)_2$ it is 0·20+0·78 = 0·98 V. During the charging, the potential of the positive electrode becomes steady at +0·60 V and that of the negative electrode becomes steady at a value below −0·78 V, which leads to a potential greater than 1·4 V at the terminals; during

(6) It would be useful for systematic experimental research to be performed on this highly hypothetical interpretation.

the discharging, the potential of the positive electrode cannot fall below +0·07 V and that of the negative electrode cannot rise above −0·72 V, or else the accumulator is entirely discharged, which corresponds to a potential of about 0·8 V at the terminals. In practice an electromotive force of about 1·4 V (instead of 1·26 V) is usually observed when the charging current is cut; the observed potentials at the terminals are usually about 1·6 V (instead of 1.4 V) during charging and 1·1 V (instead of 0·98 V) during discharging.

4. BIBLIOGRAPHY

[1] E. Deltombe, N. de Zoubov and M. Pourbaix, *Comportement électrochimique du nickel. Diagramme d'équilibres tension-pH du système* Ni–H_2O, *à* 25°C. *Corrosion du nickel; nickelage, accumulateurs au nickel* (Rapport technique RT.23 of CEBELCOR, 1955).

[2] G. Charlot, *L'analyse qualitative et les réactions en solution*, Masson, Paris, 1957.

[3] R. Piontelli, Sul comportamento elettrochimico dei metalli, *Ricerca Scientifica*, 17 September–October 1947; Lecture delivered at the XIth Int. Congr. of Chem., London, July, 1947.

[4] A. G. Petcherskaia and V. V. Stender, Potentiels de dégagement d'hydrogène dans les solutions acides, *J. Fiz. Khim.* **24**, 856–9 (1950).

[5] B. Foresti, Comportement électrochimique du nickel en présence d'hydrogène, *Gazz. Chim. Ital.* **67**, 399–407 (1937).

[6] S. I. Berezina, L'électrode Ni–H, *Doklad. Akad. Naouk. S.S.S.R.* **77**, 53–55 (1951).

[7] D. MacGillavry and R. W. Swenson, *The Potentials of Nickel in Electrolyte Solutions in the Presence of Air* (Techn. Report No. III, Nav. Research Washington D.C., 1950).

[8] D. MacGillavry, J. J. Singer and J. H. Rosenbaum, Metal–solution potentials of nickel in foreign ion solutions, *J. Chem. Phys.* **19**, 1195–1202 (1951).

[9] International Nickel Co. Inc. (*a*) *Corrosion with Data on the Characteristics of Monel, Nickel and Inconel* (1944). (*b*) *Nickel and Nickel-base Alloys. Their use in the design of Corrosion-resistant Machinery and Equipment* (Technical Bulletin T.13, 1948). (*c*) *The Resistance of Nickel and its Alloys to Corrosion by Caustic Alkalis* (Technickel Bulletin T.6, 1949).

[10] V. Rothmund, Ueber den Einfluss der Anionen auf die Passivierbarkeit der Metalle, *Z. Phys. Chem.* **110**, 384–93 (1924).

[11] M. Pourbaix, Corrosion du fer par les solutions de soude caustique [Thesis, Brussels, 1945 (extract)], *Bull. Techn. A.I. Br.*, 1946, pp. 67–86; 1947, pp. 109–20.

[12] L. M. Voltchkova, L. G. Antonova and A. J. Krasilschikov, Comportement anodique du nickel dans les solutions alcalines, *J. Fiz. Khim.* **23**, 714–18 (1949).

[13] L. Colombier, *L'état passif des métaux. Étude de la passivité du nickel* (Thèse, Nancy, 1936).

[14] J. Besson, *Étude comparée de l'oxydation par voie humide des hydroxydes nickeleux, cobalteux, manganeux et ferreux* (Thèse, Paris, 1947).

[15] G. F. Hüttig and A. Peter, Das System Nickel (II) oxyd/Wasser, *Z. anorg. allgem. Chem.* **189**, 183–9 (1930).

[16] K. H. Gayer and A. B. Garrett, The equilibria of nickel hydroxide $Ni(OH)_2$ in solutions of HCl and NaOH at 25°C, *J. Amer. Chem. Soc.* **71**, 2973–5 (1949).

[17] K. H. Gayer and L. Woontner, Hydrolysis of $CoCl_2$ and $NiCl_2$ at 25°C, *J. Amer. Chem. Soc.* **74**, 1436–7 (1952).

[18] A. Brenner and G. Riddell, Nickel plating on steel, *J. Res. Nat. Bur. Stand.* **37**, 31 (1946); Deposition of Ni and Co by chemical reduction, *Bur. Stand.* **39**, 385 (1947).

[19] R. Kremann and R. Müller, *Handbuch der allgemeinen Chemie,* VIII, No. 2, Akad. Verlagges, Leipzig, 1931, pp. 718–29.

[20] M. Pourbaix, Corrosion, passivité et passivation du fer. Le rôle du pH et du potentiel, [Thesis, Brussels, 1945 (extract)], *Mémoires Soc. Roy. Belge Ingénieurs et Industriels,* March 1951.

[21] M. Pourbaix and N. de Zoubov, Iron, Section 12.1 of this *Atlas* (p. 307).

[22] A. Hickling and J. E. Spice, The anodic behaviour of metals. III. Nickel, *Trans. Faraday Soc.* **43**, 762–9 (1947).

[23] D. R. Turner, Anode polarization effects of nickel in sulphuric acid, *J. Electr. Soc.* **98**, 434–42 (1951).

[24] M. Pourbaix, *Domaines de corrosion du fer, du cuivre et du nickel,* Unpublished paper, 1943.

[25] W. Feitknecht and A. Collet, Zur Chemie und Morphologie der basischen Salze zweiwertiger Metalle. VII. Ueber basische Nickelchloride, *Helv. Chim. Acta,* **22**, 1428–44 (1939).
[26] R. Näsänen, Die potentiometrische Bestimmung des Löslichkeitsproduktes von Ni (II) und Co (II) hydroxyd, *Ann. Acad. Sc. Fennicae,* A. **59**, 3–9 (1945).
[27] H. T. S. Britton, Electrometric study of the precipitation of hydroxides. Part I. Precipitation of Magnesium, Manganous, Ferrous, Cobalt, Nickel and Thorium hydroxides by use of the hydrogen electrode, *J. Chem. Soc.* 2110–2120 (1925).

SECTION 13.1

RUTHENIUM [1]

N. de Zoubov and M. Pourbaix

SUMMARY

(1) Shortened and adapted version of the Rapport technique RT.58 of CEBELCOR [1].

1. SUBSTANCES CONSIDERED AND SUBSTANCES NOT CONSIDERED

	Oxidation number (Z)	Considered	Not considered	$\mu°$(cal.)	Name, colour, crystalline system
Solid substances	0	**Ru**	-	0	Ruthenium, silvery grey, hex.
	+2	-	**RuO** hydr.	-	Hydrated ruthenous oxide RuO . H_2O or $Ru(OH)_2$
	+3	$\mathbf{Ru_2O_3}$ hydr.	-	−67 930 (2)	Hydrated ruthenium sesquioxide $Ru_2O_3 . 3H_2O$ or $Ru(OH)_3$, black (3)
	»	-	$\mathbf{Ru_2O_3}$	-	Ruthenium sesquioxide, blue–black
	+4	$\mathbf{RuO_2}$ hydr.	-	−40 700	Hydrated ruthenic oxide $RuO_2 . 2H_2O$ or ruthenic hydroxide $Ru(OH)_4$, black (3)
	»	-	$\mathbf{RuO_2}$	-	Ruthenic oxide, dark blue, quad.
	+5	-	$\mathbf{Ru_2O_5}$	-	Ruthenium pentoxide, black
	+6	-	$\mathbf{RuO_3}$	-	Ruthenium trioxide or ruthenic anhydride
	+8	$\mathbf{RuO_4}$	-	−26 100 (2)	Ruthenium tetroxide, yellow
Dissolved substances	+2	-	Ru^{++} ?	21 000 (2)	Ruthenous ion, blue
	+3	-	Ru^{+++}	-	Trivalent ruthenium ion, yellow
	+4	-	Ru^{++++}	-	Ruthenic ion, red–brown
	+6	RuO_4^{--}	-	−61 600 (2)	Ruthenate ion, orange
	»	-	RuO_2^{++}	-	Ruthenyl ion, green
	+7	RuO_4^-	-	−48 000 (2)	Perruthenate ion, green
	+8	H_2RuO_5	-	−81 600 (2)	"Hyperruthenic" acid, golden yellow
	»	$HRuO_5^-$	-	−66 300 (2)	"Dihyperruthenate" ion, golden yellow

2. REACTIONS AND EQUILIBRIUM FORMULAE

2.1. TWO DISSOLVED SUBSTANCES

2.1.1. *Relative stability of the dissolved substances*

Z = +8

1. $H_2RuO_5 = HRuO_5^- + H^+$ $\qquad \log\frac{(HRuO_5^-)}{(H_2RuO_5)} = -11.22 + pH$

+2 → +6

2. $Ru^{++} + 4H_2O = RuO_4^{--} + 8H^+ + 4e^-$ $\qquad E_0 = 1.563 - 0.1182\,pH + 0.0148\log\frac{(RuO_4^{--})}{(Ru^{++})}$

+2 → +7

3. $Ru^{++} + 4H_2O = RuO_4^- + 8H^+ + 5e^-$ $\qquad E_0 = 1.368 - 0.0945\,pH + 0.0118\log\frac{(RuO_4^-)}{(Ru^{++})}$

+2 → +8

4. $Ru^{++} + 5H_2O = H_2RuO_5 + 8H^+ + 6e^-$ $\qquad E_0 = 1.307 - 0.0788\,pH + 0.0098\log\frac{(H_2RuO_5)}{(Ru^{++})}$

+6 → +7

5. $RuO_4^{--} = RuO_4^- + e^-$ $\qquad E_0 = 0.590 + 0.0591\log\frac{(RuO_4^-)}{(RuO_4^{--})}$

---

(2) Ru_2O_3 hydr. and Ru^{++}: values deduced from equilibrium potentials given by Latimer.
RuO_4: value calculated by us [1].
RuO_4^{--}, RuO_4^- and H_2RuO_5: values deduced from equilibrium potentials given by Silverman and Lévy [2].
$HRuO_5^-$: value deduced from the pK of the reaction $H_2RuO_5 = HRuO_5^- + H^+$ given by Charlot [3].

(3) These values of $\mu°$ for the oxides correspond to the following values for the hydrated oxides or hydroxides:

$Ru(OH)_3$: −119 000 cal., $\qquad$ $Ru(OH)_4$ = −154 080 cal.

$+7 \rightarrow +8$

6. $RuO_4^- + H_2O = H_2RuO_5 + e^-$ $\qquad E_0 = 1.001 + 0.0591 \log \frac{(H_2RuO_5)}{(RuO_4^-)}$

7. $RuO_4^- + H_2O = HRuO_5^- + H^+ + e^-$ $\qquad E_0 = 1.660 - 0.0591\,pH + 0.0591 \log \frac{(HRuO_5^-)}{(RuO_4^-)}$

2.1.2. *Limits of the domains of relative predominance of the dissolved substances*

1'. $H_2RuO_5/HRuO_5^-$ $\qquad pH = 11.22$

2'. Ru^{++}/RuO_4^{--} $\qquad E_0 = 1.563 - 0.1182\,pH$
3'. Ru^{++}/RuO_4^- $\qquad E_0 = 1.368 - 0.0945\,pH$
4'. Ru^{++}/H_2RuO_5 $\qquad E_0 = 1,307 - 0.0788\,pH$
5'. RuO_4^{--}/RuO_4^- $\qquad E_0 = 0.590$
6'. RuO_4^-/H_2RuO_5 $\qquad E_0 = 1.001$
7'. $RuO_4^-/HRuO_5^-$ $\qquad E_0 = 1.660 - 0.0591\,pH$

2.2. TWO SOLID SUBSTANCES

Limits of the domains of relative stability of the solid substances

$0 \rightarrow +3$

8. $2\,\mathbf{Ru} + 3H_2O = \mathbf{Ru_2O_3} + 6H^+ + 6e^-$ $\qquad E_0 = 0.738 - 0.0591\,pH$

$+3 \rightarrow +4$

9. $\mathbf{Ru_2O_3} + H_2O = 2\,\mathbf{RuO_2} + 2H^+ + 2e^-$ $\qquad E_0 = 0.937 - 0.0591\,pH$

$+4 \rightarrow +8$

10. $\mathbf{RuO_2} + 2H_2O = \mathbf{RuO_4} + 4H^+ + 4e^-$ $\qquad E_0 = 1.387 - 0.0591\,pH$

2.3. ONE SOLID SUBSTANCE AND ONE DISSOLVED SUBSTANCE

Solubility of the solid substances

$Z = +8$

11. $\mathbf{RuO_4} + H_2O = H_2RuO_5$ $\qquad \log(H_2RuO_5) = -0.88$
12. $\mathbf{RuO_4} + H_2O = HRuO_5^- + H^+$ $\qquad \log(HRuO_5^-) = -12.10 + pH$

$0 \rightarrow +2$

13. $\mathbf{Ru} = Ru^{++} + 2e^-$ $\qquad E_0 = 0.455 + 0.0295 \log(Ru^{++})$

$0 \rightarrow +6$

14. $\mathbf{Ru} + 4H_2O = RuO_4^{--} + 8H^+ + 6e^-$ $\qquad E_0 = 1.193 - 0.0788\,pH + 0.0098 \log(RuO_4^{--})$

$+2 \rightarrow +3$

15. $2Ru^{++} + 3H_2O = \mathbf{Ru_2O_3} + 6H^+ + 2e^-$ $\qquad E_0 = 1.304 - 0.1773\,pH - 0.0591 \log(Ru^{++})$

$+2 \rightarrow +4$

16. $Ru^{++} + 2H_2O = \mathbf{RuO_2} + 4H^+ + 2e^-$ $\qquad E_0 = 1.120 - 0.1182\,pH - 0.0295 \log(Ru^{++})$

$+3 \rightarrow +6$

17. $\mathbf{Ru_2O_3} + 5H_2O = 2RuO_4^{--} + 10H^+ + 6e^-$ $\qquad E_0 = 1.649 - 0.0985\,pH + 0.0197 \log(RuO_4^{--})$

$+4 \rightarrow +6$

18. $\mathbf{RuO_2} + 2H_2O = RuO_4^{--} + 4H^+ + 2e^-$ $\qquad E_0 = 2.005 - 0.1182\,pH + 0.0295 \log(RuO_4^{--})$

$+4 \rightarrow +7$

19. $\mathbf{RuO_2} + 2H_2O = RuO_4^- + 4H^+ + 3e^-$ $\qquad E_0 = 1.533 - 0.0788\,pH + 0.0197 \log(RuO_4^-)$

$+4 \rightarrow +8$

20. $\mathbf{RuO_2} + 3H_2O = H_2RuO_5 + 4H^+ + 4e^-$ $\qquad E_0 = 1.400 - 0.0591\,pH + 0.0148 \log(H_2RuO_5)$

$+7 \rightarrow +8$

21. $RuO_4^- = \mathbf{RuO_4} + e^-$ $\qquad E_0 = 0.950 - 0.0591 \log(RuO_4^-)$

3. EQUILIBRIUM DIAGRAM AND ITS INTERPRETATION

3.1. ESTABLISHMENT OF THE DIAGRAM

Using relations (1)–(21) established in paragraph 2, we have constructed Fig. 1 which represents the conditions of thermodynamic equilibrium of the system ruthenium–water at 25°C, in the presence of solutions free from substances with which ruthenium can form complexes or insoluble salts.(4)

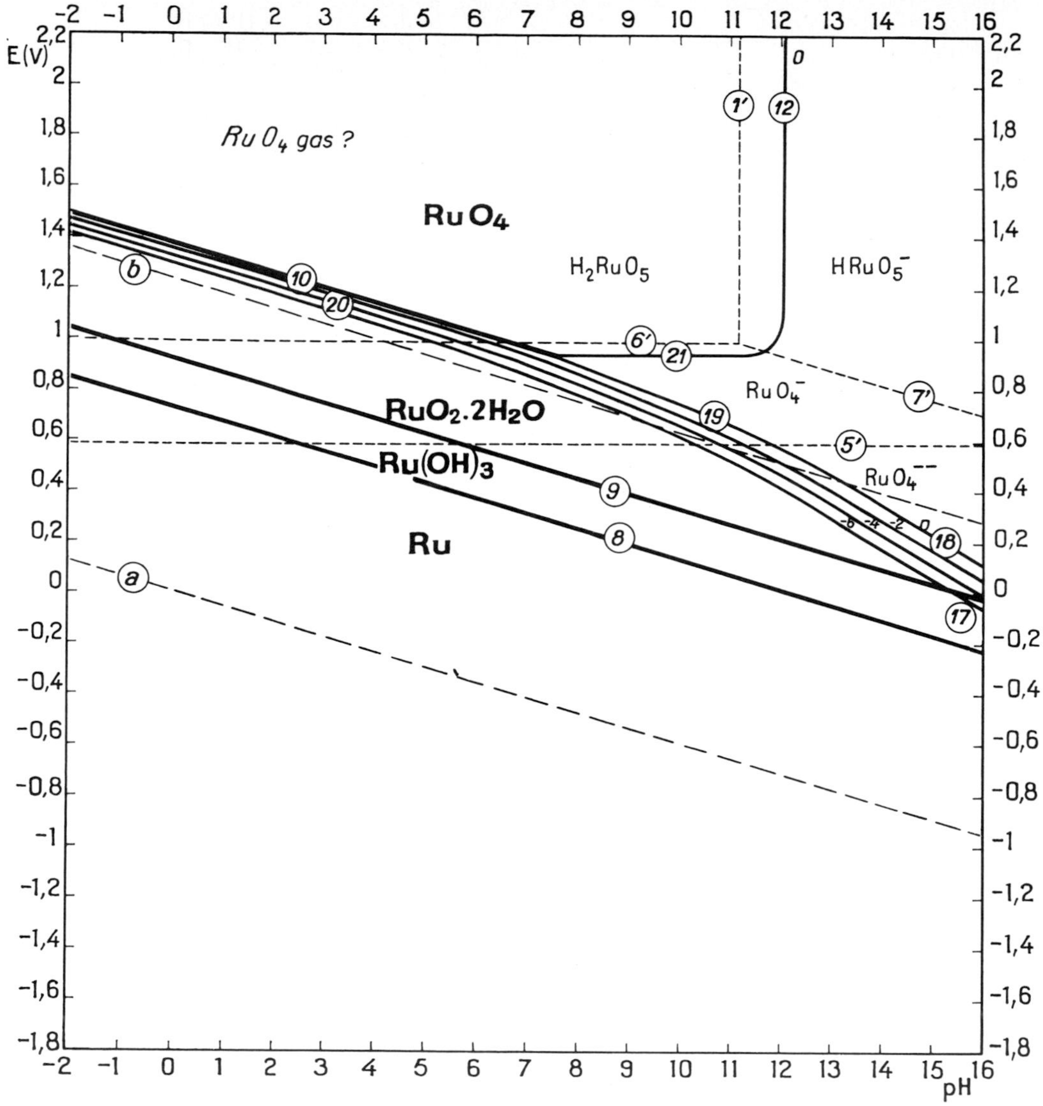

FIG. 1. Potential–pH equilibrium diagram for the system ruthenium–water, at 25°C (in the presence of solutions free from complexing substances).

In this diagram the only solid substances that we have considered, apart from metallic ruthenium, are $Ru(OH)_3$, $RuO_2 . 2H_2O$ and RuO_4, which are the only three oxides or hydroxides for which we have free enthalpy values. For want of thermodynamic data, we have not considered the hydroxide $Ru(OH)_2$, or the oxides Ru_2O_3, Ru_2O_5 and RuO_3 whose existence is uncertain.

(4) We have not considered in Fig. 1 the Ru^{++} ion because it is very likely a ruthenium chloride complex [1].

Charlot [3] states that chlorides and bromides form soluble complexes with ruthenium at valencies +3, +4, +6 and +8, and that ammonia and oxalates form complexes with ruthenium at valency +3. Also, it is probable that chlorides produce complexes with ruthenium at valency +2.

According to Martin [4], sulphates can form the complex $RuO_2(SO_4)_2^{--}$.

With regard to insoluble salts, we know that brown–black sulphides are formed by the action of H_2S.

From Fig. 1 we have derived Fig. 2 showing the theoretical conditions of corrosion, immunity and passivation of ruthenium at 25°C, in the absence of substances with which it can form soluble complexes or insoluble salts.

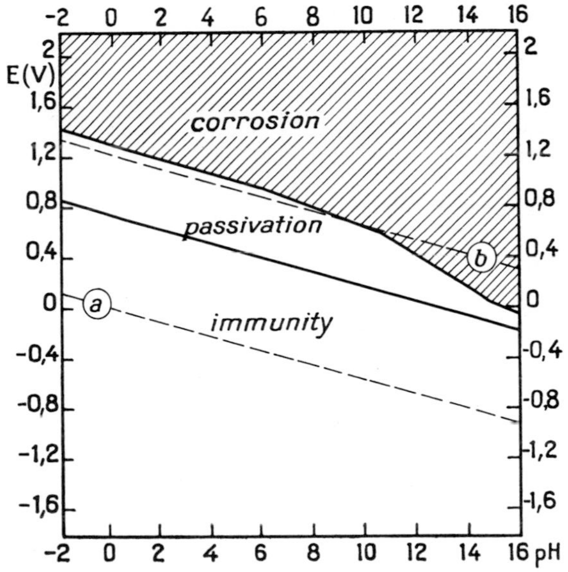

FIG. 2. Theoretical domains of corrosion, immunity and passivation of ruthenium, at 25°C (in the absence of complexing substances).

3.2. STABILITY AND CORROSION OF RUTHENIUM

In Figs. 1 and 2 ruthenium appears to be a very noble metal, as its domain of stability has a large zone in common with the domain of stability of water. However, like osmium, it is appreciably less noble than the other four metals of the platinum group: rhodium and palladium, iridium and platinum. It is found in the native state in nature, together with the other "platinum-type" metals, but in smaller quantities.

In accordance with Figs. 1 and 2, ruthenium is unaffected by water. It is not attacked by non-complexing acid solutions, but is easily corroded by alkaline oxidizing solutions (solutions of peroxides or alkali-metal hypochlorites); this property of ruthenium, which is also possessed by osmium, is used profitably in the separation of these two metals from the other platinoids.

On fusion with an alkaline oxidizing substance (e.g. a mixture of KOH and KNO_3, $KClO_3$ or $KMnO_4$), ruthenium is converted into green perruthenate RuO_4^-, which then decomposes into orange ruthenate RuO_4^{--}.

When used as an anode in a non-complexing solution, e.g. nitric acid, ruthenium is passivated.

When used as a cathode ruthenium absorbs a large quantity of hydrogen, as do all the metals of the platinum group; this absorption may be as great as 1 500 vol. of hydrogen per volume of metal. The hydrogen overpotential of ruthenium is very small; for a ruthenium regulus in a 1 M sulphuric acid solution it is, according to Thiel and Hammerschmidt [5], 0·43±0·03 mV for a current density of 0·03 to 0·25 mA/cm^2.

3.3. ELECTRO-DEPOSITION OF RUTHENIUM. ELECTRO-PLATING OF RUTHENIUM

It follows from Fig. 1 that ruthenium can easily be obtained in the metallic state by reduction of its solutions. This reduction can be brought about *chemically* by adding metallic zinc to acid solutions of chlorides or chloro-salts of tri- or tetravalent ruthenium. A transient blue coloration, due to the formation of ions of divalent ruthenium, is observed. On treating a solution of ruthenium chloride or a ruthenate with hydrazine, a mixture of hydroxides and colloidal metallic ruthenium is obtained. This mixture is very easily oxidized by the air.

Ruthenium can be *electro-deposited* from solutions of nitrosohalides. In order to obtain a shiny adherent deposit one can employ, for example, a solution 0·005 M in $RuNOCl_3$ (1·2 g/l) and 0·5 M in HCl, at a current density of 2 to 5 mA/cm^2 [6], or a solution 0·017 M in $RuNOCl_3$ (4 g/l) and containing 20 cm^3 of concentrated sulphuric acid per litre, at a temperature above 75°C.

3.4. STABILITY OF THE HYDROXIDE $Ru(OH)_3$

The hydroxide $Ru(OH)_3$ can be prepared either by addition of alkali to a solution of trivalent ruthenium chloride (Wöhler *et al.* [7]), or by reduction of a solution of tetravalent ruthenium chloride $K_2Ru(OH)Cl_5$ with hydrogen (Ipatiev and Sviagintsev [8]).

In agreement with Fig. 1, it is stable in the presence of water and aqueous solutions of all pH's free from oxidizing or reducing agents. It can easily be oxidized to ruthenium oxide $RuO_2 . 2H_2O$ or $Ru(OH)_4$, and can easily be reduced to elementary ruthenium.

3.5. STABILITY OF RUTHENIC OXIDE RuO_2

In most of its compounds ruthenium exerts the valency +4. As Fig. 1 shows, this is the stable state in the presence of oxygen, except in very alkaline solution when the stable valency state is +6. Except for this case, derivatives of valencies other than +4 tend to revert to the valency of +4 by spontaneous oxidation or reduction: thus $RuO_2 . 2H_2O$ can be obtained by spontaneous decomposition of the tetroxide RuO_4 in the presence of water, or by reduction of solutions of "hyperruthenic" acid H_2RuO_5 with hydrogen peroxide, or by reduction of solutions of "hyperruthenates" $HRuO_5^-$ with alcohol, or by acidification of solutions of perruthenates RuO_4^- or ruthenates RuO_4^{--} (e.g. with nitric acid or carbon dioxide) ([7] and [9]), or by oxidation of $Ru(OH)_3$ in the air (Charonnat [10]).

According to Fig. 1, $RuO_2.2H_2O$ should be insoluble in non-complexing acid solutions; in aerated alkaline solutions it dissolves in the hexavalent state to give ruthenates RuO_4^{--} (reaction 18).

The *anhydrous* dioxide RuO_2, which is quadratic or amorphous and has a characteristic dark blue colour, does not appear in the equilibrium diagram for the system ruthenium–water. It is obtained only at very high temperatures, by roasting the metal in a current of oxygen in a muffle-furnace, or by dehydration of the hydroxide at about 450°, or by heating ruthenium chloride or sulphide to about 400° in a current of oxygen. The properties of the anhydrous dioxide, in particular its solubility, differ from those of its hydrate: RuO_2 is unattacked by acids and can be dissolved to give orange ruthenates by fusion with an alkaline substance.

3.6. STABILITY OF THE RUTHENATES RuO_4^{--} AND THE PERRUTHENATES RuO_4^-

As is shown by Fig. 1, the orange ruthenate (RuO_4^{--}) solutions, in which ruthenium has a valency of +6, are stable in very alkaline media free from reducing agents. If the pH is lowered below 12 the ruthenates decompose to give the black hydrated dioxide $RuO_2 . 2H_2O$ and green perruthenates RuO_4^- according to the reactions $RuO_4^{--} + 4H^+ + 2e^- \rightarrow RuO_2 . 2H_2O$ (18) and $RuO_4^{--} \rightarrow RuO_4^- + e^-$ (5), i.e. according to the overall reaction

$$3RuO_4^{--} + 4H^+ \rightarrow RuO_2.2H_2O + 2RuO_4^- \quad [9].$$

The green perruthenate (RuO_4^-) solutions are always unstable; in solutions of pH greater than about 12 they tend to decompose into ruthenates RuO_4^{--} and O_2 according to the reactions $RuO_4^- + e^- \rightarrow RuO_4^{--}$ (5) and $2H_2O \rightarrow O_2 + 4H^+ + 4e^-$ (*b*), i.e. according to the overall reaction

$$4RuO_4^- + 2H_2O \rightarrow 4RuO_4^{--} + O_2 + 4H^+ \quad [10];$$

at pH's below 12 the decomposition tends to take place with the formation of $RuO_2 . 2H_2O$ and O_2 according to the reactions $RuO_4^- + 4H^+ + 3e^- \rightarrow RuO_2.2H_2O$ (19) and $2H_2O \rightarrow O_2 + 4H^+ + 4e^-$ (*b*), i.e. according to the overall reaction $4RuO_4^- + 6H_2O + 4H^+ \rightarrow 4RuO_2 . 2H_2O + 3O_2$. At pH's below about 7·5 the decomposition can also give rise to the formation of tetroxide RuO_4 and "hyperruthenic" acid H_2RuO_5, which are both unstable according to reactions (21) and (6).

3.7. STABILITY OF RUTHENIUM TETROXIDE RuO_4

The volatile yellow ruthenium tetroxide RuO_4, whose stability domain in Fig. 1 is situated above the stability domain of water, is very unstable in the presence of aqueous solutions. This distinguishes it from osmium tetroxide OsO_4, which is also volatile.

RuO_4 and its solutions can be obtained in small quantities by the action of hypochlorites, chlorine, permanganates or alkali metal peroxides on ruthenium or its derivatives, and also by the electrolysis of ruthenium chloride solutions.

The yellow RuO_4 is very soluble in water with the formation of "hyperruthenic" acid H_2RuO_5. The solubility is 0·13 mole/l (i.e. 21·54 g/l) at 25°C ([9] and [11]). The H_2RuO_5 so formed decomposes rapidly when exposed to light, forming a black deposit of hydrated dioxide $RuO_2 . 2H_2O$ (reaction 20). Hydrochloric acid reduces RuO_4 to tetra- and trivalent complexes, being itself oxidized to chlorine; alkalis and ammonia easily form unstable "hyperruthenates" $HRuO_5^-$ with RuO_4. These decompose with the formation of perruthenates RuO_4^- and ruthenates RuO_4^{--} (reactions 7 and 5).

4. BIBLIOGRAPHY

[1] N. DE ZOUBOV and M. POURBAIX, *Comportement électrochimique du ruthénium. Diagrammes d'équilibres tension–pH du système* Ru–H_2O, *à* 25°C (Rapport technique RT.58 of CEBELCOR, 1958).

[2] M. D. SILVERMAN and H. A. LÉVY, Polarographic studies of ruthenium in oxidation states IV, VI, VII and VIII, *J. Amer. Chem. Soc.* **76**, 3319 (1954).

[3] G. CHARLOT, *L'analyse qualitative et les réactions en solution*, 4th ed., Masson, Paris, 1957, p. 270.

[4] F. S. MARTIN, A sexavalent ruthenium sulfate, *J. Chem. Soc.* 3055–9 (1952).

[5] A. THIEL and W. HAMMERSCHMIDT, II. Ueber den Zusammenhang zwischen der Ueberspannung des Wasserstoffs an reinen Metallen und gewissen Eigenschaften der Metalle, *Z. anorg. allgem. Chem.* **132**, 23 (1923).

[6] *Platinum Metals Review*, **1**, 19 (1957) (Electrodeposition of ruthenium).

[7] L. WÖHLER, PH. BALZ and L. METZ, Die Oxyde des Rutheniums, *Z. anorg. allgem. Chem.* **139**, 205–19 (1924).

[8] W. N. IPATIEV and O. E. SVIAGINTSEV, *J. Chimie Générale U.R.S.S.* **61**, 823 (1929).

[9] R. E. CONNICK and C. R. HURLEY, Chemistry of Ru (VI), (VII) and Ru (VIII). Reactions, oxidation potentials and spectra, *J. Amer. Chem. Soc.* **74**, 5012–15 (1952).

[10] P. PASCAL, *Traité de Chimie minérale* (*Le ruthénium*, by R. CHARONNAT), vol. XI, Masson, Paris, 1932, pp. 383–442.

[11] H. U. VON VOGEL, *Chemiker-Kalender* (Springer-Verlag, Berlin–Göttingen–Heidelberg, 1956), p. 124.

SECTION 13.2

RHODIUM (¹)

J. VAN MUYLDER and M. POURBAIX

SUMMARY

(¹) Adapted and shortened version of the Rapport technique RT.59 of CEBELCOR [1].

1. SUBSTANCES CONSIDERED AND SUBSTANCES NOT CONSIDERED

	Oxidation number (Z)	Considered	Not considered	μ^0(cal.)	Name, colour, crystalline system
Solid substances	0	**Rh**	–	0	Rhodium, grey–white, cub.
	+1	**Rh_2O**	–	–20 000	Rhodium sub-oxide, light grey
	+2	**RhO**	–	–18 000	Rhodous oxide, grey
	+3	**Rh_2O_3**	–	–52 500	Rhodium sesquioxide, grey–black, rhomb.
	»	–	**Rh_2O_3** hydr.	–	Hydrated rhodium sesquioxide $Rh_2O_35H_2O$, light yellow
	+4	**RhO_2**	–	–15 000 (2)	Rhodic oxide, yellow–brown to brown–black
	»	–	**RhO_2** hydr.	–	Hydrated rhodic oxide RhO_22H_2O, dark green
	+6	–	**RhO_3** hydr.	–	Rhodium trioxide or rhodic anhydride, bluish
Dissolved substances	+1	Rh^+	–	14 000 (2)	Hyporhodous ion
	+2	Rh^{++}	–	28 000 (2)	Rhodous ion
	+3	Rh^{+++}	–	55 000 (2)	Rhodic ion
	+6	RhO_4^{--}	–	–15 000 (2)	Rhodate ion, dark purple

2. REACTIONS AND EQUILIBRIUM FORMULAE

2.1. TWO DISSOLVED SUBSTANCES

2.1.1. *Relative stability of the dissolved substances*

$+1 \rightarrow +2$

1. $Rh^+ = Rh^{++} + e^-$ $\quad E_0 = 0.600 + 0.0591 \log \frac{(Rh^{++})}{(Rh^+)}$

$+1 \rightarrow +6$

2. $Rh^+ + 4H_2O = RhO_4^{--} + 8H^+ + 5e^-$ $\quad E_0 = 1.717 - 0.0946\,pH + 0.0118 \log \frac{(RhO_4^{--})}{(Rh^+)}$

$+2 \rightarrow +3$

3. $Rh^{++} = Rh^{+++} + e^-$ $\quad E_0 = 1.198 + 0.0591 \log \frac{(Rh^{+++})}{(Rh^{++})}$

$+2 \rightarrow +6$

4. $Rh^{++} + 4H_2O = RhO_4^{--} + 8H^+ + 4e^-$ $\quad E_0 = 1.995 - 0.1182\,pH + 0.0148 \log \frac{(RhO_4^{--})}{(Rh^{++})}$

$+3 \rightarrow +6$

5. $Rh^{+++} + 4H_2O = RhO_4^{--} + 8H^+ + 3e^-$ $\quad E_0 = 2.261 - 0.1576\,pH + 0.0197 \log \frac{(RhO_4^{--})}{(Rh^{+++})}$

2.1.2. *Limits of the domains of relative predominance of the dissolved substances*

1'. Rh^+ / Rh^{++} $\quad E_0 = 0.600$
2'. Rh^+ / RhO_4^{--} $\quad E_0 = 1.717 - 0.0946\,pH$
3'. Rh^{++} / Rh^{+++} $\quad E_0 = 1.198$
4'. Rh^{++} / RhO_4^{--} $\quad E_0 = 1.995 - 0.1182\,pH$
5'. Rh^{+++} / RhO_4^{--} $\quad E_0 = 2.261 - 0.1576\,pH$

2.2. TWO SOLID SUBSTANCES

Limits of the domains of relative stability of the solid substances

$0 \rightarrow +1$

6. $2\mathbf{Rh} + H_2O = \mathbf{Rh_2O} + 2H^+ + 2e^-$ $\quad E_0 = 0.796 - 0.0591\,pH$

$+1 \rightarrow +2$

7. $\mathbf{Rh_2O} + H_2O = 2\mathbf{RhO} + 2H^+ + 2e^-$ $\quad E_0 = 0.882 - 0.0591\,pH$

$+1 \rightarrow +3$

8. $\mathbf{Rh_2O} + 2H_2O = \mathbf{Rh_2O_3} + 4H^+ + 4e^-$ $\quad E_0 = 0.877 - 0.0591\,pH$

(2) Values deduced from equilibrium potentials given by Latimer.

$+2 \rightarrow +3$

9. $2\,\mathbf{RhO} + H_2O = \mathbf{Rh_2O_3} + 2H^+ + 2e^-$ $\qquad E_0 = 0.871 - 0.0591\,pH$

$+3 \rightarrow +4$

10. $\mathbf{Rh_2O_3} + H_2O = 2\,\mathbf{RhO_2} + 2H^+ + 2e^-$ $\qquad E_0 = 1.730 - 0.0591\,pH$

2.3. ONE DISSOLVED SUBSTANCE AND ONE SOLID SUBSTANCE

Solubility of the solid substances

$Z = +1$

11. $2Rh^+ + H_2O = \mathbf{Rh_2O} + 2H^+$ $\qquad \log(Rh^+) = 3.31 - pH$

$Z = +3$

12. $2Rh^{+++} + 3H_2O = \mathbf{Rh_2O_3} + 6H^+$ $\qquad \log(Rh^{+++}) = 2.56 - 3\,pH$

$0 \rightarrow +1$

13. $\mathbf{Rh} = Rh^+ + e^-$ $\qquad E_0 = 0.600 + 0.0591 \log(Rh^+)$

$0 \rightarrow +2$

14. $\mathbf{Rh} = Rh^{++} + 2e^-$ $\qquad E_0 = 0.600 + 0.0295 \log(Rh^{++})$

$0 \rightarrow +3$

15. $\mathbf{Rh} = Rh^{+++} + 3e^-$ $\qquad E_0 = 0.799 + 0.0197 \log(Rh^{+++})$

$+1 \rightarrow +2$

16. $\mathbf{Rh_2O} + 2H^+ = 2Rh^{++} + H_2O + 2e^-$ $\qquad E_0 = 0.396 + 0.0591\,pH + 0.0591 \log(Rh^{++})$

$+1 \rightarrow +3$

17. $\mathbf{Rh_2O} + 2H^+ = 2Rh^{+++} + H_2O + 4e^-$ $\qquad E_0 = 0.801 + 0.0295\,pH + 0.0295 \log(Rh^{+++})$

18. $2Rh^+ + 3H_2O = \mathbf{Rh_2O_3} + 6H^+ + 4e^-$ $\qquad E_0 = 0.975 - 0.0886\,pH - 0.0295 \log(Rh^+)$

$+2 \rightarrow +3$

19. $2Rh^{++} + 3H_2O = \mathbf{Rh_2O_3} + 6H^+ + 2e^-$ $\qquad E_0 = 1.349 - 0.1773\,pH - 0.0591 \log(Rh^{++})$

$+3 \rightarrow +4$

20. $Rh^{+++} + 2H_2O = \mathbf{RhO_2} + 4H^+ + e^-$ $\qquad E_0 = 1.881 - 0.2364\,pH - 0.0591 \log(Rh^{+++})$

$+3 \rightarrow +6$

21. $\mathbf{Rh_2O_3} + 5H_2O = 2RhO_4^{--} + 10H^+ + 6e^-$ $\qquad E_0 = 2.211 - 0.0985\,pH + 0.0197 \log(RhO_4^{--})$

$+4 \rightarrow +6$

22. $\mathbf{RhO_2} + 2H_2O = RhO_4^{--} + 4H^+ + 2e^-$ $\qquad E_0 = 2.452 - 0.1182\,pH + 0.0295 \log(RhO_4^{--})$

3. EQUILIBRIUM DIAGRAMS AND THEIR INTERPRETATION

3.1. ESTABLISHMENT OF THE DIAGRAMS

Using relations (1)–(22) we have constructed Figs. 1–3, which represent the conditions of thermodynamic equilibrium of the system rhodium–water at 25°C.

Figure 1 does not take into account any dissolved forms of rhodium; it is probably valid for solutions completely free from complexing substances.

Figure 2 takes into account, as dissolved forms of rhodium, only the ions Rh^{+++} and RhO_4^{--}, which do in fact represent complexes of tri- and hexavalent rhodium. It is probably fairly true qualitatively for solutions containing chloride.

Figure 3 takes into account the four ions mentioned in paragraph 1: Rh^+, Rh^{++}, Rh^{+++} and RhO_4^{--}. It probably has no practical interest.

It is probable that none of the four rhodium ions mentioned above actually exists and that, just as in the case of platinum, there are no real rhodium salts; the formulae attributed to certain simple salts of rhodium represent these substances only in the solid state; on contact with water they are immediately converted into complexes. Like the other metals of the platinum group, rhodium has a great ability to form complex ions, notably with ammonia, the halogens, cyanides and nitrites.

Charlot [2] describes the following complexes: $RhCl_6^{---}$ (yellow), $Rh(OH)_3Cl_3^{---}$ (red–brown), $Rh(C_2O_4)_3^{---}$, $Rh(SCN)_3$ (orange), $Rh(SCN)_6^{---}$ (garnet-red) and $Rh(CN)_6^{---}$.

From Fig. 1 we have derived Fig. 4, which represents the theoretical conditions of immunity and passivation of rhodium at 25°C in the absence of substances with which rhodium can form soluble complexes.

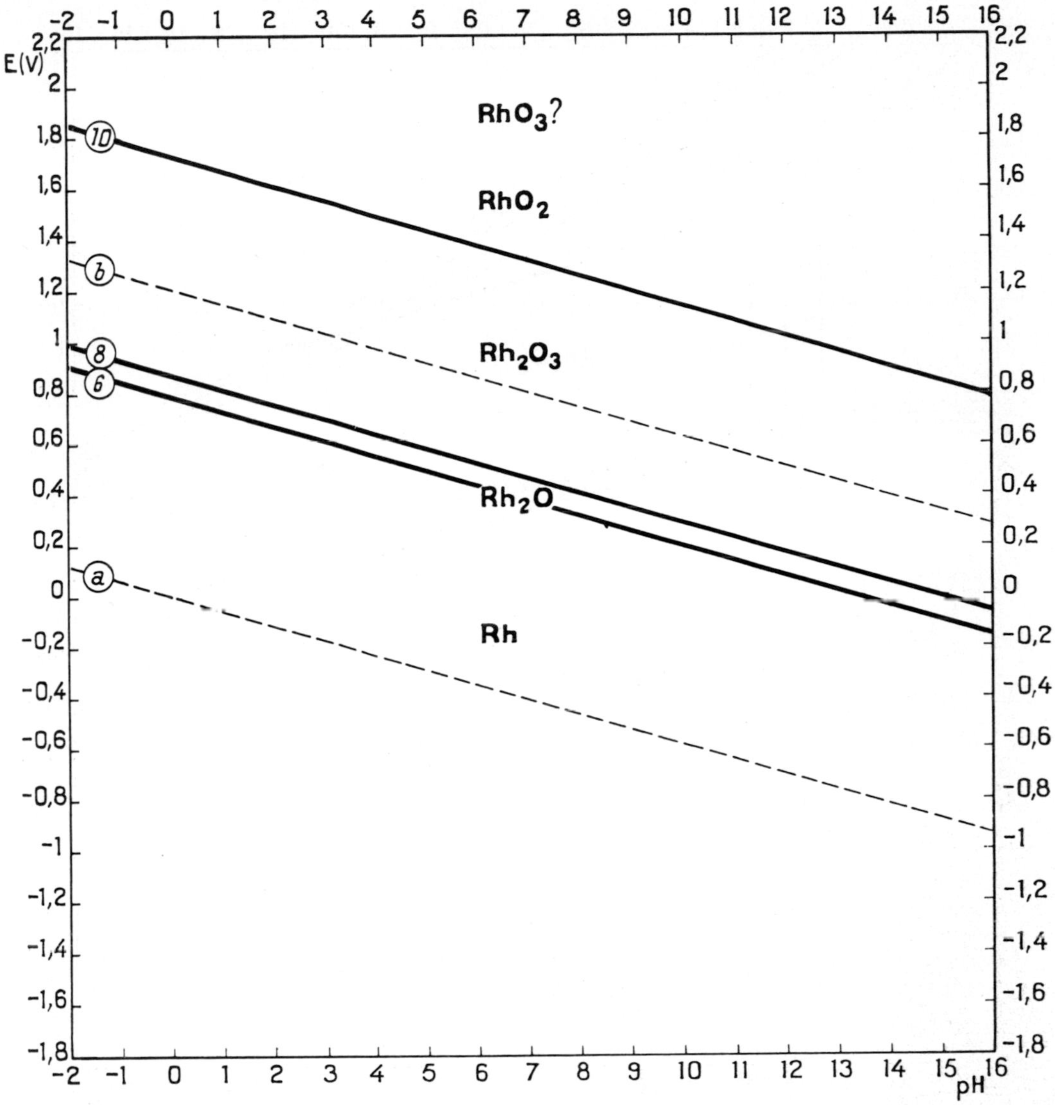

FIG. 1. Potential–pH equilibrium diagram for the system rhodium–water, at 25°C.
(Taking into account no dissolved forms of rhodium: approximately true for solutions free from complexing substances.)

Figure 5, which is derived from Fig. 2, represents, in a very approximate manner, the same conditions in the presence of chlorides.

3.2. STABILITY AND CORROSION OF RHODIUM

Rhodium appears, from Figs. 1 and 4, to be a very noble metal, as its stability domain covers the greater part of that of water. In nature it is found in the native state, usually together with other platinum-type metals, and often with gold.

In accordance with these figures, rhodium is stable in the presence of non-complexing aqueous solutions of all pH's. At temperatures around 25°C it is not affected by water or aqueous solutions of caustic alkalis; it is not attacked by acids or oxidizing agents, not even by aqua regia (which does not agree with Figs. 2 and 5 for solutions containing chloride).

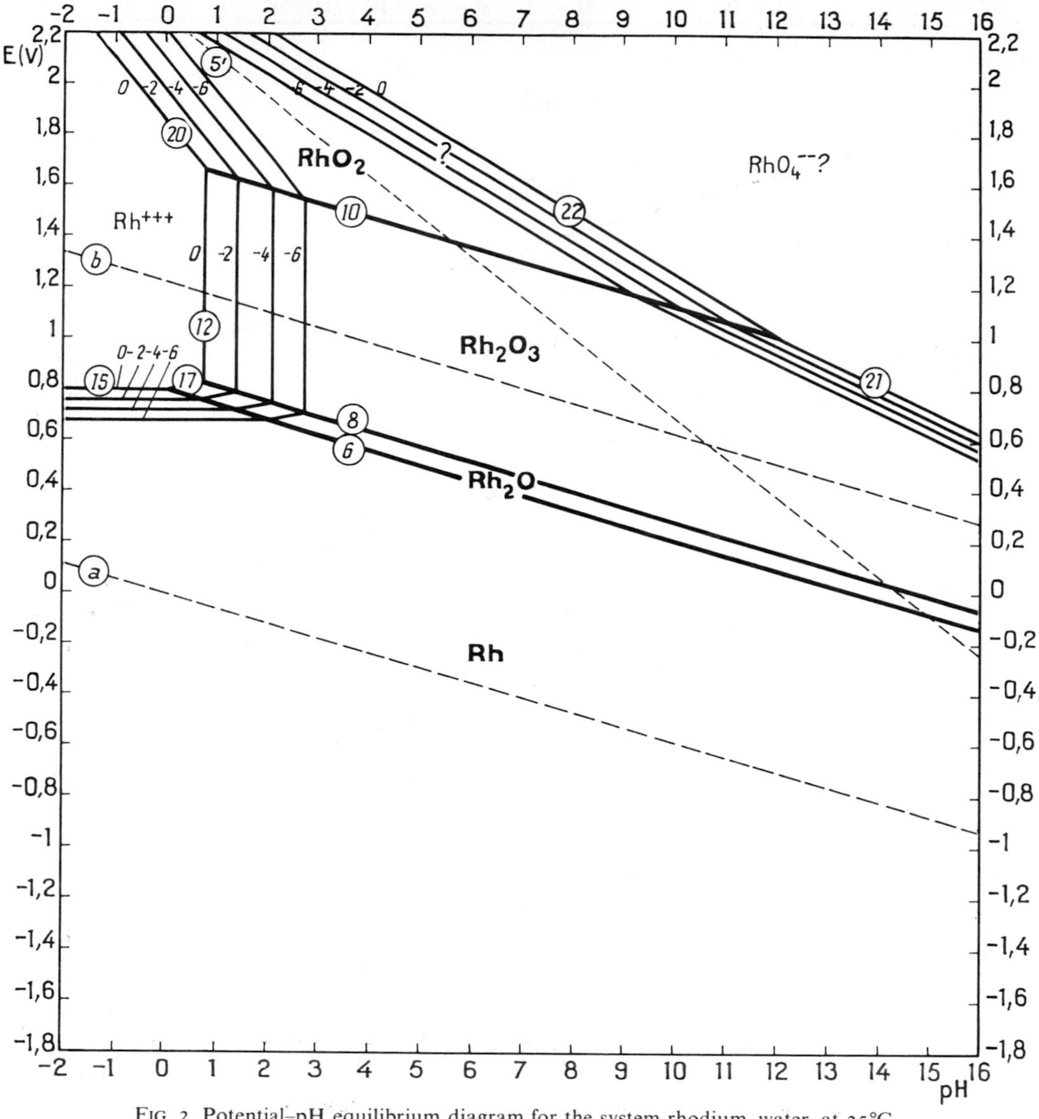

FIG. 2. Potential–pH equilibrium diagram for the system rhodium–water, at 25°C. (Taking into account as dissolved forms of rhodium only the ions Rh^{+++} and RhO_4^{--}.)

The resistance of rhodium to aggressive chemical reagents is remarkable, on the whole surpassing that of platinum. It is illustrated by the following example given by Rhodes [3]: "An electrolytic coating of rhodium 2·5 μ thick deposited on the inside of a silver vessel and exposed for half an hour to the action of boiling aqua regia shows no change in appearance. No loss in weight can be detected after this attack."

The behaviour of massive rhodium therefore appears to be completely in agreement with the predictions of Fig. 1. However, the physical state of the metal can modify its reactivity very considerably. In the finely divided state (e.g. the *rhodium blacks*, which are extremely finely divided black powders) rhodium dissolves fairly readily in hot concentrated sulphuric acid and in aqua regia; it also dissolves,

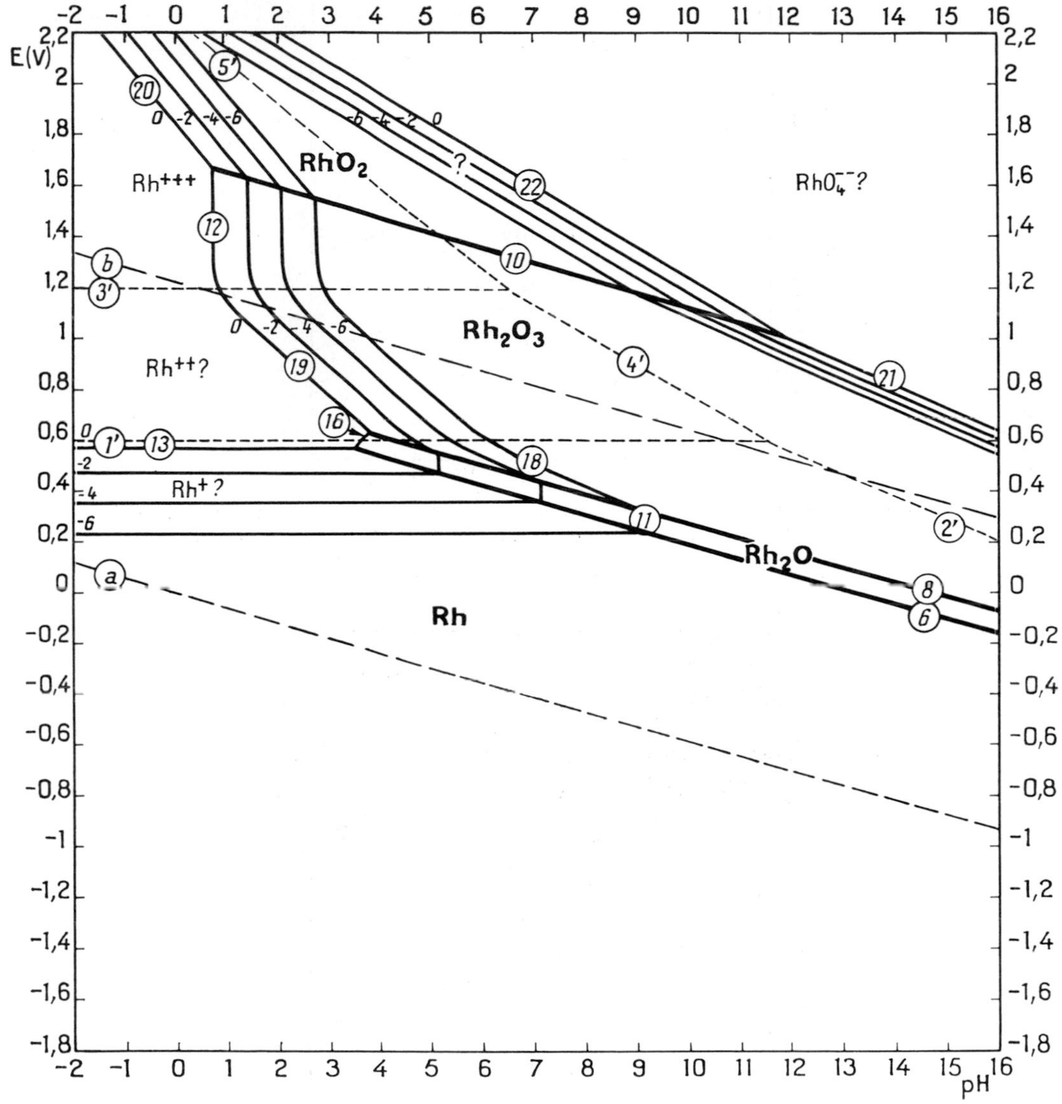

FIG. 3. Potential–pH equilibrium diagram for the system rhodium–water, at 25°C. (Taking into account all the dissolved forms of rhodium described by Latimer.)

in the course of time, in hydrochloric acid in contact with the air. This dissolution, which is in agreement with the predictions of Fig. 2, most probably takes place through the formation of complex rhodium ions in which the metal is in the trivalent state. When rhodium is heated in air or oxygen its oxidation rate increases as the temperature rises, up to about 1000–1100°C; the final oxidation product is the oxide of trivalent rhodium, Rh_2O_3. Rhodium is also converted into Rh_2O_3 by alkaline fusion with Na_2CO_3 and $NaNO_3$, KOH and KNO_3, Na_2O_2 or NaOH.

When used as an anode rhodium is in general unaffected, notably in hydrochloric solutions (Newbery [4]) and sulphuric solutions (Rhodes [3]).

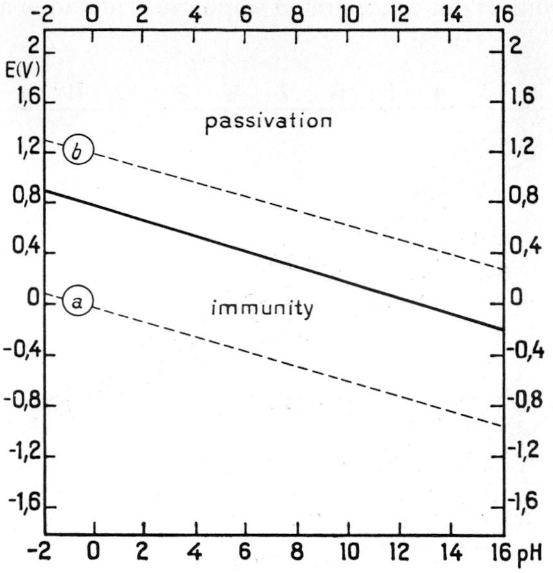

FIG. 4. Theoretical domains of corrosion, immunity and passivation of rhodium, at 25°C, in solutions free from complexing substances. (Derived from Fig. 1.)

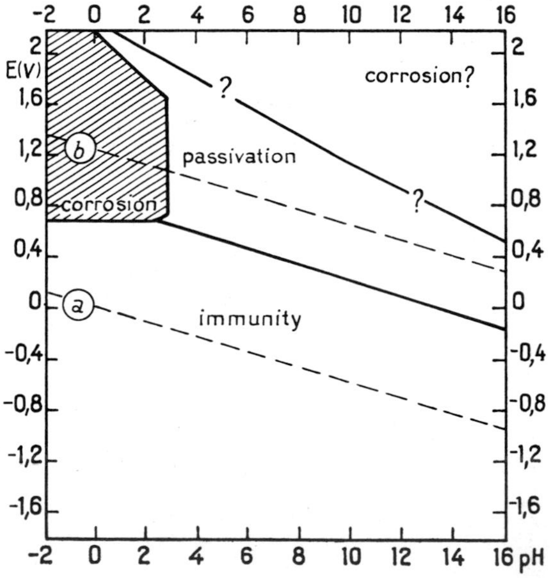

FIG. 5. Theoretical domains of corrosion, immunity and passivation of rhodium, at 25°C, in the presence of solutions containing complexing substances. (Derived from Fig. 2.)

According to Butler and Drever [5], the anodic polarization of rhodium in dilute sulphuric acid (0·1 M) or dilute caustic soda (0·1 M) causes a layer of adsorbed oxygen to be formed on the metal when the current density is small (about 10 $\mu A/cm^2$), while at higher current densities a rhodium peroxide appears.

3.3. ELECTRO-DEPOSITION OF RHODIUM. ELECTRO-PLATING OF RHODIUM

From Fig. 2 it follows that rhodium can easily be obtained in the metallic state by the reduction of its solutions. For this purpose rhodium sulphate or rhodium phosphate solutions are generally used. They are prepared respectively by adding a concentrated solution of rhodium sulphate or rhodium phosphate to dilute sulphuric acid, in such quantities that there is a concentration of 2 g of metallic rhodium and 20 c.c. of sulphuric acid per litre (Rhodes [3]).

The final solutions, although described as simple solutions of rhodium sulphate and rhodium phosphate, are in fact solutions containing rhodium complexes.

The solutions are electrolysed at 35–40°C, with a cathodic current density of 1–4 A/dm^2, using cathodes of Pt, Pd, Au, Ni, Cu, Ag or "white gold", all of which are metals that can be rhodium-plated directly.

3.4. STABILITY AND FORMATION OF THE RHODIUM OXIDES

According to Figs. 1 and 2, the rhodium oxides should all be insoluble in non-complexing solutions; they should be soluble in acid chloride solutions, and in alkaline chloride solutions containing a powerful oxidizing agent.

In actual fact, according to Wöhler and Müller [6], Rh_2O is insoluble in acids and aqua regia, although Latimer considers that it is probably very soluble at pH = 0; in very alkaline solutions its behaviour is practically unknown.

RhO, which has properties analogous to those of Rh_2O (Wöhler and Müller [6]) is thermodynamically unstable with respect to Rh_2O and Rh_2O_3, according to the free enthalpy values assumed above, and should therefore tend to decompose to give a mixture of these two oxides.

Anhydrous Rh_2O_3 is also insoluble in acids (including aqua regia) and in very alkaline solutions free from oxidizing agents. Its hydrated form, the pale yellow $Rh_2O_3 . 5H_2O$, dissolves readily in mineral acids (HCl, H_2SO_4, HNO_3) and in certain organic acids (notably in CH_3COOH when the hydrated oxide is kept moist). In alkaline solution it is oxidized by chlorine to give the greenish oxide $RhO_2 . 2H_2O$ and purple rhodate ions RhO_4^{--}. This behaviour is in satisfactory agreement with Fig. 2. The position occupied by Rh_2O_3 in Figs. 1 and 2 show that it is the stable oxide in the presence of oxygen, except in the presence of alkaline complexing solutions when it may tend to be oxidized to the valency +6. It is to be considered as an oxidizing agent.

Anhydrous RhO_2, which is yellow–brown to brown–black in colour and can be obtained by heating a mixture of rhodium, caustic potash and potassium nitrate to red-heat, is insoluble in acids and alkalis. Its dark-green hydrate can be obtained by the anodic oxidation of solutions containing complexed rhodium, and, as shown above, by the oxidation of Rh_2O_3 (or Na_3RhCl_6) with chlorine in alkaline solution. RhO_2 and its hydrate are powerful oxidizing agents, as shown by Figs. 1 and 2; they oxidize hydrochloric acid to chlorine, and react with Na_2O_2 and $Na_2S_2O_8$ producing a vigorous evolution of oxygen.

4. BIBLIOGRAPHY

[1] J. VAN MUYLDER and M. POURBAIX, *Comportement électrochimique du rhodium. Diagrammes d'équilibres tension–pH du système* Rh–H_2O, *à* 25°C (Rapport technique RT.59 of CEBELCOR, 1958).
[2] G. CHARLOT, *L'analyse qualitative et les réactions en solution,* 4th ed., Masson, Paris, 1957.
[3] E. RHODES, La pratique moderne du rhodiage, *Chim. et Ind.* **75**, No. 6 (June 1956).
[4] E. NEWBERY, Chlorine overvoltage, *J. Chem. Soc.* **119,** 483 (1921).
[5] J. BUTLER and G. DREVER, The mechanism of electrolytic processes. Part I. The anodic oxidation of some metals of the platinum group, *Trans. Faraday Soc.* **32**, 429 (1936).
[6] L. WÖHLER and W. MÜLLER, Die Chloride und Oxyde des Rhodiums, *Z. anorg. allgem. Chem.* **149**, 125–38 (1925).

SECTION 13.3

PALLADIUM(1)

N. DE ZOUBOV and M. POURBAIX

SUMMARY

1. *Substances considered and substances not considered.*

2. *Reactions and equilibrium formulae.*

2.1. Two solid substances.
Limits of the domains of relative stability of the solid substances.

2.2. One solid substance and one dissolved substance.
Solubility of the solid substances.

3. *Equilibrium diagram and its interpretation.*

3.1. Establishment of the diagram.

3.2. Stability and corrosion of palladium.

3.3. Electro-deposition of palladium. Electro-plating of palladium.

3.4. Palladium electrode for the measurement of pH.

3.5. Stability of palladous oxide and hydroxide.

3.6. Stability of palladic hydroxide.

3.7. Stability of palladium peroxide.

4. *Bibliography.*

(1) Shortened and adapted version of the Rapport Technique RT.60 of CEBELCOR [1].

1. SUBSTANCES CONSIDERED AND SUBSTANCES NOT CONSIDERED

	Oxidation number (Z)	Considered	Not considered	μ^0(cal.)	Name, colour, crystalline system
Solid substances	− 0.5	Pd_2H	–	− 1 097 (2)	Palladium α-hydride
	0	Pd	–	0	Palladium, white, f.c.cub.
	+ 1	–	Pd_2O	–	Palladium sub-oxide, black
	+ 2	PdO hydr.	–	a. −15 310	Hydrated palladium oxide or palladous hydroxide $Pd(OH)_2$, brown to yellow(3)
	»	»	–	b. −14 400	Palladous oxide, grey, quad.
	+ 3	–	Pd_2O_3 hydr.	–	Hydrated sesquioxide $Pd_2O_3 . xH_2O$, brown–black
	+ 4	PdO_2 hydr.	–	−12 820	Hydrated palladic oxide or palladic hydroxide $Pd(OH)_4$, brown(3)
	+ 6	PdO_3	–	24 100 (4)	Palladium peroxide
Dissolved substances	+ 2	Pd^{++}	–	45 500	Palladous ion, red–brown
	»	–	PdO_2^{--}	–	Palladite ion
	+ 4	–	PdO_3^{--}	–	Palladate ion

2. REACTIONS AND EQUILIBRIUM FORMULAE(5)

2.1. TWO SOLID SUBSTANCES

Limits of the domains of relative stability of the solid substances

$-0.5 \rightarrow 0$

1. $Pd_2H = 2Pd + H^+ + e^-$ $\qquad E_0 = 0.048 - 0.0591\,pH$

$0 \rightarrow +2$

2. $Pd + H_2O = PdO + 2H^+ + 2e^-$ $\qquad$ a. $E_0 = 0.897 - 0.0591\,pH$; b. $= 0.917 - 0.0591\,pH$

$+2 \rightarrow +4$

3. $PdO + H_2O = PdO_2 + 2H^+ + 2e^-$ $\qquad$ a. $E_0 = 1.283 - 0.0591\,pH$; b. $= 1.263 - 0.0591\,pH$

$+4 \rightarrow +6$

4. $PdO_2 + H_2O = PdO_3 + 2H^+ + 2e^-$ $\qquad E_0 = 2.030 - 0.0591\,pH$

2.2. ONE SOLID SUBSTANCE AND ONE DISSOLVED SUBSTANCE

Solubility of the solid substances

$Z = +2$

5. $Pd^{++} + H_2O = PdO + 2H^+$ $\qquad$ a. $\log(Pd^{++}) = -2.35 - 2\,pH$; b. $= -3.02 - 2\,pH$

$0 \rightarrow +2$

6. $Pd = Pd^{++} + 2e^-$ $\qquad E_0 = 0.987 + 0.0295 \log(Pd^{++})$

$+2 \rightarrow +4$

7. $Pd^{++} + 2H_2O = PdO_2 + 4H^+ + 2e^-$ $\qquad E_0 = 1.194 - 0.1182\,pH - 0.0295 \log(Pd^{++})$

---

(2) Value deduced from the dissociation pressure $p_{H_2} = 0{\cdot}0246$ atm. of the reaction $Pd_2H = 2Pd + \frac{1}{2}H_2$, determined by Gillespie and Hall [2].

(3) This value of $\mu^0_{PdO} = -15\,310$ cal. corresponds to $\mu^0_{Pd(OH)_2} = -72\,000$ cal. This value of $\mu^0_{PdO_2} = -12\,820$ cal. corresponds to $\mu^0_{Pd(OH)_4} = -126\,200$ cal.

(4) The value deduced from the potential $E_0 = 1{\cdot}22$ V indicated by Jirsa [4] for the equilibrium PdO_2/PdO_3 in a 1N NaOH solution.

(5) In the reactions involving PdO, the letter *a* refers to hydrated PdO or palladous hydroxide $Pd(OH)_2$ whose free enthalpy of formation is −72 000 cal.; the letter *b* refers to anhydrous PdO whose free enthalpy of formation is −14400 cal.

3. EQUILIBRIUM DIAGRAM AND ITS INTERPRETATION

3.1. ESTABLISHMENT OF THE DIAGRAM

Using relations (1)–(7) we have constructed, in Fig. 1, an equilibrium diagram for the system palladium–water, at 25°C. The thermodynamic data used in constructing the portion of the diagram concerning the palladium oxides and hydride are very uncertain; the conclusions drawn from this figure are therefore very much subject to caution.

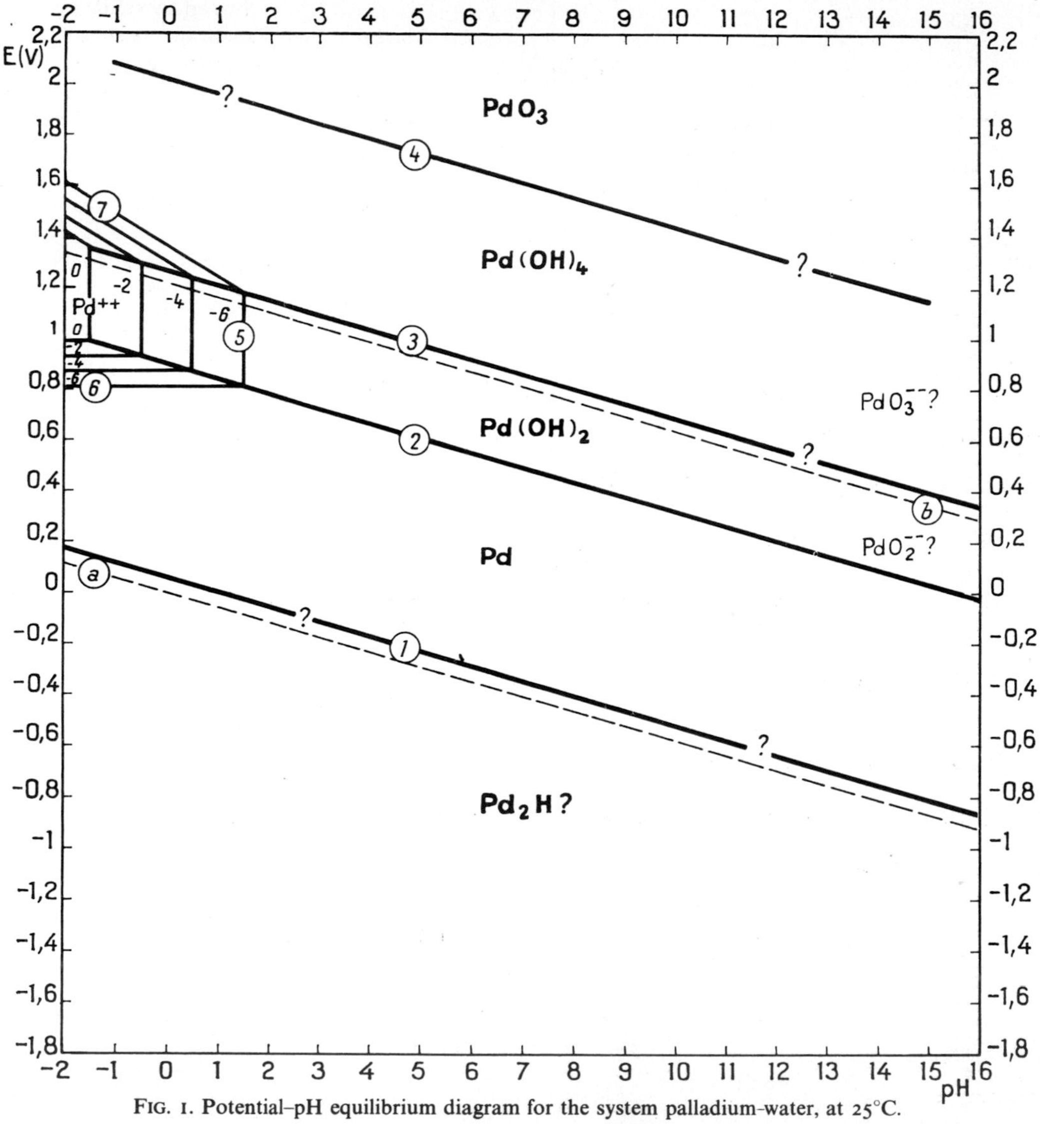

FIG. 1. Potential–pH equilibrium diagram for the system palladium-water, at 25°C.

The diagram is valid only in the absence of substances with which palladium can form soluble complexes or insoluble salts.

Charlot [3] states that, in the valency state +2, palladium forms very stable complexes with ammonia, cyanides, nitrites, etc.; its principal sparingly soluble salts are: the iodide PdI_2, the sulphide PdS, the cyanide $Pd(CN)_2$, the acetylide PdC_2, and a compound with dimethylglyoxime.

From Fig. 1 we have derived Fig. 2, which represents the theoretical domains of corrosion, immunity and passivation of palladium.

3.2. STABILITY AND CORROSION OF PALLADIUM

From Figs. 1 and 2 palladium appears to be a very noble metal, as its domain of thermodynamic stability covers the greater part of that of water. Like the other platinum-group metals, it is found in nature in the native state.

According to these diagrams metallic palladium is thermodynamically stable in the presence of aqueous solutions of all pH's free from vigorous oxidizing agents, reducing agents and complexing substances. In actual fact, palladium is not attacked at all by water, even at high temperatures; it is not tarnished when exposed to moist air. Solutions of non-oxidizing acids (acetic, hydrofluoric, oxalic, sulphuric acids) do not affect it at room temperature.

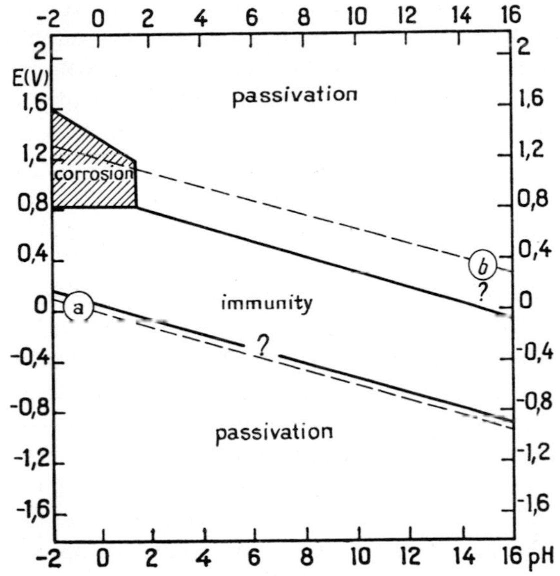

FIG. 2. Theoretical domains of corrosion, immunity and passivation of palladium, at 25°C.

As shown by Figs. 1 and 2, palladium is dissolved by solutions which are both very acid and powerfully oxidizing: hydrochloric acid, which hardly affects palladium in the absence of oxidizing agents, attacks it slightly in the presence of oxygen, more rapidly if the acid contains chlorine, and very rapidly if it is mixed with nitric acid; in these three cases red–brown chloropalladous acid is formed; aqua regia is the most effective solvent for palladium. Dilute nitric acid attacks it slowly; more concentrated nitric acid (specific gravity 1·33) corrodes it fairly rapidly, particularly when the acid contains nitrous compounds.

Palladium is perfectly resistant to cold alkaline solutions (KOH, NaOH), even if they contain oxidizing agents; this fact is not in agreement with the hypothetical formation of soluble palladites shown in Fig. 1, which may be due to the formation of a protective film (PdO?) more stable than the $Pd(OH)_2$ considered in this diagram.

When used as an electrolytic anode palladium may be corroded in very acid solutions, according to Figs. 1 and 2, except when the electrode potential is relatively high, in which case the metal can cover itself with peroxide.

In practice, a palladium anode dissolves readily in concentrated hydrochloric acid, but only slightly in the dilute acid. It does not dissolve in 2 M nitric acid or sodium nitrate solution, but becomes covered with a brown film.

During the anodic polarization of palladium in normal sodium hydroxide solution (pH = 13·7), Jirsa [4] observed several jumps in the potential, which he believed to correspond to the gradual oxidation of the metal through the successive stages $Pd \rightarrow Pd_2O \rightarrow PdO \rightarrow PdO_2 \rightarrow PdO_3$, occurring respectively at the potentials +0·15, +0·4 to 0·5, +0·95 and +1·22 V. These results are not in general agreement with Fig. 1, which may require considerable modification.

In alkaline solutions a palladium anode becomes covered with a brown film, and is thus passivated.

On reduction, palladium can form hydrides. We have represented these by the formula Pd_2H, which corresponds to the substance studied by Gillespie and Hall [2] and is the α-hydride of palladium.

In agreement with Figs. 1 and 2, palladium is thermodynamically less stable than its hydride when in the presence of hydrogen, and therefore tends to be converted into the hydride. At potentials below those indicated by line (1) there exists a domain of cathodic passivation of palladium.

When used as an electrolytic cathode palladium usually behaves in a characteristic manner, on account of its special ability to dissolve hydrogen. At room temperature it can absorb 370 times its own volume of hydrogen, and at 100°C up to 650 times its own volume; consequently one does not generally observe any evolution of gas at the beginning of the electrolysis. The absorption of hydrogen by palladium is accompanied by a change in the crystalline structure of the metal, probably owing to the formation, not only of α and β solid solutions, but also of a hydride Pd_2H or (Pd_4H_2) ([5] and [6]).

3.3. ELECTRO-DEPOSITION OF PALLADIUM. ELECTRO-PLATING OF PALLADIUM (see [5] and [7])

From Fig. 1 it follows that palladium can be very easily obtained in the metallic state by reduction of its solutions.

This reduction can be performed *chemically* by treating solutions of palladous salts (chloride $PdCl_2$) with hydrogen, metals (magnesium, zinc, iron, mercury), inorganic compounds (ferrous salts, sulphurous and phosphorous acids, carbon monoxide, phosphine) or organic compounds (methane, ethylene, formaldehyde, formic acid, hydrazine, hydroxylamine).

Palladium is easily *electro-deposited* on most common metals; the deposit of palladium thus formed can protect these metals against corrosion if it is not porous. Experience shows that the electroplating of palladium gives the best results when it is deposited on silver-, copper- or nickel-based materials, i.e. relatively noble metals on which palladium can be deposited without any formation of hydrogen. It is therefore best to copper- or nickel-plate objects made of iron, steel, tin, etc., before palladium-plating them.

3.4. PALLADIUM ELECTRODE FOR THE MEASUREMENT OF pH

Palladium has a particularly small hydrogen overpotential: the reaction $H_2 = 2H^+ + 2e^-$ takes place almost reversibly on the metal, even more reversibly than on platinum; palladium, like platinum, can therefore be used to make hydrogen electrodes for the measurement of pH. The great solubility of hydrogen in palladium enables palladium electrodes, previously saturated with hydrogen, to be used for the measurement of pH, without being permanently immersed in a current of hydrogen, as is the case for platinum; their potential remains steady for long periods at the equilibrium value corresponding to the pressure under which they are operating. If this pressure is atmospheric, the potential depends on the pH according to the following relation, at 25°C: $E_0 = -0{\cdot}0591$ pH (*a*).

3.5. STABILITY OF PALLADOUS OXIDE AND HYDROXIDE

Palladous hydroxide $Pd(OH)_2$ (or $PdO.H_2O$) can be prepared by precipitation from a solution of a palladous salt (nitrate, chloride) with an alkali metal hydroxide, or by the hydrolysis of a slightly acid palladous salt solution. From Fig. 1, $Pd(OH)_2$ appears to be slightly soluble in acids (to give palladous ions) and in alkalis (to give palladites PdO_2^{--}, which we have been able to represent only qualitatively owing to lack of thermodynamic data). The solubility of $Pd(OH)_2$ depends to a large extent on its degree of hydration; the more it is hydrated, the greater is the solubility: when freshly precipitated in the cold it dissolves readily in dilute acids and weak acids (acetic acid); the product obtained after drying over a water bath is insoluble in acetic acid and fairly insoluble in nitric and sulphuric acids. The solubility in solutions of alkali metal hydroxides is also affected by the degree of hydration. Anhydrous PdO, which can be prepared only with difficulty, by the dehydration of $Pd(OH)_2$ at 750–800°C, is insoluble in acids even when boiling, which is not in agreement with the free enthalpy values assumed in paragraph 1, according to which PdO should be more soluble than $Pd(OH)_2$.

It is therefore probable that the free enthalpy of formation of anhydrous palladous oxide is lower than the value assumed for this study (−14400 cal.).

As is shown by Fig. 1, palladous hydroxide is stable in the presence of water. It can easily be reduced in the cold to metallic palladium, in particular by formic acid, acetic acid, hydrogen peroxide and hydrogen; in the case of hydrogen the reduction is very vigorous and takes place with incandescence.

3.6. STABILITY OF PALLADIC HYDROXIDE

Palladic hydroxide $Pd(OH)_4$ (or $PdO_2 . 2H_2O$) can be prepared by the chemical oxidation (using ozone) or the electrochemical oxidation of solutions of palladous salts (nitrate, chloride, sulphate).

As is shown by Fig. 1, $Pd(OH)_4$ is a powerful oxidizing agent, unstable in air, in which it decomposes with the evolution of oxygen; it is reduced, more vigorously than $Pd(OH)_2$, by hydrogen, organic acids and hydrogen peroxide. When freshly precipitated it dissolves in hydrochloric acid, being reduced to palladous ions Pd^{++}, and partially oxidizing the acid to chlorine; nitric and sulphuric acids also dissolve it at room temperature.

Even when freshly precipitated, $Pd(OH)_4$ is insoluble in dilute solutions of NaOH; it is soluble in a 10 N solution of KOH, which may indicate the existence of soluble palladates, represented in Fig. 1 by the symbol PdO_3^{--}.

3.7. STABILITY OF PALLADIUM PEROXIDE

"Perpalladic" oxide PdO_3 or palladic anhydride, a very powerful oxidizing agent and a very unstable substance, should be formed, according to Jirsa [4], by the anodic polarization of palladium in 1 N KOH solution at 1·22 V.

4. BIBLIOGRAPHY

[1] N. DE ZOUBOV, J. VAN MUYLDER and M. POURBAIX, *Comportement électrochimique du palladium. Diagramme d'équilibres tension–pH du système* Pd–H_2O, à 25°C (Rapport technique RT.60 of CEBELCOR, 1957).

[2] L. J. GILLESPIE and F. P. HALL, The palladium–hydrogen equilibrium and palladium hydride, *J. Amer. Chem. Soc.* **48**, 1207–19 (1926).

[3] G. CHARLOT, *L'analyse qualitative et les réactions en solution,* 4th ed., Masson, Paris, 1957.

[4] F. JIRSA, Zur Theorie der elektrolytischen Sauerstoffentwicklung bei anodischer Polarisation. II. Die Anodenverhältnisse des Palladiums in alkalischen Laugen, *Z. Phys. Chem.* **113**, 241–7 (1924).

[5] J. DE MENT, H. C. DAKE and E. R. ROBERTS, *Rarer Metals. Palladium,* Temple Press, London, 1950, pp. 239–46.

[6] D. T. HURD, *An Introduction to the Chemistry of the Hydrides. The Noble Metals,* John Wiley, New York, 1952, pp. 190–2.

[7] E. TEWS, Zur Galvanotechnik des Palladiums, *Metalloberfläche,* **10**, 193–6 (1956).

SECTION 13.4

OSMIUM (1)

N. DE ZOUBOV and M. POURBAIX

SUMMARY

1. *Substances considered and substances not considered.*

2. *Reactions and equilibrium formulae.*

2.1. Two dissolved substances.

2.1.1. Relative stability of the dissolved substances.

2.1.2. Limits of the domains of relative predominance of the dissolved substances.

2.2. Two solid substances.

Limits of the domains of relative stability of the solid substances.

2.3. One solid substance and one dissolved substance.

Solubility of the solid substances.

2.4. One dissolved substance and one gaseous substance.

Solubility of the gaseous substance OsO_4.

2.5. One solid substance and one gaseous substance.

Limits of the domains of relative stability of OsO_2 and OsO_4.

3. *Equilibrium diagram and its interpretation.*

3.1. Establishment of the diagram.

3.2. Stability and corrosion of osmium.

3.3. Stability of osmium dioxide OsO_2.

3.4. Stability of the osmates OsO_4^{--}.

3.5. Stability of osmium tetroxide OsO_4.

3.6. Passivating action of osmium tetroxide.

4. *Bibliography.*

(1) Shortened and adapted version of the Rapport technique RT.61 of CEBELCOR [1].

1. SUBSTANCES CONSIDERED AND SUBSTANCES NOT CONSIDERED

	Oxidation number (Z)	Considered	Not considered	μ^0(cal.)	Name, colour, crystalline system
Solid substances	0	**Os**	–	0	Osmium, blue–grey, hex.
	+2	–	**OsO**	–	Osmous oxide, black
	+3	–	**Os_2O_3**	–	Osmium sesquioxide, dark brown
	»	–	» hydr.	–	Hydrated osmium sesquioxide $Os_2O_3.3H_2O$ or osmium hydroxide $Os(OH)_3$, red–brown
	+4	**OsO_2** hydr.	–	– *50 000*	Hydrated osmic oxide $OsO_2.2H_2O$ or osmic nydroxide $Os(OH)_4$, black (²)
	»	–	**OsO_2**	–	Osmic oxide, black, quad.
	+5	–	**Os_2O_5** ?	–	Osmium pentoxide
	+8	**OsO_4**	–	– 70 *700*	Osmium tetroxide, yellow, monocl.
	»	–	**OsO_4**	– 70 *500*	Osmium tetroxide, white
Dissolved substances	+6	OsO_4^{--}	–	– 89 *250* (³)	Osmate ion, yellow to red
	+8	H_2OsO_5	–	–126 *640* (³)	"Hyperosmic" acid, colourless
	»	$HOsO_5^-$	–	–113 *000* (³)	"Dihyperosmate" ion, orange–yellow
	»	OsO_5^{--}	–	– 93 *250* (³)	"Hyperosmate" ion, orange–yellow
Gaseous substance	+8	*OsO_4*	–	– 67 *900*	Osmium tetroxide, colourless

2. REACTIONS AND EQUILIBRIUM FORMULAE

2.1. TWO DISSOLVED SUBSTANCES

2.1.1. *Relative stability of the dissolved substances*

$Z = +8$

1. $H_2OsO_5 = HOsO_5^- + H^+$ $\qquad \log\frac{(HOsO_5^-)}{(H_2OsO_5)} = -10.00 + pH$

2. $HOsO_5^- = OsO_5^{--} + H^+$ $\qquad \log\frac{(OsO_5^{--})}{(HOsO_5^-)} = -14.50 + pH$

$+6 \rightarrow +8$

3. $OsO_4^{--} + H_2O = H_2OsO_5 + 2e^-$ $\qquad E_0 = 0.418 + 0.0295\log\frac{(H_2OsO_5)}{(OsO_4^{--})}$

4. $OsO_4^{--} + H_2O = HOsO_5^- + H^+ + 2e^-$ $\qquad E_0 = 0.714 - 0.0295\,pH + 0.0295\log\frac{(HOsO_5^-)}{(OsO_4^{--})}$

5. $OsO_4^{--} + H_2O = OsO_5^{--} + 2H^+ + 2e^-$ $\qquad E_0 = 1.142 - 0.0591\,pH + 0.0295\log\frac{(OsO_5^{--})}{(OsO_4^{--})}$

2.1.2. *Limits of the domains of relative predominance of the dissolved substances*

1'. $H_2OsO_5/HOsO_5^-$ $\qquad pH = 10.00$
2'. $HOsO_5^-/OsO_5^{--}$ $\qquad pH = 14.50$

3'. OsO_4^{--}/H_2OsO_5 $\qquad E_0 = 0.418$
4'. $OsO_4^{--}/HOsO_5^-$ $\qquad E_0 = 0.714 - 0.0295\,pH$
5'. OsO_4^{--}/OsO_5^{--} $\qquad E_0 = 1.142 - 0.0591\,pH$

(²) This value $\mu^0_{OsO_2} = -50\ 000$ cal. corresponds to $\mu^0_{Os(OH)_4} = -16\ 380$ cal.
(³) Values calculated by us [1] or deduced from the dissociation constants estimated by Sauerbrunn and Sandell [2].

2.2. TWO SOLID SUBSTANCES

Limits of the domains of relative stability of the solid substances

$0 \rightarrow +4$

6. $\mathbf{Os} + 2H_2O = \mathbf{OsO_2} + 4H^+ + 4e^-$ $E_0 = 0.687 - 0.0591\,pH$

$+4 \rightarrow +8$

7. $\mathbf{OsO_2} + 2H_2O = \mathbf{OsO_4} + 4H^+ + 4e^-$ $E_0 = 1.005 - 0.0591\,pH$

2.3. ONE SOLID SUBSTANCE AND ONE DISSOLVED SUBSTANCE

Solubility of the solid substances

$Z = +8$

8. $\mathbf{OsO_4} + H_2O = H_2OsO_5$ $\log(H_2OsO_5) = -0.55$
9. $\mathbf{OsO_4} + H_2O = HOsO_5^- + H^+$ $\log(HOsO_5^-) = -10.55 + pH$

$0 \rightarrow +6$

10. $\mathbf{Os} + 4H_2O = OsO_4^{--} + 8H^+ + 6e^-$ $E_0 = 0.994 - 0.0788\,pH + 0.0098\log(OsO_4^{--})$

$0 \rightarrow +8$

11. $\mathbf{Os} + 5H_2O = H_2OsO_5 + 8H^+ + 8e^-$ $E_0 = 0.850 - 0.0591\,pH + 0.0074\log(H_2OsO_5)$

$+4 \rightarrow +6$

12. $\mathbf{OsO_2} + 2H_2O = OsO_4^{--} + 4H^+ + 2e^-$ $E_0 = 1.607 - 0.1182\,pH + 0.0295\log(OsO_4^{--})$

$+4 \rightarrow +8$

13. $\mathbf{OsO_2} + 3H_2O = H_2OsO_5 + 4H^+ + 4e^-$ $E_0 = 1.013 - 0.0591\,pH + 0.0148\log(H_2OsO_5)$

$+6 \rightarrow +8$

14. $OsO_4^{--} = \mathbf{OsO_4} + 2e^-$ $E_0 = 0.402 - 0.0295\log(OsO_4^{--})$

2.4. ONE DISSOLVED SUBSTANCE AND ONE GASEOUS SUBSTANCE

Solubility of the gaseous substance OsO_4

$Z = +8$

15. $OsO_4 + H_2O = H_2OsO_5$ $\log\frac{p_{OsO_4}}{(H_2OsO_5)} = -1.50$

16. $OsO_4 + H_2O = HOsO_5^- + H^+$ $\log\frac{p_{OsO_4}}{(HOsO_5^-)} = 8.50 - pH$

17. $OsO_4 + H_2O = OsO_5^{--} + 2H^+$ $\log\frac{p_{OsO_4}}{(OsO_5^{--})} = 22.99 - 2\,pH$

$+6 \rightarrow +8$

18. $OsO_4^{--} = OsO_4 + 2e^-$ $E_0 = 0.463 + 0.0295\log\frac{p_{OsO_4}}{(OsO_4^{--})}$

2.5. ONE SOLID SUBSTANCE AND ONE GASEOUS SUBSTANCE

Limits of the domains of relative stability of $\mathbf{OsO_2}$ *and* OsO_4

$+4 \rightarrow +8$

19. $\mathbf{OsO_2} + 2H_2O = OsO_4 + 4H^+ + 4e^-$ $E_0 = 1.035 - 0.0591\,pH + 0.0148\log p_{OsO_4}$

3. EQUILIBRIUM DIAGRAM AND ITS INTERPRETATION

3.1. ESTABLISHMENT OF THE DIAGRAM

Using the relations given in the preceding paragraph we have constructed Fig. 1, which represents the conditions of thermodynamic equilibrium of the system osmium–water, at 25°C.

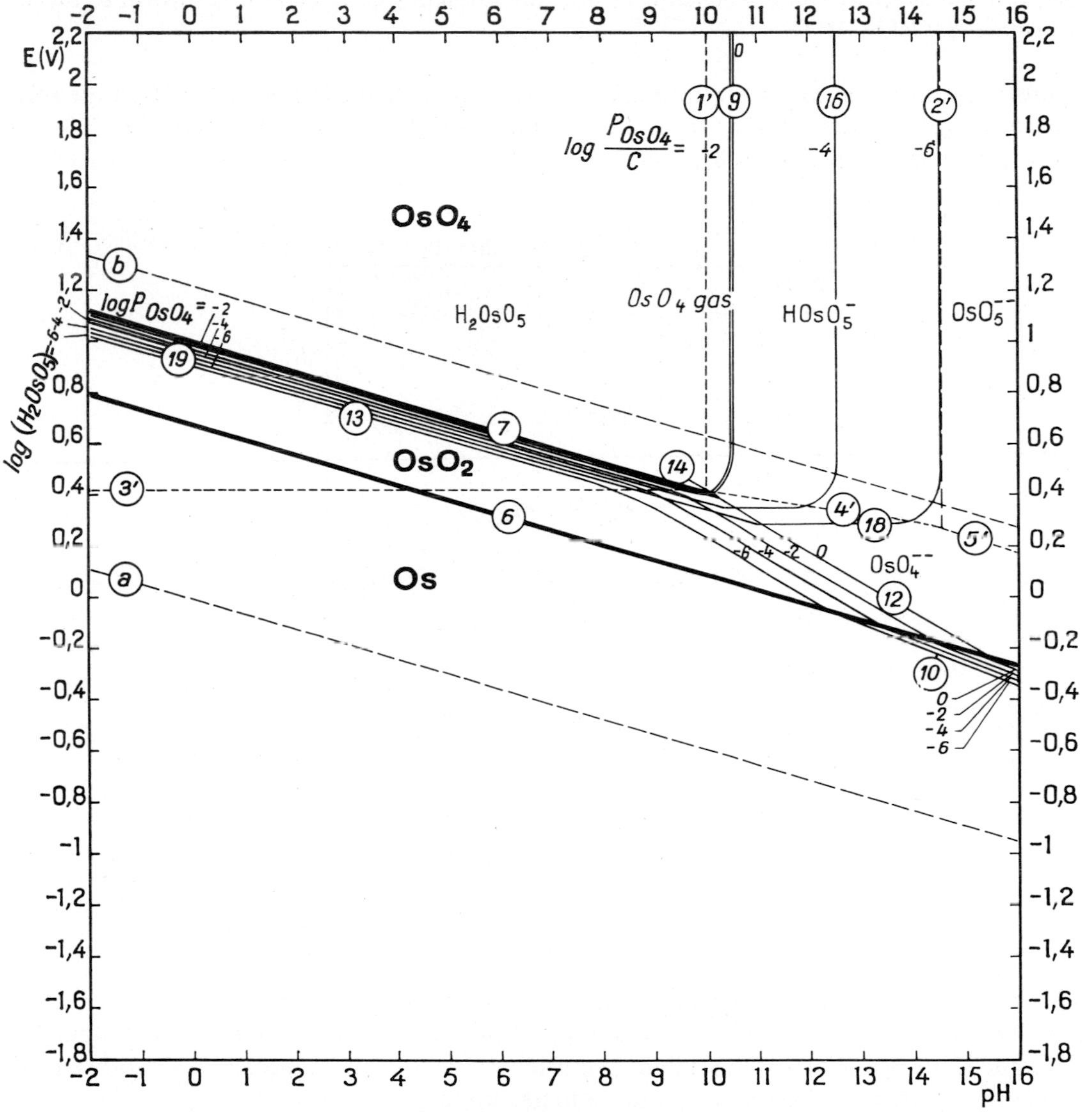

FIG. 1. Potential–pH equilibrium diagram for the system osmium–water, at 25°C.

Figure 2, which is derived from Fig. 1, indicates the theoretical conditions of corrosion, immunity and passivation of osmium at 25°C. Figures 1 and 2 are valid only in the absence of substances with which osmium can form soluble complexes or insoluble salts. For this reason we have not taken into account the complex ions $OsCl_6^{---}$ and the red $OsCl_6^{--}$ existing in acid solutions, nor the blue ion Os^{++}, most probably a complex containing chlorine, which is unstable and rapidly oxidized by the air.

Osmium forms a large number of *complexes*, including ([3], [4]):

at valency +2: $Os(CN)_6^{----}$;
at valencies +3 and +4: complexes with the ligands Cl^-, Br^-, I^-, NO_2^-, $C_2O_4^{--}$, NO, NH_3, ... ;
at valency +5: a complex with ethylene diamine [5];
at valency +6: $OsO_2X_4^{--}$, where X represents a halogen;
at valency +8: OsO_3N^-.

The principal *sparingly soluble compounds* are: the sulphides OsS_2 and OsS_4 (brown to black), and barium osmate $BaOsO_4 . H_2O$.

Figure 3 represents, according to formulae (15), (16) and (17), the influence of pH on the solubility of the gaseous tetroxide OsO_4 (in the three dissolved forms H_2OsO_5, $HOsO_5^-$ and OsO_5^{--}) for various values of the partial pressure of OsO_4.

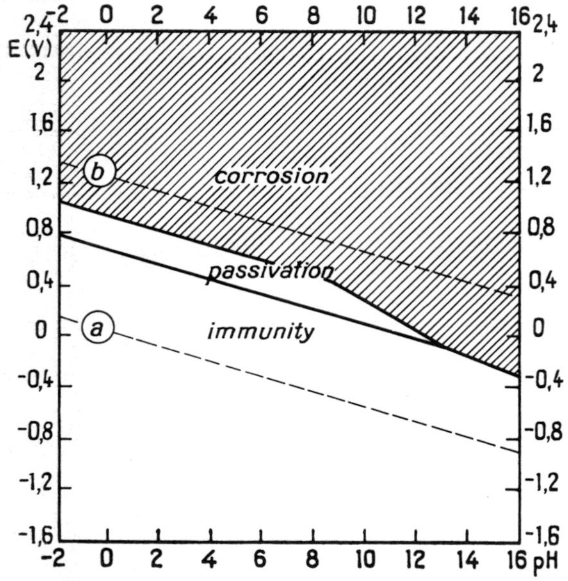

FIG. 2. Theoretical domains of corrosion, immunity and passivation of osmium, at 25°C.

3.2. STABILITY AND CORROSION OF OSMIUM ([12] and [13])

From Figs. 1 and 2, osmium appears to be a very noble metal, as it has a large zone of stability in common with that of water. Unlike the other platinum-type metals osmium is never found in the free state, but is always mixed with iridium (osmiridium) and small quantities of the other platinum-group metals; laurite, or ruthenium sulphide, contains up to 3 per cent of it.

According to these diagrams, osmium is thermodynamically stable in the presence of aqueous solutions of all pH's free from powerful oxidizing agents and complexing substances.

Even at room temperature, powdery osmium is oxidized by the air, turning black with the formation of peroxide OsO_4. The compact metal (crystallized, molten or agglomerated) is not so readily oxidized: depending on its physical state, a temperature of 200–400°C is required before oxidation begins. The degree of division of osmium considerably influences its chemical behaviour: powdery osmium is oxidized to its tetroxide by any oxidizing acid solution (HNO_3, hot concentrated H_2SO_4, H_2O_2); compact osmium is not attacked by oxidizing acids, not even by aqua regia. In the absence of air, hydrochloric acid will not even attack divided osmium; in the presence of oxygen a slight reaction takes place; at 150°C concentrated hydrochloric acid slowly dissolves spongy osmium, forming a yellow–green solution containing tri- or tetravalent osmium.

In agreement with Figs. 1 and 2, osmium is rapidly attacked by alkaline oxidizing solutions (hypochlorites, alkali metal bisulphates, nitrates, etc.), forming soluble osmates OsO_4^{--}. This property, which is shared by ruthenium, is made use of in the separation of these two metals from the other plantinoids.

On fusion with an alkaline oxidizing mixture (KOH, NaOH, ... in the presence of air), osmium is converted into an osmate (yellow to red).

When used as an anode in the electrolysis of an acid or alkaline solution, osmium is converted into its peroxide.

In agreement with the equilibrium diagram Fig. 1, osmium can easily be obtained in the metallic state by reducing solutions of hexavalent osmium (OsO_4^{--}) or tetravalent osmium ($OsCl_6^{--}$). The following reducing agents can be used: hydrogen, metals (zinc, mercury, silver), inorganic salts (ferrous sulphate, stannous chloride), organic substances (formic acid, formates, acetylene). These reducing agents generally give a brown colloidal suspension of metallic osmium and hydrated dioxide.

Important quantities of osmium are prepared by the decomposition of certain osmium compounds by heating in the absence of air. These compounds must be free from certain other substances, such as ammonium compounds and sulphides.

Like all the platinum-group metals, osmium in the divided state absorbs large quantities of hydrogen—up to 1 600 vol. of gas per volume of metal at room temperature; in the compact state the absorption is infinitesimally small.

3.3. STABILITY OF OSMIUM DIOXIDE OsO_2

The thermodynamic data given for osmium dioxide are very uncertain; moreover, we do not know whether the free enthalpy value that we have assumed concerns the anhydrous oxide OsO_2, or whether this applies to the hydrated oxide $OsO_2 . 2H_2O$ (or hydroxide $Os(OH)_4$); the representation of the stability of OsO_2 given in Fig. 1 is therefore only approximate.

According to this figure the dioxide OsO_2 should be stable and insoluble in acid, neutral and slightly alkaline solutions free from oxidizing, reducing and complexing substances. In the presence of very alkaline non-oxidizing solutions it should decompose with the formation of an osmate and metallic osmium, according to the reactions

$$OsO_2 + 4OH^- \rightarrow OsO_4^{--} + 2H_2O + 2e^- \quad (12)$$

and

$$OsO_2 + 2H_2O + 4e^- \rightarrow Os + 4OH^- \quad (6)$$

overall reaction

$$3OsO_2 + 4OH^- \rightarrow 2OsO_4^{--} + Os + 2H_2O.$$

In the presence of oxidizing solutions it should be converted into tetroxide OsO_4, or "hyperosmic" acid H_2OsO_5 (in acid or neutral solutions), or into osmate OsO_4^{--} or "hyperosmate" $HOsO_5^-$ and OsO_5^{--} (in alkaline solutions).

In practice, as Latimer describes, the dioxide does actually dissolve in very alkaline oxidizing solutions, forming osmates; in particular it reacts with hyperosmates to form osmates, according to the reversible reaction

$$OsO_2 + HOsO_5^- + 3OH^- \rightarrow 2OsO_4^{--} + 2H_2O.$$

The hydroxide dissolves in hydrochloric acid, readily when moist and with difficulty when dry, forming chlorine complexes; the solution turns successively purplish red, yellow, green and yellowish brown. Sulphuric and nitric acids dissolve OsO_2, oxidizing it to tetroxide; hydrogen peroxide acts similarly.

In the finely divided state osmium dioxide is rapidly oxidized to tetroxide by the air; it must be preserved, handled and even weighed in an atmosphere of nitrogen or carbon dioxide.

Hydrogen, hydrogen sulphide and carbon monoxide reduce the "active" dioxide to metallic osmium, even at room temperature.

3.4. STABILITY OF THE OSMATES OsO_4^{--}

Corresponding to the trioxide OsO_3, which has not yet been isolated, there are numerous well-defined salts: the easily soluble, yellow to dark red osmates OsO_4^{--}.

According to Fig. 1 the osmates should be stable in alkaline solutions free from oxidizing and reducing agents. Oxidizing agents should convert them into "hyperosmates" $HOsO_5^-$ or OsO_5^{--}; reducing agents should convert them into the dioxide OsO_2 or metallic osmium. On neutralization or acidification they should decompose into volatile OsO_4 and solid OsO_2, according to the reactions

	OsO_4^{--}	$\rightarrow$	$OsO_4 + 2e^-$	(18)
and	$OsO_4^{--} + 4H^+ + 2e^-$	$\rightarrow$	$OsO_2 + 2H_2O$	(12)
overall reaction	$2OsO_4^{--} + 4H^+$	$\rightarrow$	$OsO_4 + OsO_2 + 2H_2O.$	

In actual fact, solutions of osmates have an alkaline reaction. They are oxidized to the tetroxide OsO_4 by chlorine, and are reduced to the dioxide OsO_2 by alcohol, formaldehyde, carbon monoxide and acrolein. They smell of tetroxide, and are easily hydrolysed to give a black precipitate of hydrated dioxide $OsO_2 . 2H_2O$; the hydrolysis is favoured by acids, even by very weak ones.

As we have already seen, and in agreement with the conclusions drawn from Fig. 1 (line 10), the osmates can easily be prepared by the action of alkaline oxidizing solutions on metallic osmium; NaOH or Na_2O_2 may be used, for example [6].

On fusing osmium with alkali metal hydroxides in the presence of air, readily soluble osmates are again obtained.

3.5. STABILITY OF OSMIUM TETROXIDE OsO_4

At ordinary temperatures osmium tetroxide exists in the three states (gaseous, solid and liquid). Two varieties of the solid tetroxide are known: the yellow stable form and the colourless or white labile form. The tetroxide is volatile and its vapour is poisonous.

In Fig. 3, we have used formulae (15), (16) and (17) to represent the influence of pH on the solubility of gaseous OsO_4 (in the dissolved forms H_2OsO_5, $HOsO_5^-$ and OsO_5^{--}) at 25°C, for various values of the partial pressure of OsO_4. From this diagram one can deduce the vapour pressure of OsO_4 existing above a "hyperosmic" solution, for a given concentration and pH. For example, it can be seen that the equilibrium partial pressure of a 0·01 M H_2OsO_5 solution is $10^{-3.5}$ atm. (i.e. 0·00032 atm.) at pH's below 9·5, at 25°C; this pressure is no more than 10^{-6} atm. at pH = 12·5.

The tetroxide dissolves in water without decomposing, forming an almost colourless aqueous solution (hardly yellow at all).

The exact composition of "hyperosmic" acid is unknown; the formula H_2OsO_5 ($OsO_4 . H_2O$) that is frequently attributed to it is a simplified formula; Sauerbrunn and Sandell [2] represent "hyperosmic" acid by the general formula $H_{2n}OsO_{4+n}$.

Alkaline solutions of the tetroxide are orange–yellow. Unlike RuO_4, osmium tetroxide and its solutions are relatively stable in air, since a part of their stability domain lies in common with that of water (Fig. 1).

Osmium tetroxide is one of the most powerful oxidizing agents known: the oxidizing power of a saturated OsO_4 solution is almost equivalent to that of bromine. This "oxygen-carrying" property is used in histological work and in some chemical reactions: decolorization of an indigo solution, separation of iodine from an acid solution of potassium iodide, conversion of alcohol into aldehyde[7], with the advantage that OsO_4 does not form substitution products.

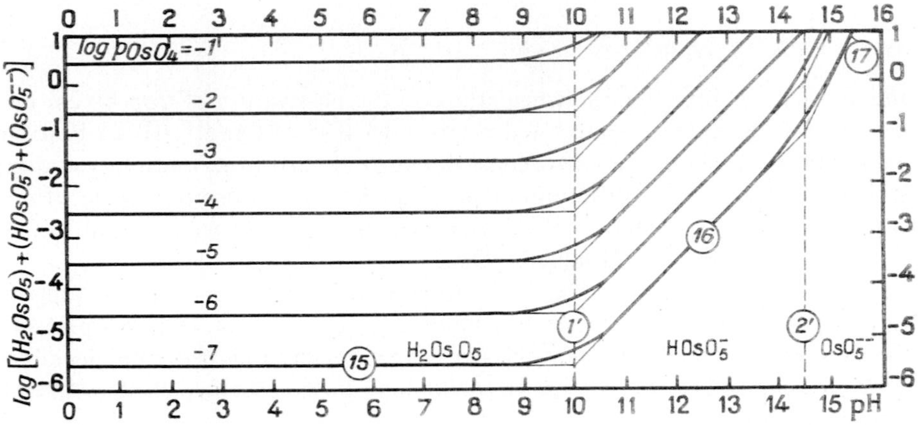

FIG. 3. Equilibrium between gaseous OsO_4 and solutions of octavalent osmium, at 25°C.

OsO_4 is easily reduced by organic matter, for instance by alcohol to the tetravalent state [black $Os(OH)_4$] in acid or slightly alkaline solution, and by alkali metal formates to the metallic state; metallic Os is precipitated as a bluish-black powder by other organic substances of various types, such as unsaturated hydrocarbons, ether, fatty substances, tannin, glucides and uric acid.

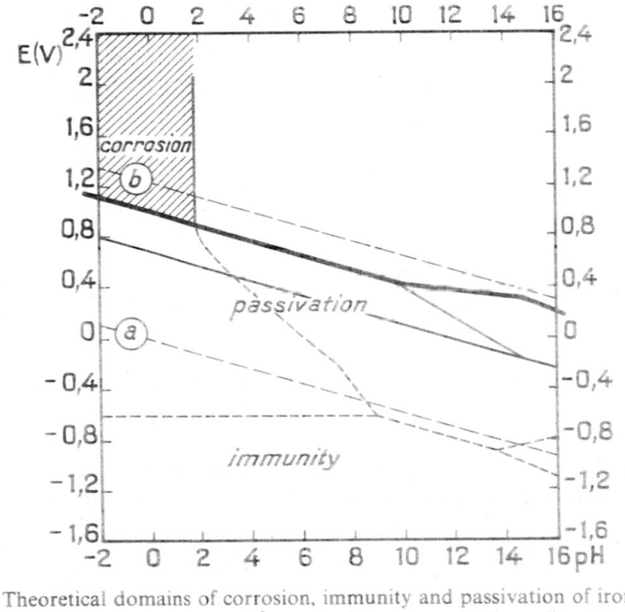

FIG. 4. Theoretical domains of corrosion, immunity and passivation of iron in the presence of solutions containing 10^{-2} g-mol of "hyperosmate" per litre (1·9 g Os/l).

Inorganic reducing agents such as metals (excluding the precious metals) reduce OsO_4 to lower oxides of osmium or to metallic osmium: ferrous salts, stannous salts and iodides convert the tetroxide into a black or brown powder of hydrated osmium dioxide; certain substances reduce the peroxide to the hexavalent state: for instance nitrites form alkaline osmates. Acid solutions of H_2OsO_5 are reduced by trivalent titanium first to the tetravalent state and then to the trivalent state.

In agreement with the equilibrium diagram (Fig. 1), osmium tetroxide is obtained by the oxidation of osmium and all its compounds.

3.6. PASSIVATING ACTION OF OSMIUM TETROXIDE

Proceeding as we have already done when studying the passivation of iron by chromates, molybdates, tungstates, vanadates, pertechnetates and perrhenates ([8], [9] and [10]) we have superimposed (in Fig. 4) the diagram representing the theoretical domains of corrosion, immunity and passivation of iron and those lines which, in the equilibrium diagram for the system osmium–water (Fig. 1) represent the conditions under which the reduction of solutions 0·01 M in "hyperosmate" can lead to the formation of solid substances: i.e. OsO_2 and metallic Os.

Comparing this figure with the similar ones for the above-mentioned passivating substances, it can be concluded that, of all these substances, osmium tetroxide and its solutions present the greatest chances of effectiveness, exceeding those of the pertechnetates even, as the domain of passivation of iron is even larger in the presence of osmium tetroxide than in the presence of pertechnetates (see p. 75 of the present publication).

These conclusions agree with the experimental results obtained by Cartledge [11]: "hyperosmic" acid and the TcO_4^- ion are the only known substances assuring such a good protection of iron in acid and neutral media.

4. BIBLIOGRAPHY

[1] N. DE ZOUBOV and M. POURBAIX, *Comportement électrochimique de l'osmium. Diagramme d'équilibres tension–*pH *du système* Os–H_2O, *à* 25°C (Rapport technique RT.61 of CEBELCOR, 1958).

[2] R. D. SAUERBRUNN and E. B. SANDELL, The ionization constants of osmic (VIII) acid, *J. Amer. Chem. Soc.* **75**, 4170–2 (1953).

[3] G. CHARLOT, *L'analyse qualitative et les réactions en solution,* 4th ed., Masson, Paris, 1957, p. 271.

[4] P. E. WENGER, *Traité de Chimie analytique qualitative minérale,* Librairie de l'Université Georg, S.A. Genève, 1946, pp. 113–16.

[5] F. D. DWYER and J. W. HOGARTH, Pentavalent osmium, *J. Amer. Chem. Soc.* **75**, 1008–9 (1953).

[6] *Deutsche Goldschmiede Ztg.* **33**, kleine Nr 22, p. 5 (1930).

[7] J. DE MENT, H. C. DAKE and E. R. ROBERTS, *Rarer metals,* Temple Press, London, 1950, pp. 248–52.

[8] M. POURBAIX and N. DE ZOUBOV, *Sur les conditions de passivation du fer par les chromates, molybdates, tungstates et vanadates* (Rapport technique RT.43 of CEBELCOR, 1957).

[9] N. DE ZOUBOV and M. POURBAIX, *Comportement électrochimique du technétium. Diagramme d'équilibres tension–*pH *du système* Tc–H_2O, *à* 25°C (Rapport technique RT.50 of CEBELCOR, 1957).

[10] N. DE ZOUBOV and M. POURBAIX, *Comportement électrochimique du rhénium. Diagramme d'équilibres tension–*pH *du système* Re–H_2O, *à* 25°C (Rapport technique RT.51 of CEBELCOR, 1957).

[11] G. H. CARTLEDGE, The passivation of iron by osmium (VIII) oxide and the origin of the Flade potential, *J. Phys. Chem.* **60**, 1571–5 (1956).

[12] P. PASCAL, *Traité de Chimie minérale,* volume XI (*Osmium*), Masson, Paris, 1932.

[13] *Gmelins Handbuch der anorganischen Chemie, Osmium,* S.N. 66, Verlag Chemie, G.m.b.H., Berlin, 1939.

SECTION 13.5

IRIDIUM[1]

J. VAN MUYLDER and M. POURBAIX

SUMMARY

(1) Shortened and adapted version of the Rapport technique RT.62 of CEBELCOR [1].

1. SUBSTANCES CONSIDERED AND SUBSTANCES NOT CONSIDERED

	Oxidation number (Z)	Considered	Not considered	μ^0(cal.)	Name, colour, crystalline system
Solid substances	0	**Ir**	–	0	Iridium, shiny white, f.c. cub.
	+2	–	**IrO**	–	Iridous oxide
	+3	Ir_2O_3 hydr.	–	−42 000	Hydrated iridium sesquioxide $Ir_2O_3xH_2O$, yellow–green to blue–black
	+4	IrO_2 hydr.	–	−28 000	Hydrated iridic oxide $IrO_2.2H_2O$ or iridic hydroxide $Ir(OH)_4$, blue to black (2)
	"	–	IrO_2	–	Iridic oxide, black
	+6	–	IrO_3	–	Iridium peroxide
Dissolved substances	+3	Ir^{+++}	–	80 000	Iridic ion
	+6	IrO_4^{--}	–	−47 000 (3)	Iridate ion
Gaseous substance	+8	–	IrO_4	–	Iridium tetroxide

2. REACTIONS AND EQUILIBRIUM FORMULAE

2.1. TWO DISSOLVED SUBSTANCES

2.1.1. *Relative stability of the dissolved substances*

$+3 \rightarrow +6$

1. $Ir^{+++} + 4H_2O = IrO_4^{--} + 8H^+ + 3e^-$ $\qquad E_0 = 1.448 - 0.1576\,pH + 0.0197 \log \frac{(IrO_4^{--})}{(Ir^{+++})}$

2.1.2. *Limits of the domains of relative predominance of the dissolved substances*

1'. Ir^{+++}/IrO_4^{--} $\qquad E_0 = 1.448 - 0.1576\,pH$

2.2. TWO SOLID SUBSTANCES

Limits of the domains of relative stability of the solid substances

$0 \rightarrow +3$

2. $2Ir + 3H_2O = Ir_2O_3 + 6H^+ + 6e^-$ $\qquad E_0 = 0.926 - 0.0591\,pH$

$0 \rightarrow +4$

3. $Ir + 2H_2O = IrO_2 + 4H^+ + 4e^-$ $\qquad E_0 = 0.926 - 0.0591\,pH$

$+3 \rightarrow +4$

4. $Ir_2O_3 + H_2O = 2IrO_2 + 2H^+ + 2e^-$ $\qquad E_0 = 0.926 - 0.0591\,pH$

2.3. ONE SOLID SUBSTANCE AND ONE DISSOLVED SUBSTANCE

Solubility of the solid substances

$Z = +3$

5. $2Ir^{+++} + 3H_2O = Ir_2O_3 + 6H^+$ $\qquad \log(Ir^{+++}) = -3.79 - 3\,pH$

$0 \rightarrow +3$

6. $Ir = Ir^{+++} + 3e^-$ $\qquad E_0 = 1.156 + 0.0197 \log(Ir^{+++})$

$+3 \rightarrow +4$

7. $Ir^{+++} + 2H_2O = IrO_2 + 4H^+ + e^-$ $\qquad E_0 = 0.233 - 0.2364\,pH - 0.0591 \log(Ir^{+++})$

$+3 \rightarrow +6$

8. $Ir_2O_3 + 5H_2O = 2IrO_4^{--} + 10H^+ + 6e^-$ $\qquad E_0 = 1.680 - 0.0985\,pH + 0.0197 \log(IrO_4^{--})$

$+4 \rightarrow +6$

9. $IrO_2 + 2H_2O = IrO_4^{--} + 4H^+ + 2e^-$ $\qquad E_0 = 2.057 - 0.1182\,pH + 0.0295 \log(IrO_4^{--})$

---

(2) This value $\mu^0_{IrO_2} = -28\,000$ cal. corresponds to $\mu^0_{Ir(OH)_4} = -141\,380$ cal.

(3) This value is deduced from the value $E_0^0 < 0.4$ V given by Latimer for the reaction $IrO_2 + 4OH^- = IrO_4^{--} + 2H_2O + 2e^-$, at pH = 14.

3. EQUILIBRIUM DIAGRAM AND ITS INTERPRETATION

3.1. ESTABLISHMENT OF THE DIAGRAM

Figure 1, established according to equations (1)–(9), represents the conditions of thermodynamic equilibrium of the system iridium–water, at 25°C.

Figure 2, deduced from Fig. 1, represents the theoretical conditions of corrosion, immunity and passivation of iridium at 25°C.

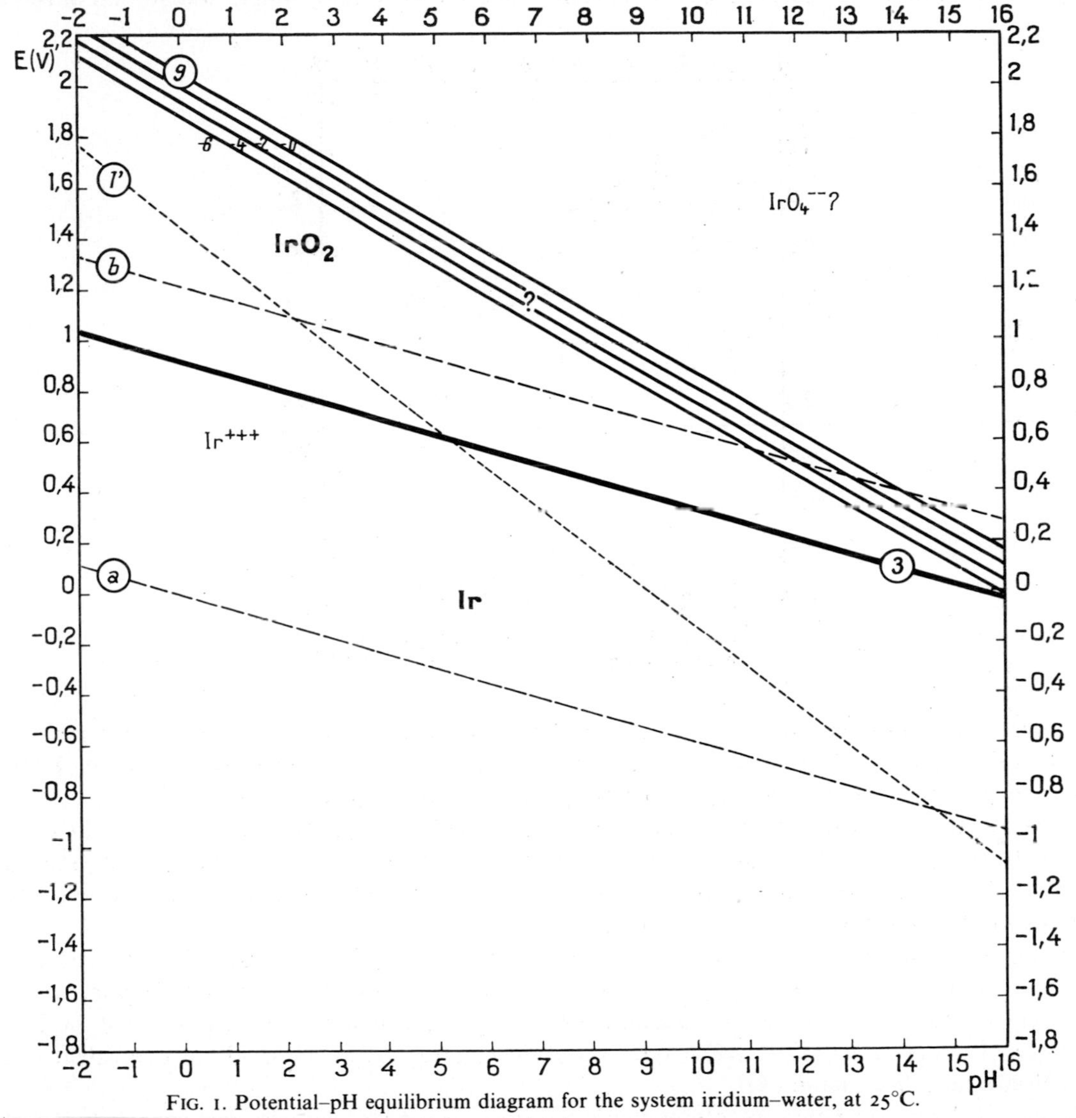

FIG. 1. Potential–pH equilibrium diagram for the system iridium–water, at 25°C.

These diagrams are valid only in the absence of substances with which iridium can form soluble complexes or insoluble salts.

The following are some of the complexes formed by iridium, according to Charlot [2]: $IrCl_6^{---}$, $Ir(SCN)_3$, $Ir(CN)_6^{---}$, $Ir(C_2O_4)_3^{---}$, $IrCl_6^{--}$, ammine complexes.

In actual fact, as is the case for platinum, there probably exist no true iridium salts; almost all its salts are, in reality, complexes, of infinite variety of colour.

3.2. STABILITY AND CORROSION OF IRIDIUM

From Fig. 1, iridium appears to be a very noble metal, as its domain of stability covers the majority of that of water. Native iridium is encountered in nature, usually associated with its "platinum-type" congeners and occasionally with gold.

In agreement with this diagram, iridium is stable in the presence of aqueous solutions of all pH's free from complexing substances. At temperatures around 25°C it is unaffected by water or aqueous solutions of caustic alkalis; acids and oxidizing agents (including aqua regia) do not attack it. The resistance of iridium to aggressive chemical reagents is noteworthy, and comparable to that of rhodium;

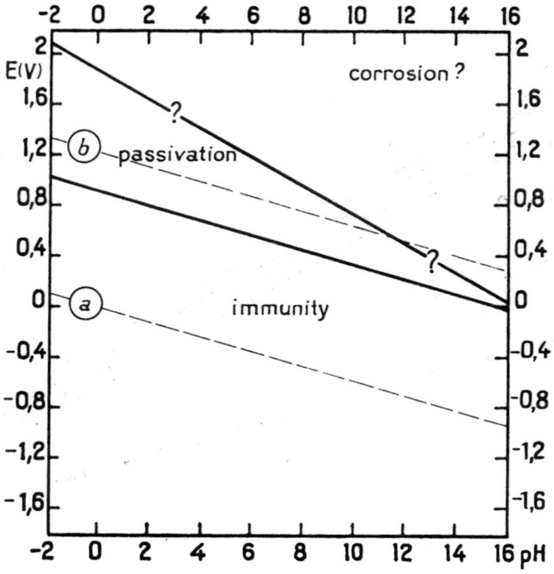

FIG. 2. Theoretical domains of corrosion, immunity and passivation of iridium, at 25°C.

alkalis, even when molten, are without action on iridium in the absence of air; for the metal to be attacked and converted to iridates it must be fused with an alkaline oxidizing mixture (molten KOH and KNO_3); certain of these iridates are soluble and certain insoluble in water (Pascal [3]).

However, the physical state of the metal can appreciably modify its reactivity, as is the case with rhodium. In the finely divided state (e.g. the "iridium blacks"), iridium is soluble in hot concentrated aqua regia. The dissolution most probably takes place through the formation of complex ions in which iridium exerts the valency +3 or +4.

On heating in air or oxygen, iridium is tarnished owing to superficial oxidation to IrO_2; at temperatures above about 1130°C the oxide decomposes, and the metal becomes shiny once again.

At temperatures of 750–1000°C, iridium loses weight through volatilization; most probably it is an oxide of octavalent iridium IrO_4 that evaporates, analogous to the oxide of octavalent osmium OsO_4 (Wöhler and Witzmann [4]).

Zhukov [5] observed that, at atmospheric pressure and 25°C, iridium can absorb 807 times its own volume of hydrogen.

When used as an anode, iridium is not usually attacked, even in the presence of any chlorine liberated by the electrolysis (Newbery [6]). According to Butler and Drever [7], oxygen is adsorbed on to the metal surface when an iridium anode is polarized in the presence of dilute sulphuric acid or dilute caustic soda, even when the potential is low (i.e. below the oxygen overpotential) (?). No peroxide is formed, contrary to the cases of platinum and rhodium. On anodically polarizing iridium at a constant temperature and current density, in the presence respectively of a 1 M sulphuric acid solution and a 2 M caustic potash solution, Foerster and Piguet [8] observed that the electrode potential of the metal first increases to a maximum value, and then decreases, tending to stabilize itself at a lower value. According to the explanation of the experimenters, this temporary variation of the anode potential results from an attack undergone by iridium during prolonged electrolysis; as the electrode becomes progressively rougher owing to the attack, its potential, which increases at first, ultimately decreases.

When used as a cathode, iridium absorbs hydrogen, which gradually penetrates into the metal. According to Cailletet and Collardeau [9], a gas cell can be constructed using a cathode of iridium sponge in the presence of acidulated water.

3.3. STABILITY OF THE IRIDIUM OXIDES

According to Fig. 1, the oxide of tetravalent iridium, IrO_2, should be insoluble in acid solutions, and should be soluble in alkaline oxidizing solutions.

In practice, *anhydrous* IrO_2 (blue to black), which can be prepared by heating a mixture of iridium, KOH and KNO_3 to red heat, or by heating finely divided iridium in air, is insoluble in acids (including aqua regia), and in bases.

On the other hand, when it is freshly prepared (e.g. by treating a boiling alkali metal iridochloride solution with KOH or NaOH in the presence of air), the *hydrate* $IrO_2 . 2H_2O$ or $Ir(OH)_4$ (blue–black) is soluble in hydrochloric acid, nitric acid and sulphuric acid; it is, however, only slightly soluble in alkalis.

On ageing or desiccation, it becomes practically insoluble in all acids (Wöhler and Witzmann [10]).

It readily gives rise to purplish-blue colloidal solutions, and on fusion with alkaline oxidizing substances it forms iridates IrO_4^{--}. Its position in Fig. 1 shows that IrO_2 is the form of iridium stable in the presence of oxygen, and is to be regarded as an oxidizing agent. According to the free enthalpy values assumed in this investigation, the oxide of trivalent iridium Ir_2O_3 is thermodynamically unstable with respect to iridium and IrO_2, and should therefore tend to decompose to give a mixture of these substances.

The anhydrous oxide Ir_2O_3 is practically impossible to prepare (Pascal [3]); its hydrated form $Ir_2O_3 . xH_2O$ (yellow–green to blue–black) is readily soluble in acids and alkalis, and is easily oxidized to $IrO_2 . 2H_2O$ by the common oxidizing agents, including air.

4. BIBLIOGRAPHY

[1] J. Van Muylder and M. Pourbaix, *Comportement électrochimique de l'iridium. Diagramme d'équilibres tension–pH du système* Ir–H_2O, *à* 25°C (Rapport technique RT.62 of CEBELCOR, 1958).
[2] G. Charlot, *L'analyse qualitative et les réactions en solution*, 4th edn., Masson, Paris, 1957.
[3] P. Pascal, *Traité de Chimie minérale*, vol. XI (*Iridium*), Masson, Paris, 1932.
[4] L. Wöhler and W. Witzmann, Feste Lösungen bei der Dissoziation von Iridiumoxyden, *Z. Elektrochem.* **14,** 107 (1908).
[5] I. I. Zhukov, *Inst. Fiz. Chim. Anal.* **3**, 636 (1926–7); quoted by P. Pascal [3].
[6] E. Newbery, Chlorine overvoltage, *J. Chem. Soc.* **119**, 483 (1921).
[7] J. Butler and G. Drever, The mechanism of overvoltage processes. Part I. The anodic oxidation of some metals of the platinum group, *Trans. Faraday Soc.* **32**, 429 (1936).
[8] F. Foerster and A. Piguet, Zur Kenntnis der anodischen Sauerstoffentwicklung, *Z. Elektrochem.* **10**, 715 (1904).
[9] L. Cailletet and E. Collardeau, Recherches sur la condensation des gaz de l'électrolyse par les corps poreux et en particulier par les métaux de la famille du platine, *C.R. Acad. Sc.*, 1894, p. 830.
[10] L. Wöhler and W. Witzmann, Die Oxyde des Iridiums, *Z. anorg. allgem. Chem.* **57,** 323 (1908).

SECTION 13.6

PLATINUM (1)

J. Van Muylder, N. de Zoubov and M. Pourbaix

SUMMARY

(1) Shortened and adapted version of the Rapport technique RT.63 of CEBELCOR [1].

1. SUBSTANCES CONSIDERED AND SUBSTANCES NOT CONSIDERED

	Oxidation number (Z)	Considered	Not considered	μ^0(cal.)	Name, colour, crystalline system
Solid substances	0	**Pt**	–	0	Platinum, white, f.c.cub.
	+2	**PtO** hydr.	–	–11 *510*	Hydrated oxide $PtO.H_2O$ or platinous hydroxide $Pt(OH)_2$, black (2)
	»	–	**PtO**	–	Platinous oxide, purple–grey
	+2.67	–	$\mathbf{Pt_3O_4}$	–	Platino–platinic oxide
	+3	–	$\mathbf{Pt_2O_3}$ hydr.	–	Platinum sesquioxide
	+4	$\mathbf{PtO_2}$ hydr.	–	–20 *000* (3)	Hydrated platinic oxide PtO_2xH_2O, brown
	»	–	$\mathbf{PtO_2}$	–	Platinic oxide blue to black
	+6	$\mathbf{PtO_3}$ hydr.	–	–16 *000* (4)	Hydrated perplatinic oxide PtO_3xH_2O, yellow
Dissolved substances	+2	Pt^{++}	–	54 *800*	Platinous ion
	+4	–	PtO_3^{--}	–	Platinate ion
	»	–	PtO^{++}	–	Platinyl ion
	»	–	$Pt(OH)^{+++}$	–	?
	+6	–	PtO_4^{--}	–	Perplatinate ion

2. REACTIONS AND EQUILIBRIUM FORMULAE

2.1. TWO SOLID SUBSTANCES

Limits of the domains of relative stability of the solid substances

$0 \rightarrow +2$

1. $\mathbf{Pt} + H_2O = \mathbf{PtO} + 2H^+ + 2e^-$ $\qquad E_0 = 0.980 - 0.0591\ pH$

$+2 \rightarrow +4$

2. $\mathbf{PtO} + H_2O = \mathbf{PtO_2} + 2H^+ + 2e^-$ $\qquad E_0 = 1.045 - 0.0591\ pH$

$+4 \rightarrow +6$

3. $\mathbf{PtO_2} + H_2O = \mathbf{PtO_3} + 2H^+ + 2e^-$ $\qquad E_0 = 2.000 - 0.0591\ pH$

2.2. ONE SOLID SUBSTANCE AND ONE DISSOLVED SUBSTANCE

Solubility of the solid substances

$Z = +2$

4. $Pt^{++} + H_2O = \mathbf{PtO} + 2H^+$ $\qquad \log(Pt^{++}) = -7.06 - 2\ pH$

$0 \rightarrow +2$

5. $\mathbf{Pt} = Pt^{++} + 2e^-$ $\qquad E_0 = 1.188 + 0.0295 \log(Pt^{++})$

$+2 \rightarrow +4$

6. $Pt^{++} + 2H_2O = \mathbf{PtO_2} + 4H^+ + 2e^-$ $\qquad E_0 = 0.837 - 0.1182\ pH - 0.0295 \log(Pt^{++})$

---

(2) The value $\mu^0_{PtO} = -11\ 510$ cal. corresponds to $\mu^0_{Pt(OH)_2} = -68\ 200$ cal.
(3) Value determined by Brewer [2].
(4) The value calculated from estimated data given by Latimer.

3. EQUILIBRIUM DIAGRAM AND ITS INTERPRETATION

3.1. ESTABLISHMENT OF THE DIAGRAM

Using equations (1)–(6) established in paragraph 2, we have constructed Fig. 1, which represents the conditions of thermodynamic equilibrium of the system platinum–water, at 25°C.

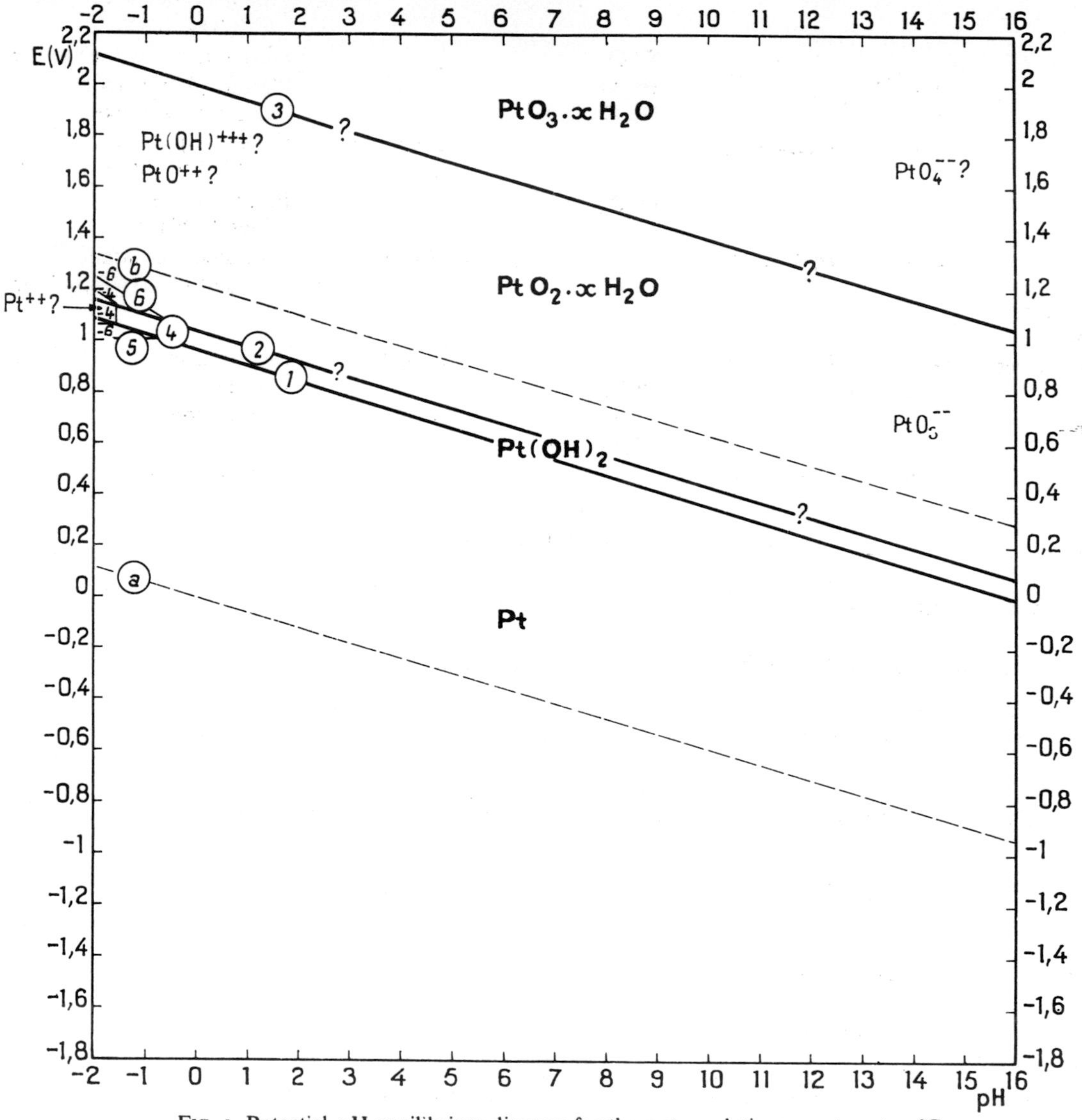

FIG. 1. Potential–pH equilibrium diagram for the system platinum–water, at 25°C.

From Fig. 1 we have derived Fig. 2, which shows the theoretical conditions of corrosion, immunity and passivation of platinum, at 25°C.

Figures 1 and 2 are valid only in the absence of substances with which platinum can form soluble complexes or insoluble compounds.

Platinum very readily forms complex ions. The complexes known at present number several thousands; some of the more important ones, given by Charlot [3] are: the chloroplatinous, cyanoplatinous, thiocyanoplatinous, platinonitrite, amminoplatinous, oxaloplatinous, chloroplatinic, iodoplatinic, cyanoplatinic, amminoplatinic, and platininitrite complexes.

Most probably platinum forms no real salts; according to Pascal [4], the formulae attributed to certain simple salts of platinum represent them only in the solid state: mere contact with water converts them immediately into complex compounds.

3.2. STABILITY AND CORROSION OF PLATINUM

From Figs. 1 and 2 platinum appears to be a very noble metal, as its domain of stability covers the majority of the domain of stability of water. In nature platinum is encountered in the native state in a mineral called "platinum ore", in which it is associated with the five other metals of the platinum group: iridium, osmium, palladium, rhodium and ruthenium.

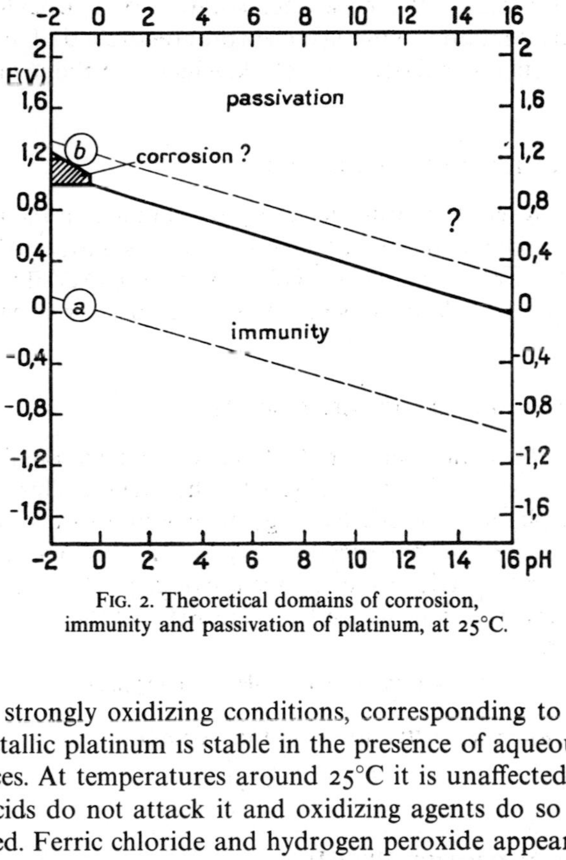

FIG. 2. Theoretical domains of corrosion, immunity and passivation of platinum, at 25°C.

Except under certain strongly oxidizing conditions, corresponding to the portion of Fig. 1 lying below lines (5) and (1), metallic platinum is stable in the presence of aqueous solutions of all pH's free from complexing substances. At temperatures around 25°C it is unaffected by water or aqueous solutions of caustic alkalis. Acids do not attack it and oxidizing agents do so only with difficulty, except when complexes are formed. Ferric chloride and hydrogen peroxide appear to have no action.

The best known and most widely used reagent for attacking platinum is aqua regia. This combines the oxidizing action of nitric acid with the complexing action of hydrochloric acid, and dissolves platinum as chloroplatinic acid H_2PtCl_6. Pure hydrochloric acid hardly attacks platinum, but if the acid contains dissolved chlorine the metal is attacked, since, like aqua regia, the acid then combines an oxidizing and a complexing action.

According to Marie ([5], [6]), platinum can be oxidized by the following oxidizing agents at room temperature: $K_2S_2O_8$, $K_2Cr_2O_7$, $KClO_3$, concentrated HNO_3, $K_3Fe(CN)_6$, and $KMnO_4$ in sulphuric or caustic solution. The oxidation products formed under these conditions are probably mainly platinic oxide PtO_2, with the possible formation of platinous hydroxide $Pt(OH)_2$ and platinous ions Pt^{++}, whose existence, however, is subject to doubt.

Hot concentrated sulphuric acid attacks platinum slightly, particularly when it is finely divided. In the absence of air platinum resists the action of fused alkalis, even at a dull red heat; in the presence of air fused alkalis corrode it vigorously.

When used as an anode, platinum is generally unattacked, notably in solutions of sulphuric, nitric and even hydrochloric acids, and also in solutions of caustic alkalis. Generally it becomes covered with platinum oxide PtO_2 or PtO_3, which, if the metal is not in the divided state, forms a protective layer on it. If the metal is in the divided state, e.g. platinum black, the oxide is not protective; it separates as a brown film, enabling an anodic attack to occur.

When used as a cathode, platinum generally absorbs a considerable quantity of hydrogen, which, according to Hurd [7], is mainly occluded in the cracks and structural faults of the metal. Thiel and Hammerschmidt [8] observed that, at room temperature, a platinum cathode can absorb up to thirty-five times its own volume of hydrogen.

Platinum used as a cathode remains generally unattacked although, according to Haber [9], a platinum cathode dipped in a relatively concentrated solution of hydrochloric acid (8 to 36 per cent) or of sodium chloride (20 per cent and more) becomes progressively dull and rough, and loses weight. In the presence of sulphuric acid the cathode turns black, which is explained by the absorption of hydrogen by the platinum.

3.3. ELECTRO-DEPOSITION AND ELECTRO-PLATING OF PLATINUM

It follows from Fig. 1 that platinum can very easily be obtained in the metallic form by the reduction of its solutions. This is usually carried out by electrolysis of solutions of complex salts of platinum, using a cathode made of copper, platinum, "white gold", brass or nickel silver. One can use in particular solutions of sodium or potassium platinate, sodium platinimitrite or a halogenoplatinate (especially potassium chloroplatinate).

3.4. PLATINUM ELECTRODE FOR THE MEASUREMENT OF pH

Platinum is stable under the conditions of potential and pH corresponding to the equilibrium state of the reaction $H_2 = 2H^+ + 2e^-$, indicated in Fig. 1 by the line (*a*). This reaction takes place almost reversibly on the surface of platinum, which has a great tendency to dissolve hydrogen. So platinum can, as is well known, be used for the construction of hydrogen electrodes for the measurement of pH, particularly if it is employed in the divided state and is previously saturated with hydrogen by cathodic treatment. The potential of this electrode depends on the pH and the hydrogen pressure according to the following relation, at 25°C:

$$E_0 = 0{\cdot}000 - 0{\cdot}0591\ \text{pH} - 0{\cdot}0295 \log p_{H_2}.$$

When the hydrogen pressure is 1 atm., this relation becomes

$$E_0 = -\ 0{\cdot}0591\ \text{pH}.$$

3.5. STABILITY OF PLATINOUS HYDROXIDE $Pt(OH)_2$

Black platinous hydroxide, which can be obtained in various hydration states by neutralizing a solution of platinous chloride in the absence of air, appears from Fig. 1 to be stable in the presence of water and non-complexing solutions free from reducing agents and powerful oxidizing agents. It is insoluble in alkaline solutions and in dilute solutions of nitric and sulphuric acids; when freshly precipitated it is soluble in concentrated solutions of these two acids, and also in hydrochloric acid with the formation of chloroplatinous acid H_2PtCl_4. After drying at 400°C, platinous hydroxide is insoluble both in acids and in bases.

As is shown by its position in Fig. 1, $Pt(OH)_2$ can act as an oxidizing agent and as a reducing agent: it oxidizes hydrogen, hydriodic acid, sulphurous acid and arsenious acid respectively to water, iodine, sulphuric acid and arsenic acid, being itself reduced to platinum. It reduces hydrogen peroxide, ozone and permanganate respectively to water, oxygen and manganese dioxide, being itself oxidized to hydrated platinic oxide $PtO_2 . xH_2O$.

3.6. STABILITY OF PLATINIC OXIDE PtO_2

Platinic oxide, like the other platinum oxides, exists in various diversely coloured hydration states. From Fig. 1 it appears to be the form of platinum thermodynamically stable in the presence of oxygen at atmospheric pressure and 25°C. It is stable in the presence of water and non-complexing acid or neutral solutions; it is readily soluble in aqueous solutions of caustic alkalis with the formation of platinates PtO_3^{--} [or $Pt(OH)_6^{--}$], and in ammonia in which it forms amminoplatinic complexes. When freshly precipitated, the tetrahydrated oxide $PtO_2 . 4H_2O$ is readily soluble in dilute acids.

The black anhydrous oxide PtO_2, insoluble in most acids and aqua regia, should be soluble in concentrated sulphuric acid to form $Pt(OH)_2^{++}$ (or PtO^{++}) and $Pt(OH)^{+++}$ cations (Latimer [10]).

Its position in Fig. 1 shows that hydrated PtO_2 is a fairly powerful oxidizing agent; it can oxidize hydrogen; it oxidizes boiling acetic and oxalic acids.

3.7. STABILITY OF PLATINUM PEROXIDE PtO_3

According to Marie [5], such an oxide appears as a yellow film on platinum when it is polarized anodically in normal H_2SO_4 solution. Its position in Fig, 1 shows that PtO_3 is an unstable substance tending to decompose into PtO_2 and oxygen; it is a powerful oxidizing agent, oxidizing water to oxygen, and chlorides and iodides in acid solution respectively to chlorine and iodine. It is insoluble in dilute solutions of nitric and sulphuric acids, but dissolves in the concentrated acids, probably being reduced to the tetra- or divalent state; it dissolves also in hydrochloric acid (probably forming chlorine and chloroplatinic complexes).

4. BIBLIOGRAPHY

[1] J. VAN MUYLDER, N. DE ZOUBOV and M. POURBAIX, *Comportement électrochimique du platine. Diagramme d'équilibres tension–*pH *du système* Pt–H_2O, *à* 25°C. (Rapport technique RT.63 of CEBELCOR, 1958).

[2] L. BREWER, Thermodynamic properties of the oxides and their vaporization processes, *Chem. Rev.* **52**, 1 (1953).

[3] G. CHARLOT, *L'analyse qualitative et les réactions en solution*, 4th ed., Masson, Paris, 1957.

[4] P. PASCAL, *Traité de Chimie minérale*, Vol. XI, Masson, Paris, 1932.

[5] C. MARIE, Sur l'oxydation électrolytique du platine, *C.R. Acad. Sc.* **145**, 117 (1907).

[6] C. MARIE, Sur l'oxydabilité du platine, *C.R. Acad. Sc.* **146**, 475 (1908).

[7] D. T. HURD, *An Introduction to the Chemistry of the Hydrides*, Wiley, New York, 1952, p. 190.

[8] A. THIEL and W. HAMMERSCHMIDT, Ueber den Zusammenhang zwischen der Ueberspannung des Wasserstoffs an reinen Metallen und gewissen Eigenschaften der Metalle, *Z. anorg. Chem.* **132**, 15–35 (1924).

[9] F. HABER, Ueber Elektrolyse der Salzsäure nebst Mitteilungen über kathodische Formation von Blei, *Z. anorg. Chem.* **16**, 447 (1898).

[10] W. LATIMER, *Oxidation Potentials*, 2nd ed., Prentice-Hall, New York, 1952.

SECTION 14.1

COPPER[1]

N. DE ZOUBOV, C. VANLEUGENHAGHE, and M. POURBAIX

SUMMARY

1. *Substances considered and substances not considered.*

2. *Reactions and equilibrium formulae.*

2.1. Two dissolved substances.

2.1.1. Relative stability of the dissolved substances.

2.1.2. Limits of the domains of relative predominance of the dissolved substances.

2.2. Two solid substances.

Limits of the domains of relative stability of copper and its oxides.

2.3. One solid substance and one dissolved substance.

Solubility of the solid substances.

2.4. One gaseous substance and one solid substance.

Relative stability of copper and its hydride.

3. *Equilibrium diagrams and their interpretation.*

3.1. Establishment of the diagrams.

3.2. Stability and corrosion of copper.

3.3. Stability and formation of the copper oxides.

3.4. Electrolysis of acid solutions of copper. Electrolytic refining of copper. Copper voltameter.

3.5. Formation and stability of copper hydride CuH.

4. *Bibliography.*

(1) Adapted version of a previously published account [1]; see also [2].

Subsequent to the present account, a similar study including the derivatives of trivalent copper has been published. (Rapport Technique RT.100 of CEBELCOR, 1961.)

1. SUBSTANCES CONSIDERED AND SUBSTANCES NOT CONSIDERED

	Oxidation number (Z)	Considered	Not considered	μ^0(cal.)	Name, colour, crystalline system
Solid substances	− I	–	**CuH**	–	Hydride, red–brown, f.c.cub.
	0	**Cu**	–	0	Copper, red, cub.
	+ 0.5	–	**Cu_4O**	–	Sub-oxide, olive green
	+ I	**Cu_2O**	–	−34 980	Cuprous oxide or oxydule, red, cub.
	»	–	**Cu_2O** hydr.	–	Hydrated cuprous oxide or cuprous hydroxide Cu(OH), yellow
	+ 2	**CuO**	–	*a.* −30 400	Cupric oxide, black, monocl. or cub.
	»	» hydr.	–	*b.* −28 610	Hydrated cupric oxide or cupric hydroxide $Cu(OH)_2$, light blue (²)
	+ 3	–	**Cu_2O_3**	–	Sesquioxide, reddish purple
	+ 4	–	**CuO_2**	–	Peroxide, brown–black
Dissolved substances	+ I	Cu^+	–	12 000	Cuprous ion, colourless
	+ 2	Cu^{++}	–	15 530	Cupric ion, light blue
	»	$HCuO_2^-$	–	−61 420	Bicuprite ion, blue
	»	CuO_2^{--}	–	−43 500	Cuprite ion, blue
	+ 3	–	Cu^{+++}	–	Copper (III) ion
	»	–	CuO_2^-	–	Cuprate ion, red or brown
Gaseous substance	− I	*CuH* ?	–	64 000	Hydride

2. REACTIONS AND EQUILIBRIUM FORMULAE (³)

2.I. TWO DISSOLVED SUBSTANCES

2.I.I. *Relative stability of the dissolved substances*

Z = + 2

1. $Cu^{++} + 2H_2O = HCuO_2^- + 3H^+$ $\qquad \log\frac{(HCuO_2^-)}{(Cu^{++})} = -26.72 + 3\,pH$

2. $Cu^{++} + 2H_2O = CuO_2^{--} + 4H^+$ $\qquad \log\frac{(CuO_2^{--})}{(Cu^{++})} = -39.88 + 4\,pH$

3. $HCuO_2^- = CuO_2^{--} + H^+$ $\qquad \log\frac{(CuO_2^{--})}{(HCuO_2^-)} = -13.15 + pH$

+ I → + 2

4. $Cu^+ = Cu^{++} + e^-$ $\qquad E_0 = 0.153 + 0.0591\log\frac{(Cu^{++})}{(Cu^+)}$

5. $Cu^+ + 2H_2O = HCuO_2^- + 3H^+ + e^-$ $\qquad E_0 = 1.733 - 0.1773\,pH + 0.0591\log\frac{(HCuO_2^-)}{(Cu^+)}$

6. $Cu^+ + 2H_2O = CuO_2^{--} + 4H^+ + e^-$ $\qquad E_0 = 2.510 - 0.2364\,pH + 0.0591\log\frac{(CuO_2^{--})}{(Cu^+)}$

(²) This value of μ^0_{CuO} corresponds to $\mu^0_{Cu(OH)_2} = -85\,300$ cal.
(³) In the reactions involving CuO, the letter *a* refers to anhydrous CuO, whose free enthalpy of formation is −30 400 cal.; the letter *b* refers to $CuO.H_2O$ or $Cu(OH)_2$, whose free enthalpy of formation is −85 300 cal.

2.1.2. *Limits of the domains of relative predominance of the dissolved substances*

1'.	Cu^{++} / $HCuO_2^-$	pH = 8.91
2'.	Cu^{++} / CuO_2^{--}	pH = 9.97
3'.	$HCuO_2^-$ / CuO_2^{--}	pH = 13.15
4'.	Cu^+ / Cu^{++}	$E_0 = 0.153$
5'.	Cu^+ / $HCuO_2^-$	$E_0 = 1.733 - 0.1773\,pH$
6'.	Cu^+ / CuO_2^{--}	$E_0 = 2.510 - 0.2364\,pH$

2.2. TWO SOLID SUBSTANCES

Limits of the domains of relative stability of copper and its oxides

$0 \rightarrow +1$

7. $2\,\mathbf{Cu} + H_2O = \mathbf{Cu_2O} + 2H^+ + 2e^-$ $E_0 = 0.471 - 0.0591\,pH$

$0 \rightarrow +2$

8. $\mathbf{Cu} + H_2O = \mathbf{CuO} + 2H^+ + 2e^-$ a. $E_0 = 0.570 - 0.0591\,pH$
   b. $= 0.609 - 0.0591\,pH$

$+1 \rightarrow +2$

9. $\mathbf{Cu_2O} + H_2O = 2\,\mathbf{CuO} + 2H^+ + 2e^-$ a. $E_0 = 0.669 - 0.0591\,pH$
   b. $= 0.747 - 0.0591\,pH$

2.3. ONE SOLID SUBSTANCE AND ONE DISSOLVED SUBSTANCE

Solubility of the solid substances

$Z = +1$

10. $2Cu^+ + H_2O = \mathbf{Cu_2O} + 2H^+$ $\log(Cu^+) = -0.84 - pH$

$Z = +2$

11. $Cu^{++} + H_2O = \mathbf{CuO} + 2H^+$ a. $\log(Cu^{++}) = 7.89 - 2pH$
    b. $= 9.21 - 2pH$

12. $\mathbf{CuO} + H_2O = HCuO_2^- + H^+$ a. $\log(HCuO_2^-) = -18.83 + pH$
    b. $= -17.52 + pH$

13. $\mathbf{CuO} + H_2O = CuO_2^{--} + 2H^+$ a. $\log(CuO_2^{--}) = -31.98 + 2pH$
    b. $= -30.67 + 2pH$

$0 \rightarrow +1$

14. $\mathbf{Cu} = Cu^+ + e^-$ $E_0 = 0.520 + 0.0591\log(Cu^+)$

$0 \rightarrow +2$

15. $\mathbf{Cu} = Cu^{++} + 2e^-$ $E_0 = 0.337 + 0.0295\log(Cu^{++})$
16. $\mathbf{Cu} + 2H_2O = HCuO_2^- + 3H^+ + 2e^-$ $E_0 = 1.127 - 0.0886\,pH + 0.0295\log(HCuO_2^-)$
17. $\mathbf{Cu} + 2H_2O = CuO_2^{--} + 4H^+ + 2e^-$ $E_0 = 1.515 - 0.1182\,pH + 0.0295\log(CuO_2^{--})$

$+1 \rightarrow +2$

18. $\mathbf{Cu_2O} + 2H^+ = 2Cu^{++} + H_2O + 2e^-$ $E_0 = 0.203 + 0.0591\,pH + 0.0591\log(Cu^{++})$
19. $\mathbf{Cu_2O} + 3H_2O = 2HCuO_2^- + 4H^+ + 2e^-$ $E_0 = 1.783 - 0.1182\,pH + 0.0591\log(HCuO_2^-)$
20. $\mathbf{Cu_2O} + 3H_2O = 2CuO_2^{--} + 6H^+ + 2e^-$ $E_0 = 2.560 - 0.1773\,pH + 0.0591\log(CuO_2^{--})$
21. $Cu^+ + H_2O = \mathbf{CuO} + 2H^+ + e^-$ $E_0 = 0.620 - 0.1182\,pH - 0.0591\log(Cu^+)$

2.4. ONE GASEOUS SUBSTANCE AND ONE SOLID SUBSTANCE

Relative stability of copper and its hydride

$-1 \rightarrow 0$

22. $CuH = \mathbf{Cu} + H^+ + e^-$ $E_0 = -2.775 - 0.0591\,pH - 0.0591\log p_{CuH}$

3. EQUILIBRIUM DIAGRAMS AND THEIR INTERPRETATION

3.1. ESTABLISHMENT OF THE DIAGRAMS

Using the equilibrium formulae given in paragraph 2, we have constructed two potential–pH equilibrium diagrams for the system copper–water, at 25°C. The solid substances considered in Fig. 1 are: Cu, Cu_2O and CuO, and in Fig. 2: Cu, Cu_2O and $Cu(OH)_2$.

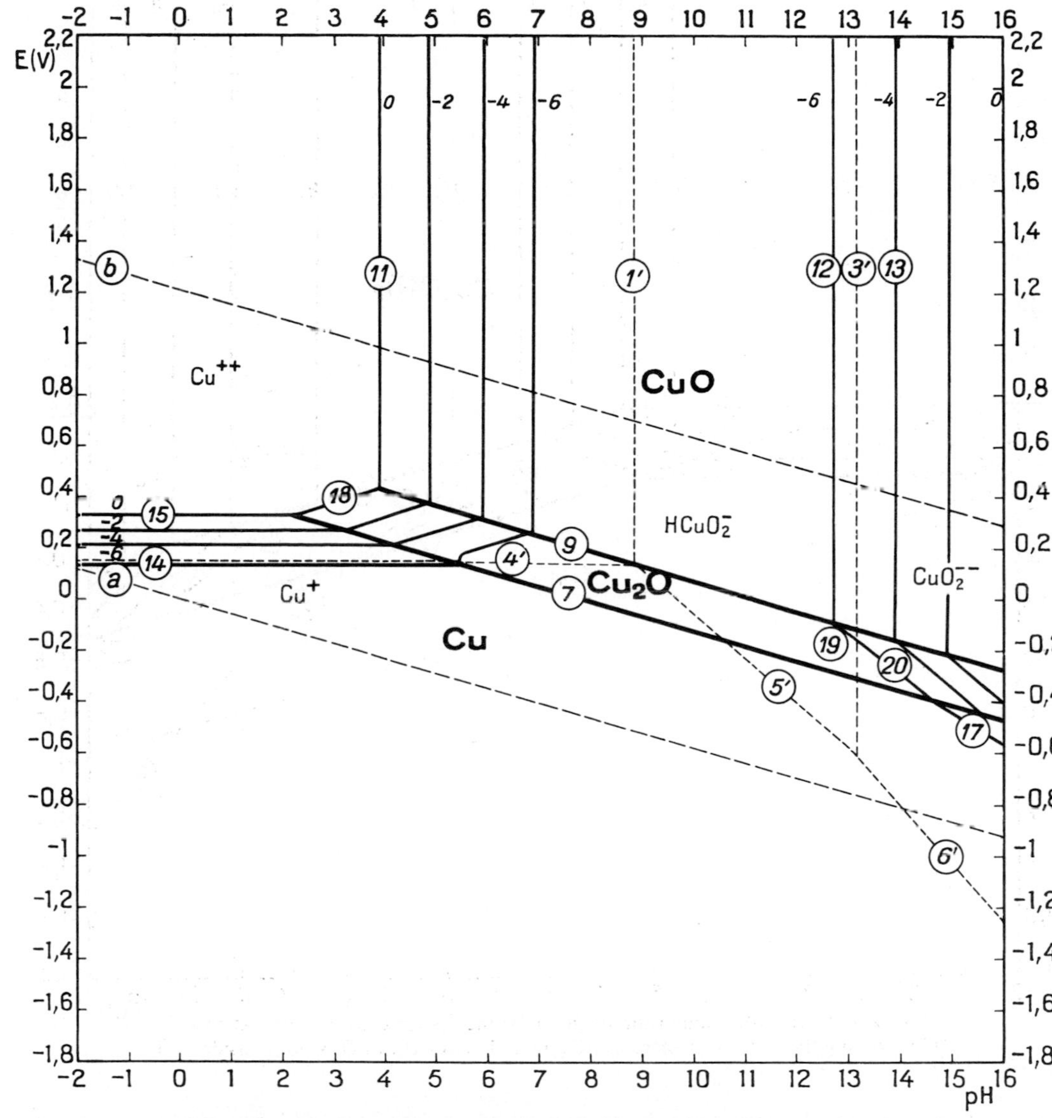

FIG. 1. Potential–pH equilibrium diagram for the system copper–water, at 25°C. [Considering the solid substances Cu, Cu_2O and CuO. $Cu(OH)_2$ is not considered.]

From the free enthalpy values given in paragraph 1, the hydroxide $Cu(OH)_2$ is less stable than the oxide CuO and tends to be converted into the oxide with an affinity of 30 *400* -- 28 *610* = 1 790 cal.; Fig. 1 therefore represents stable equilibria and Fig. 2 represents metastable equilibria.

In establishing the diagrams we have not considered the following substances, for which we do not have sufficient thermodynamic data:(4)

—*solid substances:* the hydride CuH; the sub-oxide Cu_4O whose existence is very doubtful; the unstable cuprous hydroxide CuOH which changes very quickly into Cu_2O; the sesquioxide Cu_2O_3; the peroxide CuO_2 which appears to exist only in the presence of a large quantity of hydrogen peroxide;

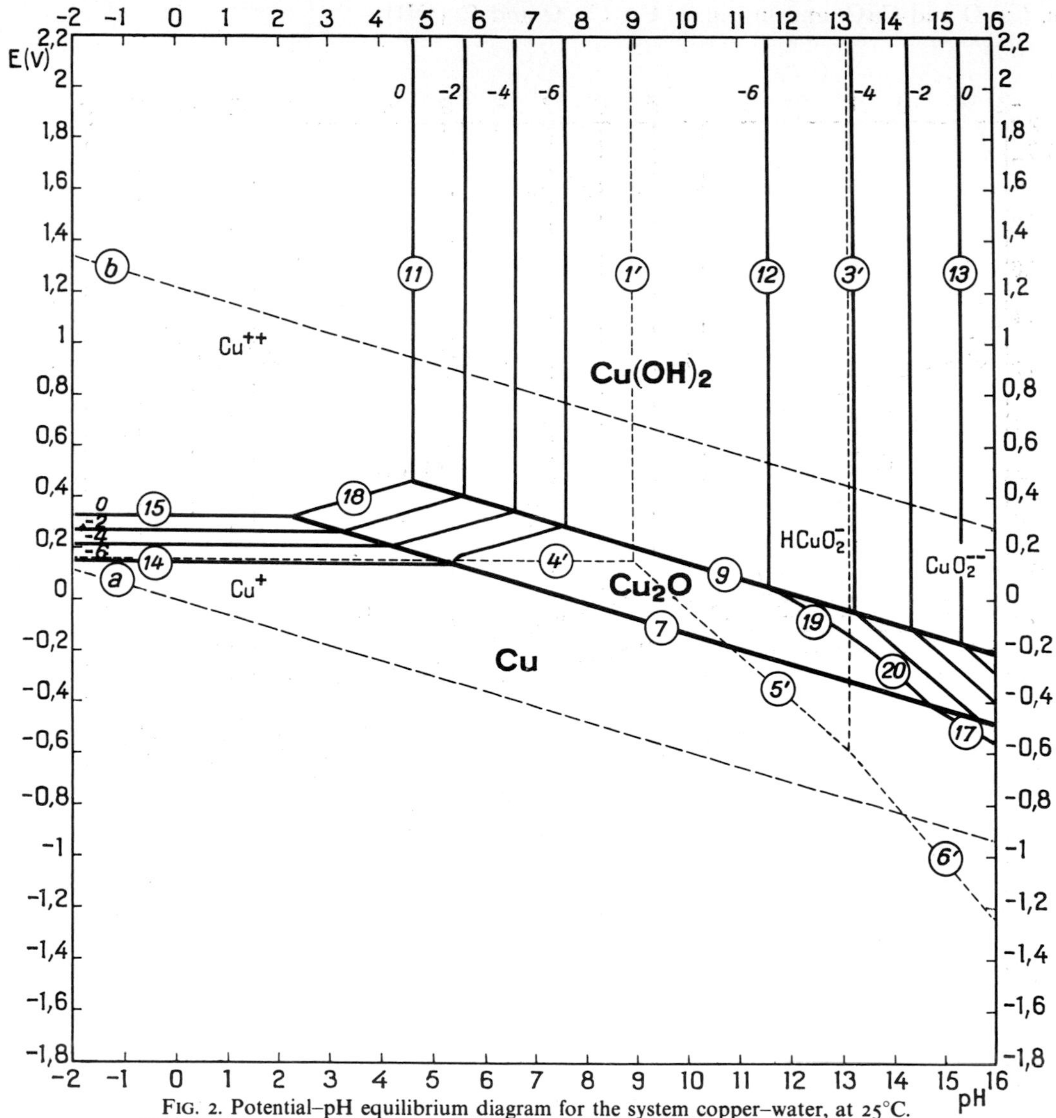

FIG. 2. Potential–pH equilibrium diagram for the system copper–water, at 25°C.
[Considering the solid substances Cu, Cu_2O and $Cu(OH)_2$. CuO is not considered.]

—*dissolved substances:* the ions containing copper of valency +3, which are sometimes formed by the action of persulphate on cupric ions (copper of valency +3 exists as sparingly soluble compounds and complexes [3]).

Figure 3, derived from Fig. 1, represents the theoretical conditions of corrosion, immunity and passivation of copper for the case of passivation by the formation of the oxides Cu_2O and CuO.

(4) Cu_2O_3 and the ions Cu^{+++} and CuO_2^- have been considered in a later study (see note, p. 384).

Using formulae (1′), (3′), (11), (12) and (13) we have constructed Fig. 4, which represents the influence of pH on the solubility of cupric oxide CuO and cupric hydroxide $Cu(OH)_2$.

These diagrams are, of course, valid only in the absence of substances with which copper can form soluble complexes or insoluble compounds.

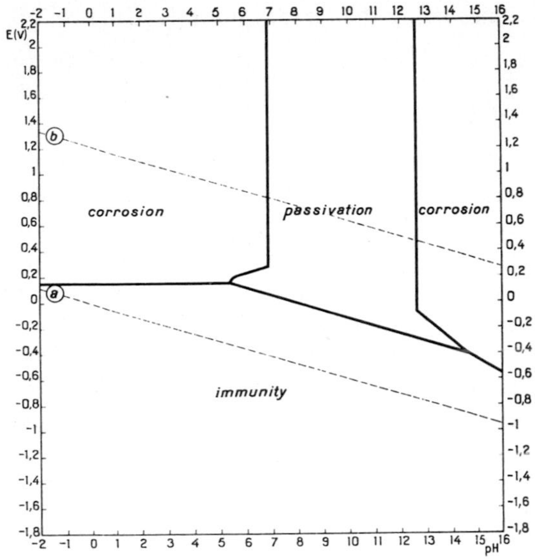

FIG. 3. Domains of corrosion, immunity and passivation of copper, at 25°C. (Derived from Fig. 1.)

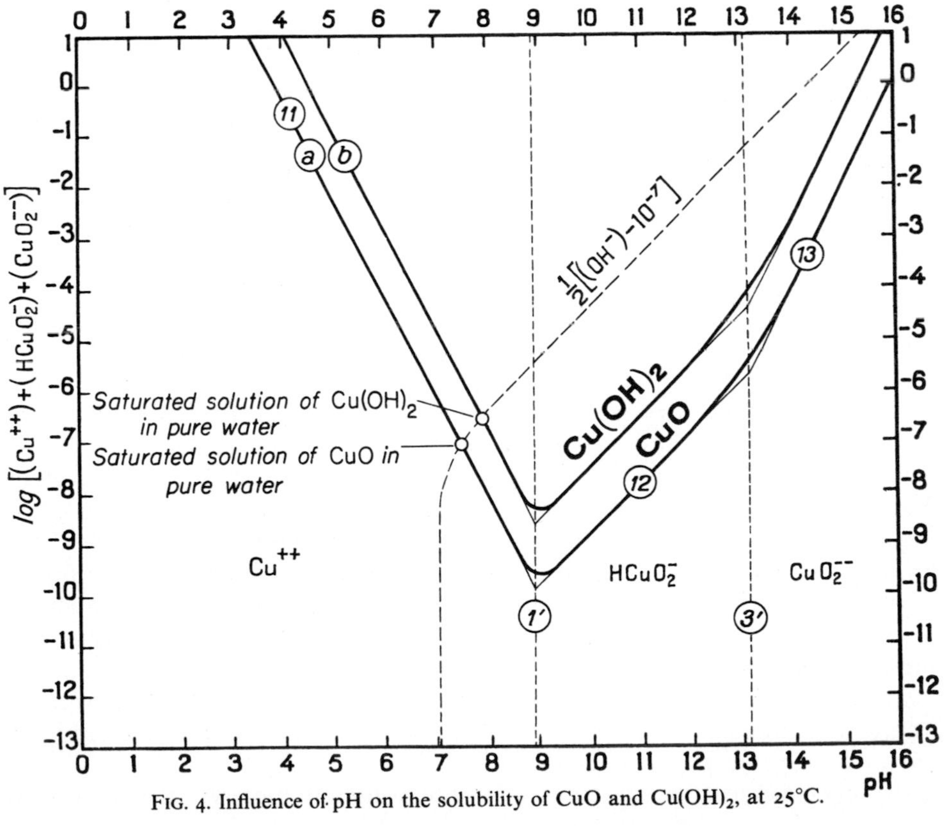

FIG. 4. Influence of pH on the solubility of CuO and $Cu(OH)_2$, at 25°C.

Copper forms a large number of complexes; Charlot [3] mentions the following: for copper of valency +1, the complexes with Cl^-, CN^-, NH_3, $S_2O_3^{--}$, which are colourless; for copper of valency +2, the yellow $CuCl^+$ complexes, the intense blue ammine complexes, the brown complexes with SCN^-, and the complexes $CuBr^+$, $CuP_2O_7^{--}$, $Cu(NO_2)_3^-$, $Cu(C_2O_4)_2^{--}$, and CuY^{--}

Most cuprous salts are sparingly soluble: e.g. CuCN, CuCl, CuBr, CuSCN and CuI; many cupric salts are also, the least soluble ones being the ferrocyanide $K_2Cu[Fe(CN)_6]$, the sulphide CuS and the carbonate $CuCO_3$ [3].

3.2. STABILITY AND CORROSION OF COPPER

Figures 1, 2 and 3 show that copper is a relatively noble metal (in the absence of complexing substances at least). It is actually found in nature (in the Great Lake region of North America).

In agreement with Fig. 3, copper is not corroded by non-complexing solutions free from oxidizing agents; on the other hand, it is corroded by acid or strongly alkaline solutions containing oxidizing agents. Practically neutral or slightly alkaline solutions should passivate the metal, the corrosion being greatly checked by the formation of oxide films.

It should be possible to prevent copper from being corroded, even in the presence of acid or alkaline oxidizing solutions, by judicious cathodic protection in such a way as to bring the potential of the metal to below about +0·1 V in acid solution and about +0·1 to −0·6 V in neutral or alkaline solution, depending on the pH.

Carefully de-aerated water does not corrode copper at all. Dissolved air causes the metal to become covered with a layer of oxides, slightly greenish brown in colour and turning darker on prolonged oxidation. The conditions under which this layer is, or is not, protective are not yet very well known. In certain cases the brown–green layer becomes porous, enabling the metal to be attacked to a certain extent: the corrosion then becomes more pronounced and a crust of black oxide, or sometimes a deposit of verdigris, appears [4].

The presence of dissolved carbonic acid in the water prevents the formation of a protective film of oxide [5].

In the presence of ammonium salts or cyanides, which form very stable complexes with Cu^+ ions, the domain of corrosion of copper is considerably larger than in Fig. 3 [1]: the domain of passivation almost completely disappears and the upper limit of the domain of immunity is brought down to considerably lower electrode potentials. These substances therefore produce vigorous corrosion of copper, even in the absence of oxidizing agents ([1], [2]).

3.3. STABILITY AND FORMATION OF THE COPPER OXIDES

In agreement with Figs. 1 and 2, *cuprous oxide* Cu_2O is sometimes formed cathodically during the electrolysis of slightly acid solutions of copper sulphate, e.g. in copper voltameters in particular; it is also formed on a copper anode used for the electrolysis of solutions of sulphuric acid, alkaline bases or sodium chloride [4]. Dilute solutions of hydrofluoric, sulphuric and phosphoric acids, and also the principal organic acids, dissolve Cu_2O with disproportionation into Cu^{++} ions and metallic Cu (lines 18 and 7 of Figs. 1 and 2).

Cupric oxide CuO is formed in particular by the electrolysis of a solution of alkaline bases or potassium chlorate, using a copper anode. It dissolves in dilute acids (lines 11) and is slightly soluble in alkaline solutions (lines 12 and 13). It also dissolves in ammonia in the presence of ammonium salts.

Cupric hydroxide $Cu(OH)_2$, which is less stable than cupric oxide CuO (see section 1), is obtained by neutralizing a solution of copper sulphate or by electrolysing a solution of an alkali metal sulphate or nitrate using a copper anode [6]. Like the oxide CuO, it is practically insoluble in water, but dissolves in dilute acids, and also in solutions of bases or alkali metal carbonates. It is oxidized by concentrated hydrogen peroxide to give *copper peroxide* CuO_2.

In Fig. 4 the formulae given in paragraph 2 have been used to represent the influence of pH on the solubility of CuO and $Cu(OH)_2$. According to this diagram, the solubility of each of these compounds in pure water, and the pH of the saturated solutions thus obtained are respectively:

for CuO: $10^{-7.0}$ g-ions Cu^{++}/l, i.e. 0·008 mg CuO/l and pH = 7·5;
for $Cu(OH)_2$: $10^{-6.5}$ g-ions Cu^{++}/l, i.e. 0·03 mg $Cu(OH)_2$/l and pH = 7·9.

This value for the solubility of $Cu(OH)_2$ in water practically agrees with a value determined by Oka [10] [$10^{-6.27}$ moles/l, i.e. 0·05 mg $Cu(OH)_2$/l]; the value for the solubility of CuO does not agree with the values determined by Remy and Kuhlmann [11] ($6{\cdot}77 \times 10^{-5}$ and $8{\cdot}86 \times 10^{-5}$ moles/l, i.e. 5·4 and 5·5 mg CuO/l).

The values assumed for the logarithms of the solubility products $(Cu^{++}).(OH^-)^2$ of CuO and $Cu(OH)_2$, given by Latimer, do not necessarily agree with all the values given in the literature, which are themselves sometimes conflicting. Some values of these logarithms are:

for CuO:

Value assumed by us	−20·12
,, ,, ,, Feitknecht [9]	−22

for $Cu(OH)_2$:

Value assumed by us	−18·81
,, ,, ,, Näsänen and Tamminen [7]	−19·66
,, ,, ,, Geloso and Deschamps [8]	−18·30
,, ,, ,, Feitknecht [9]	−18·80

3.4. ELECTROLYSIS OF ACID SOLUTIONS OF COPPER. ELECTROLYTIC REFINING OF COPPER. COPPER VOLTAMETER.

The electrolysis of acid solutions of copper depends on the fact that an electric current is passed between two electrodes immersed in the solution, the potentials of which are situated respectively above and below the equilibrium potential of the reaction $Cu = Cu^{++} + 2e^-$, the value of which at 25°C is given by equation (15). At the negative electrode copper is deposited by reduction, according to the reaction $Cu^{++} + 2e^- \rightarrow Cu$, and at the positive electrode copper is dissolved by oxidation, by the reverse reaction $Cu \rightarrow Cu^{++} + 2e^-$.

If these two reactions are the only ones which occur, they both take place with a current yield of 100 per cent, from Faraday's law; the *refining* and *plating* producees 1·185 g of copper at the cathode per amp–hour; the copper voltameter will then allow the exact measurement of the quantity of current passed.

In the case of *copper refining*, it is generally important that the anodic and cathodic potentials both remain close to the equilibrium potential of the reaction: $Cu = Cu^{++} + 2e^-$ (15). Too high a cathodic potential (situated below line (*a*)) can cause the formation of hydrogen at the cathode simultaneously with the deposition of copper, which reduces the current yield and one obtains cathodic copper containing hydrogen. A too anodic potential can cause the dissolution of noble metals, which then are deposited at the cathode instead of being left as a slime when disintegration of the anodes occurs.

In the case of the *copper voltameter*, it is necessary that the cathode potential does not drop below line (*a*), or otherwise the currents measured would be too low. The solution must also be practically free from oxygen, which would be reduced at the cathode, causing an underestimation of the current. We must also prevent the pH rising above approximately 2 to 3, in order to prevent the formation of the oxide Cu_2O at the electrodes, which would result in an overestimation of the current.

3.5. FORMATION AND STABILITY OF COPPER HYDRIDE CuH

A gaseous copper hydride CuH has been obtained by the electrolysis of a dilute solution of a copper salt [12]. According to Newbery [13], one also obtains unstable copper hydrides of variable composition during the boosting of a copper cathode when a normal sulphuric acid solution is electrolysed. From the free enthalpy value given by Latimer, the hydride CuH should be formed only at very negative potential [i.e. $-2{\cdot}7$ V from equation (22)].

There also exists a red–brown solid hydride CuH, which has been obtained by the reduction of a solution of copper sulphate with sodium hypophosphite or hypophosphorous acid at about 70°C [14].

4. BIBLIOGRAPHY

[1] M. POURBAIX, *Thermodynamique des solutions aqueuses diluées. Représentation graphique du rôle du* pH *et du potentiel* (Thesis, Delft, 1945, Béranger, Paris and Liège).

[2] M. POURBAIX, *Leçons sur la corrosion électrochimique* (Part 3) (Rapport technique RT.49 of CEBELCOR, July 1957).

[3] G. CHARLOT, *L'analyse qualitative et les réactions en solution*, 4th ed., Masson, Paris, 1957, p. 222.

[4] P. PASCAL, *Nouveau traité de Chimie minérale*, Vol. III, Masson, Paris, 1957.

[5] H. UHLIG, *The Corrosion Handbook*, J. Wiley, London, 1948, p. 63.

[6] *Gmelins Handbuch der anorganischen Chemie, Kupfer*, S.N. 60, 8th ed., Verlag Chemie, 1958, Part B, p. 101.

[7] R. NÄSÄNEN and V. TAMMINEN, The equilibria of cupric hydroxysalts in mixed aqueous solutions of cupric and alkali salts, at 25°C, *J. Amer. Chem. Soc.* **71**, 1994–8 (1949).

[8] M. GELOSO and P. DESCHAMPS, Études de sels basiques insolubles et calculs des produits de solubilité, *C.R. Acad. Sc.* **225**, 742–4 (1947).

[9] W. FEITKNECHT, Ueber die Löslichkeitsprodukte der Oxyde und des Hydroxyds von Kupfer und über die Löslichkeit von Kupferhydroxyd in Natronlauge, *Helv. Chim. Acta*, **27**, 771–5 (1944).

[10] Y. OKA, *J. Chem. Soc. Japan*, **61**, 311–20 (1940).

[11] H. REMY and A. KUHLMANN, Löslichkeitsbestimmungen an schwer löslichen Stoffen. II. Wasserlöslichkeit der Oxyde von Be, Al, Zn, Cd, Cu und Ag, *Z. anal. Chem.* **65**, 161 (1924).

[12] LEDUC, *C.R. Acad. Sc.* **113**, 71 (1891).

[13] E. NEWBERY, The life period of the overvoltage compounds, *J. Chem. Soc.* **125**, 511 (1924).

[14] D. HURD, *An Introduction to the Chemistry of the Hydrides*, John Wiley, New York; Chapman Hall, London, 1952, p. 194.

SECTION 14.2

SILVER [1]

C. VANLEUGENHAGHE, M. POURBAIX and P. VAN RYSSELBERGHE

SUMMARY

(1) Shortened and adapted version of a previously published treatise [1].

1. SUBSTANCES CONSIDERED AND SUBSTANCE NOT CONSIDERED

	Oxidation number (Z)	Considered	Not considered	μ^0(cal.)	Name, colour, crystalline system
Solid substances	0	**Ag**	–	0	Silver, grey, cub.
	+0.5	–	Ag_4O	–	Sub-oxide
	+1	**Ag_2O**	–	*a*. – 2 586	Argentous oxide, brown–black, cub.
	»	» hydr.	–	*b*. 12 726 (2)	Hydrated oxide or hydroxide AgOH, white
	+2	**AgO**	–	2 600	Argentic oxide Ag_2O_2, grey–black, cub.
	+3	**Ag_2O_3**	–	20 800	Sesquioxide, ? , cub.
Dissolved substances	+1	Ag^+	–	18 430	Argentous ion, colourless
	»	AgO^-	–	– 5 490	Argentite ion, ?
	+2	Ag^{++}	–	64 100	Argentic ion, ?
	+3	AgO^+	–	53 900	Argentyl ion, ?

2. REACTIONS AND EQUILIBRIUM FORMULAE(3)

2.1. TWO DISSOLVED SUBSTANCES

2.1.1. *Relative stability of the dissolved substances*

Z = +1

1. $Ag^+ + H_2O = AgO^- + 2H^+$ $\quad \log\frac{(AgO^-)}{(Ag^+)} = -24.04 + 2pH$

+1 → +2

2. $Ag^+ = Ag^{++} + e^-$ $\quad E_0 = 1.980 + 0.0591 \log\frac{(Ag^{++})}{(Ag^+)}$

+1 → +3

3. $Ag^+ + H_2O = AgO^+ + 2H^+ + 2e^-$ $\quad E_0 = 1.998 - 0.0591\,pH + 0.0295 \log\frac{(AgO^+)}{(Ag^+)}$

4. $AgO^- = AgO^+ + 2e^-$ $\quad E_0 = 1.288 + 0.0295 \log\frac{(AgO^+)}{(AgO^-)}$

+2 → +3

5. $Ag^{++} + H_2O = AgO^+ + 2H^+ + e^-$ $\quad E_0 = 2.016 - 0.1182\,pH + 0.0591 \log\frac{(AgO^+)}{(Ag^{++})}$

2.1.2. *Limits of the domains of relative predominance of the dissolved substances*

1'. Ag^+/AgO^- $\quad pH = 12.02$

2'. Ag^+/Ag^{++} $\quad E_0 = 1.980$

3'. Ag^+/AgO^+ $\quad E_0 = 1.998 - 0.0591\,pH$

4'. AgO^-/AgO^+ $\quad E_0 = 1.288$

5'. Ag^{++}/AgO^+ $\quad E_0 = 2.016 - 0.1182\,pH$

2.2. TWO SOLID SUBSTANCES

Limits of the domains of relative stability of silver and its oxides

0 → +1

6. $2\mathbf{Ag} + H_2O = \mathbf{Ag_2O} + 2H^+ + 2e^-$ $\quad$ *a*. $E_0 = 1.173 - 0.0591\,pH$; *b*. $= 1.505 - 0.0591\,pH$

+1 → +2

7. $\mathbf{Ag_2O} + H_2O = 2\mathbf{AgO} + 2H^+ + 2e^-$ $\quad$ *a*. $E_0 = 1.398 - 0.0591\,pH$; *b*. $= 1.066 - 0.0591\,pH$

+2 → +3

8. $2\mathbf{AgO} + H_2O = \mathbf{Ag_2O_3} + 2H^+ + 2e^-$ $\quad E_0 = 1.569 - 0.0591\,pH$

---

(2) Charlot [2] gives pK = 12·1 for the reaction $AgOH = AgO^- + H^+$. From this we can deduce

$\mu^0_{AgOH} = \mu^0_{AgO^-} - (12{\cdot}1 \times 1{,}363) = -21\,982$ cal. and $\mu^0_{Ag_2O\,hydr.} = 2\mu^0_{AgOH} - \mu^0_{H_2O} = +12\,726$ cal.

(3) In reactions in which Ag_2O takes part, letter *a* refers to anhydrous Ag_2O, whose free enthalpy of formation is −2 586 cal; letter *b* refers to hydrated Ag_2O or AgOH, whose free enthalpy of formation is −21 982 cal.

2.3. ONE SOLID SUBSTANCE AND ONE DISSOLVED SUBSTANCE

Solubility of silver and its oxides

$Z = +1$

9. $2Ag^{+} + H_2O = \mathbf{Ag_2O} + 2H^{+}$ a. $\log(Ag^{+}) = 6.33 - pH$
   b. $= 11.95 - pH$

10. $\mathbf{Ag_2O} + H_2O = 2AgO^{-} + 2H^{+}$ a. $\log(AgO^{-}) = -17.72 + pH$
   b. $= -12.10 + pH$

$Z = +2$

11. $Ag^{++} + H_2O = \mathbf{AgO} + 2H^{+}$ $\log(Ag^{++}) = -3.53 - 2pH$

$Z = +3$

12. $2AgO^{+} + H_2O = \mathbf{Ag_2O_3} + 2H^{+}$ $\log(AgO^{+}) = -11.10 - pH$

$0 \rightarrow +1$

13. $\mathbf{Ag} = Ag^{+} + e^{-}$ $E_0 = 0.799 + 0.0591 \log(Ag^{+})$

14. $\mathbf{Ag} + H_2O = AgO^{-} + 2H^{+} + e^{-}$ $E_0 = 2.220 - 0.1182\,pH + 0.0591 \log(AgO^{-})$

$+1 \rightarrow +2$

15. $Ag^{+} + H_2O = \mathbf{AgO} + 2H^{+} + e^{-}$ $E_0 = 1.772 - 0.1182\,pH - 0.0591 \log(Ag^{+})$

16. $AgO^{-} = \mathbf{AgO} + e^{-}$ $E_0 = 0.351 - 0.0591 \log(AgO^{-})$

$+1 \rightarrow +3$

17. $2Ag^{+} + 3H_2O = \mathbf{Ag_2O_3} + 6H^{+} + 4e^{-}$ $E_0 = 1.670 - 0.0886\,pH - 0.0295 \log(Ag^{+})$

18. $2AgO^{-} + H_2O = \mathbf{Ag_2O_3} + 2H^{+} + 4e^{-}$ $E_0 = 0.960 - 0.0295\,pH - 0.0295 \log(AgO^{-})$

$+2 \rightarrow +3$

19. $2Ag^{++} + 3H_2O = \mathbf{Ag_2O_3} + 6H^{+} + 2e^{-}$ $E_0 = 1.360 - 0.1773\,pH - 0.0591 \log(Ag^{++})$

3. EQUILIBRIUM DIAGRAM AND ITS INTERPRETATION

3.1. ESTABLISHMENT OF THE DIAGRAM

Using the equilibrium formulae established in paragraph 2, we have constructed Fig. 1, which represents the stable equilibria of the system silver–water, at 25°C. Figure 2, deduced from Fig. 1, represents the theoretical conditions of corrosion, immunity and passivation of silver, at 25°C. In Fig. 3 we have used equations (1′), (9) and (10) to represent the influence of pH on the solubility of Ag_2O and AgOH.

These diagrams are valid only in the absence of substances with which silver can form soluble complexes or insoluble salts. Silver forms a large number of complexes, some of which are very stable, e.g. the thiosulphuric and cyanide complexes of monovalent silver. Almost all silver salts are sparingly soluble; the nitrate, perchlorate, fluoride, acetate and chlorate are soluble [2].

3.2. STABILITY AND CORROSION OF SILVER

Silver is a very noble metal: its domain of stability covers a very large portion of the domain of stability of water.

It is found in the native state in nature, often mixed with other metals (Au, Hg, Sb, Cu, Pt in particular).

Silver is perfectly stable in the presence of water and aqueous solutions of all pH's free from oxidizing agents and complexing substances; it is not attacked appreciably by dry or moist air (provided that the air is free from ozone, sulphuric acid, halogens and ammonia [8]).

In agreement with Figs. 1 and 2, silver can be dissolved by acid oxidizing solutions to give colourless Ag^{+} ions (HNO_3, concentrated H_2SO_4, HCl in the presence of oxidizing agents). In neutral or moderately acid media, very powerful oxidizing agents (such as ozone or the persulphates) oxidize solutions of Ag^{+} to give the black oxides AgO and Ag_2O_3 which are unstable in the presence of water and decompose it with the evolution of oxygen. In very acid media these oxidizing agents can lead to the formation of black solutions of divalent silver, whose constitution is not known with certainty (Ag^{++} ions?, nitric or other complexes?)(4) [3]; these solutions, whose potential is around 2 V, are powerful oxidizing agents. As Noyes *et al.* have shown [3], they oxidize H_2O_2 to O_2, Mn^{++} to MnO_4^-, Ce^{+++} to Ce^{++++}, Tl^+ to Tl^{+++}, VO^{++} to VO_2^+, IO_3^- to IO_4^- and NH_4^+ to N_2 and oxides of nitrogen; the dilution of these solutions leads, together with an increase of pH, and according to reactions similar to those represented by lines (2′), (3′) and (5′), to the disproportionation of the divalent silver Ag^{++}

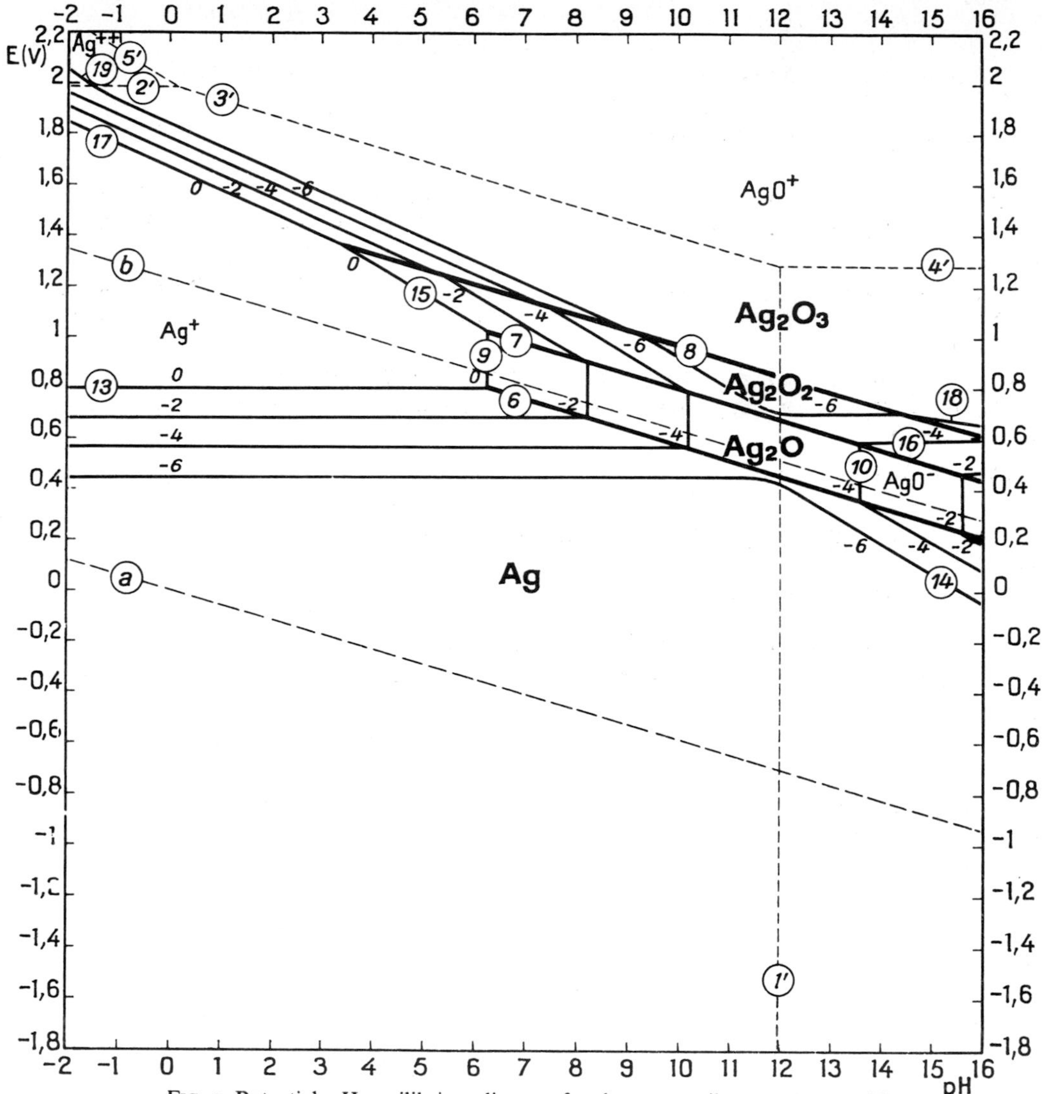

FIG. 1. Potential–pH equilibrium diagram for the system silver–water, at 25°C.

into trivalent silver AgO^+ and monovalent silver Ag^+, according to line (3′), with the separation of basic substances containing Ag_2O_3.

In alkaline solutions, silver is generally stable; in the presence of oxidizing agents it covers itself with a film of brown Ag_2O, slightly soluble in caustic alkali solutions; silver is attacked by fused hydroxides in the presence of oxygen.

(4) In nitric acid solution, Ag^{++} ions probably exist in the form of complexes, which would make Ag_2O_3 more soluble than is shown by lines (19) and (17) of Fig. 1.

As Hickling and Taylor have shown by oscillographic means [4], the anodic polarization of silver in the presence of a solution of NaOH leads first of all to the formation of a protective layer of Ag_2O; this seems to appear at potentials practically equal to those indicated by line (6) which corresponds to the equilibrium Ag/Ag_2O. The Ag_2O then becomes covered, at potentials above those indicated by lines (7) and (8), with an unstable trivalent oxide Ag_2O_3, which decomposes to give the divalent oxide AgO; during this decomposition the potential falls again, stabilizing itself in the neighbourhood of line (7); the anode which is most probably covered with a mixture of Ag_2O and AgO, is then the site of an evolution of oxygen.

The electrolysis of solutions of Ag^+ ions at sufficiently low current densities using a silver anode leads to the anodic dissolution of silver entirely in the monovalent state and the cathodic separation of metal without any risk of secondary reactions; these conditions (which are not obtained in the copper voltameter) enable silver voltameters to function perfectly.

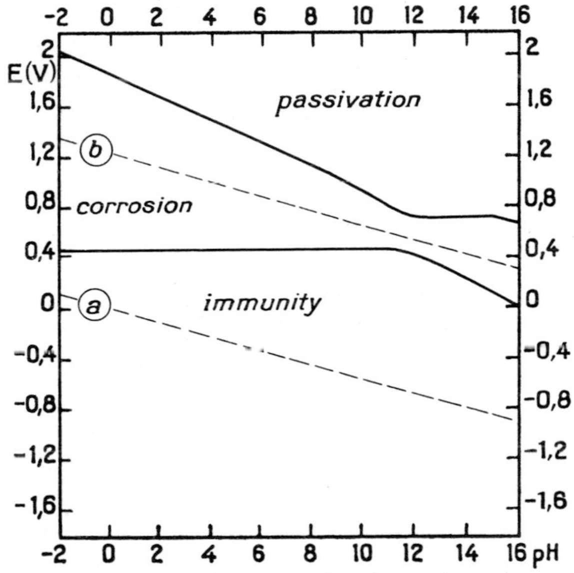

FIG. 2. Theoretical domains of corrosion, immunity and passivation of silver, at 25°C.

The electrolysis of solutions of Ag^+ ions at high current densities can lead to the deposition of black oxides AgO and Ag_2O_3 on the anode, if the anode potential is sufficiently high; these oxides, which are unstable in the presence of water, decompose it with the evolution of oxygen if the electrolysis current is broken.

Figure 2, deduced from Fig. 1, shows that any sufficiently powerful oxidizing action can cause silver to be corroded, except at high potentials when the oxide Ag_2O_3 is stable. The oxides Ag_2O and AgO are too soluble to afford protection of silver by passivation; according to Fig. 2, this corrosion of silver by a sufficient oxidizing action should be a minimum at a pH of about 12.

3.3. STABILITY AND FORMATION OF THE SILVER OXIDES

Three oxides of silver exist with certainty: Ag_2O, AgO and Ag_2O_3. The sub-oxide Ag_4O, described by many investigators, may only be a solid solution of silver in the oxide Ag_2O [5].

The oxide of monovalent silver Ag_2O is the best-known oxide. As we have seen in paragraph 3.2, it can be produced by the controlled anodic oxidation of silver in alkaline solutions. In agreement with Fig. 1, the oxide Ag_2O is an amphoteric substance; it is soluble in acid media with the formation of Ag^+

ions and in very alkaline media with the formation of AgO^- ions. This property was established with certainty by Johnston *et al.* [7] as early as 1933. Figure 3 represents, according to the formulae given in paragraph 2, the influence of pH on the solubility of Ag_2O and AgOH. It gives the solubility of Ag_2O in pure water and the pH of the saturated solution respectively as:

$$10^{-3.85} \text{ g-ions } Ag^+/l, \text{ i.e. } 16.2 \text{ mg } Ag_2O/l \quad \text{and pH} = 10.15.$$

This value for the solubility of Ag_2O in water does not agree with those given in the literature, which vary between the following extremes: 25 mg Ag_2O/l [6] and 52 mg Ag_2O/l [7].

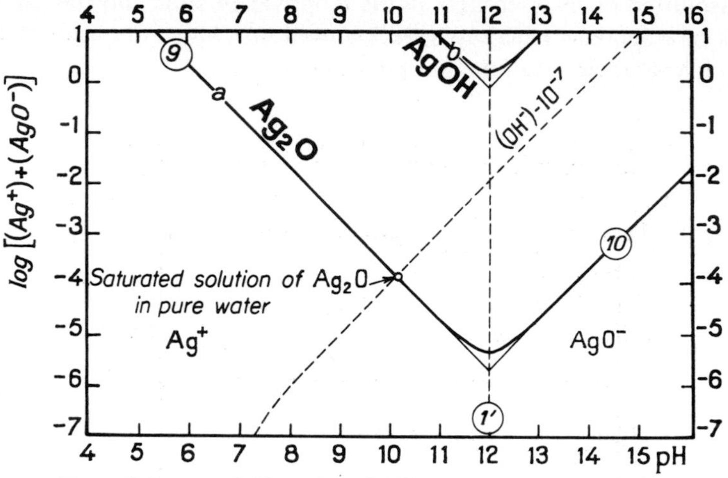

FIG. 3. Influence of pH on the solubility of Ag_2O and AgOH, at 25°C.

The oxide of divalent silver AgO or Ag_2O_2 can be obtained by the anodic oxidation of silver using an alkaline lye or dilute sulphuric acid as the electrolyte [8]. It can be reduced to monovalent silver by dilute nitric acid or ammonia.

The oxide of trivalent silver Ag_2O_3, which is formed during the anodic oxidation of silver, has not been obtained in the pure state. The position of its domain of relative stability above line (*b*) characterizes it as a substance that is very unstable in the presence of water and as a powerful oxidizing agent.

4. BIBLIOGRAPHY

[1] P. DELAHAY, M. POURBAIX and P. VAN RYSSELBERGHE, *Diagramme potentiel–*pH *de l'argent. Comportement électrochimique et corrosion de l'argent* (C.R. 2ᵉ Reunion du CITCE, Milan, 1950; Tamburini, 1951).

[2] G. CHARLOT, *L'analyse qualitative et les réactions en solution,* 4th ed., Masson, Paris, 1957.

[3] A. NOYES *et al.*, Argentic salts in acid solution, *J. Amer. Chem. Soc.* I. **57**, 1221 (1935); II. **57**, 1229 (1935); III. **57**, 1238 (1935); IV. **59**, 1316 (1937); V. **59**, 1326 (1937).

[4] A. HICKLING and D. TAYLOR, The anodic behaviour of metals. IV. Silver, *Disc. Faraday Soc.* **1**, 277–85 (1947).

[5] FAIVRE, Thesis, Paris, 1943.

[6] A. NOYES and D. KOHR, Das Lösungsgleichgewicht zwischen Silberchlorid, Silberoxyd und Lösungen von Kaliumchlorid und Hydroxyd, *Z. Phys. Chem.* **42**, 336 (1903).

[7] H. L. JOHNSTON, F. CUTA and A. GARRETT, The solubility of silver oxide in water, in alkali and in alkaline salt solutions. The amphoteric character of silver hydroxide, *J. Amer. Chem. Soc.* **55**, 2311 (1933).

[8] P. PASCAL, *Nouveau traité de chimie minérale*, Vol. III, Masson, Paris, 1957.

SECTION 14.3

GOLD[1]

J. VAN MUYLDER and M. POURBAIX

SUMMARY

---

[1] Rapport CEFA/R.4 of the Commission des Études Fondamentales et Applications of CEBELCOR.

1. SUBSTANCES CONSIDERED AND SUBSTANCES NOT CONSIDERED

	Oxidation number (Z)	Considered	Not considered		μ^0(cal.)	Name, colour, crystalline system
Solid substances	0	**Au**	–		0	Gold, yellow, f.c.cub.
	+1	–	**Au_2O** anh.		–	Aurous oxide
	»	–	» hydr.		–	Aurous hydroxide AuOH
	+3	**Au_2O_3** hydr.	–	*a.*	31 470	Hydrated auric oxide or hydroxide $Au(OH)_3$, rust–brown (²)
	»	» anh.	–	*b.*	39 000	Anhydrous auric oxide, brown–black
	+4	**AuO_2**	–		48 000 (³)	Gold peroxide
Dissolved substances	+1	Au^+	–		39 000	Aurous ion
	+3	Au^{+++}	–		103 600	Auric ion
	»	–	AuO^+		–	"Auryl" ion
	»	H_3AuO_3	–		– 61 800	Auric acid
	»	$H_2AuO_3^-$	–		– 45 800	Monoaurate ion
	»	$HAuO_3^{--}$	–		– 27 600	Diaurate ion
	»	AuO_3^{---}	–		– 5 800	Triaurate ion

2. REACTIONS AND EQUILIBRIUM FORMULAE (⁴)

2.1. TWO DISSOLVED SUBSTANCES

2.1.1. *Relative stability of the dissolved substances*

$Z = +3$

1. $Au^{+++} + 3H_2O = H_3AuO_3 + 3H^+$ $\qquad \log\frac{(H_3AuO_3)}{(Au^{+++})} = -\ 3.43 + 3\,pH$

2. $H_3AuO_3 = H_2AuO_3^- + H^+$ $\qquad \log\frac{(H_2AuO_3^-)}{(H_3AuO_3)} = -\ 11.74 + pH$

3. $H_2AuO_3^- = HAuO_3^{--} + H^+$ $\qquad \log\frac{(HAuO_3^{--})}{(H_2AuO_3^-)} = -\ 13.35 + pH$

4. $HAuO_3^{--} = AuO_3^{---} + H^+$ $\qquad \log\frac{(AuO_3^{---})}{(HAuO_3^{--})} = -\ 15.99 + pH$

$+1 \rightarrow +3$

5. $Au^+ = Au^{+++} + 2e^-$ $\qquad E_0 = 1.401 + 0.0295\log\frac{(Au^{++}}{(Au^{+}}$

6. $Au^+ + 3H_2O = H_3AuO_3 + 3H^+ + 2e^-$ $\qquad E_0 = 1.502 - 0.0886\,pH + 0.0295\log\frac{(H_3Au}{(Au^-}$

7. $Au^+ + 3H_2O = H_2AuO_3^- + 4H^+ + 2e^-$ $\qquad E_0 = 1.849 - 0.1182\,pH + 0.0295\log\frac{(H_2Au}{(Au^-}$

8. $Au^+ + 3H_2O = HAuO_3^{--} + 5H^+ + 2e^-$ $\qquad E_0 = 2.243 - 0.1477\,pH + 0.0295\log\frac{(HAu(}{(Au^-}$

(²) This value for $\mu^0_{Au_2O_3}$ corresponds to $\mu^0_{Au(OH)_3} = -69\ 300$ cal.

(³) Value calculated from $E^0_0 = 1{\cdot}75$ V given by Charlot [1] for the equilibrium Au/AuO_2.

(⁴) For the equilibria involving Au_2O_3, the values marked *a* refer to hydrated Au_2O_3($Au_2O_3.3H_2O$ or $Au(OH)_3$), and the values marked *b* refer to anhydrous Au_2O_3.

2.1.2. *Limits of the domains of relative predominance of the dissolved substances*

1'.	Au^{+++} / H_3AuO_3	$pH = 1.14$
2'.	H_3AuO_3 / $H_2AuO_3^-$	$pH = 11.74$
3'.	$H_2AuO_3^-$ / $HAuO_3^{--}$	$pH = 13.35$
4'.	$HAuO_3^{--}$ / AuO_3^{---}	$pH = 15.99$
5'.	Au^+ / Au^{+++}	$E_0 = 1.401$
6'.	Au^+ / H_3AuO_3	$E_0 = 1.502 - 0.0886\ pH$
7'.	Au^+ / $H_2AuO_3^-$	$E_0 = 1.849 - 0.1182\ pH$
8'.	Au^+ / $HAuO_3^{--}$	$E_0 = 2.243 - 0.1477\ pH$

2.2. TWO SOLID SUBSTANCES

Limits of the domains of relative stability of gold and its oxides

$0 \rightarrow +3$

9. $2\,\mathbf{Au} + 3H_2O = \mathbf{Au_2O_3} + 6H^+ + 6e^-$
 - a. $E_0 = 1.457 - 0.0591\ pH$
 - b. $ = 1.511 - 0.0591\ pH$

$+3 \rightarrow +4$

10. $\mathbf{Au_2O_3} + H_2O = 2\,\mathbf{AuO_2} + 2H^+ + 2e^-$
 - a. $E_0 = 2.630 - 0.0591\ pH$
 - b. $ = 2.465 - 0.0591\ pH$

2.3. ONE SOLID SUBSTANCE AND ONE DISSOLVED SUBSTANCE

Solubility of the solid substances

$Z = +3$

11. $2Au^{+++} + 3H_2O = \mathbf{Au_2O_3} + 6H^+$
 - a. $\log(Au^{+++}) = -2.08 - 3pH$
 - b. $\phantom{\log(Au^{+++})} = 0.69 - 3pH$

12. $\mathbf{Au_2O_3} + 3H_2O = 2H_3AuO_3$
 - a. $\log(H_3AuO_3) = -5.53$
 - b. $ = -2.74$

13. $\mathbf{Au_2O_3} + 3H_2O = 2H_2AuO_3^- + 2H^+$
 - a. $\log(H_2AuO_3^-) = -17.24 + pH$
 - b. $ = -14.48 + pH$

14. $\mathbf{Au_2O_3} + 3H_2O = 2HAuO_3^{--} + 4H^+$
 - a. $\log(HAuO_3^{--}) = -30.59 + 2pH$
 - b. $\phantom{\log(HAuO_3^{--})} = -27.83 + 2pH$

$0 \rightarrow +1$

15. $\mathbf{Au} = Au^+ + e^-$ $\quad E_0 = 1.692 + 0.0591 \log(Au^+)$

$0 \rightarrow +3$

16. $\mathbf{Au} = Au^{+++} + 3e^-$ $\quad E_0 = 1.498 + 0.0197 \log(Au^{+++})$
17. $\mathbf{Au} + 3H_2O = H_3AuO_3 + 3H^+ + 3e^-$ $\quad E_0 = 1.565 - 0.0591\ pH + 0.0197 \log(H_3AuO_3)$
18. $\mathbf{Au} + 3H_2O = H_2AuO_3^- + 4H^+ + 3e^-$ $\quad E_0 = 1.796 - 0.0788\ pH + 0.0197 \log(H_2AuO_3^-)$
19. $\mathbf{Au} + 3H_2O = HAuO_3^{--} + 5H^+ + 3e^-$ $\quad E_0 = 2.059 - 0.0985\ pH + 0.0197 \log(HAuO_3^{--})$

$+3 \rightarrow +4$

20. $Au^{+++} + 2H_2O = \mathbf{AuO_2} + 4H^+ + e^-$ $\quad E_0 = 2.507 - 0.2364\ pH - 0.0591 \log(Au^{+++})$
21. $H_3AuO_3 = \mathbf{AuO_2} + H_2O + H^+ + e^-$ $\quad E_0 = 2.305 - 0.0591\ pH - 0.0591 \log(H_3AuO_3)$
22. $H_2AuO_3^- = \mathbf{AuO_2} + H_2O + e^-$ $\quad E_0 = 1.611 - 0.0591 \log(H_2AuO_3^-)$
23. $HAuO_3^{--} + H^+ = \mathbf{AuO_2} + H_2O + e^-$ $\quad E_0 = 0.822 + 0.0591\ pH - 0.0591 \log(HAuO_3^{--})$

3. EQUILIBRIUM DIAGRAM AND ITS INTERPRETATION

3.1. ESTABLISHMENT OF THE DIAGRAM

Figure 1, established from relations (1)–(23), represents the conditions of thermodynamic equilibrium of the system gold–water, at 25°C. Figure 2, which is deduced from Fig. 1 on the basis of certain assumptions, shows the theoretical conditions of corrosion, immunity and passivation of gold, at 25°C.

These figures are valid only in the absence of substances with which gold can form soluble complexes or insoluble compounds. Gold, in the trivalent state in particular, very readily forms complex ions in aqueous solution.

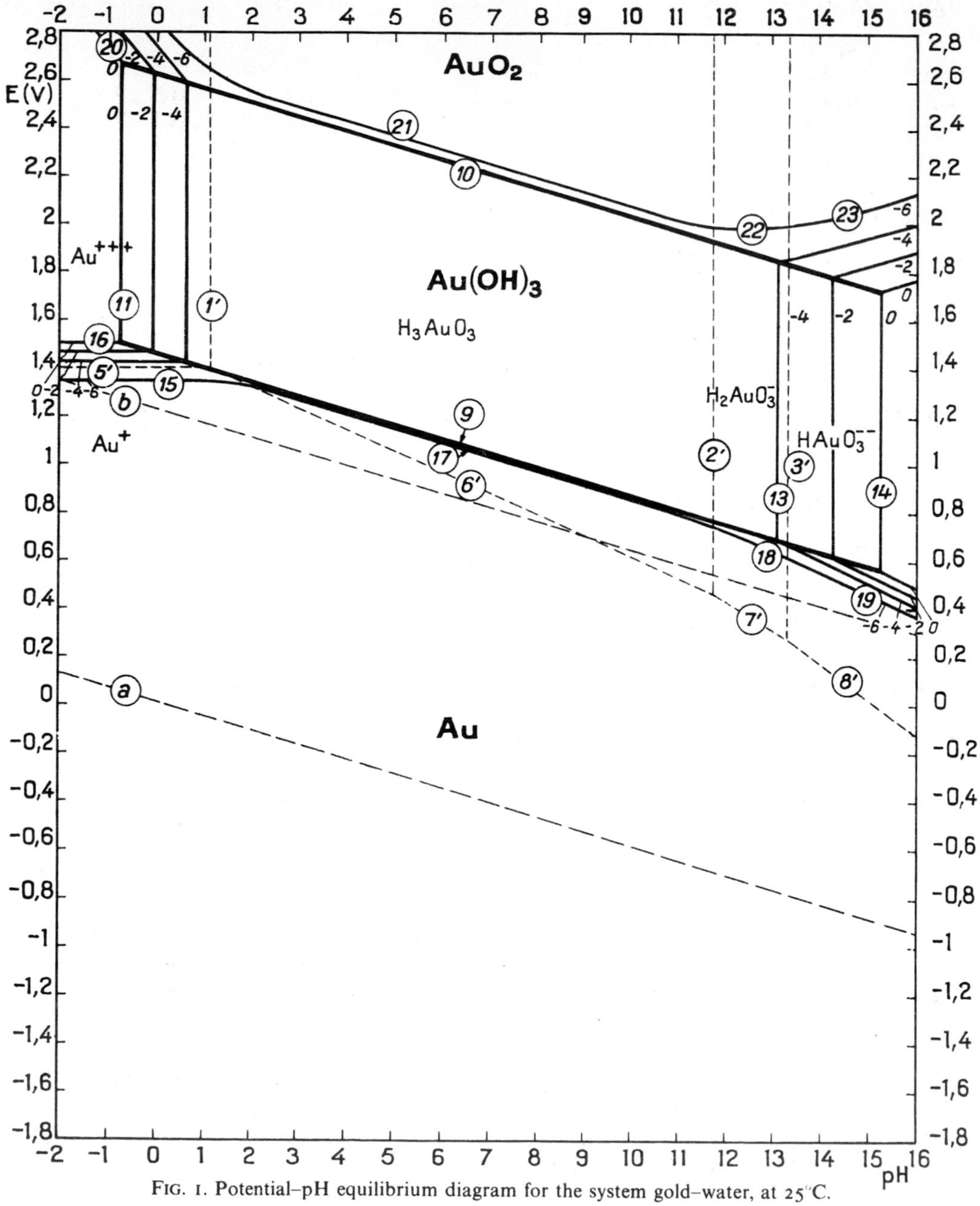

FIG. 1. Potential–pH equilibrium diagram for the system gold–water, at 25°C.

Charlot [1] mentions the following complexes as being the more important ones: yellow–red hydrochloric complexes ($AuCl_4^-$, $AuCl_3OH^-$, etc.), red–brown hydrobromic complexes ($AuBr_4^-$) and red–brown thiocyanide complexes [$Au(SCN)_4^-$]; monovalent gold forms stable colourless thiosulphuric complexes and extremely stable cyanide complexes. Gold sulphide Au_2S_3 (black) is sparingly soluble.

3.2. STABILITY AND CORROSION OF GOLD

As its domain of stability covers a very large area in Fig. 1, including the whole of the domain of stability of water, gold is a very noble metal, i.e. it can be oxidized only with difficulty.

In nature it is found mainly in the native state disseminated in quartz rocks and gold-bearing films, and in alluvial deposits, or diggings, arising from the disintegration of these rocks.

Gold is perfectly stable in the presence of water and aqueous solutions of all pH's free from complexing substances; it is unaffected by moist or dry air, even when heated.

At room temperature it is not attacked by acids unless they are both complexing and oxidizing; i.e. it is not attacked by the halogen hydracids, sulphuric acid, nitric acid or orthophosphoric acid. It is also unaffected by lyes of caustic alkalis.

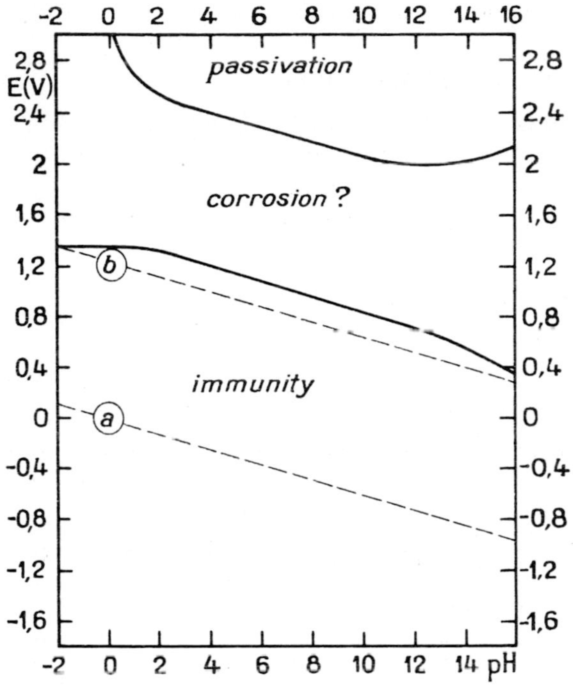

FIG. 2. Theoretical conditions of corrosion, immunity and passivation of gold, at 25°C.

In agreement with Figs. 1 and 2, gold can be attacked by very oxidizing systems whose reduction potentials are high (e.g. above 1·4 V for pH = 0). Thiessen and Schutza [2] describe the partial formation of auric oxide Au_2O_3 by the action of a mixture of oxygen and ozone.

However, gold is readily attacked only by reagents which are both complexing and oxidizing. In this respect, aqua regia is particularly effective, as it combines the oxidizing action of nitric acid with the complexing action of chlorine. In general the reaction produces a mixture of complexes: chloroauric acid $HAuCl_4$ and aurinitric acid $HAu(NO_3)_4$.

Other reagents capable of attacking gold by oxidation and the formation of complexes are: chlorine water (according to Reynolds *et al.* [3]), nitrates, hypochlorites, chlorates, permanganates and peroxides (including H_2O_2) in the presence of halogen hydracids; hydrogen peroxide in the presence of alkali metal cyanides; nitric acid and the higher oxides of lead and chromium in the presence of orthophosphoric acid. Gold is hardly attacked at all by fused alkalis, except in the presence of oxidizing agents such as the alkali metal nitrates.

When used as an electrolytic anode, gold may be either attacked or passivated, depending on whether the oxidation current density is below or above a certain value called the "limiting current density" (Gmelin [4]), which varies with the nature, concentration and temperature of the solution.

This behaviour is observed when the electrolyte is hydrochloric, sulphuric or nitric acid, or caustic soda or potash solution. The results obtained by Schutt and Walton [5] for a normal HCl solution are as follows:

t(°C)......................	15	25	35	45	55	65
I(A/cm²)..................	0.606	0.790	0.960	1.01	1.12	1.29

When a gold anode is passivated, oxygen is evolved on it (together with chlorine when the gold is passivated in the presence of hydrochloric acid), and at the same time the anode becomes covered with a protective layer of gold peroxide AuO_2 or Au_2O_4. This is unstable in the presence of water, and decomposes it with the evolution of oxygen if the electrolysis current is broken.

3.3. ELECTRO-DEPOSITION OF GOLD. ELECTRO-GILDING

It follows from Fig. 1 that gold can very easily be obtained in the metallic state by the reduction of its solutions. The normal procedure is to electrolyse solutions in which gold is present as complexes (chlorides, bromides, cyanides or ferrocyanides) using cathodes of silver, copper and their alloys. Other metals such as Zn, Cd, Pb, Ni, Fe have to be copper- or brass-plated before being electro-gilded.

3.4. STABILITY OF THE OXIDES AND HYDROXIDE OF GOLD

3.4.1. *Auric oxide and hydroxide*

In agreement with Fig. 1, hydrated auric oxide $Au_2O_3.3H_2O$ or auric hydroxide $Au(OH)_3$ is a fairly powerful oxidizing agent, thermodynamically unstable in the presence of water and aqueous solutions, in which it is capable of being reduced to gold with the evolution of oxygen. For example,

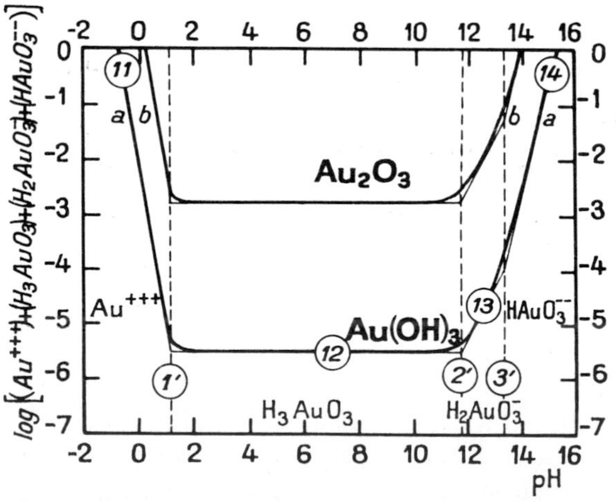

FIG. 3. Influence of pH on the solubility of auric oxide and hydroxide, at 25°C.

it can oxidize hydrogen, hydrogen peroxide, chromic oxide, alcohol and certain organic acids (e.g. CH_3CO_2H).

It is amphoteric, dissolving in very acid solutions to give auric ions Au^{+++} and in very alkaline solutions to give aurate ions $H_2AuO_3^-$ and $HAuO_3^{--}$.

Figure 3 is an approximate representation of the influence of pH on the solubility of anhydrous auric oxide Au_2O_3 and hydrated auric oxide $Au_2O_3.3H_2O$ or $Au(OH)_3$ in non-complexing solutions. It shows that these two substances dissolve in water and aqueous solutions of pH between 2 and 10·5 with the formation of undissociated auric acid H_3AuO_3. Their solubilities are constant in this domain of pH and are respectively $10^{-2.74}$ g-at Au/l (i.e. 360 mg Au/l) and $10^{-5.53}$ g-at Au/l (i.e. 6 mg Au/l); the solubility increases at pH's below 2 with the formation of Au^{+++} cations and at pH's above 10·5 with the formation of aurates $H_2AuO_3^-$ and $HAuO_3^{--}$ With regard to the hydroxide $Au(OH)_3$, the value given in Fig. 3 ($10^{-5.53}$ g-at Au/l) agrees with that given by Johnston and Leland [6], which is due to the fact that the μ^0 given by Latimer was calculated from data provided by these investigators; it is in poor agreement with the other values given in the literature, which are in themselves divergent and which are generally much lower, e.g. the $10^{-11.65}$ g-at Au/l given by Jirsa and Jelinek [7]. Pascal [8] attributes this disagreement either to the fact that the information given in the literature corresponds to false equilibria, or to the fact that the substance used was not pure. It follows that auric hydroxide is probably less soluble than is shown in Fig. 1, and that, consequently, the middle part of the corrosion domain shown in Fig. 2 probably does not exist owing to passivation; for this reason we have marked the domain of corrosion with a question mark.

3.4.2. *Gold peroxide AuO_2*

Gold peroxide appears on gold which is anodically polarized in acid and alkaline solutions. From Fig. 1 it seems to be a particularly unstable substance with a great tendency to decompose into Au_2O_3 and O_2; it is a powerful oxidizing agent, oxidizing chlorides to chlorine, for example.

It dissolves in very acid and very alkaline solutions, being reduced to the trivalent state and evolving oxygen.

4. BIBLIOGRAPHY

[1] G. Charlot, *L'analyse qualitative et les réactions en solution*, 4th ed., Masson, Paris, 1957.
[2] P. Thiessen and H. Schutza, Zur Oxydation des Goldes, *Z. anorg. allgem. Chem.* **243,** 32 (1940).
[3] Reynolds, Spiller and Allen, quoted by P. Pascal [8].
[4] *Gmelins Handbuch der anorganischen Chemie, Gold,* S.N.62, 1954.
[5] W. Schutt and W. Walton, The anodic passivation of gold, *Trans. Faraday Soc.* **30,** 918 (1934).
[6] H. L. Johnston and H. L. Leland, The solubility of gold hydroxide in alkali and equilibria in the saturated solutions, *J. Amer. Chem. Soc.* **60,** 1439 (1938).
[7] F. Jirsa and H. Jelinek, *Z. Elektrochem.* **30,** 286 (1924).
[8] P. Pascal, *Nouveau traité de Chimie minérale,* Vol. VIII, Masson, Paris, 1957.

SECTION 15.1

ZINC([1])

N. DE ZOUBOV and M. POURBAIX

SUMMARY

([1]) Shortened and adapted version of a previously published account [1].

1. SUBSTANCES CONSIDERED AND SUBSTANCES NOT CONSIDERED

	Oxidation number (Z)	Considered	Not considered	μ^0(cal.)	Name, colour, crystalline system
Solid substances	− 2	–	ZnH_2	–	Zinc hydride, white
	0	Zn	–	0	Zinc, silvery white, hex.
	+ 2	ZnO hydr.	–	*a*. − 76 936 (²)	Zinc hydroxide ε-$Zn(OH)_2$, white, orthorh.(³)
	»	»	–	*b*. − 76 876 (²)	"Inactive" zinc oxide, white
	»	» hydr.	–	*c*. − 76 623 (²)	Zinc hydroxide γ-$Zn(OH)_2$, white(³)
	»	» »	–	*d*. − 76 445 (²)	Zinc hydroxide β-$Zn(OH)_2$, white, orthorh.(³)
	»	»	–	*e*. − 75 687 (²)	"Active" zinc oxide, white
	»	» hydr.	–	*f*. − 75 246 (²)	Zinc hydroxide α-$Zn(OH)_2$, white, hex.(³)
	»	» »	–	*g*. − 75 164 (²)	Zinc hydroxide $Zn(OH)_2$, white, amorphous(³)
	+ 3	–	Zn_2O_3 hydr.	–	Hydrated zinc sesquioxide $Zn_2O_3 . H_2O$
	+ 3.33	–	Zn_3O_5 hydr.	–	?
	+ 4	–	ZnO_2	–	Zinc peroxide
	»	–	» hydr.	–	Hydrated zinc peroxide $ZnO_2 . H_2O$
Dissolved substances	+ 2	Zn^{++}	–	− 35 184	Zincic ion, colourless
	»	$ZnOH^+$	–	− 78 700 (²)	Zincyl ion, colourless
	»	$HZnO_2^-$	–	−110 900 (²)	Bizincate ion, colourless
	»	ZnO_2^{--}	–	− 93 030	Zincate ion, colourless

2. REACTIONS AND EQUILIBRIUM FORMULAE (⁴)

2.1. TWO DISSOLVED SUBSTANCES

2.1.1. *Relative stability of the dissolved substances*

$Z = +2$

1. $Zn^{++} + H_2O = ZnOH^+ + H^+$ $\qquad \log\frac{(ZnOH^+)}{(Zn^{++})} = -9.67 + pH$

2. $ZnOH^+ + H_2O = HZnO_2^- + 2H^+$ $\qquad \log\frac{(HZnO_2^-)}{(ZnOH^+)} = -17.97 + 2pH$

3. $Zn^{++} + 2H_2O = HZnO_2^- + 3H^+$ $\qquad \log\frac{(HZnO_2^-)}{(Zn^{++})} = -27.63 + 3pH$

4. $HZnO_2^- = ZnO_2^{--} + H^+$ $\qquad \log\frac{(ZnO_2^{--})}{(HZnO_2^-)} = -13.17 + pH$

(²) ZnO: values calculated from the solubility products of the various oxides and hydroxides, determined by Feitknecht [2].
$ZnOH^+$: value calculated by taking $k = 2{\cdot}2 \times 10^{-10}$ (Kolthoff and Kameda [3]) for the equilibrium constant of the hydrolysis reaction: $Zn^{++} + H_2O = ZnOH^+ + H^+$.
$HZnO_2^-$: value obtained by taking pK = 16·7 (Charlot [4]) for the equilibrium constant of the reaction $Zn(OH)_2 = HZnO_2^- + H^+$.

(³) These values of μ^0 for the oxides correspond to the following values for the hydroxides:

(*a*) ε-$Zn(OH)_2$ = − 133 626 cal., (*d*) β-$Zn(OH)_2$ = − 133 135 cal.,
(*c*) γ-$Zn(OH)_2$ = − 133 313 cal., (*f*) α-$Zn(OH)_2$ = − 133 936 cal.,
(*g*) amorphous $Zn(OH)_2$ = − 131 854 cal.

(⁴) In the reactions involving ZnO, the letter *a* refers to ε-$Zn(OH)_2$, whose free enthalpy of formation is − 133 626 cal.; the letter *g* refers to amorphous $Zn(OH)_2$, whose free enthalpy of formation is − 131 854 cal.

2.1.2. *Limits of the domains of relative predominance of the dissolved substances*

1'.	$Zn^{++}/ZnOH^{+}$	$pH = 9.67$
2'.	$ZnOH^{+}/HZnO_2^{-}$	$pH = 8.98$
3'.	$Zn^{++}/HZnO_2^{-}$	$pH = 9.21$
4'.	$HZnO_2^{-}/ZnO_2^{--}$	$pH = 13.11$

2.2. TWO SOLID SUBSTANCES

Limits of the domains of relative stability of the solid substances

$0 \rightarrow +2$

5. $\mathbf{Zn} + H_2O = \mathbf{ZnO} + 2H^+ + 2e^-$
 $a.\ E_0 = -0.439 - 0.0591\ pH$
 $g.\ \quad = -0.400 - 0.0591\ pH$

2.3. ONE SOLID SUBSTANCE AND ONE DISSOLVED SUBSTANCE

Solubility of the solid substances

$Z = +2$

6. $Zn^{++} + H_2O = \mathbf{ZnO} + 2H^+$
 $a.\ \log(Zn^{++}) = 10.96 - 2pH$
 $g.\ \quad = 12.26 - 2pH$

7. $\mathbf{ZnO} + H_2O = HZnO_2^- + H^+$
 $a.\ \log(HZnO_2^-) = -16.68 + pH$
 $g.\ \quad = -15.37 + pH$

8. $\mathbf{ZnO} + H_2O = ZnO_2^{--} + 2H^+$
 $a.\ \log(ZnO_2^{--}) = -29.78 + 2pH$
 $g.\ \quad = -28.48 + 2pH$

$0 \rightarrow +2$

9. $\mathbf{Zn} = Zn^{++} + 2e^-$ $\quad E_0 = -0.763 + 0.0295\log(Zn^{++})$
10. $\mathbf{Zn} + 2H_2O = HZnO_2^- + 3H^+ + 2e^-$ $\quad E_0 = 0.054 - 0.0886\,pH + 0.0295\log(HZnO_2^-)$
11. $\mathbf{Zn} + 2H_2O = ZnO_2^{--} + 4H^+ + 2e^-$ $\quad E_0 = 0.441 - 0.1182\,pH + 0.0295\log(ZnO_2^{--})$

3. EQUILIBRIUM DIAGRAM AND ITS INTERPRETATION

3.1. ESTABLISHMENT OF THE DIAGRAM

Using the equilibrium formulae established in paragraph 2 we have drawn Fig. 1, which represents the conditions of thermodynamic equilibrium of the system zinc–water, at 25°C. Of all the oxides and hydroxides of zinc existing in aqueous solution, only the most stable form, ε-$Zn(OH)_2$, has been considered.

This figure is valid only in the absence of substances with which zinc can form soluble complexes or insoluble compounds. According to Charlot [4] and Gmelin [5], zinc forms the following complexes: ammine, cyanide, thiocyanide, oxalic and hydrochloric complexes, and complexes with ethylene diamine, pyridine, aniline and hydrazine. There is a large number of sparingly soluble zinc compounds, including the following: the white sulphide ZnS, zinc cobalticyanide, ammoniaco–zincic phosphate, the iodate $Zn(IO_3)_2$ and zinc carbonate ([2], [4]).

Figure 2*a*, deduced from Fig. 1 on the basis of certain assumptions, represents the theoretical conditions of corrosion, immunity and passivation of zinc, for the case in which the metal is passivated by a film of zinc ε-hydroxide. Figure 2*b* represents these conditions for zinc in the presence of solutions containing bicarbonate [1].

Figure 4, established from equations (6), (7) and (8), represents the influence of pH on the solubility of the oxides and hydroxides of zinc. The two curves (*a*) and (*g*) refer respectively to ε-$Zn(OH)_2$ and amorphous $Zn(OH)_2$, which are respectively the least soluble and the most soluble varieties of hydroxide considered in paragraph 1.

3.2. STABILITY, CORROSION AND FORMATION OF ZINC

From Figs. 1 and 2, zinc appears to be a base metal, as it has no domain of stability in common with that of water; it is found in the native state only very exceptionally, in certain rocks.

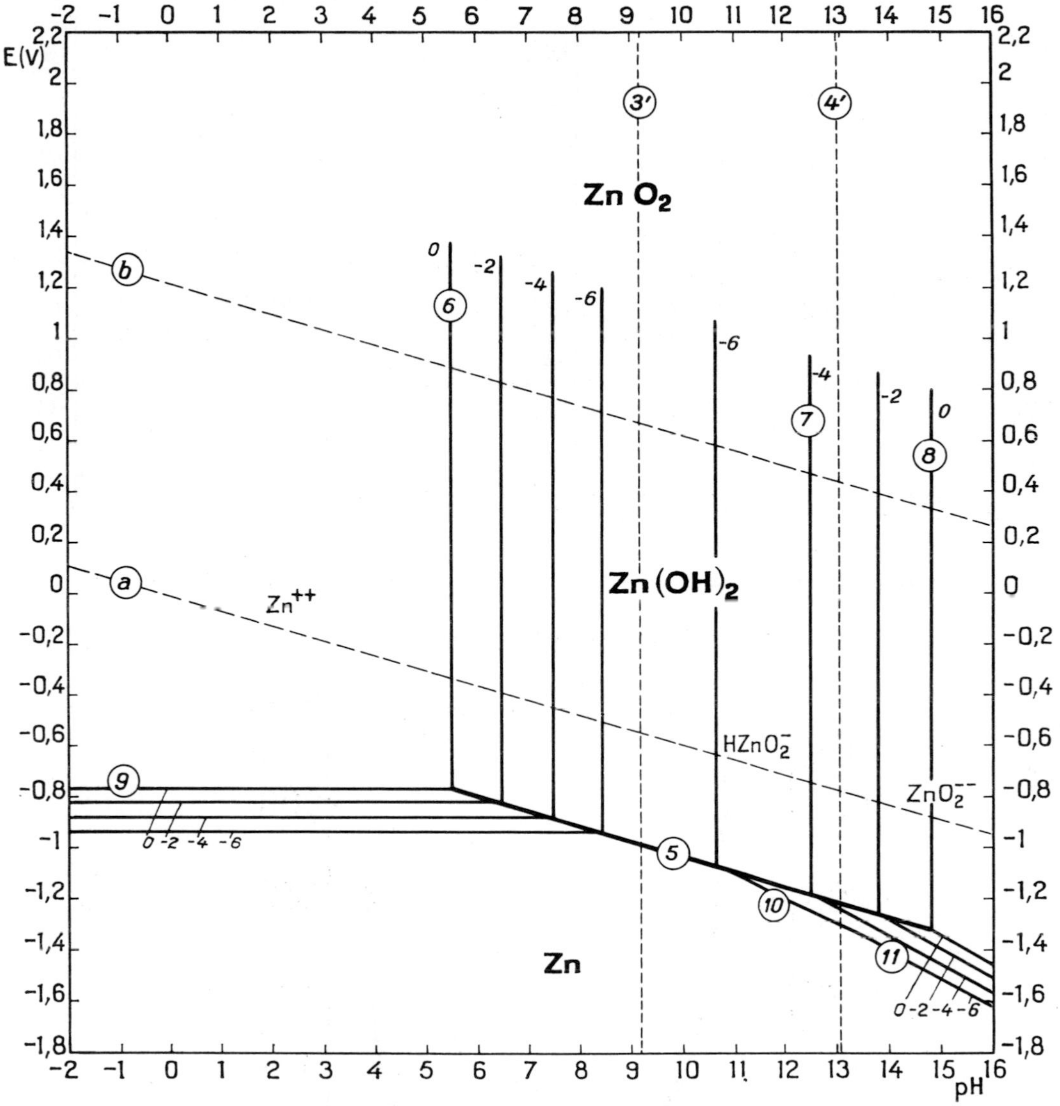

FIG. 1. Potential–pH equilibrium diagram for the system zinc–water, at 25°C. [Established by considering ε-$Zn(OH)_2$.]

It is thermodynamically unstable in the presence of water and aqueous solutions, and tends to dissolve with the evolution of hydrogen in acid, neutral or very alkaline solutions. This reaction often takes place extremely slowly when the zinc is very pure, in the presence of sulphuric acid for instance; this is due to the large hydrogen overpotential of zinc (see Section 2, p. 119). The attack is very rapid if the zinc is put in contact with a metal of low hydrogen overpotential, such as platinum; an abundant evolution of hydrogen on the platinum then occurs simultaneously with the corrosion of the zinc.

In agreement with Figs. 1 and 2*a*, zinc, in the presence of moderately alkaline solutions of pH between about 8·5 and 10·5, can cover itself with a film of hydroxide. Figure 3, which represents some results obtained by Chatalov [6] concerning the influence of pH on the corrosion rate of zinc,

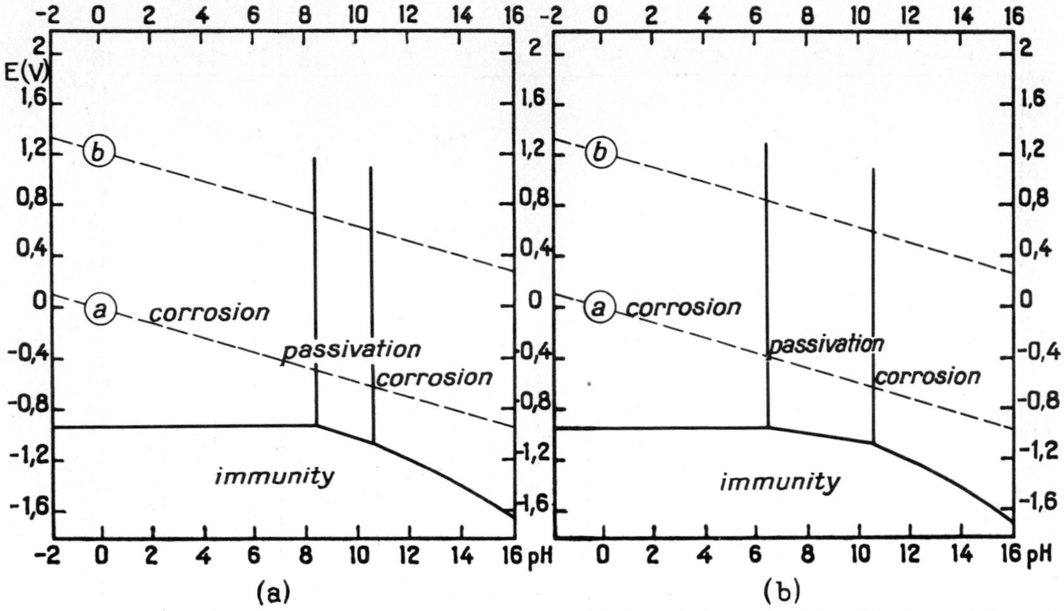

(*a*) Deduced from Fig. 1, for solutions free from CO_2.

(*b*) For solutions containing CO_2 (1 g-mol/l).

FIG. 2. Theoretical conditions of corrosion, immunity and passivation of zinc, at 25°C.

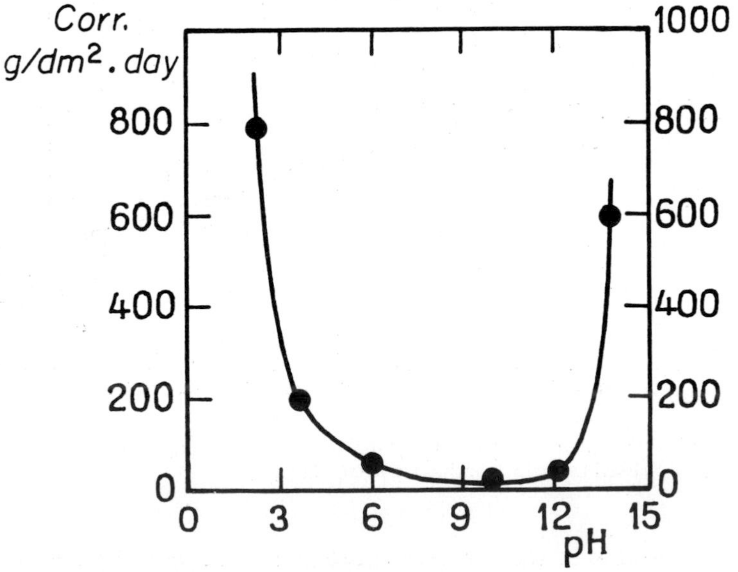

FIG. 3. Influence of pH on the corrosion rate of zinc (Chatalov).

shows that the corrosion rate is actually a minimum at these pH's. Feitknecht [2] observed that various varieties of the hydroxide can be formed when zinc corrodes in aqueous solutions. It seems, although it is not yet certain, that a protective coating of solubility comparable to that of ε-$Zn(OH)_2$, made up of a mixture of zinc oxide and zinc carbonate, is formed when there is an intensive relative movement between zinc and aerated distilled water. These conditions are approximately obtained when, for example, rainwater runs down a steeply inclined zinc roof, and there is a real possibility of passivation in this case [11].

On the other hand, in the case of standing distilled water, local differences of pH inevitably arise, with alkalinization in the "cathodic" zones, where reduction of the dissolved oxygen takes place. In agreement with Fig. 2*a*, this leads to corrosion in the relatively acid anodic zones, with the deposition of more or less passivating zinc hydroxide in the alkaline zones: this results in localized corrosion of the metal.

Depending on the conditions, therefore, zinc may have a good or a poor resistance to relatively pure waters; in general it will be resistant to hard bicarbonate waters, mainly because the presence of bicarbonate has the effect of broadening the domain of passivation shown in Fig. 2*a* at lower pH's; as is shown in Fig. 2*b*, additional passivation is obtained, corresponding to the stability of passivating zinc carbonate.

On account of the large hydrogen overpotential of zinc [7], it is possible to prepare metallic zinc by the reduction of aqueous solutions of zinc salts. As is well known, this reduction is brought about industrially by the electrolysis of acid solutions (buffered with acetic acid and acetates) or alkaline solutions (zincates or cyanide complexes). The reduction can also be carried out chemically, by treating these solutions with powerful reducing agents (e.g. magnesium).

According to Hurd [8], zinc hydride ZnH_2, a non-volatile white solid, can be obtained by the interaction of zinc dimethyl and lithium or aluminium hydride. We were unable to consider this hydride when establishing the equilibrium diagram through lack of thermodynamic data.

3.3. STABILITY AND FORMATION OF THE ZINC OXIDES AND HYDROXIDES

According to Fig. 4, the zinc hydroxides are amphoteric, dissolving in acid solutions to give zincic ions Zn^{++} and in alkaline solutions to give bizincate or zincate ions $HZnO_2^-$ and ZnO_2^{--} [reactions (6), (7) and (8)].

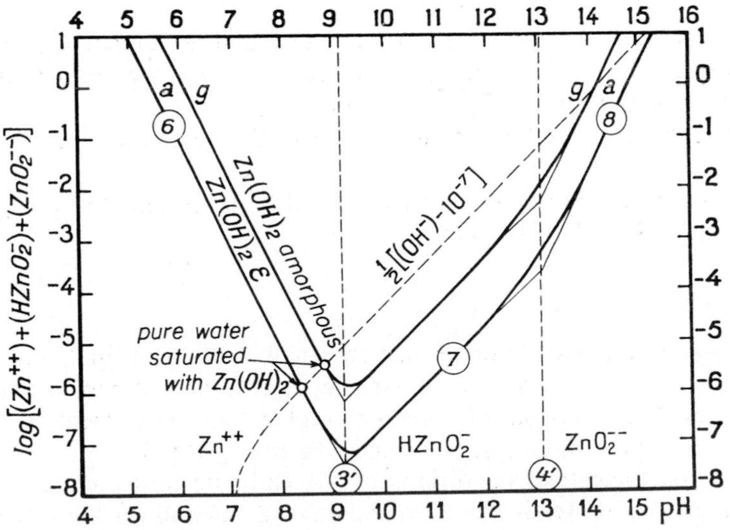

FIG. 4. Influence of pH on the solubility of the zinc hydroxides, at 25°C.

Figure 4 represents the influence of pH on the solubility of ε-$Zn(OH)_2$ and amorphous $Zn(OH)_2$ which are respectively the least soluble and the most soluble of the seven varieties of hydroxide studied by Feitknecht [2], and whose solubility products $(Zn^{++}).(OH^-)^2$ are given below [5]:

(*) ε-$Zn(OH)_2$	$8{\cdot}41 . 10^{-18} = 10^{-17{\cdot}075}$
"inactive" ZnO	$9{\cdot}21 . 10^{-18} = 10^{-17{\cdot}036}$
γ-$Zn(OH)_2$	$1{\cdot}40 . 10^{-17} = 10^{-16{\cdot}854}$
(*) β-$Zn(OH)_2$	$1{\cdot}90 . 10^{-17} = 10^{-16{\cdot}722}$
"active" ZnO	$6{\cdot}86 . 10^{-17} = 10^{-16{\cdot}164}$
(*) α-$Zn(OH)_2$	$1{\cdot}43 . 10^{-16} = 10^{-15{\cdot}845}$
(*) amorphous $Zn(OH)_2$	$1{\cdot}66 . 10^{-16} = 10^{-15{\cdot}780}$

It is in the region between the lines (*a*) and (*g*) that the precipitation and ageing of all the other zinc oxides and hydroxides will take place. According to Fig. 4, these oxides and hydroxides have a minimum solubility at pH = 9·3: this minimum solubility is $10^{-5{\cdot}9}$ g-ion/l (i.e. 0·0822 mg Zn/l) for amorphous $Zn(OH)_2$, and $10^{-7{\cdot}2}$ g-ion/l (i.e. 0·0041 mg Zn/l) for the ε-hydroxide. From Fig. 4, the characteristics of a solution formed by saturating pure water with zinc hydroxide, at 25°C, are as follows:

	Water saturated with amorphous $Zn(OH)_2$	Water saturated with ε-$Zn(OH)_2$
pH	8·85	8·40
$\log(Zn^{++})$	−5·45	−5·90
$(Zn(OH)_2)$(mg/l)	0·353	0·125

According to Feitknecht, zinc α-hydroxide is formed by the incomplete precipitation of a zincic solution at a pH of about 7. The product of the complete precipitation of a solution of a zinc salt by a base is the unstable amorphous hydroxide, resulting from the transformation of the α-$Zn(OH)_2$; the amorphous hydroxide becomes converted into β-hydroxide or oxide, depending on the operating conditions [2] in a slightly alkaline or neutral solution. In very alkaline solutions amorphous $Zn(OH)_2$ is rapidly converted into γ-$Zn(OH)_2$, which has never been observed in the corrosion products. The allotropic β-form can also be obtained directly from a very dilute zincate solution. In agreement with the table of free enthalpies of formation given in paragraph 1, ε-$Zn(OH)_2$ is the most stable compound of the system zinc–water, at 25°C. It is formed by slow separation from a zincate solution.

Zinc oxide appears in various more or less active forms. The most inactive forms are prepared by the high temperature calcination of zinc hydroxide or carbonate. Spontaneous dehydration of the amorphous hydroxide produces the "active" oxide.

A zinc peroxide of composition corresponding to ZnO_2 has been prepared by the action of 1 M NaOH on a solution of zinc hydroxide and hydrogen peroxide, and by the action of concentrated H_2O_2 on an ammoniacal solution of $ZnSO_4$ or $Zn(NO_3)_2$ [5].

For want of thermodynamic data concerning this peroxide, it is marked purely as a rough guide in Fig. 1.

Pierron [9] describes the formation of the oxides $Zn_2O_3 . H_2O$ and $ZnO_2 . H_2O$ at room temperature, and the formation of $Zn_3O_5 . H_2O$ at 60°C.

3.4. REACTIVE ZINC ANODES

On account of its electronegative character and its small "self-corrosion", zinc is a metal which lends itself well to use as a reactive anode for the sacrificial protection of iron and other metals. Pure zinc anodes, when mounted in a favourable medium such as an encasement of gypsum and clay (bentonite), enable current yields of about 90 per cent to be obtained [10].

Figure 5 represents the theoretical conditions of the cathodic protection of iron by means of zinc, respectively for the case of protective zinc hydroxide (Fig. 5*a*) and for the case of non-protective

---

[5] The hydroxides marked (*) were identified by Feitknecht in the corrosion products of zinc.

zinc hydroxide (Fig. 5*b*). The "backfills" employed industrially for the cathodic protection of buried structures by reactive zinc anodes are mainly intended to promote the formation of the non-protective hydroxide; the conditions under which anodes encased in this way are efficient correspond to the chequered zone in Fig. 5.

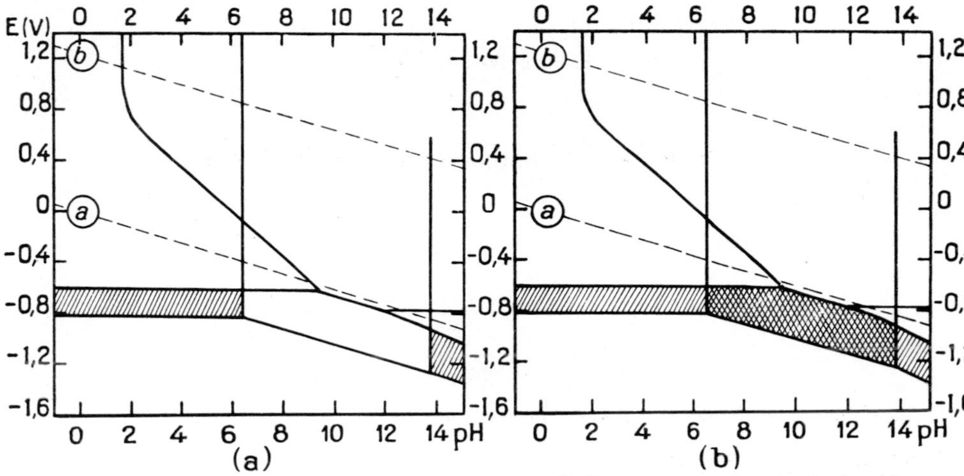

(*a*) For protective zinc hydroxide. (*b*) For non-protective zinc hydroxide.

FIG. 5. Theoretical conditions of cathodic protection of iron by means of zinc (for zinc in contact with a solution containing 0·01 g-ion Zn/l).

It is often used in preference to magnesium, being cheaper. Its use is particularly applicable to those cases in which a good current yield is required without the deterioration of a coating sensitive to alkalis (the general conditions of potential, current and resistivity being satisfied).

4. BIBLIOGRAPHY

[1] P. DELAHAY, M. POURBAIX and P. VAN RYSSELBERGHE, *Diagramme potentiel–pH du zinc. Comportement électrochimique et corrosion du zinc* (C.R. 2ᵉ Réunion du CITCE, Milan, 1950).

[2] W. FEITKNECHT, Principes chimiques et thermochimiques de la corrosion des métaux dans une solution aqueuse, démontrés par l'exemple du zinc, *Métaux et Corrosion*, **23,** 192–203 (1947).

[3] I. M. KOLTHOFF and T. KAMEDA, The hydrolysis of zinc sulphate solutions, solubility product of hydrous zinc oxide and the composition of the latter precipitated from zinc sulfate solutions, *J. Amer. Chem. Soc.* **53,** 832–42 (1931).

[4] G. CHARLOT, *L'analyse qualitative et les réactions en solution,* 4th ed., Masson, Paris, 1957.

[5] *Gmelins Handbuch der anorganischen Chemie, Zink,* S.N.32, Verlag Chemie, G.m.b.H., Weinheim, 1956.

[6] A. YA. CHATALOV, Effet du pH sur le comportement électrochimique des métaux et leur résistance à la corrosion, *Doklad. Akad. Nauk S.S.S.R.* **86,** 775–7 (1952).

[7] A. G. PETCHERSKAIA and V. V. STENDER, Potentiels de dégagement d'hydrogène dans les solutions acides, *J. Fiz. Khim. S.S.S.R.* **24,** 856–9 (1950).

[8] D. T. HURD, *An Introduction to the Chemistry of the Hydrides,* New York, 1952, pp. 196–197.

[9] M. P. PIERRON, Combinaison des hydrates d'oxydes métalliques avec l'eau oxygénée en solution alcaline; influence des produits en résultant sur la stabilisation ou la décomposition de ces solutions, *Bull. Soc. Chim.* **17,** 291–3 (1950).

[10] J. VAN MUYLDER and M. POURBAIX, *Comportement des anodes réactives en magnésium et en zinc* (Rapport technique RT.34 of CEBELCOR, 1956).

[11] M. POURBAIX, Corrosion des toitures en zinc, *Métaux et Corrosion*, **23,** 215–25 (1948).

SECTION 15.2

CADMIUM[1]

E. DELTOMBE, M. POURBAIX and N. DE ZOUBOV

SUMMARY

[1] Shortened and adapted version of the Rapport technique RT.3 of CEBELCOR [1].

1. SUBSTANCES CONSIDERED AND SUBSTANCES NOT CONSIDERED

	Oxidation number (Z)	Considered	Not considered	μ^0(cal.)	Name, colour, crystalline system
Solid substances	−2	−	CdH_2 ?	−	Cadmium hydride, white
	0	Cd	−	0	α-Cadmium, grey, hex.
	"	−	Cd	140	β-Cadmium
	+2	CdO hydr.	−	*a*. −56 440 (²)	"Inactive" cadmium hydroxide $Cd(OH)_2$, white, rhomb.(³)
	"	" "	−	*b*. −55 650 (²)	"Active" cadmium hydroxide $Cd(OH)_2$, white(³)
	"	"	−	*c*. −53 790	Cadmium oxide, brown, cub.
Dissolved substances	+2	Cd^{++}	−	−18 580	Cadmous ion, colourless
	"	$HCdO_2^-$	−	−86 500 (²)	Bicadmite ion, colourless
	"	−	CdO_2^{--}	−	Cadmite ion, colourless
Gaseous substances	−1	*CdH*	−	55 730	Cadmium hydride

2. REACTIONS AND EQUILIBRIUM FORMULAE (⁴)

2.1. TWO DISSOLVED SUBSTANCES

2.1.1. *Relative stability of the dissolved substances*

Z = +2

1. $Cd^{++} + 2H_2O = HCdO_2^- + 3H^+$ $\quad \log\frac{(HCdO_2^-)}{(Cd^{++})} = -33.34 + 3pH$

2.1.2. *Limits of the domains of relative predominance of the dissolved substances*

1'. $Cd^{++}/HCdO_2^-$ $\quad pH = 11.11$

2.2. TWO SOLID SUBSTANCES

Limits of the domains of relative stability of the solid substances

0 → +2

2. $Cd + H_2O = CdO + 2H^+ + 2e^-$
$\quad a.\ E_0 = 0.005 - 0.0591\,pH$
$\quad b.\ \ \ \ \ = 0.023 - 0.0591\,pH$
$\quad c.\ \ \ \ \ = 0.063 - 0.0591\,pH$

2.3. ONE DISSOLVED SUBSTANCE AND ONE SOLID SUBSTANCE

Solubility of the solid substances

Z = +2

3. $Cd^{++} + H_2O = CdO + 2H^+$
$\quad a.\ \log(Cd^{++}) = 13.81 - 2pH$
$\quad b.\ \ \ \ \ \ \ \ \ \ \ \ \ \ \ \ = 14.39 - 2pH$
$\quad c.\ \ \ \ \ \ \ \ \ \ \ \ \ \ \ \ = 15.76 - 2pH$

(²) CdO: Values established by Feitknecht and Reinmann [2].
$HCdO_2^-$: Value calculated from the solubility of $Cd(OH)_2$ in NaOH given by Piater [3].

(³) The value $\mu^0_{CdO} = -56\,440$ cal. corresponds to $\mu^0_{\text{inactive } Cd(OH)_2} = -113\,130$ cal.
The value $\mu^0_{CdO} = -55\,650$ cal. corresponds to $\mu^0_{\text{active } Cd(OH)_2} = -112\,340$ cal.

(⁴) For the reactions involving CdO, the letter *a* refers to "inactive" $Cd(OH)_2$, whose free enthalpy of formation is −113 130 cal.; the letter *b* refers to "active" $Cd(OH)_2$, whose free enthalpy of formation is −112 340 cal.; the letter *c* refers to anhydrous CdO, whose free enthalpy of formation is −53 790 cal.

4. $CdO + H_2O = HCdO_2^- + H^+$ a. $\log(HCdO_2^-) = -19.54 + pH$
b. $= -18.96 + pH$
c. $= -17.59 + pH$

$0 \rightarrow +2$

5. $Cd = Cd^{++} + 2e^-$ $E_0 = -0.403 + 0.0295 \log(Cd^{++})$
6. $Cd + 2H_2O = HCdO_2^- + 3H^+ + 2e^-$ $E_0 = 0.583 - 0.0886\,pH + 0.0295 \log(HCdO_2^-)$

2.4. ONE GASEOUS SUBSTANCE AND ONE SOLID SUBSTANCE

Limits of the domains of relative stability of cadmium and its hydride

$-1 \rightarrow 0$

7. $CdH = Cd + H^+ + e^-$ $E_0 = -2.417 - 0.0591\,pH - 0.0591 \log p_{CdH}$

3. EQUILIBRIUM DIAGRAM AND ITS INTERPRETATION

3.1. ESTABLISHMENT OF THE DIAGRAM

Using formulae (1)–(7) we have constructed Fig. 1, which represents the potential–pH diagram for the stable equilibria of the system cadmium–water, at 25°C; in establishing the diagram we have considered the "inactive" hydroxide $Cd(OH)_2$, which is thermodynamically the most stable form of all the oxides, anhydrous and hydrated, considered in paragraph 1.

Figure 2 shows the theoretical conditions of corrosion, immunity and passivation of cadmium, at 25°C. It is derived from Fig. 1, assuming as a first approximation that corrosion does or does not take place depending on whether the solubility of cadmium or its "inactive" hydroxide is above or below 10^{-6} g-at/l.

Figure 4, established from formulae (1′), (3) and (4), shows the influence of pH on the solubility of the anhydrous and hydrated oxides of cadmium, at 25°C.

These diagrams are valid only in the absence of substances with which cadmium can form soluble complexes or insoluble salts. According to Charlot [4] most anions form complexes with Cd^{++}, e.g. Cl^-, Br^-, I^-, NO_3^-, SO_4^{--} and $S_2O_3^{--}$. Complexes are also formed with NH_3 and HCN. In general cadmium complexes are not very stable. A large number of salts and basic salts of cadmium are sparingly soluble or very sparingly soluble, e.g. the carbonate, the cyanide, the phosphate and the sulphide.

3.2. STABILITY AND CORROSION OF CADMIUM

In Figs. 1 and 2 the upper limit of the domain of stability of cadmium practically coincides with the lower limit of the domain of stability of water at atmospheric pressure. Cadmium can therefore be considered as being at the dividing line between noble and base metals (see p. 80); it is less noble than lead, appreciably more noble than zinc, and slightly more noble than iron.

The electrochemical equilibrium diagram for cadmium (Fig. 1) and the theoretical diagram of corrosion, immunity and passivation (Fig. 2) are, on the whole, fairly similar to the corresponding diagrams for zinc, but incorporate a greater domain of immunity owing to the greater solution potential of cadmium.

The action of aqueous solutions on cadmium will therefore be qualitatively similar to their action on zinc, although cadmium will have a better general resistance to corrosion; this agrees with the observation of Uhlig [5] and Silman [6] that cadmium is less sensitive than zinc to corrosion by both acid and alkaline media.

In accordance with Figs. 1 and 2, cadmium can corrode in acid and very alkaline solutions, but in general corrosion is appreciable only in the presence of oxidizing or complexing substances (e.g. ammonia or cyanides); in the absence of such substances, pure cadmium, like lead and zinc, corrodes only very slightly, on account of the large hydrogen overpotential; for a current density of 1 A/dm^2,

Blum and Hogaboom [7] give the following overpotentials: 0·746 V for zinc, 1·090 V for lead and 1·134 V for cadmium.

In alkaline solutions cadmium can become covered with a film of hydroxide; according to Figs. 1 and 2, the formation of this film should be particularly easy at pH's of about 10–13.

As Huber has shown [8], this hydroxide constitutes a protective layer, when it is obtained by the anodic passivation of the metal, at least. The domain of stability of $Cd(OH)_2$ is therefore a domain

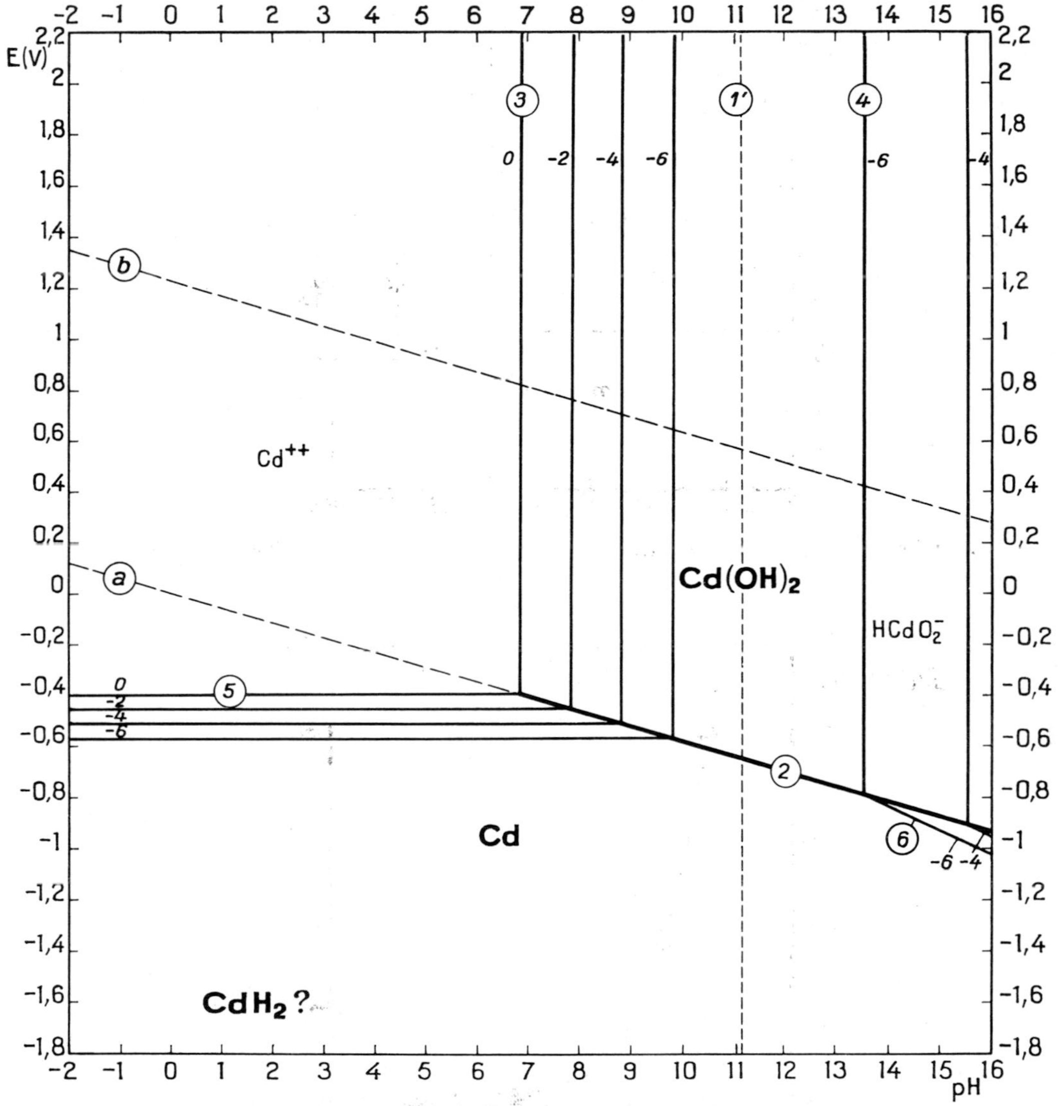

FIG. 1. Potential–pH equilibrium diagram for the system cadmium–water, at 25°C.

of real passivation of the metal; however, like the domain of passivation of zinc it has the disadvantage of being relatively narrow.

Figure 3 represents some experimental results of Chatalov [9] concerning the influence of pH on the corrosion rate of cadmium. These results do not include measurements for very alkaline solutions of pH above 12, which would be useful to verify if the corrosion of cadmium increases at pH's above 13, as would be predicted from Fig. 2.

Figure 2 also shows that in the absence of complexing substances, cadmium can easily be cathodically protected by lowering its electrode potential to below −0·60 V in acid or neutral solutions, i.e. to a potential practically equal to the potential of cathodic protection of iron. In agreement with Figs. 1 and 2, the electro-deposition of cadmium is generally very easily brought about.

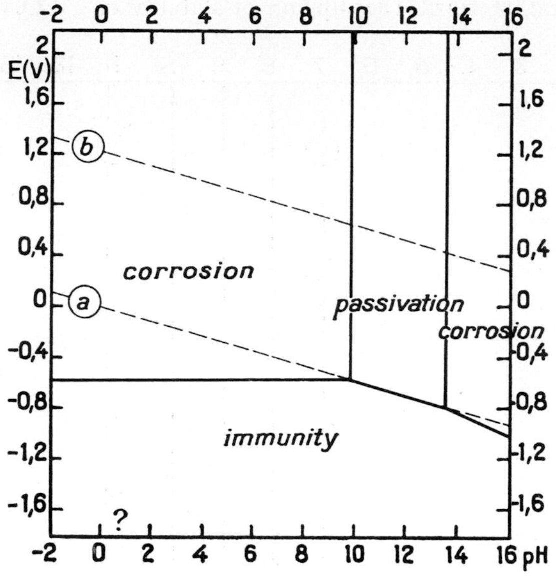

FIG. 2. Theoretical conditions of corrosion, immunity and passivation of cadmium, at 25°C.

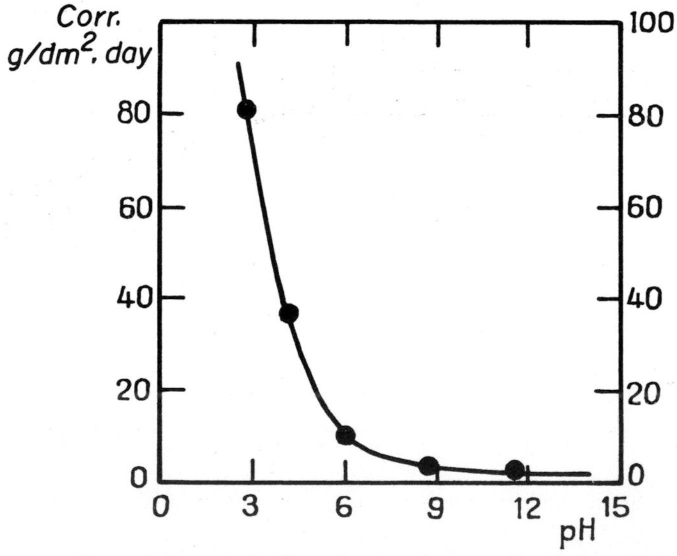

FIG. 3. Influence of pH on the corrosion rate of cadmium (Chatalov).

Hurd [10] mentions the existence of a white solid cadmium hydride, having a formula corresponding approximately to CdH_2, thermodynamically unstable and tending to decompose into hydrogen and cadmium; for want of thermodynamic data we have been able to represent it in Fig. 1 only as a rough guide.

3.3. STABILITY AND FORMATION OF CADMIUM HYDROXIDE

The oxidation of cadmium in acid or neutral media gives rise to the formation of the colourless divalent ion Cd^{++}, which is converted into the white hydroxide $Cd(OH)_2$ on increasing the pH of the solution. Cadmium hydroxide dissolves at high pH's to give the colourless bicadmite ion $HCdO_2^-$ which is the predominant dissolved form of cadmium at pH's above 11·1; it is approximately at this pH that $Cd(OH)_2$ has its minimum solubility. The hydroxide is therefore soluble in both acid and alkaline media; the amphoteric character of this compound has been described by Piater [3].

From Fig. 4, the characteristics of pure water saturated with various varieties of the oxide and hydroxides of cadmium are:

	pH	$\log(Cd^{++})$	mg Cd/l
"inactive" $Cd(OH)_2$	9·40	−4·95	1·26
"active" $Cd(OH)_2$	9·55	−4·75	2·00
anhydrous CdO	10·00	−4·30	5·63

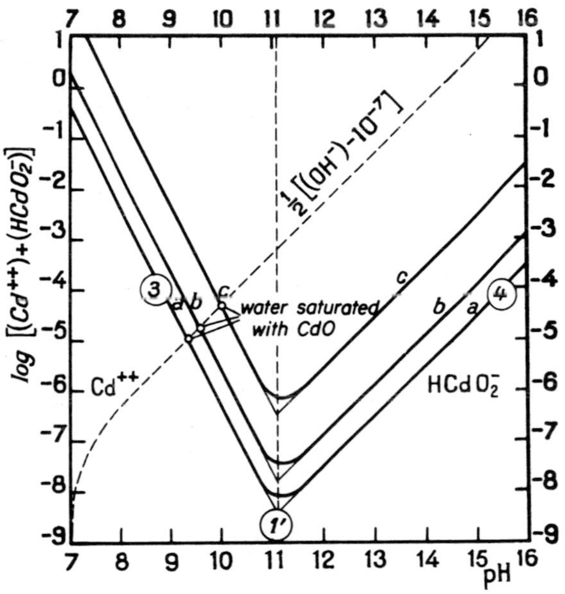

FIG. 4. Influence of pH on the solubility of cadmium, at 25°C.
(*a*, "inactive" $Cd(OH)_2$; *b*, "active" $Cd(OH)_2$; *c*, anhydrous CdO.)

The conversion of metallic cadmium into hydroxide can be effected by oxidation in an alkaline medium. Huber [8] has shown that the passivating film obtained by the anodic polarization of cadmium consists of hydroxide $Cd(OH)_2$; the anhydrous oxide CdO initially formed is unstable in water and becomes converted into "active" $Cd(OH)_2$ which turns into "inactive" $Cd(OH)_2$ by the process of ageing ([2], [8]).

Very alkaline oxidizing solutions should dissolve cadmium to give bicadmite ions $HCdO_2^-$.

4. BIBLIOGRAPHY

[1] E. DELTOMBE and M. POURBAIX, *Comportement électrochimique du cadmium. Diagramme d'équilibres tension–pH du cadmium* (Rapport technique RT.3 of CEBELCOR, 1953).

[2] W. FEITKNECHT and R. REINMANN, *Beitrag zum Potential–pH Diagramm von Cadmium in chloridhaltigen Lösungen* (C.R. 3e Réunion du CITCE, Berne, 1951, pp. 93–101; Manfredi, Milan, 1952).

[3] J. PIATER, Ueber Amphoterie des Cadmiumhydroxydes, *Z. anorg. allgem. Chem.* **174,** 321–41 (1928).

[4] G. CHARLOT, *L'analyse qualitative et les réactions en solution*, 4th ed., Masson, Paris, 1957.
[5] H. H. UHLIG, *The Corrosion Handbook*, Wiley, New York, 1948, p. 837.
[6] H. SILMAN, *Chemical and Electroplated Finishes*, 2nd ed., Chapman & Hall, London, 1952, p. 379.
[7] W. BLUM and G. B. HOGABOOM, *Principles of Electroplating and Electroforming*, McGraw-Hill, New York, 1949, p. 424.
[8] K. HUBER, *Zur Struktur anodisch erzeugter Hydroxyddeckschichten auf Cadmium* (C.R. 3e Réunion du CITCE, Berne, 1951, pp. 117–22; Manfredi, Milan, 1952).
[9] A. YA. CHATALOV, Effet du pH sur le comportement électrochimique des métaux et leur résistance à la corrosion, *Doklad. Akad. Naouk S.S.S.R.* **86**, No. 4, 775–7 (1952).
[10] D. T. HURD, *An Introduction to the Chemistry of the Hydrides*, Wiley, London, New York, 1952, p. 197.

SECTION 15.3

MERCURY (1)

N. DE ZOUBOV and M. POURBAIX

SUMMARY

1. *Substances considered and substances not considered.*

2. *Reactions and equilibrium formulae.*

2.1. Two dissolved substances.

2.1.1. Relative stability of the dissolved substances.

2.1.2. Limits of the domains of relative predominance of the dissolved substances.

2.2. One solid substance and one liquid substance.

Limits of the domains of relative stability of mercury and the oxide HgO.

2.3. One dissolved substance and one solid or liquid substance.

Solubility of mercury and the oxide HgO.

2.4. One gaseous substance and one liquid substance.

Limits of the domains of relative stability of mercury and the hydride HgH.

3. *Equilibrium diagram and its interpretation.*

3.1. Establishment of the diagram.

3.2. Stability and formation of mercury.

3.3. Stability and formation of the mercury oxides.

4. *Bibliography.*

(1) Rapport CEFA/R.6 of the Commission des Études Fondamentales et Applications of CEBELCOR.

1. SUBSTANCES CONSIDERED AND SUBSTANCES NOT CONSIDERED

	Oxidation number (Z)	Considered	Not considered	μ^0 (cal.)	Name, colour, crystalline system
Solid substances	+ 1	-	**Hg_2O** ?	-	Mercurous oxide, brown–black
	+ 2	**HgO**	-	a. −13 990	Mercuric oxide, red, orthorh.(2)
	»	»	-	b. −13 959	Mercuric oxide, yellow, orthorh.(2)
	+ 4	-	**HgO_2**	-	Mercury peroxide, brick red, amorphous
Liquid substance	0	***Hg***	-	0	Mercury, silvery grey
Dissolved substances	+ 1	Hg_2^{++}	-	36 350	Mercurous ion, colourless
	+ 2	Hg^{++}	-	39 380	Mercuric ion, colourless
	»	$Hg(OH)_2$	-	−65 700	Mercuric hydroxide
	»	$HHgO_2^-$	-	−45 420	Mercurate ion
Gaseous substance	− 1	*HgH*	-	52 600	Mercurous hydride

2. REACTIONS AND EQUILIBRIUM FORMULAE (3)

2.1. TWO DISSOLVED SUBSTANCES

2.1.1. *Relative stability of the dissolved substances*

$Z = +2$

1. $Hg^{++} + 2H_2O = Hg(OH)_2 + 2H^+$ $\qquad \log\frac{(Hg(OH)_2)}{(Hg^{++})} = -6.09 + 2\,pH$

2. $Hg(OH)_2 = HHgO_2^- + H^+$ $\qquad \log\frac{(HHgO_2^-)}{(Hg(OH)_2)} = -14.88 + pH$

$+1 \rightarrow +2$

3. $Hg_2^{++} = 2Hg^{++} + 2e^-$ $\qquad E_0 = 0.920 + 0.0295\log\frac{(Hg^{++})^2}{(Hg_2^{++})}$

4. $Hg_2^{++} + 4H_2O = 2Hg(OH)_2 + 4H^+ + 2e^-$ $\qquad E_0 = 1.279 - 0.1182\,pH + 0.0295\log\frac{(Hg(OH)_2)^2}{(Hg_2^{++})}$

5. $Hg_2^{++} + 4H_2O = 2HHgO_2^- + 6H^+ + 2e^-$ $\qquad E_0 = 2.159 - 0.1773\,pH + 0.0295\log\frac{(HHgO_2^-)^2}{(Hg_2^{++})}$

2.1.2. *Limits of the domains of relative predominance of the dissolved substances*

1'. $Hg^{++}/Hg(OH)_2$ $\qquad pH = 3.04$

2'. $Hg(OH)_2/HHgO_2^-$ $\qquad pH = 14.88$

3'. Hg_2^{++}/Hg^{++} $\qquad E_0 = 0.920 + 0.0295\log C$

4'. $Hg_2^{++}/Hg(OH)_2$ $\qquad E_0 = 1.279 - 0.1182\,pH + 0.0295\log C$

5'. $Hg_2^{++}/HHgO_2^-$ $\qquad E_0 = 2.159 - 0.1773\,pH + 0.0295\log C$

3''. Hg_2^{++}/Hg^{++} et **HgO** $\qquad$ a. $E_0 = 1.001 - 0.0591\,pH$
$\qquad$ b. $= 1.002 - 0.0591\,pH$

4''. $Hg_2^{++}/Hg(OH)_2$ et **HgO** $\qquad$ a. $E_0 = 1.180 - 0.1182\,pH$
$\qquad$ b. $= 1.181 - 0.1182\,pH$

---

(2) Bauer and Johnston [1] give the value $\mu^0_{red\ HgO} = -13\,963 \pm 35$ cal. and point out that the question of whether the yellow oxide and the red oxide differ solely in grain size or whether they are allotropic varieties has not yet been settled.

(3) In the reactions involving HgO, the letter *a* refers to red HgO, whose free enthalpy of formation is −13 990 cal.; the letter *b* refers to yellow HgO, whose free enthalpy of formation is −13 959 cal.

4‴. Hg_2^{++} /$Hg(OH)_2$ et **Hg** pH = 4.31

5″. Hg_2^{++} /$HHgO_2^-$ et **HgO** a. $E_0 = 1.620 - 0.1477\,pH$
b. $= 1.621 - 0.1477\,pH$

2.2. ONE SOLID SUBSTANCE AND ONE LIQUID SUBSTANCE

Limits of the domains of relative stability of mercury and the oxide **HgO**

$0 \rightarrow +2$

6. **Hg** $+ H_2O =$ **HgO** $+ 2H^+ + 2e^-$ a. $E_0 = 0.926 - 0.0591\,pH$
b. $= 0.927 - 0.0591\,pH$

2.3. ONE DISSOLVED SUBSTANCE AND ONE SOLID OR LIQUID SUBSTANCE

Solubility of mercury and the oxide **HgO**

a. Solubilities in gram-ions or gram-molecules per litre

$Z = +2$

7. $Hg^{++} + H_2O =$ **HgO** $+ 2H^+$ a. $\log(Hg^{++}) = 2.44 - 2\,pH$
b. $= 2.46 - 2\,pH$

8. **HgO** $+ H_2O = Hg(OH)_2$ a. $\log(Hg(OH)_2) = -3.65$
b. $= -3.63$

9. **HgO** $+ H_2O = HHgO_2^- + H^+$ a. $\log(HHgO_2^-) = -18.53 + pH$
b. $= -18.51 + pH$

$0 \rightarrow +1$

10. 2**Hg** $= Hg_2^{++} + 2e^-$ $E_0 = 0.788 + 0.0295 \log(Hg_2^{++})$

$0 \rightarrow +2$

11. **Hg** $+ 2H_2O = Hg(OH)_2 + 2H^+ + 2e^-$ $E_0 = 1.034 - 0.0591\,pH + 0.0295 \log(Hg(OH)_2)$
12. **Hg** $+ 2H_2O = HHgO_2^- + 3H^+ + 2e^-$ $E_0 = 1.474 - 0.0886\,pH + 0.0295 \log(HHgO_2^-)$

$+1 \rightarrow +2$

13. $Hg_2^{++} + 2H_2O = 2$**HgO** $+ 4H^+ + 2e^-$ a. $E_0 = 1.064 - 0.1182\,pH - 0.0295 \log(Hg_2^{++})$
b. $= 1.065 - 0.1182\,pH - 0.0295 \log(Hg_2^{++})$

b. Solubilities in gram-atoms of mercury per litre

7′. Hg^{++}/**HgO** a. $\log C = 2.44 - 2\,pH$
b. $= 2.46 - 2\,pH$

8′. **HgO**/$Hg(OH)_2$ a. $\log C = -3.65$
b. $= -3.63$

9′. **HgO**/$HHgO_2^-$ a. $\log C = -18.53 + pH$
b. $= -18.51 + pH$

10′. **Hg** /Hg_2^{++} $E_0 = 0.779 + 0.0295 \log C$
11′. **Hg** /$Hg(OH)_2$ $E_0 = 1.034 - 0.0591\,pH + 0.0295 \log C$
12′. **Hg** /$HHgO_2^-$ $E_0 = 1.474 - 0.0886\,pH + 0.0295 \log C$
13′. Hg_2^{++}/**HgO** a. $E_0 = 1.073 - 0.1182\,pH - 0.0295 \log C$
b. $= 1.074 - 0.1182\,pH - 0.0295 \log C$

2.4. ONE GASEOUS SUBSTANCE AND ONE LIQUID SUBSTANCE

Limits of the domains of relative stability of **Hg** *and the hydride HgH*

$-1 \rightarrow 0$

14. *HgH* $=$ **Hg** $+ H^+ + e^-$ $E_0 = -2.281 - 0.0591\,pH - 0.0591 \log p_{HgH}$

3. EQUILIBRIUM DIAGRAM AND ITS INTERPRETATION

2.1. ESTABLISHMENT OF THE DIAGRAM

Figure 1 represents the domains of relative predominance of mercury in the four dissolved forms Hg_2^{++}, Hg^{++}, $Hg(OH)_{2\ aq.}$ and $HHgO_2^-$; for the diatomic Hg_2^{++} ions, whose domain of predominance varies with the concentration of dissolved mercury, we have drawn the limits of this domain for four dissolved mercury concentrations, of respectively 10^{-6}, 10^{-4}, 10^{-2} and 10^{0} g-at/l [equations (3′), (4′) and (5′)].

Figure 2 represents the stable equilibria of the system mercury–water for various total dissolved mercury concentrations, of respectively 10^{-6}, 10^{-4}, 10^{-2} and 10^{0} g-ion/l (i.e. respectively 0·2, 20, 2 006 and 200 600 mg Hg/l)(4).

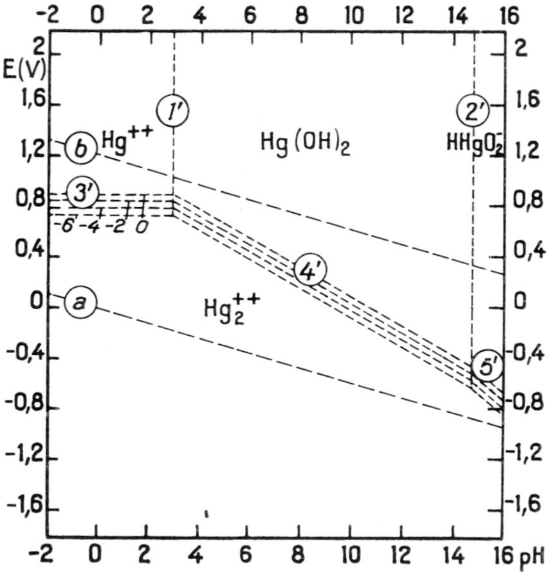

FIG. 1. Domains of relative predominance of the dissolved substances for various mercury concentrations, at 25°C.

Figure 2 was obtained by superimposing on to Fig. 1 lines (6) and (14) (which separate the domains of stability of the metal, solid red HgO and gaseous HgH) and the lines (7′)–(13′) (which represent the solubilities of each of these substances in all the dissolved forms). In the case of mercury dissolved in the diatomic form Hg_2^{++}, the limits of predominance represented in Fig. 2 refer to solutions saturated with Hg or HgO in the case of concentrations below 1 g-at Hg/l (lines 3″, 4″ and 4‴) and to solutions containing 1 g-at Hg/l for the regions of the diagram in which the saturation concentration of HgO is above 1 g-at/l (line 3′).(4)

Figure 3 shows the influence of pH on the solubility of red mercuric oxide, in its three dissolved forms Hg^{++}, $Hg(OH)_{2\ aq.}$ and $HHgO_2^-$.

Figures 1–3 are valid only in the absence of substances with which mercury can form soluble complexes or insoluble salts. The mercuric cation Hg^{++} forms a large number of complexes which

(4) These lines refer only to ideal solutions, whose concentrations are equal to their activities.

are often quite stable: $HgCl_2$, hydrobromic complexes, hydriodic complexes (in particular HgI_4^{--}), thiocyanic complexes up to $Hg(SCN)_4^{--}$, hydrocyanic complexes: $Hg(CN)_2$ and $Hg(CN)_4^{--}$; ammine complexes (not very stable), sulphurous complexes and thiosulphuric complexes.

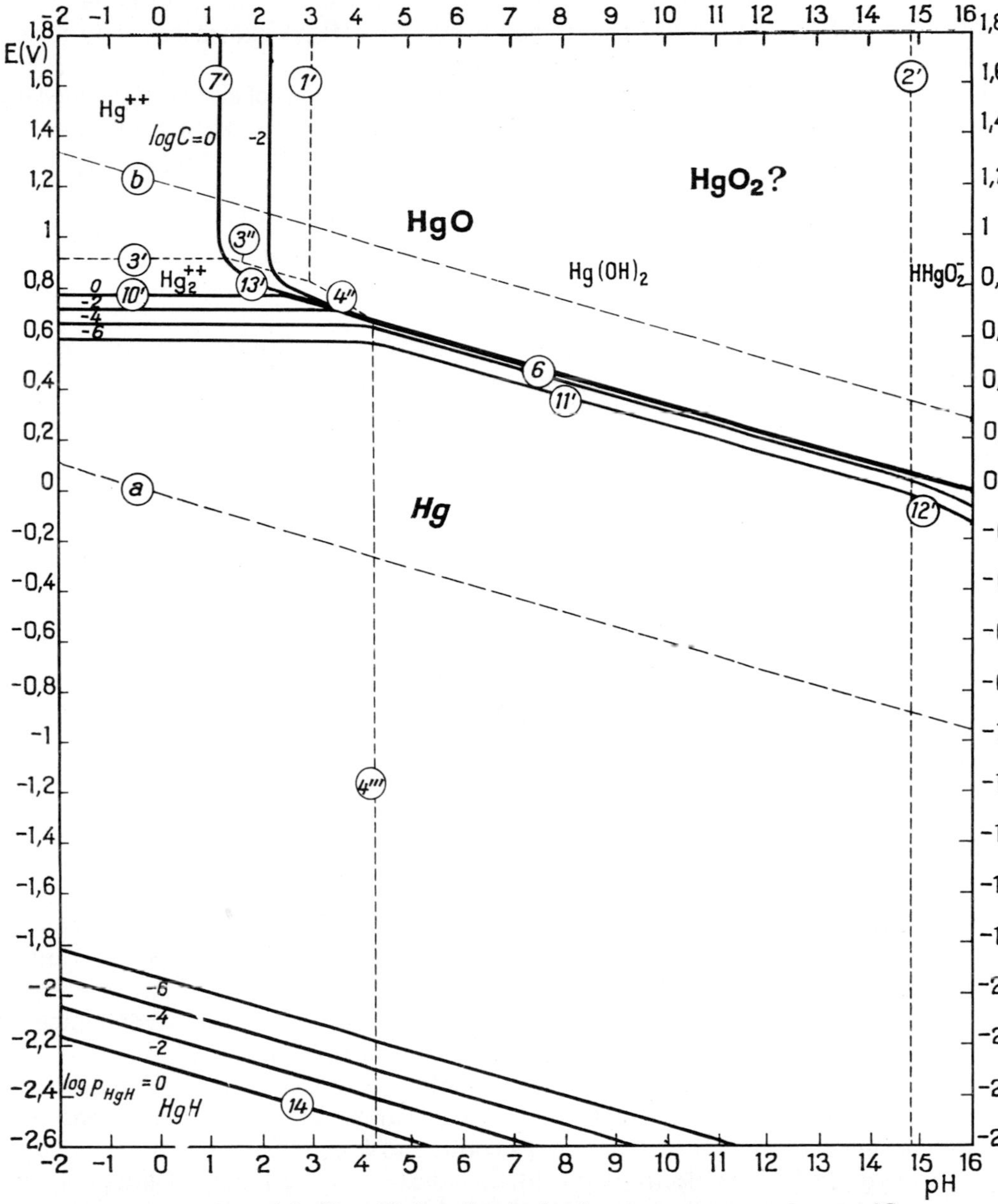

FIG. 2. Potential–pH equilibrium diagram for the system mercury–water, at 25°C.
The part of the diagram inside the line log C = 0 refers to solutions saturated with mercury or red HgO; the part outside this line concerns non-saturated solutions containing 1 g-at of dissolved mercury per litre (200 g/l?) in the form of Hg_2^{++} and Hg^{++}

The following compounds of monovalent mercury are sparingly soluble: the halides (white or yellow), the chromate (red), the iodide (green), the sulphide (black); the other salts are white. Divalent mercury forms the following sparingly soluble compounds: HgI_2 (red), $Hg(SCN)_2$ (white), HgS (usually black, but a red form can be obtained by a dry process) which is insoluble in ammonium sulphide and slightly soluble in the presence of excess sodium sulphide to give HgS_2^{--} [2].

3.2. STABILITY AND FORMATION OF MERCURY

According to Fig. 2, mercury is a very noble metal, as its domain of thermodynamic stability has a large area in common with the domain of thermodynamic stability of water. In nature elementary mercury is encountered in drops, mainly in seams of cinnabar (HgS) and more rarely in measures not containing cinnabar, the essential source of mercury.

Mercury is practically unaffected by non-oxidizing aqueous solutions of all pH's, provided that they are free from complexing substances (notably ammonia and ammonium salts): e.g. dilute solutions of sulphuric and hydrochloric acid free from oxygen, caustic soda solutions free from oxygen. Mercury reduces concentrated sulphuric acid to H_2S and sulphur.

In acid solutions of pH below about 3 or 4, a relatively slight oxidizing action causes the metal to dissolve in the mercurous state (at electrode potentials between about +0·6 and +0·9 V); a more vigorous oxidizing action (at electrode potentials above about +0·9 V) causes it to dissolve in the

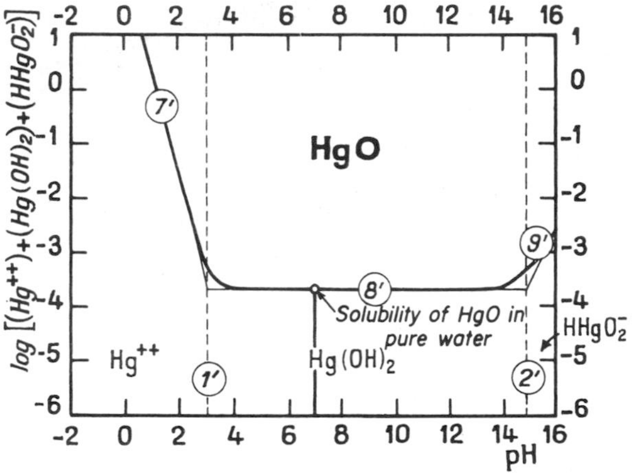

FIG. 3. Influence of pH on the solubility of red HgO, at 25°C.

mercuric state. In neutral or alkaline solutions the metal is oxidized directly to the mercuric state, with the formation of relatively soluble HgO. For example, mercury is dissolved by nitric acid at 25°C to give mercurous nitrite; it is dissolved by acid solutions of ferric chloride and vanadic acid; it becomes covered with HgO in the presence of water and alkaline solutions containing oxygen; the formation of HgO is very rapid in the presence of ozone or permanganate.

The large hydrogen overpotential of mercury enables many electrochemical reductions to be brought about by using the metal as a cathode (in particular the electrolysis operations performed in polarography using a mercury-drop cathode). According to Fig. 2, mercury can be reduced to the unstable gaseous hydride HgH at electrode potentials indicated by the family of lines (14). We have not been able to find any information about this hydride, except for a reference to it by Hurd [3], who describes the transient formation of HgH when an electric discharge takes place in a tube containing mercury vapour and hydrogen.

In agreement with Fig. 2, mercury can easily be obtained by reducing solutions of its salts; a large number of metals (including copper) may be used as reducing agents, as may stannous salts, ferrous salts, etc.

With many metals mercury forms amalgams, some of which have reducing properties which have acquired a large number of analytical applications (e.g. amalgams of sodium, zinc, bismuth, aluminium and lead).

3.3. STABILITY AND FORMATION OF THE MERCURY OXIDES

It will be recalled that it is not yet known whether the red and yellow varieties of mercuric oxide are two allotropic forms of HgO, or whether they differ solely in grain size.

As shown above, HgO can be prepared by the oxidation of mercury. In agreement with Fig. 2, it can also be obtained by the alkalinization of mercuric solutions of Hg^{++} ions, or mercurous solutions of Hg_2^{++} ions. In the latter case, HgO and metallic Hg are formed simultaneously by the disproportionation of the Hg_2^{++} ions according to the reactions

$$Hg_2^{++} + 2H_2O \rightarrow 2HgO + 4H^+ + 2e^- \quad (13)$$

and

$$Hg_2^{++} + 2e^- \rightarrow 2Hg \quad (10)$$

overall reaction

$$2Hg_2^{++} + 2H_2O \rightarrow 2HgO + 2Hg + 4H^+$$

In agreement with Fig. 3, HgO is an amphoteric oxide, slightly soluble in water ($10^{-3.62}$ g-at Hg/l for the red variety, i.e. 51·5 mg HgO/l) [4] and very soluble in very acid solutions. Mercuric oxide can be used to bring about certain oxidations, at potentials indicated by line (6) in Fig. 2, in which case it is reduced to mercury; it oxidizes hydrogen peroxide to oxygen, sulphurous acid to sulphuric acid, phosphorous and hypophosphorous acids to phosphoric acid; it also oxidizes hydroxylamine and hydrazine.

Mercurous oxide is unknown: the brown–black Hg_2O quoted in the literature appears in fact to be a mixture of Hg and HgO.

Owing to a lack of thermodynamic data, the peroxide HgO_2 was not considered in the establishment of the equilibrium diagram. It has been prepared and studied by Anthropoff and Pellini [5]. It is formed during the catalytic decomposition of hydrogen peroxide in the presence of mercury, at room temperature. HgO_2 is a brick-red powder which is very unstable and decomposes to give HgO and O_2 in the presence of moisture; when absolutely dry it does not decompose immediately. HgO_2 has the general properties of peroxides: it decolorizes $KMnO_4$ solution and liberates iodine from iodide solutions. Acids dissolve the peroxide to give mercuric salts and hydrogen peroxide.

4. BIBLIOGRAPHY

[1] T. W. BAUER and H. L. JOHNSTON, Low temperature heat capacities of inorganic solids. XV. The heat capacity and entropy of red mercuric oxide, *J. Amer. Chem. Soc.* **75**, 2217–19 (1953).

[2] G. CHARLOT, *L'analyse qualitative et les réactions en solution*, 4th ed., Masson, Paris, 1957, pp. 234–7.

[3] D. T. HURD, *An Introduction to the Chemistry of the Hydrides*, Wiley, New York, 1952, pp. 197–8.

[4] H. U. VON VOGEL, *Chemiker-Kalender*, Springer-Verlag, Berlin–Göttingen–Heidelberg, 1956, p. 118.

[5] P. PASCAL, *Traité de Chimie minérale*, Vol. VIII (*Mercure*), Masson, Paris, 1933.

SECTION 16.1

GALLIUM(1)

C. VANLEUGENHAGHE, N. DE ZOUBOV and M. POURBAIX

SUMMARY

(1) Rapport technique RT.74 of CEBELCOR (August 1958).

1. SUBSTANCES CONSIDERED AND SUBSTANCES NOT CONSIDERED

	Oxidation number (Z)	Considered	Not considered	μ^0 (cal.)	Name, colour, crystalline system
Solid substances	0	**Ga**	–	0	Gallium, grey–white, rhomb.
	+1	**Ga_2O**	–	– 75 200	Sub-oxide, brown–black
	+2	–	**GaO**	–	Gallous oxide, grey
	+3	–	**Ga_2O_3** anh.	–	β-Sesquioxide, white, monocl. or orthorh.
	»	**Ga_2O_3** anh.	–	a. –237 200	α-Sesquioxide, white, rhomb.
	»	» hydr.	–	b. –227 930	Trihydrated oxide or hydroxide $Ga(OH)_3$, white
	»	–	**Ga_2O_3** hydr.	–	Hydrated oxide ($Ga_2O_3 . H_2O$ or GaO . OH)
	»	–	» »	–	Hydrated oxide ($Ga_2O_3 . 2H_2O$)
	»	–	» »	–	Hydrated oxide ($3Ga_2O_3 . 5H_2O$)
Liquid substances	–3	–	***GaH_3***	–	Hydride, colourless
	»	–	***Ga_2H_6***	–	Hydride, colourless
	–1	–	***GaH***	–	Hydride
Dissolved substances	+2	Ga^{++}	–	– 21 000	Gallous ion, colourless
	+3	Ga^{+++}	–	– 36 600	Gallic ion, colourless
	»	$GaOH^{++}$	–	– 89 800	Gallyl ion, colourless
	»	GaO^{+}	–	– 85 400 (2)	Gallyl ion, colourless
	»	GaO_2^{-}	–	–121 300	Gallate ion, colourless
	»	$HGaO_3^{--}$	–	–164 000	Bigallate ion, colourless
	»	GaO_3^{---}	–	–148 000	Gallate ion, colourless

2. REACTIONS AND EQUILIBRIUM FORMULAE (3)

2.1. Two dissolved substances

2.1.1. *Relative stability of the dissolved substances*

Z = +3

1. $Ga^{+++} + H_2O = GaOH^{++} + H^+$ $\qquad \log\frac{(GaOH^{++})}{(Ga^{+++})} = -2.56 + pH$

2. $GaOH^{++} = GaO^+ + H^+$ $\qquad \log\frac{(GaO^+)}{(GaOH^{++})} = -3.20 + pH$

3. $GaO^+ + H_2O = GaO_2^- + 2H^+$ $\qquad \log\frac{(GaO_2^-)}{(GaO^+)} = -15.25 + 2\,pH$

4. $GaO_2^- + H_2O = HGaO_3^{--} + H^+$ $\qquad \log\frac{(HGaO_3^{--})}{(GaO_2^-)} = -10.27 + pH$

5. $HGaO_3^{--} = GaO_3^{---} + H^+$ $\qquad \log\frac{(GaO_3^{---})}{(HGaO_3^{--})} = -11.74 + pH$

+2 → +3

6. $Ga^{++} = Ga^{+++} + e^-$ $\qquad E_0 = -0.677 + 0.0591 \log\frac{(Ga^{+++})}{(Ga^{++})}$

7. $Ga^{++} + H_2O = GaOH^{++} + H^+ + e^-$ $\qquad E_0 = -0.525 - 0.0591\,pH + 0.0591 \log\frac{(GaOH^{++})}{(Ga^{++})}$

8. $Ga^{++} + H_2O = GaO^+ + 2H^+ + e^-$ $\qquad E_0 = -0.334 - 0.1182\,pH + 0.0591 \log\frac{(GaO^+)}{(Ga^{++})}$

---

(2) Value calculated from the equilibrium constant $K = 10^{-3.2}$ of the reaction $GaOH^{++} = GaO^+ + H^+$ (Charlot [8]).

(3) For the equilibrium involving Ga_2O_3, the values marked *a* refer to anhydrous Ga_2O_3 and the values marked *b* refer to $Ga_2O_3 . 3H_2O$ [or $Ga(OH)_3$]. The value –227 *930* cal. assumed for the free enthalpy of formation of Ga_2O_3 in the hydrated form corresponds to $\mu^0_{Ga_2O_3 \cdot 3H_2O} = -398\ 000$ cal. and $\mu^0_{Ga(OH)_3} = -199\ 000$ cal.

9. $Ga^{++} + 2H_2O = GaO_2^- + 4H^+ + e^-$ $E_0 = 0.567 - 0.2364\,pH + 0.0591 \log \frac{(GaO_2^-)}{(Ga^{++})}$

10. $Ga^{++} + 3H_2O = HGaO_3^{--} + 5H^+ + e^-$ $E_0 = 1.174 - 0.2955\,pH + 0.0591 \log \frac{(HGaO_3^{--})}{(Ga^{++})}$

11. $Ga^{++} + 3H_2O = GaO_3^{---} + 6H^+ + e^-$ $E_0 = 1.868 - 0.3546\,pH + 0.0591 \log \frac{(GaO_3^{---})}{(Ga^{++})}$

2.1.2. *Limits of the domains of relative predominance of the dissolved substances*

1'.	$Ga^{+++}/GaOH^{++}$	pH = 2.56
2'.	$GaOH^{++}/GaO^+$	pH = 3.20
3'.	GaO^+/GaO_2^-	pH = 7.62
4'.	$GaO_2^-/HGaO_3^{--}$	pH = 10.27
5'.	$HGaO_3^{--}/GaO_3^{---}$	pH = 11.74
6'.	Ga^{++}/Ga^{+++}	$E_0 = -0.677$
7'.	$Ga^{++}/GaOH^{++}$	$E_0 = -0.525 - 0.0591\,pH$
8'.	Ga^{++}/GaO^+	$E_0 = -0.334 - 0.1182\,pH$
9'.	Ga^{++}/GaO_2^-	$E_0 = 0.567 - 0.2364\,pH$
10'.	$Ga^{++}/HGaO_3^{--}$	$E_0 = 1.174 - 0.2955\,pH$
11'.	Ga^{++}/GaO_3^{---}	$E_0 = 1.868 - 0.3546\,pH$

2.2. TWO SOLID SUBSTANCES

Limits of the domains of relative stability of gallium and its oxides

$0 \rightarrow +1$

12. $2\mathbf{Ga} + H_2O = \mathbf{Ga_2O} + 2H^+ + 2e^-$ $E_0 = -0.401 - 0.0591\,pH$

$0 \rightarrow +3$

13. $2\mathbf{Ga} + 3H_2O = \mathbf{Ga_2O_3} + 6H^+ + 6e^-$ a. $E_0 = -0.485 - 0.0591\,pH$
b. $= -0.419 - 0.0591\,pH$

$+1 \rightarrow +3$

14. $\mathbf{Ga_2O} + 2H_2O = \mathbf{Ga_2O_3} + 4H^+ + 4e^-$ a. $E_0 = -0.527 - 0.0591\,pH$
b. $= -0.428 - 0.0591\,pH$

2.3. ONE SOLID SUBSTANCE AND ONE DISSOLVED SUBSTANCE

Solubility of gallium and its oxides

$Z = +3$

15. $2Ga^{+++} + 3H_2O = \mathbf{Ga_2O_3} + 6H^+$ a. $\log(Ga^{+++}) = 2.23 - 3\,pH$
b. $= 5.60 - 3\,pH$

16. $2GaOH^{++} + H_2O = \mathbf{Ga_2O_3} + 4H^+$ a. $\log(GaOH^{++}) = -0.33 - 2\,pH$
b. $= 3.04 - 2\,pH$

17. $2GaO^+ + H_2O = \mathbf{Ga_2O_3} + 2H^+$ a. $\log(GaO^+) = -3.56 - pH$
b. $= -0.19 - pH$

18. $\mathbf{Ga_2O_3} + H_2O = 2GaO_2^- + 2H^+$ a. $\log(GaO_2^-) = -18.81 + pH$
b. $= -15.44 + pH$

19. $\mathbf{Ga_2O_3} + 3H_2O = 2HGaO_3^{--} + 4H^+$ a. $\log(HGaO_3^{--}) = -29.08 + 2\,pH$
b. $= -25.70 + 2\,pH$

20. $\mathbf{Ga_2O_3} + 3H_2O = 2GaO_3^{---} + 6H^+$ a. $\log(GaO_3^{---}) = -40.81 + 3\,pH$
b. $= -37.44 + 3\,pH$

$0 \rightarrow +3$

21. $\mathbf{Ga} = Ga^{+++} + 3e^-$ $E_0 = -0.529 + 0.0197 \log(Ga^{+++})$

22. $\mathbf{Ga} + H_2O = GaOH^{++} + H^+ + 3e^-$ $E_0 = -0.479 - 0.0197\,pH + 0.0197 \log(GaOH^{++})$

23. $\mathbf{Ga} + H_2O = GaO^+ + 2H^+ + 3e^-$ $E_0 = -0.415 - 0.0394\,pH + 0.0197 \log(GaO^+)$

24. $\mathbf{Ga} + 2H_2O = GaO_2^- + 4H^+ + 3e^-$ $E_0 = -0.114 - 0.0788\,pH + 0.0197 \log(GaO_2^-)$

25. $\mathbf{Ga} + 3H_2O = HGaO_3^{--} + 5H^+ + 3e^-$ $E_0 = 0.088 - 0.0985\,pH + 0.0197 \log(HGaO_3^{--})$

26. $\mathbf{Ga} + 3H_2O = GaO_3^{---} + 6H^+ + 3e^-$ $E_0 = 0.319 - 0.1182\,pH + 0.0197 \log(GaO_3^{---})$

3. EQUILIBRIUM DIAGRAM AND ITS INTERPRETATION

3.1. ESTABLISHMENT OF THE DIAGRAM

Using formulae (1)–(26) we have constructed Fig. 1, which is a potential–pH equilibrium diagram for the system gallium–water, at 25°C. As we do not have adequate thermodynamic data for the oxides GaO ([2], [3]), β-Ga_2O_3, $Ga_2O_3 . H_2O$ [4], $Ga_2O_3 . 2H_2O$ and $3Ga_2O_3 . 5H_2O$ [5], or for the hydrides GaH_3 and Ga_2H_6 [6] and GaH [7], we have not taken these substances into account when establishing the equilibrium diagram.

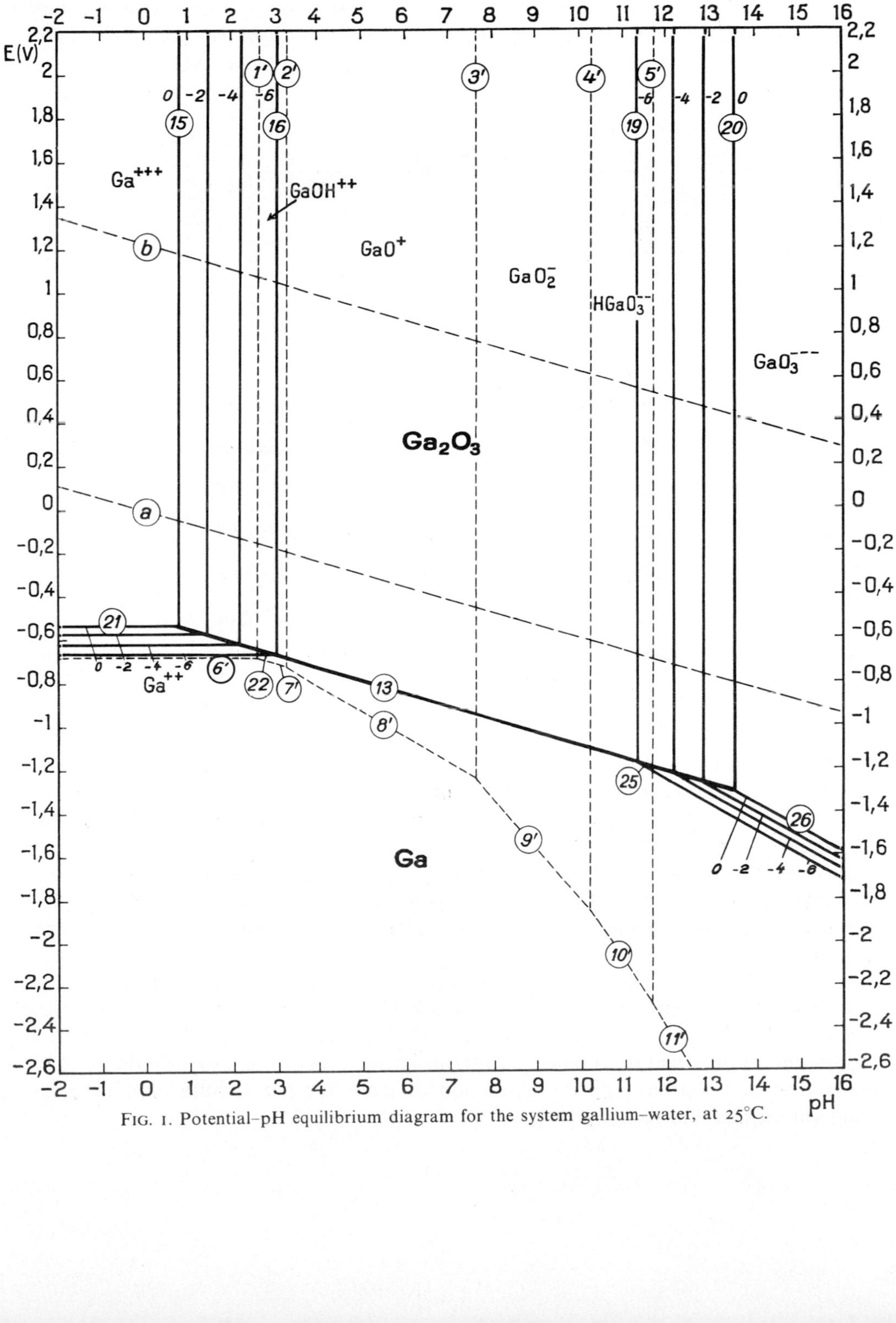

FIG. 1. Potential–pH equilibrium diagram for the system gallium–water, at 25°C.

In the diagram we have considered only the more stable of the two forms of sesquioxide given in paragraph 1, i.e. anhydrous α-Ga_2O_3. The diagram is, of course, valid only in the absence of substances with which gallium can form soluble complexes or insoluble compounds. Gallium forms the same complexes as aluminium [8]; the complexes formed with organic acids and hydroxyacids are, however, more stable than those formed by aluminium [9]. As sparingly soluble compounds, Charlot [8] mentions the ferrocyanide and the sulphide.

3.2. STABILITY, CORROSION AND ELECTRO-DEPOSITION OF GALLIUM

Figure 2, derived from Fig. 1, represents the theoretical conditions of corrosion, immunity and passivation of gallium, at 25°C, in the absence of substances with which gallium can form soluble complexes or insoluble salts. The diagram assumes the possibility of passivation by the formation of a layer of α-Ga_2O_3.

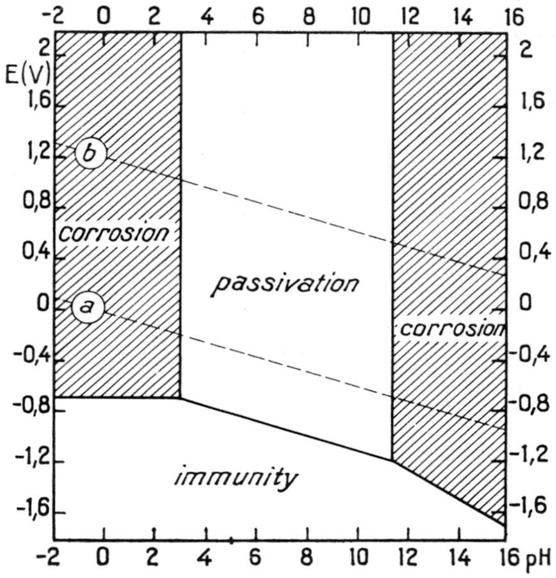

FIG. 2. Theoretical conditions of corrosion, immunity and passivation of gallium, at 25°C, assuming passivation by a film of α-Ga_2O_3.

From Figs. 1 and 2 gallium appears to be a base metal, but considerably less reactive than aluminium. In agreement with these diagrams, gallium becomes covered with a film of oxide in the presence of water; the protectivity of this film does not appear to be perfect, however: although the metal is completely unaffected by water free from air, even when boiling, it is tarnished by water containing oxygen [9]. Gallium is hardly attacked by slightly acid or slightly alkaline solutions which are non-complexing; it is appreciably attacked, possibly with the evolution of hydrogen, by very acid solutions (nitric acid, hydrofluoric acid, sulphuric acid) and very alkaline solutions (caustic soda or potash).

In agreement with Fig. 1, gallium can be electro-deposited from sufficiently acid or sufficiently alkaline solutions; for instance one can employ an alkaline solution of gallate (Lecoq de Boisbaudran [10], Hoffman [11]) or an acid solution of sulphate (Dennis and Bridgman [12], Richards and Boyer [13]). The aluminium obtained from bauxite contains about 0·02 per cent of gallium. A recent method due to de la Brétègue recommends the extraction of gallium from sodium aluminate solutions by electrolysing with a mercury cathode [14].

3.3. STABILITY OF THE GALLIUM OXIDES AND HYDROXIDE

As was mentioned in paragraph 1, the only oxides taken into account in the establishment of Fig. 1 were Ga_2O and anhydrous Ga_2O_3 and its trihydrate $Ga_2O_3 . 3H_2O$.

According to the free enthalpy values assumed here, the oxide Ga_2O is unstable with respect to Ga and Ga_2O_3, and therefore tends to decompose into a mixture of these two substances according to the electrochemical reactions (12) and (14), i.e. according to the overall chemical reaction $3Ga_2O \rightarrow 4Ga + Ga_2O_3$. Ga_2O does not therefore appear on the equilibrium diagram. The existence of Ga_2O is, in fact, uncertain: Brukl and Ortner [2] obtained a brown solid of composition Ga_2O by heating the "sesquioxide" Ga_2O_3 with gallium, but Klemm and Schnick [15] showed that the oxide thus prepared, whose composition is intermediate between that of GaO and that of Ga_2O, does not produce any new lines on the X-ray diagram; from thermal measurements they conclude that the oxide so prepared is merely a mixture of Ga and Ga_2O_3. According to Sidgwick [3], monovalent gallium does not exist.

For want of thermodynamic data we have not considered an oxide of divalent gallium, GaO, whose existence has not been sufficiently proved [2], and which would be oxidized by water [3]. There is little proof of the existence of compounds of divalent gallium other than the halogen compounds [24], and possibly the sulphide, although a reducing solution containing Ga^{++} ions, or possibly a gallous complex, can be prepared [3]. It is probably that divalent gallous compounds disproportionate, on being ionized, into metallic gallium and trivalent gallic ions.

The *sesquioxide* Ga_2O_3 exists in numerous varieties, and appears to behave in a similar manner to Al_2O_3 [16]. The β-form [17], most probably monotropic [18], appears to be the form which is thermodynamically stable at all temperatures; it crystallizes in the monoclinic and orthorhombic systems and is insoluble in mineral acids, both dilute and concentrated [18], while the α-form, which crystallizes in the hexagonal or rhombohedral systems, reacts slowly with dilute mineral acids ([18], [19]). A γ-form also exists [20]; Roy *et al.* have even found two more forms which they call δ and ε [17]. Latimer does not state the precise allotropic form to which he has attributed the free enthalpy of formation $-237{\cdot}2$ kcal; it most probably is the rhombohedral or ternary variety (α-Ga_2O_3) of which the enthalpy of formation ΔH_{20^0} was found to be $257^{\pm}$ 1 kcal. by Klemm and Schnick [15] and was used in calculating the value of $\mu^0_{Ga_2O_3}$ adopted here.

Ga_2O_3 forms several *hydrates*. For want of thermodynamic data we have been able to consider only the trihydrate $Ga_2O_3 . 3H_2O$. According to the free enthalpies assumed here, the trihydrate is less stable than anhydrous Ga_2O_3, into which it tends to be converted with an affinity of about $237-228 = 9$ kcal. In the establishment of Fig. 1 we have considered only the more stable of these two forms, i.e. anhydrous Ga_2O_3.

The monohydrated oxide $Ga_2O_3 . H_2O$, or GaO . OH, has a structure comparable to that of the diaspore AlO . OH [4]. Neogi and Nandi speak of a dihydrated oxide $Ga_2O_3 . 2H_2O$ [5]. In agreement with what has just been said, Sidgwick [3] considers that the trihydrate $Ga_2O_3 . 3H_2O$ [or hydroxide $Ga(OH)_3$] is metastable; according to Milligan and Weiser [21], the di- and trihydrates are merely mixtures of the monohydrate GaO . OH and highly hydrated oxides. According to Roy [17], if one adds alkali to a solution of a gallium salt, a gel is formed first of all; this gel is a slightly crystallized gallium–water complex, which crystallizes on ageing to form either the monohydrate GaO . OH or, directly, an anhydrous oxide α-Ga_2O_3 or γ-Ga_2O_3 (see also [21] and [22]). At room temperature the only stable hydrate appears to be GaO . OH, which is converted into β-Ga_2O_3 on heating to 300°C ([17], [23]). For want of thermodynamic data we were not able to consider the monohydrate GaO . OH.

Figure 3 indicates, according to equilibrium formulae (15)–(20), the influence of pH on the solubility of α-Ga_2O_3 and $Ga_2O_3 . 3H_2O$ [or $Ga(OH)_3$], which, like the oxides and hydroxides of aluminium, are amphoteric. Also shown in this diagram are some experimental values of the solubility of $Ga(OH)_3$ given by Charlot [8] and Fricke and Blencke [25]; the theoretical characteristics of the solutions obtained by saturating pure water with $Ga(OH)_3$ or α-Ga_2O_3 are also given. The disagreement between the theoretical values and the experimental values most probably results from the uncertainty concerning the state of development of the anhydrous or hydrated Ga_2O_3 considered. Figure 4

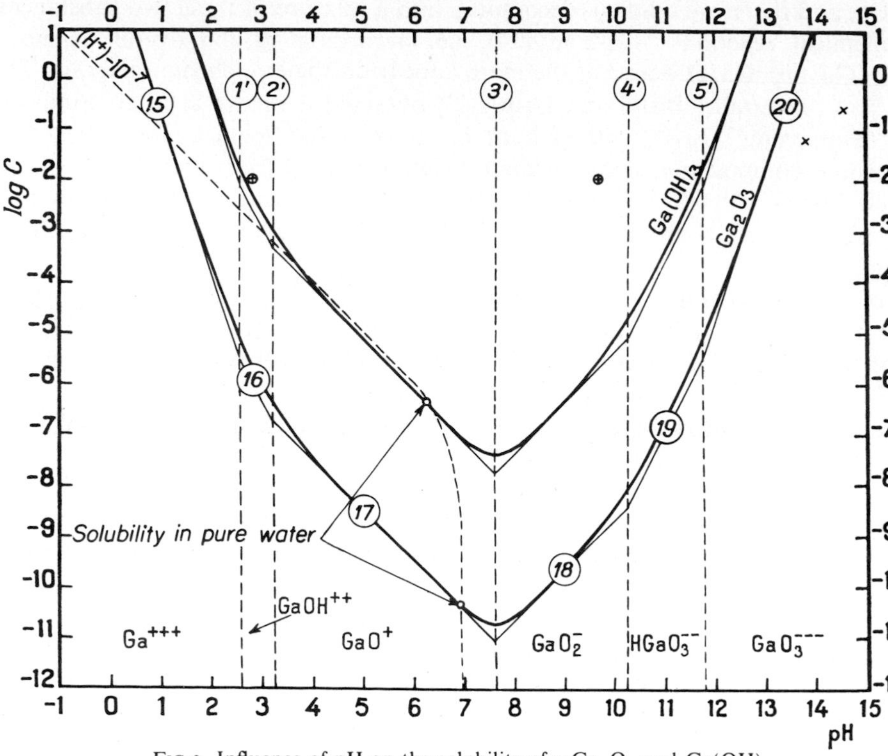

FIG. 3. Influence of pH on the solubility of α-Ga_2O_3 and $Ga(OH)_3$. (Approximate diagram.)
C represents the concentration of gallium in solution in all its dissolved forms (g-at Ga/l).
⊕ Charlot [8]; × Fricke and Blencke [25].

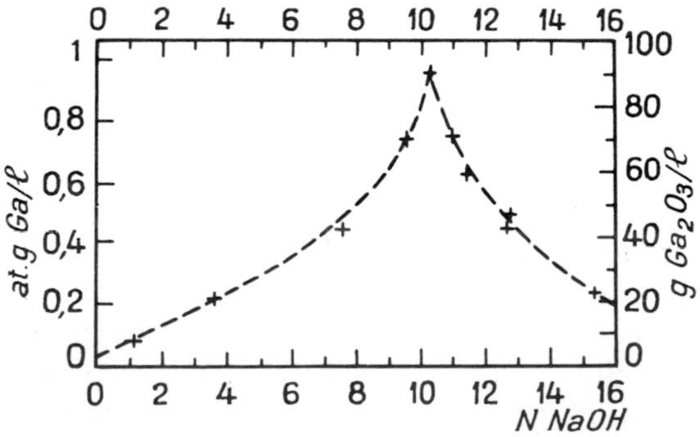

FIG. 4. Solubility of $Ga(OH)_3$ in aqueous solutions of NaOH (after Fricke and Blencke [25]).

shows the experimental results of Fricke and Blencke [25] concerning the solubility of $Ga(OH)_3$ in aqueous solutions of NaOH, at 18–20°C. The solubility is a maximum in 10·3 N NaOH; above this concentration solid trisodic gallate is formed [9]. $Ga(OH)_3$ is very soluble in ammonia, which enables Ga to be separated from Al, Fe and other metals.

4. BIBLIOGRAPHY

[1] W. M. LATIMER, *Oxidation Potentials*, 2nd ed., Prentice-Hall, New York, 1952.
[2] A. BRUKL and G. ORTNER, Die Oxyde des Galliums, *Z. anorg. allgem. Chem.* **203,** 23–25 (1932).
[3] N. V. SIDGWICK, *The Chemical Elements and their Compounds*, Vol. I, Oxford, 1950, pp. 458–80.
[4] J. BOEHM and G. KAHAN. Ueber ein Galliumhydroxyd, *Z. anorg. allgem. Chem.* **238,** 350–2 (1938).
[5] P. NEOGI and S. K. NANDI, New compounds of gallium, *J. Ind. Chem. Soc.* **13,** 399–403 (1936).
[6] E. WIBERG and T. JOHANNSEN, Ueber einen flüchtigen Galliumwasserstoff der Formel Ga_2H_6, *Die Chemie*, (*Angew. Chem.*) **55,** 38–40 (1942).
[7] J. L. MARGRAVE, Binding energies of gaseous diatomic hydrides and halides of group II and group III metals, *J. Phys. Chem.* **58**, 528–60 (1954).
[8] G. CHARLOT, *L'analyse qualitative et les réactions en solution*, 4th ed., Masson, Paris, 1957.
[9] P. PASCAL, *Traité de Chimie minérale*, Vol. VII, 1932, pp. 437–53.
[10] LECOQ DE BOISBAUDRAN, *Ann. Chim. Phys.* **6**, 2 (1884).
[11] J. I. HOFFMAN, Preparation of pure gallium, *J. Res. N.B.S.* **13,** 665–72 (1934).
[12] L. M. DENNIS and J. A. BRIDGMAN, *Gallium, J. Amer. Chem. Soc.* **40,** 1531–61 (1918).
[13] T. W. RICHARDS and S. BOYER, The purification of gallium by electrolysis and the compressibility and density of gallium, *J. Amer. Chem. Soc.* **41,** 133–4 (1919).
[14] X, Le gallium, métal d'avenir, *L'Usine nouvelle*, January, 1958, p. 36.
[15] W. KLEMM and I. SCHNICK, Die Bildungswärme von Gallium I-Oxyd, *Z. anorg. allgem. Chem.* **226,** 353 (1936).
[16] L. BREWER, The thermodynamic properties of the oxides and their vaporization processes, *Chem. Rev.* **52,** 1–76 (p. 38) (1953).
[17] R. ROY, V. G. HILL and E. F. OSBORN, Polymorphism of Ga_2O_3 and the system Ga_2O_3–H_2O, *J. Amer. Chem. Soc.* **74,** No. 3, 719–22 (1952).
[18] A. W. LAUBENGAYER and H. R. ENGLE, The sesquioxide and hydroxides of gallium, *J. Amer. Chem. Soc.* **61,** 1210–14 (1939).
[19] *Gmelins Handbuch der anorganischen Chemie*, Achte Auflage XII, S.N.36, Berlin, Verlag Chemie, G.m.b.H., 1936.
[20] J. BOEHM, Ueber Galliumoxyd und hydroxyd, *Angew. Chem.* **53,** 131 (1940).
[21] W. O. MILLIGAN and H. B. WEISER, X-Ray studies on the hydrous oxides. VIII. Gallium, indium and thallic oxides, *J. Amer. Chem. Soc.* **59,** 1670 (1937).
[22] H. B. WEISER, *Inorganic Colloid-Chemistry*. Vol. II. *The Hydrous Oxides and Hydroxides*, Wiley, London, 1935, pp. 120–1.
[23] V. G. HILL, R. ROY and E. F. OSBORN, The system alumina–gallia–water, *J. Amer. Ceram. Soc.* **35**, p. 135 (1952).
[24] A. W. LAUBENGAYER and F. B. SCHIRMER, The chlorides of gallium, *J. Amer. Chem. Soc.* **62**, 1578–83 (1940).
[25] R. FRICKE and W. BLENCKE, Beiträge zur Chemie des Galliums, *Z. anorg. allgem. Chem.* **143**, 184–200 (1925).

SECTION 16.2

INDIUM[1]

C. VANLEUGENHAGHE and M. POURBAIX

SUMMARY

[1] Rapport technique RT.75 of CEBELCOR (August 1958).

1. SUBSTANCES CONSIDERED AND SUBSTANCES NOT CONSIDERED

	Oxidation number (Z)	Considered	Not considered	μ^0 (cal.)	Name, colour, crystalline system
Solid substances	− 3	–	$(InH_3)_x$	–	Hydride, white
	0	**In**	–	0	Indium, silvery white, f.c.quad.
	+ 1	–	In_2O	–	Sub-oxide, black, hex.
	+ 2	–	InO	–	Monoxide, white
	+ 3	In_2O_3 anh.	–	*a*. −196 400	Sesquioxide, pale yellow, cub. or amorphous
	»	» hydr.	–	*b*. −193 930	Trihydrated oxide or hydroxide $In(OH)_3$, white
Dissolved substances	+ 1	In^+	–	− 3 200 (2)	"Hypoindous" ion
	+ 2	In^{++}	–	− 12 400 (2)	Indous ion
	+ 3	In^{+++}	–	− 23 700	Indic ion, colourless
	»	$InOH^{++}$	–	− 75 100 (2)	Indyl ion
	»	–	$In(OH)_2^+$	–	Indyl ion
	»	InO_2^-	–	−104 000 (2)	Indate ion
Gaseous substance	− 1	*InH*	–	45 000	Hydride

2. REACTIONS AND EQUILIBRIUM FORMULAE (3)

2.1. TWO DISSOLVED SUBSTANCES

2.1.1. *Relative stability of the dissolved substances*

$Z = +3$

1. $In^{+++} + H_2O = InOH^{++} + H^+$ $\qquad \log\frac{(InOH^{++})}{(In^{+++})} = -3.88 + pH$

2. $InOH^{++} + H_2O = InO_2^- + 3H^+$ $\qquad \log\frac{(InO_2^-)}{(InOH^{++})} = -20.38 + 3\,pH$

$+1 \rightarrow +2$

3. $In^+ = In^{++} + e^-$ $\qquad E_0 = -0.400 + 0.0591 \log\frac{(In^{++})}{(In^+)}$

$+1 \rightarrow +3$

4. $In^+ = In^{+++} + 2e^-$ $\qquad E_0 = -0.443 + 0.0295 \log\frac{(In^{+++})}{(In^+)}$

5. $In^+ + H_2O = InOH^{++} + H^+ + 2e^-$ $\qquad E_0 = -0.330 - 0.0295\,pH + 0.0295 \log\frac{(InOH^{++})}{(In^+)}$

6. $In^+ + 2H_2O = InO_2^- + 4H^+ + 2e^-$ $\qquad E_0 = 0.262 - 0.1182\,pH + 0.0295 \log\frac{(InO_2^-)}{(In^+)}$

$+2 \rightarrow +3$

7. $In^{++} = In^{+++} + e^-$ $\qquad E_0 = -0.489 + 0.0591 \log\frac{(In^{+++})}{(In^{++})}$

---

(2) The free enthalpies of In^+ and In^{++} were calculated from the equilibrium potentials given by Hepler *et al.* [1]; the free enthalpy of $InOH^{++}$ was calculated from the equilibrium constant of the reaction $In^{+++} + H_2O = InOH^{++} + H^+$, $K = 1.4 \times 10^{-4}$ given by Hepler [2] and Hepler and Hugus [3]; the free enthalpy of InO_2^- was calculated from the equilibrium constant of the reaction $In(OH)_3 = InO_2^- + H_2O + H^+$, $K = 10^{-16}$ given by Charlot [4]. We have, however, replaced $InO_3H_2^-$, the symbol given by Charlot, by $InO_2^- + H_2O$.

(3) For the equilibria involving In_2O_3, the values marked *a* refer to anhydrous In_2O_3 and the values marked *b* refer to trihydrated In_2O_3 or $In(OH)_3$. The value −193 930 cal. assumed for the free enthalpy of formation of In_2O_3 in the form of $In(OH)_3$ corresponds to $\mu^0_{In(OH)_3} = -182\,000$ cal.

2.1.2. *Limits of the domains of relative predominance of the dissolved substances*

1'.	In^{+++} / $InOH^{++}$	$pH = 3.88$
2'.	$InOH^{++}$/InO_2^-	$pH = 6.79$
3'.	In^+ / In^{++}	$E_0 = -0.400$
4'.	In^+ / In^{+++}	$E_0 = -0.443$
5'.	In^+ / $InOH^{++}$	$E_0 = -0.330 - 0.0295\ pH$
6'.	In^+ / InO_2^-	$E_0 = 0.262 - 0.1182\ pH$
7'.	In^{++} / In^{+++}	$E_0 = -0.489$

2.2. TWO SOLID SUBSTANCES

Limits of the domains of relative stability of indium and its oxide $\mathbf{In_2O_3}$

$0 \rightarrow +3$

8. $2\,\mathbf{In} + 3H_2O = \mathbf{In_2O_3} + 6H^+ + 6e^-$
   a. $E_0 = -0.190 - 0.0591\ pH$
   b. $ = -0.172 - 0.0591\ pH$

2.3. ONE SOLID SUBSTANCE AND ONE DISSOLVED SUBSTANCE

Solubility of indium and its oxide $\mathbf{In_2O_3}$

$Z = +3$

9. $2In^{+++} + 3H_2O = \mathbf{In_2O_3} + 6H^+$
   a. $\log(In^{+++}) = 7.73 - 3\ pH$
   b. $\phantom{\log(In^{+++})} = 8.65 - 3\ pH$

10. $2InOH^{++} + H_2O = \mathbf{In_2O_3} + 4H^+$
   a. $\log(InOH^{++}) = 3.85 - 2\ pH$
   b. $\phantom{\log(InOH^{++})} = 4.77 - 2\ pH$

11. $\mathbf{In_2O_3} + H_2O = 2InO_2^- + 2H^+$
   a. $\log(InO_2^-) = -17.05 + pH$
   b. $ = -16.13 + pH$

$0 \rightarrow +1$

12. $\mathbf{In} = In^+ + e^-$ $\quad E_0 = -0.139 + 0.0591 \log(In^+)$

$0 \rightarrow +3$

13. $\mathbf{In} = In^{+++} + 3e^-$ $\quad E_0 = -0.342 + 0.0197 \log(In^{+++})$

14. $\mathbf{In} + H_2O = InOH^{++} + H^+ + 3e^-$ $\quad E_0 = -0.266 - 0.0197\ pH + 0.0197 \log(InOH^{++})$

15. $\mathbf{In} + 2H_2O = InO_2^- + 4H^+ + 3e^-$ $\quad E_0 = 0.146 - 0.0788\ pH + 0.0197 \log(InO_2^-)$

$+1 \rightarrow +3$

16. $2In^+ + 3H_2O = \mathbf{In_2O_3} + 6H^+ + 4e^-$
   a. $E_0 = -0.216 - 0.0886\ pH - 0.0295 \log(In^+)$
   b. $ = -0.189 - 0.0886\ pH - 0.0295 \log(In^+)$

2.4. ONE SOLID SUBSTANCE AND ONE GASEOUS SUBSTANCE

Limits of the domains of relative stability of indium and the hydride InH

$-1 \rightarrow 0$

17. $InH = \mathbf{In} + H^+ + e^-$ $\quad E_0 = -1.951 - 0.0591\ pH - 0.0591 \log p_{InH}$

3. EQUILIBRIUM DIAGRAM AND ITS INTERPRETATION

3.1. ESTABLISHMENT OF THE DIAGRAM

Figures 1 and 2, established by means of the equilibrium relations (1)–(17) given in paragraph 2, represent the conditions of thermodynamic equilibrium of the system indium–water, at 25°C. The only solid compound of trivalent indium which appears in Fig. 1 is the anhydrous oxide In_2O_3, which is probably the stable form of the oxide of trivalent indium. According to the free enthalpy values given in paragraph 1, the hydrated oxide $In_2O_3 \cdot 3H_2O$ [or hydroxide $In(OH)_3$] is less stable than the anhydrous oxide In_2O_3, and tends to be converted into the latter with an affinity of 196·4–193·9 = 2·5 kcal. For want of sufficient thermodynamic data, we have not considered the oxides InO and In_2O prepared by Thiel and Luckmann [5].

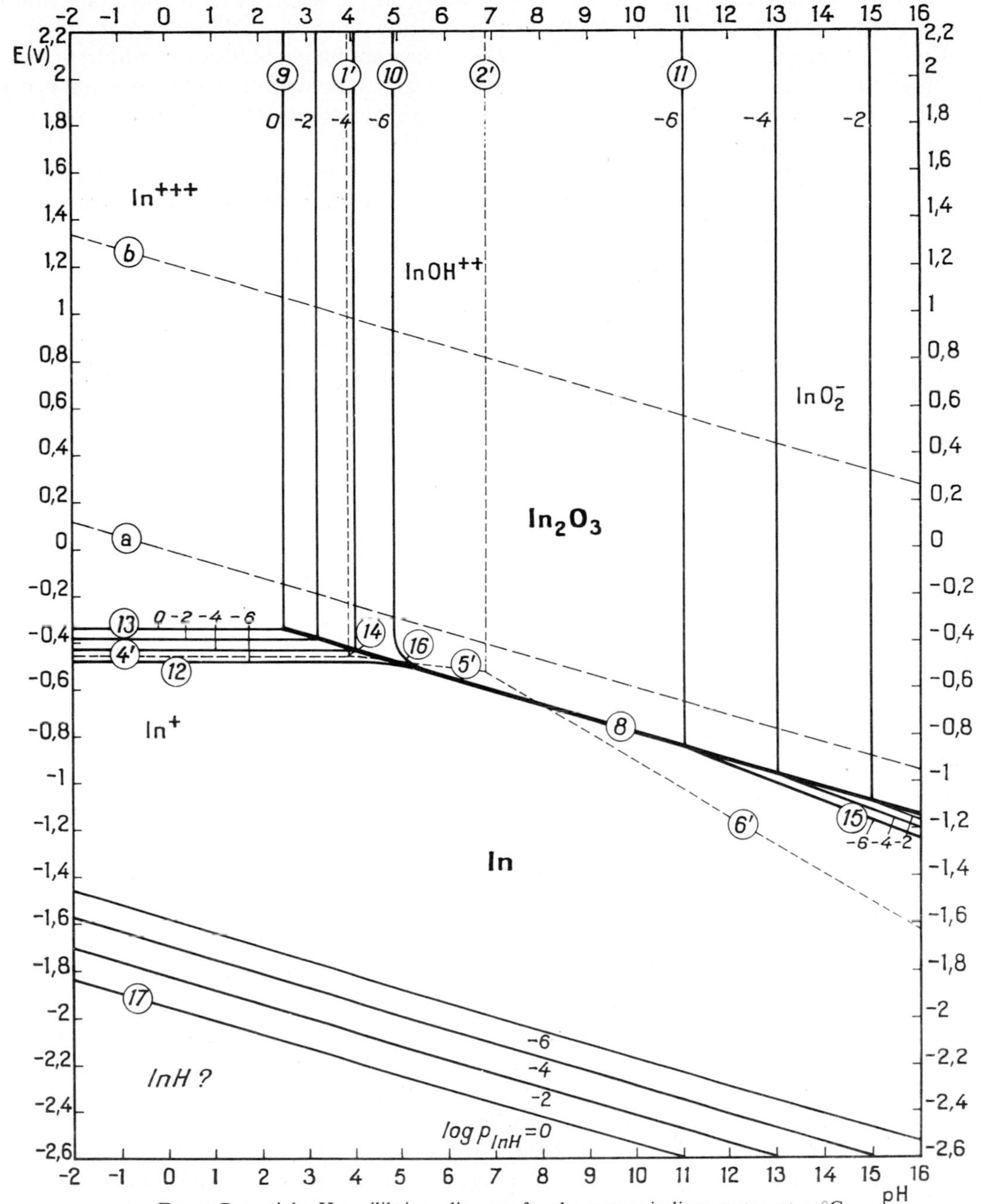

FIG. 1. Potential–pH equilibrium diagram for the system indium–water, at 25°C.

3.2. RELATIVE STABILITY OF INDIUM AND ITS OXIDE In_2O_3

Figure 1 represents the conditions of thermodynamic equilibrium of the system indium–water, at 25°C, in the absence of substances with which indium can form soluble complexes or insoluble salts. There are a large number of indium *complexes*; the principal ones are those formed with the anions of organic compounds, in particular the oxalic complex $In(C_2O_4)_2^-$ [4] and the complex ions formed with chlorides and fluorides (InF^{++} and InF_2^+ [3]). The anhydrous iodate $In(IO_3)_3$, the carbonate $In_2(CO_3)_3$ and the phosphate $InPO_4$ are *sparingly soluble*.

From Figs. 1 and 2, *indium* appears to be a base metal, as the whole of its domain of stability lies below that of water. In the presence of definitely acid or alkaline solutions, indium tends to dissolve with the evolution of hydrogen. This reaction actually takes place in dilute solutions of sulphuric acid and nitric acid [6] and in oxalic acid. In 2 N sulphuric acid, at 25°C, the hydrogen overpotential is 0·533 V ± 0·007 V [7]. The dissolution seems to be speeded up by the presence of dissolved oxygen in the solution [8]. Indium does not appear to be attacked by acetic acid.

According to Wenger [9] alkali metal hydroxides give a white precipitate of indium hydroxide, soluble in excess alkali. However, Remy [10] mentions that the dissolved hydrated oxide is reprecipitated

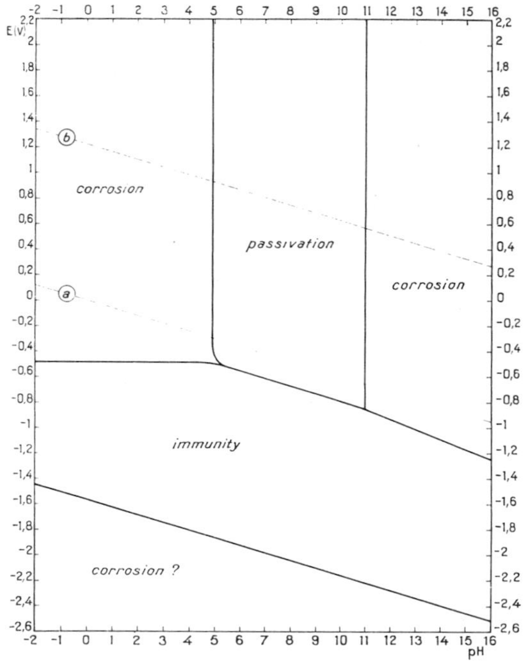

FIG. 2. Theoretical conditions of corrosion, immunity and passivation of indium, at 25°C.

after a certain time from the alkaline solution, most probably on account of the formation of another variety of indium hydroxide having a smaller solubility product.

In non-complexing solutions of pH of about 3–5 or 11–15, indium tends to cover itself with a film of *oxide* In_2O_3, which must be protective, as indium is not corroded by water at room temperature [6]. Water seems to be without action on indium up to 100°C [9].

According to Figs. 1 and 2, a powerful reducing action can corrode indium with the formation of a volatile hydride InH, which is most probably unstable, and whose existence is, in fact, uncertain [11]. A hydride InH_3, not considered in Fig. 1, has been prepared by the reduction of indium chloride with lithium hydride according to the reaction $InCl_3 + 3LiH = InH_3 + 3LiCl$ [12].

Baths for the *electro-deposition* of indium are usually chloride-, sulphate- or sulphamate-based. Fluoroborate-, fluorosilicate- and fluoride-based baths have also been patented [13]. Dextrose or sodium cyanide is often added to chloride-based baths [14].

Indium can also be obtained by reducing its oxide with carbon in a stream of hot hydrogen. Metallic indium is precipitated when excess zinc is added to a solution of an indium salt [15].

3.3. STABILITY OF MONO- AND DIVALENT INDIUM

The cation In^{++} does not appear in Fig. 1. Its concentration is always below the concentration of In^{+++} ions or In^{+} ions, the ion In^{+} itself being the predominant form only at very low dissolved indium concentrations, below about 10^{-5} g-at/l (i.e. 1·15 mg/l). In reality, In^{+} and In^{++} probably exist as chloride complexes [16] and not as simple ions. The following compounds of monovalent indium are known: the oxide, the sulphide, the selenide, the telluride, the chloride, the bromide and possibly the iodide.

3.4. SOLUBILITY OF INDIUM OXIDE In_2O_3

Figure 3 represents the influence of pH on the solubility of the two forms of the trivalent oxide In_2O_3: the anhydrous form and the trihydrated form (or hydroxide). The two curves arise from equilibrium relations (9), (10) and (11) established in paragraph 2.3.

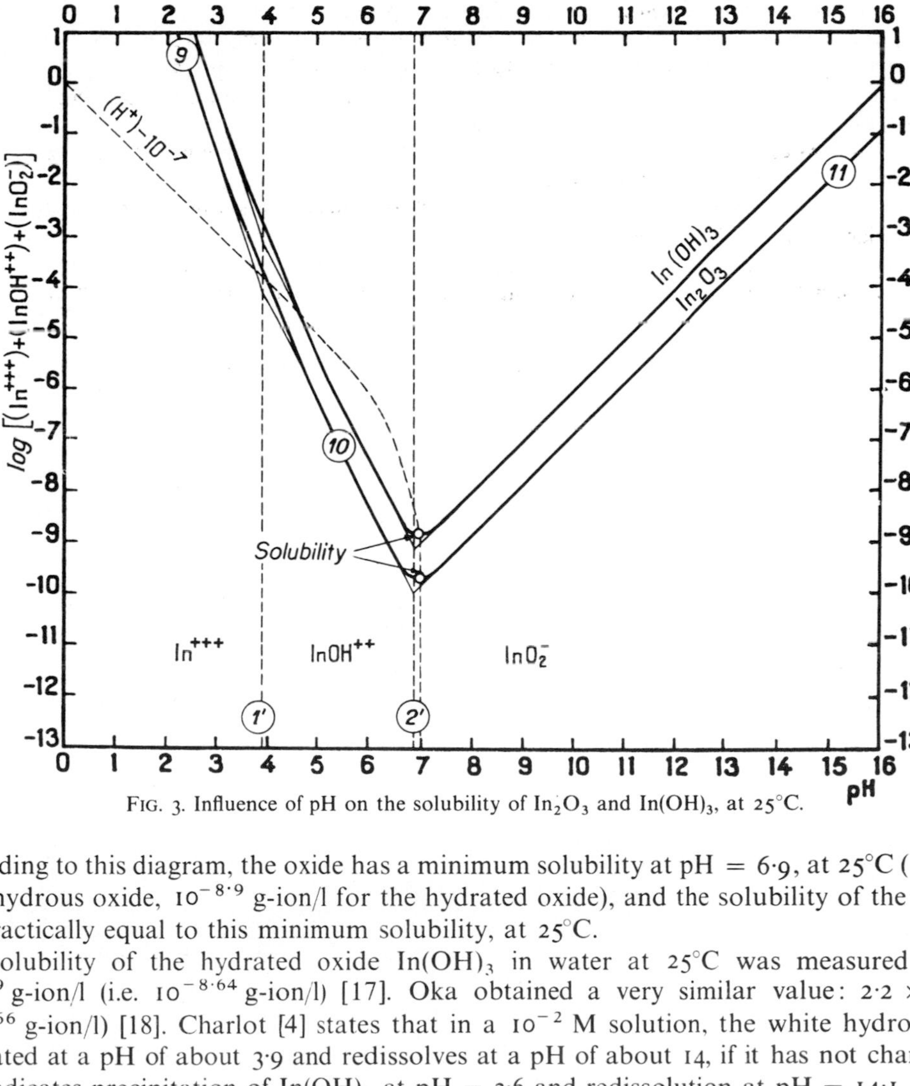

FIG. 3. Influence of pH on the solubility of In_2O_3 and $In(OH)_3$, at 25°C.

According to this diagram, the oxide has a minimum solubility at pH = 6·9, at 25°C ($10^{-9.8}$ g-ion/l for the anhydrous oxide, $10^{-8.9}$ g-ion/l for the hydrated oxide), and the solubility of the oxide in pure water is practically equal to this minimum solubility, at 25°C.

The solubility of the hydrated oxide $In(OH)_3$ in water at 25°C was measured by Moeller: $2{\cdot}3 \times 10^{-9}$ g-ion/l (i.e. $10^{-8.64}$ g-ion/l) [17]. Oka obtained a very similar value: $2{\cdot}2 \times 10^{-9}$ g-ion/l (i.e. $10^{-8.66}$ g-ion/l) [18]. Charlot [4] states that in a 10^{-2} M solution, the white hydroxide $In(OH)_3$ is precipitated at a pH of about 3·9 and redissolves at a pH of about 14, if it has not changed its form. Figure 3 indicates precipitation of $In(OH)_3$ at pH = 3·6 and redissolution at pH = 14·1, for a 10^{-2} M solution.

According to Remy [10], the oxide In_2O_3 is insoluble in alkali metal hydroxides and ammonia.

4. BIBLIOGRAPHY

[1] L. G. Hepler, Z. Z. Hugus and W. M. Latimer, The stability of the lower oxidation states of indium in aqueous solutions, *J. Amer. Chem. Soc.* **75**, 5652–4 (1953).
[2] L. G. Hepler, *Problems in the aqueous chemistry of indium*, U. S. Atomic Energy Comm. U.C.R.L.–2202, May 1953.
[3] L. G. Hepler and Z. Z. Hugus, Hydrolysis and halide complexing of indium, *J. Amer. Chem. Soc.* **74,** 6115–18 (1952).
[4] G. Charlot, *L'analyse qualitative et les réactions en solution*, 4th ed., Masson, Paris, 1957, p. 203.
[5] A. Thiel and H. Luckmann, Studien über das Indium, *Z. anorg. allgem. Chem.* **172,** 353–71 (1928).
[6] P. Pascal, *Traité de Chimie minérale*, Vol. VII, Masson, Paris, 1932, pp. 455–72.
[7] A. Thiel and W. Hammerschmidt, Ueber den Zusammenhang zwischen der Ueberspannung des Wasserstoffs an reinen Metallen und gewissen Eigenschaften der Metalle, *Z. anorg. allgem. Chem.* **132**, 15–35 (p. 23) (1923).
[8] H. H. Uhlig, *The Corrosion Handbook,* Wiley, New York, 1948, pp. 119–20.
[9] P. E. Wenger, *Traité de Chimie analytique qualitative minérale*, Geneva, 1946, pp. 235–7.
[10] H. Remy, *Treatise on Inorganic Chemistry,* Vol. I, Elsevier, 1956, pp. 375–80.
[11] D. T. Hurd, *Introduction to the Chemistry of the Hydrides*, Wiley, New York, 1952, p. 198.
[12] N. G. Gaylord, *Reduction with Complex Metal Hydrides*, Interscience, 1956, p. 55.
[13] T. Moeller and B. Hopkins, The electrochemistry of indium, *Trans. Electrochem. Soc.* **93,** No. 3, 84–93 (1948).
[14] Metal Industry, *Handbook and Directory,* 1958, p. 24.
[15] J. de Ment, H. C. Dake and E. R. Roberts, *Rarer Metals*, Temple Press, London, 1949, pp. 22–23.
[16] A. Thiel, Studien über das Indium, *Z. anorg. allgem. Chem.* **40,** 280–336 (1904).
[17] T. Moeller, Contribution to the chemistry of indium. An electrometric study of the precipitation of hydrous indium hydroxide, *J. Amer. Chem. Soc.* **63,** 2625–8 (1941).
[18] Y. Oka, *J. Chem. Soc. Japan,* **61,** 311–20 (1940). Quoted by A. Seidell and W. F. Linke, *Solubilities of Inorganic and Organic Compounds*, Supplement to the 3rd edition, Van Nostrand, New York, 1952, p. 254.

SECTION 16.3

THALLIUM[1]

C. VANLEUGENHAGHE, K. SCHWABE and M. POURBAIX

SUMMARY

1. *Substances considered and substances not considered.*

2. *Reactions and equilibrium formulae.*

   2.1. Two dissolved substances.

      2.1.1. Relative stability of Tl^{+} and Tl^{+++}

      2.1.2. Limits of the domains of relative predominance of Tl^{+} and Tl^{+++}

   2.2. Two solid substances.
   Limits of the domains of relative stability of thallium and its oxides.

   2.3. One solid substance and one dissolved substance.
   Solubility of thallium and its oxides.

   2.4. One gaseous substance and one solid substance.
   Limits of the domains of relative stability of thallium and the hydride TlH.

3. *Equilibrium diagram and its interpretation.*

   3.1. Establishment of the diagram.

   3.2. Stability, corrosion and passivation of thallium.

   3.3. Stability of thallous and thallic salts.

4. *Bibliography.*

[1] Rapport technique RT.76 of CEBELCOR.

1. SUBSTANCES CONSIDERED AND SUBSTANCES NOT CONSIDERED

	Oxidation number (Z)	Considered	Not considered	μ^0(cal.)	Name, colour, crystalline system
Solid substances	0	**Tl**	–	0	Thallium, bluish-white, hex.
	+1	**Tl_2O** hydr.	–	*a.* –34 310	Hydrated oxide or hydroxide TlOH, light yellow, rhomb.
	»	» anh.	–	*b.* –33 100 (²)	Anhydrous oxide, reddish, cub.
	+3	**Tl_2O_3** hydr.	–	*c.* –75 930	Hydrated sesquioxide or hydroxide $Tl(OH)_3$, brown, hex.
	»	» anh.	–	*d.* –63 000	Anhydrous sesquioxide, brown or black, hex.
	+3.33	–	**Tl_3O_5**	–	
Dissolved substances	+1	Tl^+	–	–7 755	Thallous ion, colourless
	+2	–	Tl^{++}	–	–
	+3	Tl^{+++}	–	50 000	Thallic ion
	»	–	TlO^+	–	Thallyl ion
	»	–	$TlOH^{++}$	–	Thallyl ion
	»	–	$Tl(OH)_2^+$	–	Thallyl ion
Gaseous substance	–1	*TlH*	–	43 000	Hydride

2. REACTIONS AND EQUILIBRIUM FORMULAE (³)

2.1. TWO DISSOLVED SUBSTANCES

2.1.1. *Relative stability of Tl^+ and Tl^{+++}*

$+1 \rightarrow +3$

1. $Tl^+ = Tl^{+++} + 2e^-$ $\quad E_0 = 1.252 + 0.0295 \log \frac{(Tl^{+++})}{(Tl^+)}$

2.1.2. *Limit of the domains of relative predominance of Tl^+ and Tl^{+++}*

1'. Tl^+/Tl^{+++} $\quad E_0 = 1.252$

2.2. TWO SOLID SUBSTANCES

Limits of the domains of relative stability of thallium and its oxides

$0 \rightarrow +1$

2. $2Tl + H_2O = Tl_2O + 2H^+ + 2e^-$
 - *a.* $E_0 = 0.485 - 0.0591\,pH$
 - *b.* $\quad = 0.512 - 0.0591\,pH$

$+1 \rightarrow +3$

3. $Tl_2O + 2H_2O = Tl_2O_3 + 4H^+ + 4e^-$
 - *ac.* $E_0 = 0.778 - 0.0591\,pH$
 - *bd.* $\quad = 0.905 - 0.0591\,pH$

(²) Value given by Brewer [1].

(³) In the equations and equilibrium formulae involving Tl_2O the values marked *a* refer to the hydrated oxide $Tl_2O.H_2O$ or TlOH; the values marked *b* refer to the anhydrous oxide. The value –34 310 cal. for the free enthalpy of hydrated Tl_2O corresponds to $\mu^0_{TlOH} = -45\,500$ cal.

In the equations and equilibrium formulae involving Tl_2O_3, the values marked *c* refer to the hydrated oxide $Tl_2O_3 . 3H_2O$ or $Tl(OH)_3$; the values marked *d* refer to the anhydrous oxide. The value –75 930 cal. for the free enthalpy of hydrated Tl_2O_3 corresponds to $\mu^0_{Tl(OH)_3} = -123\,000$ cal.

2.3. ONE SOLID SUBSTANCE AND ONE DISSOLVED SUBSTANCE

Solubility of thallium and its oxides

$Z = +1$

4. $2Tl^{+} + H_2O = \mathbf{Tl_2O} + 2H^{+}$ — a. $\log(Tl^{+}) = 13.90 - pH$
   b. $= 14.34 - pH$

$Z = +3$

5. $2Tl^{+++} + 3H_2O = \mathbf{Tl_2O_3} + 6H^{+}$ — c. $\log(Tl^{+++}) = -2.15 - 3\,pH$
   d. $= -2.60 - 3\,pH$

$0 \rightarrow +1$

6. $\mathbf{Tl} = Tl^{+} + e^{-}$ — $E_0 = -0.336 + 0.0591 \log(Tl^{+})$

$+1 \rightarrow +3$

7. $2Tl^{+} + 3H_2O = \mathbf{Tl_2O_3} + 6H^{+} + 4e^{-}$ — c. $E_0 = 1.189 - 0.0887\,pH - 0.0295 \log(Tl^{+})$
   d. $= 1.329 - 0.0887\,pH - 0.0295 \log(Tl^{+})$

2.4. ONE GASEOUS SUBSTANCE AND ONE SOLID SUBSTANCE

Limits of the domains of relative stability of thallium and the hydride TlH

$-1 \rightarrow 0$

8. $TlH = \mathbf{Tl} + H^{+} + e^{-}$ — $E_0 = -1.865 - 0.0591\,pH - 0.0591 \log p_{TlH}$

3. EQUILIBRIUM DIAGRAM AND ITS INTERPRETATION

3.1. ESTABLISHMENT OF THE DIAGRAM (4)

Using equilibrium relations (1)–(8) we have established Fig. 1. According to the free enthalpy values given in paragraph 1, the hydroxide TlOH is more stable than the anhydrous oxide Tl_2O; the latter tends to turn into the hydrated oxide with an affinity approximately equal to 34·3–33·1 = 1·2 kcal. The hydroxide $Tl(OH)_3$ is more stable than the anhydrous oxide Tl_2O_3, which tends to turn into the hydrated oxide with an affinity approximately equal to 75·9–63·0 = 12·9 kcal. For this reason the hydroxides were chosen in preference to the anhydrous oxides for the establishment of Fig. 1.

For want of thermodynamic data we were not able to consider the ion Tl^{++} which may exist in appreciable quantities [2], nor the ions TlO^{+} [3], $TlOH^{++}$ and $Tl(OH)_2^{+}$ [4].

Figure 1 is valid only in the absence of substances with which thallium can form complexes or insoluble salts. Thallium forms a large number of complexes. Charlot [3] mentions the following ones in particular: the hydrochloric complexes up to $TlCl_6^{---}$ (not very stable), the sulphuric complexes (also not very stable), and the complexes formed with organic anions containing hydroxyl groups, and with F^{-}, $C_2O_4^{--}$, etc.

The phosphate $TlPO_4$ and the chloride TlCl are sparingly soluble.

3.2. STABILITY, CORROSION AND PASSIVATION OF THALLIUM

Figure 2, deduced from Fig. 1, represents the theoretical conditions of corrosion, immunity and passivation of thallium, at 25°C, in the absence of substances with which thallium can form soluble complexes or insoluble salts.

From Figs. 1 and 2, thallium appears to be a fairly base metal. Its domain of thermodynamic stability has only a small area in common with that of water.

---

(4) A potential–pH equilibrium diagram was presented by Delahay *et al.* at the 3rd Meeting of CITCE [5]. A similar diagram is given by Charlot [3].

In acid or neutral solutions, thallium tends to decompose the water with the evolution of hydrogen. Charlot [3] points out that thallium is actually attacked by dilute nitric and sulphuric acids. In pure

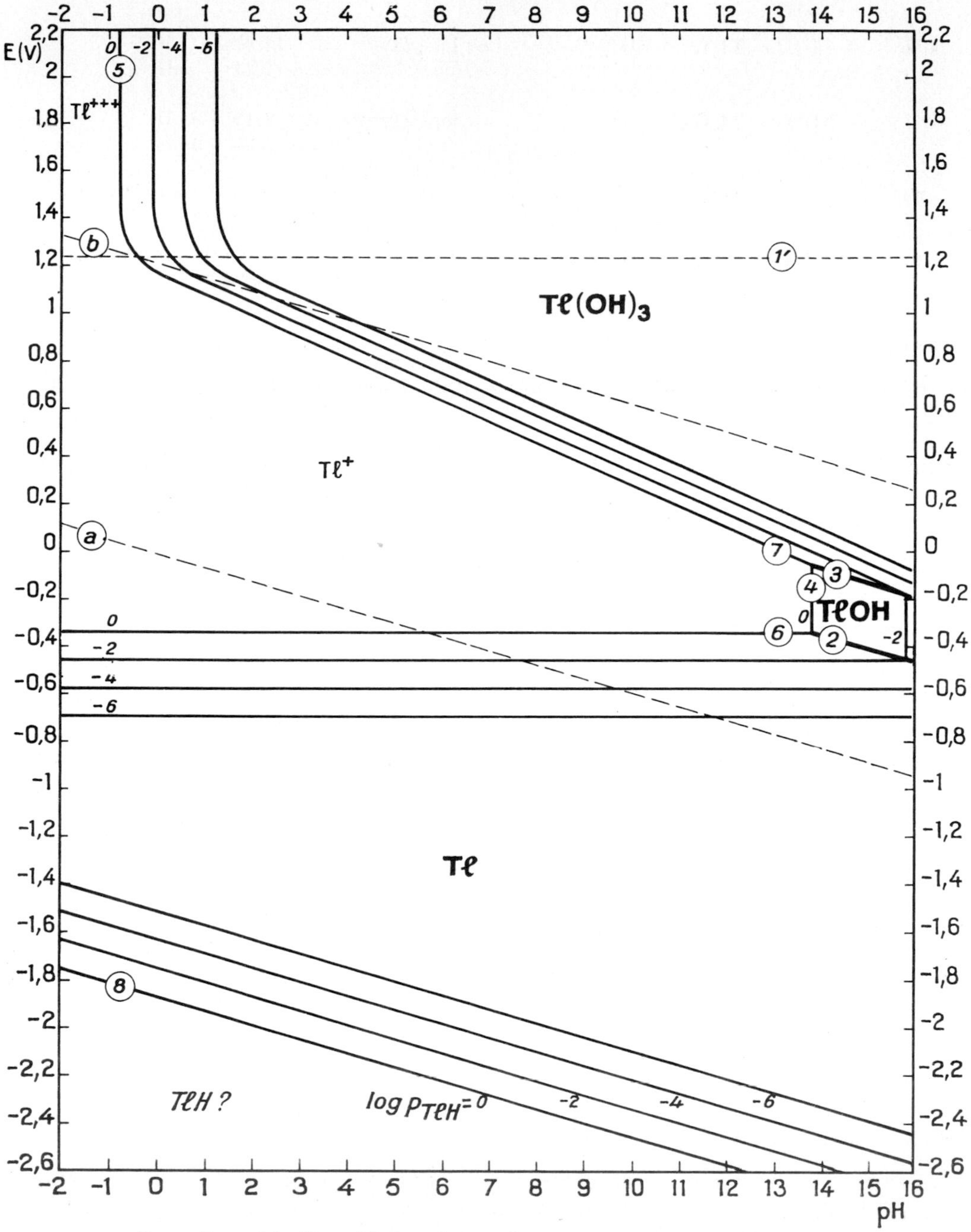

FIG. 1. Potential–pH equilibrium diagram for the system thallium–water, at 25°C.

water, however, freshly prepared thallium retains its shiny appearance [6]. Thallium is hardly attacked by concentrated hydrochloric acid, owing to the formation of TlCl, which is sparingly soluble and protects the metal [3]. In sufficiently alkaline solutions thallium behaves as a noble metal.

The anodic behaviour of thallium is characterized by the fact that the metal dissolves as thallous ions whatever the pH of the solution (provided that it is below 14), at a potential independent of the pH of the solution.

If the electrode potential is further increased, the metal is passivated, owing to the formation of insoluble protective thallic hydroxide. Machu and Khairy [7] found that, in solutions of HCl or NaCl, the passivation takes place in two stages. It seems that a thallous compound is formed in the first phase of the passivation and that this turns into a thallic salt in the second phase. The thallous salt formed is probably the sparingly soluble TlCl. In solutions of perchloric acid and sodium sulphate they found that the passivation takes place in a single stage. Besson [8] has shown that the anodic deposit formed

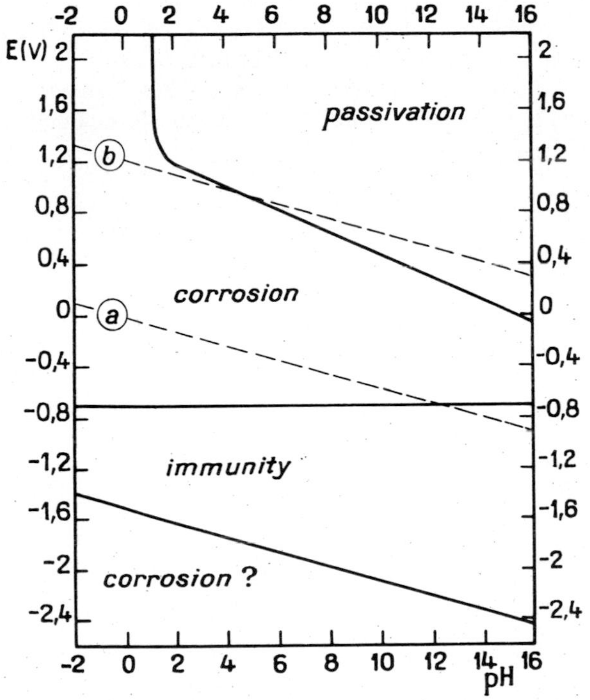

FIG. 2. Theoretical conditions of corrosion, immunity and passivation of thallium, at 25°C.

during the electrolysis of a nitric solution of thallium consists of sesquioxide Tl_2O_3, hydrated to a greater or lesser degree. According to Fig. 1, a powerful reducing action can cause thallium to corrode with the formation of a *volatile hydride* TlH, which is most probably very unstable [9]. We do not know whether such a cathodic corrosion of the metal has actually been observed.

3.3. STABILITY OF THALLOUS AND THALLIC SALTS

The *thallous salts* are oxidized only by very powerful oxidizing agents such as MnO_4^- and Cl_2 in very acid media [3]. On the other hand, Tl^+ is a powerful reducing agent in alkaline media.

The *thallic ion* Tl^{+++} appears only in media which are both very acid and very oxidizing. In acid media Tl^{+++} ions will be very oxidizing and will turn readily into thallous ions. They are reduced by practically all reducing agents, even H_2O_2 [10]. Charlot [3] points out that the thallic ion partially oxidizes hydrochloric acid and completely oxidizes iodides. It also oxidizes benzidine. The thallic salts are not very stable and behave like auric salts [11].

4. BIBLIOGRAPHY

[1] L. Brewer, The thermodynamic properties of the oxides and their vaporization processes, *Chem. Rev.* **52,** No. 10, 1–75 (1953).
[2] W. M. Latimer, *Oxidation Potentials,* 2nd ed., Prentice-Hall, New York, 1952, pp. 163–6.
[3] G. Charlot, *L'analyse qualitative et les réactions en solution,* 4th ed., Masson, Paris, 1957, p. 263.
[4] S. Hietanen and L. G. Sillén, Hydrolysis of metal ions, *Acta Chem. Scand.* **8**, 1607–25 (1954).
[5] P. Delahay, M. Pourbaix and P. Van Rysselberghe, *Diagrammes d'équilibres potentiel–pH de quelques éléments* (C.R. 3e Réunion du CITCE, Berne, 1951; Manfredi, Milan, 1952).
[6] *Gmelins Handbuch der anorganischen Chemie, Thallium,* S.N.38, Vol. XII, Verlag Chemie, G.m.b.H., Berlin, 1940.
[7] W. Machu and E. M. Khairy, Ueber die Passivität des Thalliums in Perchlorsäure-, Salzsäure-, Natriumchlorid- und Natriumsulfatlösungen, *Werkstoff und Korrosion* **5,** 11–17 (1954).
[8] J. Besson, Le dosage électrolytique du thallium, *Anal. Chem. Acta* **3,** 158–62 (1949).
[9] D. T. Hurd, *Chemistry of the Hydrides,* Wiley, New York, 1952, p. 199.
[10] N. V. Sidgwick, *The Chemical Elements and their Compounds,* Vol. I, Clarendon Press, Oxford, 1950, p. 467.
[11] J. de Ment, H. C. Dake and E. R. Roberts, *Rarer Metals,* Temple Press, London, 1949, pp. 33–42.

SECTION 17.1

CARBON[1]

J. VAN MUYLDER and M. POURBAIX

SUMMARY

1. *Substances considered and substances not considered.*

2. *Reactions and equilibrium formulae.*

2.1. Two dissolved substances.

2.1.1. Relative stability of the dissolved substances.

2.1.2. Limits of the domains of relative predominance of the dissolved substances.

2.2. Two gaseous substances.

2.2.1. Relative stability of the gaseous substances.

2.2.2. Limits of the domains of relative predominance of the gaseous substances.

2.3. One dissolved substance and one solid substance.
Dissolution equilibria of graphite.

2.4. One dissolved substance and one gaseous substance.
Solubility of the gaseous substances.

2.5. One solid substance and one gaseous substance.
Limits of the domains of relative stability of C, CH_4, CO and CO_2.

3. *Equilibrium diagram and its interpretation.*

3.1. Establishment of the diagram.

3.2. Stability of carbon.

3.3. Stability of methane CH_4.

3.4. Stability of methanol (methyl alcohol).

3.5. Stability of methanal (formaldehyde).

3.6. Stability of carbon monoxide CO.

3.7. Stability of formic acid and the formates.

3.8. Stability of oxalic acid and the oxalates.

3.9. Stability of carbon dioxide, carbonic acid and the carbonates.

4. *Bibliography.*

---

[1] Extract from the Rapport CEFA/R.7 of the Commission des Études Fondamentales et Applications of CEBELCOR (October 1958).

1. SUBSTANCES CONSIDERED AND SUBSTANCES NOT CONSIDERED

	Oxidation number (Z)	Considered	Not considered	μ^0(cal.)	Name, colour, crystalline system
Solid substances	0	C	–	0	Graphite, shiny black, hex.
	»	–	C	685.0	Diamond, colourless, cub.
Dissolved substances	−2	CH_3OH	–	−41 700	Methanol or methyl alcohol, colourless
	0	$HCOH$	–	−31 000	Methanal or formaldehyde, colourless
	+2	HCO_2H	–	−85 100	Formic acid, colourless
	»	HCO_2^-	–	−80 000	Formate ion, colourless
	+3	$H_2C_2O_4$	–	−166 800	Oxalic acid, colourless
	»	$HC_2O_4^-$	–	−165 120	Acid oxalate ion, colourless
	»	$C_2O_4^{--}$	–	−159 400	Oxalate ion, colourless
	+4	H_2CO_3	–	−149 000	Carbonic acid
	»	HCO_3^-	–	−140 310	Bicarbonate ion, colourless
	»	CO_3^{--}	–	−126 220	Carbonate ion, colourless
	+5	–	$H_2C_2O_6$	–	Perdicarbonic acid, colourless
	+6	–	H_2CO_4	–	Permonocarbonic acid, colourless
Gaseous substances	−4	CH_4	–	−12 140	Methane, colourless
	+2	CO	–	−32 807.9	Carbon monoxide, colourless
	+4	CO_2	–	−94 259.8	Carbon dioxide, colourless

2. REACTIONS AND EQUILIBRIUM FORMULAE

2.1. TWO DISSOLVED SUBSTANCES

2.1.1. *Relative stability of the dissolved substances*

Z = +2

1. $HCO_2H = HCO_2^- + H^+$ $\qquad \log \frac{(HCO_2^-)}{(HCO_2H)} = -3.74 + pH$

Z = +3

2. $H_2C_2O_4 = HC_2O_4^- + H^+$ $\qquad \log \frac{(HC_2O_4^-)}{(H_2C_2O_4)} = -1.23 + pH$

3. $HC_2O_4^- = C_2O_4^{--} + H^+$ $\qquad \log \frac{(C_2O_4^{--})}{(HC_2O_4^-)} = -4.20 + pH$

Z = +4

4. $H_2CO_3 = HCO_3^- + H^+$ $\qquad \log \frac{(HCO_3^-)}{(H_2CO_3)} = -6.38 + pH$

5. $HCO_3^- = CO_3^{--} + H^+$ $\qquad \log \frac{(CO_3^{--})}{(HCO_3^-)} = -10.34 + pH$

−2 → 0

6. $CH_3OH = HCOH + 2H^+ + 2e^-$ $\qquad E_0 = 0.232 - 0.0591\,pH + 0.0295 \log \frac{(HCOH)}{(CH_3OH)}$

−2 → +2

7. $CH_3OH + H_2O = HCO_2H + 4H^+ + 4e^-$ $\qquad E_0 = 0.145 - 0.0591\,pH + 0.0148 \log \frac{(HCO_2H)}{(CH_3OH)}$

8. $CH_3OH + H_2O = HCO_2^- + 5H^+ + 4e^-$ $\qquad E_0 = 0.199 - 0.0739\,pH + 0.0148 \log \frac{(HCO_2^-)}{(CH_3OH)}$

−2 → +4

9. $CH_3OH + 2H_2O = H_2CO_3 + 6H^+ + 6e^-$ $\qquad E_0 = 0.044 - 0.0591\,pH + 0.0098 \log \frac{(H_2CO_3)}{(CH_3OH)}$

10. $CH_3OH + 2H_2O = HCO_3^- + 7H^+ + 6e^-$ $\qquad E_0 = 0.107 - 0.0689\,pH + 0.0098 \log \frac{(HCO_3^-)}{(CH_3OH)}$

11. $CH_3OH + 2H_2O = CO_3^{--} + 8H^+ + 6e^-$ $\qquad E_0 = 0.209 - 0.0788\,pH + 0.0098 \log \frac{(CO_3^{--})}{(CH_3OH)}$

$0 \rightarrow +2$

12.	$HCOH + H_2O = HCO_2H + 2H^+ + 2e^-$	$E_0 = 0.056 - 0.0591\ pH + 0.0295 \log \frac{(HCO_2H)}{(HCOH)}$
13.	$HCOH + H_2O = HCO_2^- + 3H^+ + 2e^-$	$E_0 = 0.167 - 0.0886\ pH + 0.0295 \log \frac{(HCO_2^-)}{(HCOH)}$

$0 \rightarrow +4$

14.	$HCOH + 2H_2O = H_2CO_3 + 4H^+ + 4e^-$	$E_0 = -0.050 - 0.0591\ pH + 0.0148 \log \frac{(H_2CO_3)}{(HCOH)}$
15.	$HCOH + 2H_2O = HCO_3^- + 5H^+ + 4e^-$	$E_0 = 0.044 - 0.0739\ pH + 0.0148 \log \frac{(HCO_3^-)}{(HCOH)}$
16.	$HCOH + 2H_2O = CO_3^{--} + 6H^+ + 4e^-$	$E_0 = 0.197 - 0.0886\ pH + 0.0148 \log \frac{(CO_3^{--})}{(HCOH)}$

$+2 \rightarrow +3$

17.	$2HCO_2H = H_2C_2O_4 + 2H^+ + 2e^-$	$E_0 = 0.074 - 0.0591\ pH + 0.0295 \log \frac{(H_2C_2O_4)}{(HCO_2H)^2}$
18.	$2HCO_2H = HC_2O_4^- + 3H^+ + 2e^-$	$E_0 = 0.110 - 0.0886\ pH + 0.0295 \log \frac{(HC_2O_4^-)}{(HCO_2H)^2}$
19.	$2HCO_2^- = HC_2O_4^- + H^+ + 2e^-$	$E_0 = -0.111 - 0.0295\ pH + 0.0295 \log \frac{(HC_2O_4^-)}{(HCO_2^-)^2}$
20.	$2HCO_2^- = C_2O_4^{--} + 2H^+ + 2e^-$	$E_0 = 0.013 - 0.0591\ pH + 0.0295 \log \frac{(C_2O_4^{--})}{(HCO_2^-)^2}$

$+2 \rightarrow +4$

21.	$HCO_2H + H_2O = H_2CO_3 + 2H^+ + 2e^-$	$E_0 = -0.156 - 0.0591\ pH + 0.0295 \log \frac{(H_2CO_3)}{(HCO_2H)}$
22.	$HCO_2^- + H_2O = H_2CO_3 + H^+ + 2e^-$	$E_0 = -0.267 - 0.0295\ pH + 0.0295 \log \frac{(H_2CO_3)}{(HCO_2^-)}$
23.	$HCO_2^- + H_2O = HCO_3^- + 2H^+ + 2e^-$	$E_0 = -0.078 - 0.0591\ pH + 0.0295 \log \frac{(HCO_3^-)}{(HCO_2^-)}$
24.	$HCO_2^- + H_2O = CO_3^{--} + 3H^+ + 2e^-$	$E_0 = 0.227 - 0.0886\ pH + 0.0295 \log \frac{(CO_3^{--})}{(HCO_2^-)}$

$+3 \rightarrow +4$

25.	$H_2C_2O_4 + 2H_2O = 2H_2CO_3 + 2H^+ + 2e^-$	$E_0 = -0.386 - 0.0591\ pH + 0.0295 \log \frac{(H_2CO_3)^2}{(H_2C_2O_4)}$
26.	$HC_2O_4^- + 2H_2O = 2H_2CO_3 + H^+ + 2e^-$	$E_0 = -0.423 - 0.0295\ pH + 0.0295 \log \frac{(H_2CO_3)^2}{(HC_2O_4^-)}$
27.	$C_2O_4^{--} + 2H_2O = 2H_2CO_3 + 2e^-$	$E_0 = -0.547 + 0.0295 \log \frac{(H_2CO_3)^2}{(C_2O_4^{--})}$
28.	$C_2O_4^{--} + 2H_2O = 2HCO_3^- + 2H^+ + 2e^-$	$E_0 = -0.170 - 0.0591\ pH + 0.0295 \log \frac{(HCO_3^-)^2}{(C_2O_4^{--})}$
29.	$C_2O_4^{--} + 2H_2O = 2CO_3^{--} + 4H^+ + 2e^-$	$E_0 = 0.441 - 0.1182\ pH + 0.0295 \log \frac{(CO_3^{--})^2}{(C_2O_4^{--})}$

2.1.2. *Limits of the domains of relative predominance of the dissolved substances*

1'.	HCO_2H/HCO_2^-	$pH = 3.74$
2'.	$H_2C_2O_4/HC_2O_4^-$	$pH = 1.23$
3'.	$HC_2O_4^-/C_2O_4^{--}$	$pH = 4.20$
4'.	H_2CO_3/HCO_3^-	$pH = 6.38$
5'.	HCO_3^-/CO_3^{--}	$pH = 10.34$
6'.	$CH_3OH/HCOH$	$E_0 = 0.232 - 0.0591\ pH$
7'.	CH_3OH/HCO_2H	$E_0 = 0.145 - 0.0591\ pH$
8'.	CH_3OH/HCO_2^-	$E_0 = 0.199 - 0.0739\ pH$
9'.	CH_3OH/H_2CO_3	$E_0 = 0.044 - 0.0591\ pH$
10'.	CH_3OH/HCO_3^-	$E_0 = 0.107 - 0.0689\ pH$
11'.	CH_3OH/CO_3^{--}	$E_0 = 0.209 - 0.0788\ pH$
12'.	$HCOH/HCO_2H$	$E_0 = 0.036 - 0.0591\ pH$
13'.	$HCOH/HCO_2^-$	$E_0 = 0.167 - 0.0886\ pH$
14'.	$HCOH/H_2CO_3$	$E_0 = -0.050 - 0.0591\ pH$

15'.	$HCOH\,/HCO_3^-$	$E_0 = 0.044 - 0.0739\,pH$
16'.	$HCOH\,/CO_3^{--}$	$E_0 = 0.197 - 0.0886\,pH$
17'.	$HCO_2H/H_2C_2O_4$	$E_0 = 0.074 - 0.0591\,pH - 0.0295\log C$
18'.	$HCO_2H/HC_2O_4^-$	$E_0 = 0.110 - 0.0886\,pH - 0.0295\log C$
19'.	$HCO_2^-\,/HC_2O_4^-$	$E_0 = -0.114 - 0.0295\,pH - 0.0295\log C$
20'.	$HCO_2^-\,/C_2O_4^{--}$	$E_0 = 0.013 - 0.0591\,pH - 0.0295\log C$
21'.	HCO_2H/H_2CO_3	$E_0 = -0.156 - 0.0591\,pH$
22'.	$HCO_2^-\,/H_2CO_3$	$E_0 = -0.267 - 0.0295\,pH$
23'.	$HCO_2^-\,/HCO_3^-$	$E_0 = -0.078 - 0.0591\,pH$
24'.	$HCO_2^-\,/CO_3^{--}$	$E_0 = 0.227 - 0.0886\,pH$
25'.	$H_2C_2O_4/H_2CO_3$	$E_0 = -0.386 - 0.0591\,pH + 0.0295\log C$
26'.	$HC_2O_4^-\,/H_2CO_3$	$E_0 = -0.423 - 0.0295\,pH + 0.0295\log C$
27'.	$C_2O_4^{--}\,/H_2CO_3$	$E_0 = -0.547 + 0.0295\log C$
28'.	$C_2O_4^{--}\,/HCO_3^-$	$E_0 = -0.170 - 0.0591\,pH + 0.0295\log C$
29'.	$C_2O_4^{--}\,/CO_3^{--}$	$E_0 = 0.441 - 0.1182\,pH + 0.0295\log C$

2.2. TWO GASEOUS SUBSTANCES

2.2.1. *Relative stability of the gaseous substances*

$-4 \rightarrow +2$

30. $CH_4 + H_2O = CO + 6H^+ + 6e^-$ $\qquad E_0 = 0.497 - 0.0591\,pH + 0.0098\log\dfrac{p_{CO}}{p_{CH_4}}$

$-4 \rightarrow +4$

31. $CH_4 + 2H_2O = CO_2 + 8H^+ + 8e^-$ $\qquad E_0 = 0.169 - 0.0591\,pH + 0.0074\log\dfrac{p_{CO_2}}{p_{CH_4}}$

$+2 \rightarrow +4$

32. $CO + H_2O = CO_2 + 2H^+ + 2e^-$ $\qquad E_0 = -0.103 - 0.0591\,pH + 0.0295\log\dfrac{p_{CO_2}}{p_{CO}}$

2.2.2. *Limits of the domains of relative predominance of the gaseous substances*

30'.	CH_4/CO	$E_0 = 0.497 - 0.0591\,pH$
31'.	CH_4/CO_2	$E_0 = 0.169 - 0.0591\,pH$
32'.	CO/CO_2	$E_0 = -0.103 - 0.0591\,pH$

2.3. ONE DISSOLVED SUBSTANCE AND ONE SOLID SUBSTANCE

Dissolution equilibria of graphite

$0 \rightarrow +2$

33. $C + 2H_2O = HCO_2H + 2H^+ + 2e^-$ $\qquad E_0 = 0.627 - 0.0591\,pH + 0.0295\log(HCO_2H)$

34. $C + 2H_2O = HCO_2^- + 3H^+ + 2e^-$ $\qquad E_0 = 0.724 - 0.0886\,pH + 0.0295\log(HCO_2^-)$

$0 \rightarrow +4$

35. $C + 3H_2O = H_2CO_3 + 4H^+ + 4e^-$ $\qquad E_0 = 0.228 - 0.0591\,pH + 0.0148\log(H_2CO_3)$

36. $C + 3H_2O = HCO_3^- + 5H^+ + 4e^-$ $\qquad E_0 = 0.323 - 0.0739\,pH + 0.0148\log(HCO_3^-)$

37. $C + 3H_2O = CO_3^{--} + 6H^+ + 4e^-$ $\qquad E_0 = 0.475 - 0.0886\,pH + 0.0148\log(CO_3^{--})$

2.4. ONE DISSOLVED SUBSTANCE AND ONE GASEOUS SUBSTANCE

Solubility of the gaseous substances

$Z = +4$

38. $CO_2 + H_2O = H_2CO_3$ $\qquad \log\dfrac{(H_2CO_3)}{p_{CO_2}} = 1.43$

39. $CO_2 + H_2O = HCO_3^- + H^+$ $\qquad \log\dfrac{(HCO_3^-)}{p_{CO_2}} = -7.81 + pH$

40. $CO_2 + H_2O = CO_3^{--} + 2H^+$ $\qquad \log\dfrac{(CO_3^{--})}{p_{CO_2}} = -18.14 + 2\,pH$

2.5. ONE SOLID SUBSTANCE AND ONE GASEOUS SUBSTANCE

Limits of the domains of relative stability of C, CH_4, CO and CO_2

$-4 \rightarrow 0$

41. $CH_4 = C + 4H^+ + 4e^-$ $\qquad E_0 = -0.132 - 0.0591\,pH - 0.0148\log p_{CH_4}$

$0 \rightarrow +2$

42. $C + H_2O = CO + 2H^+ + 2e^-$ $\qquad E_0 = 0.518 - 0.0591\,pH + 0.0295\log p_{CO}$

$0 \rightarrow +4$

43. $C + 2H_2O = CO_2 + 4H^+ + 4e^-$ $\qquad E_0 = 0.207 - 0.0591\,pH + 0.0148\log p_{CO_2}$

3. EQUILIBRIUM DIAGRAM AND ITS INTERPRETATION

3.1. ESTABLISHMENT OF THE DIAGRAM

Using the equilibrium formulae established in paragraph 2, we have constructed Figs. 1–7.

In Figs. 1–4 we have used relations (1′)–(29′) to represent the influence of pH on the conditions of relative predominance (at the equilibrium) of the following dissolved carbon derivatives considered two by two: on the one hand, carbonic acid, bicarbonate and carbonate, and, on the other hand, respectively methanol (Fig. 1), methanal (Fig. 2), formate (Fig. 3) and oxalates (Fig. 4).

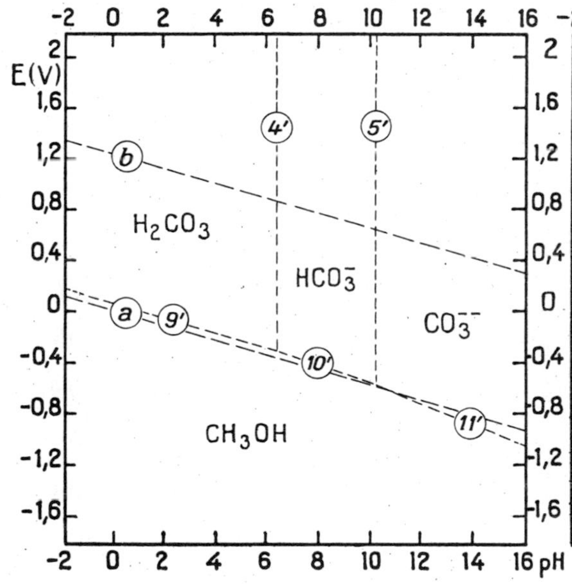

FIG. 1. Domains of relative predominance of carbon in the form of methanol and carbonates, at 25°C.

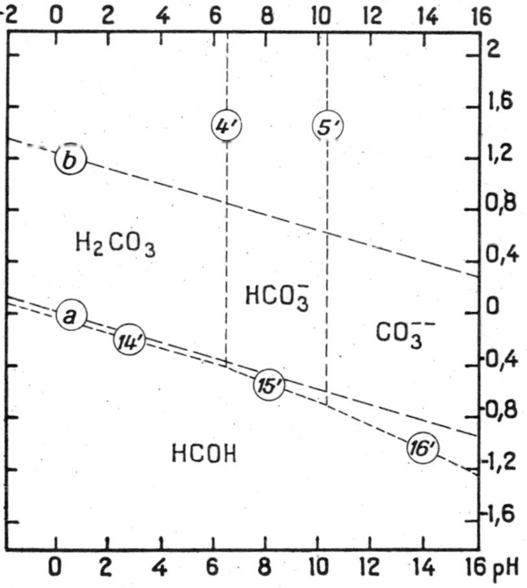

FIG. 2. Domains of relative predominance of carbon in the form of methanal and carbonates, at 25°C.

In Figs. 5 and 6 we have used relations (30′)–(32′) to represent the domain of relative predominance (at the equilibrium) of the gaseous derivatives of carbon: CH_4, CO and CO_2; in Fig. 5 we have considered all three gases (in which case CO does not appear in the diagram, as it is unstable with respect to CH_4 and CO_2); in Fig. 6 we have not considered CH_4 (thus giving us the conditions of relative predominance of CO_2 and metastable CO).

Using these diagrams in conjunction with relations (1)–(43), we have established a potential–pH equilibrium diagram for the system C(graphite)–H_2O (Fig. 7). The only dissolved and gaseous substances that we have considered are the thermodynamically stable ones: carbonic acid, bicarbonate and carbonate, methanol, carbon dioxide and methane. This diagram is valid only in the absence of substances with which the above-mentioned substances can form soluble complexes or insoluble salts.

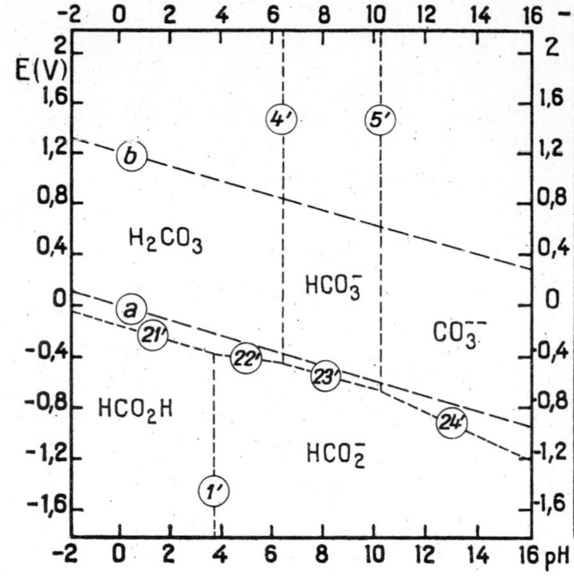

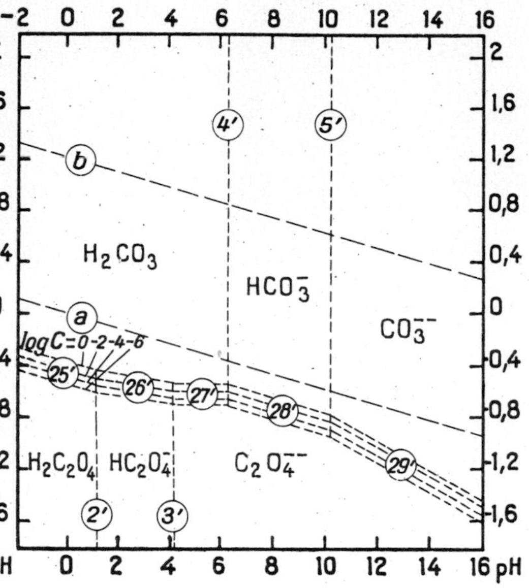

FIG. 3. Domains of relative predominance of carbon in the form of formate and carbonates, at 25°C.
Fig. 4. Domains of relative predominance of carbon in the form of oxalates and carbonates, at 25°C.

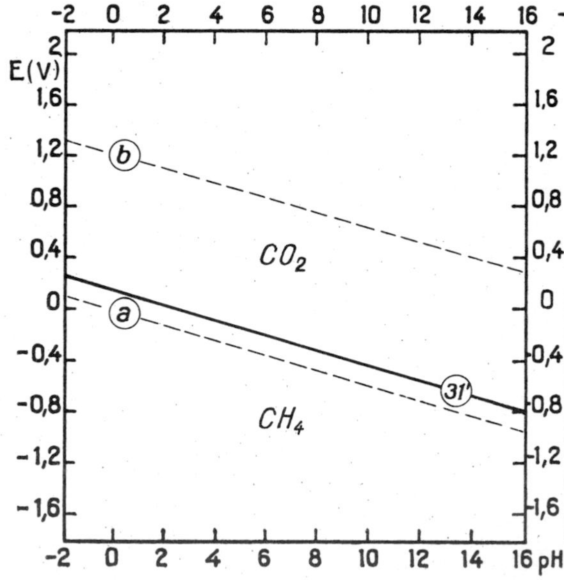

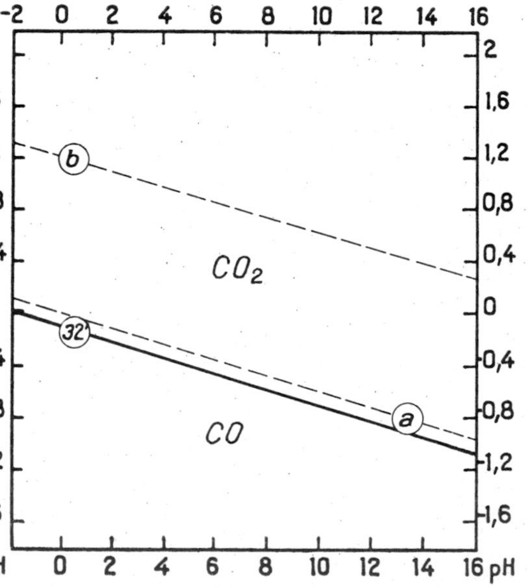

FIG. 5. Domains of relative predominance of the gaseous carbon derivatives CH_4 and CO_2 (stable equilibrium).
FIG. 6. Domains of relative predominance of the gaseous carbon derivatives CO and CO_2 (unstable equilibrium).

According to Charlot [1], the oxalates form a large number of complexes, in particular with trivalent Fe, Al and Cr, tetravalent Sn and V, hexavalent Mo and W; the carbonates form complexes which are fairly unstable with Co^{+++}, UO_2^{++}, Be^{++}, Th^{++++}, etc.

The carbonates and the oxalates are sparingly soluble in water, except for those of the alkali metals.

3.2. STABILITY OF CARBON

From Fig. 7, elementary carbon appears to be a relatively base substance, since part of its domain of stability partially covers that of water.

It is thermodynamically stable in the presence of water and aqueous solutions of pH below about 13 free from oxidizing agents.

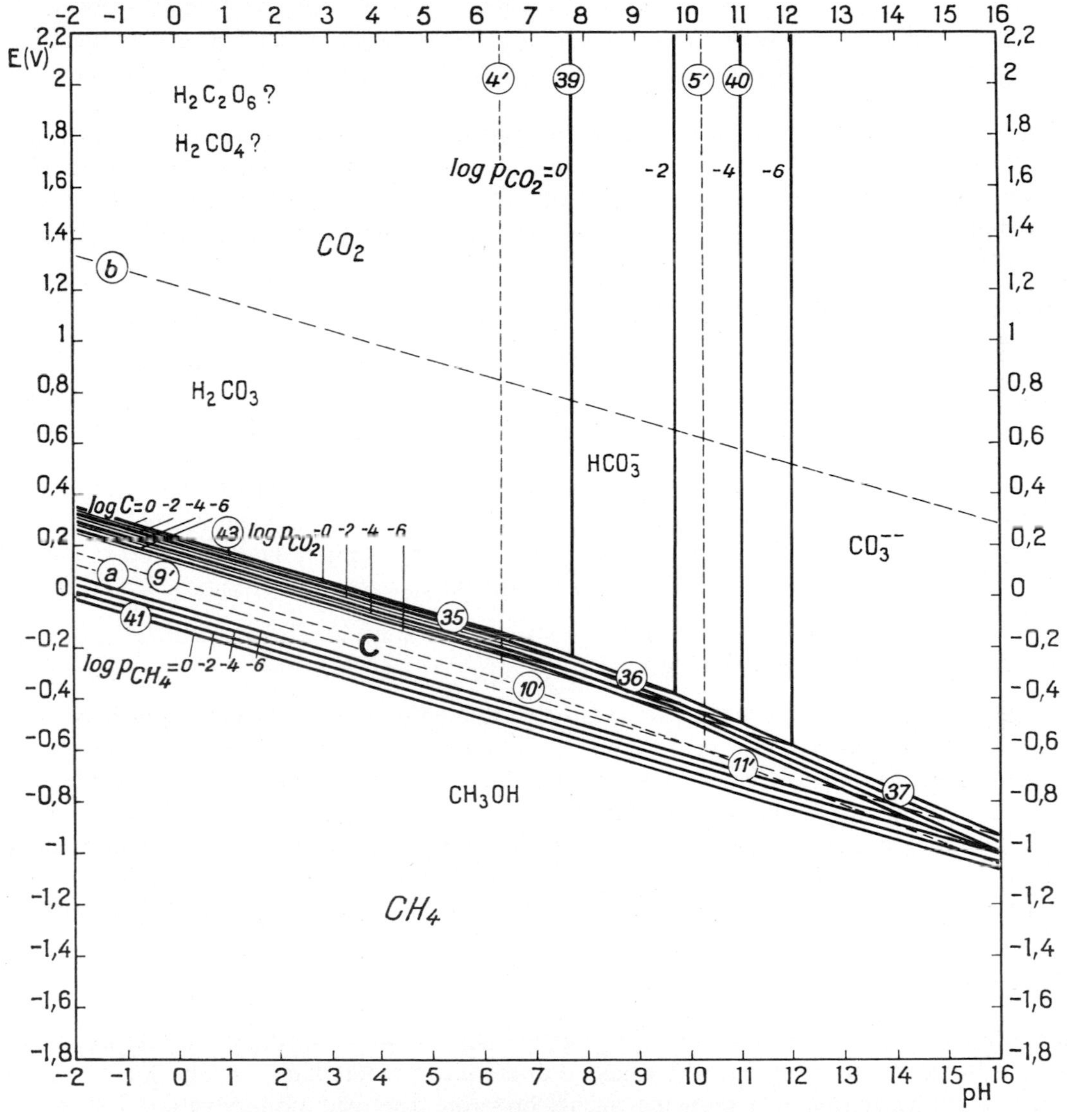

FIG. 7. Potential–pH equilibrium diagram for the system carbon–water, at 25°C. (Considering carbon in the form of graphite.)

The portion of the diagram above the line log C = 0 refers to solutions containing 1 g-at of dissolved carbon per litre in the form of $H_2CO_3 + HCO_3^- + CO_3^{--}$. The portion of the diagram below this line refers to solutions thermodynamically saturated with solid carbon.

In its natural state carbon is found in the form of diamond, graphite and impure amorphous carbon.

On account of its narrow stability domain, it is *theoretically* easy to cause carbon to react, either by oxidation when the electrode potential is above the values given by the family of lines (35), (36) and

(37), with the formation of carbon dioxide CO_2, carbonic acid H_2CO_3 and carbonates HCO_3^- and CO_3^{--}, or by reduction when the electrode potential is below the values given by the family of lines (41), with the formation of methane CH_4, methyl alcohol and other organic substances. However, it should be noted that, although energetically possible, these reactions are highly irreversible, and cannot actually be brought about under normal conditions of temperature and pressure.

3.3. STABILITY OF METHANE CH_4

According to Fig. 7, it is theoretically possible to obtain methane, together with some hydrogen, by the reduction of carbonates or carbon in the presence of aqueous solutions. This has not been confirmed, however.

Methane is a reducing agent and is thermodynamically unstable in the presence of water at atmospheric pressure; it tends to decompose into its constituent elements, carbon and hydrogen. However, under normal conditions of temperature and pressure this reaction is highly irreversible; the decomposition of methane occurs only at high temperatures.

3.4. STABILITY OF METHANOL (METHYL ALCOHOL)

According to Fig. 1, methanol can be oxidized to carbonic acid and carbonates. However, although this reaction is energetically possible as soon as the electrode potential exceeds the values given by lines (9′), (10′) and (11′), it is in fact probably highly irreversible and possible to bring about only with high overpotentials.

It follows from the equilibrium formulae given in paragraph 2 that methanol, together with carbonic acid and the carbonates, is the only dissolved substance having a domain of predominance at the equilibrium; methanol is therefore the only dissolved reducing agent to be considered in the diagram of stable equilibria (Fig. 7); methanal, the formates and the oxalates do not appear in this diagram.

3.5. STABILITY OF METHANAL (FORMALDEHYDE)

According to Fig. 2, methanal is a reducing agent, slightly unstable in the presence of water and aqueous solutions of all pH's, in which it tends to reduce the water with the evolution of hydrogen.

Methanal can theoretically be converted into carbonic acid and carbonates at electrode potentials above those given by lines (14′), (15′) and (16′).

According to Latimer [2], this conversion can be brought about by the electrolytic oxidation of methanal in an alkaline solution. Latimer also states that the electrolytic reduction of methanal, using a cathode with a large hydrogen overpotential, leads to the formation of methyl alcohol (methanol).

3.6. STABILITY OF CARBON MONOXIDE CO

According to Fig. 5, carbon monoxide CO is thermodynamically unstable with respect to methane and carbon dioxide CO_2; consequently it has no domain of predominance in Fig. 7.

Figure 6 shows that it is a reducing agent; however, the oxidation-reduction system CO/CO_2 [equation (32)] is highly irreversible and changes only with infinite slowness. Certain substances act as catalysts and make the reaction possible: pentavalent I, Ag^+, finely divided Pt and Pd (Charlot [1]).

3.7. STABILITY OF FORMIC ACID AND THE FORMATES

The positions of the domains of predominance of formic acid HCO_2H and the formates HCO_2^- in Fig. 3 show that these substances are reducing agents, thermodynamically unstable in the presence of aqueous solutions of all pH's.

In actual fact, the reducing action of formic acid and the formates on water is very slow; in solution they are practically stable in the absence of oxidizing agents, and their reducing property is not very pronounced. On the other hand, the presence of a suitable catalyst, such as finely divided palladium, markedly brings out their reducing power: hot $HgCl_2$ is reduced to Hg_2Cl_2 or even Hg; MnO_4^- is reduced to Mn^{++} (Charlot [1]). Using cathodes with large overpotentials, it is possible, according to Latimer [2], to reduce formic acid to formaldehyde and methyl alcohol.

3.8. STABILITY OF OXALIC ACID AND THE OXALATES

According to Fig. 4, oxalic acid and the oxalates are reducing agents, thermodynamically unstable in the presence of aqueous solutions. Nevertheless, their reducing action is slow, becoming appreciable only with powerful oxidizing agents (e.g. MnO_4^-) or in the presence of catalysts (e.g. finely divided Pt).

3.9. STABILITY OF CARBON DIOXIDE, CARBONIC ACID AND THE CARBONATES

Carbon dioxide CO_2, carbonic acid H_2CO_3 and the carbonates HCO_3^- and CO_3^{--} are the forms of carbon which are thermodynamically stable in the presence of water and aqueous solutions, both in the absence and in the presence of oxygen and oxidizing agents.

According to Figs. 1–7, CO_2, H_2CO_3, HCO_3^- and CO_3^{--} can be reduced to carbon and various organic substances; however, although these reactions are thermodynamically possible at electrode potentials below those given by lines (35), (36), (37) and (43); (41) and (9′), (10′) and (11′), they are highly irreversible, and cannot in fact be brought about in aqueous solution under normal conditions of temperature and pressure.

The reduction of $C^{(IV)}$ (CO_2, H_2CO_3, HCO_3^-, CO_3^{--}) to $C^{(II)}$ (CO, HCO_2H, HCO_2^-) is extremely irreversible. Charlot [1] states that it has been possible to accomplish it only by the intervention of catalysts and light, and even then with extreme slowness; in practice $C^{(IV)}$ is not reduced to $C^{(II)}$ in solution. However, Latimer [2] mentions that it is possible to reduce HCO_3^- to HCO_2^-, using a nickel catalyst. Fischer and Prziza [3] carried out the electrolytic reduction of CO_2 to HCO_2H with a zinc amalgam cathode, at a CO_2 pressure of 5 atm.

It appears to be possible to oxidize carbonic acid and the carbonates to perdicarbonic acid $H_2C_2O_6$ and permonocarbonic acid H_2CO_4 by electrolytic means (platinum anode, at about 0°C). As we have no thermodynamic data for these substances they were not considered for the establishment of the carbon–water equilibrium diagram; they are marked on it purely as a rough guide.

4. BIBLIOGRAPHY

[1] G. Charlot, *L'analyse qualitative et les réactions en solution*, 4th ed., Masson, Paris, 1957.

[2] W. Latimer, *Oxidation Potentials*, Prentice-Hall, New York, 1952.

[3] F. Fischer and O. Prziza, Ueber die elektrolytische Reduktion von unter Druck gelöstem Kohlendioxyd und Kohlenoxyd, *Ber.* **47**, 256–60 (1914).

SECTION 17.2

SILICON[1]

J. VAN MUYLDER, J. BESSON, W. KUNZ and M. POURBAIX

SUMMARY

[1] Extract from the Rapport CEFA/R.7 of the Commission des Études Fondamentales et Applications of CEBELCOR (October 1958).

1. SUBSTANCES CONSIDERED AND SUBSTANCES NOT CONSIDERED

	Oxidation number (Z)	Considered	Not considered	μ^0(cal.)	Name, colour, crystalline system
Solid substances	0	**Si**	–	0	Silicon, steel-grey, cub.
	»	–	**Si**	–	Silicon, brown, amorphous
	+2	–	**SiO**	–	Silicon monoxide, yellowish brown, amorphous
	+4	$\mathbf{SiO_2}$ anh.	–	a. −192 400	"Quartz" silica, colourless, hex.
	»	» »	–	b. −192 100	"Cristobalite" silica, colourless, cub.
	»	» »	–	c. −191 900	"Tridymite" silica, colourless, hex.
	»	» »	–	d. −190 900	Vitreous silica, colourless
	»	» »	–	e. −187 810	Hydrated silica or metamonosilicic acid H_2SiO_3, colourless, am.(2)
	»	–	$\mathbf{SiO_2}$ hydr.	–	Hydrated silica or orthomonosilicic acid H_4SiO_4, colourless, am.
Dissolved substances	+4	H_2SiO_3	–	−242 000 (3)	Metamonosilicic acid, colourless
	»	$HSiO_3^-$	–	−228 360 (3)	Acid metamonosilicate ion, colourless
	»	SiO_3^{--}	–	−212 000	Metamonosilicate ion, colourless
	»	–	(4)	–	Orthosilicic acids
Gaseous substance	−4	SiH_4	–	− 9 400	Silicon hydride, colourless

2. REACTIONS AND EQUILIBRIUM FORMULAE

2.1. TWO DISSOLVED SUBSTANCES

2.1.1. *Relative stability of the dissolved substances*

$Z = +4$

1. $H_2SiO_3 = HSiO_3^- + H^+$ $\qquad \log\frac{(HSiO_3^-)}{(H_2SiO_3)} = -10.00 + \text{pH}$

2. $HSiO_3^- = SiO_3^{--} + H^+$ $\qquad \log\frac{(SiO_3^{--})}{(HSiO_3^-)} = -12.00 + \text{pH}$

2.1.2. *Limits of the domains of relative predominance of the dissolved substances*

1'. $H_2SiO_3/HSiO_3^-$ $\qquad \text{pH} = 10.00$

2'. $HSiO_3^-/SiO_3^{--}$ $\qquad \text{pH} = 12.00$

2.2. TWO SOLID SUBSTANCES

Limits of the domains of relative stability of the solid substances

$0 \rightarrow +4$

3. $\mathbf{Si} + 2H_2O = \mathbf{SiO_2} + 4H^+ + 4e^-$

$$
\begin{aligned}
a.\ E_0 &= -0.857 - 0.0591\ \text{pH}\\
b.\quad &= -0.853 - 0.0591\ \text{pH}\\
c.\quad &= -0.851 - 0.0591\ \text{pH}\\
d.\quad &= -0.840 - 0.0591\ \text{pH}\\
e.\quad &= -0.807 - 0.0591\ \text{pH}
\end{aligned}
$$

(2) This value for $\mu^0_{SiO_2}$ corresponds to $\mu^0_{H_2SiO_3} = -187\,810 - 56\,690 = -244\,500$ cal.

(3) These values were calculated from data found by Joseph and Oakley [1] and pointed out by Latimer.

(4) In particular, we have omitted to consider the following: orthomono-, orthodi-, orthotri- and orthotetrasilicic acids H_4SiO_4, $H_6Si_2O_7$, $H_8Si_3O_{10}$ and $H_{10}Si_4O_{13}$.

2.3. ONE DISSOLVED SUBSTANCE AND ONE SOLID SUBSTANCE

Solubility of the solid substances

$Z = +4$

4. $\mathbf{SiO_2} + H_2O = H_2SiO_3$

a. $\log(H_2SiO_3) = -5.21$
b. $= -4.99$
c. $= -4.85$
d. $= -4.11$
e. $= -1.84$

5. $\mathbf{SiO_2} + H_2O = HSiO_3^- + H^+$

a. $\log(HSiO_3^-) = -15.21 + pH$
b. $= -14.99 + pH$
c. $= -14.85 + pH$
d. $= -14.11 + pH$
e. $= -11.84 + pH$

6. $\mathbf{SiO_2} + H_2O = SiO_3^{--} + 2H^+$

a. $\log(SiO_3^{--}) = -27.21 + 2\,pH$
b. $= -26.99 + 2\,pH$
c. $= -26.85 + 2\,pH$
d. $= -26.11 + 2\,pH$
e. $= -23.84 + 2\,pH$

$0 \rightarrow +4$

7. $\mathbf{Si} + 3H_2O = H_2SiO_3 + 4H^+ + 4e^-$ $\qquad E_0 = -0.780 - 0.0591\,pH + 0.0148 \log(H_2SiO_3)$
8. $\mathbf{Si} + 3H_2O = HSiO_3^- + 5H^+ + 4e^-$ $\qquad E_0 = -0.632 - 0.0739\,pH + 0.0148 \log(HSiO_3^-)$
9. $\mathbf{Si} + 3H_2O = SiO_3^{--} + 6H^+ + 4e^-$ $\qquad E_0 = -0.455 - 0.0886\,pH + 0.0148 \log(SiO_3^{--})$

2.4. ONE DISSOLVED SUBSTANCE AND ONE GASEOUS SUBSTANCE

Solubility of SiH_4

$-4 \rightarrow +4$

10. $SiH_4 + 3H_2O = H_2SiO_3 + 8H^+ + 8e^-$ $\qquad E_0 = -0.339 - 0.0591\,pH + 0.0074 \log \frac{(H_2SiO_3)}{p_{SiH_4}}$

11. $SiH_4 + 3H_2O = HSiO_3^- + 9H^+ + 8e^-$ $\qquad E_0 = -0.265 - 0.0665\,pH + 0.0074 \log \frac{(HSiO_3^-)}{p_{SiH_4}}$

12. $SiH_4 + 3H_2O = SiO_3^{--} + 10H^+ + 8e^-$ $\qquad E_0 = -0.176 - 0.0739\,pH + 0.0074 \log \frac{(SiO_3^{--})}{p_{SiH_4}}$

2.5. ONE SOLID SUBSTANCE AND ONE GASEOUS SUBSTANCE

Limits of the domains of relative stability of **Si** *and SiH_4*

$-4 \rightarrow 0$

13. $SiH_4 = \mathbf{Si} + 4H^+ + 4e^-$ $\qquad E_0 = 0.102 - 0.0591\,pH - 0.0148 \log p_{SiH_4}$

$-4 \rightarrow +4$

14. $SiH_4 + 2H_2O = \mathbf{SiO_2} + 8H^+ + 8e^-$

a. $E_0 = -0.377 - 0.0591\,pH - 0.0074 \log p_{SiH_4}$
b. $= -0.376 - 0.0591\,pH - 0.0074 \log p_{SiH_4}$
c. $= -0.375 - 0.0591\,pH - 0.0074 \log p_{SiH_4}$
d. $= -0.369 - 0.0591\,pH - 0.0074 \log p_{SiH_4}$
e. $= -0.353 - 0.0591\,pH - 0.0074 \log p_{SiH_4}$

3. EQUILIBRIUM DIAGRAM AND ITS INTERPRETATION

3.1. ESTABLISHMENT OF THE DIAGRAM

Using the equilibrium formulae given in paragraph 2 we have constructed Figs. 1 and 2.

Figure 1 is a potential–pH equilibrium diagram for the system silicon–water, considering silica in the form of quartz.

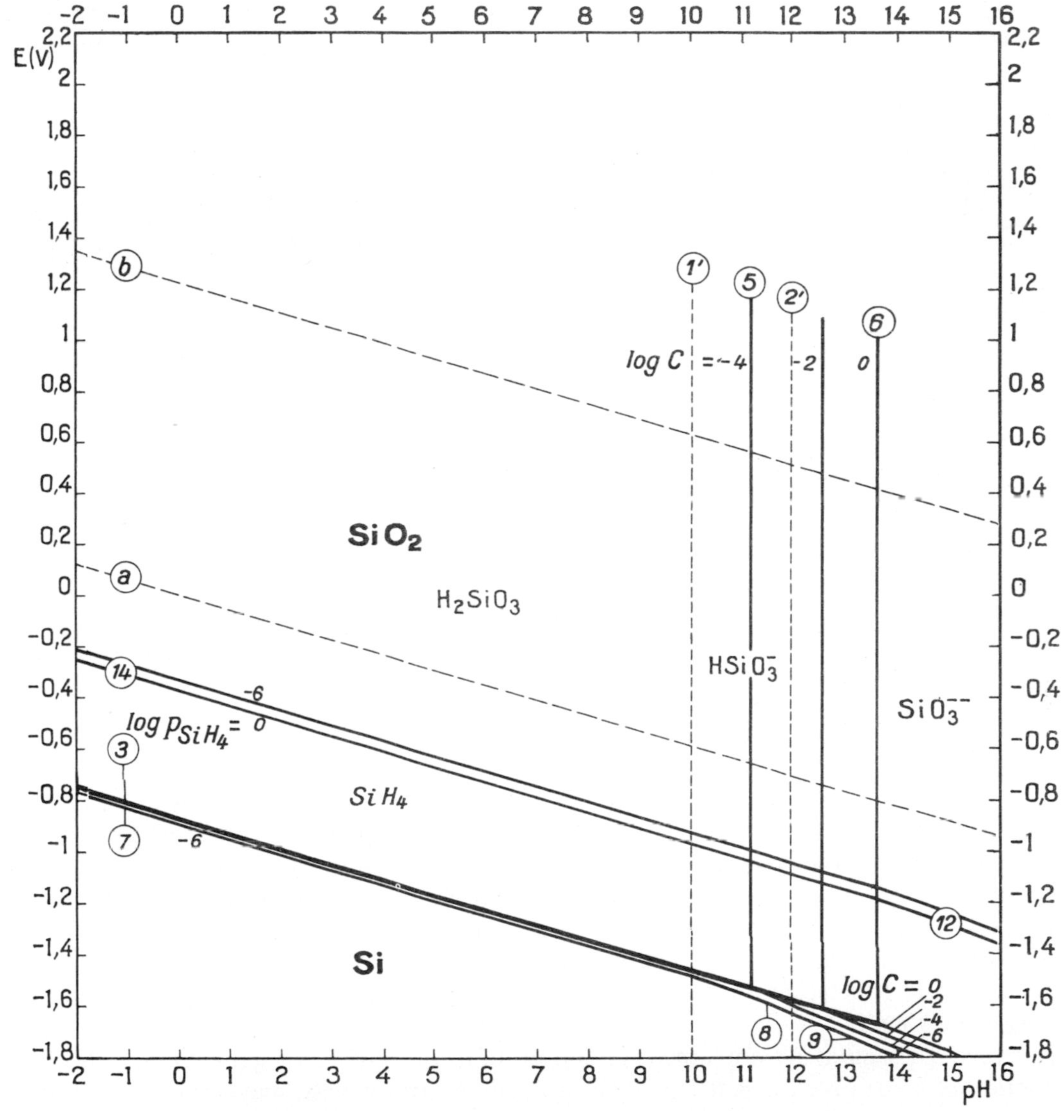

FIG. 1. Potential–pH equilibrium diagram for the system silicon–water, at 25°C. (Considering SiO_2 in the form of quartz. Approximate diagram.)

In Fig. 2 we have used relations (1′), (2′), (4), (5) and (6) to represent the influence of pH on the solubility of silica, SiO_2, in the following forms: quartz, cristobalite, tridymite, vitreous silica and amorphous hydrated silica. However, these diagrams do not take into account the complex nature of solutions of silicic acid and silicates, and are therefore only approximate. Moreover, they are valid only in the absence of substances with which silicon can form soluble complexes or insoluble salts. Charlot [2] mentions that silicon forms, in particular, unstable yellow silicomolybdic complexes with hexavalent molybdenum and fairly unstable fluorosilicic complexes, such as SiF_6^{--}. A large number of complex compounds are sparingly soluble, e.g. the aluminosilicates. The silicates are almost all insoluble, except for those of the alkali metals.

3.2. STABILITY OF SILICON

According to Fig. 1, silicon is a powerful reducing agent; together with boron, it is the most powerful reducing agent of the non-metals. It tends to decompose water with the evolution of hydrogen and gaseous silicon hydride SiH_4, and the formation of silica or silicates.

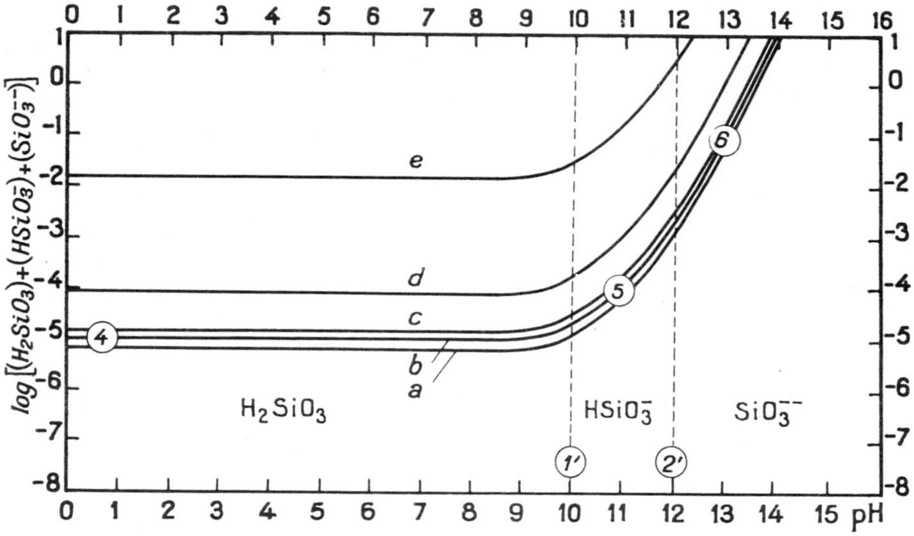

FIG. 2. Influence of pH on the solubility of silica SiO_2, at 25°C.
a, quartz; *b*, cristobalite; *c*, tridymite; *d*, vitreous silica; *e*, amorphous silica.

In actual fact, the great reactivity of silicon is not often apparent at room temperature. This seems to be due mainly to the great irreversibility of the oxidation-reduction reactions of silicon, with the result that the element displays a very great chemical stability. A second cause of this stability is probably passivation by a film of silica, in acid solution, at least (Besson and Kunz [3]). Although silicon reacts slowly with water at room temperature, as shown by Weiss and Engelhardt [4], it is not affected by acids, and is attacked by caustic alkalis only when hot, in which case silicates and silicon hydride SiH_4 are formed.

Silicon cannot be separated from aqueous solutions of its salts by electrolysis; it is usually obtained by the reduction of silica or silicates using alkali or alkaline earth metals, magnesium or aluminium.

3.3. STABILITY OF SILICON HYDRIDE SiH_4

Equilibrium diagram 1 shows that gaseous silicon hydride SiH_4 is unstable in the presence of water, which it tends to decompose with the formation of hydrogen and silica or silicates. It can be oxidized by solutions containing oxygen or other oxidizing agents such as nitric acid.

Theoretically it can be formed, together with hydrogen, by the reduction of solutions of silicic acid or silicates, but we do not know if this has been confirmed experimentally. SiH_4 can be obtained, mixed with hydrogen, by the action of acids on aluminium containing silicon as an impurity, and also by the action of hydrochloric acid on a magnesium silicide of approximate composition $SiMg_3$.

3.4. STABILITY OF SILICA SiO_2

Silica SiO_2 exists in various forms; apart from the so-called amorphous or hydrated silicas, there are at least seven crystalline varieties. The only ones encountered in nature are quartz, tridymite and cristobalite, which undergo the following reversible transformation, with extreme slowness, through the action of heat:

$$\text{quartz} \underset{}{\overset{807°}{\rightleftharpoons}} \text{tridymite} \underset{}{\overset{1\,470°}{\rightleftharpoons}} \text{cristobalite.}$$

A large number of hydration products correspond to silica SiO_2. These have the function of acids. Examples, according to Latimer [5], are H_4SiO_4, $H_6Si_2O_7$, $H_8Si_3O_{10}$ and $H_{10}Si_4O_{13}$, respectively orthomono-, orthodi-, orthotri- and orthotetrasilicic acids. There are also partial dehydration products of these acids, such as metamonosilicic acid H_2SiO_3.

All these acids, which can exist in solution, give rise to very complex equilibria. Through lack of precise data we have considered only metamonosilicic acid H_2SiO_3 in Figs. 1 and 2, to the exclusion of the condensed forms.

When alkali metal silicates are treated with dilute acids, a hydrated silica containing a variable percentage of water is obtained. Its composition can be expressed by the formula $SiO_2 . xH_2O$.

According to Fig. 1, silica is a very stable substance in the presence of water and aqueous solutions, except for alkaline solutions which dissolve it as silicates SiO_3^{--}. In this respect, we have drawn in Fig. 2 a series of curves representing diagrammatically (according to the thermodynamic data given in paragraph 1) the influence of pH on the solubility of the various varieties of silica for which we have values of the free enthalpy of formation. This figure shows that the stability of SiO_2 in alkaline media depends to a considerable extent on the variety considered.

In practice, freshly precipitated hydrated silica dissolves almost instantaneously in very alkaline solutions (NaOH, KOH); precipitated calcined silica hardly dissolves in the cold, but dissolves rapidly on boiling; quartz, even when finely powdered, is hardly attacked by these alkalis when boiling, but at 200°C it dissolves easily under pressure.

4. BIBLIOGRAPHY

[1] A. JOSEPH and H. OAKLEY, The action of silica on electrolytes, *J. Chem. Soc.* **127,** 2813 (1925).
[2] G. CHARLOT, *L'analyse qualitative et les reactions en solution*, 4th ed., Masson, Paris, 1957.
[3] J. BESSON and W. KUNZ, *Ann. Univ. Sarav.* **6,** 17 (1957).
[4] L. WEISS and T. ENGELHARDT, Ueber die Stickstoffverbindungen des Siliciums, *Z. anorg. allgem. Chem.* **65**, 88 (1909).
[5] W. LATIMER, *Oxidation Potentials,* Prentice-Hall, New York, 1952.

SECTION 17.3

GERMANIUM(¹)

N. de Zoubov, E. Deltombe, C. Vanleugenhaghe and M. Pourbaix

SUMMARY

1. *Substances considered and substances not considered.*

2. *Reactions and equilibrium formulae.*

   2.1. Two dissolved substances.

      2.1.1. Relative stability of the dissolved substances.

      2.1.2. Limits of the domains of relative predominance of the dissolved substances.

   2.2. Two solid substances.
   Limits of the domains of relative stability of germanium and its oxides.

   2.3. One solid substance and one dissolved substance.
   Solubility of germanium and its oxides.

   2.4. One solid substance and one gaseous substance.
   Relative stability of germanium and germanium hydride.

3. *Equilibrium diagrams and their interpretation.*

   3.1. Establishment of the diagrams.

   3.2. Stability and corrosion of germanium.

   3.3. Cathodic behaviour and electro-deposition of germanium.

   3.4. Stability and formation of the oxides and hydroxides of germanium.

      3.4.1. Oxides and hydroxide of divalent germanium.

      3.4.2. Germanic oxides and hydroxide.

4. *Bibliography.*

(¹) Shortened and adapted version of the Rapport technique RT.27 of CEBELCOR [1].

1. SUBSTANCES CONSIDERED AND SUBSTANCES NOT CONSIDERED

	Oxidation number (Z)	Considered	Not considered	μ^0(cal.)	Name, colour, crystalline system
Solid substances	-3	–	Ge_2H_6	–	Hydride
	-2.67	–	Ge_3H_8	–	"
	-2.5	–	Ge_4H_{10}	–	"
	-2	–	GeH_2	–	"
	-1	–	$(GeH)_x$	–	"
	0	Ge	–	0	Germanium, grey–white, cub.
	$+2$	–	GeO anh.	–	Anh. germanous oxide, black
	"	GeO hydr.	–	*a.* $-69\,900$ (*)	Hydr. germanous oxide, brown
	"	"	–	*b.* $-62\,700$ (*)	Hydr. germanous oxide, yellow
	"	–	GeO hydr.	–	Hydr. germanous oxide or germanous hydroxide $Ge(OH)_2$, orange–red
	$+4$	GeO_2	–	*c.* $-136\,100$ (*)	"Insoluble" germanic oxide, white, quad.
	"	"	–	*d.* $-132\,000$ (*)	"Precipitated" germanic oxide, white, hex.
	"	–	GeO_2	–	"Amorphous" germanic oxide
Dissolved substances	$+2$	Ge^{++}	–	0	Germanous ion
	"	–	$HGeO_2^-$	$-92\,200$ (*)	Bigermanite ion, cherry-red
	"	–	GeO_2^{--}	–	Germanite
	$+4$	H_2GeO_3	–	$-186\,800$ (*)	Germanic acid
	"	$HGeO_3^-$	–	$-175\,200$ (*)	Bigermanate ion
	"	GeO_3^{--}	–	$-157\,900$ (*)	Germanate ion
	"	–	Ge^{++++}	–	Germanic ion
	"	–	GeO_4^{----}	–	?
	"	–	$H_2Ge_2O_5$	–	Digermanic acid
	"	–	$H_2Ge_4O_9$	–	Tetragermanic acid
	"	–	$H_2Ge_5O_{11}$	–	Pentagermanic acid
	"	–	$HGe_5O_{11}^-$	–	Acid pentagermanate ion
	"	–	$Ge_5O_{11}^{--}$	–	Pentagermanate ion
	$+6$	–	$Ge_2O_7^{--}$	–	?
Gaseous substance	-4	GeH_4	–	$80\,000$ (*)	Hydride, colourless

We calculated the standard free enthalpies marked (*) as follows:

hydrated brown GeO ($-69\,900$ cal.):

We assumed the value $E_0^0 = -0{\cdot}118 \pm 0{\cdot}010$ V, given by Jolly and Latimer [2], for the standard potential of the couple brown GeO/hex. GeO_2 (according to the reaction: $GeO + H_2O = GeO_2 + 2H^+ + 2e^-$). From this we deduced: $\mu^\circ = -132\,000 + 56\,690 + (0{\cdot}118 \times 46\,120) = -69\,870$ cal.

hydrated yellow GeO ($-62\,700$ cal.):

We assumed that the free enthalpy of yellow hydr. GeO is 7 200 cal. greater than that of brown hydr. GeO ($-69\,900$ cal.), as assumed by Jolly and Latimer [2]. Thus we deduced: $\mu^0 = -69\,900 + 7\,200 = -62\,700$ cal.

quadratic GeO_2 ($-136\,100$ cal.):

We assumed the value 4·5 mg/l (i.e. $10^{-4.37}$ g-mol/l), given by Müller [3], for the solubility of quadratic GeO_2 in water (in the form of H_2GeO_3 for which $\mu^\circ = -186\,800$ cal.).
From this we deduced: $\mu^\circ = -136\,066$ cal.

hexagonal GeO_2 (−132 *000* cal.):

We assumed:

— for the enthalpy of hexagonal GeO_2: $h° = -128{\cdot}5 \pm 0{\cdot}5$ kcal., a mean proposed by Jolly and Latimer [2] for the experimental results of Becker and Roth [4] ($h° = -128{\cdot}1 \pm 0{\cdot}6$ kcal.), Hahn and Juza [5] (−128·6 kcal.) and Jolly and Latimer [2] ($-129{\cdot}2 \pm 2{\cdot}0$ kcal.).

— for the entropy of hexagonal GeO_2: $S^0 = 12$ cal./deg, a mean of the values of Jolly and Latimer [2] (13 cal./deg) and Bues and Wartenberg [6] (11·5 cal./deg).

From these we deduced: $\mu^0 = -128\,500 - (12 \times 298) = -132\,000$ cal.

$HGeO_2^-$ (−92 *200* cal.):

We assumed the value $E_B^0 = -1{\cdot}4$ V at pH = 14 (approximate value), given by Charlot [7], for the equilibrium potential of the reaction $HGeO_3^- + 2H^+ + 2e^- = HGeO_2^- + H_2O$.

From this we deduced: $\mu^0 = -175\,200 + 56\,690 + (0{\cdot}57 \times 46\,120) = -92\,220$ cal.

H_2GeO_3 (−186 *800* cal.):

We assumed the value 4·50 g/l (i.e. $10^{-1{\cdot}37}$ mole/l) for the solubility of hexagonal GeO_2 ($\mu° = -132\,000$ cal.) in water at 25°C (in the form of H_2GeO_3). This is a mean of the values of Pugh [8] (4·47 g/l) and Laubengayer and Morton [9] (4·53 g/l).

From this we deduced: $\mu° = -132\,000 - 56\,690 + (1\,363 \times 1{\cdot}37) = -186\,800$ cal.

$HGeO_3^-$ (−175 *200* cal.):

We assumed the value pK = 8·52, given by Pugh [8], for the dissociation of germanic acid according to the reaction $H_2GeO_3 = HGeO_3^- + H^+$.

From this we deduced: $\mu° = -186\,800 + (1\,363 \times 8{\cdot}52) = -175\,200$ cal.

GeO_3^{--} (−157 *900* cal.):

We assumed the value pK = 12·72, given by Pugh [8], for the dissociation of bigermanate according to the reaction $HGeO_3^- = GeO_3^{--} + H^+$.

From this we deduced: $\mu° = -175\,200 + (1\,363 \times 12{\cdot}72) = -157\,900$ cal.

GeH_4 (+80 *000* cal.):

The enthalpy of the hydride was calculated approximately from the work of Paneth and Rabinovitch [10] (see [1]).

2. REACTIONS AND EQUILIBRIUM FORMULAE

2.1. TWO DISSOLVED SUBSTANCES

2.1.1. *Relative stability of the dissolved substances*

Z = +4

1. $H_2GeO_3 = HGeO_3^- + H^+$ $\qquad \log\frac{(HGeO_3^-)}{(H_2GeO_3)} = -8.52 + pH$

2. $HGeO_3^- = GeO_3^{--} + H^+$ $\qquad \log\frac{(GeO_3^{--})}{(HGeO_3^-)} = -12.72 + pH$

+2 → +4

3. $Ge^{++} + 3H_2O = H_2GeO_3 + 4H^+ + 2e^-$ $\qquad E_0 = -0.363 - 0.1182\,pH + 0.0295\log\frac{(H_2GeO_3)}{(Ge^{++})}$

4. $Ge^{++} + 3H_2O = HGeO_3^- + 5H^+ + 2e^-$ $\qquad E_0 = -0.111 - 0.1477\,pH + 0.0295\log\frac{(HGeO_3^-)}{(Ge^{++})}$

2.1.2. *Limits of the domains of relative predominance of the dissolved substances*

1′. $H_2GeO_3/HGeO_3^-$ $\qquad pH = 8.52$

2′. $HGeO_3^-/GeO_3^{--}$ $\qquad pH = 12.72$

3′. Ge^{++}/H_2GeO_3 $\qquad E_0 = -0.363 - 0.1182\,pH$

4′. $Ge^{++}/HGeO_3^-$ $\qquad E_0 = -0.111 - 0.1477\,pH$

2.2. TWO SOLID SUBSTANCES

Limits of the domains of relative stability of germanium and its oxides

$0 \rightarrow +2$

5. **Ge** $+ H_2O =$ **GeO** $+ 2H^+ + 2e^-$
$a.\ E_0 = -0.286 - 0.0591\ pH$
$b.\ \quad = -0.130 - 0.0591\ pH$

$0 \rightarrow +4$

6. **Ge** $+ 2H_2O =$ **GeO₂** $+ 4H^+ + 4e^-$
$c.\ E_0 = -0.246 - 0.0591\ pH$
$d.\ \quad = -0.202 - 0.0591\ pH$

$+2 \rightarrow +4$

7. **GeO** $+ H_2O =$ **GeO₂** $+ 2H^+ + 2e^-$
$ac.\ E_0 = -0.206 - 0.0591\ pH$
$ad.\ \quad = -0.117 - 0.0591\ pH$
$bc.\ \quad = -0.362 - 0.0591\ pH$
$bd.\ \quad = -0.273 - 0.0591\ pH$

2.3. ONE SOLID SUBSTANCE AND ONE DISSOLVED SUBSTANCE

Solubility of germanium and its oxides

$Z = +2$

8. $Ge^{++} + H_2O =$ **GeO** $+ 2H^+$
$a.\ \log(Ge^{++}) = -9.69 - 2\ pH$
$b.\ \quad = -4.41 - 2\ pH$

$Z = +4$

9. **GeO₂** $+ H_2O = H_2GeO_3$
$c.\ \log(H_2GeO_3) = -4.37$
$d.\ \quad = -1.37$

10. **GeO₂** $+ H_2O = HGeO_3^- + H^+$
$c.\ \log(HGeO_3^-) = -12.83 + pH$
$d.\ \quad = -9.90 + pH$

11. **GeO₂** $+ H_2O = GeO_3^{--} + 2H^+$
$c.\ \log(GeO_3^{--}) = -25.60 + 2\ pH$
$d.\ \quad = -22.59 + 2\ pH$

$0 \rightarrow +2$

12. **Ge** $= Ge^{++} + 2e^-$
$E_0 = 0.000 + 0.0295 \log(Ge^{++})$

$0 \rightarrow +4$

13. **Ge** $+ 3H_2O = H_2GeO_3 + 4H^+ + 4e^-$
$E_0 = -0.182 - 0.0591\ pH + 0.0148 \log(H_2GeO_3)$

14. **Ge** $+ 3H_2O = HGeO_3^- + 5H^+ + 4e^-$
$E_0 = -0.056 - 0.0738\ pH + 0.0148 \log(HGeO_3^-)$

15. **Ge** $+ 3H_2O = GeO_3^{--} + 6H^+ + 4e^-$
$E_0 = 0.132 - 0.0886\ pH + 0.0148 \log(GeO_3^{--})$

$+2 \rightarrow +4$

16. **GeO** $+ 2H_2O = H_2GeO_3 + 2H^+ + 2e^-$
$a.\ E_0 = -0.074 - 0.0591\ pH + 0.0295 \log(H_2GeO_3)$
$b.\ \quad = -0.232 - 0.0591\ pH + 0.0295 \log(H_2GeO_3)$

17. **GeO** $+ 2H_2O = HGeO_3^- + 3H^+ + 2e^-$
$a.\ E_0 = 0.177 - 0.0886\ pH + 0.0295 \log(HGeO_3^-)$
$b.\ \quad = 0.019 - 0.0886\ pH + 0.0295 \log(HGeO_3^-)$

18. **GeO** $+ 2H_2O = GeO_3^{--} + 4H^+ + 2e^-$
$a.\ E_0 = 0.550 - 0.1182\ pH + 0.0295 \log(GeO_3^{--})$
$b.\ \quad = 0.394 - 0.1182\ pH + 0.0295 \log(GeO_3^{--})$

2.4. ONE SOLID SUBSTANCE AND ONE GASEOUS SUBSTANCE

Relative stability of germanium and germanium hydride

$-4 \rightarrow 0$

19. GeH_4 $=$ **Ge** $+ 4H^+ + 4e^-$
$E_0 = -0.867 - 0.0591\ pH - 0.0148 \log p_{GeH_4}$

3. EQUILIBRIUM DIAGRAMS AND THEIR INTERPRETATION

3.1. ESTABLISHMENT OF THE DIAGRAMS

Using relations (1)–(19) established in paragraph 2, we have constructed a potential–pH equilibrium diagram for the system germanium–water (Fig. 1). In it we have considèred only the most stable of the forms of germanium oxide given in paragraph 1, i.e. brown hydrated GeO and "insoluble" GeO_2 (white, quadratic).

In Fig. 2 we have considered brown hydrated GeO and "precipitated" GeO_2 (white, hexagonal).

In Fig. 3 we have used relations (9)–(11) to represent the influence of pH on the solubility of the two forms of GeO_2 quoted above, in solutions of tetravalent germanium (in the form of germanic acid and germanates).

From Fig. 1 we have deduced Fig. 4, which is a theoretical "corrosion, immunity and passivation" diagram for germanium.

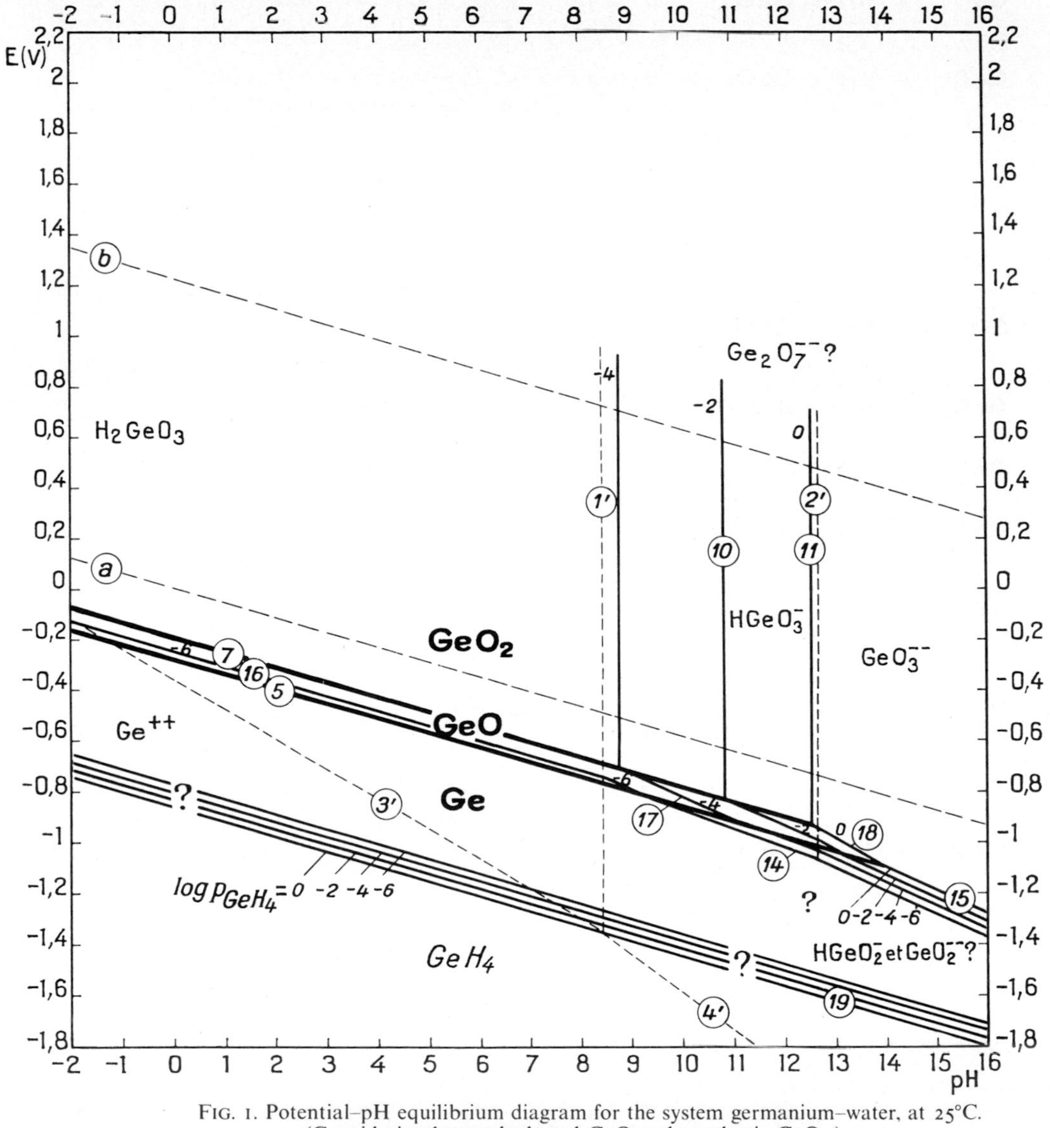

FIG. 1. Potential–pH equilibrium diagram for the system germanium–water, at 25°C. (Considering brown hydrated GeO and quadratic GeO_2.)

For want of sufficient thermodynamic data, we were not able to consider the following substances, which it would have been useful to consider for the construction of such diagrams:

—*solid substances:* we have not considered black anhydrous germanous oxide GeO whose heat of formation, according to Becker and Roth [4], is $78{\cdot}2 \pm 1{\cdot}3$ kcal., or the orange hydroxide $Ge(OH)_2$; we have not considered any of the numerous solid hydrides mentioned in the literature $(GeH)_x$, $(GeH_2)_x$, Ge_2H_6, Ge_3H_8, Ge_4H_{10}.

–*dissolved substances:* we have considered the germanite ions $HGeO_2^-$ and GeO_2^{--} only qualitatively; we have not considered pentagermanic acid $H_2Ge_5O_{11}$ or the pentagermanates $HGe_5O_{11}^-$ and $Ge_5O_{11}^{--}$ for which Charlot [7] gives the following pK's:

$$H_2Ge_5O_{11} = HGe_5O_{11}^- + H^+, \quad pK = 8.6 \text{ to } 9;$$
$$HGe_5O_{11}^- = Ge_5O_{11}^{--} + H^+, \quad pK = 12.7 \text{ to } 13.$$

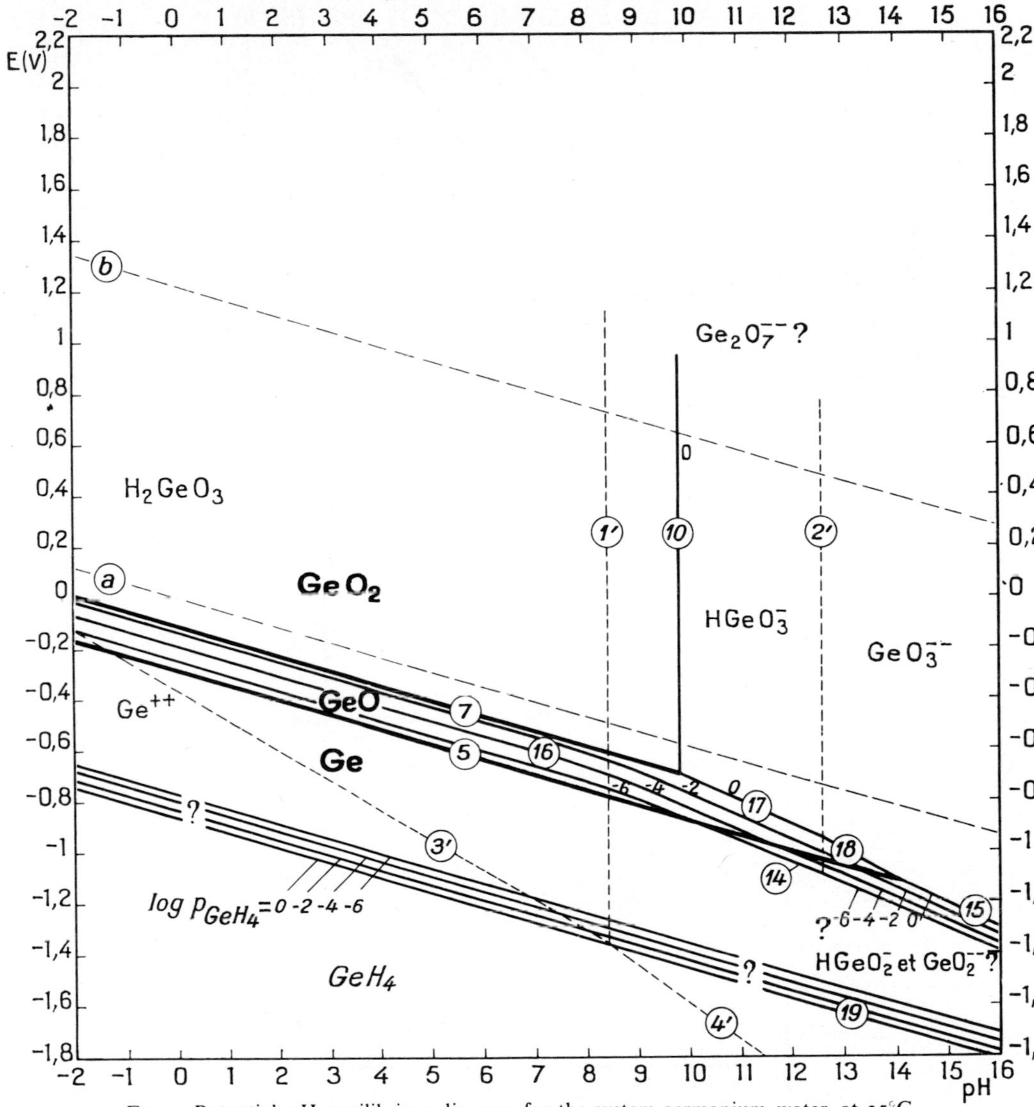

FIG. 2. Potential–pH equilibrium diagram for the system germanium–water, at 25°C. (Considering brown hydrated GeO and hexagonal GeO_2.)

It must be understood that Figs. 1–4, and consequently the interpretation of them given below, are very approximate and liable to drastic modification.

3.2. STABILITY AND CORROSION OF GERMANIUM

According to Figs. 1 and 2 germanium is a base metal, as its domain of thermodynamic stability lies entirely below that of water. It is therefore thermodynamically unstable in the presence of water.

Germanium tends to dissolve in aqueous solutions of all pH's; in neutral or acid solutions there is a possibility of the formation of relatively sparingly soluble germanous oxide GeO or relatively soluble germanic oxide. The dissolution takes place mainly in the valency state +4, with the formation of germanate, and without any appreciable formation of germanite (valency +2), in the absence of complexing substances at least.

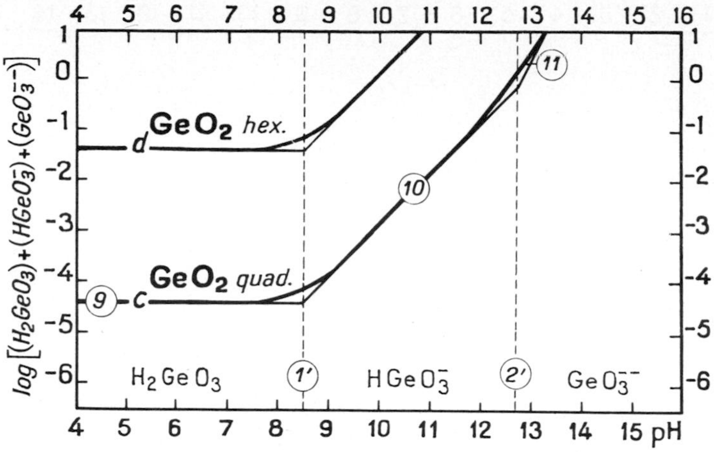

FIG. 3. Influence of pH on the solubility of quadratic GeO_2 and hexagonal GeO_2.

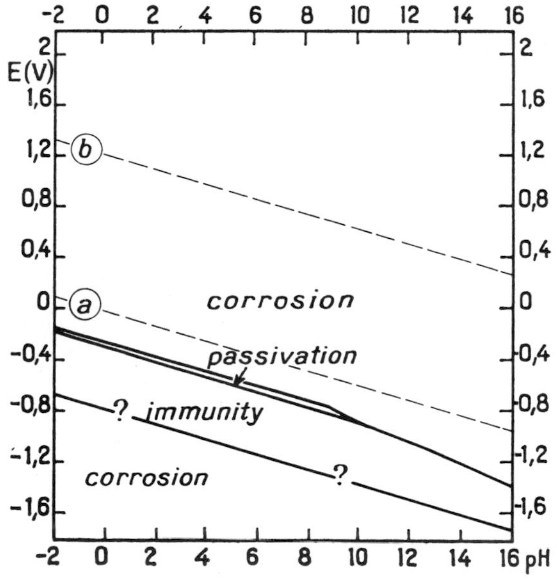

FIG. 4. Theoretical conditions of corrosion, immunity and passivation of germanium, at 25°C.

According to Figs. 1 and 2, a powerful reducing action can lead to the volatilization of germanium as its hydride GeH_4; however, the conditions of formation of this hydride, represented by the family of lines (19) are not known with precision [10].

According to Fig. 4, the domain of passivation of germanium is very small and lies entirely below the domain of stability of water, corresponding to an unstable passivation. According to this figure, germanium can be corroded all along the pH scale, which agrees with Jirsa's observation [11]. This conclusion is subject to caution, however, as it is not impossible that germanium can become covered with an oxide which is less soluble than those considered here; moreover, in the presence of certain solutions it can cover itself with sparingly soluble salts which are more or less protective. The difficulties encountered in the pickling of germanium are probably at least partly due to such facts.

Given below are some experimental data obtained by Dennis *et al.* [12], resulting from experiments carried out at room temperature for a duration of one week:

germanium is practically unaffected by water, concentrated HCl and aqueous solutions of NaOH (50 per cent), HCl (50 per cent) and H_2SO_4 (50 per cent); it is tarnished by a 10 per cent solution of NaOH and by concentrated HNO_3; dilute HNO_3 produces a white film of GeO_2 on its surface. Germanium is attacked slightly by concentrated H_2SO_4 and by HF. It dissolves rapidly in 3 per cent H_2O_2; hydrogen peroxide is, in fact, the best solvent for germanium.

3.3. CATHODIC BEHAVIOUR AND ELECTRO-DEPOSITION OF GERMANIUM

Figures 1 and 2 show that a cathode immersed in a germanium solution can be the site of the following three reactions:

the deposition of germanium;
the evolution of gaseous hydrogen;
the evolution of gaseous germanium hydride.

The relative importance of these three reactions depends mainly on the potential of the cathode and the pH of the solution in contact with the cathode, as well as on the overpotentials of these reactions.

In 1925 Paneth and Rabinovitch [10] prepared germanium hydride by the electrolysis of a solution of GeO_2 in dilute sulphuric acid between lead electrodes, using the same apparatus as they had previously used for the preparation of tin hydride SnH_4 ([13], [14]). The hydride carried along by the hydrogen formed at the cathode is separated from it by cooling. The process of formation of the GeH_4 is probably the same as for SnH_4: first of all there is electrodeposition of germanium on the lead cathode, then simultaneous evolution of hydrogen and germanium hydride on the germanium-covered cathode.

In 1950 Petcherskaia and Stender [15] measured the hydrogen overpotentials of various metals including germanium and zinc, in a 2 N H_2SO_4 solution at 25°C; they obtained the following values:

Current density (mA/cm^2)	1	5	10	20	40	60	100	200
Hydrogen overpotential (V):								
Ge	0.39	0.54	0.62	0.68	0.76	0.78	0.85	0.92
Zn	0.83	0.95	1.01	1.05	1.10	1.13	1.17	1.22

The overpotential values for germanium are, for the small current densities at least, of the same order of magnitude as those for the hydrogen overpotentials of iron, nickel and cobalt; they are therefore sufficiently great to explain the inertness of germanium towards solutions free from oxidizing agents at 25°C. On the other hand, however, they are considerably smaller than the corresponding values for zinc.

The fact that the electrodeposition of zinc in an acid bath is hindered by the presence of traces of germanium is generally interpreted as being due to germanium having a smaller hydrogen overpotential than zinc.

Here is a brief summary of the principal research carried out on the electrodeposition of germanium:

In 1927 Dennis and Tressler [16] obtained films of germanium by the electrolysis of a solution of GeO_2 in fused cryolite or fused potassium fluorogermanate in a graphite crucible. The process has the disadvantage, however, that a considerable amount of GeO is lost by evaporation.

In 1936 Schwarz *et al.* [17] systematically studied the electrodeposition of germanium in acid and alkaline aqueous solutions and came to the following conclusion: a black powdery non-adherent deposit of germanium is always obtained at first; the deposition of germanium then ceases and evolution of hydrogen and germanium hydride takes place. According to these experimenters the spongy, powdery nature of the germanium deposit is due to the simultaneous formation of hydride, which has the effect of lowering the hydrogen overpotential, favouring the formation of hydrogen.

In 1943 Lloyd and Pugh [18] directly electrolysed a solution obtained from the alkaline extraction of a germanium ore (germanite); they thus obtained a simultaneous deposition of gallium and germanium and observed that, at the end of the electrolysis, on account of the decrease in the concentration of germanium in the electrolyte, there is a decrease in the rate of deposition of germanium and a preponderance of the formation of germanium hydride.

In 1949 Fink and Dokras [19] made a very thorough investigation of the various conditions under which electrolytic deposits of germanium can be obtained; their conclusions are as follows:

in aqueous solutions (acid or alkaline), only very thin deposits of germanium can be obtained, as the deposition of germanium ceases as soon as the cathode is completely covered: after this, hydrogen evolution alone takes place. In alkaline solutions, germanium can be deposited simultaneously with other metals such as Cu, Ni and Co. The most interesting alloy thus formed is that with Cu, which has the formula Cu_3Ge;

in fused salts: an excellent deposit can be obtained starting from a solution of GeO_2 in fused sodium tetraborate, by electrolysis at about 1 000°C in a graphite crucible;

in non-aqueous solutions: very satisfactory deposits can be obtained by the electrolysis between 140 and 150°C of solutions of the iodide GeI_4 in anhydrous ethylene glycol.

Finally, in 1951, Szekely [20] perfected the non-aqueous process of Fink and Dokras: he did, in fact, obtain good deposits of germanium by electrolysing, at 59°C, a solution of $GeCl_4$ in ethylene glycol, or preferably propylene glycol using a rotating cathode. The optimum conditions are:

Concentration: 7 per cent (by volume of $GeCl_4$ in the propylene glycol);
Temperature: 59°C;
Cathodic current density: 0·4 A/cm^2;
Rate at the cathode surface: 10 m/min;
Anode: graphite.

Under these conditions the rate of deposition is 0·025 mm in 3 h. The shiny deposit can attain a thickness of at least 0·12 mm.

These studies show clearly how the three possible cathodic reactions (deposition of the metal, evolution of hydrogen and evolution of hydride) can compete with one another; consequently, the only means found so far to carry out the electrodeposition of germanium without prejudicial evolution of hydrogen or hydride is to work in the total absence of water in the electrolyte used.

3.4. STABILITY AND FORMATION OF THE OXIDES AND HYDROXIDES OF GERMANIUM

Anhydrous and hydrated oxides of both di- and tetravalent germanium are known.

3.4.1. *Oxides and hydroxide of divalent germanium*

The anhydrous oxide GeO is obtained as a black crystalline powder by the dehydration of the hydrate on heating; the dehydration is not complete until a temperature of 650°C is reached. This oxide appears to be thermodynamically unstable at temperatures below 600°C. It was not considered for the establishment of the diagrams.

The hydrated oxide, commonly called germanous hydroxide $Ge(OH)_2$, exists in two forms: when freshly precipitated in the cold, for instance by adding ammonia to a solution of it in hydrochloric acid, it is yellow and can be preserved in this state under cold water; its solubility at 25°C, according to Everest and Terrey [21], is $5{\cdot}0 \times 10^{-3}$ mole/l, i.e. $10^{-2{\cdot}3}$ mole/l. If a suspension of it in water is boiled or treated with sulphuric acid, the yellow hydrate is converted into a brown variety which is less soluble (1 to 3×10^{-4} mole/l, i.e. a mean of $10^{-3.7}$ mole/l, according to Jolly and Latimer [2] who consider this brown form to be thermodynamically stable).

As we have mentioned in paragraph 3.1, Figs. 1 and 2 were established by considering the more stable brown form. Under these conditions, germanous oxide is stable with respect to germanium and germanic oxide GeO_2, but it tends to decompose water with the evolution of hydrogen.

According to Fig. 1, which is only approximate, the germanium present in the solution obtained by saturating water with hydrated GeO exists not in the divalent form Ge^{++}, but in the tetravalent form H_2GeO_3. This dissolution, accompanied by an oxidation must also be accompanied by a simultaneous reduction, such as the decomposition of water with the evolution of hydrogen, according to the overall reaction $GeO + 2H_2O \rightarrow H_2GeO_3 + H_2$. The solubility of hydrated GeO, which is relatively small in acid and neutral solutions would be very great in very alkaline solutions.

Since the work of Hantzsch [22], germanous hydroxide has been attributed acid properties, resulting from its solubility in alkalis with the formation of germanites. Everest and Terrey [21] have shown, however, that Hantzsch's experiments were rendered inaccurate by the presence of dioxide GeO_2, which easily forms germanates; if Hantzsch's experiments are reproduced, and the presence of tetravalent germanium is carefully avoided, no reaction takes place between germanous hydroxide and alkalis according to Everest and Terrey, excluding the possibility that the hydroxide can react as an acid. As these experimenters point out, if the germanite ion $HGeO_2^-$ or GeO_2^{--} existed in an alkaline medium, it would decompose spontaneously into germanate with the deposition of germanium and/or the liberation of hydrogen.

3.4.2. *Germanic oxides and hydroxide*

The dioxide GeO_2 exists in various forms; Johnson, in his account of the inorganic compounds of germanium [23], describes three of them:

if the fused dioxide is cooled rapidly, a relatively stable *amorphous dioxide* is obtained, which is transparent and has a vitreous structure. Its solubility in water at 30°C, according to Laubengayer and Morton [9], is 5·184 g/l;

on hydrolysing germanium tetrahalides or alkali metal germanates, a *precipitated dioxide* is obtained, which has a microcrystalline hexagonal texture and is slightly less soluble than the amorphous dioxide (Pugh). Its solubility in water at 25°C is 4·53 g/l according to Laubengayer and Morton [9] and 4·47 g/l according to Pugh [8]. We have taken 4·50 g/l (see section 1);

on heating the residue obtained by evaporation of an aqueous solution of these dioxides to 380°C, a quadratic dioxide is produced, often called the *insoluble* form. This form is extraordinarily inert towards substances which react *easily* with the other two forms; it does not react with hydrofluoric acid or sulphuric acid and is attacked only very slowly by alkalis. According to Müller [3] its solubility in water at 25°C is 4·5 mg/l, and we have assumed this value for the calculation of the free enthalpies given in paragraph 1. Gulezian and Müller give 2·3 mg/l [24].

In Fig. 3 we have used relations (9), (10) and (11) to construct the solubility curves of the two crystalline forms of GeO_2.

The experimental data concerning the solubility of GeO_2 in alkaline solutions do not agree with these data. This anomaly may be due to a Tyndall effect [8].

The solubility curves given in Fig. 3 do not show the amphoteric character sometimes attributed to germanic oxide, i.e. the possibility of it dissolving also in acid media, as Ge^{++++} ions for example; we have no definite information about this. The solubility of hexagonal GeO_2 in solutions of HCl and H_2SO_4 has been studied by Pugh [8], but the behaviour of GeO_2 in these acids seems abnormal, if one assumes that the solubility in pure water is exact. We have not taken into consideration the existence of the cation of tetravalent germanium.

Corresponding to the anhydrous oxide GeO_2 there is a hydrate, obtained by the hydrolysis of the tetrachloride $GeCl_4$, for instance. This hydrate has no fixed H_2O content and loses water continuously on heating. We cannot therefore speak of a solid hydroxide $Ge(OH)_4$.

According to Figs. 1 and 2, the oxide GeO_2 is too soluble to be able to protect germanium by oxidation (Figs. 3 and 4).

4. BIBLIOGRAPHY

[1] N. DE ZOUBOV, E. DELTOMBE and M. POURBAIX, *Comportement électrochimique du germanium. Diagrammes d'équilibres tension–pH du système* Ge-H_2O, *à* 25°C (Rapport technique RT.27 of CEBELCOR, November 1955).

[2] W. L. JOLLY and W. M. LATIMER, The solubility of hydrous germanous oxide and the potential of the germanous oxide–germanic oxide couple, *J. Amer. Chem. Soc.* **74**, 5751–52 (1952); The equilibrium Ge(s)+GeO_2(s)=2GeO. The heat of formation of germanic oxide, *ibid.* **74**, 5756 (1952).

[3] J. H. MÜLLER, Further studies on the allotropy of germanic oxide, *Proc. Amer. Phil. Soc.* **65**, 193–9 (1926).

[4] G. BECKER and W. A. ROTH, Die Bildungswärmen von Indiumtrioxyd und Germaniumdioxyd, *Z. Phys. Chem.* A **161**, 69–76 (p. 75) (1932).

[5] H. HAHN and R. JUZA, Untersuchungen über die Nitride von Cadmium, Gallium, Indium und Germanium, *Z. anorg. allgem. Chem.* **244**, 121 (1940).

[6] W. BUES and H. VON WARTENBERG, Das system Ge/GeO/GeO_2, *Z. anorg. allgem. Chem.* **266**, 281–8 (1951).

[7] G. CHARLOT, *L'analyse qualitative et les réactions en solution,* 4th ed., Masson, Paris, 1957.

[8] W. PUGH, Germanium. Part IV. The solubility of germanium dioxide in acids and alkalis, *J. Chem. Soc.* 1537–41 (1929). Part V. The hydrolysis of sodium germanate and the dissociation constants of germanium acid, *ibid.*, 1994–2001.

[9] A. W. LAUBENGAYER and D. S. MORTON, Germanium XXXIX. The polymorphism of germanium dioxide, *J. Amer. Chem. Soc.* **54**, 2303–20 (1932).

[10] F. PANETH and E. RABINOVITCH, Ueber die Gruppe der flüchtigen Hydrate, *Ber.* **58**, 1138–63 (1925).

[11] F. JIRSA, Ueber die anodische Auflösung des Germaniums, *Z. anorg. allgem. Chem.* **268**, 84–88 (1952).

[12] L. M. DENNIS, K. M. TRESSLER and F. E. HANCE, Germanium. VI. Metallic germanium. Reduction of germanium dioxide. Preparation of fused germanium. Physical and chemical properties, *J. Amer. Chem. Soc.* **45**, 2033–47 (1923).

[13] F. PANETH and E. RABINOVITCH, Ueber die Gewinnung des Zinnwasserstoffs durch kathodische Reduktion, *Ber.*, **57**B, 1877–90 (1924).

[14] N. DE ZOUBOV and E. DELTOMBE, *Enthalpie libre de formation standard de l'hydrure d'étain* SnH_4 *gazeux* (Rapport technique RT.26 of CEBELCOR, 1955).

[15] A. G. PETCHERSKAIA and V. V. STENDER, Potentiels de dégagement d'hydrogène dans les solutions acides, *J. Fiz. Khim.* **24,** 856–9 (1950).

[16] L. M. DENNIS and K. M. TRESSLER, Germanium XX. Preparation of fused germanium directly from germanium dioxide, *J. Phys. Chem.* **31,** 1429–31 (1927).

[17] R. SCHWARZ, F. HEINRICH and E. HOLLSTEIN, Beiträge zur Chemie des Germaniums. 17. Ueber das elektrochemische Verhalten des Germaniums, *Z. anorg. allgem. Chem.* **229,** 146–160 (1936).

[18] D. J. LLOYD and W. PUGH, Gallium. Part VI. The separation of gallium and germanium from alkaline extracts of germanite by electrolysis, *J. Chem. Soc.* 74–6 (1943).

[19] C. G. FINK and V. M. DOKRAS, Electrodeposition and electrowinning of germanium, *Trans. Electrochem. Soc.* **95,** 80–97 (1949).

[20] G. SZEKELY, Electrodeposition of germanium, *J. Electrochem. Soc.* **98**, 318–24 (1951); B. Pat. 711065 of Sylvana Electric Products Inc., (1954).

[21] D. A. EVEREST and H. TERREY, Germanous oxide and sulfide, *J. Chem. Soc.* 2282–5 (1950).

[22] A. HANTZSCH, Ueber die Natur alkalischer Lösungen von Metallhydraten, *Z. anorg. allgem. Chem.* **30**, 289–324 (1902).

[23] O. H. JOHNSON, Germanium and its inorganic compounds, *Chem. Rev.* **51**, 431–69 (1952).

[24] C. E. GULEZIAN and J. H. MÜLLER, The conductivity of solutions of germanic oxide, *J. Amer. Chem. Soc.* **54**, 3142 (1932).

SECTION 17.4

TIN[1]

E. DELTOMBE, N. DE ZOUBOV, C. VANLEUGENHAGHE and M. POURBAIX

SUMMARY

---

(1) Shortened and adapted version of the Rapport technique RT.25 of CEBELCOR [1].

1. SUBSTANCES CONSIDERED AND SUBSTANCES NOT CONSIDERED

	Oxidation number (Z)	Considered	Not considered	μ^0(cal.)	Name, colour, crystalline system
Solid substances	0	**Sn**	–	0	Tin, white, quad.
	+2	**SnO** anh.	–	*a.* – 61 500	Stannous oxide, black, quad.
	»	» hydr.	–	*b.* – 60 910	Stannous hydroxide $Sn(OH)_2$, white(2)
	+4	**SnO_2** anh.	–	*c.* –123 200 (3)	Stannic oxide, white, quad.
	»	» hydr.	–	*d.* –114 120	Stannic hydroxide $Sn(OH)_4$, white(2)
Dissolved substances	+2	Sn^{++}	–	– 6 275	Stannous ion, colourless
	»	–	$SnOH^+$	– 60 600 (*)	Stannyl ion, colourless
	»	$HSnO_2^-$	–	– 98 000	Bistannite ion, colourless
	»	–	SnO_2^{--}	–	Stannite ion, colourless
	»	–	$Sn_2O_3^{--}$	–141 080 (*)	Distannite ion, colourless
	+4	Sn^{++++}	–	650	Stannic ion, colourless
	»	–	$HSnO_3^-$	–	Acid stannate ion, colourless
	»	SnO_3^{--}	–	–137 420 (*)	Stannate ion, colourless
	+7	–	SnO_4^-	–	Perstannate ion
Gaseous substance	–4	*SnH_4*	–	99 000 (*)	Hydride, colourless

2. REACTIONS AND EQUILIBRIUM FORMULAE

2.1. TWO DISSOLVED SUBSTANCES

2.1.1. *Relative stability of the dissolved substances*

Z = +2

1. $Sn^{++} + 2H_2O = HSnO_2^- + 3H^+$ $\log\frac{(HSnO_2^-)}{(Sn^{++})} = -15.88 + 3\,pH$

Z = +4

2. $Sn^{++++} + 3H_2O = SnO_3^{--} + 6H^+$ $\log\frac{(SnO_3^{--})}{(Sn^{++++})} = -23.47 + 6\,pH$

+2 → +4

3. $Sn^{++} = Sn^{++++} + 2e^-$ $E_0 = 0.151 + 0.0295\log\frac{(Sn^{++++})}{(Sn^{++})}$

4. $Sn^{++} + 3H_2O = SnO_3^{--} + 6H^+ + 2e^-$ $E_0 = 0.844 - 0.1773\,pH + 0.0295\log\frac{(SnO_3^{--})}{(Sn^{++})}$

5. $HSnO_2^- + H_2O = SnO_3^{--} + 3H^+ + 2e^-$ $E_0 = 0.374 - 0.0886\,pH + 0.0295\log\frac{(SnO_3^{--})}{(HSnO_2^-)}$

2.1.2. *Limits of the domains of relative predominance of the dissolved substances*

1'. $Sn^{++}/HSnO_2^-$ $pH = 5.29$
2'. Sn^{++++}/SnO_3^{--} $pH = 3.91$

3'. Sn^{++}/Sn^{++++} $E_0 = 0.151$
4'. Sn^{++}/SnO_3^{--} $E_0 = 0.844 - 0.1773\,pH$
5'. $HSnO_2^-/SnO_3^{--}$ $E_0 = 0.374 - 0.0886\,pH$

---

(2) The values of μ^0 for the oxides correspond to the following values for the hydroxides:
$Sn(OH)_2$: – 117 600 cal., $Sn(OH)_4$: – 227 500 cal.

(3) Value found by C. G. Maier, *J. Amer. Chem. Soc.* **51**, 194–206 (1929).

(*) The free enthalpies marked (*) were calculated by us ([1], [2]).

(4) For the reactions involving SnO, the letter *a* refers to anhydrous SnO and the letter *b* refers to hydrated SnO or stannous hydroxide. For the reactions involving SnO_2, the letter *c* refers to anhydrous SnO_2 and the letter *d* refers to hydrated SnO_2 or stannic hydroxide.

2.2. TWO SOLID SUBSTANCES

Limits of the domains of relative stability of tin and its oxides

$0 \rightarrow +2$

6. $Sn + H_2O = SnO + 2H^+ + 2e^-$ — a. $E_0 = -0.104 - 0.0591\,pH$; b. $= -0.091 - 0.0591\,pH$

$0 \rightarrow +4$

7. $Sn + 2H_2O = SnO_2 + 4H^+ + 4e^-$ — c. $E_0 = -0.106 - 0.0591\,pH$; d. $= -0.008 - 0.0591\,pH$

$+2 \rightarrow +4$

8. $SnO + H_2O = SnO_2 + 2H^+ + 2e^-$ — ac. $E_0 = -0.108 - 0.0591\,pH$; ad. $= 0.088 - 0.0591\,pH$; bc. $= -0.121 - 0.0591\,pH$; bd. $= 0.075 - 0.0591\,pH$

2.3. ONE SOLID SUBSTANCE AND ONE DISSOLVED SUBSTANCE

Solubility of tin and its oxides

$Z = +2$

9. $Sn^{++} + H_2O = SnO + 2H^+$ — a. $\log(Sn^{++}) = 1.07 - 2\,pH$; b. $= 1.50 - 2\,pH$

10. $SnO + H_2O = HSnO_2^- + H^+$ — a. $\log(HSnO_2^-) = -14.81 + pH$; b. $= -14.38 + pH$

$Z = +4$

11. $Sn^{++++} + 2H_2O = SnO_2 + 4H^+$ — c. $\log(Sn^{++++}) = -7.68 - 4\,pH$; d. $= -1.02 - 4\,pH$

12. $SnO_2 + H_2O = SnO_3^{--} + 2H^+$ — c. $\log(SnO_3^{--}) = -31.16 + 2\,pH$; d. $= -24.50 + 2\,pH$

$0 \rightarrow +2$

13. $Sn = Sn^{++} + 2e^-$ — $E_0 = -0.136 + 0.0295 \log(Sn^{++})$

14. $Sn + 2H_2O = HSnO_2^- + 3H^+ + 2e^-$ — $E_0 = 0.333 - 0.0886\,pH + 0.0295 \log(HSnO_2^-)$

$+2 \rightarrow +4$

15. $Sn^{++} + 2H_2O = SnO_2 + 4H^+ + 2e^-$ — c. $E_0 = -0.077 - 0.1182\,pH - 0.0295 \log(Sn^{++})$; d. $= 0.120 - 0.1182\,pH - 0.0295 \log(Sn^{++})$

16. $HSnO_2^- = SnO_2 + H^+ + 2e^-$ — c. $E_0 = -0.546 - 0.0295\,pH - 0.0295 \log(HSnO_2^-)$; d. $= -0.349 - 0.0295\,pH - 0.0295 \log(HSnO_2^-)$

17. $SnO + 2H_2O = SnO_3^{--} + 4H^+ + 2e^-$ — a. $E_0 = 0.812 - 0.1182\,pH + 0.0295 \log(SnO_3^{--})$; b. $= 0.791 - 0.1182\,pH + 0.0295 \log(SnO_3^{--})$

2.4. ONE GASEOUS SUBSTANCE AND ONE SOLID SUBSTANCE

Relative stability of tin and tin hydride

$-4 \rightarrow 0$

18. $SnH_4 = Sn + 4H^+ + 4e^-$ — $E_0 = -1.074 - 0.0591\,pH - 0.0148 \log p_{SnH_4}$

3. EQUILIBRIUM DIAGRAMS AND THEIR INTERPRETATION

3.1. ESTABLISHMENT OF THE DIAGRAMS

Figures 1 and 2 are potential–pH equilibrium diagrams for the system tin–water at 25°C.

For the establishment of Fig. 1 we considered as solid substances metallic tin and the anhydrous oxides SnO and SnO_2; for the establishment of Fig. 2 we considered as solid substances metallic tin and the hydroxides $Sn(OH)_2$ and $Sn(OH)_4$. These figures are valid only in the absence of substances with which tin can form soluble complexes or insoluble compounds. Divalent tin forms the following complexes: $SnCl^+$, $SnCl_3^-$, $SnCl_4^{--}$ and very stable oxalic complexes; tetravalent tin forms $SnCl_2^{++}$, $SnCl_3^+$, $SnCl_5^-$, $SnCl_6^{--}$ and oxalic, hydrofluoric and sulphydric complexes [3]. SnS and SnS_2 are

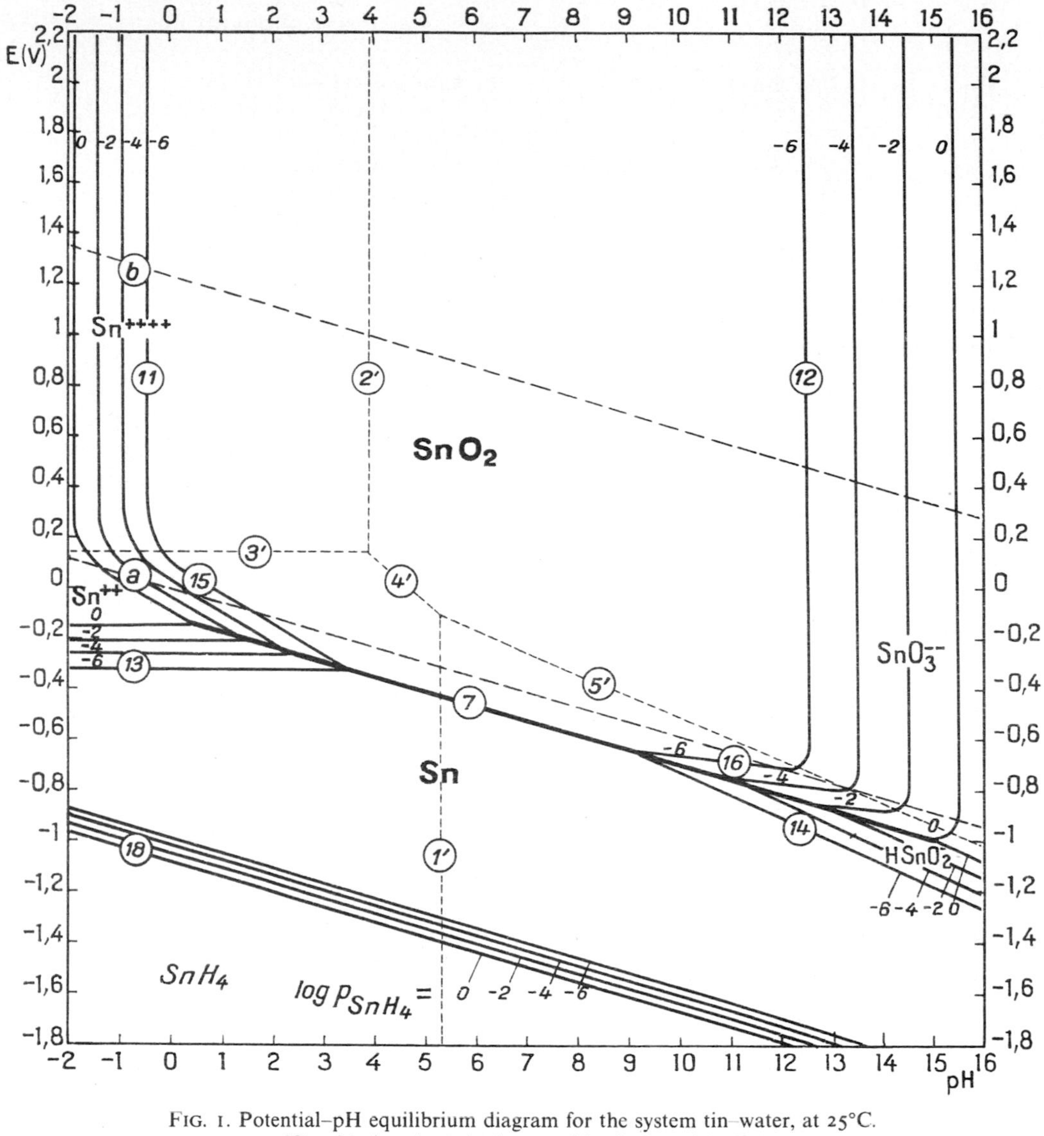

FIG. 1. Potential–pH equilibrium diagram for the system tin–water, at 25°C. (Considering the anhydrous oxides SnO and SnO_2.)

sparingly soluble [3]. For reasons which we have discussed in detail elsewhere [1], we have not considered the ions $SnOH^+$ and $Sn_2O_3^{--}$. We were not able to consider the ions SnO_2^{--}, $HSnO_3^-$ and SnO_4^- for which we do not have sufficient thermodynamic data.

We have not marked on these diagrams the compounds obtained by the action of hydrogen peroxide on stannic acid; the nature of these compounds is uncertain. Through lack of thermodynamic data we did not consider the corresponding ion SnO_4^- in establishing the diagram. The domain of predominance of this ion appears to be situated normally in the region of the diagrams corresponding to powerfully oxidizing alkaline media.

3.2. STABILITY AND CORROSION OF TIN

3.2.1. *Theoretical conditions of stability and corrosion of tin*

Figures 1 and 2 express that tin is a base metal, as its domain of thermodynamic stability has no zone in common with that of water. Tin can theoretically dissolve with the evolution of hydrogen, in

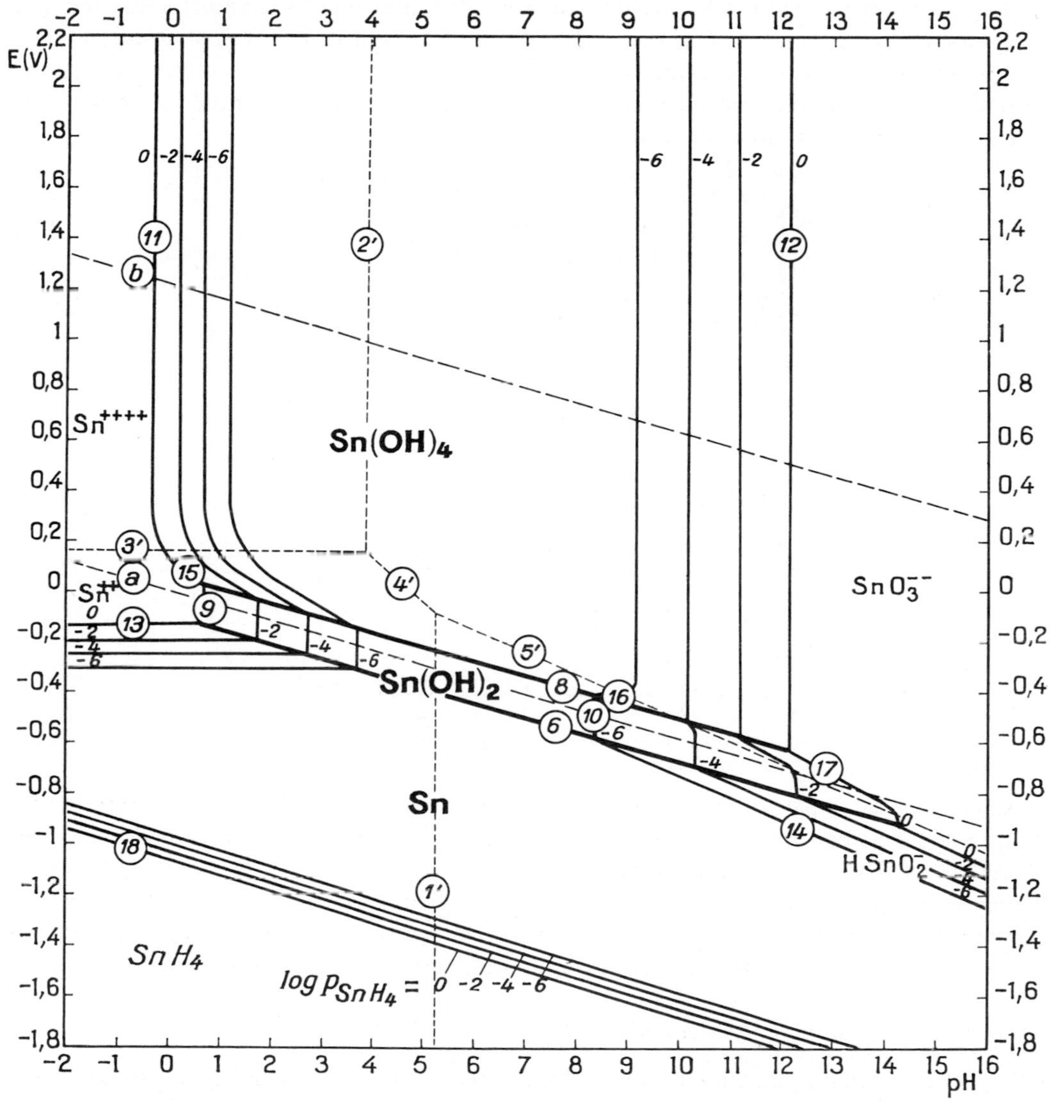

FIG. 2. Potential–pH equilibrium diagram for the system tin–water, at 25°C.
[Considering the hydroxides $Sn(OH)_2$ and $Sn(OH)_4$.]

very acid solutions and in alkaline solutions. However, on account of its large hydrogen overpotential [4], pure tin does not dissolve in practice in acids free from air and other oxidizing agents; the dissolution of tin can take place only if it is in contact with a metal of small hydrogen overpotential, or if the solution contains a depolarizing agent, such as oxygen or another oxidizing agent.

Figure 1 shows that tin can undergo reaction, not only by *oxidation*, with the formation of a layer of oxide SnO_2 or the soluble derivatives Sn^{++}, Sn^{++++}, $HSnO_2^-$ and SnO_3^{--}, but also by *reduction*, with the formation of the gaseous hydride SnH_4.

Figure 3, which is deduced from Fig. 1, represents the theoretical conditions of corrosion, immunity and passivation of tin, at 25°C.

As SnO_2 can constitute a protective film on the metal, it follows from the theoretical Fig. 3 that, in the absence of substances capable of forming with tin soluble complexes or insoluble compounds, tin will resist corrosion perfectly in moderately acid, neutral and slightly alkaline solutions, free from oxidizing agents. It will be corroded in very acid solutions as well as in alkaline solutions.

On the other hand, acid solutions and moderately alkaline solutions (pH between about 0 and 12) are passivating if they contain oxidizing agents capable of raising the potential to about +0·2 V in acid media and to −0·7 V in alkaline media.

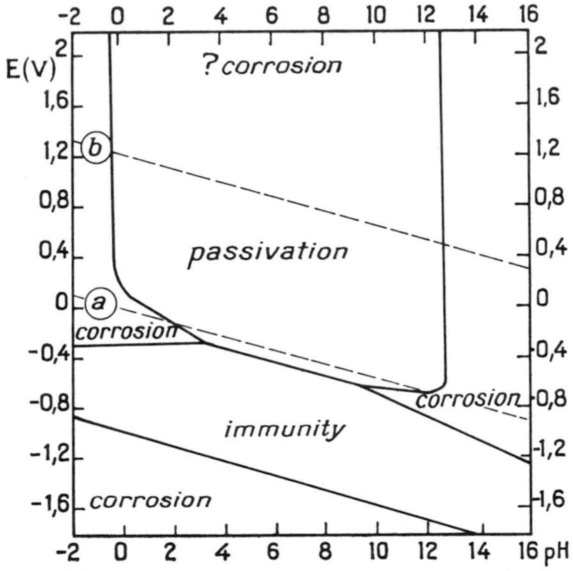

FIG. 3. Theoretical conditions of corrosion, immunity and passivation of tin, at 25°C.

It appears to be possible to bring about the cathodic protection of tin by lowering its potential to values included between two well-defined limits, which are about −0·3 and −1·0 V in very acid solutions, and −1·1 and −1·8 V in very alkaline solutions.

A strong reducing action causes, at potentials lower than those indicated by the family of lines (18), the formation of unstable gaseous tin hydride which decomposes fairly rapidly into its elements. This hydride is responsible for the corrosive cathodic domain shown at the bottom of Fig. 3.

3.2.2. *Real conditions of stability and corrosion of tin*

The theoretical conclusions which have just been put forward are in fairly good agreement with the observed facts, although the speeds at which the corrosion reactions take place are determined by the overpotentials of the various electrochemical reactions involved.

Given below is a review of certain experimental facts concerning the behaviour of tin, respectively in the absence and the presence of an electric current.

3.2.2.1. *Behaviour of tin in the absence of an electric current*

We pointed out in paragraph 3.2.1 that the hydrogen overpotential of tin is very large; it follows from this that acid and moderately alkaline solutions free from oxidizing agents will be only slightly corrosive if the tin is pure; they will be very corrosive if the metal is put in contact with substances of small hydrogen overpotential.

With regard to the experimental facts, a treatise by Britton [5] leads to the following conclusions concerning the corrosion of tin in *acid solutions*: in the absence of air the corrosion is generally slow and practically zero; in the presence of air, tin is corroded by mineral acids and most organic acids. Oxidizing acids such as nitric acid are generally corrosive, and the addition of small quantities of oxidizing agent to any acid causes an increase in the corrosion; under certain conditions a larger quantity of oxidizing agent can bring about passivation; this is the case, for example, when chromic acid is added to sulphuric or phosphoric acids, and when hydrogen peroxide is added to citric acid.

Also according to Britton, tin begins to corrode in *alkaline solutions* only when the pH is sufficiently high to dissolve the film of oxide (SnO_2) already existing on the metal; this minimum pH depends on several factors, including the composition of the solution: the presence of halogens favours passivation, as does that of silicates, phosphates, copper, silver, lead and zinc, while sulphides stimulate the activity.

In view of the well-known activating action of the halogens on most metals, it may seem paradoxical that the presence of halogens favours passivation, but one must not forget that they form very sparingly soluble basic salts of the type Sn(OH)Cl very easily with tin. In this connection Hoar [6] shows, by establishing a potential–pH diagram representing the equilibrium potentials of the systems Sn/SnO, Sn/SnO_2 and Sn/Sn(OH)Cl (the latter for a 0·1 M KCl concentration), that, under these conditions, the basic salt Sn(OH)Cl is formed in preference to any other oxide when the pH is below 2·5; under these conditions, therefore, the passivating film will be constituted at least partially of basic salt and will be formed at a lower potential than if it were constituted entirely of oxide.

Although a certain corrosion was obtained at pH = 8·4 (bicarbonate solution) with pure tin freshly scoured with emery, alkaline solutions of pH below 11 do not, in most cases, have any action on tin at room temperature. When the pH is sufficiently high, the dissolution of the tin again depends to a large extent on the presence of oxidizing agents, as in acid solutions; thus the removal of oxygen by the addition of sodium sulphite renders alkaline solutions practically harmless towards tin (Kerr [7]). As a general rule, the addition of a small quantity of oxidizing agent can greatly speed up corrosion, while the addition of a sufficiently large quantity of permanganate, perborate or chromate can prevent it completely, which explains the use of these oxidizing agents for the protection of tin against corrosion; however, this procedure requires great care, since, if an insufficient amount is added, the corrosion will be increased.

The theoretical corrosion diagram (Fig. 3) predicts a domain of passivation in slightly acid or neutral solutions, of pH between 3·5 and 9; this passivation would correspond to the metal being covered with a layer of stannic oxide SnO_2; moreover, this oxide layer is formed on the metal merely on exposure to the air. It is known that distilled water is practically without action on tin. However, certain aqueous solutions can cause *black stains* to appear on the surface of the metal. This phenomenon has been studied in particular by Brennert [8] and Hoar [6]; it sometimes happens that the oxide film pre-existing on the metal has weak points where corrosion begins; the standard equilibrium potentials of the systems Sn/SnO and Sn/SnO_2 are approximately equal in value (respectively −0·104 and −0·106 V), and consequently a new protective layer, made up of a mixture of stannous and stannic oxides, can be formed at the points of attack; Brennert was able to isolate this layer and found its composition to be about 80 per cent stannous oxide and 20 per cent stannic oxide. The black colour of the stains would thus be due to the presence of blue–black stannous oxide.

In his noteworthy study of the corrosion of tin in almost neutral solutions, Hoar [6] showed, by thermodynamically interpreting electrode potential measurements, that these black stains are connected with the formation, between the metal and the oxides covering it, of an acid solution which dissolves the stannous oxide and causes undermining; these stains occur in the case of solutions which do not form a precipitate with stannous ions (chlorides, bromides, chlorates, perchlorates, sulphates, nitrates), and do not occur in the case of solutions which form stable precipitates with stannous ions (iodates, borates, monobasic phosphate, chromates, sulphocyanates, iodides, nitrites, bicarbonates, permanganates, ferricyanides, ferrocyanides and sulphites) since, with the second group of substances, the undermining cannot take place. From this point of view, their protective action is similar to that of phosphates towards iron, or sulphates towards lead, and is interpreted by the formation of an insoluble salt at the surface of the metal.

In paragraph 3.1 we pointed out that the oxidation of stannic acid by hydrogen peroxide gives rise to the formation of compounds which have been assumed to be derivatives of hexavalent tin. The "perstannic" acid $SnO_4H \cdot 2H_2O$ thus isolated by Tanatar [9] is very sparingly soluble in water; its potassium salt is also sparingly soluble, but the sodium salt is soluble. In any case, all these substances are unstable in water which they decompose with the formation of stannic acid and hydrogen peroxide. It is well known that, in practice, tin is not resistant to solutions of hydrogen peroxide or persulphate; there is therefore reason to predict a possible corrosion domain for very oxidizing solutions.

Chatalov [10] gives a diagram (Fig. 4) indicating the influence of pH on the rate of corrosion of tin in various buffer solutions. The curve obtained clearly shows the importance of the corrosion in

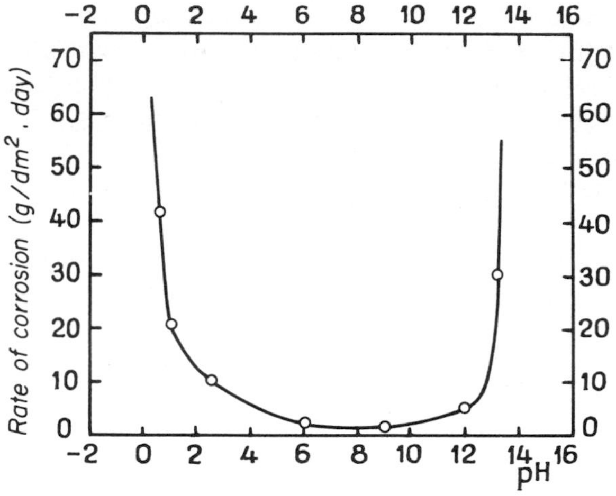

FIG. 4. Corrosion rate of tin as a function of pH (after Chatalov).

acid and alkaline solutions as compared to its lack of importance in neutral solutions. Unfortunately, Chatalov does not give any details concerning the experimental conditions under which these results were obtained.

3.2.2.2. *Anodic behaviour of tin*

From the theoretical corrosion diagram (Fig. 3) it is seen that, in certain pH domains (between −0·4 and 3·5 and between 9·5 and 12·5), a tin electrode may be expected, for a given pH, to be active or passive depending on the applied potential.

In *alkaline solutions*, this phenomenon was observed for the first time in 1906 by Goldschmidt and Eckardt [11] and occurs even at pH's higher than 13, which is probably due to a local increase in the dissolved tin concentration. These experimenters found that tin in the active state dissolves as divalent ions; in the passive state it becomes covered with a dull film; the current density at which passivation occurs is lower the more dilute the alkaline solution.

The anodic behaviour of tin in alkaline solutions plays an important part in the process of tin-plating and has been the subject of various studies, including those of Kerr [12] and Bianchi [13]; from these studies it results that the nature of the film depends on various factors, including the alkali concentration, the temperature and the current intensity: when passivation is produced by increasing the current density above a first critical value (about 80 mA/cm² in a normal NaOH solution at 40°C), the anode covers itself with a brown film of hydrated stannic oxide ($SnO_2 . H_2O$) and becomes the site of an abundant evolution of oxygen; it then ceases to give off divalent ions and dissolves as tetravalent ions, with a very small yield however; on the other hand, if after the anode has become passive the current density is reduced to a value equal to or below a second critical value (about 5 mA/cm^2 in a normal NaOH solution at 40°C), the anode becomes covered with a milky pale yellow film of a more hydrated stannic oxide ($SnO_2 . 2H_2O$), the thickness of which is determined by the equilibrium between its rate of formation and its rate of dissolution in the alkaline solution; when this film is formed, the evolution of oxygen ceases and the anode dissolves almost exclusively as tetravalent ions; the current yield can reach 94 per cent.

In the presence of oxidizing agents such as chromates, chlorates, etc., the anodic polarization curves in alkaline solutions no longer present the level portion characteristic of anodic activity: the tin becomes passive for any current density, however small it may be.

From Bianchi's observations, it can be concluded that the permeability of the oxide film to ions is greater the more hydrated the film, which agrees with the opinion that the film consisting of anhydrous SnO_2 is the only one which is actually protective.

Anodic passivation in *acid solutions* has not been so well studied; however, we should mention the work of Steinherz [14] which has brought to light, as for alkaline solutions, the existence of a critical potential above which the regular dissolution of the metal ceases and the current density falls abruptly.

In 0·1 M HCl (pH = 1) this critical potential is +0·091 V, while in 0·0375 M fluorosilicic acid (pH about 1·1) it is +0·452 V. Steinherz observed that passivation occurs in the presence of the following five acids: H_2SO_4, HCl, HBr, HI and H_2SiF_6 (the passivation produced by the halogen acids is probably due to the formation of a basic salt); on the other hand, there is no passivation in the presence of HNO_3, HIO_3, $HClO_4$ or CH_3COOH. The concentration of the acid also plays a part: when the dilution is increased, there is a rapid rise in the critical potential, which can be attributed, in the case of the halogen acids at least, to the fact that the tendency for insoluble basic salt to be formed diminishes as the dilution increases. Whether the metal is active or passive, it seems to dissolve invariably as divalent ions. The passivation phenomenon is accompanied by a darkening of the electrode, but Steinherz attributes this not to the appearance of an oxide film, but to a blackening of the electrode caused either by an irregular attack by the solution giving rise to finely divided metal, or by the appearance of impurities of the tin (carbon, etc.).

It is difficult to draw any formal conclusions from these data, taking into account the fact that the experiments were carried out in unstirred solutions; Steinherz himself points out that when a rotating electrode is used, the critical potential rises considerably: in one case, for instance, it rises from 0·1 to 0·25 V.

3.3. STABILITY OF THE OXIDES AND HYDROXIDES OF TIN

According to Fig. 2, the oxidation of tin in slightly acid, neutral or alkaline media could theoretically give rise to the formation of stannous hydroxide $Sn(OH)_2$, an amphoteric hydroxide which dissolves in acid media as stannous ions Sn^{++} and in alkaline media as stannite ions $HSnO_2^-$ and stannate ions SnO_3^{--}. A greater degree of oxidation leads to the formation of stannic hydroxide $Sn(OH)_4$, an amphoteric hydroxide which dissolves in acid media as stannic ions Sn^{++++} and in alkaline media as stannate ions SnO_3^{--}. The hydroxides $Sn(OH)_2$ and $Sn(OH)_4$ are thermodynamically less stable than the corresponding oxides SnO and SnO_2, and tend to change into these oxides with affinities respectively of 590 and 9 080 cal. In Fig. 1, we considered as solid substances, apart from metallic tin, the anhydrous oxides SnO and SnO_2. The oxide SnO does not appear on the diagram, on account of its instability in relation to Sn and SnO_2. In actual fact, in slightly acid and neutral media, the metal is oxidized directly to stannic oxide SnO_2, in agreement with Fig. 1; this figure appears to be more useful than Fig. 2 in the study of the oxidation of metal; Fig. 2 is of interest in the study of the conditions of separation and dissolution of hydroxides in the presence of stannous and stannic solutions.

The dehydration of $Sn(OH)_2$ is complete only at a high temperature, of around 100°C, probably on account of the small affinity of the conversion of $Sn(OH)_2$ into SnO. On the other hand, as Gutbier *et al.* [15] have shown, the stannic hydroxides obtained by the hydrolysis of solutions of Sn^{++++} or SnO_3^{--} ions [which do not answer to the stoichiometric formula $Sn(OH)_4$ and which exist as gels] crystallize progressively, becoming dehydrated to give the thermodynamically stable form, which is cassiterite, SnO_2. Consequently, while the equilibria represented in Fig. 1 arc stable, the equilibria represented in Fig. 2 are not stable.

The oxidation-reduction potentials of the systems Sn/SnO and Sn/SnO_2 which are respectively $-0{\cdot}104$ V (relation 6*a*) and $-0{\cdot}106$ V (relation 7*c*) at pH = 0, are very close to each other; this leads us to predict that the oxidation of tin in slightly acid and neutral media can lead to the formation of a mixture of stannous and stannic oxides, whose relative proportions will be a function of the operating conditions. We have seen in paragraph 3.2.2.1, dealing with the corrosion of tin, that this is the case with almost neutral solutions of salts forming soluble compounds with tin.

4. BIBLIOGRAPHY

[1] E. DELTOMBE, N. DE ZOUBOV and M. POURBAIX, *Comportement électrochimique de l'étain. Diagrammes d'équilibres tension–*pH *du système* Sn–H_2O *à 25°C. Corrosion de l'étain. Étamages électrolytique et chimique* (Rapport technique RT.25 of CEBELCOR, 1955).

[2] N. DE ZOUBOV and E. DELTOMBE, *Enthalpie libre de formation standard de l'hydrure d'étain* SnH_4 *gazeux* (Rapport technique RT.26 of CEBELCOR, 1955).

[3] G. CHARLOT, *L'analyse qualitative et les réactions en solution*, 4th ed., Masson, Paris, 1957.

[4] A. G. PETCHERSKAIA and V. V. STENDER, Potientiels de dégagement d'hydrogène dans les solutions acides, *J. Fiz. Khim. S.S.S.R.* **24**, 856–9 (1950).

[5] S. C. BRITTON, *The Corrosion Resistance of Tin and Tin Alloys*, Tin Research Institute, 1952.

[6] T. P. HOAR, The corrosion of tin in nearly neutral solutions, *Trans. Faraday Soc.* **33**, 1152–1167 (1937).

[7] R. KERR, The use of sodium sulphite as an addition to alkaline detergents for tinned ware, *J. Soc. Chem. Ind.* **54**, 217–21 (1935).

[8] S. BRENNERT, Ueber die Korrosion von Zinn und verzinnten Materialen unter Bildung schwarzer Flecken (Thesis, Stockholm, 1935).

[9] S. TANATAR, Perzinnsäuren und Perstannate, *Ber.* **38**, 1184–6 (1905).

[10] A. YA. CHATALOV, Influence du pH sur le comportement électrochimique des métaux et leur résistance à la corrosion, *Doklad. Akad. Naouk S.S.S.R.* **86**, 775–7 (1952).

[11] M. GOLDSCHMIDT and M. ECKARDT, Ueber die Reduktion von Nitrokörpern durch alkalische Zinnoxydullösungen, *Z. Phys. Chem.* **56**, 385–452 (1906).

[12] R. KERR, Anodic films on tin in sodium hydroxide solutions, *J. Soc. Chem. Ind.* **57**, 405–10 (1938).

[13] G. BIANCHI, La passività anodica dello stagno nelle soluzioni alcaline, *La Chim. e l'Industria* **29**, 295–7 (1947).

[14] R. STEINHERZ, Ueber Passives Zinn, *Z. Elektroch.* **30**, 279–86 (1924).

[15] A. GUTBIER, G. F. HÜTTIG and H. DOBLING, Zur Kenntnis des Systems Zinn IV Oxyd/Wasser, *Ber.* **59B**, 1232–46 (1926).

SECTION 17.5

LEAD[1]

M. Pourbaix, N. de Zoubov, C. Vanleugenhaghe and P. Van Rysselberghe

SUMMARY

(1) Shortened and adapted version of a previously published text [1].

1. SUBSTANCES CONSIDERED AND SUBSTANCES NOT CONSIDERED

	Oxidation number (Z)	Considered	Not considered	μ^0(cal.)	Name, colour, crystalline system
Solid substances	0	**Pb**	–	0	Lead, grey, cub.
	+1	–	**Pb_2O**	–	Sub-oxide, black, amorphous
	+2	**PbO** anh.	–	*a.* – 45 250	Plumbous oxide, red, quad.
	»	» »	–	*b.* – 45 050	Plumbous ox., yellow, orthorh.
	»	» hydr.	–	*c.* – 43 910	Hydrated plumbous oxide or hydroxide $Pb(OH)_2$, white, hex.(2)
	+2.67	**Pb_3O_4**	–	–147 600	Plumbo-plumbic oxide, red, quad.
	+3	**Pb_2O_3**	–	– 98 417 (3)	Sesquioxide, yellow–orange, amorphous or quad.
	+4	**PbO_2**	–	– 52 340	Dioxide, brown, quad.
Dissolved substances	+2	Pb^{++}	–	– 5 810	Plumbous ion, colourless
	»	–	$PbOH^+$	–	?
	»	$HPbO_2^-$	–	– 81 000	Biplumbite ion
	»	–	PbO_2^{--}	–	Plumbite ion
	+4	Pb^{++++}	–	72 300	Plumbic ion
	»	–	$HPbO_3^-$	–	Acid metaplumbate ion
	»	PbO_3^{--}	–	– 66 340 (3)	Metaplumbate ion
	»	PbO_4^{----}	–	– 67 421 (3)	Orthoplumbate ion
Gaseous substances	–4	–	*PbH_4*	–	Hydride
	–2	*PbH_2*	–	69 500 (3)	Hydride, colourless

2. REACTIONS AND EQUILIBRIUM FORMULAE (4)

2.1. TWO DISSOLVED SUBSTANCES

2.1.1. *Relative stability of the dissolved substances*

$Z = +2$

1. $Pb^{++} + 2H_2O = HPbO_2^- + 3H^+ \qquad \log\frac{(HPbO_2^-)}{(Pb^{++})} = -28.02 + 3\,pH$

$Z = +4$

2. $Pb^{++++} + 3H_2O = PbO_3^{--} + 6H^+ \qquad \log\frac{(PbO_3^{--})}{(Pb^{++++})} = -23.06 + 6\,pH$

3. $PbO_3^{--} + H_2O = PbO_4^{----} + 2H^+ \qquad \log\frac{(PbO_4^{----})}{(PbO_3^{--})} = -40.87 + 2\,pH$

---

(2) This value of μ^0_{PbO} corresponds to $\mu^0_{Pb(OH)_2} = -43\,910 - 56\,690 = -100\,600$ cal.

(3) The standard free enthalpy of formation of the oxide Pb_2O_3 was calculated by us from the equilibrium potential of the reaction $3Pb_2O_3 + H_2O + 2e^- = 2Pb_3O_4 + 2OH^-$, $E^0_B = 0{\cdot}40$ V given by Charlot [2]; the free enthalpy of the metaplumbate ion PbO_3^{--} was calculated by us assuming the value $E^0_B = 0{\cdot}30$ V given by Glasstone [3] for the equilibrium potential of the reaction $PbO_3^{--} + 2H_2O + 2e^- = HPbO_2^- + 3OH^-$; the free enthalpy of the orthoplumbate ion PbO_4^{----} was calculated from the value pK = 50·3 given by Charlot [2] for the reaction $Pb_3O_4 = PbO_4^{----} + 2Pb^{++}$; the value of the free enthalpy of the hydride PbH_2 is that calculated by Van Muylder and Pourbaix [4].

(4) Concerning the reactions involving PbO, the letter *a* refers to anhydrous red PbO, whose free enthalpy of formation is –45 250 cal.; the letter *b* refers to anhydrous yellow PbO, whose free enthalpy of formation is –45 050 cal.; the letter *c* refers to $Pb(OH)_2$, whose free enthalpy of formation is –100 600 cal.

$+2 \rightarrow +4$

4. $Pb^{++} = Pb^{++++} + 2e^-$ $\qquad E_0 = 1.694 + 0.0295 \log \frac{(Pb^{++++})}{(Pb^{++})}$

5. $Pb^{++} + 3H_2O = PbO_3^{--} + 6H^+ + 2e^-$ $\qquad E_0 = 2.375 - 0.1773\,pH + 0.0295 \log \frac{(PbO_3^{--})}{(Pb^{++})}$

6. $HPbO_2^- + H_2O = PbO_3^{--} + 3H^+ + 2e^-$ $\qquad E_0 = 1.547 - 0.0886\,pH + 0.0295 \log \frac{(PbO_3^{--})}{(HPbO_2^-)}$

2.1.2. *Limits of the domains of relative predominance of the dissolved substances*

1'. $Pb^{++} / HPbO_2^-$ $\qquad pH = 9.34$
2'. Pb^{++++} / PbO_3^{--} $\qquad pH = 3.84$
3'. $PbO_3^{--} / PbO_4^{----}$ $\qquad pH = 20.44$

4'. Pb^{++} / Pb^{++++} $\qquad E_0 = 1.694$
5'. Pb^{++} / PbO_3^{--} $\qquad E_0 = 2.375 - 0.1773\,pH$
6'. $HPbO_2^- / PbO_3^{--}$ $\qquad E_0 = 1.547 - 0.0886\,pH$

2.2. TWO SOLID SUBSTANCES

Limits of the domains of relative stability of the solid substances

$0 \rightarrow +2$

7. $\mathbf{Pb} + H_2O = \mathbf{PbO} + 2H^+ + 2e^-$
a. $E_0 = 0.248 - 0.0591\,pH$
b. $ = 0.252 - 0.0591\,pH$
c. $ = 0.277 - 0.0591\,pH$

$+2 \rightarrow +2.67$

8. $3\,\mathbf{PbO} + H_2O = \mathbf{Pb_3O_4} + 2H^+ + 2e^-$
a. $E_0 = 0.972 - 0.0591\,pH$
b. $ = 0.959 - 0.0591\,pH$
c. $ = 0.885 - 0.0591\,pH$

$+2.67 \rightarrow +3$

9. $2\,\mathbf{Pb_3O_4} + H_2O = 3\,\mathbf{Pb_2O_3} + 2H^+ + 2e^-$ $\qquad E_0 = 1.228 - 0.0591\,pH$

$+2.67 \rightarrow +4$

10. $\mathbf{Pb_3O_4} + 2H_2O = 3\,\mathbf{PbO_2} + 4H^+ + 4e^-$ $\qquad E_0 = 1.127 - 0.0591\,pH$

$+3 \rightarrow +4$

11. $\mathbf{Pb_2O_3} + H_2O = 2\,\mathbf{PbO_2} + 2H^+ + 2e^-$ $\qquad E_0 = 1.093 - 0.0591\,pH$

2.3. ONE SOLID SUBSTANCE AND ONE DISSOLVED SUBSTANCE

Solubility of lead and its oxides

$Z = +2$

12. $Pb^{++} + H_2O = \mathbf{PbO} + 2H^+$
a. $\log(Pb^{++}) = 12.65 - 2\,pH$
b. $\phantom{\log(Pb^{++})} = 12.80 - 2\,pH$
c. $\phantom{\log(Pb^{++})} = 13.64 - 2\,pH$

13. $\mathbf{PbO} + H_2O = HPbO_2^- + H^+$
a. $\log(HPbO_2^-) = -15.36 + pH$
b. $ = -15.22 + pH$
c. $ = -14.38 + pH$

$Z = +4$

14. $Pb^{++++} + 2H_2O = \mathbf{PbO_2} + 4H^+$ $\qquad \log(Pb^{++++}) = -8.26 - 4\,pH$
15. $\mathbf{PbO_2} + H_2O = PbO_3^{--} + 2H^+$ $\qquad \log(PbO_3^{--}) = -31.32 + 2\,pH$

$0 \rightarrow +2$

16. $\mathbf{Pb} = Pb^{++} + 2e^-$ $\qquad E_0 = -0.126 + 0.0295 \log(Pb^{++})$
17. $\mathbf{Pb} + 2H_2O = HPbO_2^- + 3H^+ + 2e^-$ $\qquad E_0 = 0.702 - 0.0886\,pH + 0.0295 \log(HPbO_2^-)$

$+2 \rightarrow +2.67$

18. $3Pb^{++} + 4H_2O = \mathbf{Pb_3O_4} + 8H^+ + 2e^-$ $\qquad E_0 = 2.094 - 0.2364\,pH - 0.0886 \log(Pb^{++})$
19. $3HPbO_2^- + H^+ = \mathbf{Pb_3O_4} + 2H_2O + 2e^-$ $\qquad E_0 = -0.390 + 0.0295\,pH - 0.0886 \log(HPbO_2^-)$

$+2 \rightarrow +4$

20. $\mathbf{PbO} + 2H_2O = PbO_3^{--} + 4H^+ + 2e^-$

$a.\ E_0 = 2.001 - 0.1182\,pH + 0.0295 \log (PbO_3^{--})$

$b.\ \quad = 1.997 - 0.1182\,pH + 0.0295 \log (PbO_3^{--})$

$c.\ \quad = 1.972 - 0.1182\,pH + 0.0295 \log (PbO_3^{--})$

21. $Pb^{++} + 2H_2O = \mathbf{PbO_2} + 4H^+ + 2e^-$ $\quad E_0 = 1.449 - 0.1182\,pH - 0.0295 \log (Pb^{++})$

22. $HPbO_2^- = \mathbf{PbO_2} + H^+ + 2e^-$ $\quad E_0 = 0.621 - 0.0295\,pH - 0.0295 \log (HPbO_2^-)$

$+2.67 \rightarrow +4$

23. $\mathbf{Pb_3O_4} + 5H_2O = 3PbO_3^{--} + 10H^+ + 4e^-$ $\quad E_0 = 2.515 - 0.1477\,pH + 0.0443 \log (PbO_3^{--})$

2.4. ONE SOLID SUBSTANCE AND ONE GASEOUS SUBSTANCE

Relative stability of lead and its hydride

$-2 \rightarrow 0$

24. $PbH_2 = \mathbf{Pb} + 2H^+ + 2e^-$ $\quad E_0 = -1.507 - 0.0591\,pH - 0.0295 \log p_{PbH_2}$

3. EQUILIBRIUM DIAGRAM AND ITS INTERPRETATION

3.1. ESTABLISHMENT OF THE DIAGRAM

Using the equilibrium formulae established in paragraph 2 we have constructed a potential–pH equilibrium diagram (Fig. 1) for the system lead–water at 25°C, considering the anhydrous red form of PbO, which is more stable than the yellow PbO and white $Pb(OH)_2$. For want of thermodynamic data we have not considered the oxide Pb_2O or the plumbites PbO_2^{--} and metaplumbates $HPbO_3^-$ which are referred to occasionally.

Figure 2 represents the theoretical conditions of corrosion, immunity and passivation of lead at 25°C; Fig. 2*a* is deduced from Fig. 1, while Fig. 2*b* refers to solutions containing CO_2.

In Fig. 3 we have used relations (1′), (12) and (13) to represent the influence of pH on the solubility of red PbO, yellow PbO and the hydroxide $Pb(OH)_2$. These diagrams are valid only in the absence of substances with which lead can form soluble complexes or insoluble salts. For the oxidation state +2, Charlot [2] points out the slightly stable complexes $PbNO_3^+$, $PbCl^+$, $PbCl_3^-$ and $Pb(CN)_4^{--}$ and the fairly stable acetic, organic hydroxyl and thiosulphuric complexes. In the oxidation state +4, lead forms complexes in a concentrated HCl medium ($PbCl_5^-$) and in a fairly concentrated H_2SO_4 medium.

Sparingly soluble compounds of lead are: $PbCl_2$, $PbBr_2$, PbI_2, PbF_2, $PbSO_4$, $PbCO_3$, etc. We have already published equilibrium diagrams for the systems $Pb–CO_2–H_2O$ and $Pb–SO_3–H_2O$ at 25°C [1].

3.2. STABILITY AND CORROSION OF LEAD

Metallic lead is thermodynamically stable in the presence of neutral or alkaline solutions free from oxidizing agents, since a portion of its stability domain lies above the line (*a*) for such solutions; lead is actually encountered occasionally in the native state. In acid solutions at atmospheric pressure lead generally tends to decompose water with the evolution of hydrogen, in which case it presents a potential included between the values indicated by line (*a*) and the value given by the lines of the family (16) which corresponds to the Pb^{++} concentration of the solution. This decomposition of water by lead is, however, usually very slow, on account of the large hydrogen overpotential of lead.

Figures 1 and 2 show in particular that metallic lead, which is generally stable in the presence of aqueous solutions free from oxidizing agents, can be dissolved by acid oxidizing solutions with the formation of divalent plumbous ions Pb^{++}; a very powerful oxidizing action can convert these divalent plumbous ions directly into brown quadrivalent lead peroxide PbO_2.

These figures also show that lead can generally be used as an electrolytic anode at high electrode potentials (for pH's between 0 and 12), without appreciable corrosion; in this case the metal becomes covered with PbO_2.

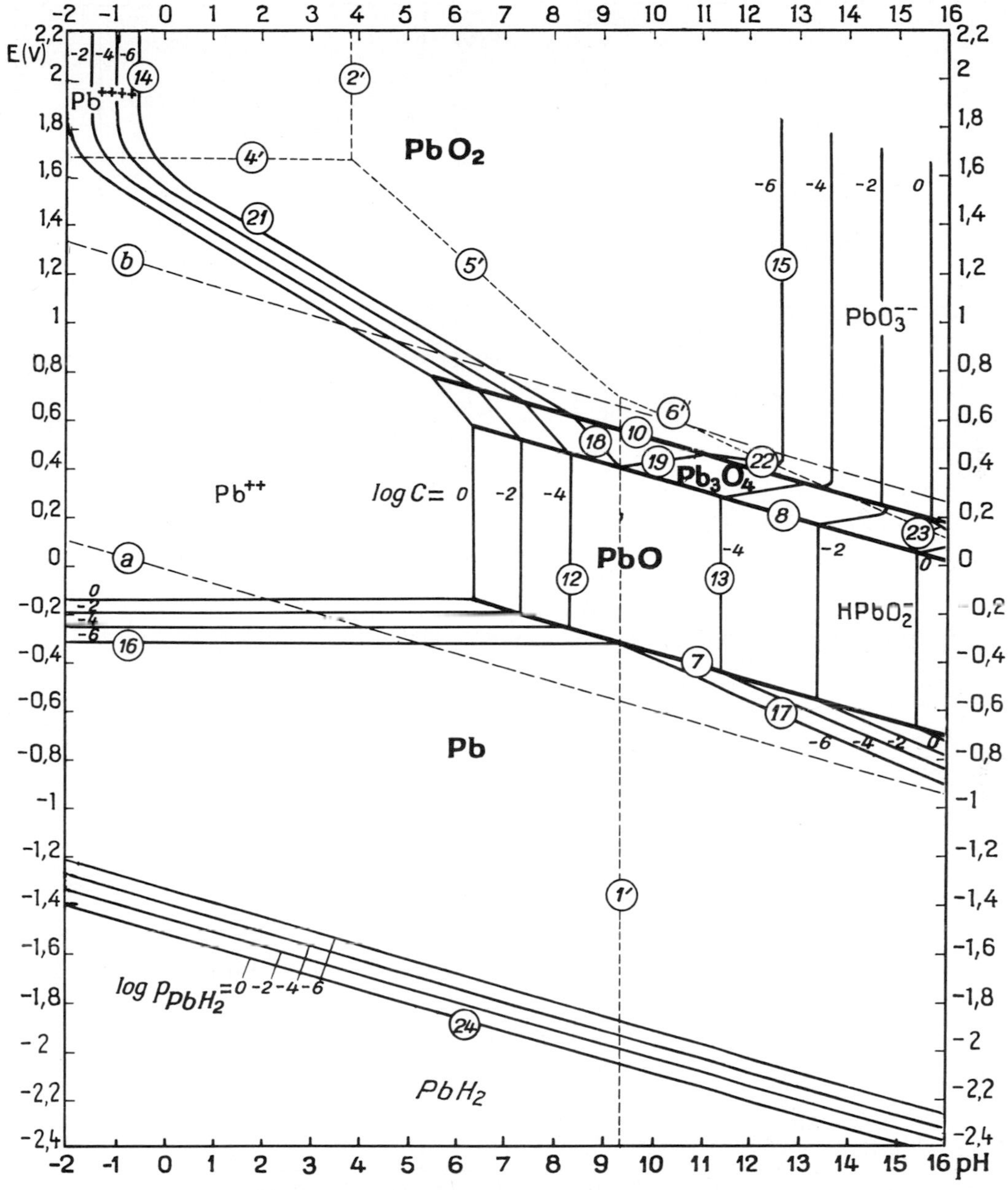

FIG. 1. Potential–pH equilibrium diagram for the system lead–water, at 25°C.

Figure 2*a* shows that in the absence of passivating substances (such as carbonates), any oxidizing action can cause lead to corrode, except at high electrode potentials, when lead peroxide PbO_2 is stable. As Schikorr [6] has pointed out, lead oxide PbO is too soluble to provide any protection for lead. Lead is therefore corroded by water free from passivating substances, and in particular by most soft waters. On the other hand, it will be resistant to hard bicarbonate waters, mainly because the presence of bicarbonate has the effect of producing a "bridge", corresponding to the stability of passivating lead carbonate, between the domains of immunity and passivation existing in Fig. 2*a* ([1], [8]) (Fig. 2*b*).

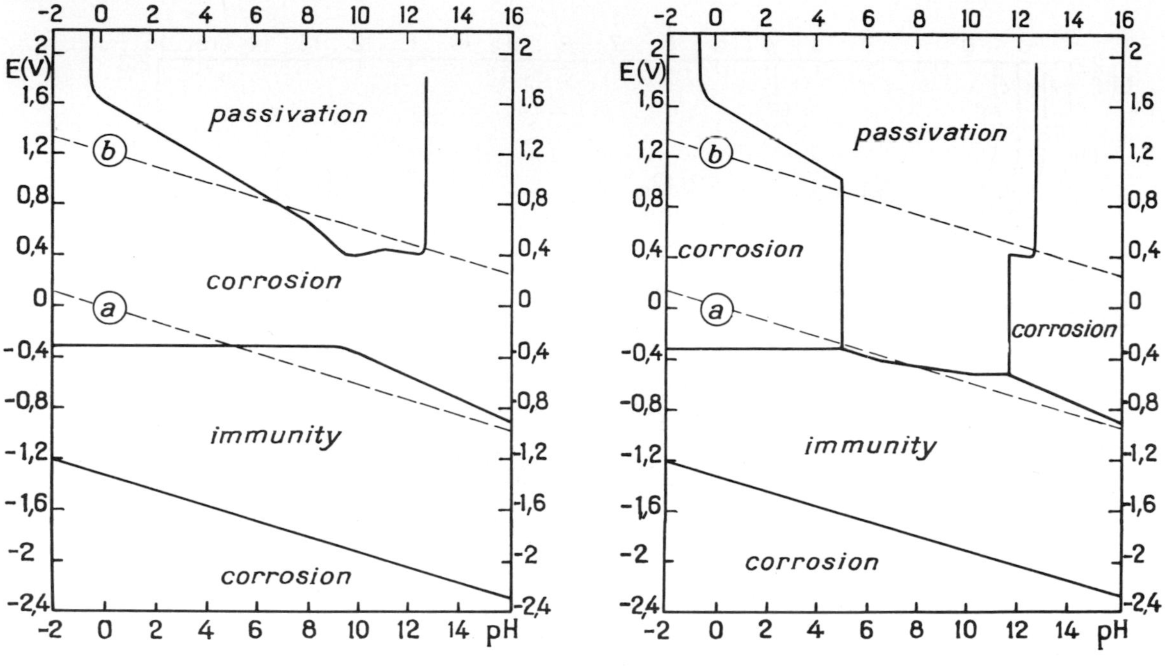

(*a*) In the absence of substances forming insoluble salts. (Deduced from Fig. 1.)

(*b*) In the presence of solutions containing CO_2. (Established for $\log\ [(H_2CO_3) + (HCO_3^-) + (CO_3^{--})] = 0$ and $\log p_{CO_2} = 0$.)

FIG. 2. Theoretical conditions of corrosion, immunity and passivation of lead, at 25°C.

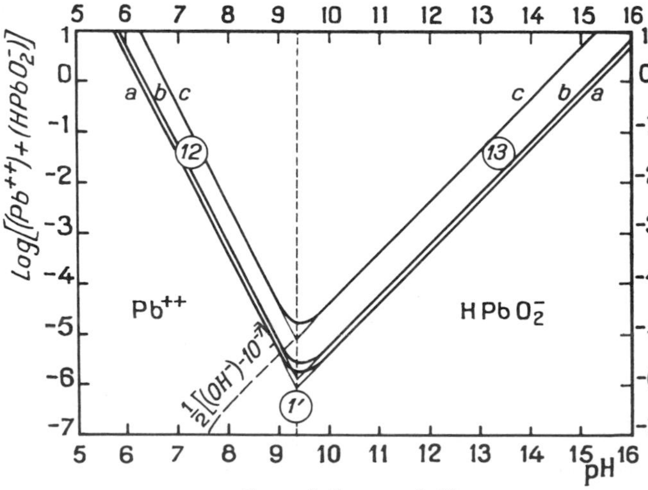

FIG. 3. Influence of pH on the solubility of red and yellow PbO and the hydroxide $Pb(OH)_2$, at 25°C.

a, red PbO; *b*, yellow PbO; *c*, $Pb(OH)_2$.

In the absence of complexing ions (such as tartrates, for instance), lead can be cathodically protected by lowering its potential to below about −0·3 V in acid or neutral solutions, or below −0·4 to −0·8 V, depending on the pH, in alkaline solutions.

A powerful reducing action at potentials below those indicated by the family of lines (24) causes the formation of unstable gaseous lead hydride, which decomposes immediately into finely divided lead and hydrogen. This hydride is responsible for the domain of cathodic corrosion at the bottom of the diagrams in Fig. 2.

For stirred aqueous solutions we have noted [4] that lead is no longer protected at very low cathodic potentials. The cathodic attack of the lead appears at well-defined electrode potentials. These potentials depend on the pH according to the following experimental relation: $E = 1{\cdot}54 - 0{\cdot}06$ pH (volt). It was from this relation that the free enthalpy of formation of lead hydride PbH_2 was calculated to be $+69\,500 \pm 4\,500$ cal. [4]. The final product of the cathodic attack consists of fine particles which separate from the cathode in a grey–black cloud. Although cathodic protection of lead can be obtained with a current density of 10 $\mu A/cm^2$, it is necessary to raise the current density to about 10 mA/cm^2 to observe cathodic corrosion [7]. This cathodic corrosion, which occurs in stirred aqueous solutions, hardly occurs at all in moist soils; the absence of such corrosion in this case seems to be due to the formation of a screen of powdery lead around the cathodically treated lead structure, produced by the decomposition of the lead hydride initially formed; this is a particularly interesting case of "cathodic passivation".

3.3. STABILITY AND FORMATION OF THE LEAD OXIDES

Figures 1 and 3 show that *plumbous oxide* PbO is amphoteric. It dissolves in acid, neutral and slightly alkaline solutions as plumbous ions Pb^{++} and in very alkaline solutions as biplumbite ions $HPbO_2^-$. It has a minimum solubility at pH = 9·34 (0·222 mg Pb/l for the red oxide).

Plumbo-plumbic oxide Pb_3O_4 or lead orthoplumbate (minium) can be obtained by the oxidation of the oxide PbO or alkaline solutions of divalent lead; further oxidation leads to the formation of lead dioxide PbO_2 or a solution of quadrivalent lead in the form of metaplumbate ions PbO_3^{--}.

The *dioxide* PbO_2 and solutions of plumbates are stable in the presence of alkaline solutions free from reducing agents, on account of the fact that lines (21) and (22) lie below line (*b*) for pH's above 7; in acid solutions, PbO_2 is thermodynamically unstable at atmospheric pressure, as lines (21) lie above line (*b*) for these solutions; it tends to be reduced to plumbous ions Pb^{++} under these conditions, decomposing the water with the evolution of oxygen; in this case, the electrode potential of the PbO_2 has a value between the values indicated by line (*b*) and the values indicated by the family of lines (21) which correspond to the Pb^{++} concentration.

PbO_2 is insoluble in neutral and moderately acid or alkaline solutions; it is slightly soluble in very acid solutions, forming plumbic ions Pb^{++++} and very soluble in very alkaline solutions, forming plumbate ions PbO_3^{--}. The position of the domain of stability of the oxide PbO_2 characterizes it to be a powerful oxidizing agent; this is confirmed in practice.

Under certain conditions it appears that *lead sesquioxide* or lead metaplumbate Pb_2O_3 can be formed. According to the free enthalpy value that we have assumed, it is thermodynamically unstable with respect to the oxides Pb_3O_4 and PbO_2. The dissolution of Pb_2O_3 in alkaline solutions according to the reaction $Pb_2O_3 + 3OH^- = HPbO_2^- + PbO_3^{--} + H_2O$, studied by Glasstone [5], leads to the formation of a solution containing equal quantities of $HPbO_2^-$ and PbO_3^{--} ions, whose equilibrium characteristics are therefore represented by line (6′).

3.4. LEAD ACCUMULATORS

We have previously ([1], [9]) examined the use of Fig. 1 for studying the operation of the lead accumulator. It will be recalled that the operation of this accumulator is due to the coupling, in a solution of sulphuric acid of pH around −0·4 and saturated with $PbSO_4$, of a positive electrode

PbO_2/Pb^{++} and a negative electrode Pb/Pb^{++} at the surface of which the following two reactions can take place:

at the electrode $PbO_2|Pb^{++}$ (approx. +1·7 V): $Pb^{++} + 2H_2O = PbO_2 + 4H^+ + 2e^-$ (21)
at the electrode $Pb|Pb^{++}$ (approx. −0·3V): $Pb = Pb^{++} + 2e^-$ (16)

corresponding to the overall reaction $Pb + PbO_2 + 4H^+ = 2Pb^{++} + 2H_2O$ whose electromotive force is 1·7 + 0·3 = 2·0 V.

When the accumulator discharges (providing electrical energy), oxidation takes place at the negative pole and reduction at the positive pole:

$-^{ve}$ pole	Pb	$\rightarrow$	$Pb^{++} + 2e^-$	$\downarrow$	(16)
$+^{ve}$ pole	$Pb^{++} + 2H_2O$	$\leftarrow$	$PbO_2 + 4H^+ + 2e^-$		(21)
overall reaction	$Pb + PbO_2 + 4H^+$	$\rightarrow$	$2Pb^{++} + 2H_2O$.		

When the accumulator is charged (external electrical energy being supplied), reduction takes place at the negative pole and oxidation at the positive pole:

$-^{ve}$ pole	Pb	$\leftarrow$	$Pb^{++} + 2e^-$	$\uparrow$	(16)
$+^{ve}$ pole	$Pb^{++} + 2H_2O$	$\rightarrow$	$PbO_2 + 4H^+ + 2e^-$		(21)
overall reaction	$2Pb^{++} + 2H_2O$	$\rightarrow$	$Pb + PbO_2 + 4H^+$.		

As both the families of lines (16) and (21) lie outside the domain of stability of water, in Fig. 1, at pH's around −0·4, the negative electrode Pb/Pb^{++} and the positive electrode PbO_2/Pb^{++} will both be unstable, and will tend to react with the electrolyte, forming respectively hydrogen (at the $-^{ve}$ pole) and oxygen (at the $+^{ve}$ pole). The accumulator will therefore discharge spontaneously when not being used, and its satisfactory operation will depend on frequent recharging.

4. BIBLIOGRAPHY

[1] P. DELAHAY, M. POURBAIX and P. VAN RYSSELBERGHE, *Diagramme potentiel–pH du plomb. Comportement électrochimique et corrosion du plomb. Accumulateurs à plomb* (Lecture given at the 2nd Meeting of CITCE, Milan, 1950; Tamburini, Milan, 1951, pp. 15–28).
[2] G. CHARLOT, *L'analyse qualitative et les réactions en solution*, 4th ed., Masson, Paris, 1957.
[3] S. GLASSTONE, Physical chemistry of the oxides of lead. Part IV: Red lead and lead sesquioxide, *J. Chem. Soc.* (*Transaction*) **121**, 1466 (1922).
[4] J. VAN MUYLDER and M. POURBAIX, *Corrosion et protection cathodiques du plomb* (Rapport technique RT.14 of CEBELCOR, July 1954).
[5] S. GLASSTONE, [3], p. 1464.
[6] G. SCHIKORR, *Korrosion und Metallschutz*, **16**, 181 (1940).
[7] C. VANLEUGENHAGHE, P. DERENNE, J. HEYMANS and J. VAN MUYLDER, *Recherches sur la protection cathodique de structures en plomb et en acier. Anodes réactives en zinc* (Rapport technique RT.64 of CEBELCOR, March 1958).
[8] M. POURBAIX and F. VANDERVELDEN, *Corrosion et incrustation des canalisations d'eau* (Rapport technique RT.67 of CEBELCOR, 1958).
[9] M. POURBAIX, *Leçons sur la corrosion électrochimique*, 3e fascicule (Rapport technique RT.49 of CEBELCOR, July 1957).

SECTION 18.1

NITROGEN(¹)

M. POURBAIX and N. DE ZOUBOV

SUMMARY

(¹) Adapted version of an extract from the Rapport CEFA/R.5 of the Commission des Études Fondamentales et Applications of CEBELCOR; see also [1].

1. SUBSTANCES CONSIDERED AND SUBSTANCES NOT CONSIDERED

	Oxidation number (Z)	Considered	Not considered	μ^0(cal.)	Name, colour, crystalline system
Solid substances	-1	–	NH_2OH	–	Hydroxylamine, white, rhomb.
	$+3$	–	N_2O_3	–	Nitrous anhydride, indigo-blue, quad.
	$+5$	–	N_2O_5	32 000	Nitric anhydride, colourless, hex.
Liquid substances	-2	–	N_2H_4	–	Hydrazine, colourless
	$+5$	–	HNO_3	$-19\,100$	Nitric acid, colourless
Dissolved substances	-3	NH_4OH	–	$-63\,050$	Ammonia; colourless
	»	NH_4^+	–	$-19\,000$	Ammonium ion, colourless
	-2	–	N_2H_4	30 560	Hydrazine
	»	–	$N_2H_4H_2^{++}$	22 500	Hydrazinium ion
	-1	–	NH_2OH	$-5\,600$	Hydroxylamine, colourless
	»	–	$NH_2OH.H^+$	$-13\,540$	Hydroxylammonium ion, colourless
	-0.33	–	HN_3	71 300	Hydrazoic acid, colourless
	»	–	N_3^-	77 700	Nitride ion
	0	–	N_2	2 994 (2)	Nitrogen, colourless
	$+1$	–	$H_2N_2O_2$	8 600	Hyponitrous acid
	»	–	$N_2O_2^{--}$	33 200	Hyponitrite ion
	»	–	$NH_2O_2^-$	18 200	?
	$+3$	HNO_2	–	$-12\,820$	Nitrous acid, colourless
	»	NO_2^-	–	$-8\,250$	Nitrite ion
	$+5$	HNO_3	–	$-26\,430$	Nitric acid, colourless
	»	NO_3^-	–	$-26\,430$	Nitrate ion, no colour of its own
	$+7$	–	HNO_4	–	Pernitric acid
Gaseous substances	-3	NH_3	–	$-3\,976$	Ammonia, colourless
	-1	–	NH	–	Imine
	-0.33	–	HN_3	78 500	Hydrazoic acid, colourless
	0	–	N	81 476	Monatomic nitrogen or "active" nitrogen, colourless
	»	N_2	–	0	Nitrogen, colourless
	$+1$	N_2O	–	24 760	Nitrous oxide, colourless
	$+2$	NO	–	20 719	Nitric oxide, colourless
	$+3$	–	N_2O_3	–	Nitrous anhydride, red–brown
	$+4$	NO_2	–	12 390	Nitrogen peroxide or dioxide, red–brown
	»	N_2O_4	–	23 491	Nitrogen peroxide or tetroxide, colourless
	$+5$	–	HNO_3	–	Nitric acid, colourless
	$+6$	–	NO_3	–	Nitrogen trioxide, slightly bluish

2. REACTIONS AND EQUILIBRIUM FORMULAE

2.1. TWO DISSOLVED SUBSTANCES

2.1.1. *Relative stability of the dissolved substances*

$Z = -3$

1. $NH_4^+ + H_2O = NH_4OH + H^+ \qquad \log\frac{(NH_4OH)}{(NH_4^+)} = -9.27 + pH$

$Z = +3$

2. $HNO_2 = NO_2^- + H^+ \qquad \log\frac{(NO_2^-)}{(HNO_2)} = -3.35 + pH$

(2) Value calculated from the solubility of pure nitrogen in water, at 25°C (178·1 mg/l).

$Z = +5$

3.	HNO_3	$= NO_3^-$	$+ H^+$	$\log \frac{(NO_3^-)}{(HNO_3)} = 0.00 + pH$

$-3 \rightarrow +3$

4.	$NH_4^+ + 2H_2O = HNO_2$		$+ 7H^+ + 6e^-$	$E_0 = 0.864 - 0.0689\ pH + 0.0098 \log \frac{(HNO_2)}{(NH_4^+)}$
5.	$NH_4^+ + 2H_2O = NO_2^-$		$+ 8H^+ + 6e^-$	$E_0 = 0.897 - 0.0788\ pH + 0.0098 \log \frac{(NO_2^-)}{(NH_4^+)}$
6.	$NH_4OH + H_2O = NO_2^-$		$+ 7H^+ + 6e^-$	$E_0 = 0.806 - 0.0689\ pH + 0.0098 \log \frac{(NO_2^-)}{(NH_4OH)}$

$+3 \rightarrow +5$

7.	$HNO_2 + H_2O = HNO_3$		$+ 2H^+ + 2e^-$	$E_0 = 0.934 - 0.0591\ pH + 0.0295 \log \frac{(HNO_3)}{(HNO_2)}$
8.	$HNO_2 + H_2O = NO_3^-$		$+ 3H^+ + 2e^-$	$E_0 = 0.934 - 0.0886\ pH + 0.0295 \log \frac{(NO_3^-)}{(HNO_2)}$
9.	$NO_2^- + H_2O = NO_3^-$		$+ 2H^+ + 2e^-$	$E_0 = 0.835 - 0.0591\ pH + 0.0295 \log \frac{(NO_3^-)}{(NO_2^-)}$

2.1.2. *Limits of the domains of relative predominance of the dissolved substances*

1'.	NH_4^+ / NH_4OH	$pH = 9.27$
2'.	HNO_2 / NO_2^-	$pH = 3.35$
3'.	HNO_3 / NO_3^-	$pH = 0.00$
4'.	NH_4^+ / HNO_2	$E_0 = 0.864 - 0.0689\ pH$
5'.	NH_4^+ / NO_2^-	$E_0 = 0.897 - 0.0788\ pH$
6'.	NH_4OH / NO_2^-	$E_0 = 0.806 - 0.0689\ pH$
7'.	HNO_2 / HNO_3	$E_0 = 0.934 - 0.0591\ pH$
8'.	HNO_2 / NO_3^-	$E_0 = 0.934 - 0.0886\ pH$
9'.	NO_2^- / NO_3^-	$E_0 = 0.835 - 0.0591\ pH$

2.2. TWO GASEOUS SUBSTANCES

2.2.1. *Relative stability of the gaseous substances*

$Z = +4$

10.	$2\mathit{NO_2}$	$= \mathit{N_2O_4}$		$\log \frac{p_{N_2O_4}}{(p_{NO_2})^2} = 0.95$

$-3 \rightarrow 0$

11.	$2\mathit{NH_3}$	$= \mathit{N_2}$	$+ 6H^+ + 6e^-$	$E_0 = 0.057 - 0.0591\ pH + 0.0098 \log \frac{p_{N_2}}{(p_{NH_3})^2}$

$0 \rightarrow +1$

12.	$\mathit{N_2} + H_2O = \mathit{N_2O}$		$+ 2H^+ + 2e^-$	$E_0 = 1.766 - 0.0591\ pH + 0.0295 \log \frac{p_{N_2O}}{p_{N_2}}$

$0 \rightarrow +2$

13.	$\mathit{N_2} + 2H_2O = 2\mathit{NO}$		$+ 4H^+ + 4e^-$	$E_0 = 1.678 - 0.0591\ pH + 0.0148 \log \frac{(p_{NO})^2}{p_{N_2}}$

$0 \rightarrow +4$

14.	$\mathit{N_2} + 4H_2O = 2\mathit{NO_2}$		$+ 8H^+ + 8e^-$	$E_0 = 1.363 - 0.0591\ pH + 0.0074 \log \frac{(p_{NO_2})^2}{p_{N_2}}$
15.	$\mathit{N_2} + 4H_2O = \mathit{N_2O_4}$		$+ 8H^+ + 8e^-$	$E_0 = 1.357 - 0.0591\ pH + 0.0074 \log \frac{p_{N_2O_4}}{p_{N_2}}$

$+1 \rightarrow +2$

16.	$\mathit{N_2O} + H_2O = 2\mathit{NO}$		$+ 2H^+ + 2e^-$	$E_0 = 1.591 - 0.0591\ pH + 0.0295 \log \frac{(p_{NO})^2}{p_{N_2O}}$

$+1 \rightarrow +4$

17. $N_2O + 3H_2O = 2NO_2 + 6H^+ + 6e^-$ $\quad E_0 = 1.229 - 0.0591\,pH + 0.0098 \log \frac{(p_{NO_2})^2}{p_{N_2O}}$

$+2 \rightarrow +4$

18. $NO + H_2O = NO_2 + 2H^+ + 2e^-$ $\quad E_0 = 1.049 - 0.0591\,pH + 0.0295 \log \frac{p_{NO_2}}{p_{NO}}$

19. $2NO + 2H_2O = N_2O_4 + 4H^+ + 4e^-$ $\quad E_0 = 1.035 - 0.0591\,pH + 0.0148 \log \frac{p_{N_2O_4}}{(p_{NO})^2}$

2.2.2. *Limits of the domains of relative predominance of the gaseous substances*

10'. NO_2 / N_2O_4 $\quad \log P = -0.65$

11'. NH_3 / N_2 $\quad E_0 = 0.060 - 0.0591\,pH - 0.0098 \log P$
12'. N_2 / N_2O $\quad E_0 = 1.766 - 0.0591\,pH$
13'. N_2 / NO $\quad E_0 = 1.674 - 0.0591\,pH + 0.0148 \log P$
14'. N_2 / NO_2 $\quad E_0 = 1.361 - 0.0591\,pH + 0.0074 \log P$
15'. N_2 / N_2O_4 $\quad E_0 = 1.357 - 0.0591\,pH$
16'. N_2O / NO $\quad E_0 = 1.582 - 0.0591\,pH + 0.0295 \log P$
17'. N_2O / NO_2 $\quad E_0 = 1.226 - 0.0591\,pH + 0.0098 \log P$
18'. NO / NO_2 $\quad E_0 = 1.049 - 0.0591\,pH$
19'. NO / N_2O_4 $\quad E_0 = 1.039 - 0.0591\,pH - 0.0148 \log P$

2.3. ONE GASEOUS SUBSTANCE AND ONE DISSOLVED SUBSTANCE

Solubility of the gaseous substances

$Z = -3$

20. $NH_4^+ = NH_3 + H^+$ $\quad \log \frac{p_{NH_3}}{(NH_4^+)} = -11.02 + pH$

21. $NH_4OH = NH_3 + H_2O$ $\quad \log \frac{p_{NH_3}}{(NH_4OH)} = -1.75$

$-3 \rightarrow 0$

22. $2NH_4^+ = N_2 + 8H^+ + 6e^-$ $\quad E_0 = 0.275 - 0.0788\,pH + 0.0098 \log \frac{p_{N_2}}{(NH_4^+)^2}$

23. $2NH_4OH = N_2 + 2H_2O + 6H^+ + 6e^-$ $\quad E_0 = 0.092 - 0.0591\,pH + 0.0098 \log \frac{p_{N_2}}{(NH_4OH)^2}$

$-3 \rightarrow +1$

24. $2NH_4^+ + H_2O = N_2O + 10H^+ + 8e^-$ $\quad E_0 = 0.647 - 0.0739\,pH + 0.0074 \log \frac{p_{N_2O}}{(NH_4^+)^2}$

25. $2NH_4OH = N_2O + H_2O + 8H^+ + 8e^-$ $\quad E_0 = 0.510 - 0.0591\,pH + 0.0074 \log \frac{p_{N_2O}}{(NH_4OH)^2}$

$-3 \rightarrow +2$

26. $NH_4^+ + H_2O = NO + 6H^+ + 5e^-$ $\quad E_0 = 0.836 - 0.0709\,pH + 0.0118 \log \frac{p_{NO}}{(NH_4^+)}$

27. $NH_4OH = NO + 5H^+ + 5e^-$ $\quad E_0 = 0.727 - 0.0591\,pH + 0.0118 \log \frac{p_{NO}}{(NH_4OH)}$

$-3 \rightarrow +3$

28. $NH_3 + 2H_2O = HNO_2 + 6H^+ + 6e^-$ $\quad E_0 = 0.755 - 0.0591\,pH + 0.0098 \log \frac{(HNO_2)}{p_{NH_3}}$

29. $NH_3 + 2H_2O = NO_2^- + 7H^+ + 6e^-$ $\quad E_0 = 0.789 - 0.0689\,pH + 0.0098 \log \frac{(NO_2^-)}{p_{NH_3}}$

$0 \rightarrow +3$

30. $N_2 + 4H_2O = 2HNO_2 + 6H^+ + 6e^-$ $\quad E_0 = 1.454 - 0.0591\,pH + 0.0098 \log \frac{(HNO_2)^2}{p_{N_2}}$

31. $N_2 + 4H_2O = 2NO_2^- + 8H^+ + 6e^-$ $\quad E_0 = 1.520 - 0.0788\,pH + 0.0098 \log \frac{(NO_2^-)^2}{p_{N_2}}$

$0 \rightarrow +5$

32. $N_2 + 6H_2O = 2HNO_3 + 10H^+ + 10e^-$ $\quad E_0 = 1.246 - 0.0591\,pH + 0.0059 \log \frac{(HNO_3)^2}{p_{N_2}}$

33. $N_2 + 6H_2O = 2NO_3^- + 12H^+ + 10e^-$ $\quad E_0 = 1.246 - 0.0709\,pH + 0.0059 \log \frac{(NO_3^-)^2}{p_{N_2}}$

$+1 \rightarrow +3$

34. $N_2O + 3H_2O = 2HNO_2 + 4H^+ + 4e^-$ $\quad E_0 = 1.297 - 0.0591\,pH + 0.0148 \log \frac{(HNO_2)^2}{p_{N_2O}}$

35. $N_2O + 3H_2O = 2NO_2^- + 6H^+ + 4e^-$ $\quad E_0 = 1.396 - 0.0886\,pH + 0.0148 \log \frac{(NO_2^-)^2}{p_{N_2O}}$

$+1 \rightarrow +5$

36. $N_2O + 5H_2O = 2HNO_3 + 8H^+ + 8e^-$ $\quad E_0 = 1.116 - 0.0591\,pH + 0.0074 \log \frac{(HNO_3)^2}{p_{N_2O}}$

37. $N_2O + 5H_2O = 2NO_3^- + 10H^+ + 8e^-$ $\quad E_0 = 1.116 - 0.0739\,pH + 0.0074 \log \frac{(NO_3^-)^2}{p_{N_2O}}$

$+2 \rightarrow +3$

38. $NO + H_2O = HNO_2 + H^+ + e^-$ $\quad E_0 = 1.004 - 0.0591\,pH + 0.0591 \log \frac{(HNO_2)}{p_{NO}}$

39. $NO + H_2O = NO_2^- + 2H^+ + e^-$ $\quad E_0 = 1.202 - 0.1182\,pH + 0.0591 \log \frac{(NO_2^-)}{p_{NO}}$

$+2 \rightarrow +5$

40. $NO + 2H_2O = HNO_3 + 3H^+ + 3e^-$ $\quad E_0 = 0.957 - 0.0591\,pH + 0.0197 \log \frac{(HNO_3)}{p_{NO}}$

41. $NO + 2H_2O = NO_3^- + 4H^+ + 3e^-$ $\quad E_0 = 0.957 - 0.0788\,pH + 0.0197 \log \frac{(NO_3^-)}{p_{NO}}$

$+3 \rightarrow +4$

42. $HNO_2 = NO_2 + H^+ + e^-$ $\quad E_0 = 1.093 - 0.0591\,pH + 0.0591 \log \frac{p_{NO_2}}{(HNO_2)}$

43. $NO_2^- = NO_2 + e^-$ $\quad E_0 = 0.895 + 0.0591 \log \frac{p_{NO_2}}{(NO_2^-)}$

44. $2HNO_2 = N_2O_4 + 2H^+ + 2e^-$ $\quad E_0 = 1.065 - 0.0591\,pH + 0.0295 \log \frac{p_{N_2O_4}}{(HNO_2)^2}$

45. $2NO_2^- = N_2O_4 + 2e^-$ $\quad E_0 = 0.867 + 0.0295 \log \frac{p_{N_2O_4}}{(NO_2^-)^2}$

$+4 \rightarrow +5$

46. $NO_2 + H_2O = HNO_3 + H^+ + e^-$ $\quad E_0 = 0.775 - 0.0591\,pH + 0.0591 \log \frac{(HNO_3)}{p_{NO_2}}$

47. $NO_2 + H_2O = NO_3^- + 2H^+ + e^-$ $\quad E_0 = 0.775 - 0.1182\,pH + 0.0591 \log \frac{(NO_3^-)}{p_{NO_2}}$

48. $N_2O_4 + 2H_2O = 2HNO_3 + 2H^+ + 2e^-$ $\quad E_0 = 0.803 - 0.0591\,pH + 0.0295 \log \frac{(HNO_3)^2}{p_{N_2O_4}}$

49. $N_2O_4 + 2H_2O = 2NO_3^- + 4H^+ + 2e^-$ $\quad E_0 = 0.803 - 0.1182\,pH + 0.0295 \log \frac{(NO_3^-)^2}{p_{N_2O_4}}$

3. EQUILIBRIUM DIAGRAMS AND THEIR INTERPRETATION

3.1. ESTABLISHMENT OF THE EQUILIBRIUM DIAGRAMS

In Fig. 1 we have used formulae (1′)–(9′) to represent the domains of relative predominance (at the equilibrium) of the dissolved compounds of nitrogen.

In Fig. 2 we have used formulae (10′)–(19′) to represent the domains of relative predominance (at the equilibrium) of the gaseous compounds of nitrogen, for a total pressure of 1 atm. of these gases considered two by two.

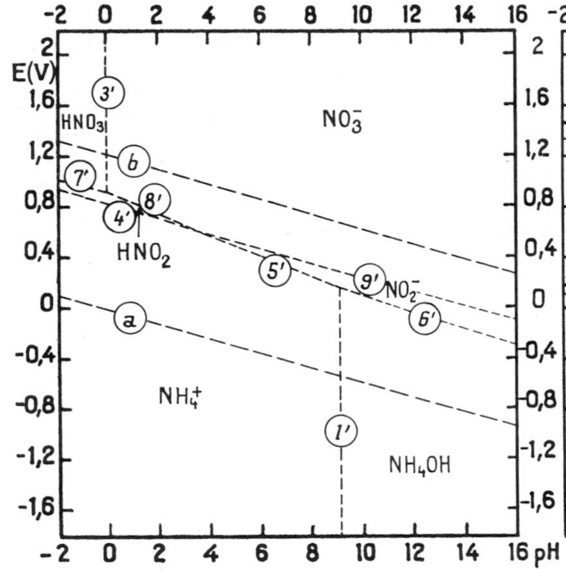

FIG. 1. Domains of relative predominance of the dissolved compounds of nitrogen, at 25°C.

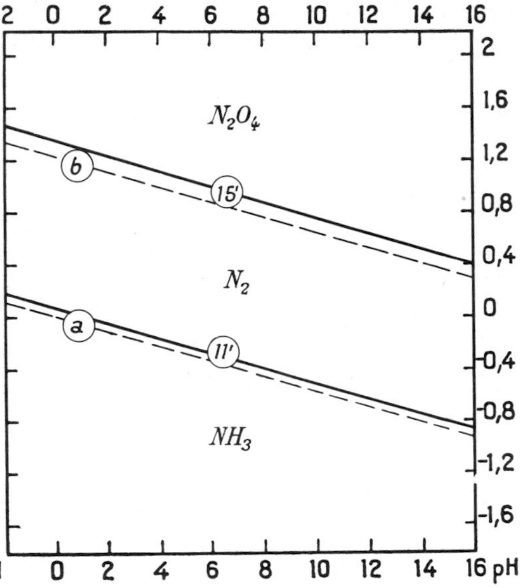

FIG. 2. Domains of relative predominance of the gaseous compounds of nitrogen, for total pressures of 1 atm., at 25°C.

Using all the formulae (1)–(49) we have constructed Fig. 3, which represents the domains of relative predominance of the dissolved compounds already represented in Fig. 1, and also the conditions under which, for the particular case of solutions containing 1 g-ion per litre of the predominant dissolved compound, the partial pressure of the predominant gaseous compound is 1 atm. (except for ammonia gas, for which we have considered pressures of 0·001 and 0·01 atm.).

In order to simplify these diagrams we have not considered the following dissolved substances, despite the fact that we have thermodynamic data which would enable us to consider them: hydrazine, hydroxylamine, hydrazoic acid, hyponitrous acid.

The equilibrium diagrams are valid only in the absence of substances with which nitrogen can form soluble complexes or insoluble salts. Nitrogen compounds form a large number of complexes; Charlot [2] points out the following: ammine complexes with metal cations (Ca^{++}, Cd^{++}, Li^{+}, Mg^{++}, Co^{++}, Hg^{++}, Ni^{++}, Cu^{++}, Co^{+++}, Ag^{+}, Cu^{+}, Zn^{++}), hydrazine complexes analogous to the ammine complexes, nitrides (deep red FeN_3^{++}), and nitrites, the best known of which is the cobaltinitrite $[Co(NO_2)_6^{---}]$.

The nitrides such as CuN_3, $Pb(N_3)_2$, TlN_3, AgN_3, $Hg_2(N_3)_2$ are sparingly soluble. Almost all the nitrites and nitrates are soluble; only the pale yellow silver nitrite, monovalent mercury nitrite and a few basic nitrates (Hg^{++}, Bi^{+++}) are sparingly soluble; the pernitrates (NO_4^-) of most heavy metals are insoluble.

Figure 3 expresses the following facts, relating to the electrochemical fixation of nitrogen, the stability of gaseous ammonia, the stability of nitrous acid and the nitrites, the reduction of nitric acid by NO and the chemical and electrochemical decomposition of nitric acid and the nitrates.

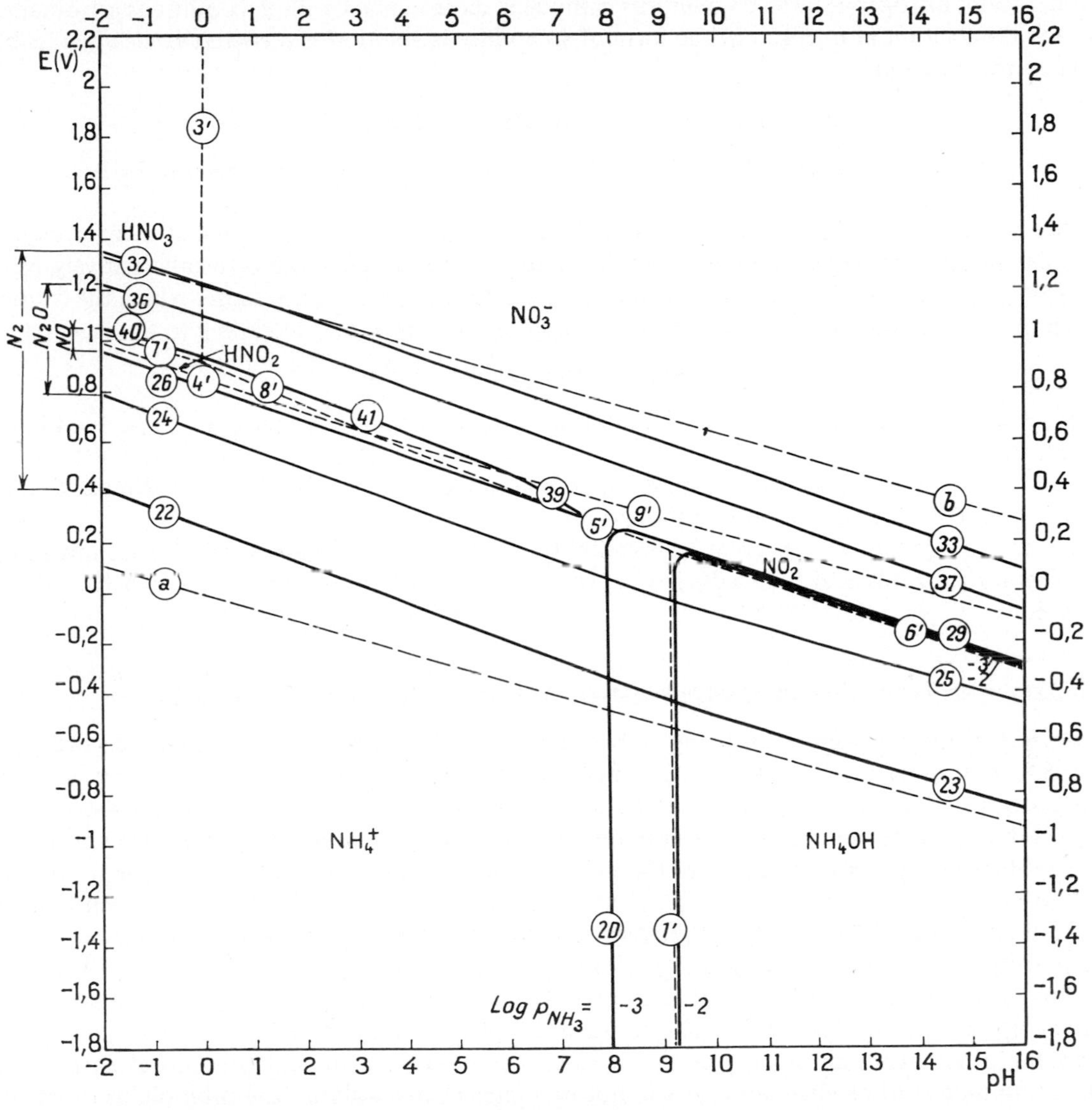

FIG. 3. Potential–pH equilibrium diagram for the system nitrogen–water, at 25°C. (The partial pressures indicated for NH_3, N_2, N_2O and NO refer to solutions containing 1 g-at of dissolved nitrogen per litre in all the forms $NH_4^+ + NH_4OH + HNO_2 + NO_2^- + HNO_3 + NO_3^-$.)

3.2. STABILITY AND ELECTROCHEMICAL FIXATION OF NITROGEN

In Fig. 2, which represents the domains of relative stability of nitrogen and its gaseous compounds at 25°C for a total pressure of 1 atm., the stability domain of diatomic nitrogen N_2 almost completely covers the stability domain of water: nitrogen is therefore thermodynamically stable under ordinary conditions. It is found in the natural state, and constitutes 79·06 per cent by volume of the air in the earth's atmosphere.

Figure 3 shows that nitrogen is not thermodynamically stable under conditions of pH and electrode potential represented by points lying outside lines (*a*) and (*b*), except for the very acid part of line (*b*) [lines (22), (23), (32) and (33)].

Consequently, if an aqueous solution is electrolysed in such a way that it evolves hydrogen at the cathode, and if nitrogen is bubbled over this cathode in close contact with it, conditions are obtained under which the fixation of nitrogen in the form of an ammonia solution is *thermodynamically* possible, according to the reaction

$$N_2 + 3H_2 + 2H_2O = 2NH_4OH \qquad (22 \text{ and } 23)$$

i.e., in the presence of a cathode and suitable catalysts it seems possible for nitrogen to be fixed in the form of ammonia.

On the other hand, if an aqueous solution is electrolysed in such a way that it evolves oxygen at the anode, and if nitrogen is bubbled over this anode in close contact with it (or alternatively N_2O, NO or a gas containing N_2, N_2O or NO, such as air), conditions are obtained under which the fixation of nitrogen in the form of a nitrate solution is *thermodynamically* possible, according to the reaction

$$N_2 + 2{\cdot}5\,O_2 + H_2O \rightarrow 2NO_3^- + 2H^+, \qquad (33)$$

i.e., in the presence of an anode and suitable catalysts, it seems possible for nitrogen to be fixed in the form of nitrates.

The combination of these two reactions, in a diaphragm cell, would involve a double fixation of nitrogen, with the formation of ammonia and nitric acid.

However, on account of the great irreversibility of the reactions considered above, nitrogen is practically non-oxidizable and non-reducible in solution [2]; such a fixation of nitrogen has not yet been effected.

3.3. STABILITY AND OXIDATION OF GASEOUS AMMONIA AND ITS AQUEOUS SOLUTIONS [3]

From Fig. 2, ammonia appears to be stable in the presence of reducing solutions; according to Fig. 3, it can be formed by the reduction of nitric or nitrous solutions. In actual fact there is a very small proportion of ammonia present in the earth's atmosphere; it is found in river- and sea-water.

The solubility conditions of gaseous ammonia are defined by relations (20) and (21), which were used to establish Fig. 4. This figure shows the influence of pH on the solubility of the gas in the two dissolved forms NH_4^+ and NH_4OH. In particular, the diagram shows that if the nitrogen content of a gas at atmospheric pressure is to be reduced to 0·0001 per cent (in which case $\log p_{NH_3} = -6$) by washing it with a solution containing 0·17 g NH_3/l [in which case $\log((NH_4^+) + (NH_4OH)) = -2$], this solution will have to have a pH equal to or below 7·0. Thus, in this case, an acid solution (e.g. sulphuric acid) need not necessarily be used to wash the gas, water alone being sufficient.

If, on the other hand, all or part of the ammonia contained in an acid solution of ammonium chloride or sulphate is to be eliminated, it will not be sufficient to alkalinize the solution, as its partial pressure of ammonia (which will have a maximum value at a pH of about 10·2) will be too small ($10^{-3·75}$, or 0·00018 atm.). As is well known, it is necessary to boil the alkalinized solution, or bubble an inert gas through it. As Fig. 3 shows, nitrogenated solutions containing 1 g-at of dissolved nitrogen per litre, can, under certain conditions of pH and electrode potential, evolve the gases N_2, N_2O and NO at atmospheric pressure, but they cannot evolve NH_3 gas at atmospheric pressure: the maximum NH_3 pressure, obtained in the lower right corner of Fig. 3, i.e. in the region in which the dissolved nitrogen exists essentially as undissociated NH_4OH, will be only slightly below 10^{-2} atm.; this pressure, the value of which depends on the NH_4OH concentration of the solution according to the relation $\log p_{NH_3} = -1{\cdot}75 + \log(NH_4OH)$ (21), is in this case $10^{-1·75}$ atm. (i.e. 0·018 atm.).

In agreement with Fig. 3, NH_3 and its solutions can be oxidized by powerful oxidizing agents, with the formation of dissolved HNO_2, NO_2^- and NO_3^-, and gaseous N_2, N_2O and NO; these oxidations are all irreversible. The halogens, hypochlorites and hypobromites oxidize NH_4^+ and NH_3 with the evolution of nitrogen [lines (22) and (23)]; when hypobromites are used, traces of NO_3^- and NO_2^- are found in solution, as well as traces of N_2O in the nitrogen evolved. The persulphates $S_2O_8^{--}$ act in the same way in the presence of Ag^+ as a catalyst.

A large number of oxides and peroxides, and a fair number of acids and salts having anions containing oxygen, react with ammonia gas, e.g. in particular, chlorine dioxide, which oxidizes NH_3 even in the cold.

The oxidation of ammonia in solution can be induced by that of another substance. Thus, when copper in contact with ammonia is oxidized by the air, part of the ammonia is oxidized to NO_2^- [3].

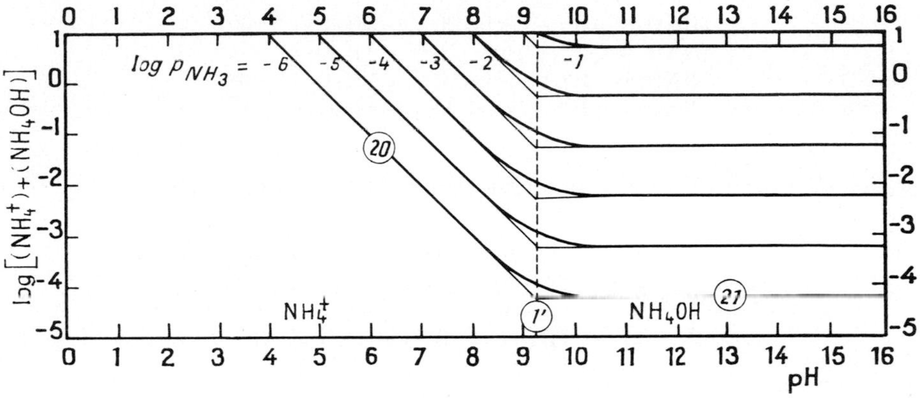

FIG. 4. Influence of pH on the solubility of gaseous NH_3, at 25°C.

Hydrogen peroxide converts ammonia solutions into nitrite, with the formation of ammonium nitrite. Manganese dioxide, in the presence of platinum sponge and in the cold, slowly oxidizes ammonia in solution to nitrite; hot $KMnO_4$ oxidizes it to nitrate.

When an ammonia solution is electrolysed, one observes at first an increasing anodic formation of nitrite, which is converted little by little into nitrate; traces of copper act as a catalyst.

Conversely, nitrites and nitrates can be reduced irreversibly to ammonia by powerful reducing agents (e.g. vanadous salts in acid media and zinc in alkaline media).

3.4. STABILITY AND DECOMPOSITION OF NITROUS ACID AND THE NITRITES

Figure 3 shows that nitrous acid HNO_2 is essentially unstable. Although HNO_2 is the predominant dissolved substance in the domain included between the lines (4′), (7′), (8′) and the abscissa pH = 3·35 (the domain in the shape of a truncated triangle), it can be thermodynamically stable in this domain only in the presence of appreciable proportions of HNO_3 or the ions NO_3^-, NH_4^+ and possibly NO_2^-, in solution; for instance, for the point whose coordinates are E = 0·740 V and pH = 1·80, the potentials of the equilibria between HNO_2 and the ions NO_3^-, NH_4^+ and NO_2^- are such that we have

$$\frac{(NO_3^-)}{(HNO_2)} = 0.12, \qquad \frac{(NH_4^+)}{(HNO_2)} = 1.00 \quad \text{and} \quad \frac{(NO_2^-)}{(HNO_2)} = 0.028.$$

We thus have a solution of nitrous acid and ammonium nitrate, with a little ammonium nitrite, containing 8·56 parts of nitrous nitrogen for 1 part of nitric nitrogen and 1 part of ammoniacal nitrogen.

Then, again, the domain of predominance of HNO_2 in Fig. 3 lies inside the regions for which the equilibrium pressures of N_2, N_2O and NO are above 1 atm. From formulae (30), (34) and (38) it can easily be calculated that the point E = 0·740 V and pH = 1·80 considered above corresponds to extremely high N_2 and N_2O pressures (respectively about 10^{62} and 10^{30} atm.), and to a more moderate, but still very appreciable, NO pressure ($10^{2.7}$ atm.).

Consequently HNO_2 tends, energetically, to decompose by oxidation according to the reaction

$$HNO_2 + H_2O = NO_3^- + 3H^+ + 2e^- \qquad (8)$$

and by reduction according to the reactions

$$\begin{array}{ll} 2HNO_2 + 6H^+ + 6e^- = N_2 + 4H_2O, & (30) \\ 2HNO_2 + 4H^+ + 4e^- = N_2O + 3H_2O, & (34) \\ HNO_2 + H^+ + e^- = NO + H_2O, & (38) \\ HNO_2 + 7H^+ + 6e^- = NH_4^+ + 2H_2O. & (4) \end{array}$$

In the absence of other oxidizing or reducing agents, this can lead only to the overall reactions

$$\begin{array}{ll} 3(8) + (30): & 5HNO_2 = 3NO_3^- + N_2 + 3H^+ + H_2O, \\ 2(8) + (34): & 4HNO_2 = 2NO_3^- + N_2O + 2H^+ + H_2O, \\ (8) + 2(38): & 3HNO_2 = NO_3^- + 2NO + H^+ + H_2O, \\ 3(8) + (4): & 4HNO_2 + H_2O = 3NO_3^- + NH_4^+ + 2H^+. \end{array}$$

Experiment shows that, of the first three of these reactions (we are not considering the fourth reaction here), only the third takes place under normal operating conditions, and this reaction is reversible ([2] and [3]). This disproportionation of nitrous acid into nitrate and nitric oxide NO has an effect on the properties of nitrous acid solutions and plays an important part in the manufacture of nitric acid by the absorption of nitrous gases in the presence of air ([1], pp. 108–110); in particular it enables us to work out the favourable influence exerted on the conversion of nitrous acid into nitric acid by bubbling gas through the mixture.

On account of its extreme oxidability, we cannot speak of a natural state for NO, as its formation under ordinary conditions is immediately followed by its conversion into nitrous anhydride N_2O_3 or nitrogen peroxide NO_2.

Nitrous acid and the nitrites can act either as oxidizing agents or reducing agents with respect to a large number of chemical systems. When HNO_2 acts as an *oxidizing agent*, it is usually converted into lower oxides of nitrogen or nitrogen itself; however, its reduction can sometimes convert it into ammonia or hydroxylamine. Nitrous acid and the nitrites oxidize hydriodic acid and the iodides to iodine, H_2S to sulphur and sulphurous and thiosulphuric acids, and arsenious acid to arsenic acid. They oxidize manganous and ferrous salts, and ferrocyanides in acid solution. Nitrous acid oxidizes the hydrogen derivatives of nitrogen (HN_3, NH_2OH, etc.) to nitrogen N_2.

When it acts as a *reducing agent*, nitrous acid is converted into nitric acid and unstable nitrogen dioxide; the latter decomposes spontaneously, with the formation of oxygen. Nitrous acid is oxidized by ozone, hydrogen peroxide, chlorine, bromine, iodine, permanganate (in acid media), the salts of Hg^{++}, Au^{+++} and Ce^{++++} and the oxides PbO_2, MnO_2, OsO_4. It reduces chloric and bromic acids (in the cold) and iodic acid (when heated) with the formation of the corresponding hydracids.

The *electrolysis* of solutions of alkali metal nitrites converts them into nitrates at the anode.

3.5. STABILITY AND DECOMPOSITION OF NITRIC ACID AND THE NITRATES

Nitric acid is a strong acid, whose pK is about zero (³) and which is therefore almost completely dissociated in solutions of pH above about 2 to 3.

Nitric acid and the nitrates are the predominant dissolved nitrogen compounds all along line (*b*) in Fig. 3, i.e. for solutions of all pH's saturated with oxygen at atmospheric pressure; this figure shows, however, that even under these oxidizing conditions, they are thermodynamically stable only in the presence of considerable proportions of nitrogen and gaseous nitrogen oxides (mainly N_2O). Nitric acid, which is colourless, exists in nature only under oxidizing conditions and even then only transiently, for example in the rainwater which falls during thunderstorms; it usually contains nitrogen and oxides of nitrogen in solution, including nitrogen peroxide NO_2 which colours it red; such is the case with "fuming" nitric acid in particular.

In agreement with Fig. 3, nitric acid is easily reduced, with the formation of dissolved nitrous and ammoniacal derivatives, gaseous nitrogen and nitrogen oxides, and other compounds (e.g. hydroxylamine) which have not been considered in the present study; thus the most important of its chemical properties is a very marked oxidizing power. The nature of the reduction products obtained depends on many factors which have not yet been sufficiently elucidated.

In many cases, nitrous acid is the first reduction product formed, e.g. according to the reaction

$$HNO_3 + 2H^+ + 2e^- \rightarrow HNO_2 + H_2O \qquad (7)$$

and this unstable HNO_2 decomposes, at low acid concentrations, to give NO, which leads to the equilibrium state of the reversible reaction $3HNO_2 = NO_3^- + 2NO + H^+ + H_2O$. At high concentrations, the decomposition of HNO_2 produces NO_2 and N_2O_4 according to reactions (42) and (44), which leads to the reversible reaction $N_2O_4 + H_2O = HNO_2 + HNO_3$ [1].

Hydrogen, which in the absence of catalysts has no action on HNO_3, reduces it in the presence of platinum sponge; the reduction can go as far as the stage NH_3. A large number of metals (Cu, Hg) reduce HNO_3 to NO. In alkaline media, $Fe(OH)_2$, Zn and Al, and in acid media, V^{++} and Cr^{++}, reduce nitrates and nitrites to NH_4OH and NH_4^+.

It is known, in particular from Tafel's works [5], that the *cathodic reduction* of HNO_3 solutions can lead to the formation of various reduction products, depending on the acid concentration and the nature of the cathode; thus one can obtain hydrogen, oxides of nitrogen, nitrous acid and nitrites, hydroxylamine and ammonium salts. For instance, Tafel observed that with an aqueous solution of HNO_3 and H_2SO_4, the yield of hydroxylamine was 1 or 100 per cent and that of ammonia was 99 or 0 per cent depending on whether the cathode was made of spongy copper or of mercury; this influence of the cathodic material is most probably due to an appreciable difference in the values of the electrode potential; that of copper is probably considerably higher than that of mercury.

4. BIBLIOGRAPHY

[1] M. Pourbaix, *Thermodynamique des solutions aqueuses diluées. Représentation graphique du rôle du pH et du potentiel*, Thesis, Delft, 1945; pref. F. E. C. Scheffer; Béranger, Paris and Liège, 1945; *Thermodynamics of Dilute Aqueous Solutions, with Application to Electrochemistry and Corrosion*, trans. J. N. Agar; pref. U. R. Evans; Ed. Arnold, London, 1949.

[2] G. Charlot, *L'analyse qualitative et les réactions en solution*, Masson, Paris, 1957, pp. 315–21.

[3] P. Pascal, *Nouveau traité de Chimie minérale*, Vol. X (*Azote*), Masson, Paris, 1956.

[4] W. M. Latimer, *Oxidation Potentials*, 2nd ed., Prentice-Hall, New York, 1952, pp. 90–105.

[5] J. Tafel, Die elektrolytische Reduktion der Salpetersäure bei Gegenwart von Salzsäure oder Schwefelsäure, *Z. anorg. allgem. Chem.* **31**, 289–325 (1902).

(³) Some experimenters indicate pK's of about 1·4.

SECTION 18.2

PHOSPHORUS(1)

J. VAN MUYLDER and M. POURBAIX

SUMMARY

1. *Substances considered and substances not considered.*

2. *Reactions and equilibrium formulae.*

2.1. Two dissolved substances.

2.1.1. Relative stability of the dissolved substances.

2.1.2. Limits of the domains of relative predominance of the dissolved substances.

2.2. Two solid substances.

Limits of the domains of stability of P and P_4H_2.

2.3. One solid substance and one gaseous substance.

Limits of the domains of stability of P, P_4H_2 and PH_3.

2.4. One solid substance and one liquid substance.

Limits of the domains of stability of P, P_4H_2 and P_2H_4.

2.5. One liquid substance and one gaseous substance.

Limits of the domains of stability of P_2H_4 and PH_3.

2.6. One dissolved substance and one solid substance.

Solubility of the solid substances.

2.7. One dissolved substance and one gaseous substance.

Solubility of the gaseous substances.

3. *Equilibrium diagrams and their interpretation.*

3.1. Establishment of the diagrams.

3.2. Stability of phosphorus.

3.3. Stability of the hydrides of phosphorus.

3.4. Stability of hypophosphorous acid and the hypophosphites.

3.5. Nickel- and cobalt-plating by chemical means.

3.6. Stability of orthophosphorous acid and the orthophosphites.

3.7. Stability of hypophosphoric acid and the hypophosphates.

3.8. Stability of orthophosphoric acid and the orthophosphates.

4. *Bibliography.*

(1) Adapted version of an extract from the Rapport CEFA/R.5 of the Commission des Études Fondamentales et Applications of CEBELCOR (June 1958).

1. SUBSTANCES CONSIDERED AND SUBSTANCES NOT CONSIDERED

	Oxidation number (Z)	Considered	Not considered	μ^0(cal.)	Name, colour, crystalline system
Solid substances	− 0.5	P_4H_2	-	16 000	Hydrogen tetraphosphide
	0	P	-	a. − 3 300	Phosphorus, red, cub.
	»	»	-	b. 0	Phosphorus, white, cub.
	»	-	P	-	Phosphorus, black, tern.
	+ 0.5	-	P_4O	-	Phosphorus sub-oxide
	+ 3	-	P_2O_3	-	Phosphorous anh., white, monocl.
	+ 4	-	P_2O_4	-	Phosphorus tetroxide, colourless, tern.
	+ 5	-	P_2O_5	-	Phosphoric anhydride, white, tern.
Liquid substance	− 2	P_2H_4	-	9 000 (²)	Hydrogen diphosphide, colourless
Dissolved substances	+ 1	H_3PO_2	-	−125 100	Hypophosphorous acid, colourless
	»	$H_2PO_2^-$	-	−122 400	Hypophosphite ion, colourless
	+ 3	H_3PO_3	-	−204 800	Orthophosphorous acid, colourless
	»	$H_2PO_3^-$	-	−202 350	Monoorthophosphite ion, colourless
	»	HPO_3^{--}	-	−194 000	Diorthophosphite ion, colourless
	»	-	HPO_2	-	Metaphosphorous acid, colourless
	»	-	$H_4P_2O_5$	-	Pyrophosphorous acid, colourless
	+ 4	$H_4P_2O_6$	-	−392 000	Hypophosphoric acid, colourless
	»	$H_3P_2O_6^-$	-	−389 000 (³)	Monohypophosphate ion, colourless
	»	$H_2P_2O_6^{--}$	-	−385 200 (³)	Dihypophosphate ion, colourless
	»	HP_2O_6	-	−375 300 (³)	Trihypophosphate ion, colourless
	»	$P_2O_6^{----}$	-	−361 700 (³)	Tetrahypophosphate ion, colourless
	+ 5	H_3PO_4	-	−274 200	Orthophosphoric acid, colourless
	»	$H_2PO_4^-$	-	−271 300	Monoorthophosphate ion, colourless
	»	HPO_4^{--}	-	−261 500	Diorthophosphate ion, colourless
	»	PO_4^{---}	-	−245 100	Triorthophosphate ion, colourless
	»	-	HPO_3	−215 800	Metaphosphoric acid, colourless
	»	-	$H_4P_2O_7$	-	Pyrophosphoric acid, colourless
	»	-	$H_5P_3O_{10}$	-	Triphosphoric acid, colourless
	»	-	$H_6P_4O_{13}$	-	Tetraphosphoric acid, colourless
	+ 6	-	$H_4P_2O_8$	-	Perphosphoric acid, colourless
	+ 7	-	H_3PO_5	-	Monoperphosphoric acid, colourless
Gaseous substances	− 3	PH_3	-	4 360	Phosphine, colourless

2. REACTIONS AND EQUILIBRIUM FORMULAE

2.1. TWO DISSOLVED SUBSTANCES

2.1.1. *Relative stability of the dissolved substances*

Z = + 1

1. $H_3PO_2 = H_2PO_2^- + H^+$ $\quad \log\frac{(H_2PO_2^-)}{(H_3PO_2)} = -\ 1.98 + pH$

Z = + 3

2. $H_3PO_3 = H_2PO_3^- + H^+$ $\quad \log\frac{(H_2PO_3^-)}{(H_3PO_3)} = -\ 1.80 + pH$

3. $H_2PO_3^- = HPO_3^{--} + H^+$ $\quad \log\frac{(HPO_3^{--})}{(H_2PO_3^-)} = -\ 6.13 + pH$

(²) Value calculated from work reported by Latimer.
(³) Values calculated from equilibrium constants indicated by Charlot[1].

$Z = +4$

4. $H_4P_2O_6 = H_3P_2O_6^- + H^+ \qquad \log \frac{(H_3P_2O_6^-)}{(H_4P_2O_6)} = -2.20 + pH$

5. $H_3P_2O_6^- = H_2P_2O_6^{--} + H^+ \qquad \log \frac{(H_2P_2O_6^{--})}{(H_3P_2O_6^-)} = -2.80 + pH$

6. $H_2P_2O_6^{--} = HP_2O_6^{---} + H^+ \qquad \log \frac{(HP_2O_6^{---})}{(H_2P_2O_6^{--})} = -7.30 + pH$

7. $HP_2O_6^{---} = P_2O_6^{----} + H^+ \qquad \log \frac{(P_2O_6^{----})}{(HP_2O_6^{---})} = -10.00 + pH$

$Z = +5$

8. $H_3PO_4 = H_2PO_4^- + H^+ \qquad \log \frac{(H_2PO_4^-)}{(H_3PO_4)} = -2.03 + pH$

9. $H_2PO_4^- = HPO_4^{--} + H^+ \qquad \log \frac{(HPO_4^{--})}{(H_2PO_4^-)} = -7.19 + pH$

10. $HPO_4^{--} = PO_4^{---} + H^+ \qquad \log \frac{(PO_4^{---})}{(HPO_4^{--})} = -12.03 + pH$

$+1 \rightarrow +3$

11. $H_3PO_2 + H_2O = H_3PO_3 + 2H^+ + 2e^- \qquad E_0 = -0.499 - 0.0591\,pH + 0.0295 \log \frac{(H_3PO_3)}{(H_3PO_2)}$

12. $H_3PO_2 + H_2O = H_2PO_3^- + 3H^+ + 2e^- \qquad E_0 = -0.446 - 0.0886\,pH + 0.0295 \log \frac{(H_2PO_3^-)}{(H_3PO_2)}$

13. $H_2PO_2^- + H_2O = H_2PO_3^- + 2H^+ + 2e^- \qquad E_0 = -0.504 - 0.0591\,pH + 0.0295 \log \frac{(H_2PO_3^-)}{(H_2PO_2^-)}$

14. $H_2PO_2^- + H_2O = HPO_3^{--} + 3H^+ + 2e^- \qquad E_0 = -0.323 - 0.0886\,pH + 0.0295 \log \frac{(HPO_3^{--})}{(H_2PO_2^-)}$

$+3 \rightarrow +4$

15. $2H_3PO_3 = H_4P_2O_6 + 2H^+ + 2e^- \qquad E_0 = 0.380 - 0.0591\,pH + 0.0295 \log \frac{(H_4P_2O_6)}{(H_3PO_3)^2}$

16. $2H_2PO_3^- = H_4P_2O_6 + 2e^- \qquad E_0 = 0.275 + 0.0295 \log \frac{(H_4P_2O_6)}{(H_2PO_3^-)^2}$

17. $2H_2PO_3^- = H_3P_2O_6^- + H^+ + 2e^- \qquad E_0 = 0.340 - 0.0295\,pH + 0.0295 \log \frac{(H_3P_2O_6^-)}{(H_2PO_3^-)^2}$

18. $2H_2PO_3^- = H_2P_2O_6^{--} + 2H^+ + 2e^- \qquad E_0 = 0.423 - 0.0591\,pH + 0.0295 \log \frac{(H_2P_2O_6^{--})}{(H_2PO_3^-)^2}$

19. $2HPO_3^{--} = H_2P_2O_6^{--} + 2e^- \qquad E_0 = 0.061 + 0.0295 \log \frac{(H_2P_2O_6^{--})}{(HPO_3^{--})^2}$

20. $2HPO_3^{--} = HP_2O_6^{---} + H^+ + 2e^- \qquad E_0 = 0.275 - 0.0295\,pH + 0.0295 \log \frac{(HP_2O_6^{---})}{(HPO_3^{--})^2}$

21. $2HPO_3^{--} = P_2O_6^{----} + 2H^+ + 2e^- \qquad E_0 = 0.570 - 0.0591\,pH + 0.0295 \log \frac{(P_2O_6^{----})}{(HPO_3^{--})^2}$

$+3 \rightarrow +5$

22. $H_3PO_3 + H_2O = H_3PO_4 + 2H^+ + 2e^- \qquad E_0 = -0.276 - 0.0591\,pH + 0.0295 \log \frac{(H_3PO_4)}{(H_3PO_3)}$

23. $H_2PO_3^- + H_2O = H_3PO_4 + H^+ + 2e^- \qquad E_0 = -0.329 - 0.0295\,pH + 0.0295 \log \frac{(H_3PO_4)}{(H_2PO_3^-)}$

24. $H_2PO_3^- + H_2O = H_2PO_4^- + 2H^+ + 2e^- \qquad E_0 = -0.260 - 0.0591\,pH + 0.0295 \log \frac{(H_2PO_4^-)}{(H_2PO_3^-)}$

25. $HPO_3^{--} + H_2O = H_2PO_4^- + H^+ + 2e^- \qquad E_0 = -0.447 - 0.0295\,pH + 0.0295 \log \frac{(H_2PO_4^-)}{(HPO_3^{--})}$

26. $HPO_3^{--} + H_2O = HPO_4^{--} + 2H^+ + 2e^- \qquad E_0 = -0.234 - 0.0591\,pH + 0.0295 \log \frac{(HPO_4^{--})}{(HPO_3^{--})}$

27. $HPO_3^{--} + H_2O = PO_4^{---} + 3H^+ + 2e^- \qquad E_0 = 0.121 - 0.0886\,pH + 0.0295 \log \frac{(PO_4^{---}}{(HPO_3^{--})}$

$+4 \rightarrow +5$

28.	$H_4P_2O_6 + 2H_2O = 2H_3PO_4 + 2H^+ + 2e^-$	$E_0 = -0.933 - 0.0591\,pH + 0.0295 \log \frac{(H_3PO_4)^2}{(H_4P_2O_6)}$
29.	$H_4P_2O_6 + 2H_2O = 2H_2PO_4^- + 4H^+ + 2e^-$	$E_0 = -0.807 - 0.1182\,pH + 0.0295 \log \frac{(H_2PO_4^-)^2}{(H_4P_2O_6)}$
30.	$H_3P_2O_6^- + 2H_2O = 2H_2PO_4^- + 3H^+ + 2e^-$	$E_0 = -0.872 - 0.0886\,pH + 0.0295 \log \frac{(H_2PO_4^-)^2}{(H_3P_2O_6^-)}$
31.	$H_2P_2O_6^{--} + 2H_2O = 2H_2PO_4^- + 2H^+ + 2e^-$	$E_0 = -0.955 - 0.0591\,pH + 0.0295 \log \frac{(H_2PO_4^-)^2}{(H_2P_2O_6^{--})}$
32.	$H_2P_2O_6^{--} + 2H_2O = 2HPO_4^{--} + 4H^+ + 2e^-$	$E_0 = -0.551 - 0.1182\,pH + 0.0295 \log \frac{(HPO_4^{--})^2}{(H_2P_2O_6^{--})}$
33.	$HP_2O_6^{---} + 2H_2O = 2HPO_4^{--} + 3H^+ + 2e^-$	$E_0 = -0.744 - 0.0886\,pH + 0.0295 \log \frac{(HPO_4^{--})^2}{(HP_2O_6^{---})}$
34.	$P_2O_6^{----} + 2H_2O = 2HPO_4^{--} + 2H^+ + 2e^-$	$E_0 = -1.039 - 0.0591\,pH + 0.0295 \log \frac{(HPO_4^{--})^2}{(P_2O_6^{----})}$
35.	$P_2O_6^{----} + 2H_2O = 2PO_4^{---} + 4H^+ + 2e^-$	$E_0 = -0.328 - 0.1182\,pH + 0.0295 \log \frac{(PO_4^{---})^2}{(P_2O_6^{----})}$

2.1.2. *Limits of the domains of relative predominance of the dissolved substances*

1'.	$H_3PO_2\ /H_2PO_2^-$	$pH = 1.98$
2'.	$H_3PO_3\ /H_2PO_3^-$	$pH = 1.80$
3'.	$H_2PO_3^-\ /HPO_3^{--}$	$pH = 6.13$
4'.	$H_4P_2O_6\ /H_3P_2O_6^-$	$pH = 2.20$
5'.	$H_3P_2O_6^-\ /H_2P_2O_6^{--}$	$pH = 2.80$
6'.	$H_2P_2O_6^{--}\ /HP_2O_6^{---}$	$pH = 7.30$
7'.	$HP_2O_6^{---}\ /P_2O_6^{----}$	$pH = 10.00$
8'.	$H_3PO_4\ /H_2PO_4^-$	$pH = 2.03$
9'.	$H_2PO_4^-\ /HPO_4^{--}$	$pH = 7.19$
10'.	$HPO_4^{--}\ /PO_4^{---}$	$pH = 12.03$

11'.	$H_3PO_2\ /H_3PO_3$	$E_0 = -0.499 - 0.0591\,pH$
12'.	$H_3PO_2\ /H_2PO_3^-$	$E_0 = -0.446 - 0.0886\,pH$
13'.	$H_2PO_2^-\ /H_2PO_3^-$	$E_0 = -0.504 - 0.0591\,pH$
14'.	$H_2PO_2^-\ /HPO_3^{--}$	$E_0 = -0.323 - 0.0886\,pH$
15'.	$H_3PO_3\ /H_4P_2O_6$	$E_0 = 0.380 - 0.0591\,pH - 0.0295 \log C$
16'.	$H_2PO_3^-\ /H_4P_2O_6$	$E_0 = 0.275 - 0.0295 \log C$
17'.	$H_2PO_3^-\ /H_3P_2O_6^-$	$E_0 = 0.340 - 0.0295\,pH - 0.0295 \log C$
18'.	$H_2PO_3^-\ /H_2P_2O_6^{--}$	$E_0 = 0.423 - 0.0591\,pH - 0.0295 \log C$
19'.	$HPO_3^{--}\ /H_2P_2O_6^{--}$	$E_0 = 0.061 - 0.0295 \log C$
20'.	$HPO_3^{--}\ /HP_2O_6^{---}$	$E_0 = 0.275 - 0.0295\,pH - 0.0295 \log C$
21'.	$HPO_3^{--}\ /P_2O_6^{----}$	$E_0 = 0.570 - 0.0591\,pH - 0.0295 \log C$
22'.	$H_3PO_3\ /H_3PO_4$	$E_0 = -0.276 - 0.0591\,pH$
23'.	$H_2PO_3^-\ /H_3PO_4$	$E_0 = -0.329 - 0.0295\,pH$
24'.	$H_2PO_3^-\ /H_2PO_4^-$	$E_0 = -0.260 - 0.0591\,pH$
25'.	$HPO_3^{--}\ /H_2PO_4^-$	$E_0 = -0.447 - 0.0295\,pH$
26'.	$HPO_3^{--}\ /HPO_4^{--}$	$E_0 = -0.234 - 0.0591\,pH$
27'.	$HPO_3^{--}\ /PO_4^{---}$	$E_0 = 0.121 - 0.0886\,pH$
28'.	$H_4P_2O_6\ /H_3PO_4$	$E_0 = -0.933 - 0.0591\,pH + 0.0295 \log C$
29'.	$H_4P_2O_6\ /H_2PO_4^-$	$E_0 = -0.807 - 0.1182\,pH + 0.0295 \log C$
30'.	$H_3P_2O_6^-\ /H_2PO_4^-$	$E_0 = -0.872 - 0.0886\,pH + 0.0295 \log C$
31'.	$H_2P_2O_6^{--}\ /H_2PO_4^-$	$E_0 = -0.955 - 0.0591\,pH + 0.0295 \log C$
32'.	$H_2P_2O_6^{--}\ /HPO_4^{--}$	$E_0 = -0.551 - 0.1182\,pH + 0.0295 \log C$
33'.	$HP_2O_6^{---}\ /HPO_4^{--}$	$E_0 = -0.744 - 0.0886\,pH + 0.0295 \log C$
34'.	$P_2O_6^{----}\ /HPO_4^{--}$	$E_0 = -1.039 - 0.0591\,pH + 0.0295 \log C$
35'.	$P_2O_6^{----}\ /PO_4^{---}$	$E_0 = -0.328 - 0.1182\,pH + 0.0295 \log C$

2.2. TWO SOLID SUBSTANCES (4)

Limits of the domains of stability of **P** *and* $\mathbf{P_4H_2}$

— 0.5 → 0

36. $\mathbf{P_4H_2} = 4\mathbf{P} + 2H^+ + 2e^-$ a. $E_0 = -0.633 - 0.0591\,pH$
b. $= -0.347 - 0.0591\,pH$

2.3. ONE SOLID SUBSTANCE AND ONE GASEOUS SUBSTANCE (4)

Limits of the domains of stability of **P**, $\mathbf{P_4H_2}$ and PH_3

— 3 → — 0.5

37. $4PH_3 = \mathbf{P_4H_2} + 10H^+ + 10e^-$ $E_0 = -0.006 - 0.0591\,pH - 0.0236 \log p_{PH_3}$

— 3 → 0

38. $PH_3 = \mathbf{P} + 3H^+ + 3e^-$ a. $E_0 = -0.111 - 0.0591\,pH - 0.0197 \log p_{PH_3}$
b. $= -0.063 - 0.0591\,pH - 0.0197 \log p_{PH_3}$

2.4. ONE SOLID SUBSTANCE AND ONE LIQUID SUBSTANCE (4)

Limits of the domains of stability of **P**, $\mathbf{P_4H_2}$ *and* $\mathbf{P_2H_4}$

— 2 → — 0.5

39. $2\mathbf{P_2H_4} = \mathbf{P_4H_2} + 6H^+ + 6e^-$ $E_0 = -0.014 - 0.0591\,pH$

— 2 → 0

40. $\mathbf{P_2H_4} = 2\mathbf{P} + 4H^+ + 4e^-$ a. $E_0 = -0.169 - 0.0591\,pH$
b. $= -0.100 - 0.0591\,pH$

2.5. ONE LIQUID SUBSTANCE AND ONE GASEOUS SUBSTANCE

Limits of the domains of stability of $\mathbf{P_2H_4}$ *and* PH_3

— 3 → — 2

41. $2PH_3 = \mathbf{P_2H_4} + 2H^+ + 2e^-$ $E_0 = 0.006 - 0.0591\,pH - 0.0591 \log p_{PH_3}$

2.6. ONE DISSOLVED SUBSTANCE AND ONE SOLID SUBSTANCE (4)

Solubility of the solid substances

— 0.5 → + 1

42. $\mathbf{P_4H_2} + 8H_2O = 4H_3PO_2 + 6H^+ + 6e^-$ $E_0 = -0.455 - 0.0591\,pH + 0.0394 \log (H_3PO_2)$
43. $\mathbf{P_4H_2} + 8H_2O = 4H_2PO_2^- + 10H^+ + 6e^-$ $E_0 = -0.376 - 0.0985\,pH + 0.0394 \log (H_2PO_2^-)$

— 0.5 → + 3

44. $\mathbf{P_4H_2} + 12H_2O = 4H_3PO_3 + 14H^+ + 14e^-$ $E_0 = -0.480 - 0.0591\,pH + 0.0169 \log (H_3PO_3)$
45. $\mathbf{P_4H_2} + 12H_2O = 4H_2PO_3^- + 18H^+ + 14e^-$ $E_0 = -0.450 - 0.0760\,pH + 0.0169 \log (H_2PO_3^-)$
46. $\mathbf{P_4H_2} + 12H_2O = 4HPO_3^{--} + 22H^+ + 14e^-$ $E_0 = -0.346 - 0.0929\,pH + 0.0169 \log (HPO_3^{--})$

— 0.5 → + 5

47. $\mathbf{P_4H_2} + 16H_2O = 4H_3PO_4 + 22H^+ + 22e^-$ $E_0 = -0.406 - 0.0591\,pH + 0.0107 \log (H_3PO_4)$
48. $\mathbf{P_4H_2} + 16H_2O = 4H_2PO_4^- + 26H^+ + 22e^-$ $E_0 = -0.383 - 0.0698\,pH + 0.0107 \log (H_2PO_4^-)$
49. $\mathbf{P_4H_2} + 16H_2O = 4HPO_4^{--} + 30H^+ + 22e^-$ $E_0 = -0.305 - 0.0806\,pH + 0.0107 \log (HPO_4^{--})$
50. $\mathbf{P_4H_2} + 16H_2O = 4PO_4^{---} + 34H^+ + 22e^-$ $E_0 = -0.176 - 0.0913\,pH + 0.0107 \log (PO_4^{---})$

(4) The formulae marked *a* concern red phosphorus and those marked *b* concern white phosphorus.

$0 \rightarrow +1$

51. P $+ 2H_2O = H_3PO_2 + H^+ + e^-$ a. $E_0 = -0,365 - 0,0591\ pH + 0,0591 \log (H_3PO_2)$
b. $= -0,508 - 0,0591\ pH + 0,0591 \log (H_3PO_2)$

52. P $+ 2H_2O = H_2PO_2^- + 2H^+ + e^-$ a. $E_0 = -0,248 - 0,1182\ pH + 0,0591 \log (H_2PO_2^-)$
b. $= -0,391 - 0,1182\ pH + 0,0591 \log (H_2PO_2^-)$

$0 \rightarrow +3$

53. P $+ 3H_2O = H_3PO_3 + 3H^+ + 3e^-$ a. $E_0 = -0,454 - 0,0591\ pH + 0,0197 \log (H_3PO_3)$
b. $= -0,502 - 0,0591\ pH + 0,0197 \log (H_3PO_3)$

54. P $+ 3H_2O = H_2PO_3^- + 4H^+ + 3e^-$ a. $E_0 = -0,419 - 0,0788\ pH + 0,0197 \log (H_2PO_3^-)$
b. $= -0,467 - 0,0788\ pH + 0,0197 \log (H_2PO_3^-)$

55. P $+ 3H_2O = HPO_3^{--} + 5H^+ + 3e^-$ a. $E_0 = -0,298 - 0,0985\ pH + 0,0197 \log (HPO_3^{--})$
b. $= -0,346 - 0,0985\ pH + 0,0197 \log (HPO_3^{--})$

$0 \rightarrow +5$

56. P $+ 4H_2O = H_3PO_4 + 5H^+ + 5e^-$ a. $E_0 = -0,383 - 0,0591\ pH + 0,0118 \log (H_3PO_4)$
b. $= -0,411 - 0,0591\ pH + 0,0118 \log (H_3PO_4)$

57. P $+ 4H_2O = H_2PO_4^- + 6H^+ + 5e^-$ a. $E_0 = -0,358 - 0,0709\ pH + 0,0118 \log (H_2PO_4^-)$
b. $= -0,386 - 0,0709\ pH + 0,0118 \log (H_2PO_4^-)$

58. P $+ 4H_2O = HPO_4^{--} + 7H^+ + 5e^-$ a. $E_0 = -0,288 - 0,0827\ pH + 0,0118 \log (HPO_4^{--})$
b. $= -0,316 - 0,0827\ pH + 0,0118 \log (HPO_4^{--})$

59. P $+ 4H_2O = PO_4^{---} + 8H^+ + 5e^-$ a. $E_0 = -0,128 - 0,0946\ pH + 0,0118 \log (PO_4^{---})$
b. $= -0,156 - 0,0946\ pH + 0,0118 \log (PO_4^{---})$

2.7. ONE DISSOLVED SUBSTANCE AND ONE GASEOUS SUBSTANCE

Solubility of the gaseous substances

$-3 \rightarrow +1$

60. $PH_3 + 2H_2O = H_3PO_2 + 4H^+ + 4e^-$ $E_0 = -0,174 - 0,0591\ pH + 0,0148 \log \frac{(H_3PO_2)}{p_{PH_3}}$

61. $PH_3 + 2H_2O = H_2PO_2^- + 5H^+ + 4e^-$ $E_0 = -0,145 - 0,0739\ pH + 0,0148 \log \frac{(H_2PO_2^-)}{p_{PH_3}}$

$-3 \rightarrow +3$

62. $PH_3 + 3H_2O = H_3PO_3 + 6H^+ + 6e^-$ $E_0 = -0,282 - 0,0591\ pH + 0,0098 \log \frac{(H_3PO_3)}{p_{PH_3}}$

63. $PH_3 + 3H_2O = H_2PO_3^- + 7H^+ + 6e^-$ $E_0 = -0,265 - 0,0690\ pH + 0,0098 \log \frac{(H_2PO_3^-)}{p_{PH_3}}$

64. $PH_3 + 3H_2O = HPO_3^{--} + 8H^+ + 6e^-$ $E_0 = -0,205 - 0,0788\ pH + 0,0098 \log \frac{(HPO_3^{--})}{p_{PH_3}}$

$-3 \rightarrow +5$

65. $PH_3 + 4H_2O = H_3PO_4 + 8H^+ + 8e^-$ $E_0 = -0,281 - 0,0591\ pH + 0,0074 \log \frac{(H_3PO_4)}{p_{PH_3}}$

66. $PH_3 + 4H_2O = H_2PO_4^- + 9H^+ + 8e^-$ $E_0 = -0,265 - 0,0665\ pH + 0,0074 \log \frac{(H_2PO_4^-)}{p_{PH_3}}$

67. $PH_3 + 4H_2O = HPO_4^{--} + 10H^+ + 8e^-$ $E_0 = -0,212 - 0,0740\ pH + 0,0074 \log \frac{(HPO_4^{--})}{p_{PH_3}}$

68. $PH_3 + 4H_2O = PO_4^{---} + 11H^+ + 8e^-$ $E_0 = -0,123 - 0,0814\ pH + 0,0074 \log \frac{(PO_4^{---})}{p_{PH_3}}$

As all the oxides of phosphorus are very soluble in water, we have not established the formulae relating to their stability conditions in the presence of aqueous solutions. Moreover, we have not established equilibrium formulae for meta- and pyrophosphorous acids HPO_2 and $H_4P_2O_5$, nor for meta- and pyrophosphoric acids HPO_3 and $H_4P_2O_7$, as these substances are not in genuine equilibrium in aqueous solutions; in general they become hydrated slowly (rapidly when the solution is heated, and in acid media) giving respectively orthophosphorous acid H_3PO_3 and orthophosphoric acid H_3PO_4.

3. EQUILIBRIUM DIAGRAMS AND THEIR INTERPRETATION

3.1. ESTABLISHMENT OF THE DIAGRAMS

Using formulae (1)–(68), we have constructed Fig. 1 (equilibrium diagram for the system phosphorus–water, taking into account the hydrides of phosphorus) and Fig. 2 (equilibrium diagram for the system phosphorus–water, not taking into account the hydrides of phosphorus and considering white phosphorus).

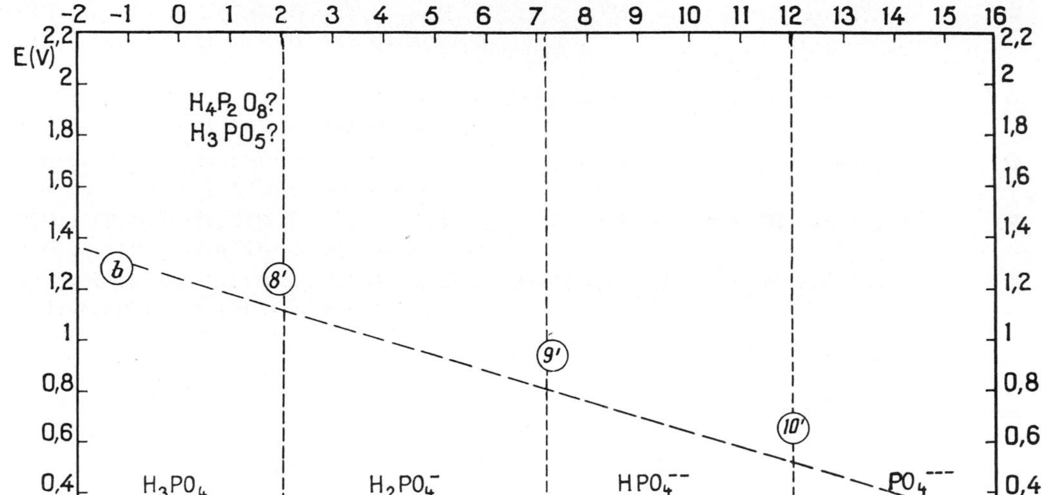

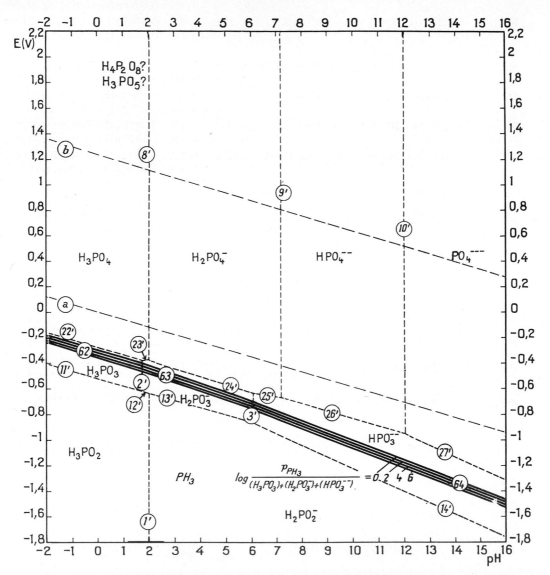

FIG. 1. Potential–pH equilibrium diagram for the system phosphorus–water, at 25°C. (Taking into account the hydrides of phosphorus.)

These figures are valid only in the absence of substances with which phosphorus can form soluble complexes or insoluble salts. According to Charlot [1], phosphorus compounds form a large number of complexes with cations; this is particularly true of the hypophosphites, the phosphates [with the ions of the Al (III) group, with V (V), Mo (VI), W (VI) and Cr (VI)], the metaphosphates, the pyrophosphates (mainly with the elements of the NH_4 and Zn groups) and the polyphosphates.

In general, the hypophosphites are soluble, as are the phosphites, the phosphates and the pyrophosphates of the alkali metals. The other phosphites, phosphates and pyrophosphates are soluble only in acid solution, to various degrees, depending on the case.

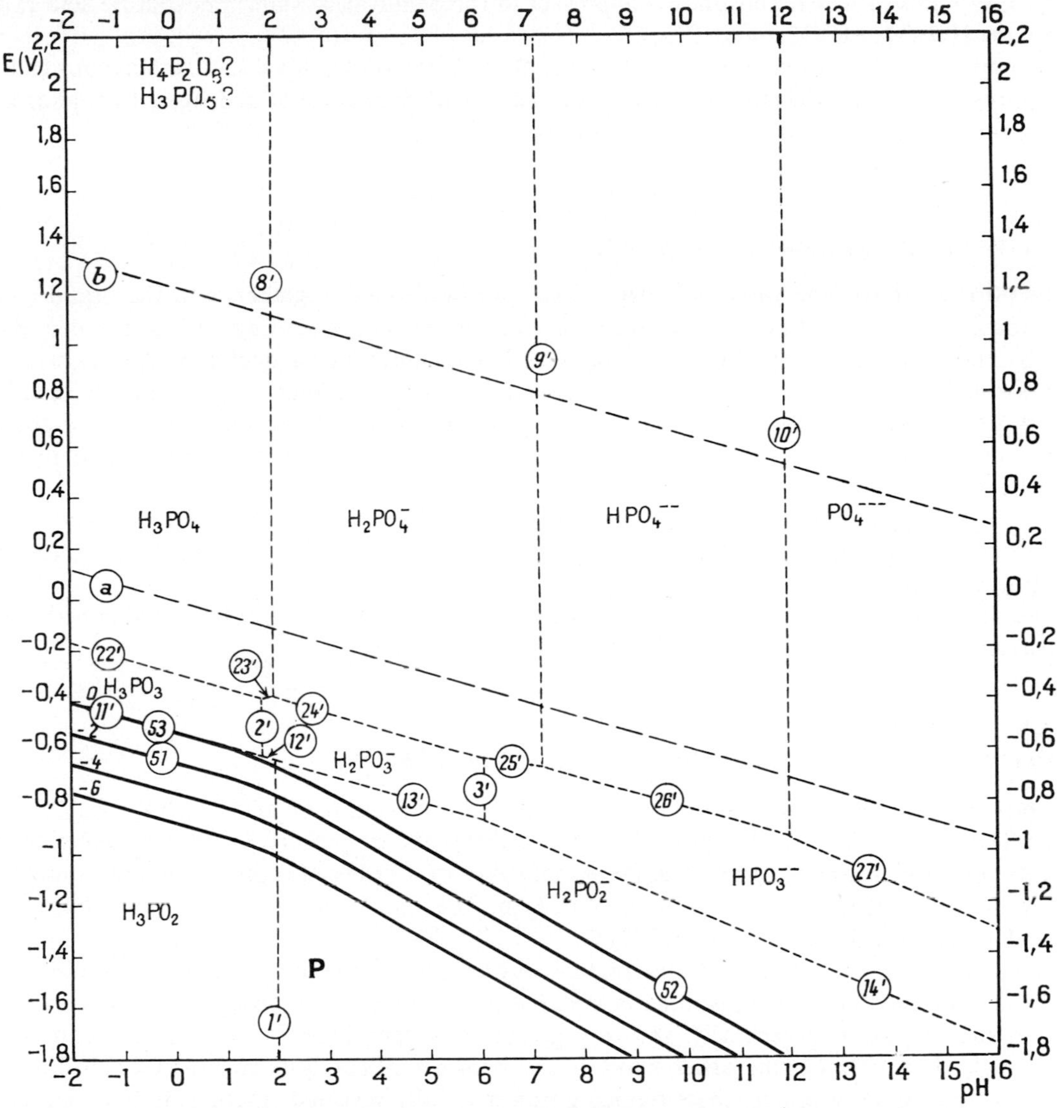

FIG. 2. Potential–pH equilibrium diagram for the system phosphorus–water, at 25°C. (Not taking into account the hydrides of phosphorus; considering white phosphorus.)

3.2. STABILITY OF PHOSPHORUS

As its domain of stability in Fig. 2 lies entirely below the domain of stability of water, phosphorus is very unstable in the presence of aqueous solutions. It is therefore a very base element, and a powerful reducing agent. It does not occur in the native state in nature, but is found in the oxidized state as mineral phosphates (apatite, wagnerite, phosphorites, etc.).

Phosphorus can be oxidized to phosphorous acid H_3PO_3 or phosphites $H_2PO_3^-$ and HPO_3^{--} (i.e. the trivalent state), by means of iodine [1], for instance, according to the reaction

$$2P + 3I_2 + 6OH^- = 6I^- + 2H_3PO_3.$$

Further oxidation, for example by means of nitric acid, potassium permanganate, chlorine, etc., produces compounds in which phosphorus is present in the pentavalent state: phosphoric acid H_3PO_4 or phosphates $H_2PO_4^-$, HPO_4^{--} and PO_4^{---}.

A comparison of Figs. 1 and 2 shows that when phosphorus is in contact with an aqueous solution, it is always unstable; it can theoretically reduce the water with formation of hydrogen, hypophosphites, phosphites, phosphates and gaseous phosphine PH_3.

3.3. STABILITY OF THE HYDRIDES OF PHOSPHORUS

As mentioned above, the gaseous hydride PH_3 can be formed, together with the liquid hydride P_2H_4, by the disproportionation of phosphorus in alkaline media; according to Fig. 1 it can also be obtained by the reduction of the hypophosphites and phosphites, in particular by means of nascent hydrogen formed at electrode potentials below those indicated by the family of lines (62), (63) and (64).

The position of the domain of stability of PH_3 below line (*a*) characterizes it to be a reducing substance, thermodynamically unstable and tending to decompose into phosphorus and hydrogen (action of heat or electric sparks).

The hydride PH_3 can be oxidized to phosphorous acid H_3PO_3 or phosphites $H_2PO_3^-$ and HPO_3^{--} (by the air), or to phosphoric acid H_3PO_4 and phosphates $H_2PO_4^-$, HPO_4^{--} and PO_4^{---} (on more vigorous oxidation).

The liquid hydride P_2H_4 and the solid hydride P_4H_2 are thermodynamically unstable with respect to the gaseous hydride PH_3; consequently, they do not appear in Fig. 1.

3.4. STABILITY OF HYPOPHOSPHOROUS ACID AND THE HYPOPHOSPHITES

The position of the domain of predominance of hypophosphorous acid H_3PO_2 and the hypophosphites $H_2PO_2^-$ in Figs. 1 and 2 show that these substances are powerful reducing agents, thermodynamically unstable in the presence of aqueous solutions of all pH's. Theoretically, they should tend to decompose water with the evolution of hydrogen, becoming converted into phosphorous acid H_3PO_3 and phosphites $H_2PO_3^{-}$ and HPO_3^{--}.

In actual fact, the reduction of water in this way is infinitely slow. In aqueous solution, hypophosphorous acid and the hypophosphites are stable in practice, in the absence of oxidizing agents, and their reducing power is generally not very great: methylene blue and iodine are reduced only infinitely slowly ([1], [2]). On the other hand, in the presence of catalysts such as Cu, Ni, Pd and C in the form of powdered graphite, their reducing power is fully revealed: methylene blue, iodine and water are then reduced ([1], [2]).

Under these conditions, hypophosphorous acid and the hypophosphites reduce the salts of the noble metals (Au, Ag, Pt, Pd), and also arsenious, cupric, cobaltous and nickelous salts with the deposition of the corresponding metal and they reduce mercuric salts to mercurous salts, being themselves oxidized to phosphorous acid and phosphites. In agreement with Figs. 1 and 2 further oxidation, by means of Cl_2, Br_2, $HClO_3$, KIO_3, HNO_3, $KMnO_4$, etc., converts hypophosphorous acid directly into phosphoric acid and phosphates.

If the hypophosphites are reduced with nascent hydrogen, one obtains the gaseous hydride PH_3 and possibly the liquid hydride P_2H_4.

The pronounced reducing property of the hypophosphites is made use of technically in the deposition of certain metals such as Ni, Co and Cr without using electric current, i.e. by simple chemical reduction.

3.5. NICKEL- AND COBALT-PLATING BY CHEMICAL MEANS

In order to study the chemical-plating of nickel [3], we have constructed Fig. 3 by superimposing the equilibrium diagram for the system nickel–water [for solutions containing 10^{-2} g-at Ni/l (0·6 g Ni^{++}/l)] on to the equilibrium diagram for the system phosphorus–water (Fig. 1 or 2). It is noticed at once that in the hatched part of Fig. 3, there is a possibility that the hypophosphites can be oxidized to phosphites and phosphates and that the Ni^{++} ions can be reduced to metallic nickel. Consequently, if we add a hypophosphite to a solution of a nickel salt, possibly in the presence of a suitable catalyst, it is theoretically possible for metallic nickel to separate out at pH's below 7; hydrogen can also be formed below line (*a*).

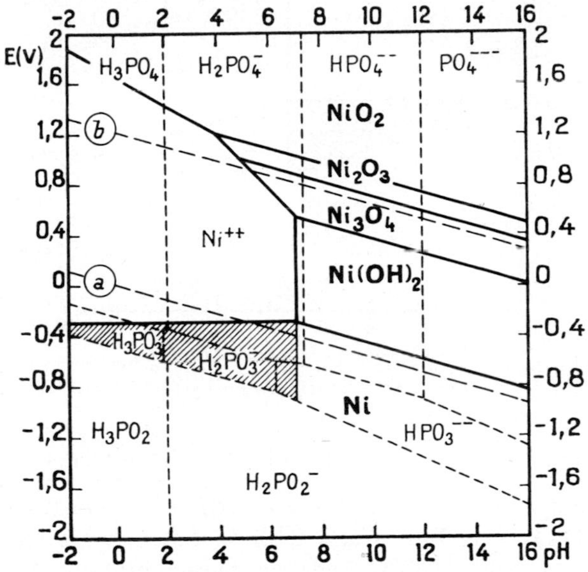

FIG. 3. Theoretical conditions for the formation of nickel by the reduction of Ni^{++} ions by hypophosphites. (For solutions containing 0·6 g Ni^{++}/l.)

The following reactions can therefore occur simultaneously during the process of nickel-plating by means of hypophosphites:
the two reductions

$$Ni^{++} + 2e^- \rightarrow Ni,$$
$$2H^+ + 2e^- \rightarrow H_2$$

and the two oxidations

$$H_2PO_2^- + H_2O \rightarrow H_2PO_3^- + 2H^+ + 2e^-,$$
$$H_2PO_2^- + 2H_2O \rightarrow H_2PO_4^- + 4H^+ + 4e^-.$$

The main reaction of chemical nickel-plating

$$Ni^{++} + H_2PO_2^- + H_2O \rightarrow Ni + H_2PO_3^- + 2H^+$$

can therefore be accompanied by the following secondary reactions:

$$4Ni^{++} + 2H_2PO_2^- + 4H_2O \rightarrow 4Ni + 2H_2PO_4^- + 8H^+,$$
$$H_2PO_2^- + H_2O \rightarrow H_2PO_3^- + H_2,$$
$$2H_2PO_2^- + 4H_2O \rightarrow 2H_3PO_4^- + 3H_2.$$

Figure 4, established in a similar manner to Fig. 3 by superimposing the two diagrams relating respectively to the system phosphorus–water and the system cobalt–water, represents the conditions of chemical cobalt-plating by the addition of hypophosphites to cobaltous solutions.

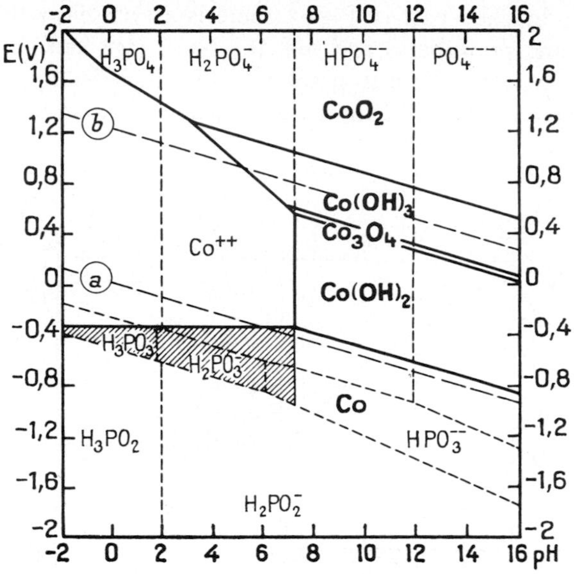

FIG. 4. Theoretical conditions for the formation of cobalt by the reduction of Co^{++} ions by hypophosphites. (For solutions containing 0·6 g Co^{++}/l.)

3.6. STABILITY OF ORTHOPHOSPHOROUS ACID AND THE ORTHOPHOSPHITES

The positions of the domains of predominance of orthophosphorous acid H_3PO_3 and the orthophosphites $H_2PO_3^-$ and HPO_3^{--}, in Figs. 1 and 2, show that they are reducing agents (less powerful ones than hypophosphorous acid H_3PO_2 and the hypophosphites $H_2PO_2^-$), thermodynamically unstable in the presence of aqueous solutions of all pH's.

Theoretically, they tend to reduce water with the evolution of hydrogen and become oxidized to phosphoric acid H_3PO_4 and phosphates $H_2PO_4^-$, HPO_4^{--} and PO_4^{---}. But, in actual fact, the reducing action of the phosphites is very slow. In aqueous solution, these substances appear to be stable and their reducing power shows itself only in the presence of catalysts (Fe^{++}, colloidal metals, HI in the light) [4].

Orthophosphorous acid and the orthophosphites slowly decolourize MnO_4^-; they reduce Ag^+ and Hg^{++}, but do not reduce Cu^{++} or As^{+++}; when heated, they reduce SO_2 with the liberation of S.

They can be oxidized to phosphoric acid and phosphates by oxidizing agents such as nitric acid, chromic acid, alkali metal chromates, etc.; they can be reduced by nascent hydrogen to gaseous PH_3.

3.7. STABILITY OF HYPOPHOSPHORIC ACID AND THE HYPOPHOSPHATES

Hypophosphoric acid $H_4P_2O_6$ and the hypophosphates $H_3P_2O_6^-$, $H_2P_2O_6^{--}$, $HP_2O_6^{---}$ and $P_2O_6^{----}$ are unstable, on the one hand with respect to phosphorous acid and the phosphites, and on the other hand with respect to phosphoric acid and the phosphates. Consequently they do not have any proper domain of predominance in Figs. 1 and 2.

Dilute solutions of these substances can, however, be preserved for a long time, without undergoing any change; nevertheless, on boiling, or in the presence of acids, ([2], [4]) they disproportionate rapidly to give a mixture of phosphorous acid and phosphoric acid.

Their reducing properties are clearly less marked than those of phosphorous acid and the phosphites. In particular, they no longer reduce metallic salts, but they still decolourize permanganate solutions and bromine water.

3.8. STABILITY OF ORTHOPHOSPHORIC ACID AND THE ORTHOPHOSPHATES

Phosphoric acid H_3PO_4 and the phosphates $H_2PO_4^-$, HPO_4^{--} and PO_4^{---} are the forms of phosphorus which are thermodynamically stable in the presence of water and aqueous solutions, both in the absence and in the presence of oxygen. As Charlot [1] points out, most compounds intermediate between PH_3 and H_3PO_4 are not in genuine equilibrium, but the oxidation-reduction systems which they give rise to change, in general, either slowly or infinitely slowly.

According to Figs. 1 and 2, phosphoric acid and the phosphates can be reduced to phosphorous acid and phosphites, hypophosphorous acid and hypophosphites, phosphorus and phosphine PH_3. However, although this reduction is theoretically possible at any potential below the values indicated by lines (22')–(27') (Figs. 1 and 2), it is, in actual fact, absolutely impossible to bring about in aqueous solution; it can only be brought about by a dry process.

It appears to be possible to oxidize phosphoric acid and the phosphates to monoperphosphoric acid H_3PO_5 and perphosphoric acid $H_4P_2O_8$, either by chemical means (the action of H_2O_2), or by electrolytic means (with a platinum anode) ([4], [5]).

4. BIBLIOGRAPHY

[1] G. Charlot, *L'analyse qualitative et les réactions en solution*, Masson, Paris, 1957.

[2] J. Coursier, *Utilisation des courbes de polarisation en chimie analytique,* Thesis, Faculté des Sciences, University of Paris, Masson, Paris, 1954.

[3] E. Deltombe, N. de Zoubov and M. Pourbaix, *Comportement électrochimique du nickel* (Rapport technique RT.23 of CEBELCOR, 1955).

[4] P. Pascal, *Nouveau traité de Chimie minérale*, Vol. X, Masson, Paris, 1956.

[5] N. Sidgwick, *The Chemical Elements and their Compounds*, Vol. I, Clarendon Press, Oxford, 1950, p. 746.

SECTION 18.3

ARSENIC[1]

J. VAN MUYLDER and M. POURBAIX

SUMMARY

[1] Shortened and adapted version of the Rapport technique RT.46 of CEBELCOR (February 1957) [1].

1. SUBSTANCES CONSIDERED AND SUBSTANCES NOT CONSIDERED

	Oxidation number (Z)	Considered	Not considered	μ^0(cal.)	Name, colour, crystalline system
Solid substances	— 1	–	As_2H_2	–	Diarsenic dihydride, brown
	— 0.5	–	As_4H_2	–	Tetra-arsenic dihydride, red–brown
	0	As	–	0	Arsenic, steel grey, rhomb.
	+ 1	–	As_2O	–	Arsenic sub-oxide
	+ 3	As_2O_3	–	—137 680	Arsenious anhydride, white, cub.
	»	–	As_2O_3	–	Arsenious anhydride, colourless, monocl.
	+ 4	–	As_2O_4	–	Arsenic peroxide
	+ 5	As_2O_5	–	—184 600	Arsenic anhydride, white, amorphous
Dissolved substances	+ 3	AsO^+	–	— 39 100	Arsenyl ion, colourless
	»	$HAsO_2$	–	— 96 250	Meta-arsenious acid, colourless
	»	AsO_2^-	–	— 83 700	Meta-arsenite ion, colourless
	»	H_3AsO_3	–	—152 940	Ortho-arsenious acid
	»	$H_2AsO_3^-$	–	—140 400	Mono-ortho-arsenite ion, colourless
	+ 5	H_3AsO_4	–	—183 800	Ortho-arsenic acid, colourless
	»	$H_2AsO_4^-$	–	—178 900	Mono-ortho-arsenate ion, colourless
	»	$HAsO_4^{--}$	–	—169 000	Di-ortho-arsenate ion, colourless
	»	AsO_4^{---}	–	—152 000	Tri-ortho-arsenate ion, colourless
	»	–	AsO_2^+	–	Arsenyl ion
	+ 7	–	AsO_3^+	–	Perarsenyl ion
Gaseous substance	— 3	AsH_3	–	42 000	Arsine, colourless

2. REACTIONS AND EQUILIBRIUM FORMULAE

2.1. TWO DISSOLVED SUBSTANCES

2.1.1. *Relative stability of the dissolved substances*

$Z = +3$

1. $AsO^+ + H_2O = HAsO_2 + H^+$ $\quad \log\frac{(HAsO_2)}{(AsO^+)} = 0.34 + pH$

2. $HAsO_2 = AsO_2^- + H^+$ $\quad \log\frac{(AsO_2^-)}{(HAsO_2)} = -9.21 + pH$

$Z = +5$

3. $H_3AsO_4 = H_2AsO_4^- + H^+$ $\quad \log\frac{(H_2AsO_4^-)}{(H_3AsO_4)} = -3.60 + pH$

4. $H_2AsO_4^- = HAsO_4^{--} + H^+$ $\quad \log\frac{(HAsO_4^{--})}{(H_2AsO_4^-)} = -7.26 + pH$

5. $HAsO_4^{--} = AsO_4^{---} + H^+$ $\quad \log\frac{(AsO_4^{---})}{(HAsO_4^{--})} = -12.47 + pH$

$+3 \rightarrow +5$

6. $AsO^+ + 3H_2O = H_3AsO_4 + 3H^+ + 2e^-$ $\quad E_0 = 0.550 - 0.0887\,pH + 0.0295\log\frac{(H_3AsO_4)}{(AsO^+)}$

7. $HAsO_2 + 2H_2O = H_3AsO_4 + 2H^+ + 2e^-$ $\quad E_0 = 0.560 - 0.0591\,pH + 0.0295\log\frac{(H_3AsO_4)}{(HAsO_2)}$

8. $HAsO_2 + 2H_2O = H_2AsO_4^- + 3H^+ + 2e^-$ $\quad E_0 = 0.666 - 0.0887\,pH + 0.0295\log\frac{(H_2AsO_4^-)}{(HAsO_2)}$

9. $HAsO_2 + 2H_2O = HAsO_4^{--} + 4H^+ + 2e^-$ $\quad E_0 = 0.881 - 0.1182\,pH + 0.0295\log\frac{(HAsO_4^{--})}{(HAsO_2)}$

10. $AsO_2^- + 2H_2O = HAsO_4^{--} + 3H^+ + 2e^-$ $\quad E_0 = 0.609 - 0.0887\,pH + 0.0295\log\frac{(HAsO_4^{--})}{(AsO_2^-)}$

11. $AsO_2^- + 2H_2O = AsO_4^{---} + 4H^+ + 2e^-$ $\quad E_0 = 0.977 - 0.1182\,pH + 0.0295\log\frac{(AsO_4^{---})}{(AsO_2^-)}$

2.1.2. *Limits of the domains of relative predominance of the dissolved substances*

1'.	AsO^+ / $HAsO_2$	pH = − 0.34
2'.	$HAsO_2$ / AsO_2^-	pH = 9.21
3'.	H_3AsO_4 / $H_2AsO_4^-$	pH = 3.60
4'.	$H_2AsO_4^-$ / $HAsO_4^{--}$	pH = 7.26
5'.	$HAsO_4^{--}$ / AsO_4^{---}	pH = 12.47
6'.	AsO^+ / H_3AsO_4	$E_0 = 0.550 - 0.0887$ pH
7'.	$HAsO_2$ / H_3AsO_4	$E_0 = 0.560 - 0.0591$ pH
8'.	$HAsO_2$ / $H_2AsO_4^-$	$E_0 = 0.666 - 0.0887$ pH
9'.	$HAsO_2$ / $HAsO_4^{--}$	$E_0 = 0.881 - 0.1182$ pH
10'.	AsO_2^- / $HAsO_4^{--}$	$E_0 = 0.609 - 0.0887$ pH
11'.	AsO_2^- / AsO_4^{---}	$E_0 = 0.977 - 0.1182$ pH

2.2. TWO SOLID SUBSTANCES

Limits of the domains of relative stability of the solid substances

$0 \rightarrow +3$

12. $2\mathbf{As} + 3H_2O = \mathbf{As_2O_3} + 6H^+ + 6e^-$ $E_0 = 0.234 - 0.0591$ pH

$0 \rightarrow +5$

13. $2\mathbf{As} + 5H_2O = \mathbf{As_2O_5} + 10H^+ + 10e^-$ $E_0 = 0.429 - 0.0591$ pH

$+3 \rightarrow +5$

14. $\mathbf{As_2O_3} + 2H_2O = \mathbf{As_2O_5} + 4H^+ + 4e^-$ $E_0 = 0.721 - 0.0591$ pH

2.3. ONE DISSOLVED SUBSTANCE AND ONE SOLID SUBSTANCE

Solubility of the solid substances

$Z = +3$

15. $2AsO^+ + H_2O = \mathbf{As_2O_3} + 2H^+$ $\log(AsO^+) = -1.02 - $ pH
16. $\mathbf{As_2O_3} + H_2O = 2HAsO_2$ $\log(HAsO_2) = -0.68$
17. $\mathbf{As_2O_3} + H_2O = 2AsO_2^- + 2H^+$ $\log(AsO_2^-) = -9.89 + $ pH

$Z = +5$

18. $\mathbf{As_2O_5} + 3H_2O = 2H_3AsO_4$ $\log(H_3AsO_4) = 4.74$
19. $\mathbf{As_2O_5} + 3H_2O = 2H_2AsO_4^- + 2H^+$ $\log(H_2AsO_4^-) = 1.15 + $ pH
20. $\mathbf{As_2O_5} + 3H_2O = 2HAsO_4^{--} + 4H^+$ $\log(HAsO_4^{--}) = -6.12 + 2$ pH
21. $\mathbf{As_2O_5} + 3H_2O = 2AsO_4^{---} + 6H^+$ $\log(AsO_4^{---}) = -18.59 + 3$ pH

$0 \rightarrow +3$

22. $\mathbf{As} + H_2O = AsO^+ + 2H^+ + 3e^-$ $E_0 = 0.254 - 0.0394$ pH $+ 0.0197 \log(AsO^+)$
23. $\mathbf{As} + 2H_2O = HAsO_2 + 3H^+ + 3e^-$ $E_0 = 0.248 - 0.0591$ pH $+ 0.0197 \log(HAsO_2)$
24. $\mathbf{As} + 2H_2O = AsO_2^- + 4H^+ + 3e^-$ $E_0 = 0.429 - 0.0788$ pH $+ 0.0197 \log(AsO_2^-)$

$0 \rightarrow +5$

25. $\mathbf{As} + 4H_2O = AsO_4^{---} + 8H^+ + 5e^-$ $E_0 = 0.648 - 0.0946$ pH $+ 0.0118 \log(AsO_4^{---})$

$+3 \rightarrow +5$

26. $\mathbf{As_2O_3} + 5H_2O = 2H_3AsO_4 + 4H^+ + 4e^-$ $E_0 = 0.580 - 0.0591$ pH $+ 0.0295 \log(H_3AsO_4)$
27. $\mathbf{As_2O_3} + 5H_2O = 2H_2AsO_4^- + 6H^+ + 4e^-$ $E_0 = 0.687 - 0.0887$ pH $+ 0.0295 \log(H_2AsO_4^-)$
28. $\mathbf{As_2O_3} + 5H_2O = 2HAsO_4^{--} + 8H^+ + 4e^-$ $E_0 = 0.901 - 0.1182$ pH $+ 0.0295 \log(HAsO_4^{--})$
29. $\mathbf{As_2O_3} + 5H_2O = 2AsO_4^{---} + 10H^+ + 4e^-$ $E_0 = 1.270 - 0.1477$ pH $+ 0.0295 \log(AsO_4^{---})$

2.4. ONE SOLID SUBSTANCE AND ONE GASEOUS SUBSTANCE

Limits of the domains of relative stability of **As** *and* AsH_3

$-3 \rightarrow 0$

30. $AsH_3 = \mathbf{As} + 3H^+ + 3e^-$ $E_0 = -0.608 - 0.0591$ pH $- 0.0197 \log p_{AsH_3}$

3. EQUILIBRIUM DIAGRAM AND ITS INTERPRETATION

3.1. ESTABLISHMENT OF THE DIAGRAM

Using formulae (1)–(30), we have constructed Fig. 1 (potential–pH equilibrium diagram for the system arsenic–water) and Fig. 2 (influence of pH on the solubility of arsenious anhydride).

These figures are valid only in the absence of substances with which arsenic can form soluble complexes or insoluble salts. According to Charlot [2], the tartrates, molybdates and tungstates form complexes with arsenic. The alkali metal arsenites and arsenates are very soluble; the other arsenites and arsenates are soluble only in acid solutions. We point out, in particular, the following two sparingly soluble arsenates: triargentic arsenate Ag_3AsO_4 (brick red), and magnesium ammonium arsenate $MgNH_4AsO_4$ (white), analogous to magnesium ammonium phosphate.

3.2. STABILITY OF ARSENIC

According to Fig. 1, elementary arsenic is a fairly noble element, as a considerable portion of its stability domain overlaps that of water. It is therefore an element which is stable in the presence of water and aqueous solutions of all pH's free from oxidizing agents.

Arsenic is not therefore affected by water free from air, and remains perfectly shiny in it; in aerated water arsenic is slowly attacked to give the very soluble arsenious anhydride As_2O_3; if a stream of air is passed through the water, the oxidation becomes fairly rapid [3].

When exposed to dry air arsenic is not oxidized at all, but on contact with moist air it undergoes a reaction at its surface and becomes covered with a black oxidation product, which can be removed by means of chlorine water or bleaching-water (oxidation to soluble arsenic acid H_3AsO_4).

At room temperature, dilute acids such as HCl, HNO_3, H_2SO_4 and H_3PO_4, when free from air, do not affect arsenic; on the other hand, it dissolves in concentrated hydrochloric acid, and hot concentrated sulphuric and nitric acids oxidize it to arsenic acid H_3AsO_4. According to Palit and Dhar, quoted by Gmelin [4], fairly dilute solutions of nitric acid (2 to 5 M) can attack arsenic at room temperature through the formation of nitrous acid HNO_2, which oxidizes arsenic to arsenious anhydride As_2O_3; the addition of reducing agents such as hydrazine N_2H_4 or sodium nitride N_3Na, which destroy the nitrous acid, prevents this attack; however, according to Millon [4], the capacity of nitric acid to react with arsenic is not increased by the presence of nitrous acid. Caustic soda solutions maintained in an atmosphere of inert gas react only slightly with arsenic; in the presence of air they oxidize arsenic to arsenite [4].

The nobility of arsenic is also confirmed by the fact that this element can be found in the natural state. It can be reduced to arsenic hydride in the presence of acid, neutral and alkaline aqueous solutions; depending on the circumstances, the reduction of arsenic can lead to the formation of arsine AsH_3, one of the solid hydrides As_2H_2 or As_4H_2, or more than one of these compounds simultaneously. AsH_3 can be obtained by the electrolysis of an acetic solution of sodium acetate using a platinum anode and an arsenic cathode; the electrolysis of aqueous solutions of HCl, H_2SO_4, H_2CrO_4, KOH and NaOH of various concentrations leads to the formation of arsine AsH_3 and diarsenic dihydride As_2H_2.

Depending on the pH and the concentration, arsenic can be oxidized to the "arsenyl" cation AsO^+, arsenious acid $HAsO_2$, arsenious anhydride As_2O_3 or arsenite AsO_2^-; further oxidation converts it into arsenic acid H_3AsO_4 or arsenates $H_2AsO_4^-$, $HAsO_4^{--}$, depending on the pH of the solution. Oxygen oxidizes arsenic to As_2O_3; oxidizing acids, such as concentrated sulphuric and nitric acids, and aqua regia, oxidize arsenic to arsenic acid H_3AsO_4; ozone, hydrogen peroxide, potassium permanganate, etc., convert arsenic to arsenates; perchloric acid, at a concentration of 60–70 per cent and at room temperature, oxidizes arsenic to the trivalent state, i.e. the anhydride As_2O_3; when heated, perchloric acid oxidizes it to the pentavalent state, i.e. arsenic acid.

Arsenic can be prepared either by the reduction of arsenites and arsenates, or by the limited oxidation of the arsenic hydrides; we give examples of these reactions in paragraphs 3.3, 3.4 and 3.5.

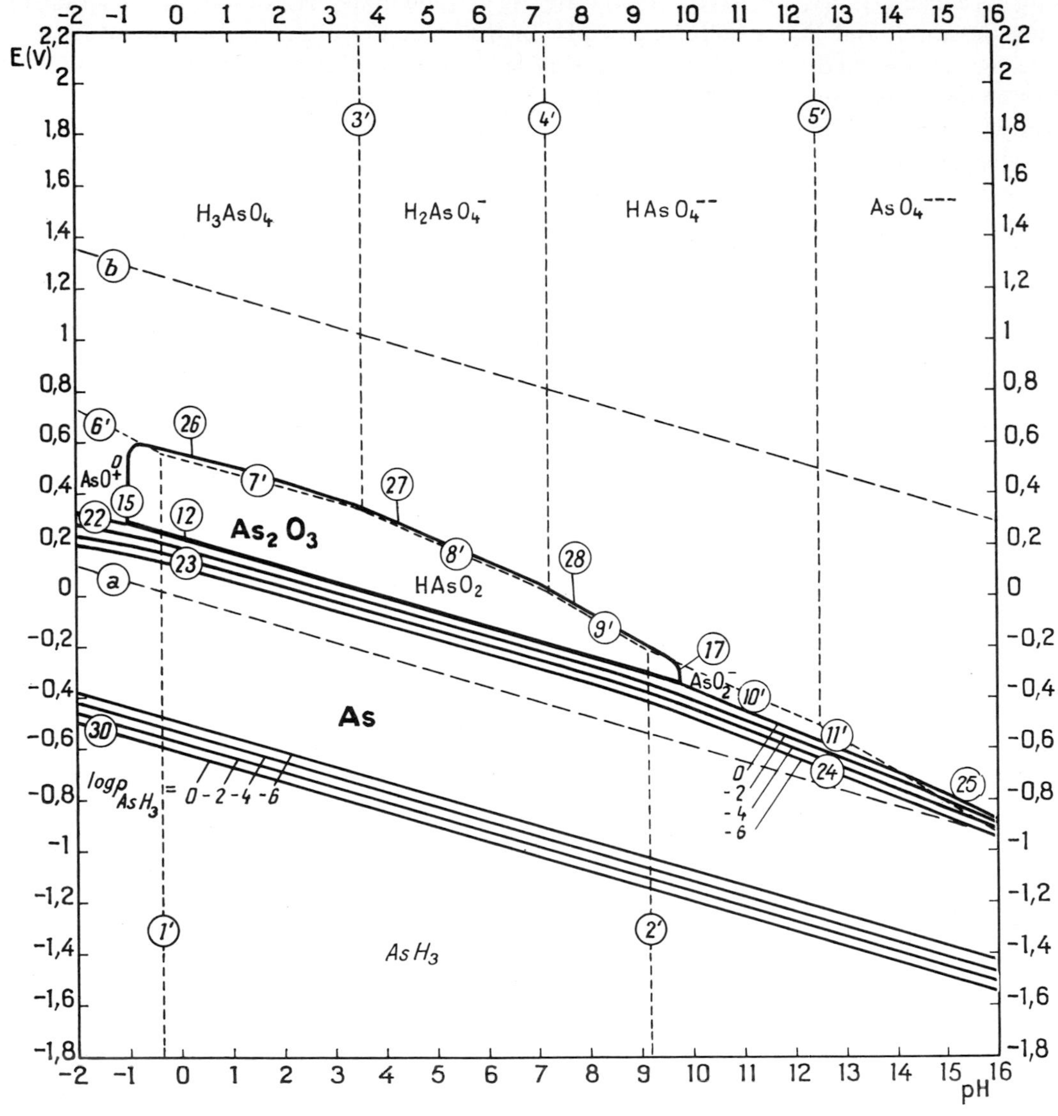

FIG. 1. Potential–pH equilibrium diagram for the system arsenic–water, at 25°C.

3.3. STABILITY OF ARSENIOUS ANHYDRIDE AND THE ARSENITES

Arsenious anhydride As_2O_3 is formed by the limited oxidation of arsenic by oxygen or perchloric acid, in the cold.

The position of its domain of stability in the equilibrium diagram (Fig. 1) shows it to be soluble, thermodynamically stable in the presence of water and acid, neutral and slightly alkaline solutions free from oxidizing agents.

According to Fig. 2, which represents the influence of pH on its solubility in solutions free from complexing substances [as given by formulae (15), (16) and (17)], As_2O_3 is an amphoteric oxide which dissolves in water and in solutions of pH between 1 and 8 with the formation of undissociated arsenious acid $HAsO_2$; the solubility is constant in this pH range and is equal to $10^{-0.68}$ g-at As/l (i.e. 0·21 g-at/l, or 21 g As_2O_3/l, which agrees with a result obtained by Anderson and Story [5]); it increases at pH's below 1 with the formation of "arsenyl" ions AsO^+, and at pH's above 8 with the formation of arsenite ions AsO_2^-.

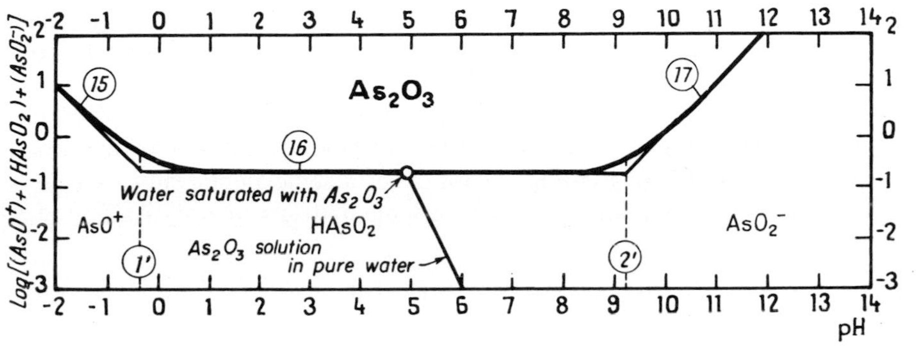

FIG. 2. Influence of pH on the solubility of arsenious anhydride, at 25°C.

It follows from Fig. 2 that, in solutions obtained by dissolving As_2O_3 in pure water of pH = 7, arsenic will exist mainly as undissociated $HAsO_2$, with a small proportion of AsO_2^-. This AsO_2^- will be produced according to the reaction $As_2O_3 + H_2O \rightarrow 2AsO_2^- + 2H^+$, i.e. with the formation of equal amounts of H^+ and AsO_2^- ions. As stated in an account published elsewhere ([6], pp. 19–27), the AsO_2^- and $HAsO_2$ concentrations in As_2O_3 solutions will depend on the pH according to the relations

$$(AsO_2^-) = (H^+) - 10^{-7.00} \quad \text{and} \quad \log(HAsO_2) = \log(AsO_2^-) + 9.21 - \text{pH}.$$

These relations enable us to represent the pH's of As_2O_3 solutions of various concentrations by a line of slope -2, in Fig. 2.

The characteristics of the solution obtained by saturating pure water with As_2O_3 will be given by the point of intersection of this line of gradient -2 with the heavy line indicating the solubility of As_2O_3; the pH coordinate of this point is 5·0, a value which has been confirmed experimentally.

This pH can also be determined by calculation, taking into account the fact that the concentrations of H^+ and AsO_2^- ions are practically equal, by putting $\log(AsO_2^-) = -\text{pH}$ in the relation $\log(AsO_2^-) = -9.89 + \text{pH}$ (17) referring to the equilibrium As_2O_3/AsO_2^-; the pH value so obtained is 4·94.

According to Fig. 1, As_2O_3 and arsenious solutions can be oxidized to arsenates and can be reduced to elementary arsenic and arsenic hydride.

The *oxidation of the arsenites* to arsenates is clearly irreversible: although theoretically possible as soon as the potential exceeds the values indicated by lines (6′), (7′), (8′), (9′), (10′) and (11′) in Fig. 1, it takes place in actual fact only at considerably higher potentials, and on condition that there is an appreciable overpotential: although the arsenates are the thermodynamically stable form of arsenic in the presence of oxygen, they can be obtained by the action of oxygen on arsenite solutions only in the presence of catalysts, such as the system iodine–iodide, for example, (Charlot [2]). In the absence of catalysts the oxidation of arsenites to arsenates requires a more powerful oxidizing agent, such as a halogen or one of its oxygen compounds, chromic acid, nitric acid, hydrogen peroxide or permanganate; this oxidation can also be brought about electrolytically, using a platinum anode.

The *reduction of the arsenites* to arsenic or arsenic hydride can be brought about chemically or electrolytically at potentials below those indicated by the family of lines (22)–(24) (for As) and the family of lines (30) (for AsH_3).

Chemically: stannous chloride $SnCl_2$ and hypophosphorous acid H_3PO_2 in hydrochloric solution reduce arsenious solutions to brown colloidal arsenic; under similar conditions, copper reduces these solutions to copper arsenide Cu_3As_2, which covers the metal with an iron grey coating. Metals which produce an evolution of "nascent hydrogen" at low electrode potentials, such as zinc in hydrochloric or sulphuric acid solution, reduce arsenious solutions with the formation of gaseous arsine AsH_3; this reaction is the basis of the classical process for the toxicological detection of arsenic in forensic medicine.

Electrolytically: arsenious solutions can be cathodically reduced, using a platinum or copper cathode, for instance. Depending on the nature of the solution, the metal used as the cathode, and the value of the current density, it is possible to obtain either arsenic alone (shiny, mat, spongy, adherent, non-adherent, etc.) or arsenic simultaneously with arsenic hydrides (mainly AsH_3 and As_2H_2).

3.4. STABILITY OF ARSENIC ANHYDRIDE AND THE ARSENATES

Arsenic anhydride As_2O_5 is the form of arsenic oxide which is thermodynamically stable in the presence of oxygen. It is very hygroscopic and very soluble in water to form arsenic acid H_3AsO_4 and arsenates $H_2AsO_4^-$, $HAsO_4^{--}$ and AsO_4^{---}; on account of its great solubility it does not appear in the equilibrium diagram (Fig. 1), which shows that arsenate solutions are thermodynamically stable in the absence of reducing agents.

The arsenates can be reduced to arsenites, to arsenic and to arsenic hydride; however, like the oxidation of arsenites to arsenates, the reduction of arsenates to arsenites is clearly irreversible: although theoretically possible as soon as the potential is below the values indicated by lines (6′), (7′), (8′), (9′), (10′) and (11′) of Fig. 1, the reaction takes place in general only at considerably lower potentials, with an appreciable overpotential: this reduction usually occurs at an appreciable rate only in very acid solutions; in alkaline solutions it is infinitely slow (Charlot [2]). Warm sulphurous acid leads to the formation of arsenious acid $HAsO_2$; hypophosphorous acid H_3PO_2 and stannous chloride form arsenic As; "nascent hydrogen" forms arsine AsH_3. The electrolytic reduction of the arsenates in acid solution is more difficult to bring about than that of the arsenites; depending on the operating conditions, it can lead to arsenic or arsine.

3.5. STABILITY OF ARSINE AsH_3

From Fig. 1 it can be seen that arsenic can be reduced to the gaseous trihydride of arsenic AsH_3 or arsine, at potentials below those indicated by the family of lines (30). As stated in paragraphs 3.2, 3.3 and 3.4, this reduction can be brought about chemically or electrolytically.

In view of the fact that its stability domain lies at very low potentials, arsine appears to be a reducing substance which is thermodynamically unstable.

Arsine is actually oxidized to arsenious acid by chloric acid $HClO_3$, and to arsenic acid or arsenates by the halogens, hot concentrated sulphuric acid, nitric acid, permanganate or ferrocyanide.

Although it tends thermodynamically to decompose into arsenic and hydrogen, arsine is practically stable in the presence of distilled water free from oxygen, at room temperature; aerated water causes the slow formation of a brown precipitate, which seems to be either arsenic or a solid lower hydride; according to Moser and Brukl [7], it is As_2H_2. When dry and pure, arsine can be kept for a long time without undergoing any change, but it readily decomposes on being warmed.

3.6. PASSIVATING ACTION OF ARSENIC COMPOUNDS

When iron or an ordinary steel corrodes in an acid, such as sulphuric acid, its electrode potential is generally around −0·2 to −0·4 volt. Under these conditions it is the elementary arsenic which is the stable form of system As–H_2O; the arsenious and arsenic compounds tend to be reduced by the iron with the formation of an arsenic cement.

It is well known that, other things being equal, the steel containers used for storing sulphuric acid are corroded less when they contain lead chamber acid than when the acid is prepared by the contact process. It is probable that this difference in behaviour is due to the fact that chamber acid contains arsenic compounds, which contact acid does not contain, and that these compounds form a deposit of arsenic on the steel which is partially protective and imperfectly passivates the metal.

3.7. ARSENIC ELECTRODES

Sometimes arsenic is used in measuring the pH of aqueous solutions and in potentiometric estimations.

The operation of the arsenic electrode in determining pH depends most probably on the equilibrium of the As/As_2O_3 system, whose electrode potential varies linearly with pH from 0 to 9, according to the relation:

$$E = 0{\cdot}234 - 0{\cdot}0591 \text{ pH} \qquad (12)$$

with the reservation, however, that the equilibrium solubility of the arsenic is very large (15 g As/l).

These deductions made from Fig. 1 correspond well with the results obtained by Tourky and Mousa [8], according to which, in the absence of air, the potential of an arsenic electrode (solid or powder) varies as indicated by relation (12) for pH's between 3 and 10.

The fact that arsenic can be used as an electrode for the measurement of pH makes possible its application on the potentiometric titration of bases and acids, especially the estimation of NaOH, HCl, HNO_3 and $H_2C_2O_4$ (Gmelin [4]).

4. BIBLIOGRAPHY

[1] J. Van Muylder and M. Pourbaix, *Comportement électrochimique de l'arsenic. Diagramme d'équilibres tension–*pH *du système* As–H_2O, *à 25°C* (Rapport technique RT.46 of CEBELCOR, February 1957).

[2] G. Charlot, *Théorie et méthode nouvelles d'analyse qualitative,* 3rd ed., Masson, Paris, 1949, p. 214.

[3] P. Pascal, *Traité de Chimie minérale*, Vol. III, Masson, Paris, 1932.

[4] *Gmelins Handbuch der anorganischen Chemie, Arsen,* S.N.17, 1952, Verlag Chemie, G.m.b.H., Weinheim, Bergstrasse.

[5] E. Anderson and LeR. G. Story, Studies on certain physical properties of As_2O_3 in water solution, *J. Amer. Chem. Soc.* **45**, 1102 (1923).

[6] M. Pourbaix, *Leçons sur la corrosion électrochimique*, 2ᵉ fascicule (Rapport technique RT.30 of CEBELCOR, 1956).

[7] L. Moser and A. Brukl, Zur Kenntnis der festen Arsenhydride, *Monatsh.* **45**, 25 (1924).

[8] A. R. Tourky and A. A. Mousa, Studies on some metal electrodes. Part VI. The arsenic electrode as a metal–metal oxide–oxygen electrode, *J. Chem. Soc.* II, 1297 (1949).

SECTION 18.4

ANTIMONY (1)

A. L. PITMAN, M. POURBAIX and N. DE ZOUBOV

SUMMARY

1. *Substances considered and substances not considered.*

2. *Reactions and equilibrium formulae.*
   2.1. Two dissolved substances.
      2.1.1. Relative stability of the dissolved substances.
      2.1.2. Limits of the domains of relative predominance of the dissolved substances.
   2.2. Two solid substances.
      Limits of the domains of relative stability of the solid substances.
   2.3. One solid substance and one dissolved substance.
      Solubility of the solid substances.
   2.4. One solid substance and one gaseous substance.
      Relative stability of antimony and stibine.

3. *Equilibrium diagram and its interpretation.*
   3.1. Establishment of the diagram.
   3.2. Stability and corrosion of antimony.
   3.3. Stability and formation of the oxides of antimony.
      3.3.1. Stability and formation of the oxides of trivalent antimony.
      3.3.2. Stability of the oxide of tetravalent antimony.
      3.3.3. Stability and formation of the oxide of pentavalent antimony and its solutions.
   3.4. Stability and formation of stibine SbH_3.
   3.5. Antimony electrodes for the measurement of pH.
      3.5.1. Antimony–antimony oxide electrode.
      3.5.2. Antimony-rod electrode.
   3.6. Passivating action of antimony solutions.

4. *Bibliography.*

---

(1) Shortened version of the Rapport technique RT.55 of CEBELCOR (January 1957) [1].

1. SUBSTANCES CONSIDERED AND SUBSTANCES NOT CONSIDERED

	Oxidation number (Z)	Considered	Not considered	μ^0(cal.)	Name, colour, crystalline system
Solid substances	− 1	–	**Sb_2H_2**	–	Antimony hydride, grey
	0	**Sb**	–	0	Antimony, grey, rhomb.
	+ 3	**Sb_2O_3** anh.	–	*a*. −149 000	Antimony trioxide or senarmontite, white, cub.
	»	» anh.	–	*b*. −147 000 (2)	Antimony trioxide or valentinite, white, orthorh.
	»	–	**Sb_2O_3** hydr.	–	Antimonious acid $HSbO_2$ag, white, amorphous
	+ 4	**Sb_2O_4** anh.	–	−165 900	Antimony tetroxide, white, orthorh.
	»	–	**Sb_2O_4** hydr.	–	Hypoantimonic acid $H_2Sb_2O_5$ or hydrated antimony tetroxide $Sb_2O_4.H_2O$
	+ 4.33	–	**Sb_6O_{13}**	–	?
	+ 5	**Sb_2O_5** anh.	–	−200 500	Antimony pentoxide, yellow, cub.
	»	–	**Sb_2O_5** hydr.	–	Antimonic acid $HSb(OH)_6$, white, amorphous
Dissolved substances	+ 3	SbO^+	–	− 42 000	Antimonyl ion, colourless
	»	$HSbO_2$	–	− 97 500 (3)	Meta-antimonious acid, white
	»	SbO_2^-	–	− 82 500	Antimonite ion $Sb(OH)_4^-$, colourless
	+ 4	–	Sb tetrav. ? (4)	–	—
	+ 5	SbO_2^+	–	− 65 500 (2)	Antimonic ion
	»	SbO_3^-		−122 930 (2)	Antimonate ion $Sb(OH)_6^-$, colourless
Gaseous substances	− 3	*SbH_3*	–	35 300	Antimonated hydrogen or stibine, colourless
	+ 2	–	*SbO*	–	?

2. REACTIONS AND EQUILIBRIUM FORMULAE

2.1. TWO DISSOLVED SUBSTANCES

2.1.1. *Relative stability of the dissolved substances*

Z = + 3

1. $SbO^+ + H_2O = HSbO_2 + H^+$ $\qquad \log\frac{(HSbO_2)}{(SbO^+)} = -\ 0.87 + \text{pH}$

2. $HSbO_2 = SbO_2^- + H^+$ $\qquad \log\frac{(SbO_2^-)}{(HSbO_2)} = -\ 11.00 + \text{pH}$

Z = + 5

3. $SbO_2^+ + H_2O = SbO_3^- + 2H^+$ $\qquad \log\frac{(SbO_3^-)}{(SbO_2^+)} = 0.54 + 2\text{pH}$

+ 3 → + 5

4. $SbO^+ + H_2O = SbO_2^+ + 2H^+ + 2e^-$ $\qquad E_0 = 0.720 - 0.0591\,\text{pH} + 0.0295 \log\frac{(SbO_2^+)}{(SbO^+)}$

5. $SbO^+ + 2H_2O = SbO_3^- + 4H^+ + 2e^-$ $\qquad E_0 = 0.704 - 0.1182\,\text{pH} + 0.0295 \log\frac{(SbO_3^-)}{(SbO^+)}$

6. $HSbO_2 + H_2O = SbO_3^- + 3H^+ + 2e^-$ $\qquad E_0 = 0.678 - 0.0886\,\text{pH} + 0.0295 \log\frac{(SbO_3^-)}{(HSbO_2)}$

7. $SbO_2^- + H_2O = SbO_3^- + 2H^+ + 2e^-$ $\qquad E_0 = 0.353 - 0.0591\,\text{pH} + 0.0295 \log\frac{(SbO_3^-)}{(SbO_2^-)}$

---

(2) Values calculated by Pitman [2].
(3) Pitman calculated $\mu^0_{HSbO_2aq.}$ to be −96 500 cal.
(4) Pascal [3] points out the possible existence of a tetravalent antimony ion.

2.1.2. *Limits of the domains of relative predominance of the dissolved substances*

1'.	SbO^+ / $HSbO_2$	pH = 0.87
2'.	$HSbO_2$ / SbO_2^-	pH = 11.00
3'.	SbO_2^+ / SbO_3^-	pH = − 0.27
4'.	SbO^+ / SbO_2^+	$E_0 = 0.720 - 0.0591\,pH$
5'.	SbO^+ / SbO_3^-	$E_0 = 0.704 - 0.1182\,pH$
6'.	$HSbO_2$ / SbO_3^-	$E_0 = 0.678 - 0.0886\,pH$
7'.	SbO_2^- / SbO_3^-	$E_0 = 0.353 - 0.0591\,pH$

2.2. TWO SOLID SUBSTANCES

Limits of the domains of relative stability of the solid substances[5]

o → +3

8. $2\mathbf{Sb} + 3H_2O = \mathbf{Sb_2O_3} + 6H^+ + 6e^-$ a. $E_0 = 0.152 - 0.0591\,pH$
   b. $= 0.167 - 0.0591\,pH$

+3 → +4

9. $\mathbf{Sb_2O_3} + H_2O = \mathbf{Sb_2O_4} + 2H^+ + 2e^-$ a. $E_0 = 0.863 - 0.0591\,pH$
   b. $= 0.819 - 0.0591\,pH$

+3 → +5

10. $\mathbf{Sb_2O_3} + 2H_2O = \mathbf{Sb_2O_5} + 4H^+ + 4e^-$ a. $E_0 = 0.671 - 0.0591\,pH$
   b. $= 0.649 - 0.0591\,pH$

+4 → +5

11. $\mathbf{Sb_2O_4} + H_2O = \mathbf{Sb_2O_5} + 2H^+ + 2e^-$ $E_0 = 0.479 - 0.0591\,pH$

2.3. ONE SOLID SUBSTANCE AND ONE DISSOLVED SUBSTANCE

Solubility of the solid substances

Z = +3

12. $2SbO^+ + H_2O = \mathbf{Sb_2O_3} + 2H^+$ a. $\log(SbO^+) = -3.05 - pH$
   b. $= -2.32 - pH$

13. $\mathbf{Sb_2O_3} + H_2O = 2HSbO_2$ a. $\log(HSbO_2) = -3.92$
   b. $= -3.19$

14. $\mathbf{Sb_2O_3} + H_2O = 2SbO_2^- + 2H^+$ a. $\log(SbO_2^-) = -14.91 + pH$
   b. $= -14.18 + pH$

Z = +5

15. $2SbO_2^+ + H_2O = \mathbf{Sb_2O_5} + 2H^+$ $\log(SbO_2^+) = -4.70 - pH$

16. $\mathbf{Sb_2O_5} + H_2O = 2SbO_3^- + 2H^+$ $\log(SbO_3^-) = -4.16 + pH$

o → +3

17. $\mathbf{Sb} + H_2O = SbO^+ + 2H^+ + 3e^-$ $E_0 = 0.212 - 0.0394\,pH + 0.0197\log(SbO^+)$

18. $\mathbf{Sb} + 2H_2O = HSbO_2 + 3H^+ + 3e^-$ $E_0 = 0.230 - 0.0591\,pH + 0.0197\log(HSbO_2)$

19. $\mathbf{Sb} + 2H_2O = SbO_2^- + 4H^+ + 3e^-$ $E_0 = 0.446 - 0.0788\,pH + 0.0197\log(SbO_2^-)$

+3 → +5

20. $\mathbf{Sb_2O_3} + 3H_2O = 2SbO_3^- + 6H^+ + 4e^-$ a. $E_0 = 0.794 - 0.0886\,pH + 0.0295\log(SbO_3^-)$
   b. $= 0.772 - 0.0886\,pH + 0.0295\log(SbO_3^-)$

21. $2SbO^+ + 3H_2O = \mathbf{Sb_2O_5} + 6H^+ + 4e^-$ $E_0 = 0.581 - 0.0886\,pH - 0.0295\log(SbO^+)$

2.4. ONE SOLID SUBSTANCE AND ONE GASEOUS SUBSTANCE

Relative stability of antimony and stibine

−3 → o

22. $SbH_3 = \mathbf{Sb} + 3H^+ + 3e^-$ $E_0 = -0.510 - 0.0591\,pH - 0.0197\log p_{SbH_3}$

---

[5] For the reactions involving $\mathbf{Sb_2O_3}$, the equations marked *a* refer to the cubic form, while the equations marked *b* refer to the orthorhombic form.

3. EQUILIBRIUM DIAGRAM AND ITS INTERPRETATION

3.1. ESTABLISHMENT OF THE DIAGRAM

In Fig. 1 we have used the equilibrium relations established in paragraph 2 [formulae (1)–(22)] to represent the conditions of thermodynamic equilibrium of all the substances considered (dissolved, solid and gaseous).

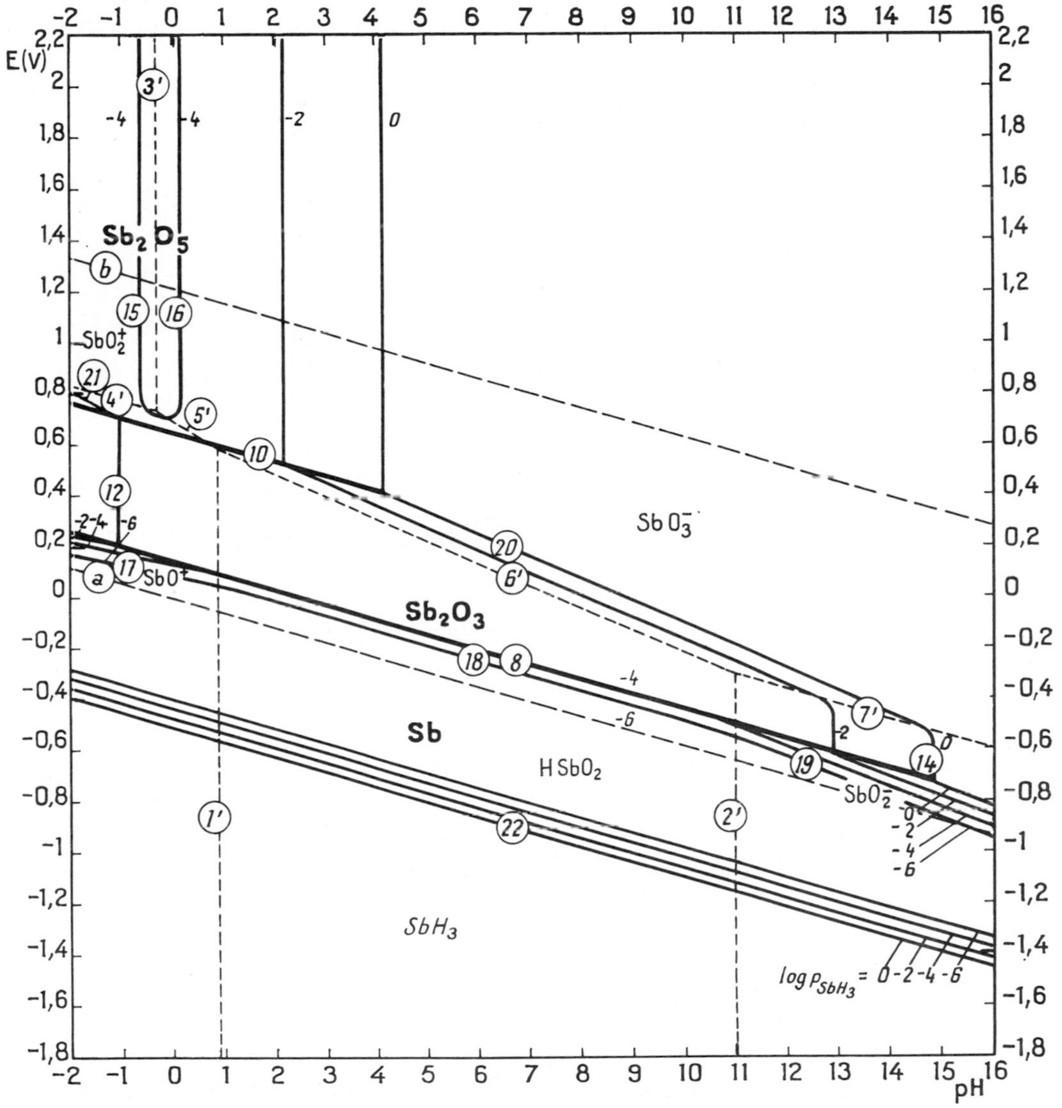

FIG. 1. Potential–pH equilibrium diagram for the system antimony–water, at 25°C.

Figure 2, which is deduced from Fig. 1 after making certain assumptions, represents the theoretical condition of corrosion and immunity of antimony.

These diagrams are valid only in the absence of substances with which antimony can form soluble complexes or insoluble salts.

In the trivalent and pentavalent states, antimony forms a large number of complexes: hydrochloric, sulphuric, tartaric, oxalic, hydrofluoric and sulphydric complexes (Charlot [4]).

The following antimony compounds are sparingly soluble: the sulphides Sb_2S_3 and Sb_2S_5, the red iodide SbI_3 which forms a precipitate in acid media, the white silver antimonate, and the basic salts SbOCl (antimonyl chloride) and SbO_2Cl.

3.2. STABILITY AND CORROSION OF ANTIMONY

In Figs. 1 and 2, the stability domain of antimony has a small area in common with the stability domain of water; antimony is therefore a slightly noble element, and can be found in the natural state.

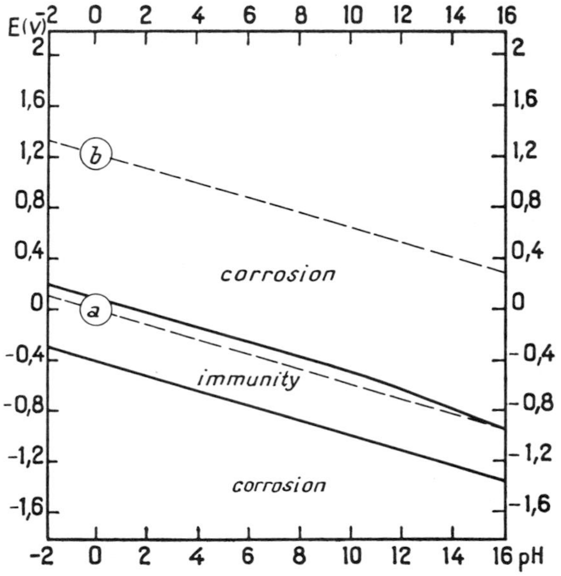

FIG. 2. Theoretical domains of corrosion and immunity of antimony, at 25°C.

As antimony is stable for all the pH's along line (*a*) and unstable at potentials slightly above those corresponding to this line, it will be unaffected in the presence of non-oxidizing solutions free from complexing substances, and will be oxidized to the tri- or pentavalent state by oxidizing solutions; in actual fact, water free from air does not attack antimony, but aerated water attacks it slowly, converting it into the fairly soluble antimonious anhydride Sb_2O_3. At room temperature, hydrochloric acid solutions free from air do not affect antimony; on the other hand, aerated solutions dissolve it slowly.

Depending on the pH and the antimony concentration, the element can be oxidized to the trivalent state in the form of the antimonyl cation SbO^+, antimonious anhydride Sb_2O_3 which dissolves as antimonious acid $HSbO_2$, and antimonite SbO_2^- [or $Sb(OH)_4^-$]. More vigorous oxidation, by means of nitric acid, mercury oxide, sodium peroxide or hydrogen peroxide, for example, oxidizes it to the pentavalent state; depending on the pH, the following substances can be formed: antimonic cations SbO_2^+, pentoxide Sb_2O_5, or antimonates SbO_3^- [or $Sb(OH)_6^-$].

At potentials below those indicated by the family of lines (22), antimony can be reduced, at all pH's, to gaseous antimony hydride SbH_3.

In Fig. 2, which is the "corrosion–immunity diagram" for antimony, there is no protection domain due to passivation by an oxide film, as both the oxides Sb_2O_3 and Sb_2O_5 are too soluble to protect antimony.

Thus there are two corrosion domains for antimony, one anodic and the other cathodic, between which there is a domain of immunity.

3.3. STABILITY AND FORMATION OF THE OXIDES OF ANTIMONY

3.3.1. *Stability and formation of the oxides of trivalent antimony*

Two allotropic varieties of antimony trioxide Sb_2O_3 are known at present: the cubic form, which exists in nature as the ore *senarmontite*, and the orthorhombic form which exists in *valentinite* [5]. According to the table given in paragraph 1, the free enthalpy of formation is smaller for the cubic form (− 149 000 cal.) than for the orthorhombic form (− 147 000 cal.); the cubic form is therefore the more stable of the two at 25°C, and it is this form which has been adopted for the establishment of the equilibrium diagram (Fig. 1). However, according to Pascal [3], the cubic form is metastable at room temperature, and stable above 570°C.

The position of the domain of stability of antimony trioxide Sb_2O_3 and antimonious solutions in the equilibrium diagram (Fig. 1) shows that they are thermodynamically stable in the presence of water and aqueous solutions free from reducing agents and powerful oxidizing agents.

They can be reduced to elementary antimony and antimony hydride; they can be oxidized to antimonic cations SbO_2^+, pentoxide Sb_2O_5 and antimonate anions SbO_3^- by means of powerful oxidizing agents such as nitric acid, alkali metal nitrates, potassium permanganate, potassium dichromate, chlorine, bromine, iodine, iodates and hydrogen peroxide.

Antimony trioxide has an amphoteric nature. In very acid media, of pH from −2 to +1, it dissolves as antimonyl ions SbO^+. In solutions of pH from 2 to 10·4 the solubility of Sb_2O_3 is independent of the pH, which indicates the formation of an undissociated substance, i.e. $HSbO_2$. More alkaline solutions dissolve the oxide as antimonite ions SbO_2^-.

The orthorhombic form can be obtained by the combustion of antimony and the slow cooling of the trioxide formed by the treatment of a boiling solution of antimony chloride in hydrochloric acid with sodium carbonate, by the decomposition of antimony oxychloride with steam at 150°C, and by roasting antimony sulphide. The cubic variety is obtained by the rapid condensation of trioxide vapour, by cooling a solution of trioxide in caustic soda, by the decomposition of a solution of emetic (antimonyl potassium tartrate) with alkalis, and by the hydrolysis of antimony oxychloride.

3.3.2. *Stability of the oxide of tetravalent antimony*

Antimony tetroxide Sb_2O_4 is found in nature as *cervantite*. As is shown by equations (9) and (11), Sb_2O_4 is thermodynamically unstable with respect to Sb_2O_3 and Sb_2O_5 at 25°C and therefore tends to decompose into a mixture of these two oxides; it does not therefore appear in the equilibrium diagram (Fig. 1). In fact, the trivalent oxide is generally oxidized directly to the pentavalent oxide.

Konopik and Zwiauer [6] have shown that aqueous solutions of Sb_2O_4 behave, in actual fact, as mixtures of trivalent and pentavalent compounds; the Sb_2O_4 therefore decomposes to give SbO_3^- ions and undissociated $HSbO_2$ in equivalent quantities, according to a reaction such as $Sb_2O_4 + H_2O \rightarrow SbO_3^- + HSbO_2 + H^+$, and a solution represented by one of the points on line (6′) (Fig. 1) is obtained. Sb_2O_4 can be reduced in particular by a solution of hydrochloric acid and potassium iodide. The existence of a hydrate $Sb_2O_4 . H_2O$, prepared by the action of an acid on a solution of Sb_2O_4 and of caustic potash, has been described. As we have no thermodynamic data for this hydrate we were unable to consider it when establishing the equilibrium diagram; the same applies to the ions of tetravalent antimony whose existence has been pointed out [3].

3.3.3. *Stability and formation of the oxide of pentavalent antimony and its solutions*

As the pentoxide Sb_2O_5 and the antimonates are stable all along line (*b*), they are the forms of antimony which are thermodynamically stable in the presence of oxygen. As Sb_2O_5 is very soluble in water and aqueous solutions (in particular in alkaline solutions, with the formation of antimonate SbO_3^-), it has only a very small stability domain in the equilibrium diagram (Fig. 1). Very acid solutions dissolve the pentoxide with the formation of antimonic cations SbO_2^+.

The pentoxide and the antimonates can be prepared by the oxidation of powdered antimony, lower oxides or antimonite solutions with powerful oxidizing agents, such as nitric acid, mercury oxide, hydrogen peroxide, bromine, iodine, iodate, iodoform, permanganate, dichromate, sodium peroxide, alkali metal nitrates, etc.

The pentoxide and its aqueous solutions can be reduced to antimonites and to antimony; the reduction from valency +5 to valency +3 can be effected by means of iodide or mercury, for example.

3.4. STABILITY AND FORMATION OF STIBINE SbH_3

In agreement with Fig. 1, gaseous stibine SbH_3 can be obtained together with hydrogen (up to 15 per cent by volume) by the electrolysis of acid or alkaline solutions using a cathode of metallic antimony at potentials below those indicated by the family of lines (22), and also by treating an antimony –zinc or an antimony–magnesium alloy with an acid.

This formation of stibine may be accompanied by the production of solid antimony hydride Sb_2H_2 not considered in Fig. 1 [7].

The position of its stability domain considerably below line (*a*) in Fig. 1 shows that stibine is a reducing substance, thermodynamically unstable, which tends to decompose into antimony and hydrogen. However, at 25°C, the decomposition rate is negligible at pH's between 1 and 13·7; in more alkaline or more acid solutions the decomposition is rapid ([7], [8], [9]).

3.5. ANTIMONY ELECTRODES FOR THE MEASUREMENT OF pH

3.5.1. *Antimony–antimony oxide electrode* ([10], [11]).

This electrode consists of a mixture of powered antimony and oxide Sb_2O_3, maintained in an atmosphere of nitrogen; the electrolyte, previously saturated with Sb_2O_3, passes slowly over the electrode.

The value of the potential of the electrode is given approximately by the relation

$$E_0 = 0.152 - 0.0591\ \text{pH}$$

which is the same as relation (8*a*), and corresponds to the equilibrium Sb/cubic Sb_2O_3. Figure 1 shows that for such an electrode to be in complete equilibrium, the solution must contain an appreciable concentration of dissolved antimony (as calculated from reaction 18); at pH's between 2 and 10, this antimony concentration is constant and equal to $10^{-3.9}$ g-at Sb/l, i.e. 10 mg Sb/l; at pH's below approximately 1 to 2 or above approximately 10 to 11, the electrode potentials can correspond to the correct values for the equilibrium Sb/cubic Sb_2O_3 [given by relation (8*a*)] only if the solution has a relatively high dissolved antimony concentration, respectively in the form of SbO^+ and SbO_2^- ions; this concentration is, for example, 10^{-3} g-at/l (121 mg Sb/l), at pH = 0 and pH = 12·6.

3.5.2. *Antimony-rod electrode*

It is well known that this electrode must be used under well-defined conditions, preferably with mechanical stirring of the solution and in the absence of dissolved oxygen.

The potential values given by Kolthoff and Hartong [12] for a temperature of 14°C are represented in Fig. 3 by the two lines (A) and (B), for which these investigators give the following equations:

for pH's between 1 and 5: $E = -0{\cdot}0415 - 0{\cdot}0485\ \text{pH}\ (14°\text{C})$ (line A),
,, ,, ,, 9 and 12: $E = -0{\cdot}009 - 0{\cdot}0536\ \text{pH}\ (14°\text{C})$ (line B).

Outside these pH domains the potential does not vary linearly with the pH.

If one assumes that the potential values at 25°C are approximately equal to those measured by Kolthoff at 14°C, it is seen that, according to Figs. 1 and 3, these values do not correspond to the equilibrium Sb/Sb_2O_3 [equation (8)]. They correspond approximately to the equilibrium H_2/H^+ for hydrogen pressures of 0·01 to 1 atm. It therefore appears as if *the antimony-rod electrode behaves approximately as a hydrogen electrode operating at a pressure of around* 0·01 *to* 1 *atm.*, the hydrogen being formed at the surface of the antimony as a result of a very slight corrosion of the metal. As the equilibrium concentration of dissolved antimony at these potentials is very small (about 10^{-10} g-at/l), the amount of dissolved antimony is undetectable.

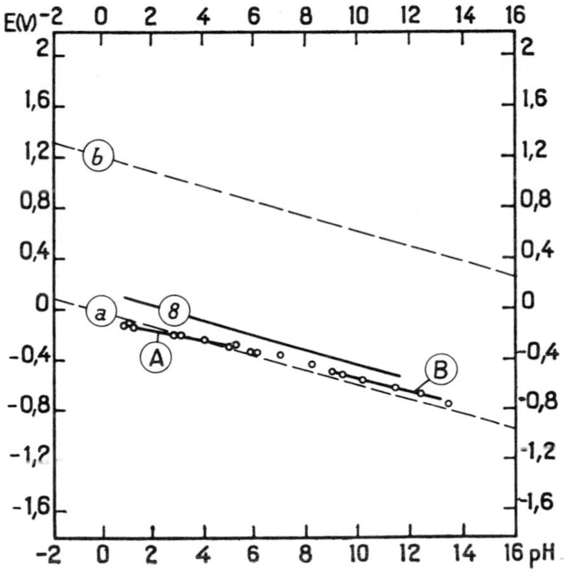

FIG. 3. Antimony electrodes.

Line 8 : Sb/Sb_2O_3 electrode, at 25°C (Schumann [11]).
Lines A and B: Rod electrode, at 14°C (Kolthoff and Hartong [12]).

The formation of the small quantity of hydrogen necessary for the satisfactory operation of this electrode requires that practically no oxidizing agent is present, in particular antimony oxide which would raise the electrode potential above the correct value and bring it nearer to the value of the antimony–antimony oxide electrode, given by relation (8).

3.6. PASSIVATING ACTION OF ANTIMONY SOLUTIONS

When iron or an ordinary steel corrodes in an acid solution, its electrode potential is generally about −0·2 to −0·4 V.

On account of its fairly noble character, antimony can be used under these conditions as a cement for the protection of iron and steel against corrosion. The cementation process can be carried out by immersing the iron or steel in a solution of Sb_2O_3 in 3 M to 10 M HCl; the iron is oxidized and a non-porous coating of metallic antimony is deposited on the iron [13]; the potential of steel cemented in this way is higher than that of non-cemented steel and in the neighbourhood of that of metallic antimony.

The corrosion resistance of these coatings has been studied by Burns and Bradley [14], who noticed their good resistance to hydrochloric and hydrofluoric solutions; they also observed that antimony cements do not resist nitric acid. These observations are in good agreement with the predictions which can be made by examining Fig. 1.

4. BIBLIOGRAPHY

[1] A. L. PITMAN, M. POURBAIX and N. DE ZOUBOV, *Comportement électrochimique de l'antimoine. Diagramme d'équilibres tension–*pH *du système* Sb–H_2O *à* 25°C (Rapport technique RT.55 of CEBELCOR, 1957).
[2] A. L. PITMAN, M. POURBAIX and N. DE ZOUBOV, Potential–pH diagram of the antimony–water system. Its applications to properties of the metal, its compounds, its corrosion, and antimony electrodes, *J. Electrochem. Soc.* **104**, 594–600 (1957).
[3] P. PASCAL, *Traité de Chimie minérale,* Vol. IV, Masson, Paris, 1933.
[4] G. CHARLOT, *L'analyse qualitative et les réactions en solution*, 4th ed., Masson, Paris, 1957, pp. 242–5
[5] M. C. BLOOM, *Amer. Min.* **24**, 281 (1939).
[6] A. N. KONOPIK and J. ZWIAUER, *Monatsheft*, **83**, 189 (1952).
[7] D. T. HURD, *Chemistry of the Hydrides*, Wiley, New York, 1952.
[8] H. W. SALZBERG and A. J. ANDREATCH, *J. Electrochem. Soc.* **101**, 528 (1954).
[9] H. J. S. SANDS, E. J. WEEKS and S. W. WORRELL, *J. Chem. Soc., Trans.,* I, **123**, 456 (1923).
[10] E. J. ROBERTS and F. FENWICK, *J. Amer. Chem. Soc.* **50**, 2125 (1928).
[11] R. SCHUMANN, *J. Amer. Chem. Soc.* **46**, 52 (1924).
[12] I. M. KOLTHOFF and B. D. HARTONG, *Rec. Trav. chim.* **44**, 113–120 (1925).
[13] R. PIONTELLI and L. FAGNANI, *Korr. und Metallsch.* **19**, 259 (1943).
[14] R. M. BURNS and W. W. BRADLEY, *Protective Coatings for Metals*, 2nd ed., Reinhold Publishing Co., New York, 1955, p. 274.

SECTION 18.5

BISMUTH [1]

J. Van Muylder and M. Pourbaix

SUMMARY

[1] Shortened version of the Rapport technique RT.48 of CEBELCOR (May 1957) [1].

1. SUBSTANCES CONSIDERED AND SUBSTANCES NOT CONSIDERED

	Oxidation number (Z)	Considered	Not considered	μ^0(cal.)	Name, colour, crystalline system
Solid substances	− 1	–	Bi_2H_2	–	Bismuth dihydride, grey
	0	Bi	–	0	Bismuth, silvery white or reddish, hex.
	+ 2	–	BiO	− 43 500	Bismuth monoxide
	+ 3	Bi_2O_3 anh.	–	a. −118 700	Bismuth trioxide, pale yellow, rhomb.
	»	» hydr.	–	b. −103 930	Bismuth hydroxide $Bi(OH)_3$, white, amorphous (3)
	+ 3.5	Bi_4O_7	–	−232 750 (2)	Oxide Bi_4O_7, grey–brown
	+ 4	Bi_2O_4	–	−109 000	Bismuth tetroxide, yellow–brown
	+ 5	Bi_2O_5	–	− 91 570 (2)	Bismuth pentoxide, dark red
Dissolved substances	+ 3	Bi^{+++}	–	14 830 (2)	Bismuthous ion, colourless
	»	$BiOH^{++}$	–	− 39 130 (2)	Hydroxybismuthous ion, colourless
	»	BiO^+	–	− 34 540	Bismuthyl ion, colourless
	»	–	BiO_2^-	–	Metabismuthite ion, colourless
	+ 5	–	BiO_3^-	–	Metabismuthate ion, colourless
Gaseous substance	− 3	BiH_3	–	55 340 (2)	Bismuthine, colourless

2. REACTIONS AND EQUILIBRIUM FORMULAE

2.1. TWO DISSOLVED SUBSTANCES

2.1.1. *Relative stability of the dissolved substances*

Z = + 3

1. $Bi^{+++} + H_2O = BiOH^{++} + H^+$ $\qquad \log\frac{(BiOH^{++})}{(Bi^{+++})} = -2.00 + pH$

2. $BiOH^{++} = BiO^+ + H^+$ $\qquad \log\frac{(BiO^+)}{(BiOH^{++})} = -3.37 + pH$

2.1.2. *Limits of the domains of relative predominance of the dissolved substances*

1'. $Bi^{+++}/BiOH^{++}$ $\qquad pH = 2.00$

2'. $BiOH^{++}/BiO^+$ $\qquad pH = 3.37$

---

(2) These free enthalpy values were determined as follows:

– Bi_4O_7 (−232 750 cal.):
Value deduced from the equilibrium potential given by Baur and Lattmann [2] for the reaction
$$2OH^- + 2Bi_2O_3 = Bi_4O_7 + H_2O + 2e^-.$$

– Bi_2O_5(- 91 570 cal.):
Value calculated from the equilibrium potential of the system BiO^+/Bi_2O_5 estimated by Latimer.

– Bi^{+++}(+14 830 cal.):
Value deduced from the pK given by Feitknecht [3] for the reaction
$$BiOCl + H_2O = Bi^{+++} + Cl^- + 2OH^-.$$

– $BiOH^{++}$(- 39 130 cal.):
Value calculated from the pK given by Charlot [4] for the reaction
$$Bi^{+++} + H_2O = BiOH^{++} + H^+.$$

– BiH_3(55 340 cal.):
Value calculated from the equilibrium potential of the system BiH_3/Bi estimated by Latimer.

(3) This value for $\mu^0_{Bi_2O_3}$ corresponds to $\mu^0_{Bi(OH)_3} = -137\,000$ cal.

2.2. TWO SOLID SUBSTANCES

Limits of the domains of relative stability of the solid substances

$0 \rightarrow +3$

3. $2\,\mathbf{Bi} + 3H_2O = \mathbf{Bi_2O_3} + 6H^+ + 6e^-$ — a. $E_0 = 0.371 - 0.0591\,pH$; b. $= 0.478 - 0.0591\,pH$

$+3 \rightarrow +3.5$

4. $2\,\mathbf{Bi_2O_3} + H_2O = \mathbf{Bi_4O_7} + 2H^+ + 2e^-$ — a. $E_0 = 1.338 - 0.0591\,pH$; b. $= 0.690 - 0.0591\,pH$

$+3.5 \rightarrow +4$

5. $\mathbf{Bi_4O_7} + H_2O = 2\,\mathbf{Bi_2O_4} + 2H^+ + 2e^-$ — $E_0 = 1.541 - 0.0591\,pH$

$+4 \rightarrow +5$

6. $\mathbf{Bi_2O_4} + H_2O = \mathbf{Bi_2O_5} + 2H^+ + 2e^-$ — $E_0 = 1.607 - 0.0591\,pH$

2.3. ONE SOLID SUBSTANCE AND ONE DISSOLVED SUBSTANCE

Solubility of the solid substances

$Z = +3$

7. $2BiOH^{++} + H_2O = \mathbf{Bi_2O_3} + 4H^+$ — a. $\log(BiOH^{++}) = 5.96 - 2\,pH$; b. $= 11.38 - 2\,pH$

8. $2BiO^+ + H_2O = \mathbf{Bi_2O_3} + 2H^+$ — a. $\log(BiO^+) = 2.59 - pH$; b. $= 8.01 - pH$

$0 \rightarrow +3$

9. $\mathbf{Bi} = Bi^{+++} + 3e^-$ — $E_0 = 0.215 + 0.0197 \log(Bi^{+++})$

10. $\mathbf{Bi} + H_2O = BiOH^{++} + H^+ + 3e^-$ — $E_0 = 0.254 - 0.0197\,pH + 0.0197 \log(BiOH^{++})$

11. $\mathbf{Bi} + H_2O = BiO^+ + 2H^+ + 3e^-$ — $E_0 = 0.320 - 0.0394\,pH + 0.0197 \log(BiO^+)$

$+3 \rightarrow +3.5$

12. $4Bi^{+++} + 7H_2O = \mathbf{Bi_4O_7} + 14H^+ + 2e^-$ — $E_0 = 2.279 - 0.4137\,pH - 0.1182 \log(Bi^{+++})$

13. $4BiOH^{++} + 3H_2O = \mathbf{Bi_4O_7} + 10H^+ + 2e^-$ — $E_0 = 2.042 - 0.2955\,pH - 0.1182 \log(BiOH^{++})$

14. $4BiO^+ + 3H_2O = \mathbf{Bi_4O_7} + 6H^+ + 2e^-$ — $E_0 = 1.644 - 0.1773\,pH - 0.1182 \log(BiO^+)$

$+3 \rightarrow +4$

15. $2Bi^{+++} + 4H_2O = \mathbf{Bi_2O_4} + 8H^+ + 2e^-$ — $E_0 = 1.910 - 0.2364\,pH - 0.0591 \log(Bi^{+++})$

16. $2BiOH^{++} + 2H_2O = \mathbf{Bi_2O_4} + 6H^+ + 2e^-$ — $E_0 = 1.792 - 0.1773\,pH - 0.0591 \log(BiOH^{++})$

17. $2BiO^+ + 2H_2O = \mathbf{Bi_2O_4} + 4H^+ + 2e^-$ — $E_0 = 1.593 - 0.1182\,pH - 0.0591 \log(BiO^+)$

$+3 \rightarrow +5$

18. $2Bi^{+++} + 5H_2O = \mathbf{Bi_2O_5} + 10H^+ + 4e^-$ — $E_0 = 1.759 - 0.1477\,pH - 0.0295 \log(Bi^{+++})$

19. $2BiOH^{++} + 3H_2O = \mathbf{Bi_2O_5} + 8H^+ + 4e^-$ — $E_0 = 1.700 - 0.1182\,pH - 0.0295 \log(BiOH^{++})$

20. $2BiO^+ + 3H_2O = \mathbf{Bi_2O_5} + 6H^+ + 4e^-$ — $E_0 = 1.605 - 0.0886\,pH - 0.0295 \log(BiO^+)$

2.4. ONE SOLID SUBSTANCE AND ONE GASEOUS SUBSTANCE

Relative stability of **Bi** *and* BiH_3

$-3 \rightarrow 0$

21. $BiH_3 = \mathbf{Bi} + 3H^+ + 3e^-$ — $E_0 = -0.800 - 0.0591\,pH - 0.0197 \log p_{BiH_3}$

3. EQUILIBRIUM DIAGRAM AND ITS INTERPRETATION

3.1. ESTABLISHMENT OF THE DIAGRAM

Using formulae (1)–(21) we have constructed Fig. 1, which represents the conditions of thermodynamic equilibrium of the system bismuth–water at 25°C, in the absence of substances with which bismuth can form soluble complexes or insoluble salts. According to Charlot [4], Cl^- ions form fairly unstable complexes with bismuth; $S_2O_3^{--}$ and I^- ions, and citrates and oxalates form more stable ones. The principal insoluble salts of bismuth are: the phosphate $BiPO_4$, the iodide BiI_3, the oxyiodide BiOI and the sulphide Bi_2S_3.

3.2. STABILITY OF BISMUTH

From Fig. 1 bismuth appears to be a fairly noble element, as a considerable area of its stability domain overlaps that of water.

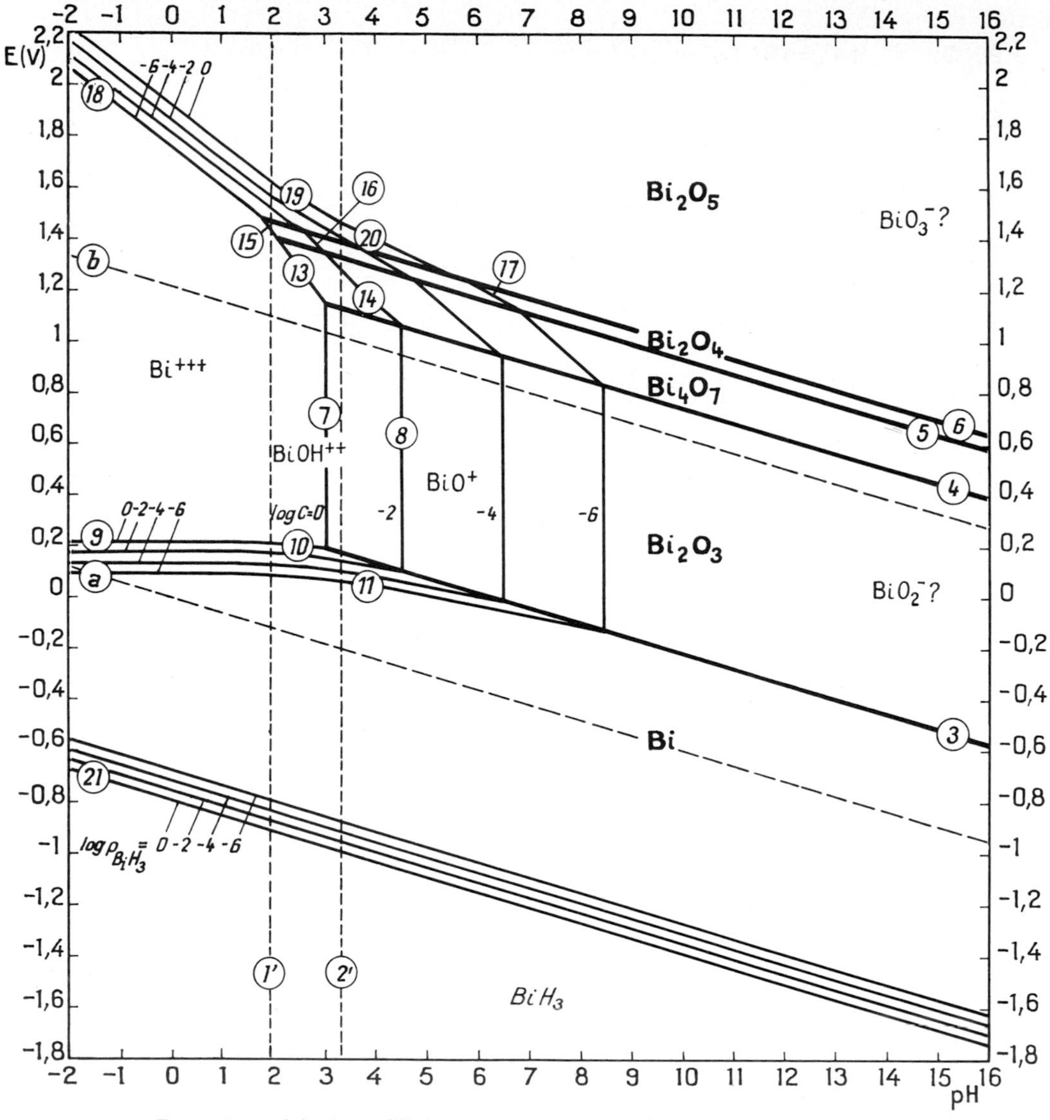

FIG. 1. Potential–pH equilibrium diagram for the system bismuth–water, at 25°C.

It is therefore stable all along the pH axis, in the presence of water or aqueous solutions free from oxidizing agents. In actual fact, bismuth is found mainly in natural state. Water free from air does not affect it, and the element preserves its metallic lustre; in aerated water it becomes covered with a layer of oxide Bi_2O_3. At room temperature, bismuth is unaffected by the air, even if the latter is moist, as long as no condensation of water takes place on its surface, in which case first white bismuthous hydroxide $Bi(OH)_3$ and then yellow trioxide Bi_2O_3 are formed, if the air is free from carbon dioxide, or a white basic carbonate is formed if the air contains carbon dioxide (Pascal [5]).

Dilute hydrochloric and sulphuric acids do not react with bismuth when they are free from air; in the presence of air they attack bismuth with the formation of Bi^{+++} ions, and possibly chloride complexes. Hot concentrated sulphuric acid dissolves bismuth, being itself reduced to SO_2. Dilute solutions of nitric acid, of density below about 1·108, do not attack bismuth; solutions of intermediate density (between about 1·108 and 1·54) (Pascal [5]) attack it, but according to Millon [6] and Quartaroli [7], nitrous acid HNO_2 must be present for this to occur; for reasons which have not yet been explained, bismuth becomes passive if it is touched with platinum, even towards nitric acid of intermediate concentration. Very concentrated solutions of nitric acid, of density above about 1·54 (?) render bismuth passive probably on account of the insolubility of the nitrate formed (Pascal [5]). Bismuth can be reduced to bismuth hydride BiH_3 at potentials below those indicated by the family of lines (21) (see paragraph 3.7).

Depending on the pH and the concentration, bismuth can be oxidized to the bismuthous cation Bi^{+++} and the bismuthyl cations $BiOH^{++}$ and BiO^+ (all colourless), and the oxide Bi_2O_3 (yellow to dark brown). Bismuth can be dissolved by oxidation, as described above, by means of hydrochloric acid in the presence of oxygen, by hot concentrated sulphuric acid and by nitric acid of suitable concentration; dissolution by oxidation can also be carried out electrolytically using a bismuth anode in the presence of aqueous solutions of acids or salts; in the latter case, the bismuth salt obtained undergoes hydrolysis and produces the corresponding bismuthyl salt (oxysalt of bismuth), for instance the oxychloride BiOCl. More vigorous oxidation converts bismuth into various higher oxides: Bi_4O_7, Bi_2O_4 and Bi_2O_5; ozone, hypochlorites, chlorates, etc., can be used to bring about this oxidation. Bismuth never dissolves in the pentavalent state.

3.3. STABILITY OF THE TRIOXIDE Bi_2O_3

Bismuth trioxide is formed by the controlled oxidation of bismuth. The position of its stability domain in Fig. 1 shows it to be a substance which is stable in the presence of water (even aerated water) and most neutral and alkaline aqueous solutions free from reducing agents; however, it dissolves easily in acid solutions to give ions in which bismuth is trivalent: Bi^{+++}, $BiOH^{++}$ and BiO^+. All these dissolved ions, which are stable in sufficiently acid media, are hydrolysed in the presence of excess water to give hydroxides or basic salts. The bismuthyl salts are derived from yellow bismuthyl hydroxide BiO(OH) by replacement of the –OH group with a –Cl, or other, radical. This hydrolysis to give basic salts is one of the most general characteristics of bismuth salts; contrary to what is observed with antimony, the hydrolysis is not prevented by adding tartaric acid.

Bismuth salts can, in general, only be dissolved in water containing a certain definite minimum of acid. When an acid solution of a bismuth salt is neutralized by a base (NaOH, KOH, NH_4OH), bismuth hydroxide $Bi(OH)_3$ or $Bi_2O_3.3H_2O$ is finally obtained; this is a white precipitate, soluble in acids and insoluble in bases; it is not therefore an amphoteric substance. In hot concentrated caustic soda a slight redissolution takes place in the form of BiO_2^- (Charlot [4]).

The hydrate $Bi(OH)_3$ or $Bi_2O_3.3H_2O$ does not appear in the equilibrium diagram, as it is thermodynamically unstable with respect to its anhydrous form Bi_2O_3. According to Fig. 1, bismuth trioxide can be oxidized to higher oxides; this conversion, which is particularly easy in alkaline solutions, can be brought about by means of the usual oxidizing agents such as ozone, chlorine, bromine, sodium peroxide, permanganate, etc. Bismuth trioxide and the cations resulting from its dissolution in acid media can be reduced to metallic bismuth. The reduction can be carried out in acid solutions and in alkaline solutions:

—*in acid solutions:* Mg, Zn, Cd, Cu, Fe, Ti^{+++} and hypophosphorous acid have been used;

—*in alkaline solutions:* $SnCl_2$ in the presence of tartaric acid, formaldehyde and glucose have been used.

However, according to Weeks and Druce [8], the action of zinc in hydrochloric acid or aluminium in caustic potash on a solution of $BiCl_3$ leads to the formation of a grey precipitate of bismuth dihydride Bi_2H_2.

3.4. STABILITY OF THE OXIDE Bi_4O_7

In the opinion of Baur and Lattmann [2], the oxide Bi_4O_7 represents a well-defined degree of oxidation, intermediate between that of the trioxide Bi_2O_3 and that of the tetroxide Bi_2O_4.

The position of its stability domain in the equilibrium diagram shows it to be an oxidizing substance, thermodynamically unstable in the presence of water. It dissolves in acid solutions to form trivalent cations, but is insoluble in alkaline solutions.

3.5. STABILITY OF THE TETROXIDE Bi_2O_4

The stability domain of this oxide lies completely below the line (*b*) relating to the equilibrium of the oxidation reaction of water at atmospheric pressure. It is therefore an oxidizing substance, unstable in the presence of water, in which it is liable to be reduced to lower oxides with the evolution of oxygen.

Bismuth tetroxide dissolves in acid solutions to form trivalent cations, at the same time evolving oxygen; it is insoluble in alkaline solutions.

It can be prepared by the electrolysis of very alkaline bismuth solutions containing tartaric acid; the oxide is obtained at the anode. According to Pascal [5], the real existence of this oxide is not absolutely certain, as the various methods of preparation always lead to the formation of a mixture of various bismuth oxides. Most of the substances which react with Bi_2O_4, and acids and reducing agents in particular, reduce it to the trivalent state, being themselves oxidized: for instance, Bi_2O_4 oxidizes manganous salts to permanganate MnO_4^- and oxidizes hydrochloric acid to chlorine.

3.6. STABILITY OF THE PENTOXIDE Bi_2O_5

Bismuth pentoxide is obtained by the oxidation of bismuth hydroxide $Bi(OH)_3$ or bismuth trioxide Bi_2O_3 dispersed in a hot potash lye. For this purpose, powerful oxidizing agents must be used: chlorine, bromine, ozone, permanganate, chlorate, hydrogen peroxide, etc.

The amount of oxygen fixed depends on the oxidizing agent employed; it is generally greatest when very concentrated caustic solutions are used. Bismuth can also be oxidized from the trivalent to the pentavalent state by electrolytic means, using a platinum anode.

The stability domain of bismuth pentoxide covers the upper part of the equilibrium diagram and lies well above line (*b*) for all pH's. This shows that the oxide is a powerful oxidizing agent; it oxidizes almost all reducing agents in acid media, in the cold, being itself reduced to trivalent bismuth: Ce^{+++} gives Ce^{++++}; Mn^{++} gives MnO_4^-, $HAsO_2$ gives H_3AsO_4, etc.

It dissolves with the evolution of oxygen in acid solutions, being reduced to the trivalent state. It is insoluble in alkaline solutions, even when they are concentrated; however, it can be dissolved by boiling concentrated solutions of caustic potash, with the formation of potassium metabismuthate $KBiO_3$; the metabismuthates are represented in Fig. 1 by the symbol BiO_3^-.

3.7. STABILITY OF BISMUTHINE BiH_3

It is seen from Fig. 1 that bismuth can be reduced to gaseous bismuth trihydride BiH_3(4), or bismuthine, at potentials below those indicated by the family of lines (21).

It has not been possible to carry out this reduction electrolytically; Paneth [9] performed it chemically by treating a mixture of finely divided bismuth and magnesium with an acid. It can also be

(4) Liquid BiH_3 boils at 22°C at a pressure of 1 atm.

carried out by reducing a bismuth salt in acid solution with a reactive metal such as magnesium. According to Weeks and Druce [8], by treating a hydrochloric solution of $BiCl_3$ with zinc or by reducing a bismuth salt with aluminium in the presence of caustic potash, a grey precipitate of solid bismuth dihydride Bi_2H_2 can be obtained. The existence of this solid hydride has yet to be confirmed.

On account of the position of its stability domain, which lies at very low potentials, the gaseous hydride BiH_3 appears to be a compound which is thermodynamically unstable and which tends to decompose into bismuth and hydrogen; this is actually observed in practice.

4. BIBLIOGRAPHY

[1] J. Van Muylder and M. Pourbaix, *Comportement électrochimique du bismuth. Diagramme d'équilibres tension–pH du système* Bi–H_2O, *à* 25°C (Rapport technique RT.48 of CEBELCOR, May 1957).
[2] E. Baur and W. Lattmann, Ueber die Potentiale der Wismutoxyde und über den alkalischen Wismutsammler, *Z. Elektrochem.* **40**, 582–5 (1934).
[3] W. Feitknecht, Gleichgewichtbeziehungen bei den schwerlöslichen basichen Salzen, *Helv. Chim. Acta,* **16**, 1302–15 (1933).
[4] G. Charlot, *Théorie et méthode nouvelles d'analyse qualitative*, 3rd ed., Masson, Paris, 1949, p. 207.
[5] P. Pascal, *Nouveau traité de Chimie minérale*, Vol. XI, Masson, Paris, 1958.
[6] E. Millon, *C. R. Acad. Sc.* **14**, 905 (1842).
[7] A. Quartaroli, Sulla cinetica delle reazioni febbrili. Contributo allo studio dell' autocatalisi, *Gazz. Chim. Ital.* **53,** 345–68 (1923).
[8] E. Weeks and J. Druce, Bismuth dihydride, *J. Chem. Soc.* **127**, 1799–1800 (1925).
[9] F. Paneth, A. Johannsen and M. Matthies, Ueber die Darstellung gasförmiger Metallhydride aus Legierungen und Lösungen, *Ber.* **55**, 769 (1922).

SECTION 19.1

OXYGEN[1]

N. DE ZOUBOV and M. POURBAIX

SUMMARY

---

[1] Rapport CEFA/R.3 of the Commission des Études Fondamentales et Applications of CEBELCOR; see also [1], [2] and [3].

1. SUBSTANCES CONSIDERED AND SUBSTANCES NOT CONSIDERED

	Oxidation number (Z)	Considered	Not considered	μ^0(cal.)	Name
Liquid substance	— 2	H_2O	-	— 56 690	Water
Dissolved substances	— 2	-	O^{--}	-	Oxide ion
	»	OH^-	-	— 37 595	Hydroxide ion
	— 1	H_2O_2	-	— 31 470	Hydrogen peroxide
	»	HO_2^-	-	— 15 610	Hydrogen peroxide ion
	»	-	O_2^{--}	-	Peroxide ion
	»	-	OH	8 530	Hydroxyl
	»	-	H^{--}	51 900	Hydride ion
	— 0.5	-	O_2^-	13 000	Hyperoxide ion
	»	-	HO_2	3 000	Perhydroxyl
	— 0.33	-	O_3^-	-	Ozonide ion
	0	-	O_2	3 950 (*)	Natural oxygen
	+ 1	H^+	-	0	Hydrogen ion
Gaseous substances	0	O_1	-	54 994	Atomic oxygen or monoxygen
	»	O_2	-	0	Natural oxygen or dioxygen
	»	O_3	-	39 060	Ozone or trioxygen.

2. REACTIONS AND EQUILIBRIUM FORMULAE

2.1. TWO DISSOLVED SUBSTANCES(**)

Dissociation of water and hydrogen peroxide

Z = 2

1. $H_2O = OH^- + H^+$ $\qquad \log(OH^-) = -14.00 + pH$

Z = —1

2. $H_2O_2 = HO_2^- + H^+$ $\qquad \log\frac{(HO_2^-)}{(H_2O_2)} = -11.63 + pH$

2.2. TWO GASEOUS SUBSTANCES

2.2.1. *Relative stability of O_1, O_2 and O_3*

3. $O_1 + H_2O = O_2 + 2H^+ + 2e^-$ $\qquad E_0 = 0.037 - 0.0591\,pH + 0.0295\log\frac{p_{O_2}}{p_{O_1}}$

4. $O_2 + H_2O = O_3 + 2H^+ + 2e^-$ $\qquad E_0 = 2.076 - 0.0591\,pH + 0.0295\log\frac{p_{O_3}}{p_{O_2}}$

2.2.2. *Limits of the domains of relative predominance of O_1, O_2 and O_3*

3'. O_1/O_2 $\qquad E_0 = 0.037 - 0.0591\,pH$

4'. O_2/O_3 $\qquad E_0 = 2.076 - 0.0591\,pH$

2.3. ONE DISSOLVED SUBSTANCE AND ONE GASEOUS SUBSTANCE

Solubility of the gaseous substances

$-2 \rightarrow 0$

5. $H_2O = O_1 + 2H^+ + 2e^-$ $\qquad E_0 = 2.421 - 0.0591\,pH + 0.0295\log p_{O_1}$

6. $2H_2O = O_2 + 4H^+ + 4e^-$ $\qquad E_0 = 1.228 - 0.0591\,pH + 0.0148\log p_{O_2}$

7. $3H_2O = O_3 + 6H^+ + 6e^-$ $\qquad E_0 = 1.511 - 0.0591\,pH + 0.0098\log p_{O_3}$

(*) Value calculated from solubility of gaseous O_2 in water at 25°C (28.31 cm^3/l for p_{O_2} = 1 atm.).

(**) In the following equations we have sometimes considered water as a dissolved substance, for simplicity.

— 1 → 0

8. $H_2O_2 = O_2 + 2H^+ + 2e^-$ $\quad E_0 = 0.682 - 0.0591\,pH + 0.0295 \log \frac{p_{O_2}}{(H_2O_2)}$

9. $HO_2^- = O_2 + H^+ + 2e^-$ $\quad E_0 = 0.338 - 0.0295\,pH + 0.0295 \log \frac{p_{O_2}}{(HO_2^-)}$

3. EQUILIBRIUM DIAGRAMS AND THEIR INTERPRETATION

3.1. ESTABLISHMENT OF THE DIAGRAMS

Using formulae (3′) and (4′) we have constructed Fig. 1, which represents the domains of relative predominance of the gaseous substances O_1, O_2 and O_3. Using all the formulae (1)–(9) we have constructed Fig. 2, which represents the equilibrium of all the oxidation and reduction reactions of oxygen considered in the present account.

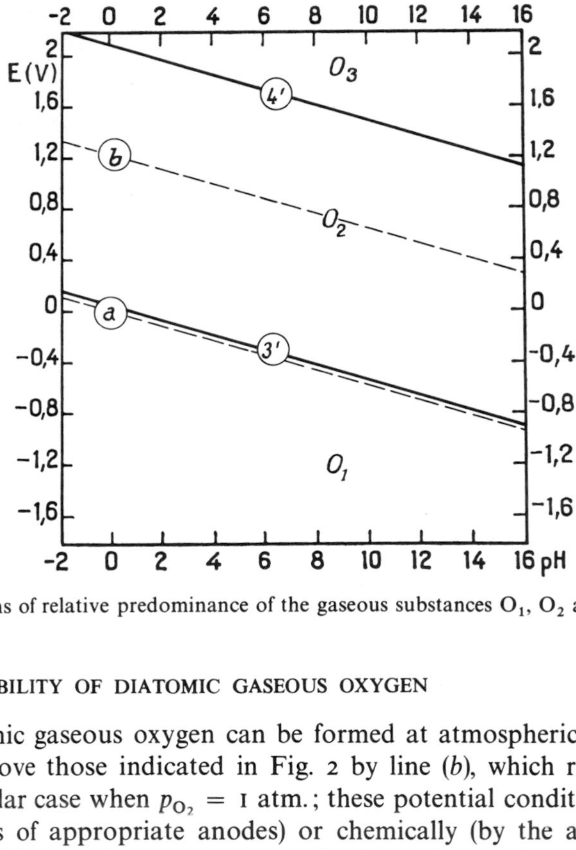

FIG. 1. Domains of relative predominance of the gaseous substances O_1, O_2 and O_3, at 25°C.

3.2. FORMATION AND STABILITY OF DIATOMIC GASEOUS OXYGEN

Theoretically, diatomic gaseous oxygen can be formed at atmospheric pressure by the oxidation of water at potentials above those indicated in Fig. 2 by line (*b*), which refers to the equilibrium of reaction (6) in the particular case when $p_{O_2} = 1$ atm.; these potential conditions can be obtained either electrolytically (by means of appropriate anodes) or chemically (by the action of oxidizing agents). As is well known, this oxidation of water to oxygen is always irreversible, irrespective of the material on whose surface it takes place; a considerable overpotential is required to bring it about [4].

Diatomic gaseous oxygen can theoretically be reduced to water according to the four electron reaction $O_2 + 4H^+ + 4e^- \rightarrow 2H_2O$ at electrode potentials below those indicated by the family of lines (6). This reaction is also highly irreversible and often takes place only with the transitory formation of hydrogen peroxide according to the two electron reactions

$$\begin{array}{lll} & O_2 + 2H^+ + 2e^- \rightarrow H_2O_2 & (8) \\ \text{and} & H_2O_2 + 2H^+ + 2e^- \rightarrow 2H_2O & \\ \hline \text{overall reaction} & O_2 + 4H^+ + 4e^- \rightarrow 2H_2O. & (6) \end{array}$$

The conditions of thermodynamic equilibrium between oxygen, on the one hand, and hydrogen peroxide and its ion HO_2^-, on the other, are shown in Fig. 2 by the family of lines (8) and (9). The

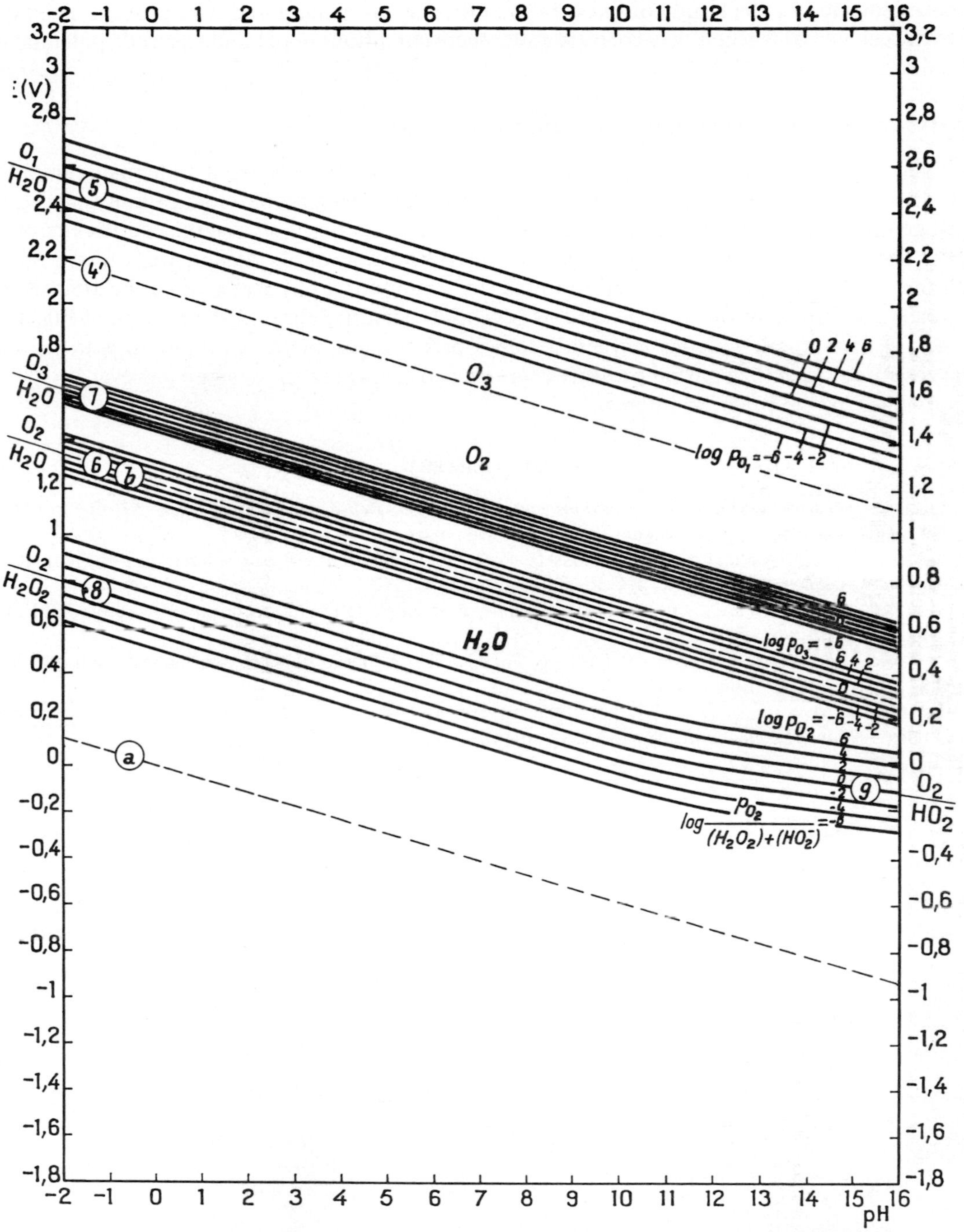

FIG. 2. Potential–pH equilibrium diagram for the system oxygen–water, at 25°C.

reduction of oxygen to hydrogen peroxide is much less irreversible than the reduction of oxygen to water, and, as Bornemann showed in 1912 [5], this can enable us to obtain, experimentally, reversible values for the potentials O_2/H_2O_2. In 1943, Berl [6] described that, if one bubbles oxygen through a porous carbon electrode immersed in an alkaline solution of hydrogen peroxide, a perfectly reversible electrode is obtained ([2]).

In actual fact, it is often easy to reduce oxygen to hydrogen peroxide (which is unstable) at potentials below those indicated by the family of lines (8) and (9): zinc, aluminium and iron produce small quantities of hydrogen peroxide when they corrode under these conditions of pH and electrode potential in an aerated solution.

3.3. FORMATION OF OZONE AND MONATOMIC GASEOUS OXYGEN

As is shown by Fig. 2, a powerful oxidation of water at very high electrode potentials can produce not only diatomic gaseous oxygen O_2, but also triatomic and even monatomic gaseous oxygen [and also hydrogen peroxide, which will not be dealt with here ([3])]. As Fig. 1 shows, the equilibrium proportion of O_3 becomes predominant with respect to the proportion of O_2 at potentials above line (4′); however, the equilibrium pressure is then too high (10^{57} atm.) for a physical sense to be attached to it.

In conclusion, we point out that at the low potentials corresponding to the portion of Fig. 1 lying below line (3′), monatomic gaseous oxygen becomes predominant at the equilibrium with respect to diatomic gaseous oxygen. The partial pressures of these two gases are then so small however (10^{-80} atm.) that this domain has no practical interest.

4. BIBLIOGRAPHY

[1] M. POURBAIX, *Thermodynamique des solutions aqueuses diluées. Représentation graphique du rôle du* pH *et du potentiel*, *Thesis*, Delft, 1945; Béranger, Paris and Liège, 1945.

[2] P. DELAHAY, M. POURBAIX and P. VAN RYSSELBERGHE, *Comportement électrochimique de l'oxygène, de l'eau oxygénée et des radicaux* OH *et* HO_2 (C.R. 2e Réunion du CITCE, Milan, 1950, pp. 42–50).

[3] M. POURBAIX, *Leçons sur la corrosion électrochimique*, 3e fascicule (Rapport technique RT.49 of CEBELCOR, 1957, pp. 24–27).

[4] A. HICKLING and S. HILL, Oxygen overvoltage. Part I: The influence of electrode material, current density, and time in aqueous solution, *Faraday Soc. Disc.* 1947, pp. 236–46.

[5] K. BORNEMANN, *Nernst Festschrift*, Knapp, Halle, 1912, p. 118.

[6] W. G. BERL, *Trans. Electrochem. Soc.* **83**, 253 (1943).

([2]) A more detailed account of this has been published elsewhere [2].

([3]) See Chapter IV, Section 1.2 (hydrogen peroxide) of this *Atlas* (p. 106).

SECTION 19.2

SULPHUR [1]

G. VALENSI, J. VAN MUYLDER and M. POURBAIX

SUMMARY

[1] Extract from the Rapport CEFA/R.15 of the Commission des Études Fondamentales et Applications of CEBELCOR.

1. SUBSTANCES CONSIDERED AND SUBSTANCES NOT CONSIDERED

	Oxidation number (Z)	Considered	Not considered	μ^0(cal.)	Name, colour, crystalline system
Solid substances	0	S	–	0	Sulphur, light yellow, orthorh.
	»	–	S	23	Sulphur, light yellow, monocl.
Dissolved substances	»	–	S	–	Sulphur, yellow, amorphous
	−2	H_2S	–	− 6 540	Hydrogen sulphide, colourless
	»	HS^-	–	3 010	Hydrogensulphide ion, colourless
	»	S^{--}	–	21 958 (2)	Sulphide ion, colourless
	−1	S_2^{--}	–	19 749 (2)	Disulphide ion, orange
	−0.67	S_3^{--}	–	17 968 (2)	Trisulphide ion, orange
	−0.50	S_4^{--}	–	16 615 (2)	Tetrasulphide ion, orange
	−0.40	S_5^{--}	–	15 689 (2)	Pentasulphide ion, orange
	+1.67	–	$S_6O_6^{--}$	–	Hexathionate ion, colourless
	+2	$H_2S_2O_3$	–	−129 900 (2)	Thiosulphuric acid, colourless
	»	$HS_2O_3^-$	–	−129 500 (2)	Acid thiosulphate ion, colourless
	»	$S_2O_3^{--}$	–	−127 200 (2)	Thiosulphate ion, colourless
	»	$S_5O_6^{--}$	–	−228 500	Pentathionate ion, colourless
	»	–	H_2SO_2	–	Sulphoxylic acid, colourless
	+2.50	$S_4O_6^{--}$	–	−244 300	Tetrathionate ion, colourless
	+3	$HS_2O_4^-$	–	−141 408 (2)	Acid dithionite ion, colourless
	»	$S_2O_4^{--}$	–	−138 000 (2)	Dithionite ion, colourless
	+3.33	$S_3O_6^{--}$	–	−229 000	Trithionate ion, colourless
	+4	H_2SO_3	–	−128 690 (2)	Sulphurous acid, colourless
	»	HSO_3^-	–	−126 000	Bisulphite ion, colourless
	»	SO_3^{--}	–	−116 100	Sulphite ion, colourless
	+5	$S_2O_6^{--}$	–	−231 000	Dithionate ion, colourless
	+6	H_2SO_4	–	−177 340	Sulphuric acid, colourless
	»	HSO_4^-	–	−179 940	Bisulphate ion, colourless
	»	SO_4^{--}	–	−177 340	Sulphate ion, colourless
	+7	$S_2O_8^{--}$	–	−262 000	Dipersulphate ion, colourless
	+8	–	H_2SO_5	–	Monopersulphuric acid, colourless
Gaseous substances	−2	*H_2S*	–	− 7 892	Hydrogen sulphide, colourless
	+2	*SO*	–	12 780	Sulphur monoxide, colourless
	+4	*SO_2*	–	− 71 790	Sulphur dioxide, colourless
	+6	–	*SO_3*	− 88 520	Sulphur trioxide, colourless

2. REACTIONS AND EQUILIBRIUM FORMULAE

2.1. TWO DISSOLVED SUBSTANCES

2.1.1. *Relative stability of the dissolved substances*

$Z = -2$

1. $H_2S = HS^- + H^+$ $\qquad \log\frac{(HS^-)}{(H_2S)} = -7.00 + pH$

2. $HS^- = S^{--} + H^+$ $\qquad \log\frac{(S^{--})}{(HS^-)} = -13,90 + pH$

---

(2) S^{--}, S_2^{--}, S_3^{--}, S_4^{--}, S_5^{--} : Values determined by Maronny and Valensi [1].

$H_2S_2O_3$, $HS_2O_3^-$, $HS_2O_4^-$: Values calculated from pK's given by Charlot [2].

$S_2O_3^{--}$, $S_2O_4^{--}$: Values given by the National Bureau of Standards (1952).

H_2SO_3 : Value calculated from the solubility of SO_2 in water.

Z = + 2

3. $H_2S_2O_3 = HS_2O_3^- + H^+$ $\quad \log \frac{(HS_2O_3^-)}{(H_2S_2O_3)} = -0.29 + \text{pH}$

4. $HS_2O_3^- = S_2O_3^{--} + H^+$ $\quad \log \frac{(S_2O_3^{--})}{(HS_2O_3^-)} = -1.69 + \text{pH}$

5. $5H_2S_2O_3 = 2S_5O_6^{--} + 4H^+ + 3H_2O$ $\quad \log \frac{(S_5O_6^{--})^2}{(H_2S_2O_3)^5} = -16.46 + 4\,\text{pH}$

6. $2S_5O_6^{--} + 3H_2O = 5HS_2O_3^- + H^+$ $\quad \log \frac{(HS_2O_3^-)^5}{(S_5O_6^{--})^2} = 14.99 + \text{pH}$

7. $2S_5O_6^{--} + 3H_2O = 5S_2O_3^{--} + 6H^+$ $\quad \log \frac{(S_2O_3^{--})^5}{(S_5O_6^{--})^2} = 6.55 + 6\,\text{pH}$

Z = + 3

8. $HS_2O_4^- = S_2O_4^{--} + H^+$ $\quad \log \frac{(S_2O_4^{--})}{(HS_2O_4^-)} = -2.50 + \text{pH}$

Z = + 4

9. $H_2SO_3 = HSO_3^- + H^+$ $\quad \log \frac{(HSO_3^-)}{(H_2SO_3)} = -1.97 + \text{pH}$

10. $HSO_3^- = SO_3^{--} + H^+$ $\quad \log \frac{(SO_3^{--})}{(HSO_3^-)} = -7.26 + \text{pH}$

Z = + 6

11. $HSO_4^- = SO_4^{--} + H^+$ $\quad \log \frac{(SO_4^{--})}{(HSO_4^-)} = -1.91 + \text{pH}$

− 2 → − 1

12. $2HS^- = S_2^{--} + 2H^+ + 2e^-$ $\quad E_0 = 0.298 - 0.0591\,\text{pH} + 0.0295 \log \frac{(S_2^{--})}{(HS^-)^2}$

13. $2S^{--} = S_2^{--} + 2e^-$ $\quad E_0 = -0.524 + 0.0295 \log \frac{(S_2^{--})}{(S^{--})^2}$

− 2 → − 0.67

14. $3HS^- = S_3^{--} + 3H^+ + 4e^-$ $\quad E_0 = 0.097 - 0.0443\,\text{pH} + 0.0148 \log \frac{(S_3^{--})}{(HS^-)^3}$

− 2 → − 0.50

15. $4HS^- = S_4^{--} + 4H^+ + 6e^-$ $\quad E_0 = 0.033 - 0.0394\,\text{pH} + 0.0098 \log \frac{(S_4^{--})}{(HS^-)^4}$

− 2 → − 0.40

16. $5HS^- = S_5^{--} + 5H^+ + 8e^-$ $\quad E_0 = 0.003 - 0.0369\,\text{pH} + 0.0074 \log \frac{(S_5^{--})}{(HS^-)^5}$

− 2 → + 2

17. $2HS^- + 3H_2O = S_2O_3^{--} + 8H^+ + 8e^-$ $\quad E_0 = 0.200 - 0.0591\,\text{pH} + 0.0074 \log \frac{(S_2O_3^{--})}{(HS^-)^2}$

18. $2S^{--} + 3H_2O = S_2O_3^{--} + 6H^+ + 8e^-$ $\quad E_0 = -0.006 - 0.0443\,\text{pH} + 0.0074 \log \frac{(S_2O_3^{--})}{(S^{--})^2}$

− 2 → + 4

19. $S^{--} + 3H_2O = SO_3^{--} + 6H^+ + 6e^-$ $\quad E_0 = 0.231 - 0.0591\,\text{pH} + 0.0098 \log \frac{(SO_3^{--})}{(S^{--})}$

− 2 → + 6

20. $H_2S + 4H_2O = HSO_4^- + 9H^+ + 8e^-$ $\quad E_0 = 0.289 - 0.0665\,\text{pH} + 0.0074 \log \frac{(HSO_4^-)}{(H_2S)}$

21. $H_2S + 4H_2O = SO_4^{--} + 10H^+ + 8e^-$ $\quad E_0 = 0.303 - 0.0739\,\text{pH} + 0.0074 \log \frac{(SO_4^{--})}{(H_2S)}$

22. $HS^- + 4H_2O = SO_4^{--} + 9H^+ + 8e^-$ $\quad E_0 = 0.252 - 0.0665\,\text{pH} + 0.0074 \log \frac{(SO_4^{--})}{(HS^-)}$

23. $S^{--} + 4H_2O = SO_4^{--} + 8H^+ + 8e^-$ $\quad E_0 = 0.149 - 0.0591\,\text{pH} + 0.0074 \log \frac{(SO_4^{--})}{(S^{--})}$

− 1 → − 0.67

24. $3S_2^{--} = 2S_3^{--} + 2e^-$ $\quad E_0 = -0.506 + 0.0295 \log \frac{(S_3^{--})^2}{(S_2^{--})^3}$

− 0.67 → − 0.50

25. $4S_3^{--} = 3S_4^{--} + 2e^-$ $\quad E_0 = -0.478 + 0.0295 \log \frac{(S_4^{--})^3}{(S_3^{--})^4}$

$-0.50 \rightarrow -0.40$

26. $5 S_4^{--} = 4 S_5^{--} + 2e^-$ $\qquad E_0 = -0.441 + 0.0295 \log \frac{(S_5^{--})^4}{(S_4^{--})^5}$

$-0.40 \rightarrow +2$

27. $2 S_5^{--} + 15 H_2O = 5 S_2O_3^{--} + 30 H^+ + 24 e^-$ $\qquad E_0 = 0.331 - 0.0739\,pH + 0.0025 \log \frac{(S_2O_3^{--})^5}{(S_5^{--})^2}$

$+2 \rightarrow +2.50$

28. $2 S_2O_3^{--} = S_4O_6^{--} + 2e^-$ $\qquad E_0 = 0.219 + 0.0295 \log \frac{(S_4O_6^{--})}{(S_2O_3^{--})^2}$

$+2 \rightarrow +4$

29. $S_2O_3^{--} + 3H_2O = 2HSO_3^- + 4H^+ + 4e^-$ $\qquad E_0 = 0.491 - 0.0591\,pH + 0.0148 \log \frac{(HSO_3^-)^2}{(S_2O_3^{--})}$

30. $S_2O_3^{--} + 3H_2O = 2SO_3^{--} + 6H^+ + 4e^-$ $\qquad E_0 = 0.705 - 0.0887\,pH + 0.0148 \log \frac{(SO_3^{--})^2}{(S_2O_3^{--})}$

$+2.50 \rightarrow +4$

31. $S_4O_6^{--} + 6H_2O = 4H_2SO_3 + 4H^+ + 6e^-$ $\qquad E_0 = 0.509 - 0.0394\,pH + 0.0098 \log \frac{(H_2SO_3)^4}{(S_4O_6^{--})}$

32. $S_4O_6^{--} + 6H_2O = 4HSO_3^- + 8H^+ + 6e^-$ $\qquad E_0 = 0.581 - 0.0788\,pH + 0.0098 \log \frac{(HSO_3^-)^4}{(S_4O_6^{--})}$

$+3 \rightarrow +4$

33. $HS_2O_4^- + 2H_2O = 2H_2SO_3 + H^+ + 2e^-$ $\qquad E_0 = -0.056 - 0.0295\,pH + 0.0295 \log \frac{(H_2SO_3)^2}{(HS_2O_4^-)}$

34. $HS_2O_4^- + 2H_2O = 2HSO_3^- + 3H^+ + 2e^-$ $\qquad E_0 = 0.060 - 0.0887\,pH + 0.0295 \log \frac{(HSO_3^-)^2}{(HS_2O_4^-)}$

35. $S_2O_4^{--} + 2H_2O = 2HSO_3^- + 2H^+ + 2e^-$ $\qquad E_0 = -0.013 - 0.0591\,pH + 0.0295 \log \frac{(HSO_3^-)^2}{(S_2O_4^{--})}$

36. $S_2O_4^{--} + 2H_2O = 2SO_3^{--} + 4H^+ + 2e^-$ $\qquad E_0 = 0.416 - 0.1182\,pH + 0.0295 \log \frac{(SO_3^{--})^2}{(S_2O_4^{--})}$

$+4 \rightarrow +5$

37. $2H_2SO_3 = S_2O_6^{--} + 4H^+ + 2e^-$ $\qquad E_0 = 0.564 - 0.1182\,pH + 0.0295 \log \frac{(S_2O_6^{--})}{(H_2SO_3)^2}$

38. $2HSO_3^- = S_2O_6^{--} + 2H^+ + 2e^-$ $\qquad E_0 = 0.455 - 0.0591\,pH + 0.0295 \log \frac{(S_2O_6^{--})}{(HSO_3^-)^2}$

39. $2SO_3^- = S_2O_6^{--} + 2e^-$ $\qquad E_0 = 0.026 + 0.0295 \log \frac{(S_2O_6^{--})}{(SO_3^{--})^2}$

$+6 \rightarrow +7$

40. $2HSO_4^- = S_2O_8^{--} + 2H^+ + 2e^-$ $\qquad E_0 = 2.123 - 0.0591\,pH + 0.0295 \log \frac{(S_2O_8^{--})}{(HSO_4^-)^2}$

41. $2SO_4^{--} = S_2O_8^{--} + 2e^-$ $\qquad E_0 = 2.010 + 0.0295 \log \frac{(S_2O_8^{--})}{(SO_4^{--})^2}$

2.1.2. *Limits of the domains of relative predominance of the dissolved substances*

1′. $H_2S\ /HS^-$ $\qquad pH = 7.00$
2′. $HS^-\ /S^{--}$ $\qquad pH = 13.90$
3′. $H_2S_2O_3/HS_2O_3^-$ $\qquad pH = 0.29$
4′. $HS_2O_3^-\ /S_2O_3^{--}$ $\qquad pH = 1.69$
5′. $H_2S_2O_3/S_5O_6^{--}$ $\qquad pH = 4.37 - 0.75 \log C$
6′. $HS_2O_3^-\ /S_5O_6^{--}$ $\qquad pH = -15.99 + 3 \log C$
7′. $S_2O_3^{--}\ /S_5O_6^{--}$ $\qquad pH = -1.26 + 0.5 \log C$
8′. $HS_2O_4^-\ /S_2O_4^{--}$ $\qquad pH = 2.50$
9′. $H_2SO_3\ /HSO_3^-$ $\qquad pH = 1.97$
10′. $HSO_3^-\ /SO_3^{--}$ $\qquad pH = 7.26$
11′. $HSO_4^-\ /SO_4^{--}$ $\qquad pH = 1.91$

12′. $HS^-\ /S_2^{--}$ $\qquad E_0 = 0.298 - 0.0591\,pH - 0.0295 \log C$
13′. $S^{--}\ /S_2^{--}$ $\qquad E_0 = -0.524 - 0.0295 \log C$
14′. $HS^-\ /S_3^{--}$ $\qquad E_0 = 0.101 - 0.0443\,pH - 0.0295 \log C$
15′. $HS^-\ /S_4^{--}$ $\qquad E_0 = 0.036 - 0.0394\,pH - 0.0295 \log C$
16′. $HS^-\ /S_5^{--}$ $\qquad E_0 = 0.007 - 0.0369\,pH - 0.0295 \log C$

17'.	$HS^- / S_2O_3^{--}$	$E_0 = 0.200 - 0.0591\ pH - 0.0074 \log C$
18'.	$S^{--} / S_2O_3^{--}$	$E_0 = -0.006 - 0.0443\ pH - 0.0074 \log C$
19'.	S^{--} / SO_3^{--}	$E_0 = 0.231 - 0.0591\ pH$
20'.	H_2S / HSO_4^-	$E_0 = 0.289 - 0.0665\ pH$
21'.	H_2S / SO_4^{--}	$E_0 = 0.303 - 0.0739\ pH$
22'.	HS^- / SO_4^{--}	$E_0 = 0.252 - 0.0665\ pH$
23'.	S^{--} / SO_4^{--}	$E_0 = 0.149 - 0.0591\ pH$
24'.	S_2^{--} / S_3^{--}	$E_0 = -0.499 \qquad - 0.0295 \log C$
25'.	S_3^{--} / S_4^{--}	$E_0 = -0.466 \qquad - 0.0295 \log C$
26'.	S_4^{--} / S_5^{--}	$E_0 = -0.426 \qquad - 0.0295 \log C$
27'.	$S_5^{--} / S_2O_3^{--}$	$E_0 = 0.328 - 0.0739\ pH + 0.0075 \log C$
28'.	$S_2O_3^{--} / S_4O_6^{--}$	$E_0 = 0.228 \qquad - 0.0295 \log C$
29'.	$S_2O_3^{--} / HSO_3^-$	$E_0 = 0.491 - 0.0591\ pH + 0.0148 \log C$
30'.	$S_2O_3^{--} / SO_3^{--}$	$E_0 = 0.705 - 0.0887\ pH + 0.0148 \log C$
31'.	$S_4O_6^{--} / H_2SO_3$	$E_0 = 0.506 - 0.0394\ pH + 0.0295 \log C$
32'.	$S_4O_6^{--} / HSO_3^-$	$E_0 = 0.578 - 0.0788\ pH + 0.0295 \log C$
33'.	$HS_2O_4^- / H_2SO_3$	$E_0 = -0.056 - 0.0295\ pH + 0.0295 \log C$
34'.	$HS_2O_4^- / HSO_3^-$	$E_0 = 0.060 - 0.0887\ pH + 0.0295 \log C$
35'.	$S_2O_4^{--} / HSO_3^-$	$E_0 = -0.013 - 0.0591\ pH + 0.0295 \log C$
36'.	$S_2O_4^{--} / SO_3^{--}$	$E_0 = 0.416 - 0.1182\ pH + 0.0295 \log C$
37'.	$H_2SO_3 / S_2O_6^{--}$	$E_0 = 0.564 - 0.1182\ pH - 0.0295 \log C$
38'.	$HSO_3^- / S_2O_6^{--}$	$E_0 = 0.455 - 0.0591\ pH - 0.0295 \log C$
39'.	$SO_3^{--} / S_2O_6^{--}$	$E_0 = 0.026 \qquad - 0.0295 \log C$
40'.	$HSO_4^- / S_2O_8^{--}$	$E_0 = 2.123 - 0.0591\ pH - 0.0295 \log C$
41'.	$SO_4^{--} / S_2O_8^{--}$	$E_0 = 2.010 \qquad - 0.0295 \log C$

2.2. ONE DISSOLVED SUBSTANCE AND ONE SOLID SUBSTANCE

Solubility of sulphur

a. In gram-molecules or gram-ions per litre

$-2 \rightarrow 0$

42.	$H_2S = \mathbf{S} + 2H^+ + 2e^-$	$E_0 = 0.142 - 0.0591\ pH - 0.0295 \log (H_2S)$
43.	$HS^- = \mathbf{S} + H^+ + 2e^-$	$E_0 = -0.065 - 0.0295\ pH - 0.0295 \log (HS^-)$
44.	$S^{--} = \mathbf{S} + 2e^-$	$E_0 = -0.476 \qquad - 0.0295 \log (S^{--})$

$-0.40 \rightarrow 0$

45.	$S_5^{--} = 5\mathbf{S} + 2e^-$	$E_0 = -0.340 \qquad - 0.0295 \log (S_5^{--})$

$0 \rightarrow +2$

46.	$2\mathbf{S} + 3H_2O = S_2O_3^{--} + 6H^+ + 4e^-$	$E_0 = 0.465 - 0.0887\ pH + 0.0148 \log (S_2O_3^{--})$
47.	$5\mathbf{S} + 6H_2O = S_5O_6^{--} + 12H^+ + 10e^-$	$E_0 = 0.484 - 0.0709\ pH + 0.0059 \log (S_5O_6^{--})$

$0 \rightarrow +2.50$

48.	$4\mathbf{S} + 6H_2O = S_4O_6^{--} + 12H^+ + 10e^-$	$E_0 = 0.416 - 0.0709\ pH + 0.0059 \log (S_4O_6^{--})$

$0 \rightarrow +4$

49.	$\mathbf{S} + 3H_2O = H_2SO_3 + 4H^+ + 4e^-$	$E_0 = 0.449 - 0.0591\ pH + 0.0148 \log (H_2SO_3)$

$0 \rightarrow +6$

50.	$\mathbf{S} + 4H_2O = HSO_4^- + 7H^+ + 6e^-$	$E_0 = 0.339 - 0.0689\ pH + 0.0098 \log (HSO_4^-)$
51.	$\mathbf{S} + 4H_2O = SO_4^{--} + 8H^+ + 6e^-$	$E_0 = 0.357 - 0.0788\ pH + 0.0098 \log (SO_4^{--})$

b. In gram-atoms of sulphur per litre

42'.	$\mathbf{S}/H_2S$	$E_0 = 0.142 - 0.0591\ pH - 0.0295 \log C$
43'.	$\mathbf{S}/HS^-$	$E_0 = -0.065 - 0.0295\ pH - 0.0295 \log C$
44'.	$\mathbf{S}/S^{--}$	$E_0 = -0.476 \qquad - 0.0295 \log C$
45'.	$\mathbf{S}/S_5^{--}$	$E_0 = -0.319 \qquad - 0.0295 \log C$
46'.	$\mathbf{S}/S_2O_3^{--}$	$E_0 = 0.456 - 0.0887\ pH + 0.0148 \log C$

47'. $\mathbf{S}/S_5O_6^{--}$ $E_0 = 0.478 - 0.0709\,pH + 0.0059\log C$

48'. $\mathbf{S}/S_4O_6^{--}$ $E_0 = 0.411 - 0.0709\,pH + 0.0059\log C$

49'. $\mathbf{S}/H_2SO_3$ $E_0 = 0.449 - 0.0591\,pH + 0.0148\log C$

50'. $\mathbf{S}/HSO_4^-$ $E_0 = 0.339 - 0.0689\,pH + 0.0098\log C$

51'. $\mathbf{S}/SO_4^{--}$ $E_0 = 0.357 - 0.0788\,pH + 0.0098\log C$

2.3. ONE DISSOLVED SUBSTANCE AND ONE GASEOUS SUBSTANCE

Solubility of the gaseous substances

a. In gram-molecules or gram-ions per litre

$Z = -2$

52. $H_2S = H_2S$ $\qquad \log\dfrac{(H_2S)}{p_{H_2S}} = -0.99$

53. $H_2S = HS^- + H^+$ $\qquad \log\dfrac{(HS^-)}{p_{H_2S}} = -7.99 + pH$

54. $H_2S = S^{--} + 2H^+$ $\qquad \log\dfrac{(S^{--})}{p_{H_2S}} = -21.90 + 2\,pH$

$Z = +4$

55. $SO_2 + H_2O = H_2SO_3$ $\qquad \log\dfrac{(H_2SO_3)}{p_{SO_2}} = 0.15$

56. $SO_2 + H_2O = HSO_3^- + H^+$ $\qquad \log\dfrac{(HSO_3^-)}{p_{SO_2}} = -1.82 + pH$

$-2 \rightarrow -0.40$

57. $5H_2S = S_5^{--} + 10H^+ + 8e^-$ $\qquad E_0 = 0.299 - 0.0739\,pH + 0.0074\log\dfrac{(S_5^{--})}{p^5_{H_2S}}$

$-2 \rightarrow +6$

58. $H_2S + 4H_2O = SO_4^{--} + 10H^+ + 8e^-$ $\qquad E_0 = 0.311 - 0.0739\,pH + 0.0074\log\dfrac{(SO_4^{--})}{p_{H_2S}}$

$+2.50 \rightarrow +4$

59. $S_4O_6^{--} + 2H_2O = 4SO_2 + 4H^+ + 6e^-$ $\qquad E_0 = 0.510 - 0.0394\,pH + 0.0098\log\dfrac{p^4_{SO_2}}{(S_4O_6^{--})}$

b. In gram-atoms of sulphur per litre

52'. H_2S/H_2S $\qquad 0 = 0.99 + \log C - \log p_{H_2S}$

53'. H_2S/HS^- $\qquad pH = 7.99 + \log C - \log p_{H_2S}$

54'. H_2S/S^{--} $\qquad pH = 10.95 + 0.5\log C - 0.5\log p_{H_2S}$

55'. SO_2/H_2SO_3 $\qquad 0 = -0.15 + \log C - \log p_{SO_2}$

56'. SO_2/HSO_3^- $\qquad pH = 1.82 + \log C - \log p_{SO_2}$

57'. H_2S/S_5^{--} $\qquad E_0 = 0.294 - 0.0739\,pH + 0.0074\log C - 0.0370\log p_{H_2}$

58'. H_2S/SO_4^{--} $\qquad E_0 = 0.311 - 0.0739\,pH + 0.0074\log C - 0.0074\log p_{H_2}$

59'. $SO_2/S_4O_6^{--}$ $\qquad E_0 = 0.516 - 0.0394\,pH - 0.0098\log C + 0.0392\log p_{SO}$

2.4. ONE SOLID SUBSTANCE AND ONE GASEOUS SUBSTANCE

Limits of the domains of relative stability of **S**, H_2S, *SO and* SO_2

$-2 \rightarrow 0$

60. $H_2S = \mathbf{S} + 2H^+ + 2e^-$ $\qquad E_0 = 0.171 - 0.0591\,pH - 0.0295\log p_{H_2S}$

$0 \rightarrow +2$

61. $\mathbf{S} + H_2O = SO + 2H^+ + 2e^-$ $\qquad E_0 = 1.507 - 0.0591\,pH + 0.0295\log p_{SO}$

$0 \rightarrow +4$

62. $\mathbf{S} + 2H_2O = SO_2 + 4H^+ + 4e^-$ $\qquad E_0 = 0.451 - 0.0591\,pH + 0.0148\log p_{SO_2}$

3. EQUILIBRIUM DIAGRAM AND ITS INTERPRETATION

3.1. ESTABLISHMENT OF THE DIAGRAM

According to the equilibrium relations given in paragraph 2, all the substances whose oxidation numbers lie between the extremes -2 (sulphides) and $+6$ (sulphates), except for solid sulphur (oxidation number 0), are thermodynamically unstable and tend to decompose. Thus the thiosulphates, dithionites, sulphites and polythionates are in false equilibrium in aqueous solution; moreover, the persulphates

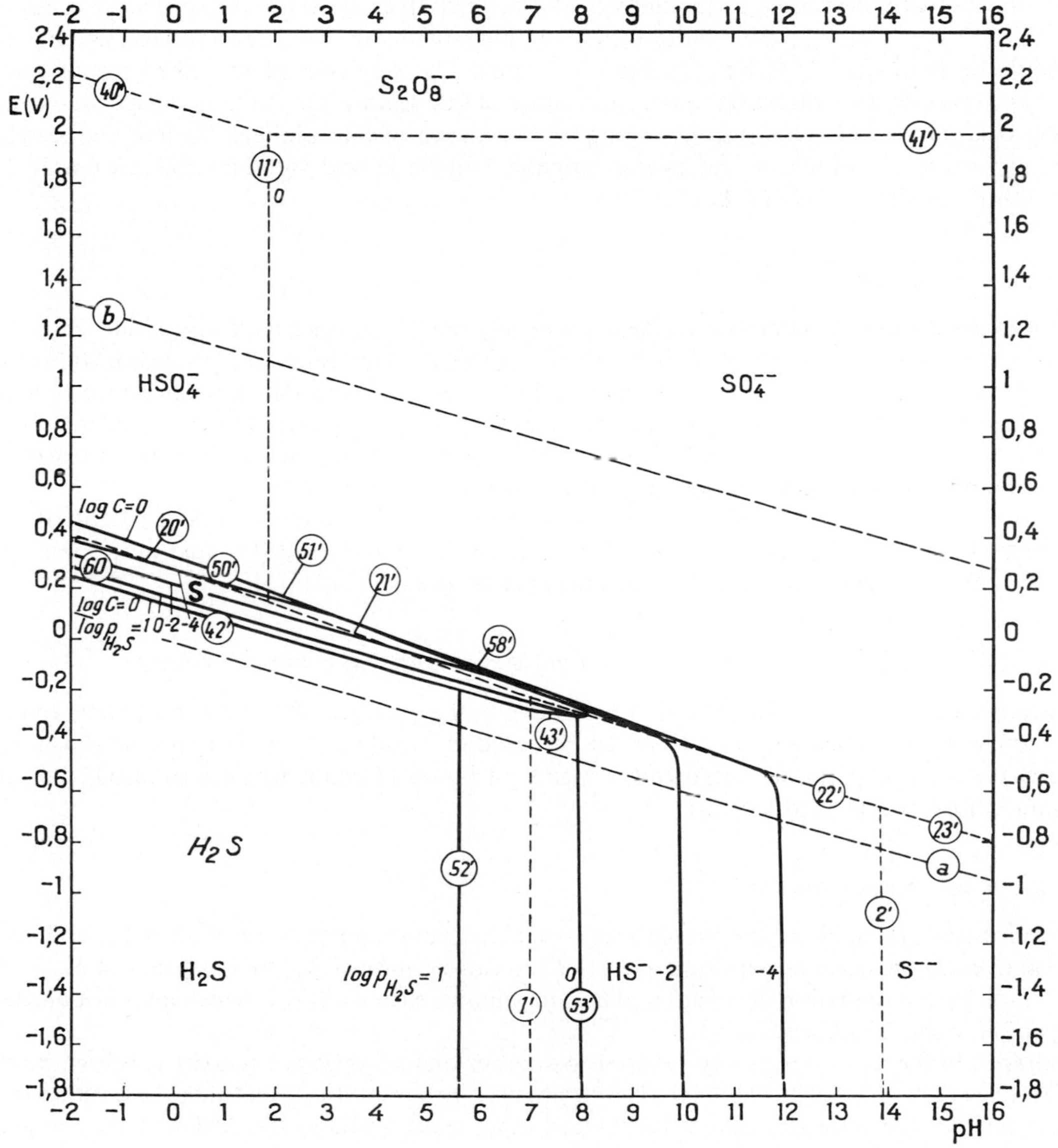

FIG. 1. Potential–pH diagram for the stable equilibria of the system sulphur–water, at 25°C.
The part of this diagram lying outside the line log C = 0 refers to solutions which are not saturated with solid sulphur but which contain 1 g-at/l (32 g/l) of sulphur, dissolved in the forms $H_2S + HS^- + S^{--} + HSO_4^- + SO_4^{--} + S_2O_8^{--}$. The part inside this line refers to solutions saturated with solid sulphur.

are unstable in water. If the equilibria were attained, only H_2S, HS^-, S^{--}, S, HSO_4^- and SO_4^{--} ought to be found in solution.

Figure 1, which is based on formulae (1)–(62), represents the potential–pH diagram for the *stable* equilibria of the system suphur–water at 25°C, for ideal solutions containing 1 g-ion of dissolved sulphur per litre (i.e. 32 g S/l) in the six forms considered: H_2S, HS^-, S^{--}, HSO_4^-, SO_4^{--} and $S_2O_8^{--}$.

For the reasons given above, this figure does not show most of the compounds which are theoretically disproportionated. It is beyond the scope of this discussion to make a complete study of the system in question, but Valensi has carried out detailed work on it [3].

Figure 1 is valid only in the absence of substances with which sulphur can form soluble complexes or insoluble salts. According to Charlot [2], various sulphur derivatives form complexes, the stability of which varies greatly according to the individual case; examples are those of the thiosulphates (with Fe^{+++}, Cr^{+++}, Ag^+, Bi^{+++}, etc.), those of the sulphites (with Ag^+ and precious metals) and those of the sulphates (with Zr^{++++}, Fe^{+++}, Mn^{++++}, etc.). The sulphides of the alkali metals and the alkaline earth metals are soluble in water; the other sulphides are insoluble in water, but dissolve to varying degrees in acid solutions, depending on the nature of the sulphide. Barium and lead thiosulphates are sparingly soluble, as are barium sulphite (soluble in acid solution) and a few anhydrous sulphates [those of Cr, Fe (III), etc.].

3.2. STABILITY OF SULPHUR

The stability domain of sulphur is triangular and very narrow. It lies completely within the stability domain of water, and in the bottom left-hand corner of this domain. Sulphur is therefore stable in the presence of water and acid solutions free from oxidizing agents; it is unstable in the presence of alkaline solutions, in which it tends to disproportionate to give hydrogensulphides HS^-, sulphides S^{--} (and polysulphides), and sulphates SO_4^{--} (and other oxidation products). In practice, these reactions are slow (Valensi [3]) and take place only in hot, very alkaline media (Charlot [2]).

In agreement with Fig. 1, sulphur can be reduced to hydrogen sulphide H_2S at potentials below those indicated by lines (42′) and (60), and can be oxidized to sulphates HSO_4^- and SO_4^{--} (and other oxidation products) at potentials above those indicated by lines (50′) and (51′).

3.3. STABILITY OF HYDROGEN SULPHIDE, THE HYDROGENSULPHIDES AND THE SULPHIDES

Figure 1 shows that H_2S, HS^- and S^{--} are stable in the presence of water and aqueous solutions of all pH's free from oxidizing agents. They can be oxidized to sulphur (e.g. by I_2 in acid media or by hot concentrated HNO_3), and to sulphate (by means of powerful oxidizing agents: MnO_4^-, Cl_2, Br_2, BrO^-, ClO^-, hot concentrated HNO_3).

3.4. STABILITY OF THE SULPHATES

The sulphates are stable in the presence of water and aqueous solutions of all pH's, both in the presence and in the absence of oxidizing agents. They can be formed by the oxidation of H_2S, HS^-, S^{--} and S, or by the oxidation of other sulphur compounds, such as SO_3^{--} which does not appear in the diagram of stable equilibria.

Theoretically the sulphates can be reduced to sulphur and sulphides at potentials below those indicated by lines (50′), (51′), (22′), (23′) and (58′). In practice, however, it is found that these reactions are highly irreversible; the sulphates cannot be reduced in aqueous media in the cold, and are completely inactive and inert under these conditions (Charlot [2]).

We point out, however, the catalytic influence of the bacterium *Vibrio desulphuricans* which enables $CaSO_4$ to be reduced to CaS in the cold; this micro-organism can bring about an anaerobic biochemical catalysis capable of burning up the carbon of vegetable detritus from arable land by means of the oxygen contained in the gypsum, i.e. capable of bringing about the following thermodynamically possible reaction:

$$2C + CaSO_4.2H_2O \rightleftharpoons HS^- + HCO_3^- + H_2CO_3 + Ca^{++}.$$

If there is any ironwork in the neighbourhood, the effect of the corrosive acidity produced is followed by the precipitation of ferrous ions by the HS^- ions, in the form of black ferrous sulphide.

The sulphides can be oxidized to dipersulphates $S_2O_8^{--}$; however, it can be seen from Fig. 1 that such an oxidation is possible only at potentials above about 2·0 V, which can be attained by only very few reagents, such as F/F^- ($E_0^0 = 2{\cdot}87$ V) and O_3/O_2 ($E_0^0 = 2{\cdot}08$ V). The dipersulphates are therefore prepared by anodic oxidation. A platinum anode is used for this purpose, dipping into a very concentrated solution of sulphuric acid or an alkali metal sulphate; the current density used is very high—between 5 and 10 A/cm^2 (Valensi [3]).

The perdisulphates are thermodynamically unstable in the presence of water, which they tend to decompose with the evolution of oxygen. These substances rate among the best oxidizing agents known. Their reduction to sulphates is catalysed by silver salts.

4. BIBLIOGRAPHY

[1] G. Maronny and G. Valensi, *Fonctions thermodynamiques standards des ions mono- et polysulfurés en solution aqueuse* (C. R. 9e Réunion du CITCE, Paris, 1957; Butterworth, London); G. Maronny, *Thesis*, Paris, 1957; *J. Chim. Phys.* **56**, 140–157 (1959).

[2] G. Charlot, *L'analyse qualitative et les réactions en solution*, 4th ed., Masson, Paris, 1957, p. 298–311.

[3] G. Valensi, *Comportement électrochimique du soufre. Diagrammes d'équilibres tension*–pH *du système* S–H_2O, *à* 25°C, 1 *atm.* [Rapport of the Commission des Études Fondamentales et Applications of CEBELCOR, R.17 (1959)].

SECTION 19.3

SELENIUM (1)

J. VAN MUYLDER and M. POURBAIX

SUMMARY

(1) Extract from the Rapport CEFA/R.15 of the Commission des Études Fondamentales et Applications of CEBELCOR, a revised version of an earlier work [1].

1. SUBSTANCES CONSIDERED AND SUBSTANCES NOT CONSIDERED

	Oxidation number (Z)	Considered	Not considered	μ^0(cal.)	Name, colour, crystalline system
Solid substances	0	**Se**	–	0	Selenium, grey, rhomb.
	»	–	**Se**	–	Selenium, red, monocl.
Dissolved substances	– 2	H_2Se	–	18 400	Hydrogen selenide, colourless
	»	HSe^-	–	23 500	Hydrogen selenide ion, colourless
	»	Se^{--}	–	42 600	Selenide ion, colourless
	+ 4	H_2SeO_3	–	–101 800	Selenious acid, colourless
	»	$HSeO_3^-$	–	– 98 300	Acid selenite ion, colourless
	»	SeO_3^{--}	–	– 89 330	Selenite ion, colourless
	+ 6	H_2SeO_4	–	–105 420	Selenic acid, colourless
	»	$HSeO_4^-$	–	–108 200	Acid selenate ion, colourless
	»	SeO_4^{--}	–	–105 420	Selenate ion, colourless
	+ 7	–	$H_2Se_2O_8$	–	Perdiselenic acid
Gaseous substance	– 2	*H_2Se*	–	17 000	Hydrogen selenide, colourless

2. REACTIONS AND EQUILIBRIUM FORMULAE

2.1. TWO DISSOLVED SUBSTANCES

2.1.1. *Relative stability of the dissolved substances*

$Z = -2$

1. $H_2Se = HSe^- + H^+$ $\qquad \log\frac{(HSe^-)}{(H_2Se)} = -3.74 + pH$

2. $HSe^- = Se^{--} + H^+$ $\qquad \log\frac{(Se^{--})}{(HSe^-)} = -14.01 + pH$

$Z = +4$

3. $H_2SeO_3 = HSeO_3^- + H^+$ $\qquad \log\frac{(HSeO_3^-)}{(H_2SeO_3)} = -2.57 + pH$

4. $HSeO_3^- = SeO_3^{--} + H^+$ $\qquad \log\frac{(SeO_3^{--})}{(HSeO_3^-)} = -6.58 + pH$

$Z = +6$

5. $H_2SeO_4 = HSeO_4^- + H^+$ $\qquad \log\frac{(HSeO_4^-)}{(H_2SeO_4)} = 2.05 + pH$

6. $HSeO_4^- = SeO_4^{--} + H^+$ $\qquad \log\frac{(SeO_4^{--})}{(HSeO_4^-)} = -2.05 + pH$

$-2 \rightarrow +4$

7. $H_2Se + 3H_2O = H_2SeO_3 + 6H^+ + 6e^-$ $\qquad E_0 = 0.360 - 0.0591\,pH + 0.0098\log\frac{(H_2SeO_3)}{(H_2Se)}$

8. $H_2Se + 3H_2O = HSeO_3^- + 7H^+ + 6e^-$ $\qquad E_0 = 0.386 - 0.0690\,pH + 0.0098\log\frac{(HSeO_3^-)}{(H_2Se)}$

9. $HSe^- + 3H_2O = HSeO_3^- + 6H^+ + 6e^-$ $\qquad E_0 = 0.349 - 0.0591\,pH + 0.0098\log\frac{(HSeO_3^-)}{(HSe^-)}$

10. $HSe^- + 3H_2O = SeO_3^{--} + 7H^+ + 6e^-$ $\qquad E_0 = 0.414 - 0.0690\,pH + 0.0098\log\frac{(SeO_3^{--})}{(HSe^-)}$

11. $Se^{--} + 3H_2O = SeO_3^{--} + 6H^+ + 6e^-$ $\qquad E_0 = 0.276 - 0.0591\,pH + 0.0098\log\frac{(SeO_3^{--})}{(Se^{--})}$

$+4 \rightarrow +6$

12.	$H_2SeO_3 + H_2O = HSeO_4^- + 3H^+ + 2e^-$	$E_0 =$	$1.090 - 0.0886\,pH + 0.0295 \log \frac{(HSeO_4^-)}{(H_2SeO_3)}$
13.	$H_2SeO_3 + H_2O = SeO_4^{--} + 4H^+ + 2e^-$	$E_0 =$	$1.151 - 0.1182\,pH + 0.0295 \log \frac{(SeO_4^{--})}{(H_2SeO_3)}$
14.	$HSeO_3^- + H_2O = SeO_4^{--} + 3H^+ + 2e^-$	$E_0 =$	$1.075 - 0.0886\,pH + 0.0295 \log \frac{(SeO_4^{--})}{(HSeO_3^-)}$
15.	$SeO_3^{--} + H_2O = SeO_4^{--} + 2H^+ + 2e^-$	$E_0 =$	$0.880 - 0.0591\,pH + 0.0295 \log \frac{(SeO_4^{--})}{(SeO_3^{--})}$

2.1.2. *Limits of the domains of relative predominance of the dissolved substances*

1'.	$H_2Se\ /HSe^-$	$pH =$	3.74
2'.	$HSe^-\ /Se^{--}$	$pH =$	14.01
3'.	$H_2SeO_3/HSeO_3^-$	$pH =$	2.57
4'.	$HSeO_3^-/SeO_3^{--}$	$pH =$	6.58
5'.	$H_2SeO_4/HSeO_4^-$	$pH =$	− 2.05
6'.	$HSeO_4^-/SeO_4^{--}$	$pH =$	2.05
7'.	$H_2Se\ /H_2SeO_3$	$E_0 =$	$0.360 - 0.0591\,pH$
8'.	$H_2Se\ /HSeO_3^-$	$E_0 =$	$0.386 - 0.0690\,pH$
9'.	$HSe^-\ /HSeO_3^-$	$E_0 =$	$0.349 - 0.0591\,pH$
10'.	$HSe^-\ /SeO_3^{--}$	$E_0 =$	$0.414 - 0.0690\,pH$
11'.	$Se^{--}\ /SeO_3^{--}$	$E_0 =$	$0.276 - 0.0591\,pH$
12'.	$H_2SeO_3/HSeO_4^-$	$E_0 =$	$1.090 - 0.0886\,pH$
13'.	H_2SeO_3/SeO_4^{--}	$E_0 =$	$1.151 - 0.1182\,pH$
14'.	$HSeO_3^-/SeO_4^{--}$	$E_0 =$	$1.075 - 0.0886\,pH$
15'.	$SeO_3^{--}\ /SeO_4^{--}$	$E_0 =$	$0.880 - 0.0591\,pH$

2.2. ONE SOLID SUBSTANCE AND ONE DISSOLVED SUBSTANCE

Solubility of selenium

$-2 \rightarrow 0$

16.	$H_2Se = \mathbf{Se} + 2H^+ + 2e^-$	$E_0 =$	$-0.399 - 0.0591\,pH - 0.0295 \log (H_2Se)$
17.	$HSe^- = \mathbf{Se} + H^+ + 2e^-$	$E_0 =$	$-0.510 - 0.0295\,pH - 0.0295 \log (HSe^-)$
18.	$Se^{--} = \mathbf{Se} + 2e^-$	$E_0 =$	$-0.924 - 0.0295 \log (Se^{--})$

$0 \rightarrow +4$

19.	$\mathbf{Se} + 3H_2O = H_2SeO_3 + 4H^+ + 4e^-$	$E_0 =$	$0.741 - 0.0591\,pH + 0.0148 \log (H_2SeO_3)$
20.	$\mathbf{Se} + 3H_2O = HSeO_3^- + 5H^+ + 4e^-$	$E_0 =$	$0.778 - 0.0739\,pH + 0.0148 \log (HSeO_3^-)$
21.	$\mathbf{Se} + 3H_2O = SeO_3^{--} + 6H^+ + 4e^-$	$E_0 =$	$0.875 - 0.0886\,pH + 0.0148 \log (SeO_3^{--})$

2.3. ONE SOLID SUBSTANCE AND ONE GASEOUS SUBSTANCE

Limits of the domains of relative stability of **Se** *and H_2Se*

$-2 \rightarrow 0$

22.	$H_2Se = \mathbf{Se} + 2H^+ + 2e^-$	$E_0 =$	$-0.369 - 0.0591\,pH - 0.0295 \log p_{H_2Se}$

2.4. ONE GASEOUS SUBSTANCE AND ONE DISSOLVED SUBSTANCE

Solubility of gaseous H_2Se

$Z = -2$

23.	$H_2Se = H_2Se$	$\log (H_2Se) = -1.03 + \log p_{H_2Se}$
24.	$H_2Se = HSe^- + H^+$	$\log (HSe^-) = -4.77 + pH + \log p_{H_2Se}$
25.	$H_2Se = Se^{--} + 2H^+$	$\log (Se^{--}) = -30.01 + 2\,pH + \log p_{H_2Se}$

3. EQUILIBRIUM DIAGRAM AND ITS INTERPRETATION

3.1. ESTABLISHMENT OF THE DIAGRAM

Using the equilibrium formulae given in paragraph 2, we have constructed Figs. 1 and 2. In Fig. 2 we have used relations (1′), (23) and (24) to represent the influence of pH and pressure on the solubility of hydrogen selenide H_2Se at 25°C.

Using this diagram and all the equations (1)–(25), we have constructed Fig. 1, which is a potential–pH equilibrium diagram for the system selenium–water, at 25°C. These diagrams are valid only in the

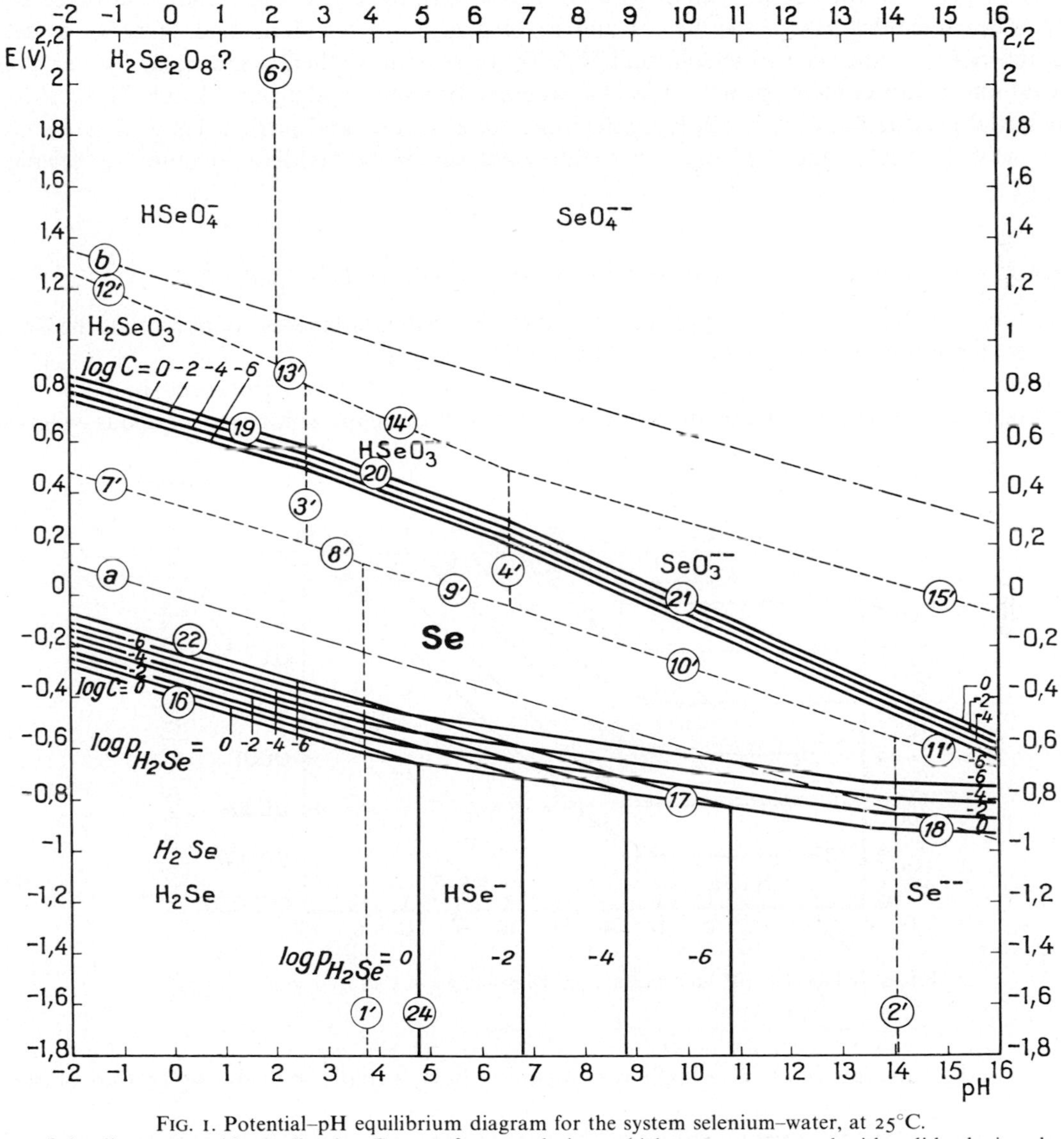

FIG. 1. Potential–pH equilibrium diagram for the system selenium–water, at 25°C.
The part of the diagram outside the line log C = 0 refers to solutions which are not saturated with solid selenium but contain 1 g-at/l (79 g/l) of selenium, dissolved in the forms

$$H_2Se + HSe^- + Se^{--} + H_2SeO_3 + HSeO_3^- + SeO_3^{--} + HSeO_4^- + SeO_4^{--}$$

The part of the diagram inside this line refers to solutions saturated with solid selenium.

absence of substances with which selenium can form insoluble compounds or soluble complexes. In this connection, the selenides, selenites and selenates of metals other than the alkali metals are generally insoluble; examples of selenium complexes are: selenophosphoric acid $PSe(OH)_3$, chromoselenic acid, cobaltiselenic complexes and complex derivatives of uranic acid and nitrosylsulphuric acid.

3.2. STABILITY OF SELENIUM

According to Fig. 1, selenium is a fairly noble substance, as a large portion of its stability domain covers that of water. It is therefore stable in the presence of water and aqueous solutions of all pH's free from oxidizing and reducing agents. We can in fact find selenium in the native state, but the combined state is greatly predominant, especially in the form of the double selenide of lead and copper.

In agreement with the equilibrium diagram it is easy both to reduce selenium (to hydrogen selenide H_2Se or other selenides HSe^- and Se^{--}) and to oxidize it (to selenious acid H_2SeO_3 or selenites $HSeO_3^-$ and SeO_3^{--}, and also to selenic acid H_2SeO_4 or selenates $HSeO_4^-$ and SeO_4^{--}). For example, when selenium is cathodically polarized in the presence of water, hydrogen selenide H_2Se is formed, after the initial production of red colloidal selenium; hot sulphuric and nitric acids oxidize selenium to selenious acid H_2SeO_3, and hydrogen peroxide oxidizes finely divided selenium to selenic acid H_2SeO_4 [2].

3.3. STABILITY OF HYDROGEN SELENIDE H_2Se AND THE SELENIDES HSe^- AND Se^{--}

Selenium can be reduced to hydrogen selenide and other selenides at potentials below those indicated by the families of lines (16), (17), (18) and (22) in Fig. 1.

As their stability domain is situated at relatively low potentials, these substances should be regarded as reducing agents, unstable in the presence of water and aqueous solutions. Aqueous solutions of

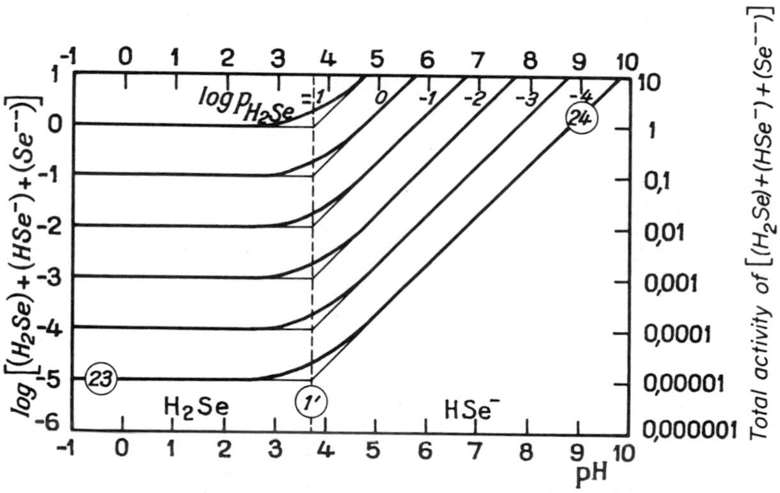

FIG. 2. Influence of pH and pressure on the solubility of hydrogen selenide, at 25°C.

H_2Se are actually unstable in air, the H_2Se decomposing fairly rapidly with the separation of selenium [2].

Figure 2 represents, for various values of the partial pressure of H_2Se, the influence of pH on the solubility of the gas in the dissolved forms H_2Se, HSe^- and Se^{--} at 25°C. It is easy to deduce from this diagram the equilibrium pressure of gaseous H_2Se above a selenious solution for a given concentration and pH.

Examples of reactions in which hydrogen selenide and the selenides act as reducing agents are: the decolorization of chlorine, bromine and iodine solutions, the reduction of sulphurous and selenious acids respectively to sulphur and selenium, the conversion of ferricyanide $Fe(CN)_6^{---}$ to ferrocyanide $Fe(CN)_6^{----}$, etc.

3.4. STABILITY OF SELENIOUS ACID AND THE SELENITES

Selenious acid H_2SeO_3 and the selenites $HSeO_3^-$ and SeO_3^{--} are stable in the presence of water and aqueous solutions free from oxidizing and reducing agents.

In accordance with the position of their domain of predominance, these substances can act both as oxidizing agents and as reducing agents. For example, the following substances can be oxidized by selenious acid and its salts: hydrogen, hydrogen sulphide, sulphurous acid, sulphites and dithionites, ortho- and hypophosphorous acids, etc. The following powerful oxidizing agents can be reduced by selenious acid and its salts: chlorine, potassium dichromate, potassium permanganate and hydrogen peroxide.

3.5. STABILITY OF SELENIC ACID AND THE SELENATES

The domain of predominance of selenic acid H_2SeO_4 and the selenates $HSeO_4^-$ and SeO_4^{--} occupies all of the upper part of the equilibrium diagram, and also covers part of the stability domain of water; these substances are therefore stable in the presence of water and aqueous solutions of all pH's, both in the presence and in the absence of oxidizing agents.

Moreover, they are oxidizing agents which are reduced by a large number of substances. In practice, these reductions are difficult to bring about, as the system SeO_3^{--}/SeO_4^{--} has a certain irreversibility (Charlot [3]). Powerful reducing agents are oxidized by these substances only when in hot, very acid media: e.g. hot concentrated HCl, trivalent titanium Ti^{+++}, SO_2 in a hot concentrated sulphuric medium [3].

It should be possible to oxidize selenic acid and the selenates electrolytically to perdiselenic acid $H_2Se_2O_8$ using a platinum anode. This acid has been represented approximately at the top of the equilibrium diagram in Fig. 1.

4. BIBLIOGRAPHY

[1] P. DELAHAY, M. POURBAIX and P. VAN RYSSELBERGHE, *Diagrammes d'équilibres potentiel–*pH *de quelques éléments* (C.R. 3e Réunion du CITCE, Berne, 1951, p. 15).

[2] *Gmelins Handbuch der anorganischen Chemie, Selen,* S.N.10, Teil A, 1953 and Teil B, 1949.

[3] G. CHARLOT, *L'analyse qualitative et les réactions en solution,* Masson, Paris, 1957.

SECTION 19.4

TELLURIUM[1]

E. DELTOMBE, N. DE ZOUBOV and M. POURBAIX

SUMMARY

1. *Substances considered and substances not considered.*
2. *Reactions and equilibrium formulae.*
   2.1. Two dissolved substances.
      2.1.1. Relative stability of the dissolved substances.
      2.1.2. Limits of the domains of relative predominance of the dissolved substances.
   2.2. Two solid substances.
      Relative stability of tellurium and its oxides.
   2.3. One solid substance and one dissolved substance.
      Solubility of the solid substances.
   2.4. One gaseous substance and one dissolved substance.
      Solubility of gaseous hydrogen telluride.
   2.5. One gaseous substance and one solid substance.
      Relative stability of tellurium and gaseous hydrogen telluride.
3. *Equilibrium diagrams and their interpretation.*
   3.1. Establishment of the diagrams.
   3.2. Stability of tellurium.
   3.3. Stability and formation of hydrogen telluride, the tellurides and the ditellurides.
   3.4. Stability and formation of tellurous anhydride and the tellurites.
   3.5. Stability and formation of telluric anhydride, telluric acid and the tellurates.
4. *Bibliography.*

[1] Shortened and adapted version of the Rapport technique RT.33 of CEBELCOR (April 1956) [1].

1. SUBSTANCES CONSIDERED AND SUBSTANCES NOT CONSIDERED

	Oxidation number (Z)	Considered	Not considered	μ^0(cal.)	Name, colour, crystalline system
Solid substances	0	**Te**	–	0	Tellurium, brown–black, amorphous
	+2	–	**TeO**	–	Monoxide, black, amorphous
	+4	**TeO_2**	–	a. – 65 320 (*)	Tellurous anhydride, white, quad.
	»	» hydr.	–	b. – 57 670 (*)	Tellurous acid H_2TeO_3 or $TeO_2 . H_2O$, white(²), amorphous
	+6	–	**TeO_3**	–	Telluric anhydride, orange–yellow
	»	**TeO_3** hydr.	–	– 74 968 (*)	Orthotelluric acid H_6TeO_6 or $TeO_3 . 3H_2O$, colourless, cub. or monocl.(²)
Dissolved substances	–2	H_2Te	–	34 100	Hydrogen telluride, colourless
	»	HTe^-	–	37 700	Acid telluride ion, colourless
	»	Te^{--}	–	52 700	Telluride ion, colourless
	–1	Te_2^{--}	–	38 750	Ditelluride ion, red
	+4	Te^{++++}	–	52 380 (*)	Tellurous ion
	»	$HTeO_2^+$	–	– 62 510 (*)	Telluryl ion
	»	–	H_2TeO_3	–	Tellurous acid
	»	$HTeO_3^-$	–	–104 340 (*)	Acid tellurite ion, colourless
	»	TeO_3^{--}	–	– 93 790 (*)	Tellurite ion, colourless
	+6	H_2TeO_4	–	–131 658 (*)	Telluric acid, colourless
	»	$HTeO_4^-$	–	–123 268 (*)	Acid tellurate ion, colourless
	»	TeO_4^{--}	–	–109 088 (*)	Tellurate ion, colourless
Gaseous substance	–2	*H_2Te*	–	33 100	Hydrogen telluride, tellurium hydride

The μ^0 values marked (*) were calculated by us as follows:

—TeO_2 (–65 320 cal.):

We assumed Schumann's value [2], $E_0^0 = +0{\cdot}5213$ V for the equilibrium potential of the reaction

$$Te + 2H_2O = TeO_2 + 4H^+ + 4e^-$$

for tetragonal TeO_2 (see *loc. cit.* [1]).

—Hydrated TeO_2 (–57 670 cal.):

We assumed the value $E_0^0 = +0{\cdot}604$ V (according to Kasarnowsky's experimental values [3]) for the equilibrium potential of the reaction $Te + 3H_2O = TeO_2 . H_2O + 4H^+ + 4e^-$ (for amorphous $TeO_2 . H_2O$) (see *loc. cit.* [1]).

—Hydrated TeO_3 (–74 968 cal.):

We assumed Latimer's value, $E_0^0 = +1{\cdot}02$ V, for the equilibrium potential of the reaction

$$TeO_2 + 4H_2O = TeO_3 . 3H_2O + 2H^+ + 2e^-.$$

—Te^{++++} (52 380 cal.):

We assumed Getman's value [4], $E_0^0 = +0{\cdot}568$ V, for the equilibrium potential of the reaction $Te = Te^{++++} + 4e^-$ (see *loc. cit.* [1]).

—$HTeO_2^+$ (–62 510 cal.):

We assumed the relation $\log (HTeO_2^+) = -2{\cdot}06 - pH$, given by Schumann's experiments [2], as the equilibrium condition for the reaction $TeO_2 + H^+ = HTeO_2^+$ (for anhydrous TeO_2) (see *loc. cit.* [1]).

(²) The value $\mu^0_{TeO_2} = -57\,670$ cal. corresponds to $\mu^0_{TeO_2 . H_2O} = -114\,360$ cal. The value $\mu^0_{TeO_2} = -74\,968$ cal. corresponds to $\mu^0_{H_6TeO_6} = -245\,038$ cal.

—$HTeO_3^-$ (−104 *340* cal.):

We assumed Kasarnowsky's [3] value, $E_0 = +0{\cdot}282$ V, for the potential of the couple $Te/TeO_2.H_2O$ in pure water saturated with $TeO_2.H_2O$; if one takes $E_0^0 = +0{\cdot}604$ V for the standard potential of this couple (at pH = 0) the pH of this saturated solution is 5·45. Assuming that the solution contains equal quantities of $HTeO_2^+$ and $HTeO_3^-$ ions, it follows that the pK of the reaction $HTeO_2^+ + H_2O = HTeO_3^- + 2H^+$ is 5·45 which gives $\mu^0_{HTeO_3^-} = -104\,340$ cal. (see *loc. cit.* [1]).

—TeO_3^{--} (−93 *790* cal.):

We assumed Blanc's value [5], pK = 7·74, for the reaction $HTeO_3^- = TeO_3^{--} + H^+$ (see *loc. cit.* [1]).

—H_2TeO_4 (−131 *658* cal.):

We assumed that (according to Latimer) the free enthalpy of solution of solid orthotelluric acid H_6TeO_6 is small and that, for approximate calculations, one can use the same free enthalpy value for the solid acid as for the dissolved acid (which amounts to the assumption that the solubility of the solid acid in its undissociated form is about 1 g-mol/l). We therefore have $\log(H_1TeO_4) = 0$ as the approximate equilibrium condition for the dissolution reaction

$$H_6TeO_6\,(s) = H_2TeO_4(aq.) + 2H_2O.$$

From it we obtain $\mu^0_{H_2TeO_4} = -245\,038 + (56\,690 \times 2) = -131\,658$ cal. (see *loc. cit.* [1]).

—$HTeO_4$ (−123 *268* cal.) and TeO_4^{--} (−109 *088* cal.):

We assumed Blanc's values [5], pK = 6·17 for the reaction $H_2TeO_4 = HTeO_4^- + H^+$ and pK = 10·39 for the

$$HTeO_4^- = TeO_4^{--} + H^+$$

(see *loc. cit.* [1]).

2. REACTIONS AND EQUILIBRIUM FORMULAE

2.1. TWO DISSOLVED SUBSTANCES

2.1.1. *Relative stability of the dissolved substances*

$Z = -2$

1. $H_2Te = HTe^- + H^+$ $\quad \log\frac{(HTe^-)}{(H_2Te)} = -2.64 + pH$

2. $HTe^- = Te^{--} + H^+$ $\quad \log\frac{(Te^{--})}{(HTe^-)} = -11.00 + pH$

$Z = +4$

3. $Te^{++++} + 2H_2O = HTeO_2^+ + 3H^+$ $\quad \log\frac{(HTeO_2^+)}{(Te^{++++})} = 1.11 + 3\,pH$

4. $HTeO_2^+ + H_2O = HTeO_3^- + 2H^+$ $\quad \log\frac{(HTeO_3^-)}{(HTeO_2^+)} = -10.90 + 2\,pH$

5. $HTeO_3^- = TeO_3^{--} + H^+$ $\quad \log\frac{(TeO_3^{--})}{(HTeO_3^-)} = -7.74 + pH$

$Z = +6$

6. $H_2TeO_4 = HTeO_4^- + H^+$ $\quad \log\frac{(HTeO_4^-)}{(H_2TeO_4)} = -6.17 + pH$

7. $HTeO_4^- = TeO_4^{--} + H^+$ $\quad \log\frac{(TeO_4^{--})}{(HTeO_4^-)} = -10.38 + pH$

$-2 \rightarrow -1$

8. $2H_2Te = Te_2^{--} + 4H^+ + 2e^-$ $\quad E_0 = -0.638 - 0.1182\,pH + 0.0295\log\frac{(Te_2^{--})}{(H_2Te)^2}$

9. $2HTe^- = Te_2^{--} + 2H^+ + 2e^-$ $\quad E_0 = -0.795 - 0.0591\,pH + 0.0295\log\frac{(Te_2^{--})}{(HTe^-)^2}$

10. $2Te^{--} = Te_2^{--} + 2e^-$ $\quad E_0 = -1.445 + 0.0295\log\frac{(Te_2^{--})}{(Te^{--})^2}$

$-2 \rightarrow +4$

11. $H_2Te = Te^{++++} + 2H^+ + 6e^-$ $\quad E_0 = 0.132 - 0.0197\,pH + 0.0098\log\frac{(Te^{++++})}{(H_2Te)}$

12. $H_2Te + 2H_2O = HTeO_2^+ + 5H^+ + 6e^-$ $\quad E_0 = 0.121 - 0.0492\,pH + 0.0098\log\frac{(HTeO_2^+)}{(H_2Te)}$

$-1 \rightarrow +4$

13. $Te_2^{--} = 2Te^{++++} + 10e^-$ $\quad E_0 = 0.286 + 0.0059\log\frac{(Te^{++++})^2}{(Te_2^{--})}$

14. $Te_2^{--} + 4H_2O = 2HTeO_2^+ + 6H^+ + 10e^-$ $\quad E_0 = 0.273 - 0.0354\,pH + 0.0059\log\frac{(HTeO_2^+)^2}{(Te_2^{--})}$

15. $Te_2^{--} + 6H_2O = 2HTeO_3^- + 10H^+ + 10e^-$ $\quad E_0 = 0.402 - 0.0591\,pH + 0.0059 \log \frac{(HTeO_3^-)^2}{(Te_2^{--})}$

16. $Te_2^{--} + 6H_2O = 2TeO_3^{--} + 12H^+ + 10e^-$ $\quad E_0 = 0.493 - 0.0709\,pH + 0.0059 \log \frac{(TeO_3^{--})^2}{(Te_2^{--})}$

$+4 \rightarrow +6$

17. $Te^{++++} + 4H_2O = H_2TeO_4 + 6H^+ + 2e^-$ $\quad E_0 = 0.920 - 0.1773\,pH + 0.0295 \log \frac{(H_2TeO_4)}{(Te^{++++})}$

18. $HTeO_2^+ + 2H_2O = H_2TeO_4 + 3H^+ + 2e^-$ $\quad E_0 = 0.953 - 0.0886\,pH + 0.0295 \log \frac{(H_2TeO_4)}{(HTeO_2^+)}$

19. $HTeO_3^- + H_2O = H_2TeO_4 + H^+ + 2e^-$ $\quad E_0 = 0.631 - 0.0295\,pH + 0.0295 \log \frac{(H_2TeO_4)}{(HTeO_3^-)}$

20. $HTeO_3^- + H_2O = HTeO_4^- + 2H^+ + 2e^-$ $\quad E_0 = 0.813 - 0.0591\,pH + 0.0295 \log \frac{(HTeO_4^-)}{(HTeO_3^-)}$

21. $TeO_3^{--} + H_2O = HTeO_4^- + H^+ + 2e^-$ $\quad E_0 = 0.584 - 0.0295\,pH + 0.0295 \log \frac{(HTeO_4^-)}{(TeO_3^{--})}$

22. $TeO_3^{--} + H_2O = TeO_4^{--} + 2H^+ + 2e^-$ $\quad E_0 = 0.892 - 0.0591\,pH + 0.0295 \log \frac{(TeO_4^{--})}{(TeO_3^{--})}$

2.1.2. *Limits of the domains of relative predominance of the dissolved substances*

1'. $H_2Te\ /HTe^-$ $\quad pH = 2.64$
2'. $HTe^-\ /Te^{--}$ $\quad pH = 11.00$
3'. $Te^{++++}/HTeO_2^+$ $\quad pH = -0.37$
4'. $HTeO_2^+\ /HTeO_3^-$ $\quad pH = 5.45$
5'. $HTeO_3^-\ /TeO_3^{--}$ $\quad pH = 7.74$
6'. $H_2TeO_4/HTeO_4^-$ $\quad pH = 6.17$
7'. $HTeO_4^-\ /TeO_4^{--}$ $\quad pH = 10.38$

8'. $H_2Te\ /Te_2^{--}$ $\quad E_0 = -0.638 - 0.1182\,pH - 0.0295 \log C$
9'. $HTe^-\ /Te_2^{--}$ $\quad E_0 = -0.795 - 0.0591\,pH - 0.0295 \log C$
10'. $Te^{--}\ /Te_2^{--}$ $\quad E_0 = -1.445 - 0.0295 \log C$
11'. $H_2Te\ /Te^{++++}$ $\quad E_0 = 0.132 - 0.0197\,pH$
12'. $H_2Te\ /HTeO_2^+$ $\quad E_0 = 0.121 - 0.0492\,pH$
13'. $Te_2^{--}\ /Te^{++++}$ $\quad E_0 = 0.286 + 0.0059 \log C$
14'. $Te_2^{--}\ /HTeO_2^+$ $\quad E_0 = 0.273 - 0.0354\,pH + 0.0059 \log C$
15'. $Te_2^{--}\ /HTeO_3^-$ $\quad E_0 = 0.402 - 0.0591\,pH + 0.0059 \log C$
16'. $Te_2^{--}\ /TeO_3^{--}$ $\quad E_0 = 0.493 - 0.0709\,pH + 0.0059 \log C$
17'. Te^{++++}/H_2TeO_4 $\quad E_0 = 0.920 - 0.1773\,pH$
18'. $HTeO_2^+\ /H_2TeO_4$ $\quad E_0 = 0.953 - 0.0886\,pH$
19'. $HTeO_3^-\ /H_2TeO_4$ $\quad E_0 = 0.631 - 0.0295\,pH$
20'. $HTeO_3^-\ /HTeO_4^-$ $\quad E_0 = 0.813 - 0.0591\,pH$
21'. $TeO_3^{--}\ /HTeO_4^-$ $\quad E_0 = 0.584 - 0.0295\,pH$
22'. $TeO_3^{--}\ /TeO_4^{--}$ $\quad E_0 = 0.892 - 0.0591\,pH$

These formulae lead to the following potential values when the two tellurium concentrations are equal, for total tellurium concentrations of respectively 1, 10^{-2}, 10^{-4} and 10^{-6} g-at/l (for the hypothetical case of ideal solutions).

			Tellurium concentration			
		g-at/l	1.	10^{-2}.	10^{-4}.	10^{-6}.
		mg/l	127 600.	1 276.	12.76.	0.13.
8'.	$H_2Te\ /Te_2^{--}$	$E_0 =$	-0.638	-0.579	-0.520	-0.461
9'.	HTe^-/Te_2^{--}	$E_0 =$	-0.795	-0.736	-0.677	-0.618
10'.	Te^{--}/Te_2^{--}	$E_0 =$	-1.445	-1.386	-1.327	-1.268
13'.	$Te_2^{--}\ /Te^{++++}$	$E_0 =$	0.286	0.274	0.262	0.250
14'.	$Te_2^{--}\ /HTeO_2^+$	$E_0 =$	0.273	0.261	0.249	0.237
15'.	$Te_2^{--}\ /HTeO_3^-$	$E_0 =$	0.402	0.390	0.378	0.366
16'.	$Te_2^{--}\ /TeO_3^{--}$	$E_0 =$	0.493	0.481	0.469	0.457

The limits of the domains of relative predominance of tellurium existing in two forms dissolved in solutions saturated with elementary tellurium are given by eliminating the term C between the two relations involving on the one hand elementary tellurium, and on the other hand respectively each of the two dissolved forms [relations (32′) to (37′)]. The following relations are thus obtained:

8″ (32′ and 33′).	H_2Te/Te_2^{--}	in the presence of	Te : $pH = 1.56$
14″ (33′ and 35′).	$Te_2^{--}/HTeO_2^+$	»	Te : $E_0 = 0.090 - 0.0295\ pH$
15″ (33′ and 36′).	$Te_2^{--}/HTeO_3^-$	»	Te : $E_0 = 0.197 - 0.0491\ pH$
16″ (33′ and 37′).	Te_2^{--}/TeO_3^{--}	»	Te : $E_0 = 0.274 - 0.0591\ pH$

These relations will be used in establishing the equilibrium diagram for the tellurium–water system.

2.2. TWO SOLID SUBSTANCES[3]

Relative stability of tellurium and its oxides

$0 \rightarrow +4$

23. $Te + 2H_2O = TeO_2 + 4H^+ + 4e^-$ a. $E_0 = 0.521 - 0.0591\ pH$
b. $= 0.604 - 0.0591\ pH$

$+4 \rightarrow +6$

24. $TeO_2 + H_2O = TeO_3 + 2H^+ + 2e^-$ a. $E_0 = 1.020 - 0.0591\ pH$
b. $= 0.850 - 0.0591\ pH$

2.3. ONE SOLID SUBSTANCE AND ONE DISSOLVED SUBSTANCE[3]

Solubility of the solid substances

a. Solubility in gram-ions or gram-molecules per litre

$Z = +4$

25. $Te^{++++} + 2H_2O = TeO_2 + 4H^+$ a. $\log(Te^{++++}) = -3.16 - 4\ pH$
b. $= 2.44 - 4\ pH$

26. $HTeO_2^+ = TeO_2 + H^+$ a. $\log(HTeO_2^+) = -2.07 - pH$
b. $= 3.55 - pH$

27. $TeO_2 + H_2O = HTeO_3^- + H^+$ a. $\log(HTeO_3^-) = -12.96 + pH$
b. $= -7.34 + pH$

28. $TeO_2 + H_2O = TeO_3^{--} + 2H^+$ a. $\log(TeO_3^{--}) = -20.71 + 2\ pH$
b. $= -15.09 + 2\ pH$

$Z = +6$

29. $TeO_3 + H_2O = H_2TeO_4$ $\log(H_2TeO_4) = 0.00$
30. $TeO_3 + H_2O = HTeO_4^- + H^+$ $\log(HTeO_4^-) = -6.17 + pH$
31. $TeO_3 + H_2O = TeO_4^{--} + 2H^+$ $\log(TeO_4^{--}) = -16.55 + 2\ pH$

$-2 \rightarrow 0$

32. $H_2Te = Te + 2H^+ + 2e^-$ $E_0 = -0.739 - 0.0591\ pH - 0.0295 \log(H_2Te)$

$-1 \rightarrow 0$

33. $Te_2^{--} = 2Te + 2e^-$ $E_0 = -0.840 - 0.0295 \log(Te_2^{--})$

$0 \rightarrow +4$

34. $Te = Te^{++++} + 4e^-$ $E_0 = 0.568 + 0.0148 \log(Te^{++++})$
35. $Te + 2H_2O = HTeO_2^+ + 3H^+ + 4e^-$ $E_0 = 0.551 - 0.0443\ pH + 0.0148 \log(HTeO_2^+)$
36. $Te + 3H_2O = HTeO_3^- + 5H^+ + 4e^-$ $E_0 = 0.713 - 0.0737\ pH + 0.0148 \log(HTeO_3^-)$
37. $Te + 3H_2O = TeO_3^{--} + 6H^+ + 4e^-$ $E_0 = 0.827 - 0.0886\ pH + 0.0148 \log(TeO_3^{--})$

---

(3) For the reactions involving TeO_2, the letter *a* refers to anhydrous TeO_2, whose free enthalpy of formation is −65 320 cal.; the letter *b* refers to hydrated TeO_2, whose free enthalpy of formation is −114 *360* cal.

$+4 \rightarrow +6$

38. $\mathbf{TeO_2} + 2H_2O = H_2TeO_4 + 2H^+ + 2e^-$
 a. $E_0 = 1.020 - 0.0591\,pH + 0.0295 \log (H_2TeO_4)$
 b. $ = 0.854 - 0.0591\,pH + 0.0295 \log (H_2TeO_4)$

39. $\mathbf{TeO_2} + 2H_2O = HTeO_4^- + 3H^+ + 2e^-$
 a. $E_0 = 1.202 - 0.0886\,pH + 0.0295 \log (HTeO_4^-)$
 b. $ = 1.036 - 0.0886\,pH + 0.0295 \log (HTeO_4^-)$

40. $\mathbf{TeO_2} + 2H_2O = TeO_4^{--} + 4H^+ + 2e^-$
 a. $E_0 = 1.509 - 0.1182\,pH + 0.0295 \log (TeO_4^{--})$
 b. $ = 1.343 - 0.1182\,pH + 0.0295 \log (TeO_4^{--})$

b. Solubility in gram-atoms of tellurium per litre

25′. $Te^{++++}/\mathbf{TeO_2}$
 a. $\log C = -3.16 - 4\,pH$
 b. $ = 2.44 - 4\,pH$

26′. $HTeO_2^+/\mathbf{TeO_2}$
 a. $\log C = -2.07 - pH$
 b. $ = 3.55 - pH$

27′. $\mathbf{TeO_2}/HTeO_3^-$
 a. $\log C = -12.96 + pH$
 b. $ = -7.34 + pH$

28′. $\mathbf{TeO_2}/TeO_3^{--}$
 a. $\log C = -20.71 + 2\,pH$
 b. $ = -15.09 + 2\,pH$

29′. $\mathbf{TeO_3}/H_2TeO_4$ $\log C = 0.00$

30′. $\mathbf{TeO_3}/HTeO_4^-$ $\log C = -6.17 + pH$

31′. $\mathbf{TeO_3}/TeO_4^{--}$ $\log C = -16.55 + 2\,pH$

32′. $H_2Te/\mathbf{Te}$ $E_0 = -0.739 - 0.0591\,pH - 0.0295 \log C$

33′. $Te_2^{--}/\mathbf{Te}$ $E_0 = -0.891 - 0.0295 \log C$

34′. $\mathbf{Te}/Te^{++++}$ $E_0 = 0.568 + 0.0148 \log C$

35′. $\mathbf{Te}/HTeO_2^+$ $E_0 = 0.551 - 0.0443\,pH + 0.0148 \log C$

36′. $\mathbf{Te}/HTeO_3^-$ $E_0 = 0.713 - 0.0737\,pH + 0.0148 \log C$

37′. $\mathbf{Te}/TeO_3^{--}$ $E_0 = 0.827 - 0.0886\,pH + 0.0148 \log C$

38′. $\mathbf{TeO_2}/H_2TeO_4$
 a. $E_0 = 1.020 - 0.0591\,pH + 0.0295 \log C$
 b. $ = 0.854 - 0.0591\,pH + 0.0295 \log C$

39′. $\mathbf{TeO_2}/HTeO_4^-$
 a. $E_0 = 1.202 - 0.0886\,pH + 0.0295 \log C$
 b. $ = 1.036 - 0.0886\,pH + 0.0295 \log C$

40′. $\mathbf{TeO_2}/TeO_4^{--}$
 a. $E_0 = 1.509 - 0.1182\,pH + 0.0295 \log C$
 b. $ = 1.343 - 0.1182\,pH + 0.0295 \log C$

2.4. ONE GASEOUS SUBSTANCE AND ONE DISSOLVED SUBSTANCE

Solubility of gaseous hydrogen telluride

a. Solubility in gram-ions or gram-molecules per litre

$Z = -2$

41. $H_2Te = H_2Te$ $\log \frac{p_{H_2Te}}{(H_2Te)} = 0.73$

42. $H_2Te = HTe^- + H^+$ $\log \frac{p_{H_2Te}}{(HTe^-)} = 3.37 - pH$

43. $H_2Te = Te^{--} + 2H^+$ $\log \frac{p_{H_2Te}}{(Te^{--})} = 14.38 - 2\,pH$

$-2 \rightarrow -1$

44. $2H_2Te = Te_2^{--} + 4H^+ + 2e^-$ $E_0 = -0.595 - 0.1182\,pH - 0.0295 \log \frac{p^2_{H_2Te}}{(Te_2^{--})}$

b. Solubility in gram-atoms of tellurium per litre

41′. H_2Te/H_2Te $\log p_{H_2Te} = 0.73 + \log C$

42′. H_2Te/HTe^- $\log p_{H_2Te} = 3.37 - pH + \log C$

43′. H_2Te/Te^{--} $\log p_{H_2Te} = 14.38 - 2\,pH + \log C$

44′. H_2Te/Te_2^{--} $E_0 = -0.604 - 0.1182\,pH - 0.0591 \log p_{H_2Te} + 0.0295 \log C$

2.5. ONE GASEOUS SUBSTANCE AND ONE SOLID SUBSTANCE

Relative stability of tellurium and gaseous tellurium hydride

$-2 \rightarrow 0$

45. $H_2Te = \mathbf{Te} + 2H^+ + 2e^-$ $E_0 = -0.717 - 0.0591\ pH - 0.0295 \log p_{H_2Te}$

3. EQUILIBRIUM DIAGRAMS AND THEIR INTERPRETATION

3.1. ESTABLISHMENT OF THE DIAGRAMS

Figure 1 represents, according to equations (1′)–(22′) and for various total dissolved tellurium concentrations, the domains of relative predominance of tellurium present in solution in each of the 11 dissolved forms which we have considered.

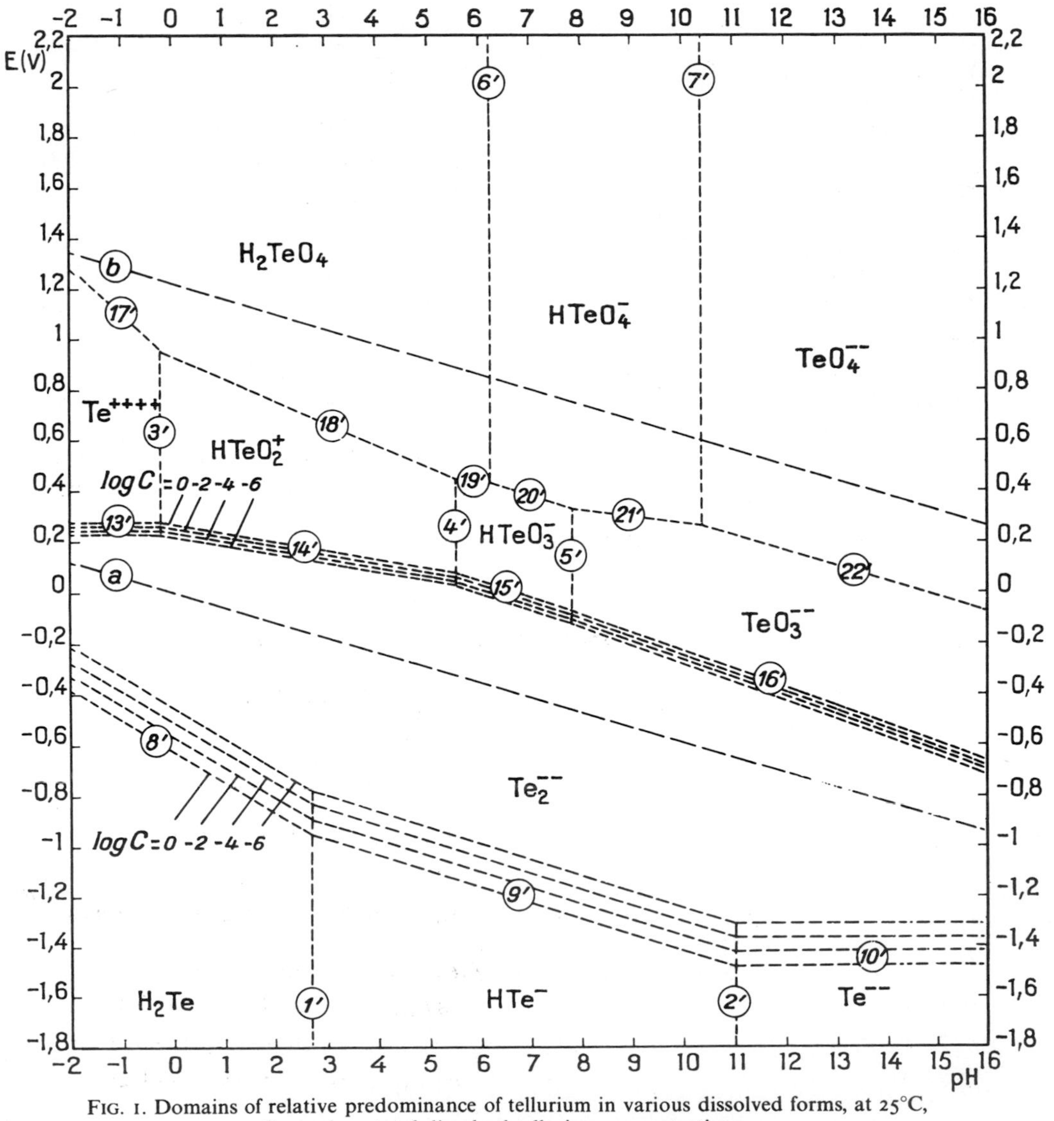

FIG. 1. Domains of relative predominance of tellurium in various dissolved forms, at 25°C, for various total dissolved tellurium concentrations.

Using relations (1)–(45) we have constructed Fig. 2, which is an electrochemical equilibrium diagram for the system tellurium–water. The form of TeO_2 considered in this diagram is the anhydrous one, which is more stable than the hydrated form $TeO_2.H_2O$.

Using equations (25')–(28') we have constructed Fig. 3, which represents the influence of pH on the solubility of TeO_2 at 25°C.

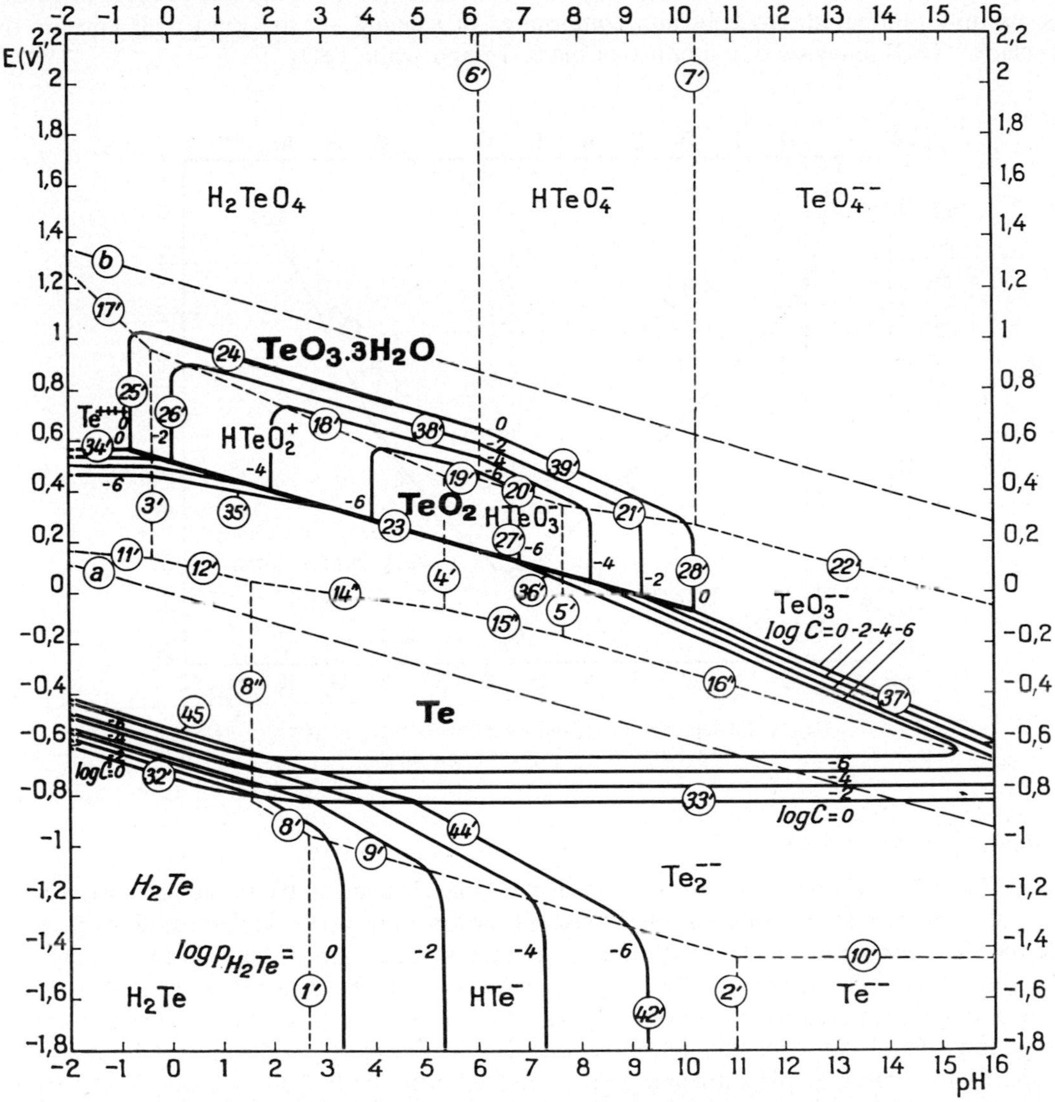

FIG. 2. Potential–pH equilibrium diagram for the system tellurium–water, at 25°C.
The portion of this diagram lying outside the line log C = 0 concerns unsaturated solutions containing 1 g-at Te/l; the portion inside this line concerns solutions which are saturated with Te or TeO_2.

In accordance with the convention which we have adopted throughout the *Atlas* for elements comprising dissolved polyatomic substances (e.g. Te_2^{--}), the portion of the figure outside the line for which log C = 0 refers to unsaturated solutions containing 1 g-at of dissolved tellurium per litre (i.e. 127 g Te/l) ([4]); the portion of the figure inside this line refers to solutions which are saturated with Te or TeO_2.

([4]) It will be recalled that this applies to "ideal" solutions.

Figure 2 is valid only in the absence of substances with which tellurium can form complexes or insoluble salts. In this connection we point out that chlorides complex hexavalent tellurium with the formation of $TeCl_6^{--}$ ions, and that the tellurides, tellurites and tellurates of metals other than the alkali metals are generally insoluble. Figures 1 and 2 represent the important valencies of tellurium, namely -2, $+4$ and $+6$, as is the case for the neighbouring elements of the same group of the periodic table (sulphur and selenium); from this point of view the equilibrium diagrams of these three elements may be usefully compared. No tellurium compounds of valency $+2$ are known; it appears that the brown–black "TeO" consists of a mixture of black Te and white TeO_2.

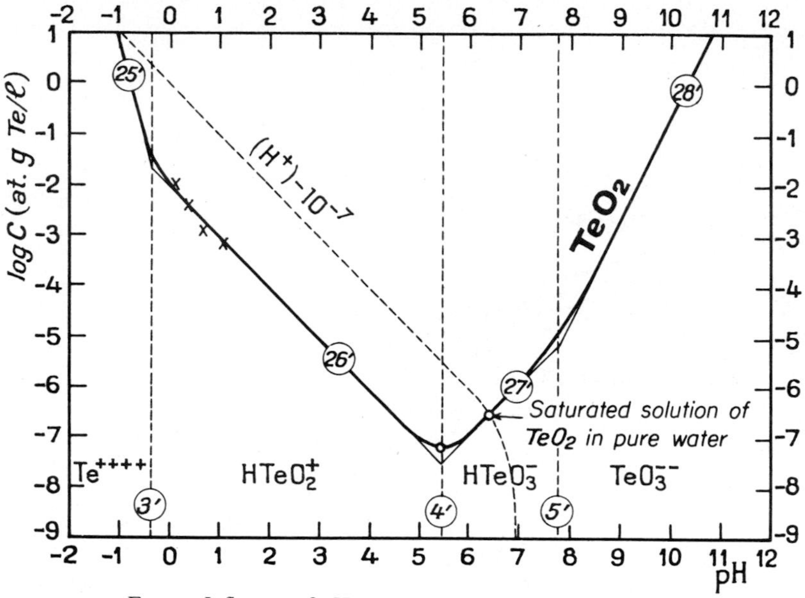

FIG. 3. Influence of pH on the solubility of TeO_2, at 25°C.
× Kasarnowsky's experimental values.

3.2. STABILITY OF TELLURIUM

From Fig. 2, tellurium appears to be a relatively noble element, stable in the presence of water and aqueous solutions free from oxidizing agents, except, however, in very alkaline solutions in which it is possible for the element to dissolve with the simultaneous formation of tellurite ions TeO_3^{--} and ditelluride ions Te_2^{--}. According to this diagram tellurium can be reduced in acid solution to give dissolved and gaseous hydrogen telluride H_2Te, and it can be reduced in alkaline solution to give ditelluride ions Te_2^{--} and possibly telluride ions Te^{--}. It can be oxidized to tellurous anhydride TeO_2 (sparingly soluble at pH's around 4 to 7) and tellurite, or to telluric oxide $TeO_3.3H_2O$ (very soluble), telluric acid and tellurate.

In actual fact aqueous solutions free from oxidizing agents have no action on tellurium unless they are very alkaline, and tellurium can be reduced electrolytically in acid solution with the formation of gaseous hydrogen telluride.

In *aerated water* tellurium becomes covered with TeO_2 which is non-protective if the tellurium is freshly precipitated, but constitutes a protective film at its surface if it is in the compact state. *Oxidizing acids*, such as nitric acid and concentrated sulphuric acid, oxidize tellurium to TeO_2 and tellurous ions; hydrogen peroxide and the peroxides oxidize it further, to telluric acid or tellurates.

On *electrolytic oxidation* in alkaline solution tellurium passes into solution as tellurite ions TeO_3^{--}, and under certain conditions a dark and not very adherent deposit can be formed on the anode (Le Blanc [6], Reichinstein [7], Winterling [8], Gallo [9]) which, according to Fig. 2, may be TeO_2 or even TeO_3; it should be noted that TeO_2 is white, but becomes darker through the reducing action of organic substances (small traces of tellurium give it a distinct brown colour); TeO_3 is brown.

On electrolytic oxidation in acid solution, tellurium again passes into solution in the tetravalent state (probably as Te^{++++} or $HTeO_2^+$ ions) and the anode becomes covered with a spongy grey–black layer (TeO_2 or TeO_3?) (Gallo, Winterling).

In solutions of certain salts (CH_3COONa, KCl, K_2SO_4), a black adherent film is formed on the anode; the latter becomes passive and only a very small amount of tellurium passes into solution (Gallo, Winterling).

In a solution of caustic potash, the *electrolytic reduction* of tellurium produces a red solution of polytelluride Te_2^{--} and elementary tellurium in the form of grey dust (Le Blanc [6]); the formation of tellurium dust in this way may result either from the decomposition of the ditelluride with the evolution of hydrogen, according to the reactions:

$$Te_2^{--} \rightarrow 2\,Te + 2\,e^- \qquad (33)$$

and

$$2\,H^+ + 2\,e^- \rightarrow H_2 \qquad (a)$$

overall reaction

$$Te_2^{--} + 2\,H^+ \rightarrow 2\,Te + H_2$$

or, according to Le Blanc, from the disproportionation of the ditelluride according to the reactions:

$$Te_2^{--} \rightarrow 2\,Te + 2\,e^- \qquad (33)$$

and

$$Te_2^{--} + 2\,e^- \rightarrow 2\,Te^{--} \qquad (10)$$

overall reaction

$$2\,Te_2^{--} \rightarrow 2\,Te + 2\,Te^{--}$$

in which case line (10') relating to the Te_2^{--}/Te^{--} equilibrium would be too low down in Fig. 2 and would have to be raised.

In acid solution, electrolytic reduction also gives a red solution of Te_2^{--} ions and tellurium dust; the hydrogen evolved at the cathode contains an appreciable quantity of gaseous hydrogen telluride (Müller and Lucas [10]).

3.3. STABILITY AND FORMATION OF HYDROGEN TELLURIDE, THE TELLURIDES AND THE DITELLURIDES

Hydrogen telluride and its dissolution products (tellurhydric acid H_2Te and the tellurides HTe^- and Te^{--}) occupy the lower part of the equilibrium diagram (Fig. 2). These substances therefore appear to be reducing compounds.

In agreement with this figure, these substances can easily be oxidized, with the separation of tellurium and, in alkaline solution, with the formation of red ditelluride Te_2^{--}. Solutions of H_2Te are in fact very unstable in the air, the H_2Te decomposing immediately with the separation of tellurium (Ernyei [11], Bruner [12]); alkaline solutions of sodium or potassium telluride are coloured red by the action of a trace of oxygen, and larger quantities of oxygen cause powdery black tellurium to separate out (Berthelot and Fabre [13], Tschugaeff and Chlopine [14], Bredig and Haber [15]).

Examples of reductions by tellurides are: the reduction of ferric chloride to ferrous chloride, the reduction of $HgCl_2$ to HgCl and the decolorization of bromine and iodine solutions.

Conversely, hydrogen telluride and tellurides will be obtained by reducing tellurium in acid solution (according to Ernyei, gaseous H_2Te is obtained by the electrolysis of 50 per cent H_2SO_4 with a tellurium cathode at $-20°C$) or by reducing ditellurides in neutral or alkaline solutions.

The red ditelluride ion Te_2^{--}, in which tellurium has a valency of -1, corresponds to the S_2^{--} ion of the disulphides; it is obtained in an analogous manner, by the reduction of elementary tellurium with telluride solutions. The position of its stability domain characterizes it as a reducing compound which can be oxidized to tellurium and reduced to telluride; these two possibilities actually occur in the disproportionation reaction $Te_2^{--} = Te + Te^{--}$ which is the reverse of the reaction by which ditellurides are formed; polytelluride solutions are, in fact, unstable, and when one tries, for example, to isolate sodium polytelluride by evaporating its solutions, decomposition to telluride and metallic tellurium takes place (Tibbals [16]).

3.4. STABILITY AND FORMATION OF TELLUROUS ANHYDRIDE AND THE TELLURITES

The position of the domain of relative stability of tellurous anhydride TeO_2 in the equilibrium diagram shows it to be very stable in water; it can be reduced to tellurium, oxidized to telluric anhydride TeO_3 or its dissolved forms, and appears to be an amphoteric oxide since it dissolves in acid solutions as $HTeO_2^+$ and Te^{++++} ions, and in neutral and alkaline solutions as $HTeO_3^-$ and TeO_3^{--} ions. Figure 3 shows the solubility curve of TeO_2 as given by relations (25')–(28'); it also gives the four values experimentally determined by Kasarnowsky [3] in hydrochloric acid solutions of various concentrations.

These experimental values lie exactly on the curve. The three values determined by Schumann [2] in perchloric acid $HClO_4$ also lie on the curve, necessarily so, since it is from these values that we calculated the free enthalpy of $HTeO_2^+$.

According to Fig. 3, TeO_2 will have a minimum solubility of $10^{-7.2}$ g-mole/l at pH = 5·45. The characteristics of the solution obtained by dissolving TeO_2 in pure water until it is saturated will be given by the coordinates of the point of intersection of the line giving the value of $[(H^+) - 10^{-7}]$ with the line showing the solubility of TeO_2; these characteristics are:

$$pH = 6{\cdot}4, \qquad (TeO_2) = 10^{-6{\cdot}55}, \qquad \text{i.e. } 0{\cdot}04 \text{ mg } TeO_2/l.$$

It is generally recognized that TeO_2 is very sparingly soluble in water; however, no precise experimental data exist in this connection; Pascal [17] and Gmelin [18] give a solubility value of around 1/150 000 due to Klein and Morel [19]; this represents a concentration of 6·6 mg TeO_2/l ($10^{-4{\cdot}38}$ mole/l); however, this very old (1884) value is only very approximate.

Tellurous anhydride is essentially the product of the direct oxidation of tellurium by oxygen. It can also be obtained by the oxidation of tellurium with dilute nitric acid.

On reduction tellurous anhydride gives tellurium. In this respect we should mention the electrolytic deposits obtained by Müller [20] by the electrolysis of a solution of 1·1 g/l of $TeO_2.H_2O$ in 1 M sulphuric acid, using a platinum cathode covered with tellurium at a potential of −0·170 V. Joliot [21] obtained a deposit of tellurium by the electrolysis of a solution which was 10^{-3} N with respect to Te^{++++} and 0·2 N with respect to HNO_3, using a gold cathode at a potential of 0·140 V.

The tellurites are oxidized to tellurates in the presence of air or permanganate. Tellurous anhydride is oxidized to tellurate by the action of hydrogen peroxide in alkaline solution. Hydrogen peroxide, chromic acid and chlorine oxidize TeO_2 to telluric acid.

3.5. STABILITY AND FORMATION OF TELLURIC ANHYDRIDE, TELLURIC ACID AND THE TELLURATES

The product of the dry oxidation of tellurous anhydride is telluric anhydride TeO_3, for which we have not been able to establish a definite stability domain in the equilibrium diagram through lack of thermodynamic data concerning it. It is a solid orange–yellow substance which is not hygroscopic and is insoluble in water and the common acids; it is converted into tellurates by boiling concentrated alkalis.

When the tellurides, tellurium or TeO_2 are oxidized with hydrogen peroxide, chromic acid in nitric solution, or chlorine, telluric acid or tellurates are obtained, in agreement with Fig. 2. Telluric acid solutions give on evaporation cubic or clinorhombic crystals of the trihydrate $TeO_3.3H_2O$ or orthotelluric acid H_6TeO_6, which is very soluble in water (about 1 to 2 g-mole/l).

The stability domains of telluric acid and its ions coincide to a certain extent with that of water; they are therefore stable in the presence of water and reducible to compounds of lower valency. As examples of reduction reactions we point out the reduction of telluric acid by hydrosulphite, hydrazine, the sugars and hydrobromic acid. The tellurates can be reduced with difficulty to tellurites.

4. BIBLIOGRAPHY

[1] E. DELTOMBE, N. DE ZOUBOV and M. POURBAIX, *Comportement électrochimique du tellure. Diagramme tension*–pH *du système* Te–H_2O *à* 25°C (Rapport technique RT.33 of CEBELCOR, April 1956).
[2] R. SCHUMANN, The free energy and heat content of tellurium dioxide and of amorphous and metallic tellurium. The reduction potential of tellurium, *J. Amer. Chem. Soc.* **47**, 356–63 (1925).
[3] J. KASARNOWSKY, Tellurige Säure als Base, *Z. Physik. Chem.* **109**, 287–301 (1924).
[4] F. H. GETMAN, A study of the tellurium electrode, *Trans. Amer. Electr. Soc.* **64**, 206–13 (1933).
[5] E. BLANC, Détermination de la constante de dissociation de quelques acides minéraux, *J. Chim. Phys.* **18**, 28–45 (1920).
[6] M. LE BLANC, Kann ein Element sowohl positive wie negative Ionen bilden? *Z. Elektrochem.* **11**, 813–18 (1905).
[7] D. REICHINSTEIN, Theorie der chemischen Affinität vom Standpunkte der polaren Aufspaltung und des Massenwirkungsgesetzes, *Z. Phys. Chem.* **97**, 257–303 (1921).
[8] A. WINTERLING, Dissert Munich T.H., 1915.
[9] G. GALLO, Équivalent électrochimique du tellure, *Gazz. Chim. Ital.* **35**, 245–77 (1905).
[10] E. MÜLLER and R. LUCAS, Ueber die Kathodische verstäubung von Tellur, *Z. Elektrochem.* **11**, 521–5 (1905).
[11] E. ERNYEI, Ueber den Tellurwasserstoff, *Z. anorg. allgem. Chem.* **25**, 313–17 (1900).
[12] L. BRUNER, Ueber Selen- und Tellurwasserstoff als Säuren, *Z. Elektrochem.* **19**, 861 (1913).
[13] M. BERTHELOT and CH. FABRE, Chaleur de formation de l'acide tellurhydrique, *C. R. Acad. Sc.* **105**, 92–5 (1887).
[14] L. TSCHUGAEFF and W. CHLOPINE, Beiträge zur Kenntnis des Reduktionsvermögens der schwefligen Säure. I. Einwirkung von Natriumhydrosulfit auf Tellur und Selen, *Ber.* **47**, 1269–75 (1914).
[15] G. BREDIG and F. HABER, Ueber Zerstäubung von Metallkathoden bei der Elektrolyse mit Gleichstrom, *Ber.* **31**, 2741–52 (1898).
[16] C. A. TIBBALS, A study in tellurides, *J. Amer. Chem. Soc.* **31**, 902–13 (1909).
[17] P. PASCAL, *Traité de Chimie minérale*, Vol. II, Masson, Paris, 1932.
[18] *Gmelins Handbuch der anorganischen Chemie, Tellur*, S.N.11, 1940, Verlag Chemie, G.m.b.H., Berlin.
[19] D. KLEIN and J. MOREL, Sur les produits obtenus dans l'attaque du tellure par l'acide nitrique, *C. R. Acad. Sc.* **99**, 540–42 (1884).
[20] E. MÜLLER, Die Kathodische Abscheidung von Tellur und Selen aus ihren Sauerstoffsäuren und ihre elektroanalytische Bestimmung, *Z. Phys. Chem.* **100**, 346–66 (1922).
[21] F. JOLIOT, Sur une nouvelle méthode d'étude du comportement électrochimique des corps en solution très diluée, *C. R. Acad. Sc.* **188**, 1106–8 (1929).

SECTION 19.5

POLONIUM [1]

J. VAN MUYLDER

SUMMARY

---

[1] Extract from the Rapport CEFA/R.15 of the Commission des Études Fondamentales et Applications of CEBELCOR.

1. SUBSTANCES CONSIDERED AND SUBSTANCE NOT CONSIDERED

	Oxidation number (Z)	Considered	Not considered	μ^0(cal.)	Name, colour, crystalline system
Solid substances	0	**Po**		0	Polonium, monocl.
	+ 4	**PoO_2** anh.	-	— *46 600*	Polonium oxide, cub. or quad.
	»	-	**PoO_2** hydr.	-	Polonium hydroxide $PoO(OH)_2$ or H_2PoO_3
	+ 6	**PoO_3**	-	— *33 000*	Polonium peroxide
Dissolved substances	+ 2	Po^{++}	-	*30 000*	Polonous ion
	+ 4	PoO_3^{--}	-	—*101 000*	Polonate ion
Gaseous substance	— 2	*PoH_2*	-	> *46 000*	Polonium hydride, colourless

2. REACTIONS AND EQUILIBRIUM FORMULAE

2.1. TWO DISSOLVED SUBSTANCES

2.1.1. *Relative stability of the dissolved substances*

$+2 \rightarrow +4$

1. $Po^{++} + 3H_2O = PoO_3^{--} + 6H^+ + 2e^-$ $\quad E_0 = 0.847 - 0.1773\,pH + 0.0295 \log \frac{(PoO_3^{--})}{(Po^{++})}$

2.1.2. *Limit of the domains of relative predominance of the dissolved substances*

1'. Po^{++}/PoO_3^{--} $\quad E_0 = 0.847 - 0.1773\,pH$

2.2. TWO SOLID SUBSTANCES

Limits of the domains of relative stability of the solid substances

$0 \rightarrow +4$

2. **Po** $+ 2H_2O =$ **PoO_2** $+ 4H^+ + 4e^-$ $\quad E_0 = 0.724 - 0.0591\,pH$

$+4 \rightarrow +6$

3. **PoO_2** $+ H_2O =$ **PoO_3** $+ 2H^+ + 2e^-$ $\quad E_0 = 1.524 - 0.0591\,pH$

2.3. ONE DISSOLVED SUBSTANCE AND ONE SOLID SUBSTANCE

Solubility of the solid substances

$Z = +4$

4. **PoO_2** $+ H_2O = PoO_3^{--} + 2H^+$ $\quad \log(PoO_3^{--}) = -1.68 + 2\,pH$

$0 \rightarrow +2$

5. **Po** $= Po^{++} + 2e^-$ $\quad E_0 = 0.651 + 0.0295 \log(Po^{++})$

$0 \rightarrow +4$

6. **Po** $+ 3H_2O = PoO_3^{--} + 6H^+ + 4e^-$ $\quad E_0 = 0.748 - 0.0886\,pH + 0.0148 \log(PoO_3^{--})$

$+2 \rightarrow +4$

7. $Po^{++} + 2H_2O =$ **PoO_2** $+ 4H^+ + 2e^-$ $\quad E_0 = 0.798 - 0.1182\,pH - 0.0295 \log(Po^{++})$

$+2 \rightarrow +6$

8. $Po^{++} + 3H_2O =$ **PoO_3** $+ 6H^+ + 4e^-$ $\quad E_0 = 1.161 - 0.0886\,pH - 0.0148 \log(Po^{++})$

$+4 \rightarrow +6$

9. $PoO_3^{--} =$ **PoO_3** $+ 2e^-$ $\quad E_0 = 1.474 - 0.0295 \log(PoO_3^{--})$

2.4. ONE GASEOUS SUBSTANCE AND ONE SOLID SUBSTANCE

Limits of the domains of relative stability of **Po** *and* PoH_2

$-2 \rightarrow 0$

10. $PoH_2 = \mathbf{Po} + 2H^+ + 2e^-$ $\qquad E_0 = -1.000 - 0.0591\,pH - 0.0295 \log p_{PoH_2}$

3. EQUILIBRIUM DIAGRAM AND ITS INTERPRETATION

3.1. ESTABLISHMENT OF THE DIAGRAM

Using the formulae given in paragraph 2 we have constructed Fig. 1, which is the equilibrium diagram for the system polonium–water at 25°C.

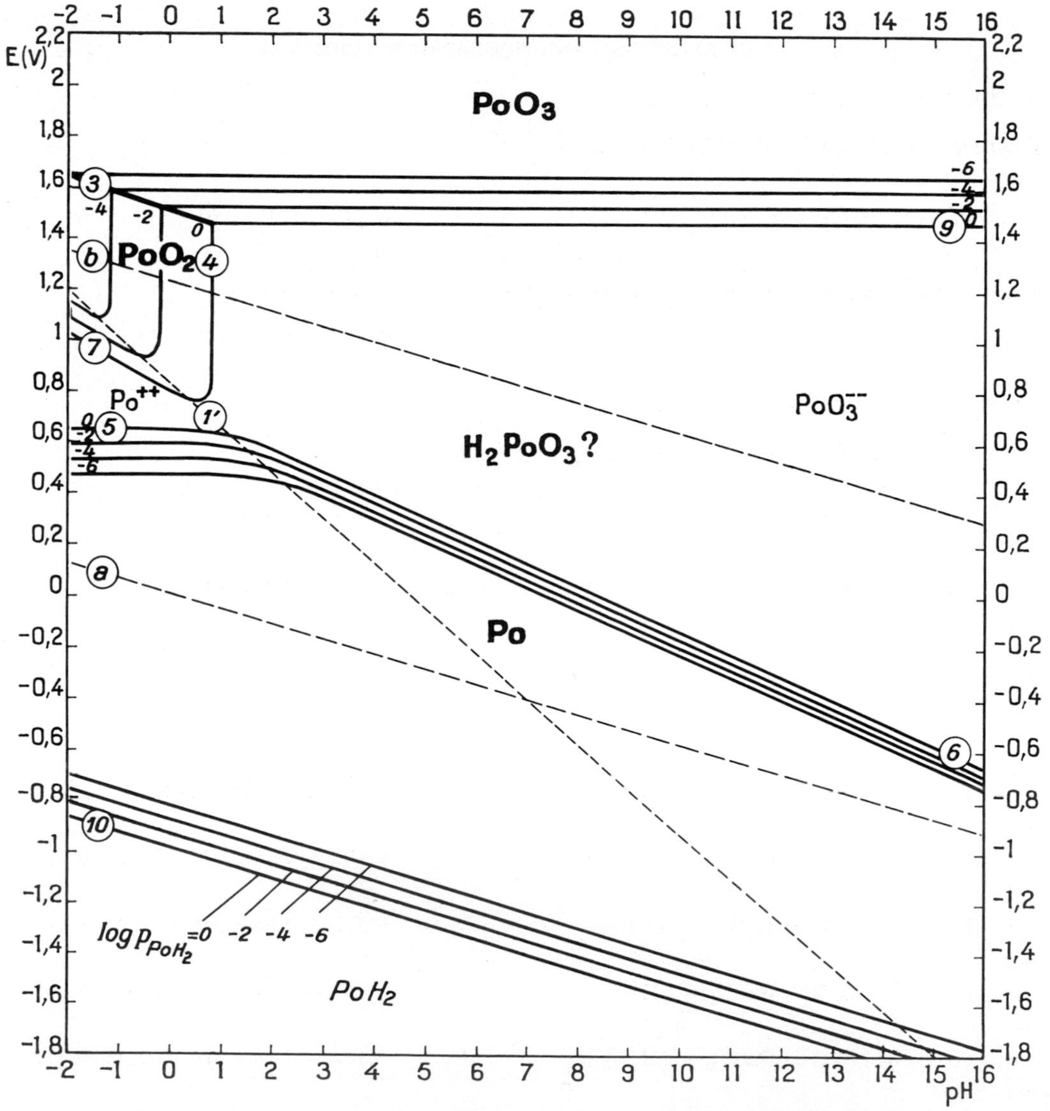

FIG. 1. Potential–pH equilibrium diagram for the system polonium–water, at 25°C.

This diagram is valid only in the absence of substances with which polonium can form soluble complexes or insoluble compounds. A nitric complex $Po(NO_3)_6^{--}$, an oxalic complex $Po(C_2O_4)_3^{--}$, and a hydrochloric complex $PoCl_6^{--}$ are known to exist.

As pure polonium has not yet been obtained in a weighable quantity, knowledge of its chemistry is still very incomplete. It is generally employed as a thin layer fixed on a metal support (Pt, Au, Ag, Ni, etc.), and there is often difficulty in distinguishing between the reactions of the polonium and those of the metal support. Moreover, as the values of the free enthalpy of formation of three of the six substances considered in the system are very uncertain, it must be realized that the diagram is only a very approximate representation of the real equilibria.

3.2. STABILITY OF POLONIUM

According to Fig. 1, polonium is a fairly noble element, as part of its stability domain lies above line (*a*). Consequently, it is theoretically stable in the presence of air or aqueous solutions of all pH's free from oxidizing agents. By oxidation, polonium can be converted into polonous ions Po^{++} or polonate ions PoO_3^{--}, depending on the pH of the solution; a sufficiently powerful oxidizing action can convert these ions respectively into the oxide PoO_2 and the peroxide PoO_3. In definitely acid or alkaline media, polonium solutions are stable; in neutral or very nearly neutral media, polonium appears to exist as polonium hydroxide H_2PoO_3 or $PoO(OH)_2$) (Guillot [1]), which we have indicated only approximately in Fig. 1 through lack of data for it. On reduction, polonium can form gaseous polonium hydride PoH_2.

The behaviour of polonium is not governed solely by thermodynamics, however; it depends also to a large extent on the radioactive properties of the element. It is considerably influenced in particular by the α-radiation, owing to the bombardment to which this radiation submits everything surrounding the element. Thus, by converting the oxygen of the air into ozone, it causes the polonium to be oxidized in the presence of media which ought not to oxidize it, taking into consideration the noble character of the element; such media are air, acid solutions (HCl, HNO_3, H_2SO_4, CH_3CO_2H, $C_2O_4H_2$) and caustic alkali solutions (KOH, NaOH) [2]. It is a question, of course, of a secondary action of the α-radiation, but this does not make it any less fundamental in its results.

3.3. STABILITY OF POLONIUM HYDRIDE

It can be seen from Fig. 1 that polonium can be reduced to polonium hydride PoH_2 at potentials below those indicated by the family of lines (10).

The reduction can be carried out chemically by treating polonium with hydrochloric acid in the presence of magnesium, or by reducing a polonium salt in acid solution with magnesium. As its stability domain is situated at very low potentials, polonium hydride appears to be an unstable substance which tends to decompose spontaneously into hydrogen and polonium; this is actually observed in practice.

3.4. STABILITY OF THE OXIDE AND PEROXIDE OF POLONIUM

3.4.1. *Polonium oxide PoO_2*

The position of its stability domain in Fig. 1 shows PoO_2 to be thermodynamically stable in the presence of aqueous solutions which are very acid and oxidizing. It can be oxidized to polonium peroxide PoO_3 and reduced to polonous ions Po^{++}; on increasing the pH, it appears that it passes into solution as polonate ions PoO_3^{--}.

3.4.2. *Polonium peroxide PoO_3*

As is shown by its position in Fig. 1, polonium peroxide is thermodynamically unstable, and is an oxidizing agent which must tend to decompose, with the evolution of oxygen, to give PoO_2 in very acid solutions and polonate ions PoO_3^{--} in other solutions.

4. BIBLIOGRAPHY

[1] M. GUILLOT, Sur les conditions de précipitation du polonium et sur quelques-uns de ses dérivés complexes, *J. Chim. Phys.* **28**, 30 (1931).
[2] *Gmelins Handbuch der anorganischen Chemie, Polonium*, S.N.13, Verlag Chemie, Berlin, 1941.

HALOGENS[1]

INTRODUCTION

The impossibility of representing all the known forms of a given non-metal on a single diagram, which has already been encountered in the case of sulphur, occurs again with the halogens. It arises from the metastability of a fair number of amphoteric oxides which ought to decompose under normal conditions if the true equilibrium were attained. Moreover, the presence of condensed ions such as HF_2^-, I_3^- and Br_3^- containing more than one atom of the halogen in question, or dissolved polyatomic molecules (dissolved Br_2, Cl_2, I_2), means that the limits of the domains of relative predominance of these ions or molecules vary with the total concentration of dissolved halogen. These domains vary not only in extent, but also in nature. For this reason we give more than one equilibrium diagram for each of the elements considered.

For *fluorine* two diagrams of stable equilibria are given, for solutions containing respectively 1 and 10^{-2} g-at F/l. For *chlorine* all the diagrams refer to a total chlorine concentration of 1 g-at/l; in addition to the diagram representing stable equilibria, three diagrams are given for metastable equilibria: these refer to the stability of the chlorates, the chlorites and the hypochlorites. For *bromine* and *iodine* we give only the diagrams representing stable equilibria, for concentrations of 1, 10^{-2}, 10^{-4} and 10^{-6} g-at Br or I/l. It would, of course, be possible to construct additional diagrams representing the metastable equilibria of the system iodine–water (relative stability of hypoiodous acid and the hypoiodites) and the system bromine–water (relative stability of hypobromous acid and the hypobromites); one could also construct equilibrium diagrams for the system chlorine–water for solutions containing 10^{-2}, 10^{-4} or 10^{-6} g-at Cl/l.

Not all the equilibria can be interpreted by means of the diagrams that we have constructed, mainly because the tendency of the anions (more particularly the simple anions) to form complexes either with heavy cations or with other anions or simple substances (in particular with those of the same family) is one of the dominant features of the chemistry of the halogens. The diagrams given can assign domains of relative predominance only to autocomplexes (polyhalides) or complexes due to the solvents (ions containing oxygen and acids). The interhalogen compounds will not therefore be dealt with here, despite the interest which they present.

In this connection we point out that fluorine differs considerably from the other halogens in its much greater tendency to form complexes; the sparingly soluble compounds may, moreover, be regarded as special cases of these complexes [1]. This tendency does not illustrate a normal periodic variation in properties, since the complexing tendency *increases* as one goes from chlorine to iodine [2].

With the exception of certain similarities between chlorine and bromine, the resemblance between the various halogens has been somewhat exaggerated, as is well illustrated by the diagrams given.

The fact that the halogen compounds have equivalent overall formulae (which is not universal, and would in any case be due only to the common degree of oxidation) does not mean that the structures of these compounds, and hence their properties, are the same. Thus the oxyacid of iodine at the valency

(1) Adapted version of the Rapport CEFA/R.12 of CEBELCOR.

considered to be 7 is H_5IO_6 and not HIO_4, and is a much more powerful oxidizing agent than $HBrO_4$ or $HClO_4$; it appears to belong to the peracid type (derived from hydrogen peroxide) rather than to the ordinary type of the two others [3].

BIBLIOGRAPHY

[1] G. CHARLOT and R. GAUGIN, *Les méthodes d'analyse des réactions en solution*, Masson, Paris, 1951, p. 299.
[2] G. URBAIN and A. SENECHAL, *Introduction à la chimie des complexes*, Hermann, Paris, 1913, p. 115.
[3] F. EPHRAIM, *Inorganic Chemistry*, 5th English translation, Gurney & Jackson, London, 1948, p. 392.

SECTION 20.1

FLUORINE (1)

C. VANLEUGENHAGHE, G. VALENSI and M. POURBAIX

SUMMARY

(1) Adapted version of an extract from Rapport CEFA/R.12 of the Commission des Études Fondamentales et Applications of CEBELCOR. Potential–pH equilibrium diagrams for the system iodine–water have been previously presented by Valensi *et al.*, in 1953 [1] as well as by Brown [2] and by Pourbaix [3] in 1955, at CITCE meetings.

1. SUBSTANCES CONSIDERED AND SUBSTANCES NOT CONSIDERED

	Oxidation number (Z)	Considered	Not considered	μ^0(cal.)	Name, colour, crystalline system
Dissolved substances	— 1	HF	–	— 70 410	Hydrofluoric acid, colourless
	»	HF_2^-	–	—137 400	Bifluoride ion, colourless
	»	F^-	–	— 66 080	Fluoride ion, colourless
	0	–	F_2	–	Dissolved fluorine
Gaseous substances	— 1	HF	–	— 64 700	Hydrofluoric acid, colourless
	0	F	–	28 190	Atomic fluorine
	»	F_2	–	0	Fluorine, greenish yellow
	+ 1	F_2O	–	9 700	Monoxide, colourless
	+ 2	–	F_2O_2	–	Dioxide, brown

2. REACTIONS AND EQUILIBRIUM FORMULAE

2.1. TWO DISSOLVED SUBSTANCES

2.1.1. *Relative stability of the dissolved substances*

Z = — 1

1. $2HF = HF_2^- + H^+$ $\qquad \log\frac{(HF_2^-)}{(HF)^2} = -2.51 + pH$

2. $HF_2^- = 2F^- + H^+$ $\qquad \log\frac{(F^-)^2}{(HF_2^-)} = -3.85 + pH$

3. $HF = F^- + H^+$ $\qquad \log\frac{(F^-)}{(HF)} = -3.18 + pH$

2.1.2. *Limits of the domains of relative predominance of the dissolved substances*

1'. HF/HF_2^- $\qquad pH = 2.51 - \log C$

2'. HF_2^-/F^- $\qquad pH = 3.85 + \log C$

3'. HF/F^- $\qquad pH = 3.18$

2.2. TWO GASEOUS SUBSTANCES

2.2.1. *Relative stability of the gaseous substances*

Z = 0

4. $2F = F_2$ $\qquad \log\frac{p_{F_2}}{p_F^2} = 4.14$

— 1 → 0

5. $2HF = F_2 + 2H^+ + 2e^-$ $\qquad E_0 = 2.806 - 0.0591\,pH + 0.0295\log\frac{p_{F_2}}{p_{HF}^2}$

— 1 → + 1

6. $2HF + H_2O = F_2O + 4H^+ + 4e^-$ $\qquad E_0 = 2.123 - 0.0591\,pH + 0.0148\log\frac{p_{F_2O}}{p_{HF}^2}$

0 → + 1

7. $F_2 + H_2O = F_2O + 2H^+ + 2e^-$ $\qquad E_0 = 1.439 - 0.0591\,pH + 0.0295\log\frac{p_{F_2O}}{p_{F_2}}$

2.2.2. *Limits of the domains of relative predominance of the gaseous fluorine compounds*

4'.	F/F_2	$\log P = -3.84$
5'.	HF/F_2	$E_0 = 2.814 - 0.0591\,pH - 0.0295 \log P$
6'.	HF/F_2O	$E_0 = 2.127 - 0.0591\,pH - 0.0148 \log P$
7'.	F_2/F_2O	$E_0 = 1.439 - 0.0591\,pH$
6''.	HF/F_2O and F^-	$E_0 = 2.137 - 0.0443\,pH - 0.0148 \log(F^-)$
6'''.	HF/F_2O and HF_2^-	$E_0 = 2.166 - 0.0516\,pH - 0.0074 \log(HF_2^-)$
6^{IV}.	HF/F_2O and HF	$E_0 = 2.184 - 0.0591\,pH - 0.0148 \log(HF)$

2.3. ONE GASEOUS SUBSTANCE AND ONE DISSOLVED SUBSTANCE

Solubility of the gaseous fluorine compounds

HF

$Z = -1$

8. $HF = HF$ $\qquad \log \frac{(HF)}{p_{HF}} = 4.19$

9. $2HF = HF_2^- + H^+$ $\qquad \log \frac{(HF_2^-)}{p^2_{HF}} = 5.87 + pH$

10. $HF = F^- + H^+$ $\qquad \log \frac{(F^-)}{p_{HF}} = 1.01 + pH$

F_2

$-1 \rightarrow 0$

11. $2HF = F_2 + 2H^+ + 2e^-$ $\qquad E_0 = 3.053 - 0.0591\,pH + 0.0295 \log \frac{p_{F_2}}{(HF)^2}$

12. $HF_2^- = F_2 + H^+ + 2e^-$ $\qquad E_0 = 2.979 - 0.0295\,pH + 0.0295 \log \frac{p_{F_2}}{(HF_2^-)}$

13. $2F^- = F_2 + 2e^-$ $\qquad E_0 = 2.866 + 0.0295 \log \frac{p_{F_2}}{(F^-)^2}$

F_2O

$-1 \rightarrow +1$

14. $2HF + H_2O = F_2O + 4H^+ + 4e^-$ $\qquad E_0 = 2.246 - 0.0591\,pH + 0.0148 \log \frac{p_{F_2O}}{(HF)^2}$

15. $HF_2^- + H_2O = F_2O + 3H^+ + 4e^-$ $\qquad E_0 = 2.209 - 0.0443\,pH + 0.0148 \log \frac{p_{F_2O}}{(HF_2^-)}$

16. $2F^- + H_2O = F_2O + 2H^+ + 4e^-$ $\qquad E_0 = 2.153 - 0.0295\,pH + 0.0148 \log \frac{p_{F_2O}}{(F^-)^2}$

3. EQUILIBRIUM DIAGRAMS AND THEIR INTERPRETATION

3.1. ESTABLISHMENT OF THE DIAGRAMS

Using the equilibrium formulae given in paragraph 2, we have constructed Figs. 1–7.

In Fig. 1 we have used relations (1'), (2') and (3') to represent the influence of pH and concentration on the conditions of relative predominance of the following three dissolved forms of fluorine: HF, HF_2^- and F^-.

By superimposing the lines given by relations (8), (9) and (10) on to Fig. 1 we have constructed Fig. 2, which represents the influence of pH on the solubility of gaseous hydrogen fluoride at various partial pressures.

Using relations (5'), (6') and (7') we have constructed Fig. 3, which represents the domains of relative predominance of gaseous fluorine F_2 and its gaseous derivatives HF and F_2O for various values of the total pressure, firstly considering all three gases (Fig. 3*a*), in which case F_2 does not appear on the diagram as it is unstable with respect to F_2O, and secondly not considering F_2O (Fig. 3*b*), in which case the conditions of relative predominance of F_2 with respect to HF appear on the diagram.

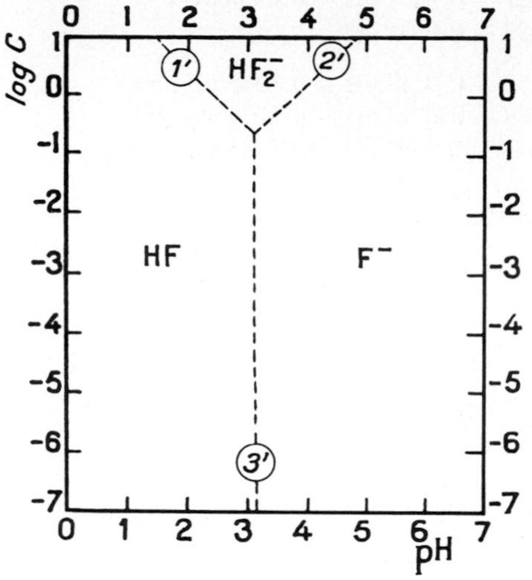

FIG. 1. Domains of relative predominance of the various dissolved forms of the system fluorine–water at 25°C.

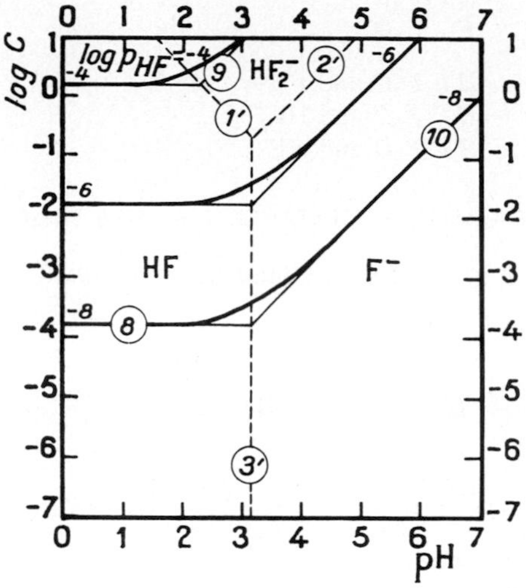

FIG. 2. Influence of pH on the solubility of gaseous HF at various partial pressures, at 25°C.

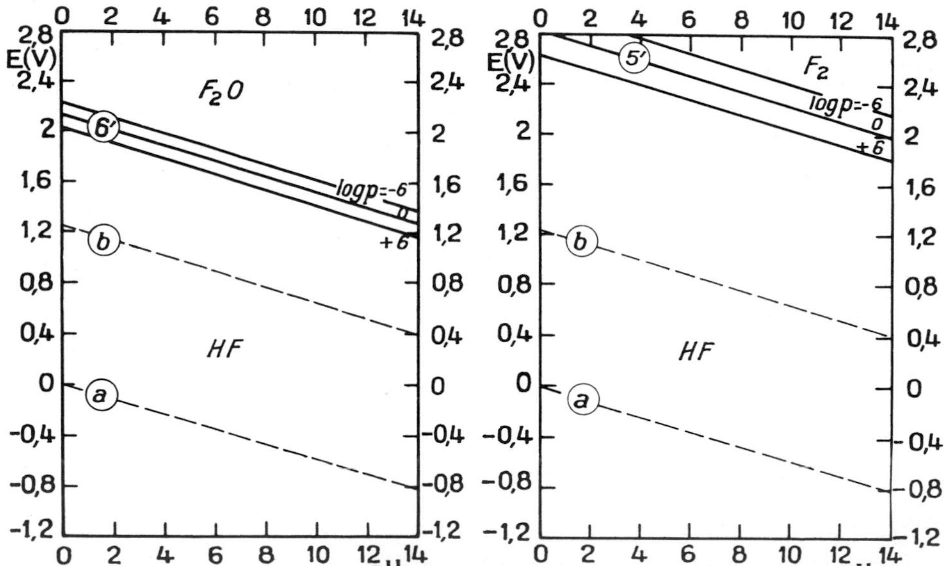

a. HF – F_2 – F_2O equilibria. *b*. HF – F_2 equilibrium.

FIG. 3. Domains of relative predominance of the gaseous fluorine compounds.

Using these figures and all the equilibrium relations given in paragraph 2, we have constructed Figs. 4 and 5, which are potential–pH equilibrium diagrams for the system fluorine–water. These two figures refer to total dissolved fluorine concentrations of respectively 10^{-2} (Fig. 4) and 1 g-at F/l (Fig. 5).

These figures are valid only in the absence of substances with which fluorine can form *soluble complexes* or *insoluble salts.* Fluorine forms a very large number of complexes with tri-, tetra- and pentavalent cations. In particular, in very slightly acid solution, the fluoride anion forms colourless,

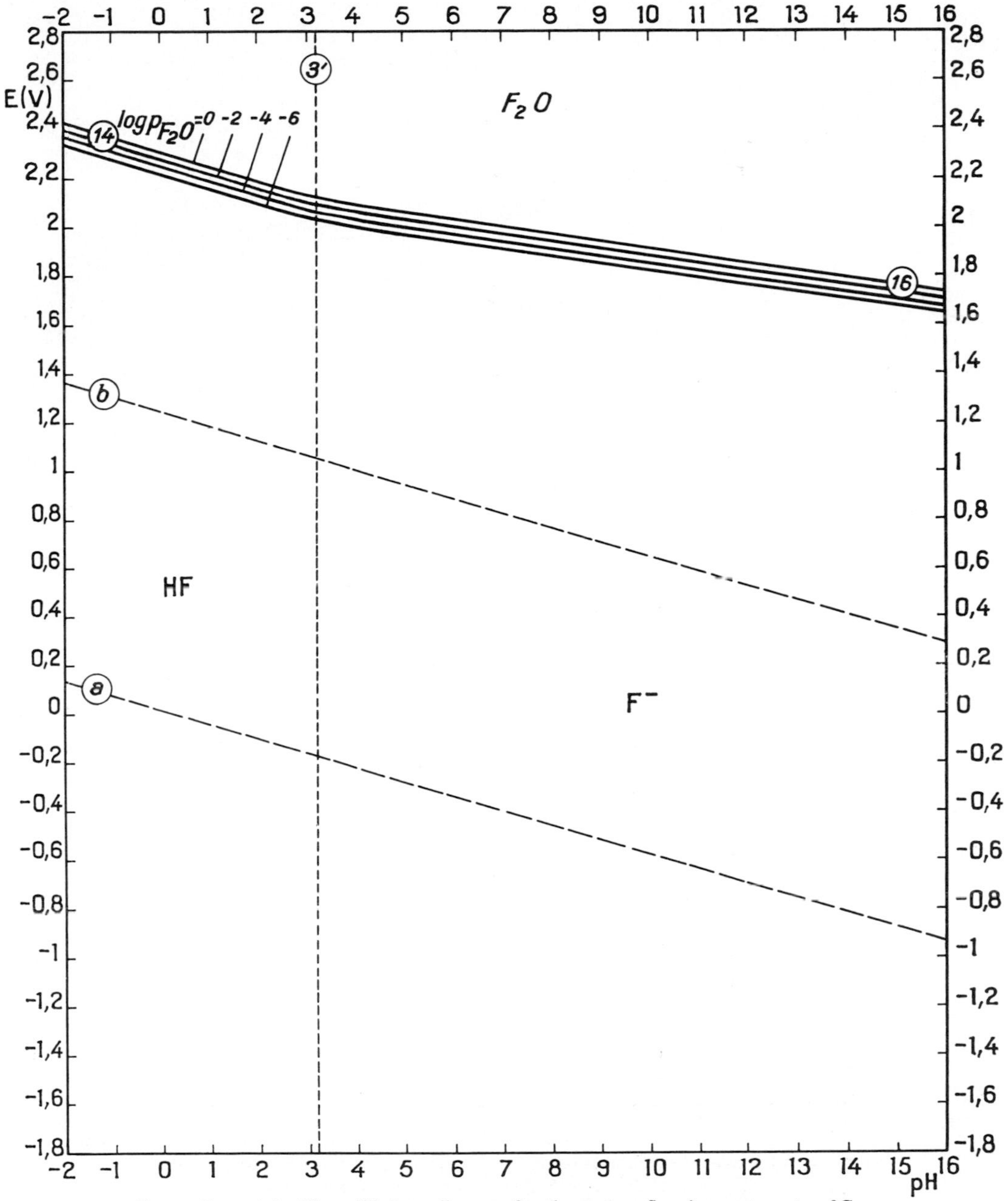

FIG. 4. Potential–pH equilibrium diagram for the system fluorine–water, at 25°C.
(For a total dissolved fluorine concentration of 10^{-2} g-at/l.)

soluble acidocomplexes, such as FeF_6^{---} and ZrF_6^{--}, with the tri- and tetravalent cations of a certain number of metallic elements. Charlot [1] points out that the most stable complexes are those formed by Al (III), Be (II), Sn (IV) and Zr (IV); the complexes formed by B (III) are fairly stable. Most fluorides are sparingly soluble, but dissolve in strongly acid media; however, even in these media the fluorides of the tetravalent metals and the rare earths are sparingly soluble.

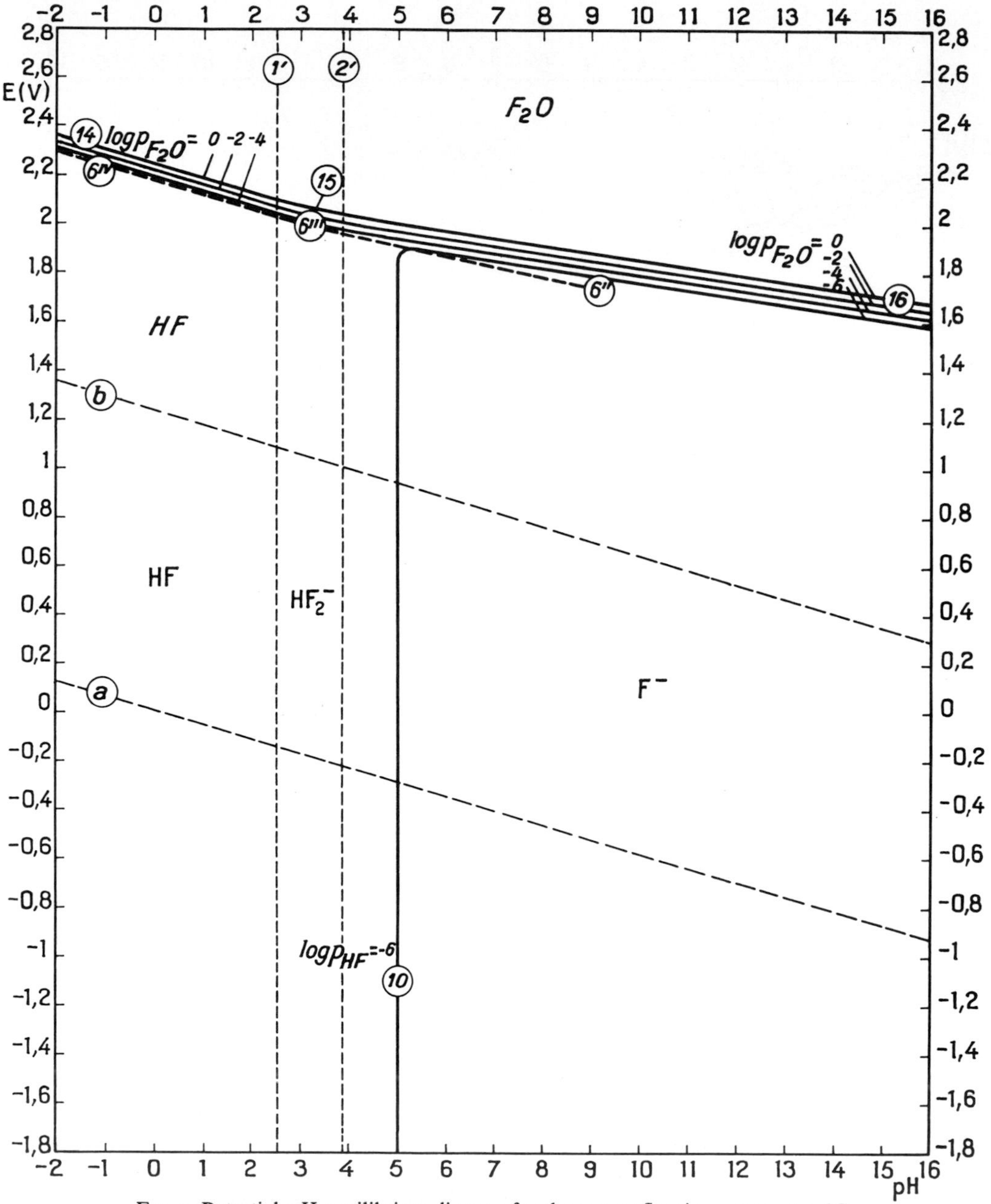

FIG. 5. Potential–pH equilibrium diagram for the system fluorine–water, at 25°C. (For a total dissolved fluorine concentration of 1 g-at/l.)

3.2. DISSOCIATION OF HYDROFLUORIC ACID

In contrast to the other halogen hydracids, hydrofluoric acid is a weak acid: it ionizes only partially to fluoride F^-; its aqueous solutions may contain an appreciable quantity of fluorine in the form of unionized hydrofluoric acid HF and partially ionized bifluoride HF_2^-.

Using a method described elsewhere [2], it is possible to predetermine graphically the pH and the composition of hydrofluoric acid solutions of various concentrations obtained by dissolving HF in pure water. This is done by means of equilibrium relations (1), (2) and (3), as is described below.

In Fig. 6 we have reproduced the limits of the domains of relative predominance of fluorine dissolved as HF, F^- and HF_2^- (as already shown in Fig. 1), and we have added lines (17–18), (19–20) and (21–22), which represent the influence of pH on the concentrations of F^-, HF_2^- and HF respectively, in hydrofluoric acid solutions. The heavy line represents the total concentration of fluorine dissolved in all of these three forms.

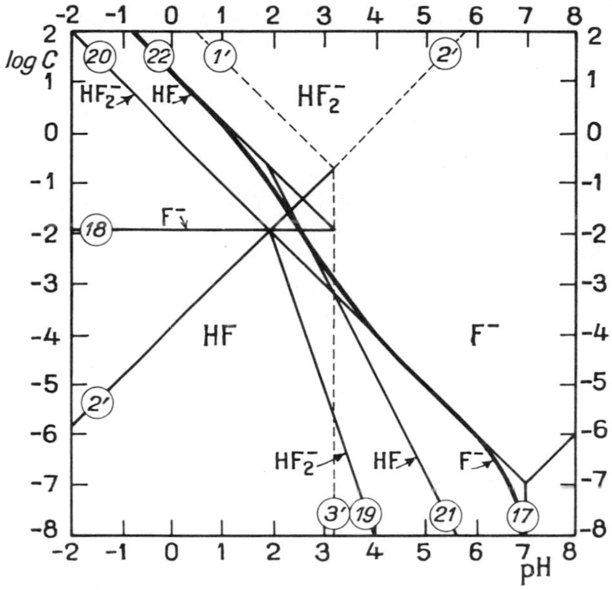

FIG. 6. pH of hydrofluoric acid solutions, at 25°C.

These lines were determined as follows:

— *In the region of Fig. 6 in which* F^- *ions are predominant with respect to* HF_2^- *ions*, i.e. below line (2′), these F^- ions are formed, essentially by the dissociation of HF according to the reaction $HF \rightarrow F^- + H^+$; the concentration of F^- ions is therefore approximately equal to the concentration of H^+ ions formed by this dissociation.
Therefore

$$\log(F^-) = \log((H^+) - 10^{-7}) \qquad (17)$$

i.e., for pH's below about 6:

$$\log(F^-) = -\,pH.$$

The HF_2^- *ion concentration* is connected with the F^- ion concentration by the relation

$$\log\frac{(F^-)^2}{(HF_2^-)} = -3.85 + pH \qquad (2) \qquad \text{or} \qquad \log(HF_2^-) = 2\log(F^-) + 3.85 - pH$$

or, when $\log(F^-) = -pH$:

$$\log(HF_2^-) = 3.85 - 3\,pH. \qquad (19)$$

which appears in Fig. 6 as the straight line (19) of gradient -3;

— *In the region of Fig. 6 in which* HF_2^- *ions are predominant with respect to* F^- *ions, i.e.* above line (2′), these HF_2^- ions are formed essentially by the dissociation of HF according to the reaction

$2HF \rightarrow HF_2^- + H^+$ (1); in this case it is the HF_2^- ion concentration, and not the F^- ion concentration which is approximately equal to the concentration of H^+ ions formed by the dissociation of HF. Therefore

$$\log(HF_2^-) = \log((H^+) - 10^{-7}), \qquad (20)$$

i.e. for pH's below about 6:

$$\log(HF_2^-) = -\,pH.$$

The F^- *ion concentration* is connected with the HF_2^- ion concentration by relation (2) which can be written

$$2\log(F^-) = \log(HF_2^-) - 3.85 + pH \quad \text{or} \quad \log(F^-) = \frac{1}{2}\log(HF_2^-) - 1.925 + \frac{1}{2}pH$$

or, when $\log(HF_2^-) = -pH$:

$$\log(F^-) = -\,1.925. \qquad (18)$$

which appears in Fig. 6 as the horizontal straight line (18).

— *Everywhere in Fig. 6*, i.e. both above and below line (2′), the *concentration of undissociated* HF is connected with the F^- concentration by the relation

$$\log\frac{(F^-)}{(HF)} = -\,3.18 + pH \quad (3) \quad \text{or} \quad \log(HF) = \log(F^-) + 3.18 - pH.$$

In the region of Fig. 6 below line (2′), where $\log(F^-) \sim -pH$ for pH's below 6, relation (3) becomes

$$\log(HF) = 3.18 - 2\,pH, \qquad (21)$$

which appears in Fig. 6 as the straight line (21) of gradient -2.

In the region of Fig. 6 below line (2′), where $\log(F^-) = -1{\cdot}925$, relation (3) becomes

$$\log(HF) = 1.26 - pH, \qquad (22)$$

which appears in Fig. 6 as the straight line (22) of gradient -1.

— It follows from the above discussion that the pH of the solutions obtained by dissolving different amounts of HF in pure water will be given in Fig. 6 by the heavy line, which represents, as a function of pH, the amount of fluorine dissolved in all of these three forms HF, HF_2^- and F^-. It can be seen that, in practice, this line approximately coincides with lines (17), (20), (21) and (22) successively. Column (*a*) below shows the pH of hydrofluoric acid solutions of various concentrations C([2]), the pH's being deduced from this heavy line in Fig. 6; the values given in columns (*b*) and (*c*) were experimentally determined, respectively by Anthony and Hudleston [3] and by Abegg [4] (from Deussen's work [5]).

log C	pH (*a*) calculated	(*b*) measured	(*c*) measured
−5	5·0	—	—
−4	4·1	—	—
−3	3·2	—	—
−2	2·6	—	2·67
−1	2·0	2·02	2·07
0	1·2	1·23	—

([2]) This refers to ideal solutions; the concentration C is calculated in moles of HF per litre; a molar solution contains 20 g HF/l.

As is shown by Figs. 1 and 6, the bifluoride ion HF_2^- is predominant only in solutions having pH's of about 3·2 and containing more than $10^{-0.7}$ g-at of dissolved fluorine per litre (i.e. 3·8 g F/l); on diluting such solutions the bifluoride decomposes into hydrofluoric acid and fluoride according to the reaction $HF_2^- \rightarrow HF + F^-$. In dilute solution hydrofluoric acid dissociates directly into fluoride according to the reaction $HF \rightarrow F^- + H^+$, the pK of which is 3·2, without appreciable formation of bifluoride HF_2^-.

Using the equilibrium formulae given above, it is in fact possible to calculate the HF, F^- and HF_2^- concentrations in a solution obtained by dissolving different amounts of HF in pure water. The composition of these solutions as a function of pH is given in Fig. 7, the pH being a function of the total dissolved fluorine concentration as is shown in Fig. 6. Figure 7 shows that in solutions of high fluorine concentration, only a small amount of bifluoride ions is formed. A 1 N solution of hydrofluoric acid (pH = 1·2) will contain only about 7·5 per cent of dissociated molecules (about 5·5 per cent bifluoride ions and 2 per cent fluoride ions).

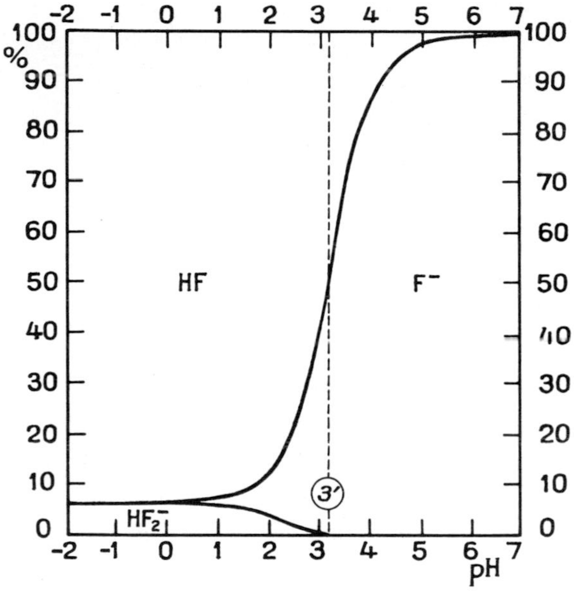

FIG. 7. Hydrolysis of hydrofluoric acid. Composition of the aqueous phase as a function of the pH of the solution.

3.3. STABILITY AND FORMATION OF FLUORINE

Fluorine is the most powerful oxidizing agent known. Several investigators have tried in vain to produce it by oxidizing substances containing fluorine, but although several of them claim that their experiments were successful, Pascal [6] considers that they have produced no formal proof of this conclusion. Figures 3–6 show that gaseous fluorine is always unstable in the presence of aqueous solutions, even if a powerful oxidizing action is brought into play, in which case it tends to react with water to give fluorine monoxide F_2O, hydrofluoric acid and fluoride, as well as oxygen and ozone. Thus the oxidation of hydrofluoric acid and fluorides in aqueous solution, both by electrolytic and chemical means, leads to the formation of the monoxide F_2O and not fluorine.

The only method of preparing fluorine is therefore the electrolysis of anhydrous hydrofluoric acid, rendered conducting by the addition of a fluoride (Moissan, 1899).

3.4. STABILITY OF GASEOUS HYDROFLUORIC ACID

Figure 2 shows a series of isobaric lines referring to partial pressure of gaseous HF equal respectively to 10^{-8}, 10^{-6} and 10^{-4} atm., plotted as a function of pH and total dissolved fluorine concentration (in the forms HF, HF_2^- and F^-). It can be seen in particular from this figure that on acidification of solutions 10^{-2} M in fluoride to a pH below 2, one will obtain solutions whose partial gaseous HF pressure will be $10^{-6.19}$ atm. (i.e. 0·00000064 atm.), at 25°C.

3.5. STABILITY AND FORMATION OF FLUORINE MONOXIDE F_2O

As described in paragraph 3.3, the fluorides and hydrofluoric acid are converted into gaseous F_2O by anodic oxidation. This method of preparing fluorine monoxide was discovered by Lebeau and Damiens [7 *a* and *b*] who electrolysed a *very concentrated* aqueous solution of acid potassium fluoride KF + 3HF using an iron or nickel anode. In this case F_2O is formed without undue formation of oxygen, on account of the high oxygen overpotential and low F_2O overpotential. The gas obtained is, however, always contaminated with oxygen.

Another method of preparing F_2O, also due to Lebeau and Damiens [7*c*], consists of passing a stream of small fluorine bubbles rapidly into a solution of caustic soda (about 2 per cent NaOH). The fluorine then reacts as follows:

$$F_2 + 2OH^- \rightarrow F_2O + H_2O + 2e^- \qquad (7)$$

and

$$F_2 + 2e^- \rightarrow 2F^- \qquad (13)$$

overall reaction

$$2F_2 + 2OH^- \rightarrow F_2O + 2F^- + H_2O.$$

The gas obtained always contains oxygen. Under the most favourable conditions a gas containing 70 per cent F_2O is obtained.

As is shown by Figs. 4 and 5, fluorine monoxide is thermodynamically unstable in the presence of water, which it tends to oxidize with the evolution of oxygen and the formation of hydrofluoric acid according to the reactions

$$F_2O + 4H^+ + 4e^- \rightarrow 2HF + H_2O \qquad (14)$$

and

$$2H_2O \rightarrow O_2 + 4H^+ + 4e^- \qquad (b)$$

overall reaction

$$F_2O + H_2O \rightarrow 2HF + O_2.$$

However, most probably on account of the great irreversibility of reaction (*b*), this reaction is very slow: F_2O can be preserved practically intact in the presence of water for 4 weeks [8]; in the presence of alkaline solutions the decomposition of F_2O is rapid and complete, especially in the case of concentrated solutions [9].

3.6. STABILITY OF THE FLUORIDES AND DISSOLVED HYDROFLUORIC ACID

As was recalled above (paragraph 3.1), the potential–pH equilibrium diagrams given in Figs. 4 and 5 are valid only in the absence of substances with which fluorine can form insoluble compounds. Most fluorides are sparingly soluble or insoluble. The only soluble ones are those of the alkali metals, silver, thallium and mercury (mercurous and mercuric). The diagrams in Figs. 4 and 5 apply only to these soluble fluorides.

Figures 4 and 5 show that the fluorides are stable in the presence of water, which they do not decompose under any circumstances.

The fluorides, like hydrofluoric acid, are converted into gaseous fluorine monoxide F_2O by anodic oxidation (see paragraph 3.5). Hydrofluoric acid, which is slightly volatile (see paragraph 3.4), is a weak acid (see paragraph 3.2), unlike the other halogen hydracids, HCl, HBr and HI, which are all strong acids.

4. BIBLIOGRAPHY

[1] G. Charlot, *L'analyse qualitative et les réactions en solution,* Masson, Paris, 1957, p. 273.

[2] M. Pourbaix, *Leçons sur la corrosion électrochimique*, 2ᵉ fascicule (Rapport technique RT.30 of CEBELCOR, February 1956, p. 22).

[3] J. D. C. ANTHONY and L. J. HUDLESTON, The freezing point of hydrofluoric acid, *J. Chem. Soc.* **127**, 1122–8 (1925).
[4] R. ABEGG, *Handbuch der anorganischen Chemie* (Die Elemente der siebenten Gruppe des periodischen systems), Leipzig, 1913, p. 40.
[5] E. DEUSSEN, Zur Kenntnis der Flusssäure, *Z. anorg. allgem. Chem.* **44**, 312 and 408 (1905).
[6] P. PASCAL, *Nouveau traité de Chimie minérale*, Vol. XVI, Masson, Paris, 1960, p. 17.
[7] P. LEBEAU and A. DAMIENS:
a. Sur un procédé facile de préparation du fluor, C.R. Acad. Sc. **181**, 916 (1925);
b. Sur l'existence d'un composé oxygéné du fluor, C.R. Acad. Sc. **185**, 652 (1927);
c. Sur un nouveau mode de préparation du fluorure d'oxygène, C. R. Acad. Sci. **188**, 1253 (1929).
[8] O. RUFF and W. MENZEL, Die Möglichkeit der Bildung höherer Sauerstoff–Fluoride und die Eigenschaften des Sauerstoff-2-Fluorids, *Z. anorg. allgem. Chem.* **198**, 39 (1931).
[9] N. V. SIDGWICK, *The Chemical Elements and their Compounds*, Vol. II, Oxford, 1951, p. 1100 et seq.

SECTION 20.2

CHLORINE (1)

G. VALENSI, E. DELTOMBE, N. DE ZOUBOV, C. VANLEUGENHAGHE and M. POURBAIX

SUMMARY

(1) Adapted version of an extract from Rapport CEFA/R.12 of the Commission des Études Fondamentales et Applications of CEBELCOR. See also [1]. A potential–pH equilibrium diagram for the system chlorine–water was presented by Valensi *et al.* at the 5th Meeting of CITCE (1953) [2].

1. SUBSTANCES CONSIDERED AND SUBSTANCES NOT CONSIDERED

	Oxidation number (Z)	Considered	Not considered	μ^0(cal.)	Name, colour, crystalline system
Dissolved substances	− I	Cl^-	-	−31 350	Chloride ion, colourless
	0	Cl_2	-	1 650	Dissolved chlorine
	+ I	$HClO$	-	−19 110	Hypochlorous acid, colourless
	»	ClO^-	-	− 8 900	Hypochlorite ion, colourless
	+ 3	$HClO_2$	-	70	Chlorous acid, colourless
	»	ClO_2^-	-	2 740	Chlorite ion, colourless
	+ 5	ClO_3^-	-	− 620	Chlorate ion, colourless
	+ 7	ClO_4^-	-	− 2470	Perchlorate ion, colourless
Gaseous substances	− I	HCl	-	−22 769	Hydrogen chloride, colourless
	0	Cl_2	-	0	Chlorine, greenish–yellow
	+ I	Cl_2O	-	22 400	Chlorine monoxide, hypochlorous anhydride, brownish
	+ 2	-	ClO	-	Chlorine oxide
	+ 4	ClO_2	-	29 500	Chlorine dioxide, orange–yellow
	+ 6	-	ClO_3	-	Chlorine trioxide, brown
	+ 7	-	Cl_2O_7	-	Chloric heptoxide, perchloric anhydride, colourless
	+ 8	-	ClO_4	-	Chlorine tetroxide, colourless

2. REACTIONS AND EQUILIBRIUM FORMULAE

2.1. TWO DISSOLVED SUBSTANCES

2.1.1. *Relative stability of the dissolved substances*

Z = + I

1. $HClO = ClO^- + H^+$ $\qquad \log\frac{(ClO^-)}{(HClO)} = -7.49 + pH$

Z = + 3

2. $HClO_2 = ClO_2^- + H^+$ $\qquad \log\frac{(ClO_2^-)}{(HClO_2)} = -1.96 + pH$

− I → 0

3. $2Cl^- = Cl_2 + 2e^-$ $\qquad E_0 = 1.395 + 0.0295\log\frac{(Cl_2)}{(Cl^-)^2}$

− I → + I

4. $Cl^- + H_2O = HClO + H^+ + 2e^-$ $\qquad E_0 = 1.494 - 0.0295\,pH + 0.0295\log\frac{(HClO)}{(Cl^-)}$

5. $Cl^- + H_2O = ClO^- + 2H^+ + 2e^-$ $\qquad E_0 = 1.715 - 0.0591\,pH + 0.0295\log\frac{(ClO^-)}{(Cl^-)}$

− I → + 3

6. $Cl^- + 2H_2O = HClO_2 + 3H^+ + 4e^-$ $\qquad E_0 = 1.570 - 0.0443\,pH + 0.0148\log\frac{(HClO_2)}{(Cl^-)}$

7. $Cl^- + 2H_2O = ClO_2^- + 4H^+ + 4e^-$ $\qquad E_0 = 1.599 - 0.0591\,pH + 0.0148\log\frac{(ClO_2^-)}{(Cl^-)}$

− I → + 5

8. $Cl^- + 3H_2O = ClO_3^- + 6H^+ + 6e^-$ $\qquad E_0 = 1.451 - 0.0591\,pH + 0.0098\log\frac{(ClO_3^-)}{(Cl^-)}$

− I → + 7

9. $Cl^- + 4H_2O = ClO_4^- + 8H^+ + 8e^-$ $\qquad E_0 = 1.389 - 0.0591\,pH + 0.0074\log\frac{(ClO_4^-)}{(Cl^-)}$

$0 \rightarrow +1$

10. $Cl_2 + 2H_2O = 2HClO + 2H^+ + 2e^-$ $\quad E_0 = 1.594 - 0.0591\,pH + 0.0295\log\frac{(HClO)^2}{(Cl_2)}$

11. $Cl_2 + 2H_2O = 2ClO^- + 4H^+ + 2e^-$ $\quad E_0 = 2.036 - 0.1182\,pH + 0.0295\log\frac{(ClO^-)^2}{(Cl_2)}$

$0 \rightarrow +3$

12. $Cl_2 + 4H_2O = 2HClO_2 + 6H^+ + 6e^-$ $\quad E_0 = 1.628 - 0.0591\,pH + 0.0098\log\frac{(HClO_2)^2}{(Cl_2)}$

13. $Cl_2 + 4H_2O = 2ClO_2^- + 8H^+ + 6e^-$ $\quad E_0 = 1.666 - 0.0788\,pH + 0.0098\log\frac{(ClO_2^-)^2}{(Cl_2)}$

$0 \rightarrow +5$

14. $Cl_2 + 6H_2O = 2ClO_3^- + 12H^+ + 10e^-$ $\quad E_0 = 1.463 - 0.0709\,pH + 0.0059\log\frac{(ClO_3^-)^2}{(Cl_2)}$

$0 \rightarrow +7$

15. $Cl_2 + 8H_2O = 2ClO_4^- + 16H^+ + 14e^-$ $\quad E_0 = 1.385 - 0.0675\,pH + 0.0042\log\frac{(ClO_4^-)^2}{(Cl_2)}$

$+1 \rightarrow +3$

16. $HClO + H_2O = HClO_2 + 2H^+ + 2e^-$ $\quad E_0 = 1.645 - 0.0591\,pH + 0.0295\log\frac{(HClO_2)}{(HClO)}$

17. $ClO^- + H_2O = HClO_2 + H^+ + 2e^-$ $\quad E_0 = 1.423 - 0.0295\,pH + 0.0295\log\frac{(HClO_2)}{(ClO^-)}$

18. $HClO + H_2O = ClO_2^- + 3H^+ + 2e^-$ $\quad E_0 = 1.703 - 0.0886\,pH + 0.0295\log\frac{(ClO_2^-)}{(HClO)}$

19. $ClO^- + H_2O = ClO_2^- + 2H^+ + 2e^-$ $\quad E_0 = 1.474 - 0.0591\,pH + 0.0295\log\frac{(ClO_2^-)}{(ClO^-)}$

$+3 \rightarrow +5$

20. $HClO_2 + H_2O = ClO_3^- + 3H^+ + 2e^-$ $\quad E_0 = 1.214 - 0.0886\,pH + 0.0295\log\frac{(ClO_3^-)}{(HClO_2)}$

21. $ClO_2^- + H_2O = ClO_3^- + 2H^+ + 2e^-$ $\quad E_0 = 1.155 - 0.0591\,pH + 0.0295\log\frac{(ClO_3^-)}{(ClO_2^-)}$

$+3 \rightarrow +7$

22. $HClO_2 + 2H_2O = ClO_4^- + 5H^+ + 4e^-$ $\quad E_0 = 1.201 - 0.0739\,pH + 0.0148\log\frac{(ClO_4^-)}{(HClO_2)}$

23. $ClO_2^- + 2H_2O = ClO_4^- + 4H^+ + 4e^-$ $\quad E_0 = 1.173 - 0.0591\,pH + 0.0148\log\frac{(ClO_4^-)}{(ClO_2^-)}$

$+5 \rightarrow +7$

24. $ClO_3^- + H_2O = ClO_4^- + 2H^+ + 2e^-$ $\quad E_0 = 1.189 - 0.0591\,pH + 0.0295\log\frac{(ClO_4^-)}{(ClO_3^-)}$

2.1.2. *Limits of the domains of relative predominance of the dissolved substances*

1'. $HClO/ClO^-$ $\quad pH = 7.49$

2'. $HClO_2/ClO_2^-$ $\quad pH = 1.96$

3'. Cl^-/Cl_2 $\quad E_0 = 1.395 - 0.0295\log C$

4'. $Cl^-/HClO$ $\quad E_0 = 1.494 - 0.0295\,pH$

5'. Cl^-/ClO^- $\quad E_0 = 1.715 - 0.0591\,pH$

6'. $Cl^-/HClO_2$ $\quad E_0 = 1.570 - 0.0443\,pH$

7'. Cl^-/ClO_2^- $\quad E_0 = 1.599 - 0.0591\,pH$

8'. Cl^-/ClO_3^- $\quad E_0 = 1.451 - 0.0591\,pH$

9'. Cl^-/ClO_4^- $\quad E_0 = 1.389 - 0.0591\,pH$

10'. $Cl_2/HClO$ $\quad E_0 = 1.594 - 0.0591\,pH + 0.0295\log C$

11'. Cl_2/ClO^- $\quad E_0 = 2.036 - 0.1182\,pH + 0.0295\log C$

12'. $Cl_2/HClO_2$ $\quad E_0 = 1.628 - 0.0591\,pH + 0.0098\log C$

13'. Cl_2/ClO_2^- $\quad E_0 = 1.666 - 0.0788\,pH + 0.0098\log C$

14'. Cl_2/ClO_3^- $\quad E_0 = 1.463 - 0.0709\,pH + 0.0059\log C$

15'. Cl_2/ClO_4^- $\quad E_0 = 1.385 - 0.0675\,pH + 0.0042\log C$

16'. $HClO/HClO_2$ $\quad E_0 = 1.645 - 0.0591\,pH$

17'. $ClO^-/HClO_2$ $\quad E_0 = 1.423 - 0.0295\,pH$

18'.	$HClO/ClO_2^-$	$E_0 = 1.703 - 0.0886\ pH$
19'.	ClO^-/ClO_2^-	$E_0 = 1.474 - 0.0591\ pH$
20'.	$HClO_2/ClO_3^-$	$E_0 = 1.214 - 0.0886\ pH$
21'.	ClO_2^-/ClO_3^-	$E_0 = 1.155 - 0.0591\ pH$
22'.	$HClO_2/ClO_4^-$	$E_0 = 1.201 - 0.0739\ pH$
23'.	ClO_2^-/ClO_4^-	$E_0 = 1.173 - 0.0591\ pH$
24'.	ClO_3^-/ClO_4^-	$E_0 = 1.189 - 0.0591\ pH$

2.2. TWO GASEOUS SUBSTANCES

2.2.1. *Relative stability of the gaseous substances*

$-1 \rightarrow 0$

25. $2\,HCl = Cl_2 + 2H^+ + 2e^-$ $\quad E_0 = 0.987 - 0.0591\ pH + 0.0295 \log \frac{p_{Cl_2}}{p^2_{HCl}}$

$-1 \rightarrow +1$

26. $2\,HCl + H_2O = Cl_2O + 4H^+ + 4e^-$ $\quad E_0 = 1.351 - 0.0591\ pH + 0.0148 \log \frac{p_{Cl_2O}}{p^2_{HCl}}$

$-1 \rightarrow +4$

27. $HCl + 2H_2O = ClO_2 + 5H^+ + 5e^-$ $\quad E_0 = 1.436 - 0.0591\ pH + 0.0118 \log \frac{p_{ClO_2}}{p_{HCl}}$

$0 \rightarrow +1$

28. $Cl_2 + H_2O = Cl_2O + 2H^+ + 2e^-$ $\quad E_0 = 1.714 - 0.0591\ pH + 0.0295 \log \frac{p_{Cl_2O}}{p_{Cl_2}}$

$0 \rightarrow +4$

29. $Cl_2 + 4H_2O = 2ClO_2 + 8H^+ + 8e^-$ $\quad E_0 = 1.549 - 0.0591\ pH + 0.0074 \log \frac{p^2_{ClO_2}}{p_{Cl_2}}$

$+1 \rightarrow +4$

30. $Cl_2O + 3H_2O = 2ClO_2 + 6H^+ + 6e^-$ $\quad E_0 = 1.494 - 0.0591\ pH + 0.0098 \log \frac{p^2_{ClO_2}}{p_{Cl_2O}}$

2.2.2. *Limits of the domains of relative predominance of the gaseous substances*

25'.	HCl/Cl_2	$E_0 = 0.997 - 0.0591\ pH - 0.0295 \log P$
26'.	HCl/Cl_2O	$E_0 = 1.355 - 0.0591\ pH - 0.0148 \log P$
27'.	HCl/ClO_2	$E_0 = 1.436 - 0.0591\ pH$
28'.	Cl_2/Cl_2O	$E_0 = 1.714 - 0.0591\ pH$
29'.	Cl_2/ClO_2	$E_0 = 1.547 - 0.0591\ pH + 0.0074 \log P$
30'.	Cl_2O/ClO_2	$E_0 = 1.491 - 0.0591\ pH + 0.0098 \log P$
25''.	HCl/Cl_2 and Cl^-	$E_0 = 1.173 - 0.0295\ pH - 0.0295 \log C$
28''.	Cl_2/Cl_2O and HClO	$E_0 = 1.714 - 0.0591\ pH$
28'''.	Cl_2/Cl_2O and ClO^-/Cl^-	$E_0 = 1.714 - 0.0591\ pH$
29''.	Cl_2/ClO_2 and ClO_3^-	$E_0 = 1.505 - 0.0656\ pH + 0.0065 \log C$

2.3. ONE GASEOUS SUBSTANCE AND ONE DISSOLVED SUBSTANCE

Solubility of the gaseous substance

a. Solubility in gram-ions or gram-molecules per litre

$Z = -1$

31 $HCl = Cl^- + H^+$ $\quad \log(Cl^-) = 6.30 + pH + \log p_{HCl}$

$Z = 0$

32. $Cl_2 = Cl_2$ $\quad \log(Cl_2) = -1.21 + \log p_{Cl_2}$

Z = +1

33. $Cl_2O + H_2O = 2HClO$ $\log(HClO) = 1.44 + \frac{1}{2}\log p_{Cl_2O}$

34. $Cl_2O + H_2O = 2ClO^- + 2H^+$ $\log(ClO^-) = -6.05 + pH + \frac{1}{2}\log p_{Cl_2O}$

Cl_2

−1 → 0

35. $2Cl^- = Cl_2 + 2e^-$ $E_0 = 1.359 + 0.0295\log\frac{p_{Cl_2}}{(Cl^-)^2}$

0 → +1

36. $Cl_2 + 2H_2O = 2HClO + 2H^+ + 2e^-$ $E_0 = 1.630 - 0.0591\,pH + 0.0295\log\frac{(HClO)^2}{p_{Cl_2}}$

37. $Cl_2 + 2H_2O = 2ClO^- + 4H^+ + 2e^-$ $E_0 = 2.072 - 0.1182\,pH + 0.0295\log\frac{(ClO^-)^2}{p_{Cl_2}}$

0 → +3

38. $Cl_2 + 4H_2O = 2HClO_2 + 6H^+ + 6e^-$ $E_0 = 1.640 - 0.0591\,pH + 0.0098\log\frac{(HClO_2)^2}{p_{Cl_2}}$

39. $Cl_2 + 4H_2O = 2ClO_2^- + 8H^+ + 6e^-$ $E_0 = 1.678 - 0.0788\,pH + 0.0098\log\frac{(ClO_2^-)^2}{p_{Cl_2}}$

0 → +5

40. $Cl_2 + 6H_2O = 2ClO_3^- + 12H^+ + 10e^-$ $E_0 = 1.470 - 0.0709\,pH + 0.0059\log\frac{(ClO_3^-)^2}{p_{Cl_2}}$

0 → +7

41. $Cl_2 + 8H_2O = 2ClO_4^- + 16H^+ + 14e^-$ $E_0 = 1.389 - 0.0675\,pH + 0.0042\log\frac{(ClO_4^-)^2}{p_{Cl_2}}$

Cl_2O

−1 → +1

42. $2Cl^- + H_2O = Cl_2O + 2H^+ + 4e^-$ $E_0 = 2.152 - 0.0295\,pH + 0.0148\log\frac{p_{Cl_2O}}{(Cl^-)^2}$

0 → +1

43. $Cl_2 + H_2O = Cl_2O + 2H^+ + 2e^-$ $E_0 = 1.679 - 0.0591\,pH + 0.0295\log\frac{p_{Cl_2O}}{(Cl_2)}$

+1 → +3

44. $Cl_2O + 3H_2O = 2HClO_2 + 4H^+ + 4e^-$ $E_0 = 1.603 - 0,0591\,pH + 0.0148\log\frac{(HClO_2)^2}{p_{Cl_2O}}$

45. $Cl_2O + 3H_2O = 2ClO_2^- + 6H^+ + 4e^-$ $E_0 = 1.661 - 0.0886\,pH + 0.0148\log\frac{(ClO_2^-)^2}{p_{Cl_2O}}$

+1 → +5

46. $Cl_2O + 5H_2O = 2ClO_3^- + 10H^+ + 8e^-$ $E_0 = 1.408 - 0.0738\,pH + 0.0074\log\frac{(ClO_3^-)^2}{p_{Cl_2O}}$

+1 → +7

47. $Cl_2O + 7H_2O = 2ClO_4^- + 14H^+ + 12e^-$ $E_0 = 1.336 - 0.0689\,pH + 0.0049\log\frac{(ClO_4^-)^2}{p_{Cl_2O}}$

ClO_2

−1 → +4

48. $Cl^- + 2H_2O = ClO_2 + 4H^+ + 5e^-$ $E_0 = 1.511 - 0.0473\,pH + 0.0118\log\frac{p_{ClO_2}}{(Cl^-)}$

0 → +4

49. $Cl_2 + 4H_2O = 2ClO_2 + 8H^+ + 8e^-$ $E_0 = 1.540 - 0.0591\,pH + 0.0074\log\frac{p^2_{ClO_2}}{(Cl_2)}$

$+1 \rightarrow +4$

50. $HClO + H_2O = ClO_2 + 3H^+ + 3e^-$ $\qquad E_0 = 1.522 - 0.0591\,pH + 0.0197 \log \frac{p_{ClO_2}}{(HClO)}$

51. $ClO^- + H_2O = ClO_2 + 2H^+ + 3e^-$ $\qquad E_0 = 1.374 - 0.0394\,pH + 0.0197 \log \frac{p_{ClO_2}}{(ClO^-)}$

$+3 \rightarrow +4$

52. $HClO_2 = ClO_2 + H^+ + e^-$ $\qquad E_0 = 1.277 - 0.0591\,pH + 0.0591 \log \frac{p_{ClO_2}}{(HClO_2)}$

53. $ClO_2^- = ClO_2 + e^-$ $\qquad E_0 = 1.160 + 0.0591 \log \frac{p_{ClO_2}}{(ClO_2^-)}$

$+4 \rightarrow +5$

54. $ClO_2 + H_2O = ClO_3^- + 2H^+ + e^-$ $\qquad E_0 = 1.152 - 0.1182\,pH + 0.0591 \log \frac{(ClO_3^-)}{p_{ClO_2}}$

$+4 \rightarrow +7$

55. $ClO_2 + 2H_2O = ClO_4^- + 4H^+ + 3e^-$ $\qquad E_0 = 1.177 - 0.0788\,pH + 0.0197 \log \frac{(ClO_4^-)}{p_{ClO_2}}$

b. Solubility in gram-atoms of chlorine per litre

31'.	HCl / Cl^-	$0 = 6.30 + pH - \log C + \log P$
32'.	Cl_2 / Cl_2	$0 = -0.91 - \log C + \log P$
33'.	Cl_2O / $HClO$	$0 = 1.44 - \log C + \frac{1}{2} \log P$
34'.	Cl_2O / ClO^-	$0 = -6.05 + pH - \log C + \frac{1}{2} \log P$
35'.	Cl^- / Cl_2	$E_0 = 1.359 \quad 0.0591 \log C + 0.0295 \log P$
36'.	Cl_2 / $HClO$	$E_0 = 1.630 - 0.0591\,pH + 0.0591 \log C - 0.0295 \log P$
37'.	Cl_2 / ClO^-	$E_0 = 2.072 - 0.1182\,pH + 0.0591 \log C - 0.0295 \log P$
38'.	Cl_2 / $HClO_2$	$E_0 = 1.640 - 0.0591\,pH + 0.0196 \log C - 0.0098 \log P$
39'.	Cl_2 / ClO_2^-	$E_0 = 1.678 - 0.0788\,pH + 0.0196 \log C - 0.0098 \log P$
40'.	Cl_2 / ClO_3^-	$E_0 = 1.470 - 0.0709\,pH + 0.0118 \log C - 0.0059 \log P$
41'.	Cl_2 / ClO_4^-	$E_0 = 1.389 - 0.0675\,pH + 0.0084 \log C - 0.0042 \log P$
42'.	Cl^- / Cl_2O	$E_0 = 2.152 - 0.0295\,pH - 0.0295 \log C + 0.0148 \log P$
43'.	Cl_2 / Cl_2O	$E_0 = 1.688 - 0.0591\,pH - 0.0295 \log C + 0.0295 \log P$
44'.	Cl_2O / $HClO_2$	$E_0 = 1.603 - 0.0591\,pH + 0.0295 \log C - 0.0148 \log P$
45'.	Cl_2O / ClO_2^-	$E_0 = 1.661 - 0.0886\,pH + 0.0295 \log C - 0.0148 \log P$
46'.	Cl_2O / ClO_3^-	$E_0 = 1.408 - 0.0738\,pH + 0.0148 \log C - 0.0074 \log P$
47'.	Cl_2O / ClO_4^-	$E_0 = 1.336 - 0.0689\,pH + 0.0098 \log C - 0.0049 \log P$
48'.	Cl^- / ClO_2	$E_0 = 1.511 - 0.0473\,pH - 0.0118 \log C + 0.0118 \log P$
49'.	Cl_2 / ClO_2	$E_0 = 1.542 - 0.0591\,pH - 0.0074 \log C + 0.0148 \log P$
50'.	$HClO$ / ClO_2	$E_0 = 1.522 - 0.0591\,pH - 0.0197 \log C + 0.0197 \log P$
51'.	ClO^- / ClO_2	$E_0 = 1.374 - 0.0394\,pH - 0.0197 \log C + 0.0197 \log P$
52'.	$HClO_2$ / ClO_2	$E_0 = 1.277 - 0.0591\,pH - 0.0591 \log C + 0.0591 \log P$
53'.	ClO_2^- / ClO_2	$E_0 = 1.160 - 0.0591 \log C + 0.0591 \log P$
54'.	ClO_2 / ClO_3^-	$E_0 = 1.152 - 0.1182\,pH + 0.0591 \log C - 0.0591 \log P$
55'.	ClO_2 / ClO_4^-	$E_0 = 1.177 - 0.0788\,pH + 0.0197 \log C - 0.0197 \log P$

3. EQUILIBRIUM DIAGRAMS AND THEIR INTERPRETATION

3.1. ESTABLISHMENT OF THE DIAGRAMS

Using the equilibrium relations indicated in paragraph 2, we have constructed Figs. 1–7. Figure 1 refers to solutions containing 1 g-at Cl/l (35·5 g Cl/l) and represents the stable equilibria of the system chlorine–water at 25°C, which contain in particular the chloride/perchlorate equilibrium. Figures 2*a*,

2b and 2c also refer to solutions containing 1 g-at Cl/l, and represent certain metastable equilibria, relating in particular to the relative stability conditions of the chlorates (Fig. 2a), the chlorites (Fig. 2b) and the hypochlorites (Fig. 2c).

Figure 3 is a potential/concentration diagram for the stable equilibria of the system chlorine–water at 25°C, for solutions of pH = 0.

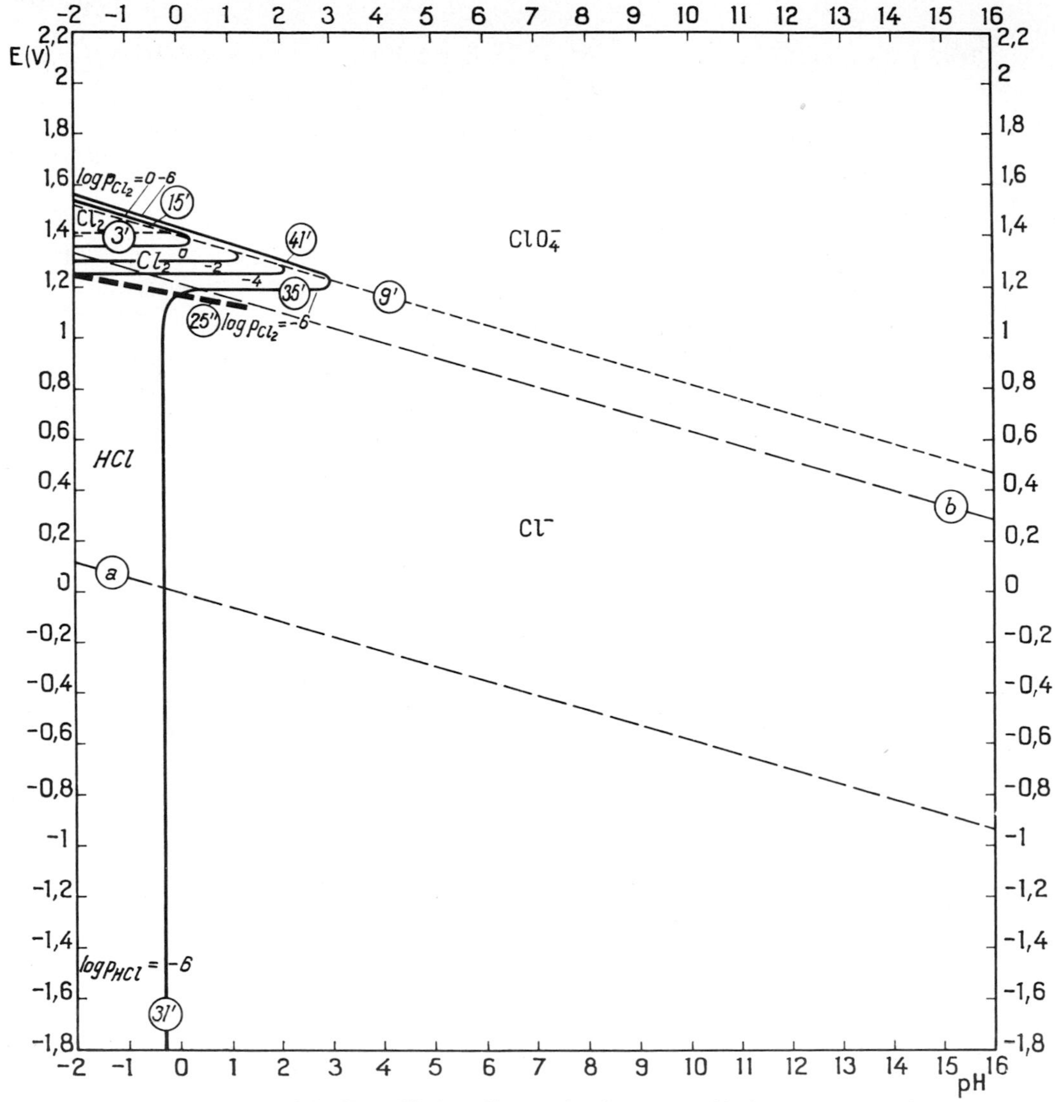

FIG. 1. Potential–pH equilibrium diagram for the system chlorine–water, at 25°C. Stable equilibria.
(For solutions containing 1 g-at Cl/l.)

Figure 4 represents the influence of pH on the solubility of gaseous HCl at various partial pressures, Fig. 5 represents the influence of pH on the dissociation of hypochlorous acid, Fig. 6 represents the influence of pH on the solubility of gaseous Cl_2O, and Fig. 7 the influence of pH on the dissociation of chlorous acid.

3.2. STABILITY OF THE CHLORIDES

Hydrochloric acid, which is a strong acid and is very slightly volatile, is completely dissociated according to the reaction $HCl \rightarrow H^+ + Cl^-$. The domain of predominance of the Cl^- ion extends all along the pH axis and completely covers the domain of stability of water.

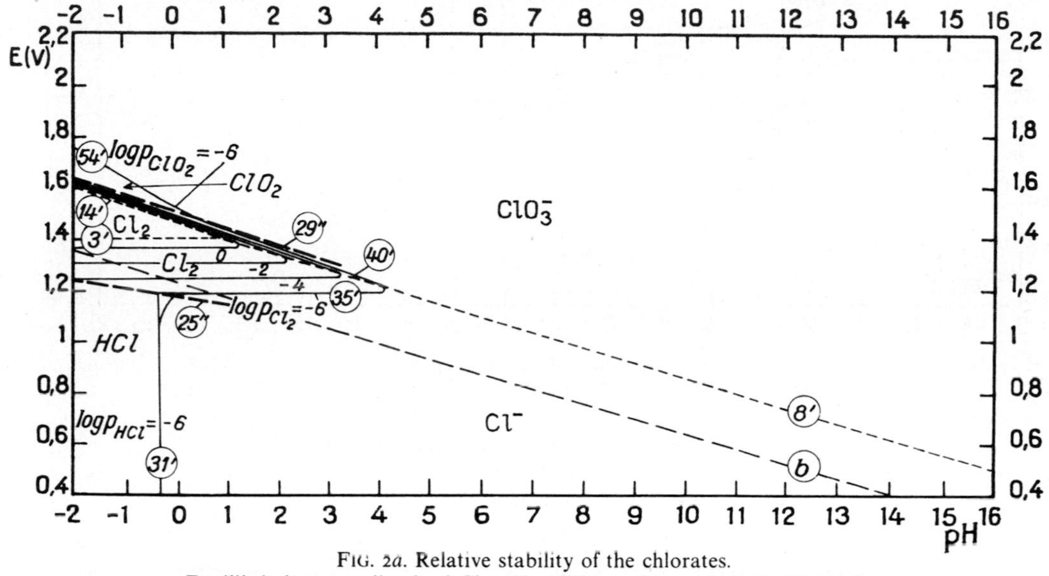

FIG. 2a. Relative stability of the chlorates.
Equilibria between dissolved Cl^-, Cl_2, ClO_3^- and gaseous HCl, Cl_2, ClO_2.

In Fig. 4 we have used equation (31′) to construct a diagram showing the logarithm of the Cl^- concentration in a solution as a function of the pH, for various partial pressures of gaseous HCl in the atmosphere in equilibrium with the solution. Conversely, one can deduce from this diagram the vapour pressure of HCl above a chloride solution of known pH and Cl^- concentration.

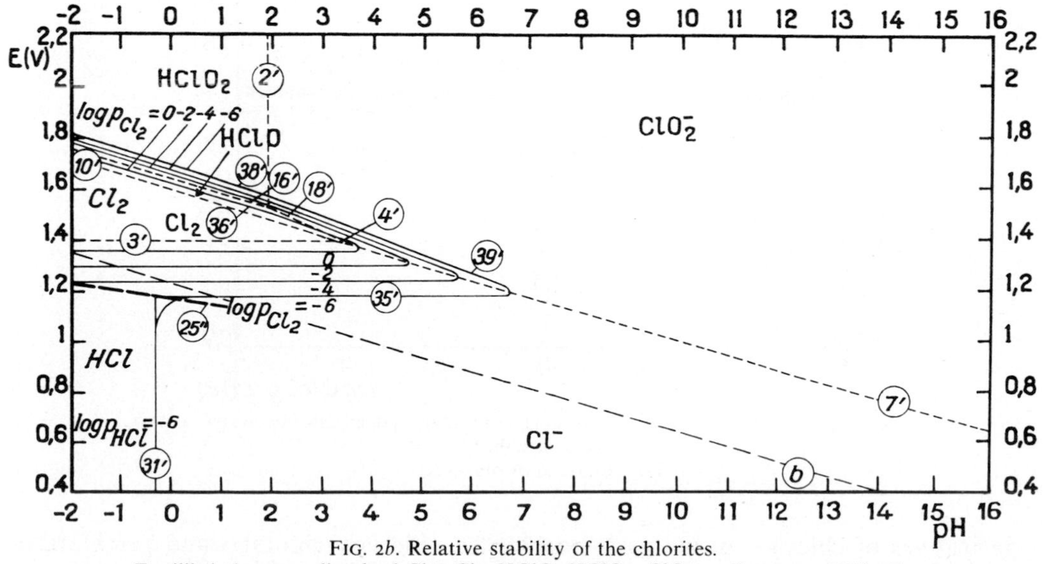

FIG. 2b. Relative stability of the chlorites.
Equilibria between dissolved Cl^-, Cl_2, HClO, $HClO_2$, ClO_2^- and gaseous HCl, Cl_2.

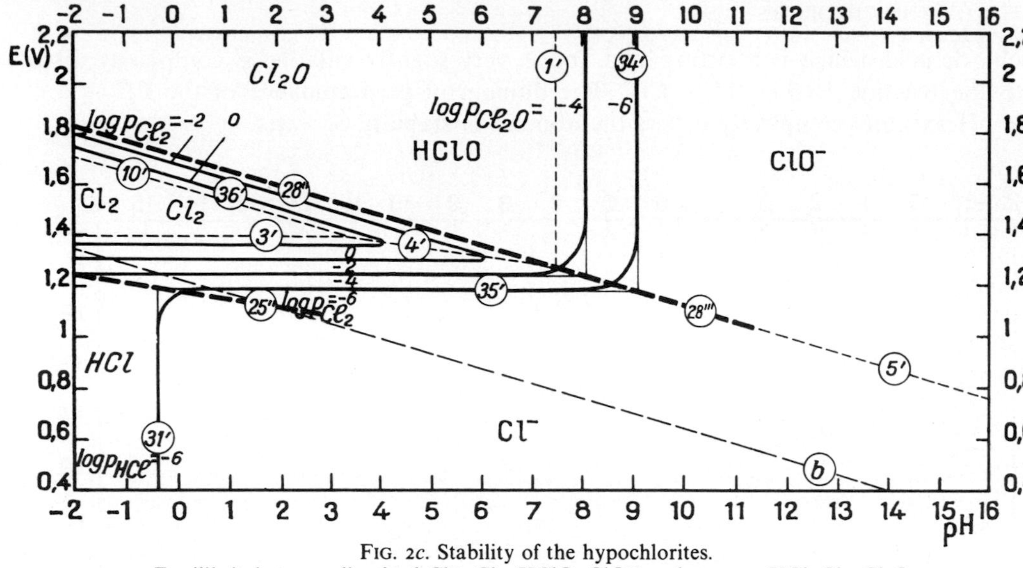

FIG. 2c. Stability of the hypochlorites.
Equilibria between dissolved Cl^-, Cl_2, HClO, ClO^- and gaseous HCl, Cl_2, Cl_2O.

FIG. 2. Potential–pH diagrams for the system chlorine–water, at 25°C.
Metastable equilibria.
(For solutions containing 1 g-at Cl/l.)

As can be seen from Figs. 1, 2 and 3, controlled oxidation of chlorides in sufficiently acid solution will lead to the formation of gaseous chlorine; in neutral or alkaline solution it will lead to the formation

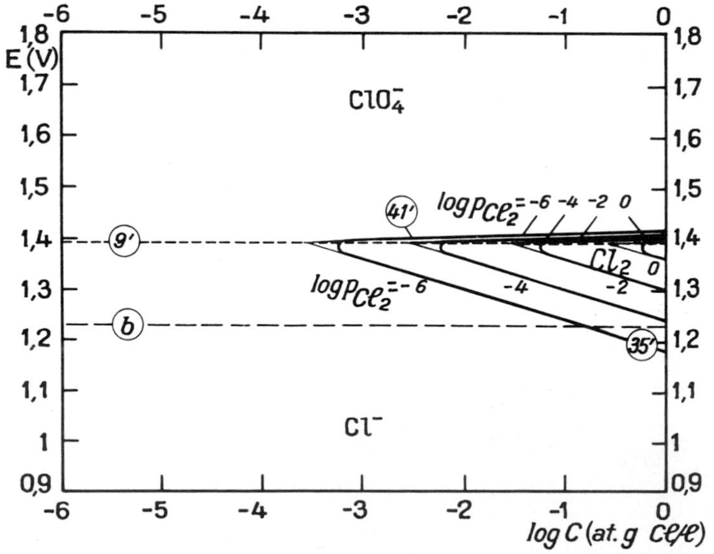

FIG. 3. Potential/concentration equilibrium diagram for the system chlorine–water, at 25°C.
Stable equilibria.
(For solutions of pH = 0.)

of oxygen derivatives of chlorine, including hypochlorites, chlorites, chlorates and perchlorates. The conditions under which these different oxidations are possible will be examined individually later.

3.3. FORMATION AND STABILITY OF GASEOUS CHLORINE

Figures 1, 2 and 3 show that gaseous chlorine has only a relatively small stability domain, and then only in acid solutions; chlorine can be obtained by the oxidation of acid solutions having a sufficiently high Cl^- concentration (Fig. 3), and this oxidation can be brought about either chemically or electrolytically. From the above mentioned figures it can be seen that very powerful oxidizing agents are needed to bring about this reaction, even if we do not take into account the chlorine overpotential.

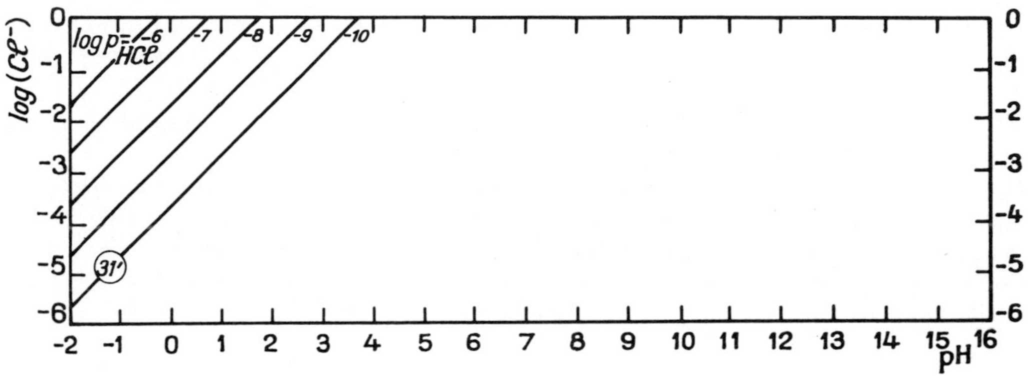

FIG. 4. Influence of pH on the solubility of gaseous HCl at various partial pressures.

In the laboratory, chlorine is usually prepared by the chemical oxidation of hot solutions of hydrochloric acid, using $KMnO_4$ or IO_3^-. With very concentrated hydrochloric acid, MnO_2 can also be used (Scheele process) [2].

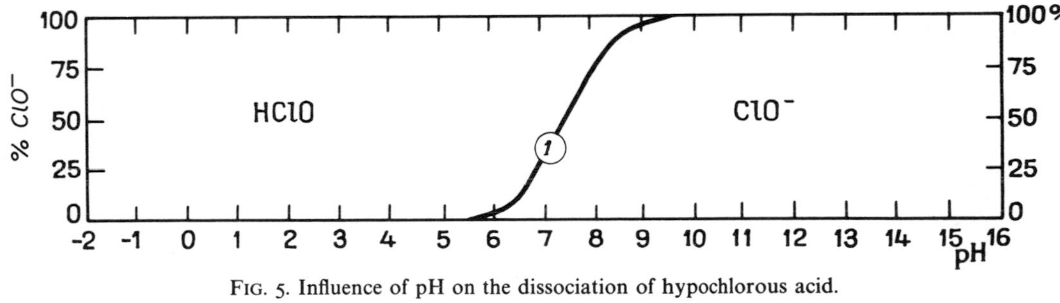

FIG. 5. Influence of pH on the dissociation of hypochlorous acid.

Industrially, chlorine is manufactured on a very large scale by the electrolysis of chloride solutions. In this process it is, of course, necessary that the anolyte should be acid, and this is realized by separating the anolyte from the alkaline catholyte by means of a diaphragm. The chlorine formed in this way is practically free from oxygen, even though the equilibrium formation potential for oxygen is lower than that for chlorine; this is due to the fact that the oxygen overpotential is a lot higher than the chlorine overpotential. When chloride solutions are electrolysed with a non-acid anolyte, as is the case when no diaphragm is used, chlorine is not obtained; depending on the temperature and current density, hypochlorite and Cl_2O (Fig. 2c), chlorate (Fig. 2a) or perchlorate (Fig. 1) can be formed.

The position of the stability domain of chlorine above that of water and the triangular shape of this domain show respectively that chlorine tends to oxidize water with the evolution of oxygen and that, in the presence of water, it can decompose on addition of alkali to give a chloride and an oxygen compound of chlorine (hypochlorite, chlorite, chlorate or perchlorate).

The *oxidation of water*, which takes place according to the reactions

	$2Cl_2 + 4e^- \rightarrow 4Cl^-$	(35)
and	$2H_2O \rightarrow O_2 + 4H^+ + 4e^-$	(b)
overall reaction	$2Cl_2 + 2H_2O \rightarrow 4Cl^- + O_2 + 4H^+$	

is always fairly slow on account of the great irreversibility of reaction (b); this gives chlorine water a certain degree of stability, despite its great oxidizing power; examples of reactions in which chlorine in the presence of water acts as an oxidizing agent are: the oxidation of hydrogen peroxide $Cl_2 + H_2O_2 \rightarrow 2Cl^- + O_2 + 2H^+$; the oxidation of the acids HI, HBr, H_2S, H_2Se and H_2Te to I_2, Br_2, S, Se and Te respectively; the oxidation of hyposulphites to sulphates, nitrites to nitrates, ferrous and stannous salts to ferric and stannic salts, ammonia to nitrogen, etc.

The affinities of the decomposition reactions of chlorine increase as the solution becomes more alkaline; according to Figs. 1 and 2 these reactions can theoretically produce hypochlorite, chlorite, chlorate and perchlorate; they can occur during the electrolysis of chloride solutions when the anodic and cathodic compartments are not separated, in which case the chlorine formed at the anode can react with the alkali formed at the cathode. Experiment shows that at temperatures around 25°C, the formation of hypochlorous acid and hypochlorites by the reactions $Cl_2 + H_2O \rightarrow HClO + Cl^- + H^+$ and $Cl_2 + H_2O \rightarrow ClO^- + Cl^- + 2H^+$ predominates over the other reactions; at 50°, the formation of chlorate by the reaction $3Cl_2 + 3H_2O \rightarrow ClO_3^- + 5Cl^- + 6H^+$ is predominant, while at low temperatures, and with a high current density, the chlorate solution is converted into perchlorate.

It should be noted that equation (32′) gives the value of the *solubility of chlorine* in water at 25°C as a function of the pressure of gaseous chlorine above the solution; conversely, it gives the partial pressure of gaseous chlorine in equilibrium with chlorine solutions of various concentrations.

3.4. FORMATION AND STABILITY OF HYPOCHLOROUS ACID, THE HYPOCHLORITES AND HYPOCHLOROUS ANHYDRIDE

Hypochlorous acid HClO is a very weak acid of pK = 7·5 (Fig. 2*c*). Figure 5 shows the influence of pH on the relative proportions of the forms HClO and ClO^- in hypochlorite solutions. Hypochlorous acid is a combination of water and hypochlorous anhydride (chlorine monoxide) Cl_2O; in

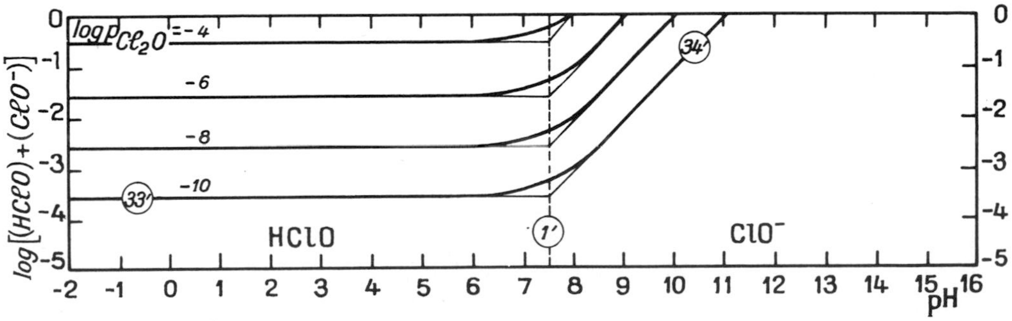

FIG. 6. Influence of pH on the solubility of gaseous Cl_2O at various partial pressures.

Fig. 6 we have used relations (33′) and (34′) to represent, as a function of pH, the solubility in water at 25°C of gaseous hypochlorous anhydride Cl_2O in the forms HClO and ClO^-, for various partial Cl_2O pressures in the atmosphere in equilibrium with these solutions.

As shown in paragraph 3.3, HClO and ClO^- can be obtained at about 25°C by the electrolytic oxidation of neutral or alkaline solutions of chlorides, or by the action of chlorine on neutral or alkaline solutions.

The position of the stability-domains of HClO and ClO^- above the domain of stability of the water (Fig. 2*c*) shows that hypochlorous acid and hypochlorites oxidize the water with the release of oxygen. This oxidation of the water is done by means of the reduction of hypochlorous acid and hypochlorites to chloride (which, for the solutions considered, containing 1 g-al Cl/l considered at Fig. 2*c*, will be evolved under atmospheric pressure at pH below 4) and in chloride (which will be predominant in solution at pH above 3·3). Here are the reactions to be considered in the different conditions of pH([2]):

pH below approximately 4

$$\begin{array}{lcll} 4HClO + 4H^+ + 4e^- & \rightarrow & 2Cl_2 + 4H_2O & (36) \\ 2H_2O & \rightarrow & O_2 + 4H^+ + 4e^- & (b) \\ \hline 4HClO & \rightarrow & O_2 + 2Cl_2 + 2H_2O & \end{array}$$

pH between approximately 3·3 and 7·5

$$\begin{array}{lcll} 2HClO + 2H^+ + 4e^- & \rightarrow & 2Cl^- + 2H_2O & (4) \\ 2H_2O & \rightarrow & O_2 + 4H^+ + 4e^- & (b) \\ \hline 2HClO & \rightarrow & O_2 + 2Cl^- + 2H^+ & \end{array}$$

pH above approximately 7·5

$$\begin{array}{lcll} 2ClO^- + 4H^+ + 4e^- & \rightarrow & 2Cl^- + 2H_2O & (5) \\ 2H_2O & \rightarrow & O_2 + 4H^+ + 4e^- & (b) \\ \hline 2ClO^- & \rightarrow & O_2 + 2Cl^-. & \end{array}$$

Except in the presence of certain catalysts (MnO_2, NiO_2, CoO_2) or under the action of light, these reactions are all slow however, especially in alkaline solution, on account of the great irreversibility of reaction (*b*) (oxidation of water to oxygen). As is the case with chlorine water, this confers a fairly large stability on neutral and alkaline solutions of hypochlorous acid and hypochlorites, in spite of their great oxidizing power.

Numerous examples of the oxidizing action of HClO and ClO^- are known: the oxidation of the elements S, Se, P, As and of H_2S, H_2SO_3, AsH_3 and PH_3 to the corresponding oxyacids; the oxidation of the oxides As_2O_3, FeO, MnO, NiO, PbO and SnO to the corresponding higher oxides; the oxidation of I^- to IO_4^- [3].

In acid solutions and in the presence of chloride, parallel to slow oxidation of water by oxygen (*b*), there will be a rapid oxidation of the chloride to chlorine (35). This will bring about the rapid overall reaction $HClO^- + Cl^- + H^+ \rightarrow Cl_2 + H_2O$ with the double formation of free chlorine [by the reduction of HClO according to reaction (36) and by oxidation of Cl^- according to reaction (35)]:

$$\begin{array}{llcll} & 2Cl^- & \rightarrow & Cl_2 + 2e^- & (35) \\ \text{and} & 2HClO + 2H^+ + 2e^- & \rightarrow & Cl_2 + 2H_2O & (36) \\ \hline \text{overall reaction} & 2HClO + 2Cl^- + 2H^+ & \rightarrow & 2Cl_2 + 2H_2O. & \end{array}$$

Consequently, hypochlorous acid solutions decompose on acidification, and this decomposition will be faster the higher the chloride concentration.

Figure 2*b*, obtained by adding those equilibria involving *chlorites* to the chlorine/chloride/hypochlorite equilibria of Fig. 2*c*, brings out the decomposition of hypochlorites into chlorides and chlorites; in alkaline media this decomposition proceeds according to the reactions

$$\begin{array}{llcll} & ClO^- + 2H^+ + 2e^- & \rightarrow & Cl^- + H_2O & (5) \\ \text{and} & ClO^- + H_2O & \rightarrow & ClO_2^- + 2H^+ + 2e^- & (19) \\ \hline \text{overall reaction} & 2ClO^- & \rightarrow & Cl^- + ClO_2^- & \end{array}$$

and is such that there is no longer any domain of thermodynamic stability for the hypochlorite ClO^- ion; in acid media, it remains for the hypochlorous acid HClO a triangular domain of stability which

([2]) We indicate here the two partial electrochemical reactions and also the resultant overall chemical reaction.

is characteristic of the disproportionation which then takes place according to the reactions

	$HClO + H^+ + 2e^-$	$\rightarrow$	$Cl^- + H_2O$	(4)
and	$HClO + H_2O$	$\rightarrow$	$HClO_2 + 2H^+ + 2e^-$	(16)
overall reaction	$2HClO$	$\rightarrow$	$Cl^- + HClO_2 + H^+.$	

If we compare Fig. 2 *a* and *c* we see that, in the presence of chloride, the stability domain of chlorates covers entirely that of the hypochlorous acid and hypochlorites. In consequence HClO and ClO^- are thermodynamically unstable towards ClO_3^- and Cl^- and have a tendency to react to the following reaction: $ClO^- + 2HClO \rightarrow ClO_3^- + 2Cl^- + 2H^+$.

Experience shows that this reaction practically does not occur at 25°C but that it attains an appreciable speed at higher temperature (50°C).

3.5. FORMATION AND STABILITY OF CHLOROUS ACID AND THE CHLORITES

In the chlorite ion ClO_2^-, chlorine is present in the oxidation state +3, intermediate between that of the hypochlorites (+1) and those of chlorine dioxide (+4), the chlorates (+5) and the perchlorates (+7). As we have just pointed out, Fig. 2*b* was obtained by adding to Fig. 2*c* lines representing the equilibrium conditions of $HClO_2$ and ClO_2^- with respect to all the substances represented in Fig. 2*c*, and by omitting from the diagram thus obtained the substances which then cease to be predominant. There is thus no longer any need to consider the hypochlorites ClO^-, which are completely replaced by the more stable chlorites ClO_2^-, nor the gaseous hypochlorous anhydride Cl_2O. Hypochlorous acid HClO retains a small domain of predominance.

Chlorous acid $HClO_2$ is a weak acid (pK = 2·0), but not so weak as hypochlorous acid (pK = 7·5); Fig. 7 shows the effect of pH on the relative proportions of the forms $HClO_2$ and ClO_2^- in chlorite solutions.

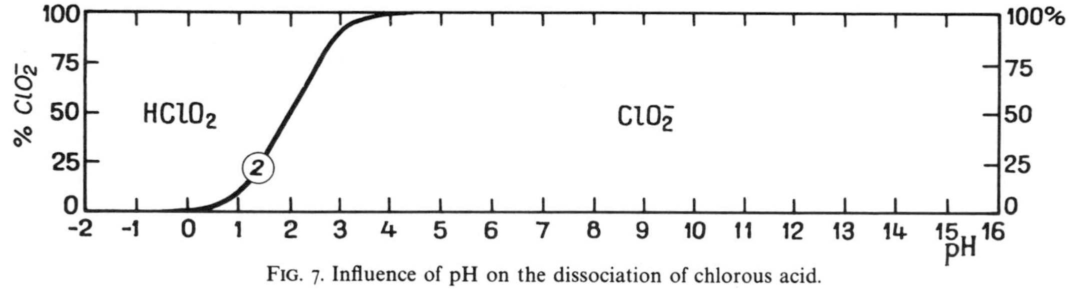

FIG. 7. Influence of pH on the dissociation of chlorous acid.

Chlorites can be obtained, together with clorates, by the disproportionation of ClO_2 in alkaline solution according to the reaction $2ClO_2 + H_2O \rightarrow ClO_2^- + ClO_3^- + 2H^+$.

Solutions of chlorous acid and chlorites, which tend to be reduced to hypochlorite and chloride, are oxidizing: they oxidize iodine to iodic acid, nitrous acid to nitric acid and sulphurous acid to sulphuric acid; they also oxidize hydrogen peroxide, ferrous salts and manganous salts. They can be oxidized to gaseous ClO_2 by ozone.

Like the other oxygen compounds of chlorine, chlorites have only a metastable equilibrium: in the presence of catalysts (Pt or Pd blacks), they rapidly decompose to give chlorate and chloride, for instance in alkaline media, according to the reactions

	$ClO_2^- + 4H^+ + 4e^-$	$\rightarrow$	$Cl^- + 2H_2O$	(7)
and	$2ClO_2^- + 2H_2O$	$\rightarrow$	$2ClO_3^- + 4H^+ + 4e^-$	(21)
overall reaction	$3ClO_2^-$	$\rightarrow$	$Cl^- + 2ClO_3^-$	

or in acid media, according to the reactions

	$HClO_2 + 3H^+ + 4e^-$	$\rightarrow$	$Cl^- + 2H_2O$	(6)
and	$2HClO_2 + 2H_2O$	$\rightarrow$	$2ClO_3^- + 6H^+ + 4e^-$	(20)
overall reaction	$3HClO_2$	$\rightarrow$	$Cl^- + 2ClO_3^- + 3H^+$	

In alkaline media the cathodic reduction of ClO_2^- ions gives chlorides directly (cf. [4]).

3.6. FORMATION AND STABILITY OF GASEOUS CHLORINE DIOXIDE ClO_2

Chlorine dioxide represents an oxidation state intermediate between the chlorites and chlorates. No acid or ion of the same degree of oxidation ($Z = +4$) is known.

ClO_2 is a powerful oxidizing agent and its aqueous solutions are not very stable, mainly on account of the relative ease with which it can be reduced to chlorite; in the absence of oxidizable substances and in the presence of alkali, it dissolves in water, decomposing with the slow formation of chlorite and chlorate according to the overall reaction $2ClO_2 + H_2O \rightarrow ClO_2^- + ClO_3^- + 2H^+$. Chlorine dioxide can oxidize chlorides to hypochlorites according to the reaction $2ClO_2 + Cl^- + H_2O \rightarrow 2HClO_2 + ClO^-$

3.7. FORMATION AND STABILITY OF THE CHLORATES AND PERCHLORATES

Chloric and perchloric acids are strong acids, existing in solution only in the form of ClO_3^- and ClO_4^- ions. Theoretically they can be formed by the disproportionation of chlorine into chloride and chlorate, on the one hand, and into chloride and perchlorate on the other.

From a purely thermodynamic point of view, the chloride–perchlorate system is the more stable (Figs. 1 and 3); it is towards this that all systems tend whence chlorine becomes oxidized to a degree intermediate between the chlorides and the perchlorates; in practice the transformation stops at the chlorate stage, since the chlorate $\rightarrow$ perchlorate transformation is very slow at room temperature; it is in this way that chloric acid is formed by the decomposition of aqueous solutions of Cl_2, or of HClO, $HClO_2$ and ClO_2; chlorates are obtained by the action of chlorine on alkaline lyes at 50°C, or by the electrolysis of chloride solutions, also at about 50°C; perchlorates are obtained at the expense of chlorates only at temperatures of around 350° or by electrolysis under certain operating conditions: a high chlorate concentration, a low temperature and a high current density. The chlorates and perchlorates are stable and do not have any oxidizing properties except in very acid solution; thus chloric acid oxidizes the hydracids HCl, HBr and HI to Cl_2, Br_2 and I_2 respectively; it also oxidizes SO_2, H_2S and the sulphides, and HNO_2, and causes certain metals (Cu, Hg, Ti, Fe) to pass from a lower to a higher degree of oxidation; perchloric acid oxidizes iodine to HIO_3; Se, S, P, As and Sb can also be oxidized in the hot; it has no action, however, on H_2S, SO_2, HNO_2 and HCl and is not reduced by ferrous salts, but is readily reduced by salts of trivalent titanium. In a concentrated dehydrating acid medium (H_2SO_4), chlorates decompose with formation of gaseous chlorine dioxide [3] (Fig. 2*a*).

4. BIBLIOGRAPHY

[1] H. VALENSI, E. DELTOMBE, N. DE ZOUBOV and M. POURBAIX, *Comportement électrochimique du chlore. Diagrammes d'équilibres tension*–pH *du système.* Cl–H_2O *à* 25°C (Rapport technique RT.44 of CEBELCOR, February 1957).

[2] G. VALENSI *et al.*, Diagrammes tension–pH des halogènes (Lecture at the 5th Meeting of CITCE, Stockholm, 1953) (unpublished).

[3] G. CHARLOT, *L'analyse qualitative et les réactions en solution,* 4th ed., Masson, Paris, 1957.

[4] J. LAMBERTON and H. DE LACHEISSERIE, Contribution expérimentale à l'étude de la stabilité électrochimique des composés du chlore en fonction du pH moyen des solutions (Lecture at the 4th Meeting of CITCE, Cambridge, 1952) (unpublished).

SECTION 20.3

BROMINE(1)

C. VANLEUGENHAGHE, G. VALENSI and M. POURBAIX

SUMMARY

(1) Adapted version of an extract from Rapport CEFA/R.12 of the Commission des Études Fondamentales et Applications of CEBELCOR. A potential–pH equilibrium diagram for the system bromine–water was presented by Valensi *et al.* at the 5th Meeting of CITCE (1953) [1].

1. SUBSTANCES CONSIDERED AND SUBSTANCES NOT CONSIDERED

	Oxidation number (Z)	Considered	Not considered	μ^0(cal.)	Name, colour, crystalline system
Solid substances	+1	–	Br_2O	–	Monoxide, brown
	+4	–	BrO_2	–	Dioxide, yellow
	+5.33	–	Br_3O_8	–	Octoxide, white
Liquid substance	0	Br_2	–	0	Bromine, dark brown
Dissolved substances	−1	Br^-	–	−24 574	Bromide ion, colourless
	−0.33	Br_3^-	–	−25 270	Tribromide ion, reddish-yellow
	−0.20	Br_5^-	–	−24 340 (*)	Pentabromide ion
	0	Br_2	–	977	Bromine
	+1	$HBrO$	–	−19 900	Hypobromous acid, straw yellow
	»	BrO^-	–	− 8 000	Hypobromite ion, colourless
	+3	–	$HBrO_2$	–	Bromous acid
	+5	$HBrO_3$	–	1 350 (*)	Bromic acid, colourless
	»	BrO_3^-	–	2 300 (*)	Bromate ion, colourless
Gaseous substances	−1	HBr	–	−12 720	Hydrobromic acid, colourless
	0	Br_2	–	751	Bromine, red–brown

The values not marked with the sign (*) are ones given by Latimer [2]. The value of $\mu^0_{Br_5^-}$ was given by Valensi in a lecture to the 5th Meeting of CITCE [1]. The value of $\mu^0_{BrO_3^-}$ is that mentioned by Lewis and Randall [3], and is in approximate agreement with that calculated by Mel *et al.* [4] (2·1 kcal. + 2 kcal.), and with that calculated by Myers (see [4]) (2·5 kcal. ± 0·3 kcal.). The value of $\mu^0_{HBrO_3}$ was calculated by us from the pK of the reaction $HBrO_3 = BrO_3^- + H^+$ (pK = 0·7) given by Charlot [5] and from the free enthalpy value for BrO_3^- that we have assumed.

2. REACTIONS AND EQUILIBRIUM FORMULAE

2.1. TWO DISSOLVED SUBSTANCES

2.1.1. *Relative stability of the dissolved substances*

Z = +1

1. $HBrO = BrO^- + H^+$ $\qquad \log\frac{(BrO^-)}{(HBrO)} = -8.73 + pH$

Z = +5

2. $HBrO_3 = BrO_3^- + H^+$ $\qquad \log\frac{(BrO_3^-)}{(HBrO_3)} = -0.70 + pH$

−1 → −0.33

3. $3Br^- = Br_3^- + 2e^-$ $\qquad E_0 = 1.051 + 0.0295\log\frac{(Br_3^-)}{(Br^-)^3}$

−1 → −0.20

4. $5Br^- = Br_5^- + 4e^-$ $\qquad E_0 = 1.068 + 0.0148\log\frac{(Br_5^-)}{(Br^-)^5}$

−1 → 0

5. $2Br^- = Br_2 + 2e^-$ $\qquad E_0 = 1.087 + 0.0295\log\frac{(Br_2)}{(Br^-)^2}$

−1 → +1

6. $Br^- + H_2O = HBrO + H^+ + 2e^-$ $\qquad E_0 = 1.331 - 0.0295\,pH + 0.0295\log\frac{(HBrO)}{(Br^-)}$

7. $Br^- + H_2O = BrO^- + 2H^+ + 2e^-$ $\qquad E_0 = 1.589 - 0.0591\,pH + 0.0295\log\frac{(BrO^-)}{(Br^-)}$

$-1 \rightarrow +5$

8. $Br^- + 3H_2O = HBrO_3 + 5H^+ + 6e^-$ $E_0 = 1.417 - 0.0493\,pH + 0.0098 \log \frac{(HBrO_3)}{(Br^-)}$

9. $Br^- + 3H_2O = BrO_3^- + 6H^+ + 6e^-$ $E_0 = 1.423 - 0.0591\,pH + 0.0098 \log \frac{(BrO_3^-)}{(Br^-)}$

$-0.33 \rightarrow -0.20$

10. $5Br_3^- = 3Br_5^- + 2e^-$ $E_0 = 1.156 + 0.0295 \log \frac{(Br_5^-)^3}{(Br_3^-)^5}$

$-0.33 \rightarrow 0$

11. $2Br_3^- = 3Br_2 + 2e^-$ $E_0 = 1.159 + 0.0295 \log \frac{(Br_2)^3}{(Br_3^-)^2}$

$-0.33 \rightarrow +1$

12. $Br_3^- + 3H_2O = 3HBrO + 3H^+ + 4e^-$ $E_0 = 1.470 - 0.0443\,pH + 0.0148 \log \frac{(HBrO)^3}{(Br_3^-)}$

13. $Br_3^- + 3H_2O = 3BrO^- + 6H^+ + 4e^-$ $E_0 = 1.856 - 0.0886\,pH + 0.0148 \log \frac{(BrO^-)^3}{(Br_3^-)}$

$-0.33 \rightarrow +5$

14. $Br_3^- + 9H_2O = 3HBrO_3 + 15H^+ + 16e^-$ $E_0 = 1.462 - 0.0554\,pH + 0.0037 \log \frac{(HBrO_3)^3}{(Br_3^-)}$

15. $Br_3^- + 9H_2O = 3BrO_3^- + 18H^+ + 16e^-$ $E_0 = 1.472 - 0.0665\,pH + 0.0037 \log \frac{(BrO_3^-)^3}{(Br_3^-)}$

$-0.20 \rightarrow 0$

16. $2Br_5^- = 5Br_2 + 2e^-$ $E_0 = 1.161 + 0.0295 \log \frac{(Br_2)^5}{(Br_5^-)^2}$

$-0.20 \rightarrow +1$

17. $Br_5^- + 5H_2O = 5HBrO + 5H^+ + 6e^-$ $E_0 = 1.305 - 0.0493\,pH + 0.0098 \log \frac{(HBrO)^5}{(Br_5^-)}$

18. $Br_5^- + 5H_2O = 5BrO^- + 10H^+ + 6e^-$ $E_0 = 1.935 - 0.0985\,pH + 0.0098 \log \frac{(BrO^-)^5}{(Br_5^-)}$

$0 \rightarrow +1$

19. $Br_2 + 2H_2O = 2HBrO + 2H^+ + 2e^-$ $E_0 = 1.574 - 0.0591\,pH + 0.0295 \log \frac{(HBrO)^2}{(Br_2)}$

20. $Br_2 + 2H_2O = 2BrO^- + 4H^+ + 2e^-$ $E_0 = 2.090 - 0.1182\,pH + 0.0295 \log \frac{(BrO^-)^2}{(Br_2)}$

$0 \rightarrow +5$

21. $Br_2 + 6H_2O = 2HBrO_3 + 10H^+ + 10e^-$ $E_0 = 1.482 - 0.0591\,pH + 0.0059 \log \frac{(HBrO_3)^2}{(Br_2)}$

22. $Br_2 + 6H_2O = 2BrO_3^- + 12H^+ + 10e^-$ $E_0 = 1.491 - 0.0709\,pH + 0.0059 \log \frac{(BrO_3^-)^2}{(Br_2)}$

$+1 \rightarrow +5$

23. $HBrO + 2H_2O = HBrO_3 + 4H^+ + 4e^-$ $E_0 = 1.460 - 0.0591\,pH + 0.0148 \log \frac{(HBrO_3)}{(HBrO)}$

24. $HBrO + 2H_2O = BrO_3^- + 5H^+ + 4e^-$ $E_0 = 1.470 - 0.0739\,pH + 0.0148 \log \frac{(BrO_3^-)}{(HBrO)}$

25. $BrO^- + 2H_2O = HBrO_3 + 3H^+ + 4e^-$ $E_0 = 1.330 - 0.0443\,pH + 0.0148 \log \frac{(HBrO_3)}{(BrO^-)}$

26. $BrO^- + 2H_2O = BrO_3^- + 4H^+ + 4e^-$ $E_0 = 1.341 - 0.0591\,pH + 0.0148 \log \frac{(BrO_3^-)}{(BrO^-)}$

2.1.2. *Limits of the domains of relative predominance of the dissolved substances*

1'. $HBrO/BrO^-$ $pH = 8.73$
2'. $HBrO_3/BrO_3^-$ $pH = 0.70$

3'. Br^-/Br_3^- $E_0 = 1.055 - 0.0591 \log C$
4'. Br^-/Br_5^- $E_0 = 1.075 - 0.0591 \log C$
5'. Br^-/Br_2 $E_0 = 1.087 - 0.0295 \log C$
6'. $Br^-/HBrO$ $E_0 = 1.331 - 0.0295\,pH$
7'. Br^-/BrO^- $E_0 = 1.589 - 0.0591\,pH$

8′.	Br^-	$/HBrO_3$	$E_0 = 1.417 - 0.0493\ pH$
9′.	Br^-	$/BrO_3^-$	$E_0 = 1.423 - 0.0591\ pH$
10′.	Br_3^-	$/Br_5^-$	$E_0 = 1.182 \quad - 0.0591 \log C$
11′.	Br_3^-	$/Br_2$	$E_0 = 1.152 \quad + 0.0295 \log C$
12′.	Br_3^-	$/HBrO$	$E_0 = 1.468 - 0.0443\ pH + 0.0295 \log C$
13′.	Br_3^-	$/BrO^-$	$E_0 = 1.854 - 0.0886\ pH + 0.0295 \log C$
14′.	Br_3^-	$/HBrO_3$	$E_0 = 1.462 - 0.0554\ pH + 0.0074 \log C$
15′.	Br_3^-	$/BrO_3^-$	$E_0 = 1.472 - 0.0665\ pH + 0.0074 \log C$
16′.	Br_5^-	$/Br_2$	$E_0 = 1.131 \quad + 0.0886 \log C$
17′.	Br_5^-	$/HBrO$	$E_0 = 1.500 - 0.0493\ pH + 0.0394 \log C$
18′.	Br_5^-	$/BrO^-$	$E_0 = 1.930 - 0.0985\ pH + 0.0394 \log C$
19′.	Br_2	$/HBrO$	$E_0 = 1.574 - 0.0591\ pH + 0.0295 \log C$
20′.	Br_2	$/BrO^-$	$E_0 = 2.090 - 0.1182\ pH + 0.0295 \log C$
21′.	Br_2	$/HBrO_3$	$E_0 = 1.482 - 0.0591\ pH + 0.0059 \log C$
22′.	Br_2	$/BrO_3^-$	$E_0 = 1.491 - 0.0709\ pH + 0.0059 \log C$
23′.	$HBrO$	$/HBrO_3$	$E_0 = 1.460 - 0.0591\ pH$
24′.	$HBrO$	$/BrO_3^-$	$E_0 = 1.470 - 0.0739\ pH$
25′.	BrO^-	$/HBrO_3$	$E_0 = 1.330 - 0.0443\ pH$
26′.	BrO^-	$/BrO_3^-$	$E_0 = 1.341 - 0.0591\ pH$

11″.	Br_3^-	$/Br_2$ and $\mathbf{Br_2}$	$E_0 = 1.149$
21″.	Br_2	$/HBrO_3$ and $\mathbf{Br_2}$	$E_0 = 1.482 - 0.0591\ pH$
22″.	Br_2	$/BrO_3^-$ and $\mathbf{Br_2}$	$E_0 = 1.490 - 0.0709\ pH$

2.2. ONE LIQUID SUBSTANCE AND ONE DISSOLVED SUBSTANCE

Solubility of liquid bromine

a. Solubility in gram-ions per litre

$Z = 0$

27.	$Br_2 = \mathbf{Br_2}$		$\log(Br_2) = -0.72$

$-1 \rightarrow 0$

28.	$2Br^- = \mathbf{Br_2} + 2e^-$	$E_0 = 1.066$	$-0.0591 \log(Br^-)$

$-0.33 \rightarrow 0$

29.	$2Br_3^- = 3\mathbf{Br_2} + 2e^-$	$E_0 = 1.096$	$-0.0591 \log(Br_3^-)$

$-0.20 \rightarrow 0$

30.	$2Br_5^- = 5\mathbf{Br_2} + 2e^-$	$E_0 = 1.056$	$-0.0591 \log(Br_5^-)$

$0 \rightarrow +1$

31.	$\mathbf{Br_2} + 2H_2O = 2HBrO + 2H^+ + 2e^-$	$E_0 = 1.596 - 0.0591\ pH + 0.0591 \log(HBrO)$

$0 \rightarrow +5$

32.	$\mathbf{Br_2} + 6H_2O = 2HBrO_3 + 10H^+ + 10e^-$	$E_0 = 1.487 - 0.0591\ pH + 0.0118 \log(HBrO_3)$
33.	$\mathbf{Br_2} + 6H_2O = 2BrO_3^- + 12H^+ + 10e^-$	$E_0 = 1.495 - 0.0709\ pH + 0.0118 \log(BrO_3^-)$

b. Solubility in gram-atoms per litre

27′.	Br_2	$/\mathbf{Br_2}$	$\log C = -0.42$
28′.	Br^-	$/\mathbf{Br_2}$	$E_0 = 1.066 \quad - 0.0591 \log C$
29′.	Br_3^-	$/\mathbf{Br_2}$	$E_0 = 1.124 \quad - 0.0591 \log C$
30′.	Br_5^-	$/\mathbf{Br_2}$	$E_0 = 1.097 \quad - 0.0591 \log C$
31′.	$\mathbf{Br_2}$	$/HBrO$	$E_0 = 1.596 - 0.0591\ pH + 0.0591 \log C$
32′.	$\mathbf{Br_2}$	$/HBrO_3$	$E_0 = 1.487 - 0.0591\ pH + 0.0118 \log C$
33′.	$\mathbf{Br_2}$	$/BrO_3^-$	$E_0 = 1.495 - 0.0709\ pH + 0.0118 \log C$

2.3. ONE LIQUID SUBSTANCE AND ONE GASEOUS SUBSTANCE

Vapour pressure of liquid bromine

Z = 0

34. $\mathbf{Br_2} = Br_2$ $\log p_{Br_2} = -0.55$

2.4. TWO GASEOUS SUBSTANCES

2.4.1. *Relative stability of gaseous bromine and gaseous hydrogen bromide*

−1 → 0

35. $2HBr = Br_2 + 2H^+ + 2e^-$ $E_0 = 0.351 - 0.0591\,pH + 0.0295 \log \frac{p_{Br_2}}{p^2_{HBr}}$

2.4.2. *Limits of the domains of relative predominance of gaseous bromine and gaseous hydrogen bromide*

35'. HBr/Br_2 $E_0 = 0.361 - 0{,}0591\,pH - 0.0295 \log P$

2.5. ONE GASEOUS SUBSTANCE AND ONE DISSOLVED SUBSTANCE

Solubility of gaseous bromine and gaseous hydrogen bromide

a. Solubility in gram-ions or gram-molecules per litre

Br_2

Z = 0

36. $Br_2 = Br_2$ $\log p_{Br_2} = 0.165 + \log(Br_2)$

−1 → 0

37. $2Br^- = Br_2 + 2e^-$ $E_0 = 1.082 + 0.0295 \log \frac{p_{Br_2}}{(Br^-)^2}$

−0.33 → 0

38. $2Br_3^- = 3Br_2 + 2e^-$ $E_0 = 1.145 + 0.0295 \log \frac{p^3_{Br_2}}{(Br_3^-)^2}$

0 → +1

39. $Br_2 + 2H_2O = 2HBrO + 2H^+ + 2e^-$ $E_0 = 1.579 - 0.0591\,pH + 0.0295 \log \frac{(HBrO)^2}{p_{Br_2}}$

0 → +5

40. $Br_2 + 6H_2O = 2HBrO_3 + 10H^+ + 10e^-$ $E_0 = 1.484 - 0.0591\,pH + 0.0059 \log \frac{(HBrO_3)^2}{p_{Br_2}}$

41. $Br_2 + 6H_2O = 2BrO_3^- + 12H^+ + 10e^-$ $E_0 = 1.492 - 0.0709\,pH + 0.0059 \log \frac{(BrO_3^-)^2}{p_{Br_2}}$

HBr

Z = −1

42. $HBr = Br^- + H^+$ $\log p_{HBr} = -8.70 - pH + \log(Br^-)$

b. Solubility in gram-ions of bromine per litre

36'. Br_2/Br_2 $\log p_{Br_2} = -0.136 + \log C$

37'. Br^-/Br_2 $E_0 = 1.082 + 0.0295 \log p_{Br_2} - 0.0591 \log C$

38'. Br_3^-/Br_2 $E_0 = 1.173 + 0.0886 \log p_{Br_2} - 0.0591 \log C$

39'. $Br_2/HBrO$ $E_0 = 1.579 - 0.0591\,pH - 0.0295 \log p_{Br_2} + 0.0591 \log C$

40'. $Br_2/HBrO_3$ $E_0 = 1.484 - 0.0591\,pH - 0.0059 \log p_{Br_2} + 0.0118 \log C$

41'. Br_2/BrO_3^- $E_0 = 1.492 - 0.0709\,pH - 0.0059 \log p_{Br_2} + 0.0118 \log C$

42'. HBr/Br^- $\log p_{HBr} = -8.70 - pH + \log C$

3. EQUILIBRIUM DIAGRAMS AND THEIR INTERPRETATION

3.1. ESTABLISHMENT OF THE DIAGRAMS

Using the equilibrium formulae established in paragraph 2, we have drawn Fig. 1, which is a potential–pH equilibrium diagram for a total dissolved bromine concentration of 1 g-at Br/l (79·9 g Br/l). Figure 2 represents four partial equilibrium diagrams, for total dissolved bromine concentrations of respectively 1, 10^{-2}, 10^{-4} and 10^{-6} g-at Br/l.

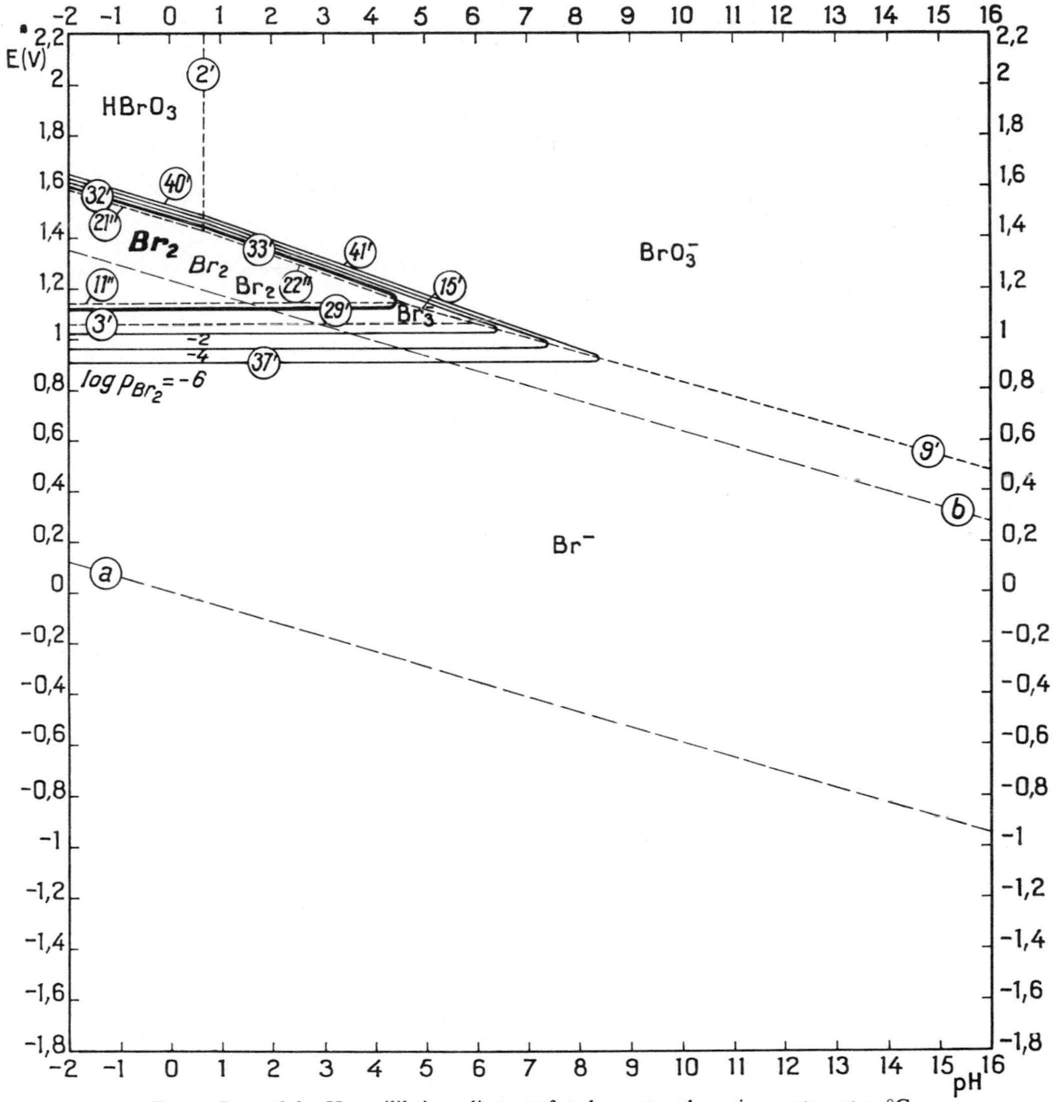

FIG. 1. Potential–pH equilibrium diagram for the system bromine–water, at 25°C.

Solutions containing 1 g-at Br/l.

Figure 3 refers to solutions of pH = 0, and represents a potential/concentration equilibrium diagram for the system bromine–water, at 25°C. Figure 4 shows the influence of pH on the solubility of gaseous hydrogen bromide, at 25°C. These diagrams are valid only in the absence of substances with which bromine can form *soluble complexes* or *insoluble salts*. Bromine forms a large number of complexes, but they are usually not very stable. Examples are: $CuBr^{+}$, $CdBr_4^{--}$, $PtBr_4^{--}$, $AuBr_2^{-}$, I_2Br^{-}, IBr_2^{-}, $TlBr_4^{-}$. Certain bromides are sparingly soluble or insoluble: AuBr, $PbBr_2$, TlBr, CuBr, AgBr, HgBr, $MoBr_2$, $PdBr_2$, $PtBr_2$; a few bromates are also sparingly soluble: $Pb(BrO_3)_2$, $Hg(BrO_3)_2$, $AgBrO_3$, $TlBrO_3$.

No account was taken of the unstable solid oxides Br_2O, BrO_2 and Br_3O_8 in the establishment of the above diagrams, since we have no thermodynamic data for these compounds.

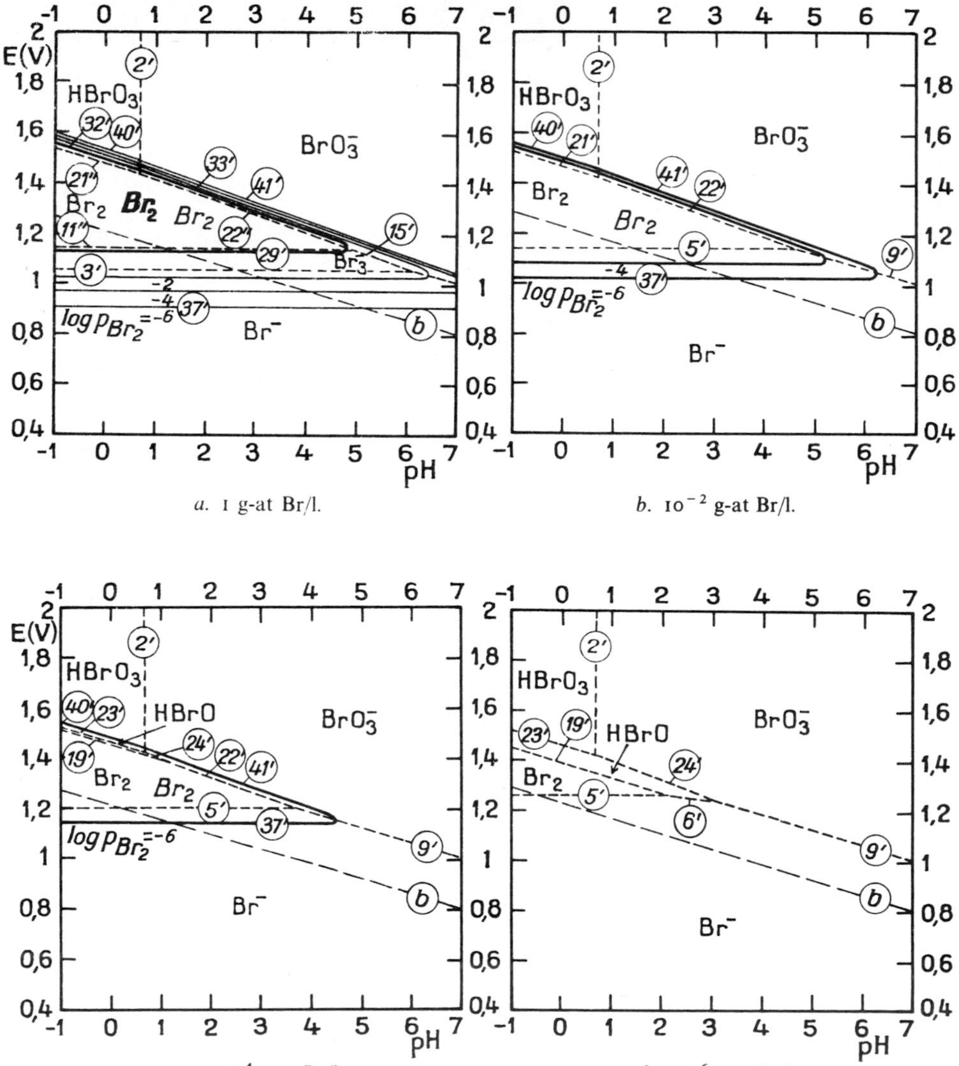

a. 1 g-at Br/l. *b.* 10^{-2} g-at Br/l.

c. 10^{-4} g-at Br/l. *d.* 10^{-6} g-at Br/l.

FIG. 2. Potential–pH equilibrium diagram for the system bromine–water, at 25°C.

3.2. FORMATION AND STABILITY OF BROMINE

In agreement with Figs. 1 and 2, bromine can be obtained by the controlled oxidation of an acid solution of a bromide.

This oxidation can be brought about chemically (e.g. using nitric acid, concentrated sulphuric acid, metallic peroxides, dichromate or hypochlorous acid), or electrolytically (using a platinum anode).

With relatively concentrated solutions (having a bromine concentration greater than about 0·38 g-at/l, i.e. 30 g Br/l), this oxidation gives rise to both liquid and gaseous bromine (the vapour pressure of liquid bromine is 0·28 atm. at 25°C). With relatively dilute solutions (having a bromine concentration lower than 0·38 g-at Br/l), the bromine formed remains in the dissolved state, presenting, nevertheless, a small partial pressure [which, for example, does not exceed $10^{-4.1}$ atm. (i.e. 0·00008 atm.) in the case of solutions containing 10^{-4} g-at Br/l].

When a bromide solution is oxidized electrolytically without a diaphragm, the bromine liberated at the anode reacts with the base formed at the cathode to give hypobromite which is unstable and is converted chemically into bromate, with the evolution of oxygen [7].

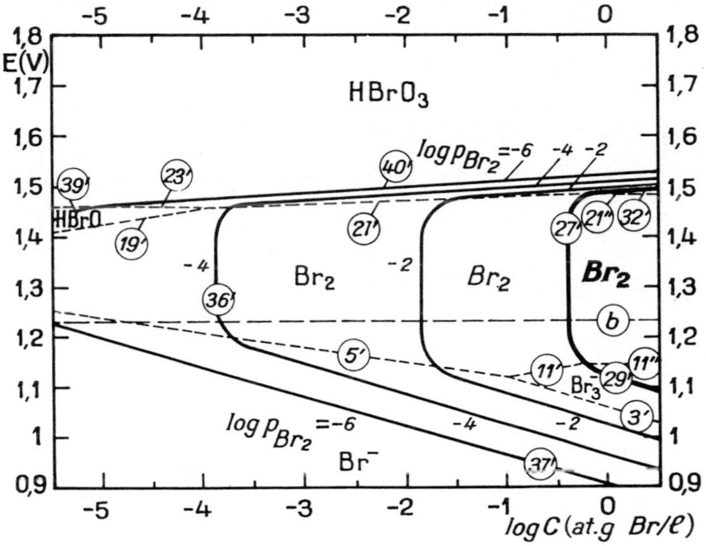

FIG. 3. Potential/concentration equilibrium diagram for the system bromine–water, at 25°C. (For solutions of pH = 0.)

The position of the stability domain of bromine in Figs. 1 and 2 characterizes it as an oxidizing substance except in highly acid solutions; in neutral, alkaline and slightly acid solutions it tends to oxidize the water with the evolution of oxygen and the formation of bromide (and polybromides such as Br_3^-); this oxidation may be accompanied by a decomposition to bromide and to bromate and hypobromite, the latter being itself unstable. Bromine water does in fact contain hypobromite and slowly evolves oxygen; this decomposition is accelerated by the action of light [1].

The overpotential of formation of bromine is of the same order of magnitude as that of chlorine [7].

3.3. STABILITY OF HYDROBROMIC ACID AND THE BROMIDES

In Figs. 1 and 2, the domain of predominance of the bromides Br^- entirely covers the domain of stability of water, except for the top left corner, where the media are very acid and oxidizing. In nature we therefore find bromine in the form of bromides, principally as magnesium and alkali metal bromides.

Hydrobromic acid is a strong acid; in aqueous solution it is completely dissociated according to the reaction $HBr \rightarrow H^+ + Br^-$. In agreement with equation (42′) and Fig. 4 which is derived from it, solutions of bromides or hydrobromic acid, even when very acid, exert only a very small partial pressure of gaseous hydrogen bromide. In this respect hydrobromic acid differs from hydrofluoric and hydrochloric acids, whose aqueous solutions are more volatile.

The high solubility of bromine in an aqueous solution of hydrobromic acid is responsible for the existence of the polybromides Br_3^- and Br_5^- and possibly of more condensed compounds. The Br_3^- ion has a domain of relative predominance only in solutions whose concentration is greater than $8{\cdot}04 \times 10^{-2}$ g-at Br/l. The Br_5^- ion is never predominant.

3.4. FORMATION AND STABILITY OF HYPOBROMOUS ACID AND THE HYPOBROMITES

Hypobromous acid HBrO has no domain of relative predominance in Fig. 2, except in very dilute solutions, whose concentration does not exceed 10^{-4} g-at/l. The formation of hypobromous acid is the result of the "hydrolysis of bromine", which consists of disproportionation according to the electrochemical reactions

$$Br_2 + 2e^- \rightarrow 2Br^- \qquad (5)$$
$$Br_2 + 2H_2O \rightarrow 2HBrO + 2H^+ + 2e^- \qquad (19)$$

and therefore corresponds to the overall chemical reaction

$$Br_2 + H_2O \rightarrow Br^- + HBrO + H^+.$$

The formation of hypobromous acid will therefore be favoured by the absence of Br^- ions [6].

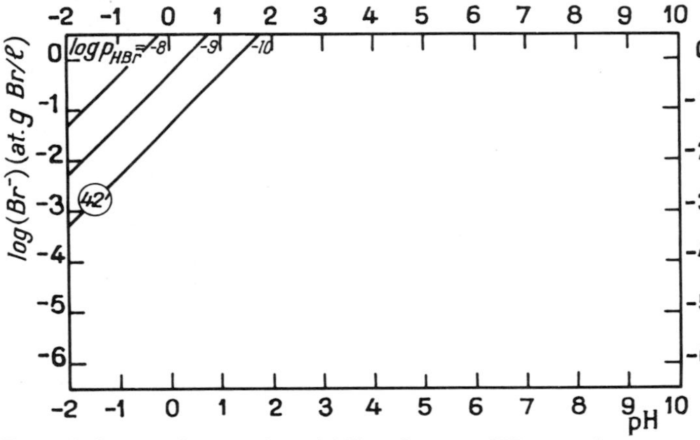

FIG. 4. Influence of pH on the solubility of gaseous HBr at various pressures.

Hypobromous acid is an oxidizing agent which is unstable in the presence of water, since its domain of relative predominance lies above the stability domain of water. Consequently it tends to decompose water with the formation of oxygen and bromine according to the electrochemical reactions

$$2H_2O \rightarrow O_2 + 4H^+ + 4e^- \qquad (b)$$
$$4HBrO + 4H^+ + 4e^- \rightarrow 2Br_2 + 4H_2O \qquad (19)$$

i.e. according to the chemical reaction

$$4HBrO \rightarrow O_2 + 2Br_2 + 2H_2O.$$

Moreover, it is generally metastable with respect to bromic acid and bromine, into which it decomposes according to the electrochemical reactions

$$HBrO + 2H_2O \rightarrow HBrO_3 + 4H^+ + 4e^- \qquad (23)$$
$$4HBrO + 4H^+ + 4e^- \rightarrow 2Br_2 + 4H_2O \qquad (19)$$

i.e., according to the chemical reaction

$$5HBrO \rightarrow HBrO_3 + 2Br_2 + 2H_2O.$$

Hypobromous acid is a weak acid (pK = 8·73); like hypobromous acid, the hypobromites BrO^- are metastable. In very alkaline solutions they decompose to give bromate and bromide according to the electrochemical reactions

$$BrO^- + 2H_2O \rightarrow BrO_3^- + 4H^+ + 4e^- \quad (26)$$
$$2BrO^- + 4H^+ + 4e^- \rightarrow 2Br^- + 2H_2O \quad (7)$$

i.e. according to the chemical reaction

$$3BrO^- \rightarrow BrO_3^- + 2Br^-.$$

This reaction occurs even in the cold, in particular during the electrolysis of a bromide solution without a diaphragm [1].

3.5. FORMATION AND STABILITY OF BROMIC ACID AND THE BROMATES

Bromic acid $HBrO_3$ is a strong acid (pK = 0·70). Bromic acid and the bromates can be obtained by the electrolytic oxidation of bromide solutions or bromine water using chlorine, fluorine or hypochlorous anhydride, or by the action of bromine on water in the presence of alkalis [8]. In this last case there is simultaneous formation of bromide, a little oxygen and unstable hypobromous acid.

Bromic acid and the bromates are powerful oxidizing agents, but the speed of their oxidation reactions is generally low [5]. Bromates are often sparingly soluble in the cold.

4. BIBLIOGRAPHY

[1] G. Valensi, Diagrammes tension–pH des halogènes (Lecture at the 5th Meeting of CITCE, Stockholm, 1953) (unpublished).
[2] W. Latimer, *Oxidation Potentials*, 2nd ed., Prentice-Hall, New York, 1952.
[3] G. N. Lewis and M. Randall, *Thermodynamics and the Free Energy of Chemical Substances*, McGraw-Hill, New York, 1923, p. 521.
[4] H. C. Mel, W. L. Jolly and W. Latimer, The heat and free energy of formation of bromate ion, *J. Amer. Chem. Soc.* **75**, 3827 (1953).
[5] G. Charlot, *L'analyse qualitative et les réactions en solution*, 4th ed., Masson, Paris, 1957.
[6] P. Pascal, *Traité de Chimie minérale*, Vol. I, Masson, Paris, 1931.
[7] H. J. Creighton, *Principles and Applications of Electrochemistry*, Wiley, New York, 1943, p. 250.
[8] N. V. Sidgwick, *The Chemical Elements and their Compounds*, Vol. II, Oxford, 1951, pp. 1139 *et seq.*

SECTION 20.4

IODINE [1]

C. VANLEUGENHAGHE, G. VALENSI and M. POURBAIX

SUMMARY

[1] Adapted version of an extract from Rapport CEFA/R.12 of the Commission des Études Fondamentales et Applications of CEBELCOR. Potential–pH equilibrium diagrams for the system iodine–water have been previously presented by Valensi *et al.*, in 1953 [1] as well as by Brown [2] and by Pourbaix [3] in 1955, at CITCE meetings.

1. SUBSTANCES CONSIDERED AND SUBSTANCES NOT CONSIDERED

	Oxidation number (Z)	Considered	Not considered	μ^0(cal.)	Name, colour, crystalline system
Solid substances	0	I_2	-	0	Iodine, grey–black, orthorh.
	+4	-	I_2O_4	-	Iodyl iodate, lemon yellow
	+4.5	-	I_4O_9	-	Iodate of trivalent iodine $I(IO_3)_3$, yellowish white
	+5	-	I_2O_5	-	Iodine pentoxide or iodic anhydride, colourless
	»	-	HIO_3	-	Iodic acid, colourless
	+7	-	HIO_4	-	Periodic acid
Dissolved substances	−1	I^-	-	−12 330	Iodide ion, colourless
	−0.33	I_3^-	-	−12 310	Triiodide ion, orange–brown
	−0.20	-	I_5^-	− 6 900 (2)	Pentaiodide ion
	0	I_2	-	3 926	Dissolved iodine, brown
	+1	I^+	-	31 290 (2)	?
	»	HIO	-	−23 500	Hypoiodous acid, colourless
	»	IO^-	-	− 8 500	Hypoiodite ion, colourless
	+3	-	HIO_2	-	Iodous acid
	+5	HIO_3	-	−33 340 (2)	Iodic acid, colourless
	»	IO_3^-	-	−32 250	Iodate ion, colourless
	+7	HIO_4	-	−15 020 (2)	Periodic acid H_5IO_6, colourless(3)
	»	IO_4^- anh.	-	−12 700 (2)	Anhydrous periodate ion, colourless
	»	-	IO_4^- hydr.	−10 520 (2)	Hydrated periodate ion ($H_4IO_6^-$), colourless
	»	HIO_5^{--}	-	−58 110 (2)	Periodate ion ($H_3IO_6^{--}$), colourless
	»	IO_5^{---}	-	−43 110 (2)	Periodate ion ($H_2IO_6^{---}$), colourless
	»	-	$I_2O_9^{----}$	-	Periodate ion, colourless
Gaseous substances	−1	*HI*	-	310	Hydrogen iodide, colourless
	0	I_2	-	4 630	Iodine, violet

2. REACTIONS AND EQUILIBRIUM FORMULAE

2.1. TWO DISSOLVED SUBSTANCES

2.1.1. *Relative stability of the dissolved substances*

Z = +1

1. $I^+ + H_2O = HIO + H^+$ $\qquad \log \frac{(HIO)}{(I^+)} = -1.39 + pH$

2. $HIO = IO^- + H^+$ $\qquad \log \frac{(IO^-)}{(HIO)} = -11.00 + pH$

Z = +5

3. $HIO_3 = IO_3^- + H^+$ $\qquad \log \frac{(IO_3^-)}{(HIO_3)} = -0.80 + pH$

---

(2) I_5^- Value taken from the communication by G. Valensi to the 5th meeting of CITCE [1].
HIO_3: value calculated from pK of the dissociation of iodic acid given by Brown [2].
I^+: value calculated from the pK of the reaction $I_2 + H_2O = I^- + H_2IO^+$ given by Bell and Gelles [4]; ($\mu^0_{H_2IO^+} = -25\,400$ cal., which corresponds to $\mu^0_{I^+} = 31\,290$ cal.).
IO_4^-: value due to Latimer and Crouthamel and quoted by Brown [2].
HIO_4, IO_4^- hydr., HIO_5^{--} and IO_5^{---}: values calculated from data supplied by Crouthamel [10].
(3) By analogy with the corresponding chlorine and bromine compounds, we have represented periodic acid by the formula HIO_4, although it is generally accepted that periodic acid answers to the formula $HIO_4 . 2H_2O$ or H_5IO_6. Similarly, we have omitted the molecule of water from the formulae of the periodate ions which are usually written $H_3IO_6^{--}$ and $H_2IO_6^{---}$

$Z = +7$

4. $HIO_4 = IO_4^- + H^+$ $\qquad \log \frac{(IO_4^-)}{(HIO_4)} = -1.70 + pH$

5. $IO_4^- + H_2O = HIO_5^{--} + H^+$ $\qquad \log \frac{(HIO_5^{--})}{(IO_4^-)} = -8.30 + pH$

6. $HIO_5^{--} = IO_5^{---} + H^+$ $\qquad \log \frac{(IO_5^{---})}{(HIO_5^{--})} = -11.00 + pH$

$-1 \rightarrow -0.33$

7. $3I^- = I_3^- + 2e^-$ $\qquad E_0 = 0.536 + 0.0295 \log \frac{(I_3^-)}{(I^-)^3}$

$-1 \rightarrow 0$

8. $2I^- = I_2 + 2e^-$ $\qquad E_0 = 0.621 + 0.0295 \log \frac{(I_2)}{(I^-)^2}$

$-1 \rightarrow +1$

9. $I^- = I^+ + 2e^-$ $\qquad E_0 = 0.946 + 0.0295 \log \frac{(I^+)}{(I^-)}$

10. $I^- + H_2O = HIO + H^+ + 2e^-$ $\qquad E_0 = 0.987 - 0.0295\,pH + 0.0295 \log \frac{(HIO)}{(I^-)}$

11. $I^- + H_2O = IO^- + 2H^+ + 2e^-$ $\qquad E_0 = 1.313 - 0.0591\,pH + 0.0295 \log \frac{(IO^-)}{(I^-)}$

$-1 \rightarrow +5$

12. $I^- + 3H_2O = HIO_3 + 5H^+ + 6e^-$ $\qquad E_0 = 1.077 - 0.0493\,pH + 0.0098 \log \frac{(HIO_3)}{(I^-)}$

13. $I^- + 3H_2O = IO_3^- + 6H^+ + 6e^-$ $\qquad E_0 = 1.085 - 0.0591\,pH + 0.0098 \log \frac{(IO_3^-)}{(I^-)}$

$-1 \rightarrow +7$

14. $I^- + 4H_2O = HIO_4 + 7H^+ + 8e^-$ $\qquad E_0 = 1.215 - 0.0517\,pH + 0.0074 \log \frac{(HIO_4)}{(I^-)}$

15. $I^- + 4H_2O = IO_4^- + 8H^+ + 8e^-$ $\qquad E_0 = 1.227 - 0.0591\,pH + 0.0074 \log \frac{(IO_4^-)}{(I^-)}$

16. $I^- + 5H_2O = HIO_5^{--} + 9H^+ + 8e^-$ $\qquad E_0 = 1.288 - 0.0665\,pH + 0.0074 \log \frac{(HIO_5^{--})}{(I^-)}$

17. $I^- + 5H_2O = IO_5^{---} + 10H^+ + 8e^-$ $\qquad E_0 = 1.370 - 0.0739\,pH + 0.0074 \log \frac{(IO_5^{---})}{(I^-)}$

$-0.33 \rightarrow 0$

18. $2I_3^- = 3I_2 + 2e^-$ $\qquad E_0 = 0.789 + 0.0295 \log \frac{(I_2)^3}{(I_3^-)^2}$

$-0.33 \rightarrow +1$

19. $I_3^- = 3I^+ + 4e^-$ $\qquad E_0 = 1.151 + 0.0148 \log \frac{(I^+)^3}{(I_3^-)}$

20. $I_3^- + 3H_2O = 3HIO + 3H^+ + 4e^-$ $\qquad E_0 = 1.213 - 0.0443\,pH + 0.0148 \log \frac{(HIO)^3}{(I_3^-)}$

21. $I_3^- + 3H_2O = 3IO^- + 6H^+ + 4e^-$ $\qquad E_0 = 1.701 - 0.0886\,pH + 0.0148 \log \frac{(IO^-)^3}{(I_3^-)}$

$-0.33 \rightarrow +5$

22. $I_3^- + 9H_2O = 3HIO_3 + 15H^+ + 16e^-$ $\qquad E_0 = 1.145 - 0.0554\,pH + 0.0037 \log \frac{(HIO_3)^3}{(I_3^-)}$

23. $I_3^- + 9H_2O = 3IO_3^- + 18H^+ + 16e^-$ $\qquad E_0 = 1.154 - 0.0665\,pH + 0.0037 \log \frac{(IO_3^-)^3}{(I_3^-)}$

$-0.33 \rightarrow +7$

24. $I_3^- + 12H_2O = 3HIO_4 + 21H^+ + 22e^-$ $\qquad E_0 = 1.276 - 0.0564\,pH + 0.0027 \log \frac{(HIO_4)^3}{(I_3^-)}$

25. $I_3^- + 12H_2O = 3IO_4^- + 24H^+ + 22e^-$ $\qquad E_0 = 1.290 - 0.0645\,pH + 0.0027 \log \frac{(IO_4^-)^3}{(I_3^-)}$

26. $I_3^- + 15H_2O = 3HIO_5^{--} + 27H^+ + 22e^-$ $\qquad E_0 = 1.357 - 0.0725\,pH + 0.0027 \log \frac{(HIO_5^{--})^3}{(I_3^-)}$

27. $I_3^- + 15H_2O = 3IO_5^{---} + 30H^+ + 22e^-$ $\qquad E_0 = 1.445 - 0.0806\,pH + 0.0027 \log \frac{(IO_5^{---})^3}{(I_3^-)}$

$0 \rightarrow +1$

28. $I_2 = 2I^+ + 2e^-$ $\quad E_0 = 1.272 + 0.0295 \log \frac{(I^+)^2}{(I_2)}$

29. $I_2 + 2H_2O = 2HIO + 2H^+ + 2e^-$ $\quad E_0 = 1.354 - 0.0591\,pH + 0.0295 \log \frac{(HIO)^2}{(I_2)}$

30. $I_2 + 2H_2O = 2IO^- + 4H^+ + 2e^-$ $\quad E_0 = 2.005 - 0.1182\,pH + 0.0295 \log \frac{(IO^-)^2}{(I_2)}$

$0 \rightarrow +5$

31. $I_2 + 6H_2O = 2HIO_3 + 10H^+ + 10e^-$ $\quad E_0 = 1.169 - 0.0591\,pH + 0.0059 \log \frac{(HIO_3)^2}{(I_2)}$

32. $I_2 + 6H_2O = 2IO_3^- + 12H^+ + 10e^-$ $\quad E_0 = 1.178 - 0.0709\,pH + 0.0059 \log \frac{(IO_3^-)^2}{(I_2)}$

$0 \rightarrow +7$

33. $I_2 + 8H_2O = 2HIO_4 + 14H^+ + 14e^-$ $\quad E_0 = 1.300 - 0.0591\,pH + 0.0042 \log \frac{(HIO_4)^2}{(I_2)}$

34. $I_2 + 8H_2O = 2IO_4^- + 16H^+ + 14e^-$ $\quad E_0 = 1.314 - 0.0676\,pH + 0.0042 \log \frac{(IO_4^-)^2}{(I_2)}$

35. $I_2 + 10H_2O = 2HIO_5^{--} + 18H^+ + 14e^-$ $\quad E_0 = 1.384 - 0.0760\,pH + 0.0042 \log \frac{(HIO_5^{--})^2}{(I_2)}$

36. $I_2 + 10H_2O = 2IO_5^{---} + 20H^+ + 14e^-$ $\quad E_0 = 1.477 - 0.0844\,pH + 0.0042 \log \frac{(IO_5^{---})^2}{(I_2)}$

$+1 \rightarrow +5$

37. $I^+ + 3H_2O = HIO_3 + 5H^+ + 4e^-$ $\quad E_0 = 1.143 - 0.0739\,pH + 0.0148 \log \frac{(HIO_3)}{(I^+)}$

38. $I^+ + 3H_2O = IO_3^- + 6H^+ + 4e^-$ $\quad E_0 = 1.155 - 0.0886\,pH + 0.0148 \log \frac{(IO_3^-)}{(I^+)}$

39. $HIO + 2H_2O = IO_3^- + 5H^+ + 4e^-$ $\quad E_0 = 1.134 - 0.0739\,pH + 0.0148 \log \frac{(IO_3^-)}{(HIO)}$

40. $IO^- + 2H_2O = IO_3^- + 4H^+ + 4e^-$ $\quad E_0 = 0.972 - 0.0591\,pH + 0.0148 \log \frac{(IO_3^-)}{(IO^-)}$

$+1 \rightarrow +7$

41. $I^+ + 4H_2O = HIO_4 + 7H^+ + 6e^-$ $\quad E_0 = 1.304 - 0.0689\,pH + 0.0098 \log \frac{(HIO_4)}{(I^+)}$

42. $HIO + 3H_2O = HIO_4 + 6H^+ + 6e^-$ $\quad E_0 = 1.290 - 0.0591\,pH + 0.0098 \log \frac{(HIO_4)}{(HIO)}$

43. $HIO + 3H_2O = IO_4^- + 7H^+ + 6e^-$ $\quad E_0 = 1.235 - 0.0689\,pH + 0.0098 \log \frac{(IO_4^-)}{(HIO)}$

44. $HIO + 4H_2O = HIO_5^{--} + 8H^+ + 6e^-$ $\quad E_0 = 1.389 - 0.0788\,pH + 0.0098 \log \frac{(HIO_5^{--})}{(HIO)}$

45. $IO^- + 4H_2O = IO_5^{---} + 8H^+ + 6e^-$ $\quad E_0 = 1.389 - 0.0788\,pH + 0.0098 \log \frac{(IO_5^{---})}{(IO^-)}$

$+5 \rightarrow +7$

46. $HIO_3 + H_2O = HIO_4 + 2H^+ + 2e^-$ $\quad E_0 = 1.626 - 0.0591\,pH + 0.0295 \log \frac{(HIO_4)}{(HIO_3)}$

47. $IO_3^- + H_2O = HIO_4 + H^+ + 2e^-$ $\quad E_0 = 1.603 - 0.0295\,pH + 0.0295 \log \frac{(HIO_4)}{(IO_3^-)}$

48. $IO_3^- + H_2O = IO_4^- + 2H^+ + 2e^-$ $\quad E_0 = 1.653 - 0.0591\,pH + 0.0295 \log \frac{(IO_4^-)}{(IO_3^-)}$

49. $IO_3^- + 2H_2O = HIO_5^{--} + 3H^+ + 2e^-$ $\quad E_0 = 1.898 - 0.0886\,pH + 0.0295 \log \frac{(HIO_5^{--})}{(IO_3^-)}$

50. $IO_3^- + 2H_2O = IO_5^{---} + 4H^+ + 2e^-$ $\quad E_0 = 2.223 - 0.1182\,pH + 0.0295 \log \frac{(IO_5^{---})}{(IO_3^-)}$

2.1.2. *Limits of the domains of relative predominance of the dissolved substances*

1′. I^+ / HIO $\quad pH = 1.39$

2′. HIO / IO^- $\quad pH = 11.00$

3′. HIO_3 / IO_3^- $\quad pH = 0.80$

4'.	HIO_4/IO_4^-	$pH = 1.70$
5'.	IO_4^-/HIO_5^{--}	$pH = 8.30$
6'.	HIO_5^{--}/IO_5^{---}	$pH = 11.00$
7'.	I^-/I_3^-	$E_0 = 0.532 - 0.0591 \log C$
8'.	I^-/I_2	$E_0 = 0.621 - 0.0295 \log C$
9'.	I^-/I^+	$E_0 = 0.946$
10'.	I^-/HIO	$E_0 = 0.987 - 0.0295\, pH$
11'.	I^-/IO^-	$E_0 = 1.313 - 0.0591\, pH$
12'.	I^-/HIO_3	$E_0 = 1.077 - 0.0493\, pH$
13'.	I^-/IO_3^-	$E_0 = 1.085 - 0.0591\, pH$
14'.	I^-/HIO_4	$E_0 = 1.215 - 0.0517\, pH$
15'.	I^-/IO_4^-	$E_0 = 1.227 - 0.0591\, pH$
16'.	I^-/HIO_5^{--}	$E_0 = 1.288 - 0.0665\, pH$
17'.	I^-/IO_5^{---}	$E_0 = 1.370 - 0.0739\, pH$
18'.	I_3^-/I_2	$E_0 = 0.782 + 0.0295 \log C$
19'.	I_3^-/I^+	$E_0 = 1.149 + 0.0295 \log C$
20'.	I_3^-/HIO	$E_0 = 1.211 - 0.0443\, pH + 0.0295 \log C$
21'.	I_3^-/IO^-	$E_0 = 1.699 - 0.0886\, pH + 0.0295 \log C$
22'.	I_3^-/HIO_3	$E_0 = 1.145 - 0.0554\, pH + 0.0074 \log C$
23'.	I_3^-/IO_3^-	$E_0 = 1.154 - 0.0665\, pH + 0.0074 \log C$
24'.	I_3^-/HIO_4	$E_0 = 1.276 - 0.0564\, pH + 0.0054 \log C$
25'.	I_3^-/IO_4^-	$E_0 = 1.290 - 0.0645\, pH + 0.0054 \log C$
26'.	I_3^-/HIO_5^{--}	$E_0 = 1.357 - 0.0725\, pH + 0.0054 \log C$
27'.	I_3^-/IO_5^{---}	$E_0 = 1.445 - 0.0806\, pH + 0.0054 \log C$
28'.	I_2/I^+	$E_0 = 1.272 + 0.0295 \log C$
29'.	I_2/HIO	$E_0 = 1.354 - 0.0591\, pH + 0.0295 \log C$
30'.	I_2/IO^-	$E_0 = 2.005 - 0.1182\, pH + 0.0295 \log C$
31'.	I_2/HIO_3	$E_0 = 1.169 - 0.0591\, pH + 0.0059 \log C$
32'.	I_2/IO_3^-	$E_0 = 1.178 - 0.0709\, pH + 0.0059 \log C$
33'.	I_2/HIO_4	$E_0 = 1.300 - 0.0591\, pH + 0.0042 \log C$
34'.	I_2/IO_4^-	$E_0 = 1.314 - 0.0676\, pH + 0.0042 \log C$
35'.	I_2/HIO_5^{--}	$E_0 = 1.384 - 0.0760\, pH + 0.0042 \log C$
36'.	I_2/IO_5^{---}	$E_0 = 1.477 - 0.0844\, pH + 0.0042 \log C$
37'.	I^+/HIO_3	$E_0 = 1.143 - 0.0739\, pH$
38'.	I^+/IO_3^-	$E_0 = 1.155 - 0.0886\, pH$
39'.	HIO/IO_3^-	$E_0 = 1.134 - 0.0739\, pH$
40'.	IO^-/IO_3^-	$E_0 = 0.972 - 0.0591\, pH$
41'.	I^+/HIO_4	$E_0 = 1.304 - 0.0689\, pH$
42'.	HIO/HIO_4	$E_0 = 1.290 - 0.0591\, pH$
43'.	HIO/IO_4^-	$E_0 = 1.235 - 0.0689\, pH$
44'.	HIO/HIO_5^{--}	$E_0 = 1.389 - 0.0788\, pH$
45'.	IO^-/IO_5^{---}	$E_0 = 1.389 - 0.0788\, pH$
46'.	HIO_3/HIO_4	$E_0 = 1.626 - 0.0591\, pH$
47'.	IO_3^-/HIO_4	$E_0 = 1.603 - 0.0295\, pH$
48'.	IO_3^-/IO_4^-	$E_0 = 1.653 - 0.0591\, pH$
49'.	IO_3^-/HIO_5^{--}	$E_0 = 1.898 - 0.0886\, pH$
50'.	IO_3^-/IO_5^{---}	$E_0 = 2.223 - 0.1182\, pH$
3''.	HIO_3/IO_3^- and $\mathbf{I_2}$	$pH = 0.8$
18''.	I_3^-/I_2 and $\mathbf{I_2}$	$E_0 = 0.714$
23''.	I_3^-/IO_3^- and $\mathbf{I_2}$	$E_0 = 1.090 - 0.0591\, pH$
28''.	I_2/I^+ and $\mathbf{I_2}$	$E_0 = 1.205$
31''.	I_2/HIO_3 and $\mathbf{I_2}$	$E_0 = 1.154 - 0.0591\, pH$
32''.	I_2/IO_3^- and $\mathbf{I_2}$	$E_0 = 1.165 - 0.0709\, pH$
37''.	I^+/HIO_3 and $\mathbf{I_2}$	$E_0 = 1.143 - 0.0739\, pH$

2.2. ONE SOLID SUBSTANCE AND ONE DISSOLVED SUBSTANCE

Solubility of solid iodine

a. Solubility in gram-ions or gram-molecules per litre

Z = 0

51. $\mathbf{I_2} = I_2$ $\qquad \log(I_2) = -2.87$

$-1 \to 0$

52. $2I^- = \mathbf{I_2} + 2e^-$ $\qquad E_0 = 0.5355 - 0.0591 \log(I^-)$

$-0.33 \to 0$

53. $2I_3^- = 3\mathbf{I_2} + 2e^-$ $\qquad E_0 = 0.534 - 0.0591 \log(I_3^-)$

$0 \to +1$

54. $\mathbf{I_2} = 2I^+ + 2e^-$ $\qquad E_0 = 1.357 + 0.0591 \log(I^+)$
55. $\mathbf{I_2} + 2H_2O = 2HIO + 2H^+ + 2e^-$ $\qquad E_0 = 1.439 - 0.0591\,pH + 0.0591 \log(HIO)$
56. $\mathbf{I_2} + 2H_2O = 2IO^- + 4H^+ + 2e^-$ $\qquad E_0 = 2.090 - 0.1182\,pH + 0.0591 \log(IO^-)$

$0 \to +5$

57. $\mathbf{I_2} + 6H_2O = 2HIO_3 + 10H^+ + 10e^-$ $\qquad E_0 = 1.186 - 0.0591\,pH + 0.0118 \log(HIO_3)$
58. $\mathbf{I_2} + 6H_2O = 2IO_3^- + 12H^+ + 10e^-$ $\qquad E_0 = 1.195 - 0.0709\,pH + 0.0118 \log(IO_3^-)$

b. Solubility in gram-atoms of iodine per litre

51'. $\mathbf{I_2}/I_2$ $\qquad \log C = -2.57$

52'. $I^-/\mathbf{I_2}$ $\qquad E_0 = 0.5355 - 0.0591 \log C$
53'. $I_3^-/\mathbf{I_2}$ $\qquad E_0 = 0.562 - 0.0591 \log C$
54'. $\mathbf{I_2}/I^+$ $\qquad E_0 = 1.357 + 0.0591 \log C$
55'. $\mathbf{I_2}/HIO$ $\qquad E_0 = 1.439 - 0.0591\,pH + 0.0591 \log C$
56'. $\mathbf{I_2}/IO^-$ $\qquad E_0 = 2.090 - 0.1182\,pH + 0.0591 \log C$
57'. $\mathbf{I_2}/HIO_3$ $\qquad E_0 = 1.186 - 0.0591\,pH + 0.0118 \log C$
58'. $\mathbf{I_2}/IO_3^-$ $\qquad E_0 = 1.195 - 0.0709\,pH + 0.0118 \log C$

2.3. TWO GASEOUS SUBSTANCES

2.3.1. *Relative stability of gaseous iodine and hydrogen iodide*

$-1 \to 0$

59. $2\mathit{HI} = \mathit{I_2} + 2H^+ + 2e^-$ $\qquad E_0 = 0.087 - 0.0591\,pH + 0.0295 \log \dfrac{p_{I_2}}{p_{HI}^2}$

2.3.2. *Limits of the domains of relative predominance of gaseous iodine and hydrogen iodide*

59'. $\mathit{HI}/\mathit{I_2}$ $\qquad E_0 = 0.097 - 0.0591\,pH - 0.0295 \log P$

2.4. ONE GASEOUS SUBSTANCE AND ONE DISSOLVED SUBSTANCE

Solubility of gaseous hydrogen iodide HI and iodine I_2

a. Solubility in gram-ions per litre

Z = −1

60. $\mathit{HI} = I^- + H^+$ $\qquad \log \dfrac{(I^-)}{p_{HI}} = 9.29 + pH$

Z = 0

61. $I_2 = \mathit{I_2}$ $\qquad \log \dfrac{p_{I_2}}{(I_2)} = -0.52$

$-1 \rightarrow 0$

62.	$2I^-$	$= I_2$	$+ 2e^-$	$E_0 = 0.636 + 0.0295 \log \frac{p_{I_2}}{(I^-)^2}$

$0 \rightarrow +1$

63.	I_2	$= 2I^+$	$+ 2e^-$	$E_0 = 1.256 + 0.0295 \log \frac{(I^+)^2}{p_{I_2}}$

$0 \rightarrow +5$

64.	I_2	$+ 6H_2O = 2HIO_3$	$+10H^+ + 10e^-$	$E_0 = 1.166 - 0.0591\,pH + 0.0059 \log \frac{(HIO_3)^2}{p_{I_2}}$
65.	I_2	$+ 6H_2O = 2IO_3^-$	$+12H^+ + 10e^-$	$E_0 = 1.175 - 0.0709\,pH + 0.0059 \log \frac{(IO_3^-)^2}{p_{I_2}}$

b. Solubility in gram-atoms of iodine per litre

60'.	HI/I^-	$pH = -9.29 + \log C - \log P$
61'.	I_2/I_2	$\log C = 0.82 + \log P$
62'.	I^-/I_2	$E_0 = 0.636 - 0.0591 \log C + 0.0295 \log P$
63'.	I_2/I^+	$E_0 = 1.256 + 0.0591 \log C - 0.0295 \log P$
64'.	I_2/HIO_3	$E_0 = 1.166 - 0.0591\,pH + 0.0118 \log C - 0.0059 \log P$
65'.	I_2/IO_3^-	$E_0 = 1.175 - 0.0709\,pH + 0.0118 \log C - 0.0059 \log P$

3. EQUILIBRIUM DIAGRAMS AND THEIR INTERPRETATION

3.1. ESTABLISHMENT OF THE DIAGRAMS

Using the equilibrium formulae established in paragraph 2, we have constructed Figs. 1 and 2, which are potential–pH diagrams representing the thermodynamically stable equilibria of the system iodine–water, at 25°C, for four different total dissolved iodine concentrations: 10^{-6}, 10^{-4}, 10^{-2} and 1 g-at I/l, i.e. respectively 0·127, 12·69, 1269 and 126 920 mgI/l.

The domains of relative predominance of the dissolved substances were determined from the formulae quoted in paragraph 2.1.2. For those reactions involving only monatomic forms of iodine, the equations of the lines which correspond to the same iodine concentration in the two dissolved forms considered, do not depend on the total iodine concentration C, while for those reactions involving a monatomic and a polyatomic form of iodine, the equations of these lines depend on the total iodine concentration C. In the equations reproduced in paragraphs 2.1.2, 2.2 and 2.4, C represents the total dissolved iodine concentration expressed in gram-atoms of iodine per litre.

In order to determine the boundary of the domains of relative predominance of iodine in two dissolved forms in solutions saturated with solid iodine, the term C is eliminated from those formulae of (51')–(58') which involve, on the one hand, solid iodine and, on the other hand, respectively each of the two dissolved forms considered. The resulting equations therefore express the limits of the domains of relative predominance of iodine in two dissolved forms in solutions saturated with iodine. They are given in paragraph 2.1.2 as equations marked with the sign ″. Figure 3 is the potential/concentration diagram for the system iodine–water at 25°C for solutions of pH = 0. Figure 4 represents the influence of pH on the solubility of HI as iodide, for various partial pressures of gaseous HI.

These equilibrium diagrams are, of course, valid only in the absence of substances with which iodine can form *soluble complexes* or *insoluble compounds*. There are a large number of soluble complexes containing iodine, including: $HgIO_4^{--}$, ICl_2^-, PbI_4^{--}, CuI_2^-, AgI_4^{---} and CdI_4^{--}. The insoluble or sparingly soluble compounds include the iodides of lead and palladium, the hypoiodites of silver and mercury, and barium periodate.

3.2. STABILITY OF HYDRIODIC ACID AND THE IODIDES

As shown by Figs. 1 and 2, *hydriodic acid* HI has no domain of predominance. It is a strong acid, completely dissociated according to the reaction $HI \rightarrow I^- + H^+$, forming iodide I^- whose domain of predominance extends all along the pH scale and almost completely covers a very large part of the

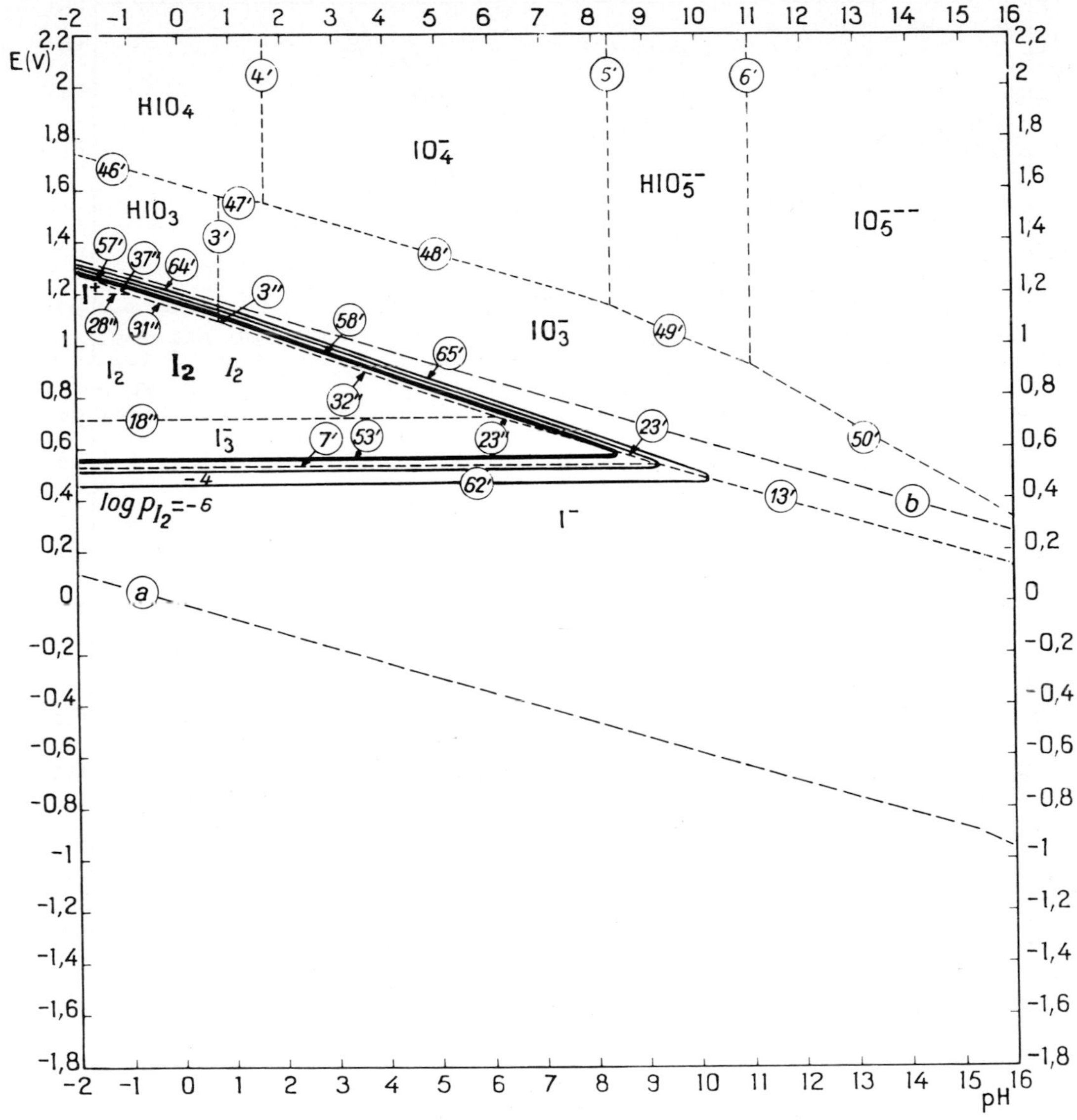

FIG. 1. Potential–pH equilibrium diagram for the system iodine–water, at 25°C, for solutions containing 1 g-at I/l.

stability domain of water, with the possibility of oxidation in the upper part of this domain. Hydriodic acid is only very slightly volatile (Fig. 4).

The *iodides* are stable in the presence of aqueous solutions free from oxidizing agents, and it is generally in this form that iodine is found in nature.

The oxidation of iodides at potentials above those indicated in Figs. 1 and 2 by line (13') leads to the formation of iodate IO_3^-, accompanied in acid media by the intermediate formation of iodine and possibly triiodide I_3^- and hypoiodite derivatives such as I^+. With relatively concentrated solutions, containing more than $10^{-2.57}$ g-at of dissolved iodine per litre (i.e. 342 mg I/l), iodine can separate out in the solid state (Figs. 1, 2*a* and 3). Further oxidation can lead to the formation of periodic acid and periodates.

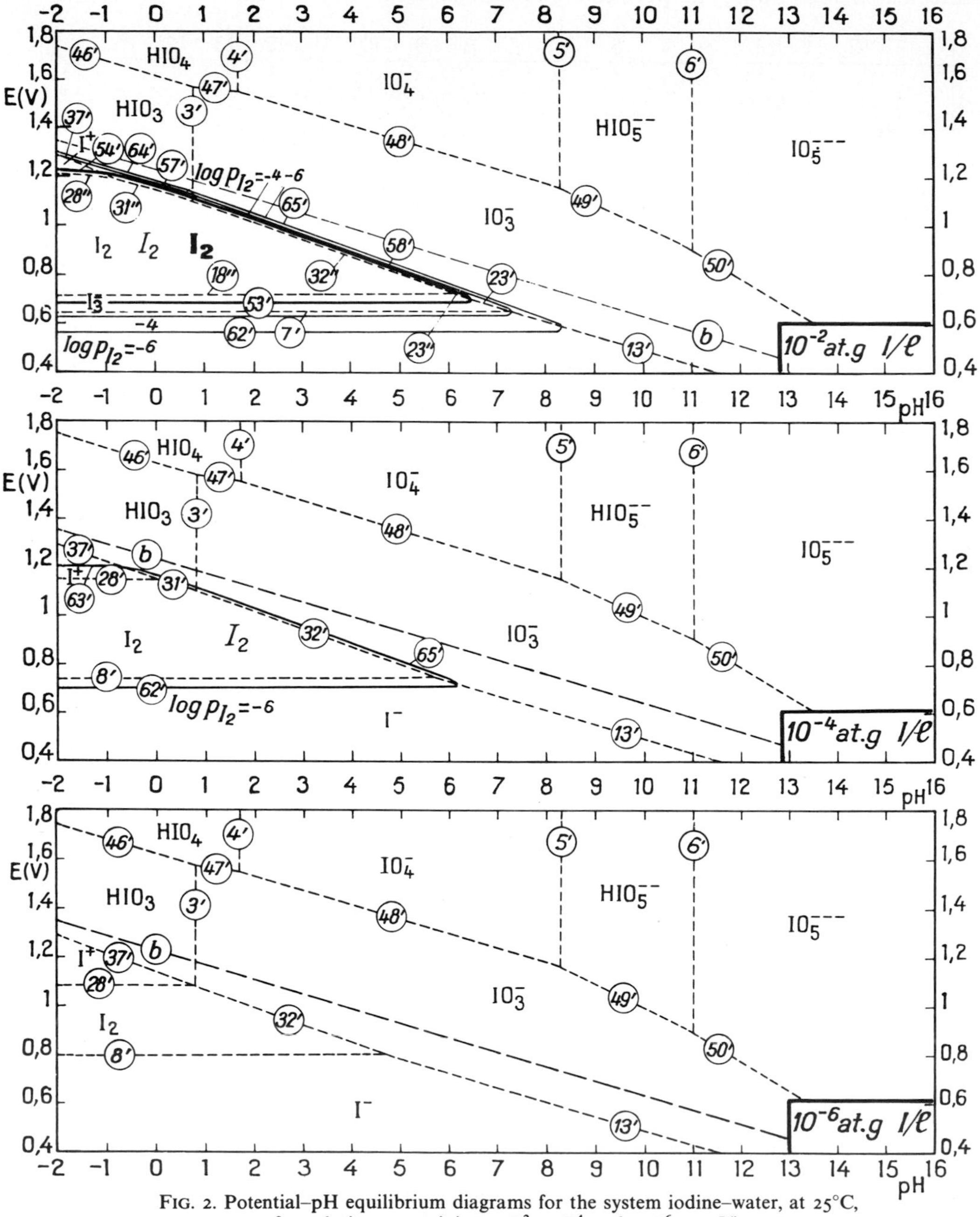

FIG. 2. Potential–pH equilibrium diagrams for the system iodine–water, at 25°C, for solutions containing 10^{-2}, 10^{-4} and 10^{-6} g-at I/l.

All oxidizing agents do in fact liberate iodine from acid solutions of iodides: oxygen, ozone, nitric acid, arsenates, antimonates, vanadates, chromates, permanganates, chlorine, bromine and ferric ions, iodates [5].

3.3. STABILITY OF IODINE

Iodine is thermodynamically stable in a triangular region which is situated in Figs. 1 and 2 in the upper left-hand region of the domain of stability of water. Iodine is therefore stable in slightly oxidizing

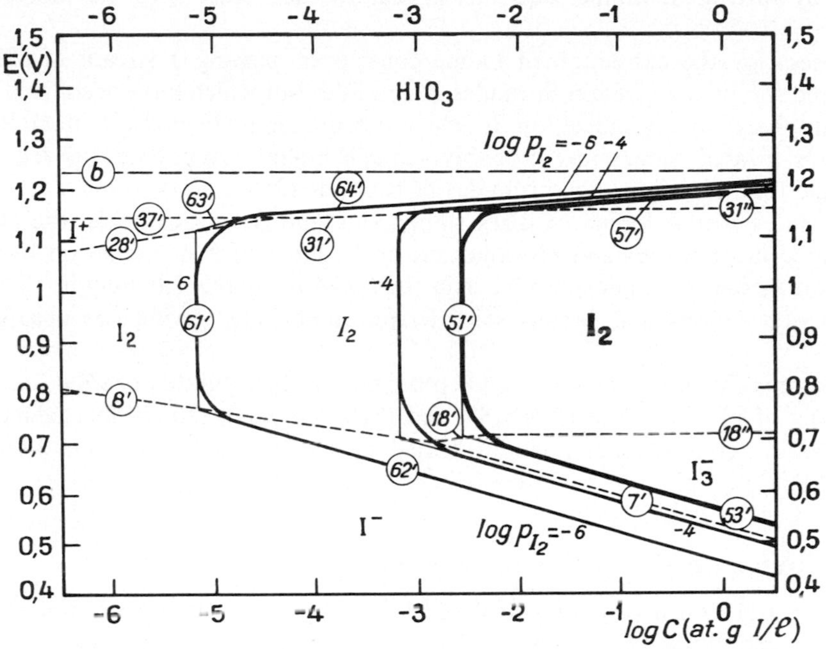

FIG. 3. Potential/concentration diagram for the system iodine–water, at 25°C. (For a solution of pH = 0).

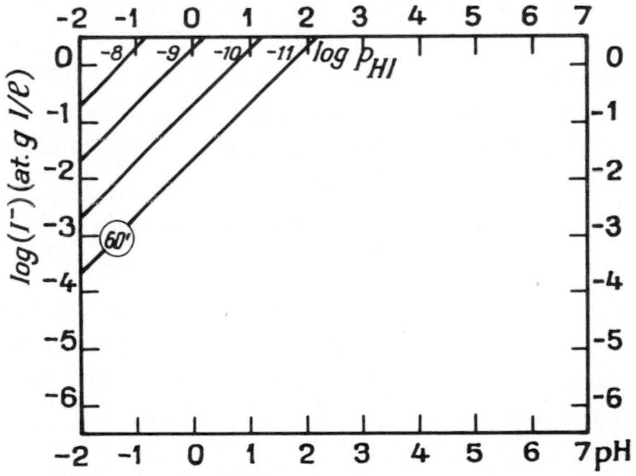

FIG. 4. Influence of pH on the solubility of HI for various partial pressures.

acid solutions. It reacts in alkaline solution to give iodate and iodide, according to the reactions

$$\begin{array}{llll} & I_2 + 6H_2O & \rightarrow & 2IO_3^- + 12H^+ + 10e^- \quad (58) \\ \text{and} & 5I_2 + 10e^- & \rightarrow & 10I^- \quad (52) \\ \hline \text{overall reaction} & 3I_2 + 3H_2O & \rightarrow & IO_3^- + 5I^- + 6H^+. \end{array}$$

It is interesting to use Figs. 1 and 2 to interpret the two main processes for the industrial extraction of iodine, as Valensi *et al.* have done [1]. Iodine is found in the form of iodates in Chile saltpetre. After concentrating aqueous solutions, the iodates are reduced to iodine with sodium sulphite. Now the SO_3 ion has in practice an oxidation potential of +0·33 V[7], which, according to Figs. 1 and 2, should reduce iodine to iodide. A too vigorous oxidation such as this is in fact a frequent accident, and is remedied by mixing in mother-liquor: the iodates then react with the iodides to give solid iodine.

Another process for the extraction of iodine consists in passing a stream of chlorine into the washings of seaweed ash, which contain bromides and iodides but which have been freed from chlorides and alkali metal sulphates by crystallization. Iodine and bromine are liberated in turn. It does not seem that much iodate is formed, since most probably a much higher overpotential is required to oxidize the iodine to iodate than to oxidize the bromides to bromine [2].

In the presence of water, iodine oxidizes sulphurous and arsenious acids, the latter reversibly. It also oxidizes hypophosphorous and phosphorous acids, but whilst its action on hypophosphorous acid is rapid in acid media, with phosphorous acid the speed is appreciable only in alkaline media [6]. Iodine also oxidizes stannous and ferrous salts, ferrocyanides, etc., giving rise usually to reversible equilibria.

Figure 3 represents the influence of electrode potential on the solubility of solid iodine and gaseous iodine for solutions of pH = 0. The lines (18″) and (31″) are given merely for didactic purposes, in view of the fact that no conditions can be represented by a point inside the domain bounded by lines (53′), (51′) and (57′).

3.4. STABILITY OF HYPOIODOUS ACID AND THE HYPOIODITES

Hypoiodous acid HIO is a very weak acid which behaves as an amphoteric electrolyte, giving rise to the following two equilibria [6]:

$$HIO = I^+ + OH^- \quad (pK = 1.39) \quad (1)$$
$$HIO = IO^- + H^+ \quad (pK = 11.0) \quad (2)$$

The I^+ cation, or rather its hydrated form H_2IO^+, can exist in an appreciable quantity only in a very acid and oxidizing aqueous solution (Figs. 1 and 2).

Hypoiodous acid and its salts are thermodynamically unstable and do not therefore appear in Figs. 1 and 2 which represent stable equilibria only. They exist only in "false equilibrium" and tend to decompose into iodide and iodate, for instance, according to the reactions

$$2IO^- + 4H^+ + 4e^- \rightarrow 2I^- + 2H_2O \quad (11)$$
and
$$IO^- + 2H_2O \rightarrow IO_3^- + 4H^+ + 4e^- \quad (40)$$
overall reaction
$$3IO^- \rightarrow 2I^- + IO_3^-.$$

This disproportionation, which is generally rapid, even in the cold, is relatively slow in very alkaline solutions [8]. Hypoiodous acid and the hypoiodites are formed transiently, together with iodides, in the reaction of water or alkalis on iodine. They can also be formed by the oxidation of iodides or the reduction of iodates or periodates [5].

3.5. STABILITY OF IODIC ACID AND THE IODATES

In accordance with Figs. 1 and 2, iodic acid HIO_3 and the iodates are stable in the presence of water. Iodates are found in nature in Chile saltpetres (sodium iodate). Iodic acid can be obtained by the action of water on its anhydride, iodine pentoxide I_2O_5, or by the oxidation of iodine with nitric acid or a chlorate [5].

Iodic acid is a strong acid of pK = 0·80. It is completely dissociated at pH's above about 2. Iodic acid and the iodates are powerful oxidizing agents.

Iodic acid is less soluble than chloric and bromic acids; the saturated aqueous solution of it is 0·5 M. We have not considered here the solid HIO_3 for lack of thermodynamic precise data concerning it. The iodates behave in solution like chlorates and bromates, but they are much more stable. The speed at which they oxidize other substances is generally slow at pH's above 5 [9]. In particular the iodates oxidize concentrated hydrochloric acid [7] according to the reaction

$$IO_3^- + 6H^+ + 2Cl^- + 4e^- = ICl_2^- + 3H_2O \qquad (E_0^0 = 1.23\ V).$$

3.6. STABILITY OF PERIODIC ACID AND THE PERIODATES

Periodic acid (para-periodic acid) of formula H_5IO_6 is only a dihydrate in appearance ([2], [5]). Its expanded formula is:

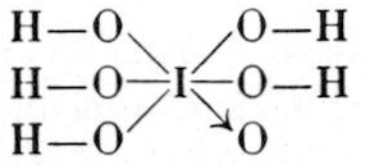

By analogy with the corresponding chlorine and bromine compounds we have, however, adopted the formula HIO_4 for periodic acid.

The acido-basic dissociation of periodic acid is quite complicated. It can be represented as follows:

$$\begin{array}{llll} H_5IO_6 & = H_4IO_6^- & + H^+ & pK_1 \\ H_4IO_6^- & = IO_4^- & + 2H_2O & pK = -1.60 \\ H_4IO_6^- & = H_3IO_6^{--} & + H^+ & pK_2 \\ H_3IO_6^{--} & = H_2IO_6^{---} & + H^+ & pK_3. \end{array}$$

An apparent dissociation constant can be *measured*, which takes account of the second of these reactions: the "dehydration" of the $H_4IO_6^-$ ion. The dissociation constants can be *calculated*, either from the structure of the substance [1], or by means of Ricci's semi-theoretical expression [12]. In the following table we give a comparison of the apparent, true and calculated pK's.

	Apparent		True	Calculated	
	[13]	[14]	[10]	[12]	[11]
pK_7	1·6	1·55	3·3	3·0	2·9
pK_2	8·4	8·27	6·7	7·0	—
pK_3	14·3	—	—	11·0	—

The free enthalpy values given in paragraph 1 were calculated from the pK values shown in large figures. It seems that the following dissociation also takes place: $2H_3IO_6^{--} = I_2O_9^{---} + 3H_2O$, but for want of thermodynamic data we were not able to consider the $I_2O_9^{---}$ ion. The IO_4^- form is thermodynamically more stable than the $H_4IO_6^-$ form; the latter is never predominant in aqueous solution in which it is 97·6 per cent destroyed, whatever the conditions which have given rise to it [2]. Periodic acid can easily be reduced to iodic acid by means of sulphuric, sulphurous or hydrochloric acids, or hydrogen sulphide [5].

The *periodates* are very powerful oxidizing agents, but act slowly. They oxidize manganese salts to permanganate in hot acid media [9]. Valensi *et al.* [1] point out that the difference between the potentials of standard equilibrium of the couples HIO_4/HIO_3 (E_0^0 = 1·626) and MnO_4^-/Mn^{++} (E_0^0 = 1·507) [15] is only 0·12 V. One would therefore be led to think that the liveliness of periodic acid is not due to its high thermodynamic level alone, but also to a small, natural overpotential (as an absolute value). In actual fact, says Valensi [16], it can only be a question of an autocatalysis, due to the manganous salts and analogous to the one which he has assumed in the action of oxygen on the polysulphides. The polarographic reduction of the periodates has been studied by Coe and Rogers [17], and by Souchay [18], and it shows an overpotential exceeding 1 V in absolute value. The periodates are very powerful oxidizing agents in alkaline media. Most reducing agents which are sufficiently powerful reduce them to iodides. The reaction is very slow in acid media, but faster in alkaline media [9]. The oxido–reduction reaction between the periodates and divalent cobalt has been studied by means of a potential–pH diagram by Jentoft and Robinson [19].

4. BIBLIOGRAPHY

[1] G. Valensi *et al.*, Diagrammes tension–pH des halogènes (5th Meeting of CITCE, Stockholm, 1953) (unpublished).

[2] M. G. Brown, *Potential*–pH *Diagrams for Iodine Compounds* [Report of 7th Meeting of CITCE (Lindau, 1955), Butterworths, London, 1957, pp. 244–56].

[3] M. Pourbaix, *On the Electrochemical Behaviour of Iodine* [Report of 7th Meeting of CITCE (Lindau, 1955), Butterworths, London, 1957, pp. 258–65].

[4] R. P. Bell and E. Gelles, The halogen cations in aqueous solution, *J. Chem. Soc.* 2734–40 (1951).

[5] N. V. Sidgwick, *The Chemical Elements and their Compounds*, Vol. II, Oxford, 1950, p. 1167.

[6] P. Pascal, *Traité de Chimie minérale*, Vol. I, Masson, Paris, 1931.

[7] G. Charlot, *Définition des divers types de potentiels d'oxydo-réduction utiles en Chimie analytique. Potentiels apparents* [Report of 2nd Meeting of CITCE (Milan, 1950), Tamburin, Milan, 1951, p. 261].

[8] C. H. Li and C. F. White, Kinetics of hypoiodite decomposition, *J. Amer. Chem. Soc.* **65**, 335 (1943).

[9] G. Charlot, *L'analyse qualitative et les réactions en solution*, 4th ed., Masson, Paris, 1957, pp. 273–89.

[10] C. E. Crouthamel, A. M. Hayes and D. S. Martin, Ionization and hydration equilibria of periodic acid, *J. Amer. Chem. Soc.* **73**, 82 (1951).

[11] A. Kossiakoff and D. Harker, The calculation of the ionization constants of inorganic oxygen acids from their structures, *J. Amer. Chem. Soc.* **60**, 2043 (1938).

[12] J. E. Ricci, The aqueous ionization constants of inorganic oxygen acids, *J. Amer. Chem. Soc.* **70**, 109 (1948).

[13] C. E. Crouthamel, H. V. Meek, D. S. Martin and C. V. Banks, Spectrophotometric studies of dilute aqueous periodate solutions, *J. Amer. Chem. Soc.* **71**, 3031–5 (1949).

[14] R. Näsänen, Studies on copper (II) periodates, *Acta Chem. Scand.* **8**, 1587–95 (1954).

[15] A. M. Moussard, J. Brenet, F. Jolas, M. Pourbaix and J. Van Muylder, *Comportement électrochimique du manganèse. Diagramme d'équilibres tension*–pH *du système* Mn–H_2O *à* 25°C (Rapport technique RT.18 of CEBELCOR, December 1954, p. 3).

[16] G. Valensi, *Contribution au diagramme potentiel*–pH *du soufre* [Report of 2nd Meeting of CITCE (Milan, 1950), Tamburini, Milan, 1951, pp. 51–68].

[17] R. H. Coe and L. B. Rogers, Electroreduction of periodate at the dropping mercury electrode. Behaviour in acidic solutions of pH less than 3, *J. Amer. Chem. Soc.* **70**, 3276–8 (1948).

[18] P. Souchay, Polarographie des periodates. Applications analytiques. *Anal. Chim. Acta,* **2**, 17–29 (1948).

[19] R. E. Jentoft and R. J. Robinson, The reaction between periodate and cobaltous ions, *J. Amer. Chem. Soc.* **75**, 4083–4 (1953).

CHAPTER V

TABLES

SECTION 1

PERIODIC CLASSIFICATION OF THE ELEMENTS

O.	I.		II.		III.		IV.		V.		VI.		VII.		VIII.		
	a.	b.	a.	b.	a.	b.	a.	b.	a.	b.	a.	b.	a.	b.			
	1.H 1,0080																
2.He 4,003	3.Li 6,940		4.Be 9,013		5.B 10,82			6.C 12,011		7.N 14,008		8.O 16,000		9.F 19,00			
10.Ne 20,183	11.Na 22,991		12.Mg 24,32		13.Al 26,98			14.Si 28,09		15.P 30,975		16.S 32,066		17 Cl 35,457			
18.Ar 39,944	19.K 39,100		20.Ca 40,08		21.Sc 44,96		22.Ti 47,90		23.V 50,95		24.Cr 52,01		25.Mn 54,94		26.Fe 55,85	27.Co 58,94	28.Ni 58,71
		29.Cu 63,54		30.Zn 65,38		31.Ga 69,72		32.Ge 72,60		33.As 74,91		34 Se 78,96		35.Br 79,916			
36.Kr 83,80	37.Rb 85,48		38.Sr 87,63		39.Y 88,92		40.Zr 91,22		41.Nb 92,91		42.Mo 95,95		43.Tc [99]		44.Ru 101,1	45.Rh 102,91	46.Pd 106,4
		47.Ag 107,880		48.Cd 112,41		49.In 114,82		50.Sn 118,70		51.Sb 121,76		52 Te 127,61		53.I 126,91			
54.Xe 131,30	55.Cs 132,91		56.Ba 137,36		57–71 Lanthanides (1)		72.Hf 178,50		73.Ta 180,95		74.W 183,86		75.Re 186,22		76.Os 190,2	77.Ir 192,2	78.Pt 195,09
		79.Au 197,0		80.Hg 200,61		81.Tl 204,39		82.Pb 207,21		83.Bi 209,00		84 Po 210		85.At [210]			
86.Rn 222	87.Fr [223]		88.Ra 226,05		89.Ac 227		90.Th 232,05		91.Pa 231		92.U 238,07		93.Np [237]		Transuranic elements		

(1) Lanthanides:

57.La	58.Ce	59.Pr	60.Nd	61.Pm	62.Sm	63.Eu	64.Gd	65.Tb	66.Dy	67.Ho	68.Er	69.Tm	70.Yb	71.Lu
138,92	140,13	140,92	144,27	[145]	150,35	152,0	157,26	158,93	162,51	164,94	167,27	168,94	173,04	174,99

(2) Transuranic elements:

94.Pu	95.Am	96.Cm	97.Bk	98.Cf	99.E	100.Fm	101.Mv
[242]	[243]	[245]	[249]	[249]	[254]	[255]	[256]

N.B.—Values in brackets [ ] are for the masses of the isotope with the longest known half-life.

SECTION 2

INTERNATIONAL ATOMIC WEIGHTS

	Symbol	Atomic No.	Atomic Weight
Actinium	Ac	89	227
Aluminium	Al	13	26·98
Americium	Am	95	[243]
Antimony	Sb	51	121·76
Argon	Ar	18	39·944
Arsenic	As	33	74·91
Astatine	At	85	[210]
Barium	Ba	56	137·36
Berkelium	Bk	97	[249]
Beryllium	Be	4	9·013
Bismuth	Bi	83	209·00
Boron	B	5	10·82
Bromine	Br	35	79·916
Cadmium	Cd	48	112·41
Calcium	Ca	20	40·08
Californium	Cf	98	[249]
Carbon	C	6	12·011
Cerium	Ce	58	140·13
Cesium	Cs	55	132·905
Chlorine	Cl	17	35·457
Chromium	Cr	24	51·01
Cobalt	Co	27	58·94
Copper	Cu	29	63·54
Curium	Cm	96	[245]
Dysprosium	Dy	66	162·51
Einsteinium	Es	99	[254]
Erbium	Er	68	167·27
Europium	Eu	63	152·0
Fermium	Fm	100	[255]
Fluorine	F	9	19·00
Francium	Fr	87	[223]
Gadolinium	Gd	64	157·26
Gallium	Ga	31	69·72
Germanium	Ge	32	72·60
Gold	Au	79	197·0
Hafnium	Hf	72	178·50
Helium	He	2	4·003
Holmium	Ho	67	164·94
Hydrogen	H	1	1·0080
Indium	In	49	114·82
Iodine	I	53	126·91
Iridium	Ir	77	192·2
Iron	Fe	26	55·85
Krypton	Kr	36	83·80
Lanthanum	La	57	138·92
Lead	Pb	82	207·21
Lithium	Li	3	6·940
Lutetium	Lu	71	174·99
Magnesium	Mg	12	24·32
Manganese	Mn	25	54·94
Mendelevium	Mv	101	[256]
Mercury	Hg	80	200·61
Molybdenum	Mo	42	95·95
Neodymium	Nd	60	144·27
Neon	Ne	10	20·183
Neptunium	Np	93	[237]
Nickel	Ni	28	58·71
Niobium	Nb	41	92·91
Nitrogen	N	7	14·008
Nobelium	No	102	
Osmium	Os	76	190·2
Oxygen	O	8	16·000
Palladium	Pd	46	106·4
Phosphorus	P	15	30·975
Platinum	Pt	78	195·09
Plutonium	Pu	94	[242]
Polonium	Po	84	210
Potassium	K	19	39·100
Praseodymium	Pr	59	140·92
Promethium	Pm	61	[145]
Protactinium	Pa	91	231
Radium	Ra	88	266·05
Radon	Rn	86	222
Rhenium	Re	75	186·22
Rhodium	Rh	45	102·91
Rubidium	Rb	37	85·48
Ruthenium	Ru	44	101·1
Samarium	Sm	62	150·35
Scandium	Sc	21	44·96
Selenium	Se	34	78·96
Silicon	Si	14	28·09
Silver	Ag	47	107·880
Sodium	Na	11	22·991
Strontium	Sr	38	87·63
Sulfur	S	16	32·066
Tantalum	Ta	73	180·95
Technetium	Tc	43	[99]
Tellurium	Te	52	127·61
Terbium	Tb	65	158·93
Thallium	Tl	81	204·39
Thorium	Th	90	232·05
Thulium	Tm	69	168·94
Tin	Sn	50	118·70
Titanium	Ti	22	47·90
Tungsten	W	74	183·86
Uranium	U	92	238·07
Vanadium	V	23	50·95
Xenon	Xe	54	131·30
Ytterbium	Yb	70	173·04
Yttrium	Y	39	88·92
Zinc	Zn	30	65·38
Zirconium	Zr	40	91·22

SEQUENCE OF ELEMENTS IN CHAPTER IV*

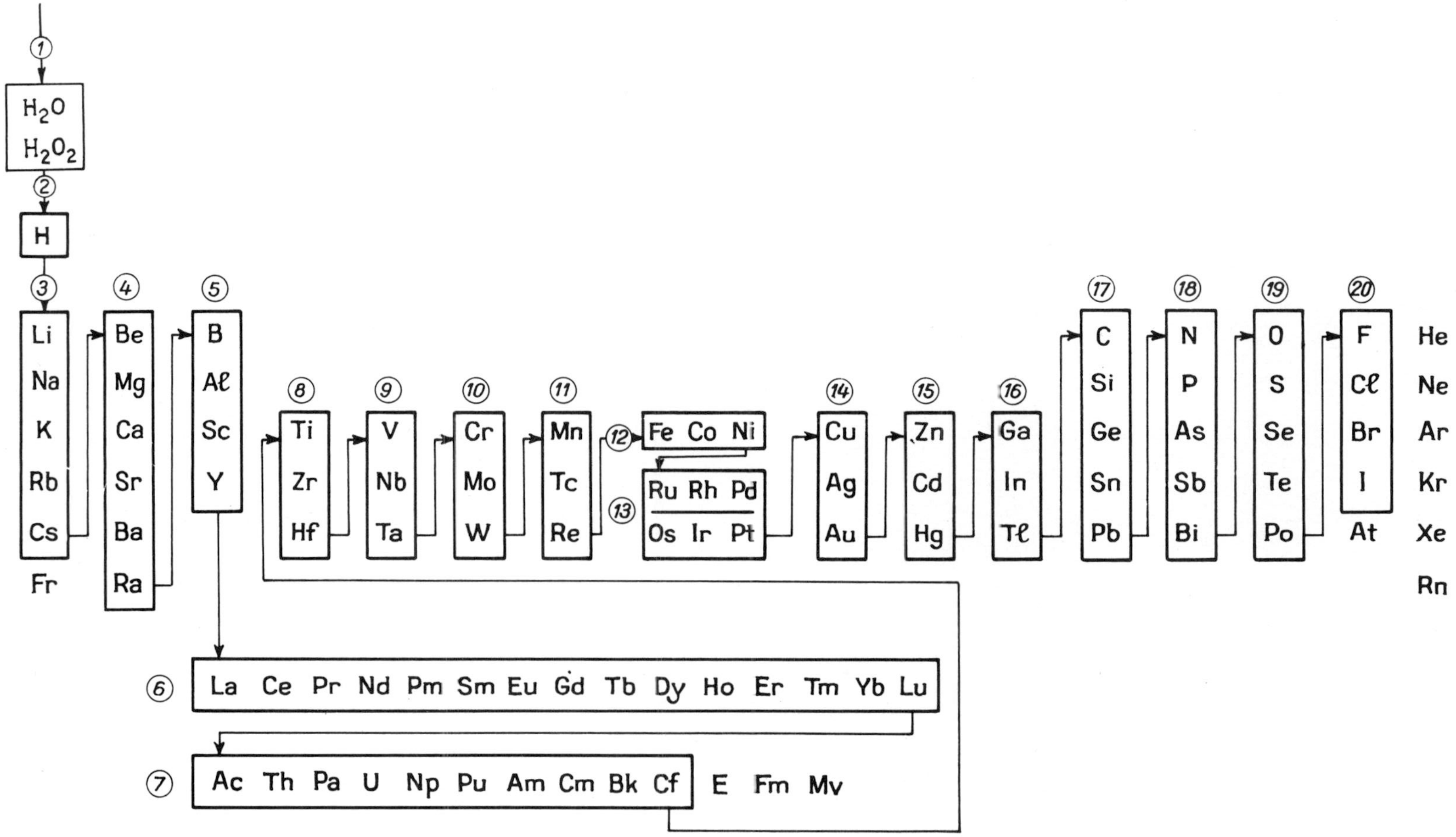

* This table is based upon a similar table in W. M. Latimer, *Oxidation Potentials*, 2nd ed., Prentice-Hall, New York, 1952.

AUTHOR INDEX

Q

R

S

SUBJECT INDEX

(**Bold figures** indicate an important reference)